PHYSICAL GEOGRAPHY
THE GLOBAL ENVIRONMENT

PHYSICAL GEOGRAPHY

H. J. de Blij
MICHIGAN STATE UNIVERSITY

Cathy T. Conrad
SAINT MARY'S UNIVERSITY

Peter O. Muller
UNIVERSITY OF MIAMI

Peter Long
YORK UNIVERSITY

Richard S. Williams, Jr
WOODS HOLE RESEARCH INSTITUTE

THE GLOBAL ENVIRONMENT

CANADIAN EDITION

OXFORD

UNIVERSITY PRESS

OXFORD

UNIVERSITY PRESS

70 Wynford Drive, Don Mills, Ontario M3C 1J9
www.oup.com/ca

Oxford University Press is a department of the University of Oxford.
It furthers the University's objective of excellence in research, scholarship,
and education by publishing worldwide in

Oxford   New York

Auckland   Cape Town   Dar es Salaam   Hong Kong   Karachi   Kuala Lumpur   Madrid   Melbourne
Mexico City   Nairobi   New Delhi   Shanghai   Taipei   Toronto

With offices in
Argentina   Austria   Brazil   Chile   Czech Republic   France   Greece   Guatemala   Hungary   Italy
Japan   Poland   Portugal   Singapore   South Korea   Switzerland   Thailand   Turkey   Ukraine   Vietnam

Oxford is a trade mark of Oxford University Press
in the UK and in certain other countries

Published in Canada
by Oxford University Press

National Library of Canada Cataloguing in Publication Data

Physical geography : the global environment / H.J. de Blij ... [et al.]. — 1st Canadian ed.

Includes index.

ISBN 0-19-542115-9

1. Physical geography—Textbooks. I. De Blij, Harm J.

GB55.P49 2005   910'.02   C2005-900048-1

1 2 3 4 - 08 07 06 05

This book is printed on permanent (acid-free) paper ∞.
Printed in Canada

In Memory of
DENNIS M. O'CONNER

whose interest and faith in this book
we recall appreciatively

HJdB

Preface to the Canadian Edition

Physical geography is truly a global science, and any textbook on the subject must be global in its scope. Yet authors will naturally focus particular attention on the landscapes most familiar to their readers, and—unfortunately for Canadian students—most introductory-level texts have been written with American or British students in mind. Building on the outstanding foundation provided by the third edition of *Physical Geography: The Global Environment*, by H.J. de Blij, Peter O. Muller, Richard S. Williams, Jr, this Canadian adaptation retains the international scope of the American original but takes advantage of Canada's exceptional physical diversity to add a wealth of new material that Canadian students can relate to, on topics ranging from wind patterns to landscape types, soil classification to hurricanes, permafrost to drought, avalanches, water use, air pollution, and weather analysis—to name only a few.

The result, we hope, is a book that will engage Canadian students and provide a solid base for lifelong exploration of the physical world in all its variety, whether in Canada or around the globe.

Acknowledgments

Cathy Conrad thanks her colleagues and students in the Department of Geography at St. Mary's University, particularly Dr Philip Giles, who provided both images and input on the text, and Erin Edmundson, a wonderful student who assisted with the websites and ancillaries, in addition to research. She is also grateful to intern Kevin Garroway, for listening to her stories and helping with the research on the maps and weather-related topics. Finally, she thanks her husband, Scott, and son, Jakob, both for their love and support and for the many new insights into the physical world that they have sparked.

Peter Long thanks his friends (faculty, staff, graduate and undergraduate students) at the Department of Geography at York University; the staff of the Scott Map Library (especially Mary McDowell and Dana Craig) and the Geography Department's Teaching Resources Centre (Mike Flosznik) for helping to find maps and other resources on some fairly arcane subjects; Professor Osamu Oshima of the University of Tokyo at Komaba, Japan; and John Radford, Chair of the Department, for permission to reprint some exceptional images from the Hans Carol slide collection. He is grateful to Dr Catherine Hickson of the Geological Survey of Canada in Vancouver who provided important information about the Anahim Volcanic Belt in B.C. He would also like to express his thanks to Dr Christopher Green, FRGS, FGS (Honorary Research Fellow, Centre for Quaternary Research, Department of Geography, Royal Holloway, University of London), for instilling in him a deep appreciation for geomorphology and Pleistocene studies when he was a callow student during the early and mid 1970s. Dr Green remains a constant inspiration. Finally, Peter thanks his wife, Christine, and son, Adam, who are a continual source of love and much support.

In addition, we are both very grateful to our colleagues Roger Phillips (York University), Gita Laidler (University of Toronto), John Menzies (Brock University), Philip Giles (St. Mary's University), Norm Catto (Memorial University of Newfoundland), and Blair Hrabi (University of Toronto), for their contributions to the new *Canadian Geographers in the Field* sections. We would also like to thank the wonderful editorial staff at Oxford University Press Canada, including Laura Macleod, Rachael Cayley, Nick Durie, Judith Turnbull, David Ward, and Phyllis Wilson.

Cathy Conrad
Peter Long

Preface to the U.S. Edition

In the decade since the appearance of this book, environmental issues have become prominent among public concerns. Even the most cursory content analysis of the popular press proves the extent to which global climate change, El Niño effects, melting glaciers, and climatic extremes have become front-page news. Add to this the technologically enhanced reportage of earthquakes in remote locales, hurricanes on their computer-predicted tracks, "millennium" floods, sun-blocking volcanic eruptions, and other natural events that briefly but vividly make the headlines, and it is clear that our collective awareness of nature's challenges have taken centre stage.

But how well are the environmental systems that underlie all this often-sensational news understood? It is quite another to have some basic understanding of how it works and what its regional and global implications are. When Mount Pinatubo erupted explosively in 1991, the consequences ranged from the climatic (a temporary but distinct cooling effect) to the strategic (the closure of United States military bases in the Philippines). One needed some background in physical as well as human geography to appreciate these linkages.

Meanwhile, slower and less dramatic changes in our Earthly environments have potentially far greater consequences. In the 1800s the planet emerged from what has been called a "Little Ice Age" and entered a phase of warming that continues, despite a major reversal in the middle decades of the twentieth century, to this day. The degree to which human activities enhance this "greenhouse warming" is a matter for informed debate, but it is essential to understand the climatic history of the entire Holocene to see it in appropriate context. Even if emission-limiting agreements more stringent than the Kyoto Protocols could be approved and implemented (and we all wish it could be so), climatic fluctuations would not cease. We live in a world of wide and often rapid environmental swings, and we should understand their impacts on human societies much better than we do.

In this book we provide a background for an understanding of the Earth's environmental systems and processes, carrying the story from the place of our planet in the solar system to the regional landscapes resulting from tectonic and erosional forces. Because this is a geography book, we tend to use spatial perspectives and approaches when we address environmental problems and issues—but our working definition of physical geography, where several sciences converge, is broad and encompassing.

The Third Edition

In this new edition of *Physical Geography: The Global Environment,* we have benefited from the comments of readers of earlier editions as well as the advice provided by Richard S. Williams, Jr., who is the author and editor of numerous scientific publications in a wide range of related fields. As those familiar with this book will note, we have made only one significant structural change, involving the combination and condensation of Units 52 and 53 of the Second Edition, thus sharpening the focus on the North American landscapes with which students tend to be most familiar. In the redesigned part openers, we have sketched the systemic frameworks that recur in the text. Dr. Williams alerted us to the growing research focus on the cryosphere, and following our reading of the relevant literature, notably in the journals *Science* and *Nature,* we recast the key figure (Fig. 2.1, page 19), recognizing *five* (not four) Earth-system spheres as the basis for this and future editions.

The new edition also brings us up to date on the continuing debate over global climate change—but only after the fundamentals of climate have been discussed. The public is bombarded with reportage, opinion pieces, and exhortations regarding global warming, but surveys show environmental literacy scores even lower than scores for spatial literacy. An informed public is needed when it comes to forging effective public policy. In this book we attempt to provide information as well as guide opinion, and we hope that these pages will enhance the quality of discourse. Comprehending global climate change requires an understanding of the diverse topics that constitute physical geography, ranging from atmospheric and oceanic systems to ice ages and glaciations, from Earth-orbit variations to biogeographic responses. One notable geographic aspect of the accumulating global-warming evidence is its regional divergence: while some areas of the planet exhibit evidence of sustained warming, others experience simultaneous cooling (for example, the Eastern Canadian winter of 2002–2003, one of the most severe in recorded history). The reasons for such apparent contradictions can be understood through the study of global environmental systems in time *and* space.

There was a time when physical geography was studied with little or no reference to human-environmental interconnections, but humanity has itself become a factor in the environmental evolution of the planet. In the text we refer frequently to this relationship, and every unit includes a box under the heading *Perspectives on the Human Environment,* in which the topic is given emphasis. In previous editions of this book, the *Perspectives* boxes proved to be a productive element, and we have strengthened this feature in this edition, using the opportunity to reflect on the impacts of environmental extremes (such as Hurricane Mitch) and their aftermaths.

As readers familiar with this book will note, we have made numerous changes to keep pace with scientific discovery as well as ongoing research. The potential impact of change in the North Atlantic Oscillation (not as well known as the El Niño/Southern Oscillation of the Pacific) is now chronicled in Unit 11. Growing understanding of the capacity of asteroids, comets, and meteor-like objects not only to kill dinosaurs but also to transform climate and land, led to substantial revision of Unit 4. The identification of a boundary separating the Indian from the Australian tectonic plates (previously regarded as a single entity) changed the text and maps in Unit 32. Minor updates abound, and not a page of this book remained unaffected.

In response to sometimes-frustrated correspondents, we added small locator maps to photographs not otherwise identified by location. Many of the photographs were taken by the senior author in the course of his fieldwork (over more than 40 years of research), and extracts from the fieldnotes provide background to the images. We hope that you will find enjoyment as well as information and explanation in the pages that follow.

Acknowledgments

During the preparation of this new edition of *Physical Geography: The Global Environment,* we received advice and guidance from many quarters. First and foremost, we thank our reviewers, who supplied valuable feedback on the previous edition and thoughtful suggestions as to how we could improve a number of units. They were:

Caroline P. Davies, University of Missouri, Kansas City
Jeremy E. Diem, Georgia State University
William L. Graf, University of South Carolina
Daniel M. Johnson, Portland State University (Ore.)
Stephen E. G. LaDochy, California State University, Los Angeles
Elliot G. McIntire, California State University, Northridge
Donald L. Morgan, Brigham Young University (Utah)
John F. Shroder, Jr., University of Nebraska at Omaha
Thomas A. Wikle, Oklahoma State University
Harry F. L. Williams, University of North Texas

We are also most grateful for the advice and/or assistance we received from the following people:

Philip L. Chaney, Auburn University (Ala.)
Christopher B. Hanson, University of Miami (Fla.)
Roger P. Miller, Black Hills State University (S.D.)
Mauri Pelto, Nichols College (Mass.)
Randall J. Schaetzl, Michigan State University
Aondover A. Tarhule, University of Oklahoma
Charles Tarnocai, Agriculture and Agri-Food Canada (Ottawa)
Verna Vander Kool, Cuyahoga Community College (Ohio)

We are indebted to our colleagues at Oxford University Press, who superbly managed the preparation of this Canadian edition from our arrival at the company in 2001 to the publication of bound books barely two years later. Our longtime friend Dr. Christopher J. Rogers, vice president and general manager of the higher education group, brought us to Oxford, set the revision process into motion, and insisted on the highest standards as he oversaw the entire project. Ms. Eman Hudson admirably handled the developmental editing, constantly exuding high energy and infectious enthusiasm. Peter Gordon not only coordinated myriad details as he smoothed us into the production process, but also entertained us fabulously with his wit and wisdom on several occasions. Mary Hopkins deftly supervised the marketing responsibilities, and Linda Harris splendidly organized the suite of ancillary publications and computer activities that accompany this book.

A special note of appreciation is reserved for those individuals who contributed so effectively to the production process. Karen Shapiro, our managing editor, marvelously coordinated the entire operation and worked tirelessly to get the best possible results. Talia Krohn did a truly outstanding job in assembling our photography program and astonished us repeatedly with her resourcefulness in obtaining usable photos no matter how outlandish our requests. Our designer, Cathleen Bennett, was especially pleasant to work with, and she deserves much of the credit for the handsome appearance of the end product. We also thank Elyse Dubin, Barbara Brown, and Erin Clancy for their invaluable assistance at crucial moments of personnel change and for their many additional efforts to keep things moving along. Special thanks, too, go to Janice G. Goodell, who worked tirelessly and effectively to correct the scanned text and to make revisions to the initial draft of the manuscript.

Last, but certainly not least, we thank our wives—Bonnie, Nancy, and Mary Ellen—for all their support and encouragement, particularly in getting us across those inevitable bumps in the road as this enterprise successfully found its congenial new home.

H. J. de Blij
Peter O. Muller
Richard S. Williams, Jr.

From the Publisher

Few subjects have been more central to human beings than the study of the physical world. Yet it is only in the past five hundred years—and particularly the last hundred and fifty—that we have begun to have any scientific understanding of the Earth and the processes that continue to shape it.

Today we are becoming aware that the most crucial social and political issues are often inextricably linked to geographic realities: from the finite nature of the world's water supplies and the location of its oil reserves to the massive changes that are already underway as a result of global warming. A basic understanding of our physical environment—its nature, history, and limitations—has never been more vital to the average citizen. And as the present century progresses, environmental issues will undoubtedly come to play an ever more central role in shaping the fate not just of nations but of every individual on Earth.

With these considerations in mind, Oxford University Press is especially proud to publish the first Canadian edition of *Physical Geography: The Global Environment*, by H.J. de Blij, Peter O. Muller, Richard S. Williams, Jr, Cathy T. Conrad, and Peter Long. Of course there is nothing uniquely Canadian about the subject of physical geography; it would be hard to imagine a more international discipline. But under its broad umbrella there are distinctive contributions made by Canadian scholars, as well as topics of special interest to students living in a country whose physical geography is one of the most diverse anywhere on the Earth. This text provides the most authoritative introduction to physical geography now available, in a way that is accessible and engaging for Canadian students.

Special Features of this Text

Physical Geography: The Global Environment includes numerous features designed to make its subject matter accessible and interesting to students. Among them are the following:

- **A stunning new four-colour design.** Physical geography is by nature one of the most visually oriented of all the sciences. *Physical Geography* takes advantage of the full colour palette to:
  - make diagrams and charts clear and easy to follow;

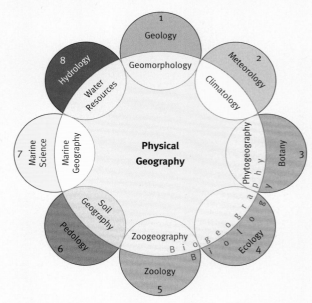

FIGURE 1.4 Schematic representation of the specialized subfields that constitute physical geography.

– make maps attractive and easy to read;

FIGURE 25.1   Soils of Canada and the United States, divided into two major classes determined by climate (after Marbut).

– present features of the natural world as realistically as possible;

The five spheres of the Earth System in harmonious interaction. Mount Tasman, South Island, New Zealand. (Authors' photo)

– and produce a text that is straightforward to navigate and inviting to read.

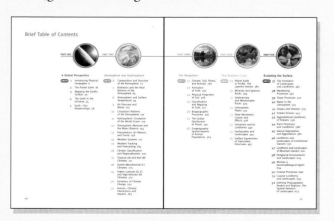

• **Student-centred learning resources.** A good textbook is not the final word on its subject but an invitation to further learning. At the end of each chapter are several pedagogical features designed with this purpose in mind, including:

– *Key Terms* listed with page references;
– *Review Questions* focusing on major themes and topics of the chapter;
– *References and Further Readings* intended to direct students to useful print resources; and
– *Web Resources* annotated by the authors to highlight their potential value for further research.

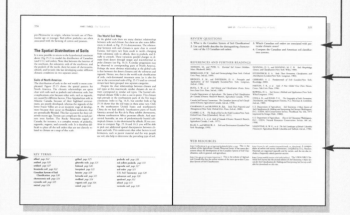

• **Canadian content where appropriate.** It's true that astronauts looking at the Earth from space see no national boundaries. But imaginary lines can still have real effects. Texts published for the U.S. market naturally reflect the needs and interests of American students and instructors. In the same way, this text highlights Canadian content where appropriate—as in the case of the Canadian System of Soil Classification—

FIGURE 25.15   Generalized spatial distribution of soils in North America using the Canadian Soil Orders (U.S. Soil Orders are in parentheses).

and uses Canadian examples to illustrate fundamental concepts—featuring Canadian maps, for example, in its discussion of standard cartographic symbols:

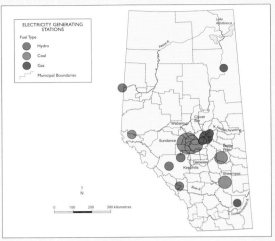

FIGURE 3.8 Alberta's electrical generating stations (fuel type and capacity), an example of a proportional symbol map.

- **International coverage.** At the same time—as the book's subtitle reminds us—physical geography is a global discipline. Hence every effort has been made to include the broadest possible range of international examples and research.

FIGURE 27.1 Global distribution of the principal terrestrial biomes.

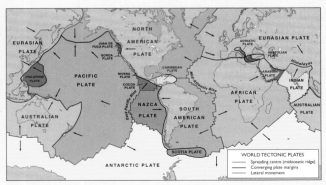

FIGURE 32.3 Lithospheric plates of the Earth. Each drifts continuously in the direction shown by the arrows. As the legend indicates, plate-margin movement falls into one of three categories: divergence (spreading), convergence, or lateral motion.

- ***Perspectives on the Human Environment.*** These special boxed features provide additional insight into important and interesting issues, beyond the coverage included in the body of the text. For instance, "Sliding Scale" places humans in the broad context of the physical world.

PERSPECTIVES ON THE HUMAN ENVIRONMENT

Sliding Scale

Imagine a couple sunbathing on Cavendish Beach. We can photograph them occupying a square of sand about 1 m on a side. If we move the camera higher, a square of 10 (10^1) m reveals their companions. When we focus on a 100 (10^2) m area, we can see a crowd of people on the beach. A picture of 1000 (10^3) m includes the beach, some sea, and some land (as in Fig. 1.6). One with an edge of 10,000 (10^4) m captures most of Prince Edward Island National Park and parts of the neighbouring north shore of Prince Edward Island.

Moving the camera still farther, we shoot a picture of a 100,000 (10^5) m square. It encompasses most of the central P.E.I. region. The next step is 1,000,000 (10^6) m. This snapshot takes in the entire province of P.E.I., some neighbouring provinces, and parts of the Atlantic Ocean, the Gulf of St. Lawrence, and the Bay of Fundy. A photo at the next level of generalization, showing a square of 10,000,000 (10^7) m, covers most of the visible Earth. And if the camera is far enough away in outer space to focus on a square of 100,000,000 (10^8) m, we see Planet Earth as a small globe. Somewhere on it is that couple lying on a square of Cavendish Beach's seaside sand.

- ***Canadian Geographers in the Field.*** Drawn from the notebooks of practising geographers, these boxes offer students direct insight into the research process.

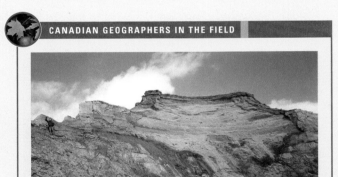

CANADIAN GEOGRAPHERS IN THE FIELD

"The shorelines of the Great Lakes are superb outdoor laboratory sites for field work investigations. This site near Port Burwell, southern Ontario on the north shore of Lake Erie reveals a complex stratigraphy of upper glaciolacustrine laminated muds, below that glaciofluvial sands and gravels and subglacial lodgement and waterlain tills in the lower half of the photograph. In a single exposure, therefore, one can find all the needed evidence of the late Wisconsinan Laurentide Ice Sheet glaciation and associated retreat sediments related to ice marginal proglacial sedimentation, first within a shallow near ice marginal proglacial zone then at the top of the section within an increasingly deeper glacial lake environment."

John Menzies, B.Sc., Ph.D., P.Geo. is Professor of Geography and Earth Sciences at Brock University.

Instructors' and Students' Supplements to Accompany the Text

Physical Geography: A Global Perspective is accompanied by a wide range of supplementary items for students and instructors alike, all designed to enhance the text's value as a teaching and learning tool.

For Students

The following students' resources are available at www.oup.com/ca/he/companion/deBlij

- **Online student study guide.** This interactive program allows students to test their understanding of key concepts through a variety of self-grading questions. As well, the site offers links to additional learning resources.
- **Natural Hazards website.** This website offers fascinating information about earthquakes, hurricanes, floods, winter weather, and other geological, meteorological, and biological hazards.

For Instructors

The following instructors' resources are available to qualifying adopters at www.oup.com/ca/he/companion/deBlij (please contact your OUP Canada sales representative):

- **Instructors' manual.** A comprehensive resource package featuring lecture outlines, teaching objectives, media resources, small group and project ideas, and review questions.
- **PowerPoint slides.** Dozens of images, including maps, charts, and diagrams, digitized for classroom use.

Finally, a comprehensive testing program is available on CD-ROM to qualified adopters (please contact your sales representative):

- **Computerized Test Item File.** Fully interactive testing software not only provides hundreds of multiple choice, true/false, and short answer questions but makes it possible to customize exams; add new questions and modify existing ones; and publish tests to a variety of media, including print and the Web.

Brief Table of Contents

PART ONE

PART TWO

xv

Contents

PART THREE The Biosphere

PART FOUR　The Restless Crust

PART FIVE　Sculpting the Surface

Perspectives Boxes by Unit

PERSPECTIVES ON THE HUMAN ENVIRONMENT

PART ONE

A Global Perspective

Relationships among the Five Spheres of the Earth System

Modern physical geographers view the Earth as the manifestation of a set of interconnected, interactive, interlocking systems that generate the forces, processes, and landscapes with which we are all familiar. These geochemical, geophysical, and biological systems, propelled by innumerable subsidiary systems in which energy and matter are transported, stored, and redeployed, forge the Earth as we know it. Thus, the planet may be viewed in terms of five gigantic open (interacting) systems represented as *spheres* of which the oldest is the lithosphere, the sphere of rocks (and earthquakes and volcanoes), and the youngest is the biosphere, the realm of plants and animals. We experience the atmosphere and its weather subsystems on a daily basis, know the Earth as the "blue planet" because the waters of the hydrosphere cover about 70 percent of its surface, and are reminded by the ice of the cryosphere in polar and high-mountain areas that ice-age conditions, once much more extensive, still prevail over parts of the globe. Dominant systems produce these discrete Earthly spheres, but interactive processes prevail, and the borders among them, transitional in nature, vary in space and time.

A Global Perspective

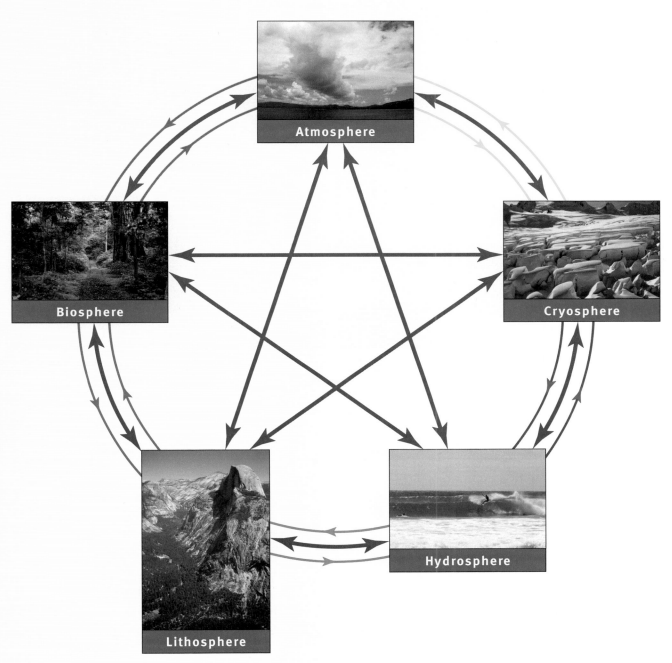

Atmosphere

Cryosphere

Biosphere

Hydrosphere

Lithosphere

Introducing Physical Geography

Planet Earth and its moon in the northern summer—clear skies in the U.S. and central Canada, a hurricane off Mexico, snow-bearing clouds over Antarctica.

OBJECTIVES

- To introduce and discuss the contemporary focus of physical geography
- To relate physical geography to the other natural and physical sciences
- To introduce the systems and modelling approaches to physical geography

This is a book about the Earth's natural environments. Its title, *Physical Geography: The Global Environment*, suggests the unifying perspective. Earth's human habitat will be examined, with a focus on the fragile layer of life that sustains humanity along with millions of species of animals and plants. Features of the natural world such as erupting volcanoes, winding rivers, advancing deserts, and changing shorelines are examined not only as physical phenomena, but also in terms of their relationships with human societies and communities.

Physical geography is a broad discipline, with physical geographers working on a variety of research topics. The Earth will therefore be discussed from various vantage points. It will be studied in space and from space, from mountaintops and in underground shafts, from clouds and ocean waves to rocks and minerals, from fertile soils and verdant forests to arid deserts and icy wastelands.

Geography

Geographers, of course, are not the only researchers studying the Earth's surface. Geologists, meteorologists, biologists, hydrologists, and scientists from many other disciplines also study aspects of the planetary surface and what lies above and below it. But only one scholarly discipline, geography, combines and integrates and, at its best, *synthesizes* knowledge from all these other fields as it makes its own research contributions. Time and again in this book you will become aware of connections among physical phenomena and between natural phenomena and human activities of which you might not have become aware in another course.

Although geography is a modern discipline in which scientists increasingly use high-technology research equipment, its roots extend to the very dawn of scholarly inquiry. When the ancient Greeks began to realize the need to organize the knowledge they were gathering, they divided it all into two areas: geography (the study of the terrestrial world) and cosmography (the study of the skies, stars, and the universe beyond). A follower of Aristotle, a scholar named Eratosthenes (ca. 275–ca. 195 B.C.E.), actually coined the term *geography* in the third century B.C.E. To him, geography was the accurate description of the Earth (*geo,* meaning Earth; *graphia,* meaning description), and during his lifetime volumes were written about rocks, soils, and plants. There was a magnificent library in Alexandria (in what is now Egypt) that came to contain the greatest collection of existing geographical studies.

Soon the mass of information (i.e., the database) concerning terrestrial geography became so large that the rubric lost its usefulness. Scientific specialization began. Some scholars concentrated on the rocks that make up the hard surface of the Earth, and geology emerged. Others studied living organisms, and biology grew into a separate discipline. Eventually even these specializations became too comprehensive. Biologists, for example, focused on plants (botany) or animals (zoology). The range of scientific disciplines expanded—and continues to do so to this day.

This, however, did not mean that geography itself lost its identity or relevance. As science became more compartmentalized, geographers realized that they could contribute in several ways, not only by conducting "basic" research, but also by maintaining that connective, integrative perspective that links knowledge from different disciplines. One aspect of this perspective relates to the "where" with which geography is popularly associated. The location or position of features on the surface of the Earth (or above or below it) may well be one of the most significant things about them. Thus geographers seek to learn not only about the features themselves, but also about their spatial relationships. The word **spatial** comes from the noun "space"—not the outer space surrounding our planet, but Earthly, terrestrial space.

The question is not only *where* things are located, but also *why* they are positioned where they are and *how* they came to occupy that position. To use more technical language: What is the cause of the variations in the distribution of phenomena we observe to exist in geographic space? What are the dynamics that shape the spatial organization of each part of the Earth's surface? These are among the central questions that geographers have asked for centuries and continue to pose today.

In some ways, geography is similar to history: both are broad, *holistic* (all-inclusive), integrating disciplines. Historians are interested in questions concerning time and chronology, whereas geographers analyze problems involving space and place. Thus geography's scope is even broader than that of history. As we will see later, historical and chronological matters concern us in physical as well as human geography. But no body of facts or data belongs exclusively to geography. To that extent, at least, geography lost the pre-eminence it enjoyed in the days of the ancient Greeks.

Fields of Geography

Specialization has also developed within geography. Although all geographers share an interest in spatial arrangements, distribution, and organization, some geographers are more interested in physical features or natural phenomena, whereas others concentrate on people and their activities. That is why reference is made in the previous paragraphs to *physical* and *human* geography, the broadest possible division of the discipline. But even within these broad areas there are subdivisions. For example, a physical geographer may work on shorelines and beaches, on soil erosion, or on climate change. A human geographer may be interested in urban problems, in geopolitical trends, or in health issues. As a result, geography today consists of a cluster of fields, many of which are shown in Fig. 1.1. Note that each of the geographic fields included (such as cultural geography, political geography, and population geography) is closely related to what is sometimes called a cognate (common-source) discipline. Thus cultural geography relates closely to anthropology, political geography to political science, population geography to demography, and so forth. In turn, all the fields of geography are

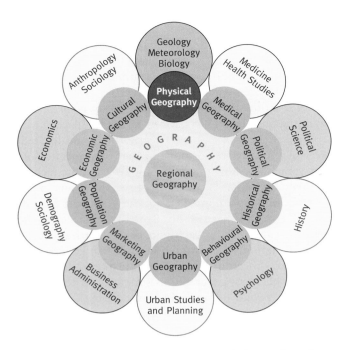

FIGURE 1.1 Schematic representation of the modern discipline of geography—physical geography highlighted—and its cognate fields.

related to each other through the spatial perspective that is geography's common bond.

Figure 1.1 is actually a simplification of the real situation in geography. Each of the fields shown consists of a combination of subfields. Cultural geography, for example, encompasses several subfields, including studies of the cultural landscape (the imprint of a culture upon the land), cultural ecology (the interrelationships between culture and nature), culture hearths (the source areas of civilizations), and cultural diffusion (the movement of innovations and ideas from place to place). Physical geography, too, is an umbrella term for an even larger number of subfields. These subfields will be examined in the units that follow. But first let us examine physical geography as a field of geography.

Physical Geography

As the words imply, physical geography is the geography of the physical world. This field, like the entire discipline, is an old one. Eratosthenes was a pioneer in physical geography at a time when scholars still were unsure about the size or shape of our planet. Eratosthenes's name is permanently enshrined in physical geography's hall of fame because of his remarkably accurate calculation of the circumference of the Earth, a measurement he based on observations of the angle of the Sun at various loca-

tions in Egypt (where he worked). This was the beginning of research in a field now known as *geodesy* (the study of the size and shape of the Earth), but for Eratosthenes it was just one of several geographic pursuits. He realized the importance of mapping his observations, and trained himself to become a skilled *cartographer* (mapmaker and/or analyst). Having concluded that the Earth was spherical (and not, as many of his colleagues believed, flat) and that parts of it were better warmed by the Sun than others, Eratosthenes drew maps of the Earth's environmental zones. He concluded—without ever having been anywhere near them—that the spherical Earth would have a hot equatorial zone, two cold polar zones, and two temperate zones lying between these. Centuries after Eratosthenes's death there still were scholars who did not believe that his ideas were essentially accurate. Here was a geographer way ahead of his time.

Other Greek geographers, and later Roman geographers, studied such physical features as mountains (including the Mediterranean region's volcanoes), rivers, coasts, and islands. Some of them were excellent observers and recorders, and what they wrote about the Mediterranean basin continues to be of interest to scientists today. A scholar named Pliny the Younger (nephew of Pliny the Elder, a scientist) witnessed the eruption of Mount Vesuvius in C.E. 79 from a boat in the nearby Bay of Naples (Fig. 1.2). He described the mushroom cloud rising above the mountain and the burial of such towns as Pompeii and Herculaneum. What he did not know, as he chronicled the disaster from a safe distance, was that his uncle, who had rushed to the scene to help the stricken, died in Vesuvius's poisonous fumes.

It is sad indeed that much of what those ancient geographers wrote has been lost over time, because what has survived is of such enormous interest. From fragments of Greek and Roman writing we know about how wide and fast-flowing the rivers were, the activity of some now-quiet volcanoes, and the density of vegetation in places where there is none today. Worse, after the Romans carried geography so far forward, Europe descended into the Dark Ages, and geography (along with science in general) stagnated. For a thousand years, geographic learning in the Arab realm of North Africa/Southwest Asia and in China advanced far beyond that of Europe. Little of what was achieved by Arab or Chinese scholars was added to the European inventory, however. In addition, many records, maps, and books were lost as a result of wars, fires, and neglect.

Physical geography revived when the age of exploration and discovery dawned around 1500. Portuguese navigators skirted the African coast; Columbus crossed the Atlantic Ocean and returned with reports of new

FIGURE 1.2 An artist's rendition of the horror and chaos in the streets of Pompeii on that fateful summer day in C.E. 79 as the huge cloud of volcanic ash and toxic gases, spewed by nearby Mount Vesuvius, descended on the town and buried it in a matter of seconds.

lands in the West. Cartographers recorded the accumulating knowledge on increasingly accurate maps. In European cities there circulated news of great rivers, snowcapped mountains, wild coasts, vast plains, forbidding escarpments, dense forests with taller trees than had ever been seen, strange and fearful animals, and alien peoples. Explorers and fortune hunters brought back hoards of gold and other valuables. Geographic knowledge could be the key to wealth.

While Europeans rushed to the new lands, scientists tried to find some order in the mass of new information that confronted them. One of the greatest of these scholars was Alexander von Humboldt (1769–1859), who travelled to the New World not for wealth but for knowledge (Fig. 1.3). He managed to travel 3000 km up the uncharted Orinoco River in northern South America, did fieldwork in Ecuador and Peru, crossed what is now Mexico, and visited Cuba before reaching the United States in 1804. Later he traversed Russia, including remote Siberia. He collected thousands of rock samples and plant specimens and made hundreds of drawings of the animals he observed. After settling down in Paris, he wrote 30 books on his American

FIGURE 1.3 A painter's depiction of the expedition of Alexander von Humboldt (standing in boat) making its way through the lowland tropics of northern South America shortly after the turn of the nineteenth century.

travels and later produced his famous six-volume series called *Cosmos,* one of the gigantic scientific achievements of the nineteenth century.

From von Humboldt's writings we can learn about the state of physical geography in his time. It is evident that physical geography had become more than the study of the surface of the Earth. Now it also included studies of the soils, vegetation and animals, the oceans, and the atmosphere. Although the term *physical geography* was firmly entrenched, it might have been more appropriate to use the term *natural geography* for this wide-ranging field.

Von Humboldt demonstrated geographic research methods in many ways. While working in the Andes Mountains of western South America, for instance, he made maps of the slopes, ranges, valleys, and other terrain features of the landscape. He also mapped the vegetation and realized that altitude, temperature, and vegetation types were interrelated. This means, of course, that altitudinal zonation also influences crop cultivation, linking physical (natural) and human geography. Observing the movement of ocean water off the Pacific coast of Peru, von Humboldt identified a cold current that, he correctly concluded, began in Antarctic waters and carried a polar chill to the western shores of equatorial South America. Again, he correctly connected this cold water and prevailing onshore wind patterns with the resulting desert conditions along the narrow Peruvian coastal plain. This ocean current, in fact, was for a long time named the Humboldt Current in his honour (more recently it has become known as the Peru Current).

Subfields of Physical Geography

The stage was now set for the development of specializations within the field of physical geography, and soon these subfields began to take shape. Over the past century, physical geography has evolved into a cluster of research foci, the most important of which are diagrammed in Fig. 1.4. Remember that the entire field of physical geography is only one of those illustrated in Fig. 1.1.

The geography of landscape, **geomorphology** (1), remains one of the most productive subfields of physical geography. As the term suggests (*geo,* meaning Earth; *morph,* meaning shape or form), this area of research focuses on the structuring of the Earth's surface. Geomorphologists seek to understand the evolution of slopes, the development of plains and plateaus, and the processes shaping dunes and caves and cliffs—the elements of the physical landscape. Often geomorphology has far-reaching implications. From the study of landscape it is possible to prove the former presence of

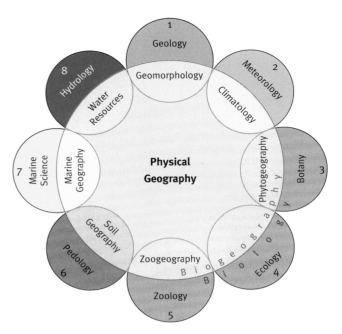

FIGURE 1.4 Schematic representation of the specialized subfields that constitute physical geography.

ice sheets and mountain glaciers, rivers, and deserts. *Geology* is geomorphology's closest ally, but the study of geomorphology can involve far more than rocks. The work of running water, moving ice, surging waves, and restless air all contribute to landscape genesis. And while these forces shape the surface above, geologic forces modify it from below.

Proceeding clockwise from the top of Fig. 1.4, we observe that *meteorology* (the branch of physics that deals with atmospheric phenomena) and physical geography combine to form **climatology** (2), the study of climates and their spatial distribution. Climatology involves not only the classification of climates and the analysis of their distribution, but also broader environmental questions, including climatic change, vegetation patterns, soil formation, and the relationships between human societies and climate.

As Fig. 1.4 indicates, the next three subfields relate physical geography to aspects of *biology.* Where biology and physical geography overlap is the broad subfield of **biogeography** (3–5), but there are specializations within biogeography itself. Physical geography combined with botany forms **phytogeography** (3), and combined with zoology it becomes **zoogeography** (5). Note that biogeography (4), itself linked to *ecology,* lies between these two subfields; in fact, both zoogeography and phytogeography are parts of biogeography. The next subfield of physical geography is related to soil science, or *pedology*. Pedologists' research tends to focus on the internal properties of soils and the processes that go on during soil development. In **soil geography** (6), research centres on the spatial patterns of soils, their distribution, and their relationships to climate, vegetation, and humankind.

Other subfields of physical geography are **marine geography** (7) and the study of **water resources** (8). Marine geography, which is related to the discipline of *marine science,* also has human as well as physical components. The human side of marine geography has to do with maritime boundaries, the competition for marine resources, and the law of the sea; therefore, this subfield is closely allied with political geography (see Fig. 1.1). The physical side of marine geography deals with coastlines and shores, beaches, river mouths, and other landscape features associated with the oceanic margins of the continents. The subfield of water resources (where *hydrology* and physical geography intersect) also has human as well as physical elements. The landmasses contain fresh water at the surface (in the form of lakes and rivers) and below (as groundwater). As we will see later in this book, the study of these waters may be approached from geomorphic as well as economic standpoints.

In the 51 units that follow, these various subfields of physical geography will be examined in some detail, and the connections between physical and human geography also will be revealed. As you will see, we must go beyond the confines of Fig. 1.4 to put our work in proper perspective. To understand the basics of physical geography, we must comprehend the general properties of our planet, not only deep below its surface, but also far beyond as it orbits the Sun as part of the solar system in our tiny corner of the vast universe. Comprehending general properties will be among our first tasks and constitute much of the remainder of Part One.

FIGURE 1.5 Toroweap Point overlooking the Grand Canyon of the Colorado River. Parts of the canyon are 1600 m deep and 29 km wide. This most famous physiographic feature of North America extends for nearly 450 km across northern Arizona, where the snowmelt-fed Colorado River has exposed hundreds of millions of years of sedimentary rock strata. The geologist-geographer John Wesley Powell led the first river expedition through this massive gorge in 1869—and gave the Grand Canyon its name.

A Century of Physical Geography

During the past century, physical geographers have made many noteworthy and interesting contributions to science. Over time, the nature of these contributions has changed. Just 100 years ago, for example, the map of the physical geography of North America was still being filled in, and physical geographers such as John Wesley Powell and Grove Karl Gilbert reported on the spectacular scenery they studied in the western United States. Through sketches and cross-sectional profiles, Powell described his journeys down the Colorado River and told the story of one of the Earth's greatest natural features, the Grand Canyon (Fig. 1.5). Gilbert analyzed the origins of prominent mountains and showed how running water could remove huge amounts of rock, carrying it from hillslope to river delta. Prominent physical features were given names, and later a famous cartographer, Erwin Raisz, drew a minutely detailed map of the physical landscape of the entire United States—a cartographic masterpiece still in use today.

Other physical geographers, explorer-scientists all, fired the imaginations of their colleagues and students. Some of their names became permanently associated with the landscapes or physical features they studied: Louis Agassiz and glaciers, William Libbey and ocean currents, Arnold Guyot and ocean-floor topography. But perhaps the most important scholar between the 1880s and 1930s was William Morris Davis (1850–1934), who taught physical geography at Harvard and several other universities. Davis was less the explorer and more the theoretician (although he travelled worldwide in pursuit of his ideas), and in a series of significant papers he published the first comprehensive theory concerning the way rocks and geologic structures are worn down by the force of running (stream) water. He coined many terms we still use today, and he moved physical geography into the modern scientific era. In Unit 42 we look at Davis's theories and see how others built upon (or countered) them.

Following Davis, specialization in physical geography became stronger, and the subfields shown in Fig. 1.4 gained identity. In the United States, Wallace Atwood took the field in a more physiographic (regional), less geomorphic direction at Harvard University, where he succeeded Davis. In Canada the geomorphic tradition remained strong, well into the twentieth century and today, with a very active group of internationally recognized geomorphologists. Climatologists such as C. Warren Thornthwaite and Wladimir P. Köppen advanced this field of physical geography, and Canadians like F. Kenneth Hare, Timothy Oke, and Marie Sanderson have more recently become recognized as significant Canadian geographers. Griffith Taylor, an Antarctic scientist who contributed to Scott's Antarctic expedition and to the development of geography in Canada, Australia, and the United States, has described the evolution of the discipline and its philosophical basis (see reference list at the end of this unit).

Many other scholars, too numerous to mention here, have contributed to the recent development of physical geography in North America. You will find much of their work cited in the end-of-unit references throughout this book. There still are physical geographers working on large, theoretical questions as Davis did (now with the aid of sophisticated quantitative techniques and computer-based approaches), but others work on highly specialized, very specific questions. These days, when you ask a physical geographer what his or her specialty is, you frequently hear such answers as hydroclimatology, periglacial processes, paleogeography, or wetland ecosystems. All this helps explain the wide range of material you will encounter in this book, which is an overview of a broad field encompassing many topics.

Systems and Models in Physical Geography

Physical geography is a multifaceted science that seeks to understand major elements of our complex world. In order to deal with this complexity, physical geographers employ numerous concepts and specialized methods, many of which will emerge in the units that follow. This section provides an introduction to that analysis by considering two general approaches to the subject: systems and models.

Systems

In recent years, many physical geographers have found it convenient to organize their approach to the field within a systems framework of thinking. A **system** may be regarded as any set of related events or objects and their interactions. A city could be described as a large and elaborate system. Each day the system receives an inflow of energy, food, water, and vast quantities of consumer goods. Most of this energy and matter is used and changed in form by the various populations that reside in the urban centre. At the same time, huge amounts of energy, manufactured goods, and services, along with sewage and other waste products, are produced in and exported from the city. Note that energy and matter freely transfer across the city's boundaries, making it an **open system** and underscoring its relationships with surrounding systems (such as the agricultural and energy-producing systems of the region of which it is a part). There are many examples of open systems throughout this book, such as a weather system or a river drainage basin. Indeed, in terms of energy flows, the Earth itself is an enormous open system that comprises several interconnected lesser systems. Although it is difficult to find one on the Earth's surface, we should also know what is meant by the term **closed system**: a self-contained system exhibiting no exchange of energy or matter across its boundaries. (One example of a closed system, when the entire Earth is considered, is the carbon cycle, which is discussed in Unit 6.)

An important property of a system is its organization as an integrated whole. Accordingly, systems often contain one or more subsystems. A **subsystem** is a component of a larger system. A subsystem can act independently, but it operates within, and is linked to, the larger system. The food distribution, manufacturing, and sewage systems are subsystems of the total city system described in the preceding paragraph. Systems and subsystems have boundaries, called *interfaces*. The transfer or exchange of energy and matter takes place at these interfaces (which may also be regarded as surfaces). Sometimes interfaces are visible: you can see where sunlight strikes the roof of a building. But often they are not visible: you cannot see the movement of groundwater, a part of the global water system, as it flows through the subterranean rocks of the geologic system. Many geographers focus their attention on these interfaces, visible or invisible, particularly when they coincide with the Earth's surface. It is here that we find the greatest activity of our dynamic world.

Two other ideas commonly used in systems approaches are those of dynamic equilibrium and feedback. A system is in **dynamic equilibrium** when it is neither growing nor getting smaller but continues to be in balance and complete operation. **Feedback** occurs when a change in one part of the system causes a change in another part of the system. Let us consider two examples. If you were to look at the sand in a specific area of Miami Beach (Fig. 1.6), you would barely perceive that the currents moving along the shore are taking away some sand and bringing in a replacement supply. There is continual movement, yet over a period of weeks the beach apparently stays the same. The beach, thus, can be said to be in a state of dynamic equilibrium.

An example of feedback, or a *feedback mechanism*, would be the case of solar radiation being reflected from a Toronto sidewalk. The sidewalk's surface receives energy from the Sun, but it also reflects and radiates some of that energy back into the atmosphere as well as losing it in other ways. The more energy the sidewalk receives, the more it reflects and reradiates. Because of the reflection and reradiation, the sidewalk does not become increasingly hotter. Without the feedback mechanisms of reflection and reradiation, it would certainly be impossible to walk on that surface at midday during summer.

A feedback mechanism that operates to keep a system in its original condition, such as the reflection or radiation from the sidewalk, is called a *negative feedback mechanism*. The opposite case, in which a feedback mechanism induces a progressively greater change from the original condition of a system, is called a *positive feedback mechanism*. In a later unit it is explained why the growth of a metropolitan area leads to higher average air temperatures. A change of this kind is an example of positive feedback.

Models

Another way that physical geographers approach the study of the Earth's phenomena is to make models of them. In his landmark book on geographic analysis, Peter Haggett defined a **model** as *the creation of an idealized representation of reality in order to demonstrate its most important properties*. Model building, therefore, is a com-

plementary way of thinking about the world. It entails the controlled simplification of a complex reality, filtering out the essential forces and patterns from the myriad details with which they are embedded in a complicated world. Such abstractions, which convey not the entire truth but a valid and reasonable part of it, are highly useful because they facilitate the development of generalizations. We saw this in the preceding discussion of the city system, which underscored some universal attributes concerning the spatial interaction between cities and the surrounding regions they serve. Systems, therefore, may also be regarded as models. Models will be used frequently in this book because they allow us to penetrate a complex subject quickly and highlight its most essential aspects.

Geographic Magnitude

In approaching the real world, we must also consider the size of the subjects and phenomena that interest us. Even speeding at 1000 km per hour, one may become uncomfortable on a 16-hour flight from Vancouver to Sydney, Australia, because, in human terms, the world is such a big place. But in studying our planet, we must not think of distance and magnitude in purely human terms.

Let us consider different sizes, or **orders of magnitude**. Figure 1.7 shows the various orders of magnitude with which we must become familiar. The scale in this figure is written in *exponential* notation. This means that 100 is written as 10^2 (10×10), 1000 is 10^3 ($10 \times 10 \times 10$), 0.01 is 10^{-2} (1/100), and so forth. This notation saves us from writing numerous zeros. The scales geographers use most often—which are shown on the right-hand side of Fig. 1.7—go from about 10^5 or 10^6 cm, the size of Point Pleasant Park in Halifax or Central Park in New York City (Fig. 1.8), up to about 10^{10} cm, beyond the order of magnitude of the Earth's circumference (see Perspective: Sliding Scale). Physical geographers sometimes have to expand their minds even further. Cosmic rays with wavelengths of 10^{-16} cm may affect our climate. The nearest fixed star is approximately 10^{18} cm away. Brighter stars much farther away sometimes help when navigating a path across the Earth's surface. Occasionally (as in Unit 4) we have to perform mental gymnastics to conceive of such distances, but one of the beauties of physical geography is that it helps us to see the world in a different way.

Let us now embark on our detailed study of the Earth. Central to this effort is the attempt to understand the environment at the Earth's surface, a habitat we must all live with in a one-to-one relationship. Nobody who has become acquainted with physical geography is ever likely to forget that.

FROM THE FIELDNOTES

FIGURE 1.6 "South Florida's Atlantic coast, looking northward beyond Miami Beach. At present the beach seen in this photograph represents a system in dynamic equilibrium, with currents flowing parallel to the coast, continuously removing sand and at the same time depositing a replacement supply."

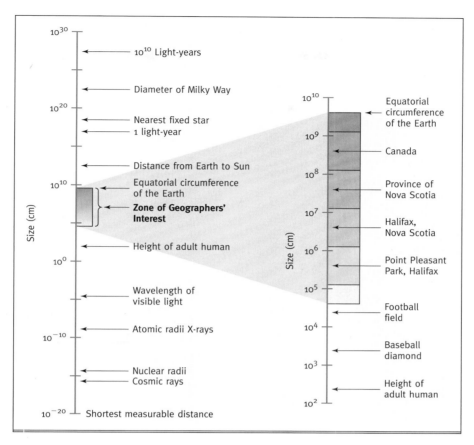

FIGURE 1.7   Orders of geographic magnitude. Geographers mostly operate in the context of the scales shown on the right, but sometimes they must think in much smaller or larger terms, as indicated at left.

PERSPECTIVES ON THE HUMAN ENVIRONMENT

Sliding Scale

Imagine a couple sunbathing on Cavendish Beach. We can photograph them occupying a square of sand about 1 m on a side. If we move the camera higher, a square of 10 (10^1) m reveals their companions. When we focus on a 100 (10^2) m area, we can see a crowd of people on the beach. A picture of 1000 (10^3) m includes the beach, some sea, and some land (as in Fig. 1.6). One with an edge of 10,000 (10^4) m captures most of Prince Edward Island National Park and parts of the neighbouring north shore of Prince Edward Island.

Moving the camera still farther, we shoot a picture of a 100,000 (10^5) m square. It encompasses most of the central P.E.I. region. The next step is 1,000,000 (10^6) m. This snapshot takes in the entire province of P.E.I., some neighbouring provinces, and parts of the Atlantic Ocean, the Gulf of St. Lawrence, and the Bay of Fundy. A photo at the next level of generalization, showing a square of 10,000,000 (10^7) m, covers most of the visible Earth. And if the camera is far enough away in outer space to focus on a square of 100,000,000 (10^8) m, we see Planet Earth as a small globe. Somewhere on it is that couple lying on a square of Cavendish Beach's seaside sand.

FIGURE 1.8   Central Park really does occupy a central location on the totally built up island of Manhattan. This north-looking view of the 340-hectare green space shows the park, first laid out in 1856, flanked by tall buildings in all directions. Central Park for many years has been the subject of geographic studies, ranging from biogeography (the survival of plants and animals in this unique setting) to human geography (the behaviour of people as they use the park for purposes ranging from open-air symphony concerts to skateboarding).

KEY TERMS

biogeography *page 10*	**marine geography** *page 11*	**spatial** *page 7*
climatology *page 10*	**model** *page 13*	**subsystem** *page 12*
closed system *page 12*	**open system** *page 12*	**system** *page 12*
dynamic equilibrium *page 13*	**orders of magnitude** *page 13*	**water resources** *page 11*
feedback *page 13*	**phytogeography** *page 10*	**zoogeography** *page 10*
geomorphology *page 10*	**soil geography** *page 11*	

REVIEW QUESTIONS

1. Define the term *spatial* and show how it is central to the study of geography.
2. What contributions did the Greeks and Romans make to the early evolution of physical geography?
3. What is physical geography? How does it differ from other sciences?
4. Define the eight major subfields of physical geography. What are their major foci of study? How do these differ from other fields in the natural and social sciences?
5. Define the terms *system, subsystem, open system, dynamic equilibrium,* and *feedback.*
6. Define the term *model,* and describe how models can help us understand our complex physical world.

REFERENCES AND FURTHER READINGS

ATWOOD, W. W. *The Physiographic Provinces of North America* (New York: Ginn, 1940).

CHORLEY, R. J., et al. *The History of the Study of Landforms, or the Development of Geomorphology. Vol. 2: The Life and Work of William Morris Davis* (New York: Wiley, 1973).

GAILE, G. L., and WILLMOT, C. J., Eds. *Geography in America* (Columbus, Ohio: Merrill, 1989), 28–94, 112–146.

GOUDIE, A. S., et al., Eds. *The Encyclopedic Dictionary of Physical Geography* (Cambridge, Mass.: Blackwell, 3rd ed., 1994).

GREGORY, K. J. *The Changing Nature of Physical Geography* (New York: Oxford Univ. Press, 2000).

HAGGETT, P. *Locational Analysis in Human Geography* (London: Edward Arnold, 1965), 19.

HANCOCK, P. L., and SKINNER, B. J., Eds. *Oxford Companion to the Earth* (New York: Oxford Univ. Press, 2001).

JAMES, P. E., and MARTIN, G. J. *All Possible Worlds: A History of Geographical Ideas* (New York: Wiley, 3rd ed., 1993).

MARCUS, M. G. "Coming Full Circle: Physical Geography in the Twentieth Century," *Annals of the Association of American Geographers,* 69 (1979), 521–532.

ORME, A. R., Ed. *The Physical Geography of North America* (New York: Oxford Univ. Press, 2001).

PATTISON, W. D. "The Four Traditions of Geography," *Journal of Geography,* 63 (1964), 211–216.

Rediscovering Geography: New Relevance for Science and Society (Washington, DC: National Academy Press, 1997).

SANDERSON, M. *Griffith Taylor: Antarctic Scientist and Pioneer Geographer* (Ottawa: Carleton University Press, 1988).

TAYLOR, G., Ed. *Geography in the Twentieth Century* (London: Methuen, 1951).

THOMAS, D., and GOUDIE, A. S., Eds. *The Dictionary of Physical Geography* (Malden, Mass.: Blackwell, 3rd ed., 2000).

TINKLER, K. *A Short History of Geomorphology* (London: Croom Helm, 1985).

WOLMAN, M. G. "Contemporary Value of Geography: Applied Physical Geography and the Environmental Sciences," in A. Rogers et al., Eds. *The Student's Companion to Geography* (Cambridge, Mass.: Blackwell, 1992), 3–7.

WEB RESOURCES

http://www.aag.org A general introduction to the field of geography, including specialty groups in physical geography.

http://www.cag-acg.ca The Canadian Association of Geographers (CAG). The CAG is the national organization representing practising geographers from public and private sectors and from universities.

The Planet Earth

The five spheres of the Earth System in harmonious interaction. Mount Tasman, South Island, New Zealand. (Authors' photo)

OBJECTIVES

- To define and highlight the five spheres of the Earth System

- To highlight the general characteristics of the Earth's continents

- To introduce the world's ocean basins and the topographic characteristics of the seafloor

W hen U.S. astronauts for the first time left Earth's orbit and reached the Moon, they were able to look back at our planet and see it as no one had ever seen it before. The television cameras aboard their spacecraft beamed spectacular pictures of the Earth, seen on television sets around the globe. As colour-enhanced photos later showed, against the dark sky the Earth displayed a range of vivid colours, from the blue of the oceans to the green of forests to the brown of sparsely vegetated land to the great white swirls of weather systems in the atmosphere (see photo, p. 6). The astronauts, however, also saw things no camera could adequately transmit. Most of all, they were struck by the smallness of our world in the vastness of the universe, what architect Buckminster Fuller called "Spaceship Earth." It was difficult to conceive that all 6-plus billion humans and their works were confined to, and dependent upon, so tiny a planet. Every participant in those Moon missions returned with a sense of awe—and a heightened concern over the fragility of our terrestrial life-support systems.

In the units that follow, we will examine these systems and learn, among other things, how serious the threat of irreversible damage to them may be. We should remember that all the systems we will study—weather and climate, oceanic circulation, soil formation, vegetation growth, landform development, and erosion—ultimately are parts of one great Earth System. Even though this total Earth System is an open system with respect to energy flows, the amount of matter on and in the Earth is pretty much fixed. Little new matter is being added to supplement what we use up, and so far nothing of consequence permanently leaves the Earth. This means that our material resource base is finite; that is, parts of it can be used up. It also means that any hazardous products we create must remain a part of our environment.

Spheres of the Earth System

Our planet consists of a set of interacting shells or "spheres," some of them extending over the entire globe, others covering it partially. The **atmosphere** is the blanket of air that adheres to the Earth's surface. It is our life layer, the mixture of gases we breathe. It begins a few metres within the soil or on the water's surface, and its outermost periphery can be tracked to a height of about 60,000 km above the Earth. Heat energy from the Sun keeps the atmosphere in motion, causing weather systems to form and travel across land and sea. The atmosphere is most dense at sea level and thins out with increasing altitude.

Below the atmosphere lies the outermost shell of the solid Earth, the **lithosphere** (*lithos* means rock). The lithosphere's upper surface is sculpted into the almost endless variety of landforms and physical landscapes that form the Earth's scenery. The lithosphere continues under the oceans, where the surface of the seafloor is created by forces quite different from those on land.

Constituting about 71 percent of the Earth's surface, the oceans lie between the atmosphere and the lithosphere. This is the largest segment of the **hydrosphere**, which contains all the water that exists on and within the solid surface of the Earth and in the atmosphere above. The oceans are the primary moisture source for the precipitation that falls on the landmasses, carried there in the constantly moving atmosphere.

The **cryosphere** includes all forms of frozen water, including glaciers, floating ice, snow cover, and permafrost (permanently frozen subsoil). Although it could logically be regarded as a component of the hydrosphere, the cryosphere does have its own distinct properties, and many scientists in recent years have come to recognize it as a full-fledged Earth sphere. It should be noted, however, that the cryosphere is the only one of these spheres that is discontinuous across our planet.

The **biosphere** is the zone of life, the home of all living things. This includes the Earth's vegetation, animals, and human beings. Since there are living organisms in the soil and plants are rooted in soil, part of the soil layer (which is otherwise a component of the lithosphere) may be included in the biosphere.

These five spheres—atmosphere, lithosphere, hydrosphere, cryosphere, and biosphere—are the key Earth layers with which we shall be concerned in our study of physical geography. But other shells of the Earth also play their roles. Not only are there outer layers atop the effective atmosphere, but there also are spheres inside the Earth, beneath the lithosphere. In turn, the lithosphere is affected by forces and processes from above. Thus it is important to keep in mind the interactions among the five spheres—they are not separate and independent segments of our planet, but constantly interacting subsystems of the total **Earth System**.

These systemic interrelationships are diagrammed in Fig. 2.1. The atmosphere, lithosphere, hydrosphere, cryosphere, and biosphere are the main components of the physical world. They are linked together in any one place and over the Earth as a whole. As the diagram demonstrates, physical geographers study the phenomena within these spheres and the multiple interactions among them. Within the total Earth System, the five

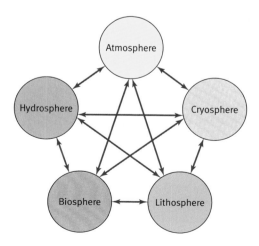

FIGURE 2.1 The five spheres of the Earth System and their interrelationships.

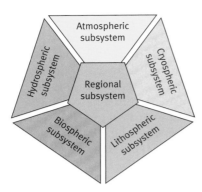

FIGURE 2.2 The Earth System and its subsystems. A regional subsystem encompasses parts of the other five subsystems.

spheres or subsystems also interconnect at any given place to form a **regional subsystem** (Fig. 2.2). We are interested in the special ways in which the five major subsystems work together to form a regional subsystem. In a sense each regional subsystem is unique, but there are enough similarities between the ways in which our five spheres interact to produce the landscapes we live on for us to group some types of regional subsystems together. The rationale for grouping places together into regions is discussed in several units in this book.

Hemispheres

In addition to five layered spheres (the atmosphere, lithosphere, hydrosphere, cryosphere, and biosphere), the Earth can also be divided into **hemispheres** (from the ancient Greek, *hemi*, meaning half; *sphaira*, meaning sphere). The northern half of the globe, from the Equator to the North Pole, is the Northern Hemisphere; the southern half is the Southern Hemisphere. There are many differences between the two hemispheres, which will be seen in later units that treat patterns of seasonality, planetary rotational effects, and the regionalization of climates. Perhaps the most obvious difference concerns the distribution of land and sea (Fig. 2.3). The Earth's continental landmasses are far more heavily concentrated in the Northern Hemisphere (which contains about 70 percent of the total land area); the Southern Hemisphere has much less land and much more water than the Northern Hemisphere. Moreover, the polar areas of each hemisphere differ considerably. The Northern Hemisphere polar zone—the *Arctic*—consists of peripheral islands covered mostly by thick ice and a central mass of sea ice floating atop the Arctic Ocean (Fig. 2.3, inset map A). The Southern Hemisphere polar zone—the *Antarctic*—is dominated by a large

continental landmass covered with the world's largest continuous ice sheet (inset map B).

The Earth can be further divided into Eastern and Western Hemispheres. Technically, the Eastern Hemisphere lies to the east of an imaginary line drawn from pole to pole through the Royal Observatory in Greenwich, England (part of the city of London), and on through the middle of the Pacific Ocean on the opposite side of the world. In practice, however, the Western Hemisphere consists of the half of the Earth centred on the Americas, and the Eastern Hemisphere contains all of Eurasia and Africa. So there is a precise use, based on a grid drawn on the globe (which is elaborated in Unit 3), and a more general use of this hemispheric division.

A look at any globe representing the Earth suggests yet another pair of hemispheres: a **land hemisphere** and a **water** (or oceanic) **hemisphere**. The landmasses are concentrated on one side of the Earth to such a degree that it is appropriate to refer to that half of the Earth as the land hemisphere (Fig. 2.4). This hemisphere is centred on Africa, which lies surrounded by the other continents: the Americas to the west, Eurasia to the north and northeast, Australia to the southeast, and Antarctica to the south. The opposite hemisphere, the water hemisphere, is dominated by the Earth's greatest ocean, the Pacific. When you look at a globe from above the centre of the Pacific Ocean, only the fringes of the landmasses appear along the margins of this huge body of water.

Continents and Oceans

There is an old saying to the effect that "the Earth has six continents and seven seas." In fact, that generalization is not too far off the mark (see Fig. 2.3). The Earth does have six continental landmasses: Africa, South America, North America, Eurasia (Europe and Asia occupy a single large landmass), Australia, and Antarctica. As for the seven seas, there are five great oceanic bodies of water and several smaller seas. The Pacific Ocean is the largest of all. The Indian Ocean lies between Africa and Australia. The North Atlantic Ocean and the South Atlantic Ocean may be regarded as two discrete oceans that are dissimilar in a number of ways. Encircling Antarctica is the Southern Ocean. Sixth, and largest of the smaller seas, is the Arctic Ocean, which lies beneath the floating Arctic icecap.

The seventh body of water often identified with these oceans is the Mediterranean Sea, which lies between Europe and Africa and is connected to the interior sea of Eurasia, the Black Sea. The Mediterranean is not of oceanic dimensions, but unlike the Caribbean or the Arabian Sea, it also is not merely an extension of an ocean. The Mediterranean is very nearly landlocked and has only one narrow natural outlet through the Strait of Gibraltar, between Spain and Morocco.

In our study of weather and climate, the relative location, general dimensions, and the topography of the landmasses are important, because these influence the movement of moisture-carrying air.

The Landmasses

Only about 29 percent of the surface of the Earth is constituted by land; 71 percent is water or ice. Thus less than one-third of our planet is habitable by human beings, but much of this area is too dry, too cold, or too rugged to allow large concentrations of settlement. Our livable world where permanent settlement is possible—known as the **ecumene**—is small indeed (see Perspective: Human Population and Natural Processes).

Each of the six continental landmasses possesses unique physical properties. *Africa,* which accounts for just over 20 percent of the total land area, is at the heart of the land hemisphere. Of all the landmasses, Africa alone lies astride the Equator in such a way that large segments of it occupy the Northern as well as the Southern Hemisphere. Africa often is called the plateau continent, because much of its landmass lies above 1000 m in elevation, and coastal plains are relatively narrow. As Fig. 2.3 reveals, a fairly steep escarpment rises near the coast in many parts of Africa, leading rapidly up to the plateau surface of the interior. African rivers that rise in the interior plunge over falls and rapids before reaching the coast, limiting their navigability. Furthermore, Africa lacks a physical feature seen on all the other landmasses: a linear mountain range comparable to South America's Andes, North America's Rocky Mountains, Eurasia's Himalayas, or Australia's Great Dividing Range. The reason for this will become clear when the geomorphic history of that continent is discussed.

South America, occupying 12 percent of the world's land, is much smaller than Africa (Table 2.1). The topography of this landmass is dominated in the west by the gigantic Andes Mountains, which exceed 6000 m in height in many places. East of the mountains, the surface becomes a plateau interrupted by the basins of major rivers, among which the Amazon is by far the largest. The Andes constitute a formidable barrier to the cross-continental movement of air, which has a major impact on the distribution of South America's climates.

North America, with one-sixth of the total land area, is substantially larger than South America. This landmass extends from Arctic to tropical environments. Western North America is mainly mountainous; the great Rocky Mountains stretch from Alaska to Mexico. West of the Rockies lie other major mountain ranges, such as the Sierra Nevada and the Cascades. East of the Rocky Mountains lie extensive plains covering a vast area from Hudson Bay south to the Gulf of Mexico and curving up along the Atlantic seaboard as far north as New York City. Another north–south-trending mountain range, the Appalachians, rises between the coastal and interior lowlands of the East. Thus the continental topography is somewhat funnel-shaped. This means that air from both polar and tropical areas can penetrate the heart of the continent, without topographic obstruction, from north and south. As a result, summer weather there can be tropical, whereas winter weather exhibits Arctic-like extremes.

Eurasia (covering 36.5 percent of the land surface) is by far the largest landmass on Earth, and all of it lies in the Northern Hemisphere. The topography of Europe and Asia is dominated by a huge mountain chain that extends from west to east across the hybrid continent. It has many names in various countries, the most familiar of which are the Alps in Central Europe and the Himalayas in South Asia. In Europe, the Alps lie between the densely populated North European Lowland to the north and the subtropical Mediterranean lands to the south. In Asia, the Himalayas form but one of many great mountain ranges that emanate from central Asia northeastward into Russia's Siberia, eastward into China, and southeastward into South and Southeast Asia. Between and below these ranges lie several of the world's most densely populated river plains, including China's Huang He (Yellow) and Chang Jiang (Yangzi) and India's Ganges.

Australia is the world's smallest continent (constituting less than 6 percent of the total land area) and topographically its lowest. The Great Dividing Range lies near the continent's eastern coast, and its highest peak reaches a mere 2217 m. Australia's northern areas lie in the tropics, but its southern coasts are washed by the outer fringes of Antarctic waters.

Antarctica, the "frozen continent," lies almost entirely buried by the world's largest and thickest ice sheet. Beneath the ice, Antarctica (constituting the remaining 9.3 percent of the world's land area) has a varied topography that includes the southernmost link in the Andean mountain chain (the backbone of the Antarctic Peninsula). Currently very little of this underlying landscape is exposed, but Antarctica was not always a frigid polar landmass. As will be discussed in more detail later, the Antarctic ice, the air above it, and the waters around it are critically important in the global functioning of the atmosphere, hydrosphere, and biosphere.

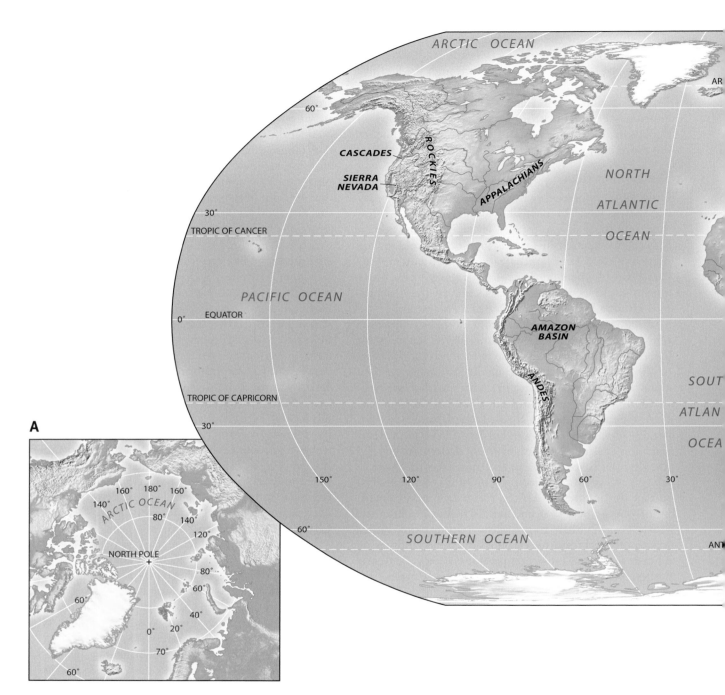

FIGURE 2.3 Distribution of land and sea on the Earth's surface. The continents are shown in topographic relief; the terrain of the ocean floor is shown in Fig. 2.6.

The Ocean Basins

Before the twentieth century, the ocean basins were unknown territory. Only the tidal fringes of the continents and the shores of deep-sea islands revealed glimpses of what might lie below the vast world ocean. Then sounding devices were developed, and some of the ocean-floor topography became apparent, at least in cross-sectional profile. Next, equipment was built that permitted the collection of rock samples from the seabed. And now marine scientists are venturing down to deep areas of the ocean floor and can watch volcanic eruptions in progress through the portholes of deep-sea submersibles. The

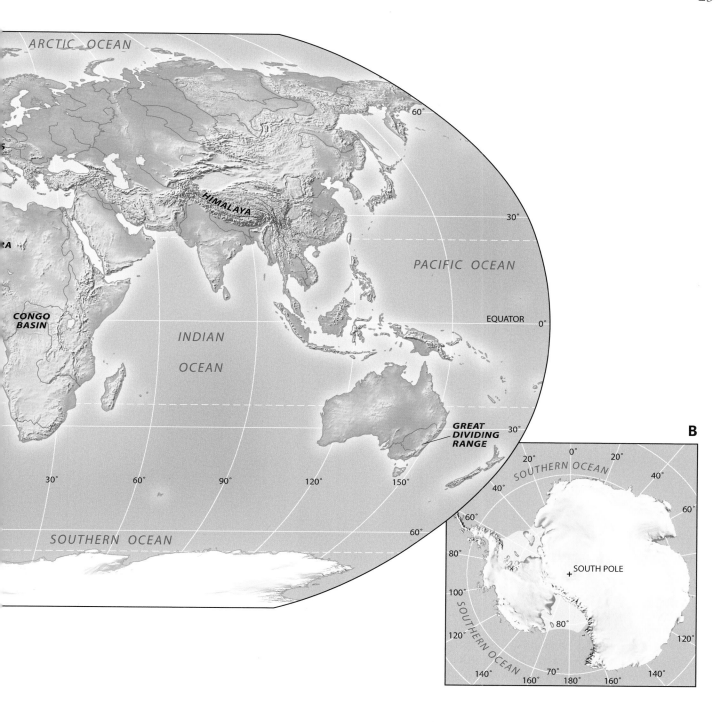

secrets of the submerged 71 percent of the lithosphere are finally being revealed.

When the seafloors were mapped and the composition and age of rock samples were determined, a remarkable discovery was made: the deep ocean floors are geologically different from the continental landmasses. The ocean floors have a varied topography, but this topography is not simply an extension of what we see on land. There are ridges and valleys and mountains and plains, but these are not comparable to the Appalachians or the Amazon Basin.

We return to this topic in Part Four. For the present we should acquaint ourselves with the main features of the ocean basins. If all the water were removed from

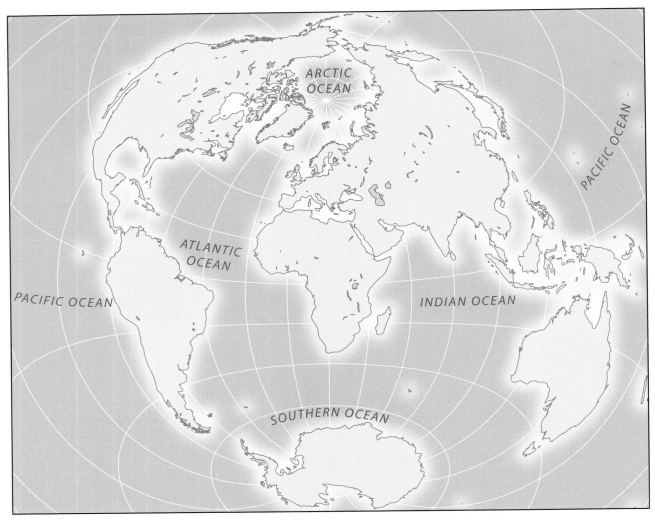

FIGURE 2.4 Land Hemisphere. This is the half of the globe that contains most of the world's landmasses, which surround the African continent.

the ocean basins, they would reveal the topography shown in Fig. 2.6. The map reveals that the ocean basins can be divided into three regions: (1) the margins of the continents, (2) the abyssal zones—extensive, mound-studded plains at great depth, and (3) a system of ridges flanked by elaborate fractures and associated relief.

The continental margin consists of the continental shelf, continental slope, and continental rise. The **continental shelf** is the very gently sloping, relatively shallow, submerged plain at the edge of the continent. The map shows the continental shelves to be continuations of the continental landmasses (see especially the areas off eastern North America, southeastern South America, and northwestern Europe). Generally these shelves extend no deeper than 180 m. Their average width is about 80 km, but some are as wide as 1000 km. Because the continental shelves are extensions of the

landmasses, the continental geologic structure continues to their edges. During the most recent ice age, when much ocean water was taken up by the ice sheets, sea levels dropped enough to expose most of these continental shelves. Rivers flowed across them and carved valleys that can still be seen on detailed maps. The oceans today are fuller than in the past, and they have flooded the extensive plains at the margins of the continents.

At a depth of about 180 m, the continental shelf ends at a break in slope that is quite marked in some places and less steep in others. At this discontinuity the **continental slope** begins and plunges steeply downward. Often at the foot of the continental slope there is a transitional **continental rise** of gently downsloping seafloor (Fig. 2.6). The continental rise leads into the abyssal zone. This zone consists mainly of the **abyssal plains**, large expanses of lower-relief ocean floor. The

Table 2.1 Dimensions of the Landmasses

Landmass	Area km²	Percentage of Land Surface	Highest Mountain	Elevation (m)
Africa	30,300	20.2	Kilimanjaro	5,861
South America	17,870	11.9	Aconcagua	6,919
North America	24,350	16.3	McKinley	6,158
Eurasia	54,650	36.5	Everest	8,848
Australia	8,290	5.6	Kosciusko	2,217
Antarctica	13,990	9.3	Vinson Massif	5,110

PERSPECTIVES ON THE HUMAN ENVIRONMENT

Human Population and Natural Processes

This book focuses on the physical systems, forces, and processes that modify natural landscapes, but at this early stage we should take note of the human factor and its impact on the natural world. As we will note later, animals, from worms to wallabies, play their roles in modifying landscapes by burrowing, digging, grazing, browsing, and even, as with beavers, felling trees and building dams. But no species in the history of this planet has transformed natural landscapes to the degree humans have. We have converted entire regions to irrigated agriculture, terraced cultivable hillslopes, confined and controlled whole river systems, and reconstructed shorelines. We are also deforesting vast areas, destroying soil cover, gouging huge open-pit mines, and building and paving once natural surfaces into megacities so large that they become global-scale landscape features in their own right. In the first half of the twentieth century, geographers began to distinguish between **natural landscapes**, those areas of the planet still essentially subject to the physical processes we discuss here, and **cultural landscapes**, in which human intervention dominates to such an extent that physical processes have become subordinate. As the human population has grown, the cultural has gained as the natural has receded.

Population grew explosively during the twentieth century, from 1.5 billion in 1900 to more than 6 billion in 2000. Although the overall rate of growth has been declining in recent decades, the world still is adding about 75 million people per year to a total that already exceeded 6.3 billion in 2003. And while population in some areas of the world has begun to stabilize and even decline (Russia, Japan, most of Europe), it continues to mushroom elsewhere, notably in South and Southwest Asia. But sheer numbers are no guide to a population's impact on the natural world. Highly developed, rich societies place demands on the resources of our planet that translate into massive intervention (in the United States, think of the Tennessee Valley Authority, the Colorado and Mississippi Rivers, the agricultural Midwest, the northeastern seaboard's Megalopolis that stretches from north of Boston to south of Washington D.C.). More populous but less developed and less demanding societies cannot afford to bend nature to their needs and tend to live subject to its uncertainties, as do the vast majority of the people in Bangladesh.

It is nevertheless useful to have a sense of the spatial distribution of the world's population (Fig. 2.5). Our technological, environment-controlling capacities notwithstanding, this map still represents the historic accommodation humans made as populations entered and adjusted to habitats capable of supporting them. Two of the three great clusters—East Asia and South Asia—still represent dominantly rural, agricultural populations, despite what is happening on Asia's Pacific

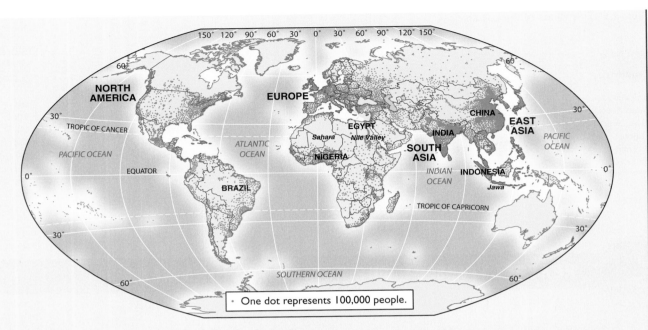

FIGURE 2.5 Spatial distribution of the world's population in 2003. The way people have arranged themselves in geographic space represents the totality of their adjustments to the environments that are capable of supporting human settlement. Individual countries are identified on the world political map in Appendix A.

Rim. The third and smallest of the major clusters, Europe, is the most modernized, industrialized, and urbanized of the three, but this population's impact on the region's natural environments by many measures is greater than that of the other two.

As Fig. 2.5 shows, about 90 percent of the world's people live on a relatively small fraction (about one-fifth) of the land. Fertile river lowlands and deltas still contain the highest regional densities; altitudinally, more than three-quarters of all humankind resides below 500 m; and nearly 70 percent live within 500 km of a seacoast. This leaves large parts of the planet with sparse human populations, including deserts such as the Sahara, high-latitude regions such as Siberia, and mountains such as the Himalayas. But even there, as we will see, humans make their impact. To the atmosphere, biosphere, lithosphere, hydrosphere, and cryosphere, should we add the *demosphere?*

abyssal plains form the floors of the deepest areas of each ocean, except for even deeper *trenches,* which occur at the foot of some continental slopes (as along the Pacific margin of Asia). The abyssal zone is not featureless, however, and the extensive plains are diversified by numerous hills and seamounts, all of which are of volcanic origin. (*Seamounts* are volcanic mountains reaching over 1000 m above the seafloor.) There also are lengthy valleys, as though rivers had carved them here more than 1800 m below the water surface. The origin of these valleys remains uncertain.

The third major ocean-floor feature is a global system of **midoceanic ridges**. These ridges are high, submarine, volcanic mountain ranges. The existence of one such ridge, the Mid-Atlantic Ridge, was long known to scientists. But its properties were not understood until quite recently, when it became clear that midoceanic ridges also extend across the Indian, Pacific, and Southern Ocean floors (Fig. 2.6). As is noted in Part Four, these midoceanic ridges are the scenes of active submarine volcanism and major movements of the Earth's crust. When scientists were able to observe them for the first time, they brought back dramatic records of violent eruptions, superheated water, and exotic marine life forms populating these active ridges that had never been seen before.

The active character of the midoceanic ridges and the geologic properties of the ocean floor become

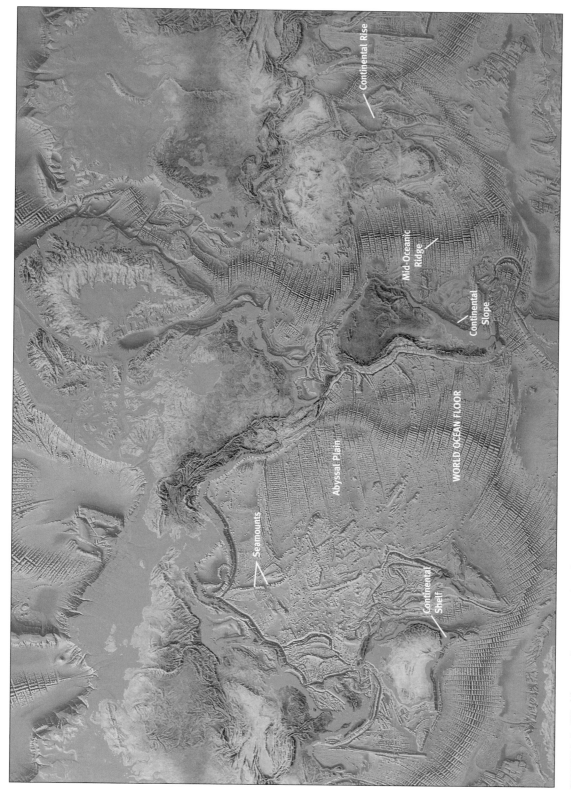

Continental Rise

Mid-Oceanic Ridge

Continental Slope

Abyssal Plain

WORLD OCEAN FLOOR

Seamounts

Continental Shelf

FIGURE 2.6 World ocean floor. Examples of the major features highlighted in the text on pages 24–26 are labelled.

important to us when we study their implications in geomorphology. But the configuration of the ocean floors affects the movement of ocean water just as the topography on land influences the movement of air. The ocean basins are filled with water that, like the air, is in constant motion. Great permanent circulation systems have developed in the oceans, and these systems affect the weather and climate on neighbouring continents. Our water-dominated planet is finally yielding secrets it has held for eons.

KEY TERMS

abyssal plains *page 24*

atmosphere *page 19*

biosphere *page 19*

continental rise *page 24*

continental shelf *page 24*

continental slope *page 24*

cryosphere *page 19*

cultural landscapes *page 25*

Earth System *page 19*

ecumene *page 21*

hemisphere *page 20*

hydrosphere *page 19*

land hemisphere *page 20*

lithosphere *page 19*

midoceanic ridge *page 26*

natural landscapes *page 25*

regional subsystem *page 20*

water hemisphere *page 20*

REVIEW QUESTIONS

1. Name the Earth's five spheres or interacting shells.

2. What is the regional subsystem and how does it relate to the Earth's five spheres?

3. What is the difference between the land hemisphere and the water hemisphere?

4. Compare and contrast the distribution of continental landmasses in the Northern and Southern Hemispheres.

5. Describe the basic spatial patterns exhibited by the distribution of the world's population.

6. Describe the major topographic features of the world's ocean basins.

REFERENCES AND FURTHER READINGS

BROAD, W. J.   *The Universe Below: Discovering the Secrets of the Deep Sea* (New York: Simon and Schuster, 1997).

DE BLIJ, H. J., and MULLER, P. O.   *Geography: Realms, Regions, and Concepts* (Hoboken, N.J.: Wiley, 11th ed., 2004).

"The Dynamic Earth," *Scientific American* (September 1983; special issue).

EMILIANI, C.   *Planet Earth: Cosmology, Geology, and the Evolution of Life and the Environment* (New York: Cambridge Univ. Press, 1992).

HANCOCK, P. L., and SKINNER, B. J., Eds.   *Oxford Companion to the Earth* (New York: Oxford Univ. Press, 2001).

LODDERS, K., and FEGLEY, B., Jr.   *The Planetary Scientist's Companion* (New York: Oxford Univ. Press, 1998).

National Geographic Atlas of the World (Washington, D.C.: National Geographic Society, 7th ed., 1999).

NEWMAN, J. L., and MATZKE, G. E.   *Population: Patterns, Dynamics, and Prospects* (Englewood Cliffs, N.J.: Prentice-Hall, 1984).

Oxford Atlas of the World (New York: Oxford Univ. Press, 9th ed., 2001).

SEIBOLD, E., and BERGER, W. H.   *The Sea Floor: An Introduction to Marine Geology* (New York: Springer Verlag, 1996).

THOMAS, D. S. G., and GOUDIE, A. S., Eds.   *The Dictionary of Physical Geography* (Malden, Mass.: Blackwell, 3rd ed., 2000).

WEB RESOURCES

http://earthobservatory.nasa.gov Visible Earth directory, a searchable directory of images, visualizations, and animations of the Earth.

Mapping the Earth's Surface

The United Kingdom was the world's (colonial) superpower when the global grid was laid out, so the British could decide where the Prime Meridian would lie. The Eastern and Western Hemispheres meet in this doorway of the Royal Observatory at Greenwich, near London. (Authors' photo)

OBJECTIVES

- To introduce the reference system for locations on the Earth's surface

- To describe the most important characteristics of maps and the features of common classes of map projections

- To discuss the elements of map interpretation and contemporary cartographic techniques

W hen you go to a new city, your process of learning about it begins at the hotel where you stay or in your new home. You then locate the nearest important service facilities, such as supermarkets and shopping centres. Gradually your knowledge of the city, and your activity space within it, expands. This slow pace of learning about the space you live in repeats the experience of every human society as it learned about the Earth. Early in the learning process, directions concerning the location of a particular place have to be taken from or given to someone. The most common form of conveying such information is the **map**, which Phillip Muehrcke has defined as *any geographical image of the environment*. We have all seen sketch maps directing us to a place for a social gathering. The earliest maps were of a similar nature, beginning with maps scratched in the dust or sand.

Although humans have been drawing maps throughout most of their history, the oldest surviving maps date only from about 2500 B.C.E. They were drawn on clay tablets in Mesopotamia (modern-day Iraq) and represented individual towns, the entire known country, and the early Mesopotamian view of the world (Fig. 3.1). The religious and astrological text above the map (Fig. 3.1A) indicates that the Mesopotamian idea of space was linked to ideas about humankind's place in the universe. This is a common theme in **cartography**—the science, art, and technology of mapmaking and map use. Even today, maps of newly discovered space, such as star charts, raise questions in our minds of where we, as humans, fit into the overall scheme of things.

The Spherical Earth

If you look out your window, there is no immediate reason for you to suppose that the Earth's surface is anything but flat. It takes a considerable amount of travelling and observation to reach any other conclusion. Yet, the notion of the Earth as a sphere is a longstanding one and was accepted by several Greek philosophers as far back as 350 B.C.E. By 200 B.C.E. the Earth's circumference (approximately 40,000 km) had been accurately estimated by Eratosthenes to within a few percentage points of its actual size. The idea of a spherical Earth continued to be challenged, however, and was not universally accepted until the Magellan expedition successfully circumnavigated the globe in the early sixteenth century.

Dividing the Earth

When a sphere is cut into two parts, the edges of the cut form circles. Once the Earth was assumed to be spherical, it was logical to divide it by means of circles. Sometime between the development of the wheel and the measurement of the planet's circumference, mathematicians had decided that the circle should be divided into 360 parts by means of 360 straight lines radiating from the centre of the circle. The angle between two of these lines was called a **degree**. For such a large circle as the Earth's circumference, further subdivisions became

A

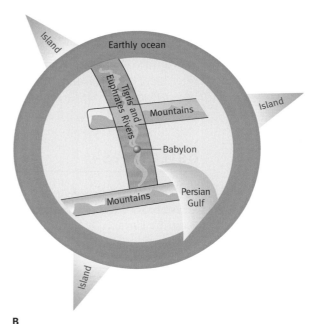

B

FIGURE 3.1 Mesopotamian world map. The original (A) was drawn in clay about 4500 years ago, with an explanatory text (top). An interpretive diagram (B) indicates its principal features.

necessary. Each degree was divided into 60 *minutes*, and each minute was further subdivided into 60 *seconds*.

With a system for dividing the curved surface of the Earth, the problem became the origin and layout of these circles. Two sets of information could be used to tackle this problem. First, a sense of direction had been gained by studying the movements of the Sun, Moon, and stars. In particular, the Sun at midday was always located in the same direction, which was designated as *south*. Knowing this, it was easy to arrive at the concepts of *north, east,* and *west*. The division of the circle could refine these directional concepts. The second piece of information was that some geographical locations in the Mediterranean region, fixed by star measurements, could be used as reference points for the division of the Earth.

Using this knowledge, it was possible to imagine a series of "lines" on the Earth's surface (in actuality, circles around the spherical Earth), some running north–south and some running east–west, which together form a grid. The east–west lines of this grid are still called **parallels**, the name the Greeks gave them; the north–south lines are called **meridians**. As we can see in Fig. 3.2, the two sets of lines differ. Parallels never intersect with one another, whereas meridians intersect at the top and bottom points (poles) of the sphere.

Latitude and Longitude

The present-day divisions of the globe stem directly from the Earth grids devised by ancient Greek geographers. The parallels are called lines of latitude. The parallel running around the middle of the globe, the **Equator**, is defined as zero degrees latitude. As Fig. 3.3A illustrates, **latitude** is the angular distance, measured in degrees north or south, of a point along a parallel from

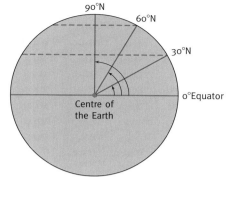

A

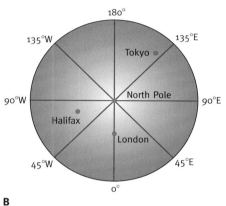

B

FIGURE 3.3 Latitude and longitude. Viewed from the side (A), lines of latitude (including the Equator) are horizontal parallels. Lines of longitude, the meridians, appear to radiate from a centre point when viewed from above the North Pole (B); they converge again at the South Pole.

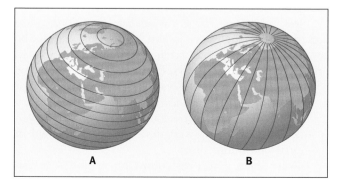

FIGURE 3.2 Parallels (A) and meridians (B) on a globe. Parallels run east–west; meridians run north–south.

the Equator. Lines of latitude in both the Northern and Southern Hemispheres are defined this way. Thus Vancouver has a latitude of 49 degrees, 15 minutes north of the Equator (49°15′N), and Sydney, Australia, a latitude of 33 degrees, 55 minutes south (33°55′S). The "top" of the Earth, the *North Pole,* is at latitude 90°N; the "bottom," the *South Pole,* is at 90°S.

The meridians are called lines of longitude. In 1884, the meridian that passes through the Royal Observatory at Greenwich in London, England, was established as the global starting point for measuring longitude. This north–south line is called the **Prime Meridian** and is defined as having a longitude of zero degrees. **Longitude** is the angular distance, measured in degrees east or west, of a point along a meridian from the Prime Meridian. The other meridians are ascertained as if we were looking down on the Earth from above the North Pole, as Fig. 3.3B indicates. Measurements are taken both east and west from the Prime Meridian. Therefore, Vancouver has a longitude of 123 degrees, 04 minutes west of the Greenwich meridian (123°04′W), and Sydney has a longitude of 151 degrees, 17 minutes east (151°17′E).

Because meridians converge at the North and South Poles, the actual distance contained in one degree of longitude varies from 111 km at the Equator to zero at the poles. In contrast, the length of a degree of latitude is about 111 km anywhere between 0° and 90°N or S. We say "about" because the Earth is not a perfect sphere—it bulges slightly at the Equator and is flattened at the poles. The Greek geographers, however, knew nothing of this. They had a more immediate and difficult problem to confront: how could they represent the three-dimensional Earth on a flat chart?

Today, for an increasingly large number of people, measurement of latitude and longitude has become a routine daily experience thanks to an exciting recent technological development. With the aid of a relatively inexpensive GPS receiver, anyone can now determine their exact geographic position. The **global positioning system (GPS)** was developed by the U.S. Department of Defense for a variety of military applications, but its use by scientists, private industry, and the public at large continues to expand. The GPS involves a constellation of more than two dozen satellites that orbit the Earth at an altitude of 20,000 km. A GPS receiver, either handheld or mounted in a vehicle, detects signals simultaneously from several satellites to precisely calculate its latitude and longitude (and even its elevation). Over the past few years, that capability quickly resulted in widespread applications of GPS technology, not only for on-board navigational purposes in ships, aircraft, cars, and trucks, but also to locate and monitor the movements of such vehicles (and even individuals).

Map Projections

If you have ever tried to cut the skin off an orange or any other spherical surface and then lay it flat on a table, you realize that this is not an easy task. At least some part of the skin must be stretched to make it completely flat. Cylinders or cones may be cut easily to be laid out flat without distortion, but not a sphere, which in geometric and cartographic terms is an *undevelopable* surface, incapable of being flattened. Once the ancient Greeks had accepted the idea that the Earth was a sphere, they had to determine how best to represent the round Earth on a flat surface. There is no totally satisfactory solution to this problem, but the early mapmakers soon invented many of the partial solutions that are still used commonly today.

The Greeks had noted that a light placed at the centre of a globe casts shadows along the meridians and parallels. These shadows, which form lines, can be "projected" outward onto some surface that can later be cut and laid out flat. The resulting series of projected lines on the new surface is called a **map projection**, which may be defined as an orderly arrangement of meridians and parallels, produced by any systematic method, that can be used for drawing a map of the spherical Earth on a flat surface. All modern map projections, it should be added, are constructed mathematically.

Properties of Map Projections

Any map projection has three variable properties: scale, area, and shape. **Scale** is the ratio of the size of an object on the map to the actual size of the object it represents. For example, consider a model globe that has a diameter of 25 cm. It represents the real Earth, whose diameter is 12,900 km. Therefore, 1 cm of the globe represents 516 km (12,900 km divided by 25 km), or 51,600,000 cm, on the real Earth. So we say that the scale of the model globe is 1 to 51,600,000, or 1:51,600,000. Why must we use such large numbers instead of saying 1 (cm) to 516 (km)? Because the first rule of fractions is that the numerator and the denominator must always be given in the same mathematical units.

The *area* of a section of the Earth's surface is found by multiplying its east–west distance by its north–south distance. This calculation is simple for rectangular pieces of land, but tedious for territories with more complicated shapes. In many map projections, complex real areas can be well represented simply by controlled shrinking (scaling down the distances). Manitoba has the same area relative to other Canadian provinces on a model globe as in the real world. The only difference is that the scale has changed.

Now consider *shape*. When a map projection preserves the true shape of an area, it is said to be conformal. Shape can often be preserved in map projections—but not always. In the real world, the shape of Saskatchewan is almost a rectangle. On a map with a scale of 1:50,000 for north–south distances and a scale of 1:200,000 for east–west distances, Saskatchewan is squeezed in the east–west direction and stretched in the north–south direction.

In creating a map projection from a globe, we can preserve one, or sometimes two, of the properties of scale, area, and shape. But it is not possible to preserve all three at once over all parts of the map. Try it for yourself by drawing a shape on a plastic ball and then cutting the ball to make a flat, two-dimensional map. You will be forced to compromise. To minimize this problem, the Greeks followed the rule cartographers still use: select the map projection best suited to the particular geographical purpose at hand.

Types of Map Projections

Since the time of the pioneering Greeks, mapmakers have devised hundreds of projections to flatten the globe so that all of it is visible at once. Indeed, mathematically it is possible to create an infinite number of map projections. In practice, however, these cartographic transformations of the three-dimensional, spherical surface of the Earth have tended to fall into a small number of categories. The four most common classes of map projections are considered here: cylindrical, conic, plane, and equal-area.

A **cylindrical projection** involves the transfer of the Earth's latitude/longitude grid from the globe to a cylinder, which is then cut and laid flat. When this operation is completed, the parallels and the meridians appear on the opened cylinder as straight lines intersecting at right angles. On any map projection, the least distortion occurs where the globe touches, or is *tangent* to, the geometric object it is projected onto; the greatest distortion occurs farthest from this place of contact. In Fig. 3.4A we observe in the left-hand diagram that the globe and the cylinder are tangent along the parallel of the Equator. The parallel of tangency between a globe and the surface onto which it is projected is called the **standard parallel**. The right-hand diagram of Fig. 3.4A shows a globe larger than the cylinder, and two standard parallels result. This projection reduces distortion throughout the map, and is particularly useful for representing the low-latitude zone straddling the Equator between the pair of standard parallels.

Mathematical modifications have increased the utility of cylindrical projections, the best known of which was devised in 1569 by the Flemish cartographer Gerhardus Mercator. In a **Mercator projection** (Fig. 3.5), the spacing of parallels increases toward the poles. This increase is in direct proportion to the false widening between normally convergent meridians that is necessary to draw those meridians as parallel lines. Although this produced extreme distortion in the area of the polar latitudes, it provided a tremendously important service for navigators using the newly perfected magnetic compass. Unlike with any other map projection, a straight line drawn on this one is a line of true

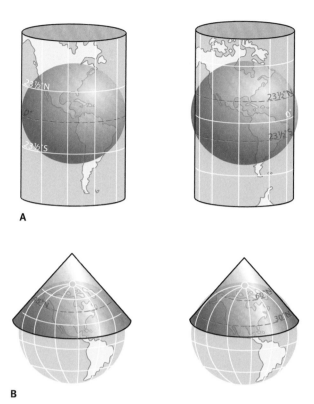

FIGURE 3.4 Construction of cylindrical (A) and conic (B) projections with one and two standard parallels.

and constant compass bearing. Such lines are called *rhumb lines*. Once a navigator has determined from the Mercator map of the world the compass direction to be travelled, the ship can easily be locked onto this course.

Cones can be cut and laid out flat as easily as cylinders, and the **conic projection** has been in use almost as long as the cylindrical. A conic projection involves the transfer of the Earth's latitude/longitude grid from a globe to a cone, which is then cut and laid flat. Figure 3.4B shows the derivation of the two most common conic projections, the one- and two-standard-parallel cases. On a conic projection, meridians are shown as straight lines that converge toward the (North) Pole. Parallels appear as arcs of concentric circles with the same centre point that shorten as the latitude increases. This projection is best suited for the middle latitudes, such as the United States and Europe, where distortion is minimal if the apex of the imaginary cone is positioned directly above the North Pole.

Planar projections, in which an imaginary plane touches the globe at a single point, exhibit a wheel-like symmetry around the point of tangency between the

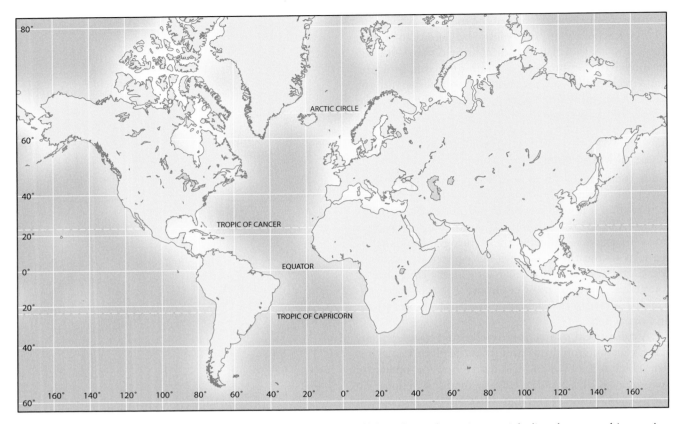

FIGURE 3.5 The Mercator projection, which produces straight parallels and meridians. Any straight line drawn on this map is a (rhumb) line of constant compass bearing, a tremendous advantage for long-distance navigation.

plane and the sphere. Planar projections were the first map projections developed by the ancient Greeks. Today they are most frequently used to represent the polar regions (Fig. 3.6). One type of planar projection, the *gnomonic,* possesses an especially useful property: a straight line on this projection is the shortest route between two points on the Earth's surface. This has vital implications in this age of intercontinental jet travel. Long international flights seek to follow the shortest routes, and these are found on the spherical Earth by imagining the globe to be cut exactly in half along a straight line running through the origin and destination cities. When a sphere is cut in half, the circle formed along the edge of the cut is called a *great circle.* (*Small circles* are the edges of all other cuts when a sphere is divided into two unequal portions.) Long-distance air traffic usually follows great-circle routes, such as the one shown between New York and London in Fig. 3.6.

Through the mathematical manipulation of projective geometry, it is possible to derive an unlimited number of map projections that go beyond the convenience and simplicity of the cylinder, cone, and plane. Among

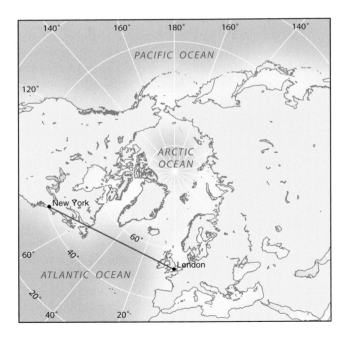

FIGURE 3.6 The great-circle route from New York to London, which becomes a straight line on this polar gnomonic projection.

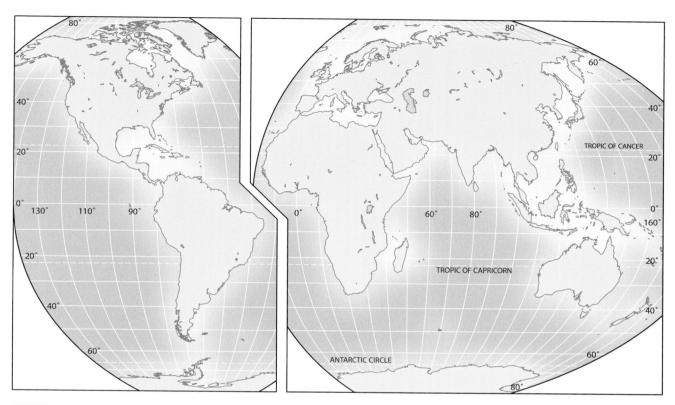

FIGURE 3.7 Equal-area projection. All areas mapped are represented in their correct relative sizes. This flat polar quartic equal-area projection—in interrupted form—was developed in 1949 for the U.S. Coast and Geodetic Survey by F. W. McBryde and P. D. Thomas.

these other types of map projections, **equal-area projections** rank among the most important. An equal-area projection is one in which all the areas mapped are represented in correct proportion to one another. Thus on a world map of this type, the relative areal sizes of the continents are preserved. True shape, however, must be sacrificed. Nonetheless, good equal-area projections attempt to limit the distortion of shape so that the continental landmasses are still easily recognizable. This should be carefully noted in Fig. 3.7, which displays the flat polar quartic projection. Because they maintain the areal relationships of every part of the globe, equal-area projections are particularly useful for mapping the worldwide spatial distributions of land-based phenomena. The map in Fig. 3.7 also possesses another feature you have undoubtedly observed by now: it is not a continuous representation but is *interrupted*. This device helps the cartographer minimize distortion, devote most of the projection to the parts that project best, and de-emphasize areas of the globe that are not essential to the distribution at hand (such as omitting large parts of the oceans in mappings of land-based phenomena).

Map Interpretation

One of the most important functions of maps is to communicate their content effectively and efficiently. Because so much spatial information exists in the real world, cartographers must first carefully choose the information to be included and deleted in order to avoid cluttering the map with less-relevant data. Thus *maps are models:* their compilers simplify the complexity of the real world, filtering out all but the most essential information. Even so, a considerable amount of information remains, and all of it must be compressed into the small confines of the final map. To facilitate that task, cartographers have learned to encode their spatial messages through the use of symbolization. Decoding this cartographic shorthand is not a difficult task, and the place to begin is the map's key or **legend** (or sometimes its written caption), in which symbols and colours are identified. These symbols usually correspond to the different categories of geographic data: dimensionless *points,* one-dimensional *lines,* two-dimensional *areas,* and three-dimensional *volumes* or *surfaces.*

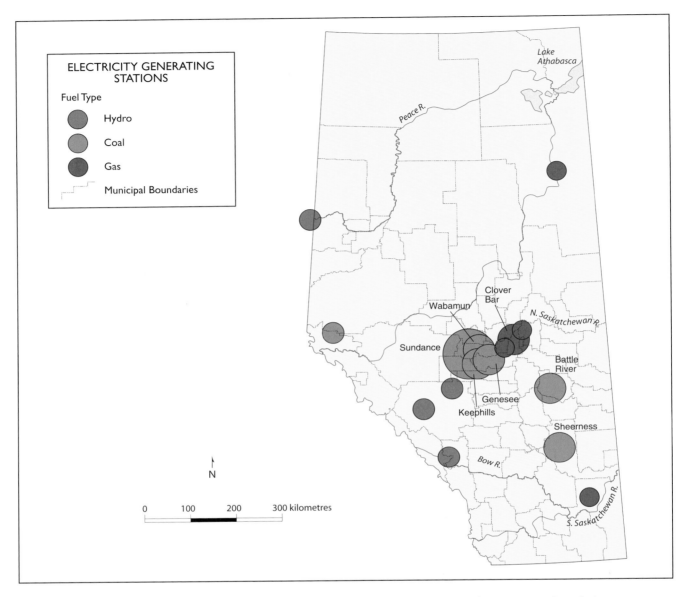

FIGURE 3.8 Alberta's electrical generating stations (fuel type and capacity), an example of a proportional symbol map.

Point symbols tell us the location of each occurrence of the phenomenon being mapped and, frequently, its quantity. This is illustrated in Fig. 3.8, which is a map of electrical generating stations in Alberta. A dot or circle marks the spot of each such location, whose generating capacity can be ascertained in the legend. Taken together, all these point symbols exhibit the provincial distribution of this phenomenon.

Line symbols represent linkages and/or flows that exist between places. The map in Fig. 3.9 shows the pattern of crude oil and gas pipelines in the province of Alberta.

Area symbols portray two-dimensional spaces, with colours representing specific quantitative ranges. An example is seen in Fig. 3.10, which maps population density (persons/km²) by census division in Alberta in 1996. The northern part of the province is representative of a relatively low population density, as indicated by the light shading, whereas the areas around Edmonton, Red Deer, and Calgary have higher population densities, as represented with darker shading.

Volume symbols describe *surfaces* that can be generalizations of real surfaces (such as the world topo-

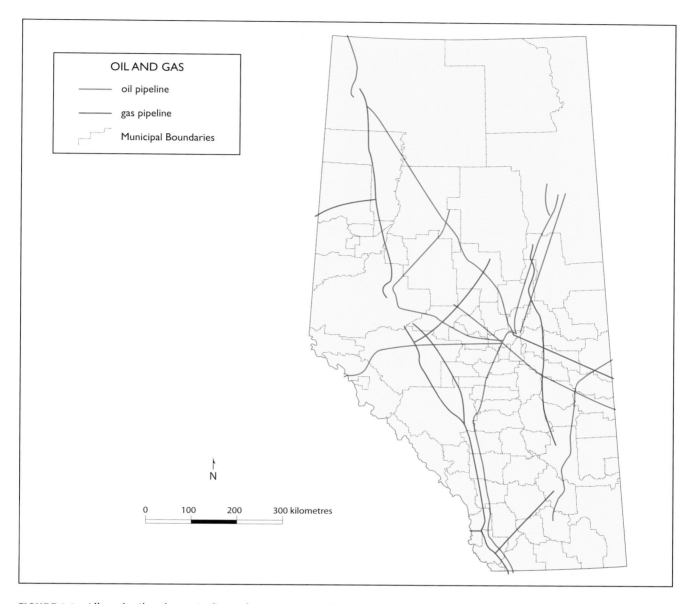

FIGURE 3.9 Alberta's oil and gas pipelines, demonstrating a line-mapping technique.

graphic relief map in Fig. 2.3) or representations of conceptual surfaces. An example of the latter is provided in Fig. 3.11, which shows Alberta's January daily mean temperatures (1971 to 2000). Bands of "warmer" temperatures can be seen to the southwest corner, with bands of progressively colder temperatures toward the north. This mapping technique is known as **isarithmic (isoline) mapping** and consists of numerous **isolines** that connect all places possessing the same value of a given phenomenon or "height" above the flat base of the surface. In Fig. 3.11 the boundary lines between

colour zones, as the legend indicates, connect all points reporting that particular temperature.

Perhaps the best known use of isolines in physical geography is the representation of surface relief by **contouring**. As Fig. 3.12 demonstrates, each contour line represents a specific and constant elevation, and all the contours together provide a useful generalization of the surface being mapped. A more practical example of contouring is shown in Fig. 3.13, where the landscape portrayed in Fig. 3.13A corresponds to the *topographic map* of that terrain in Fig. 3.13B. By comparing the two

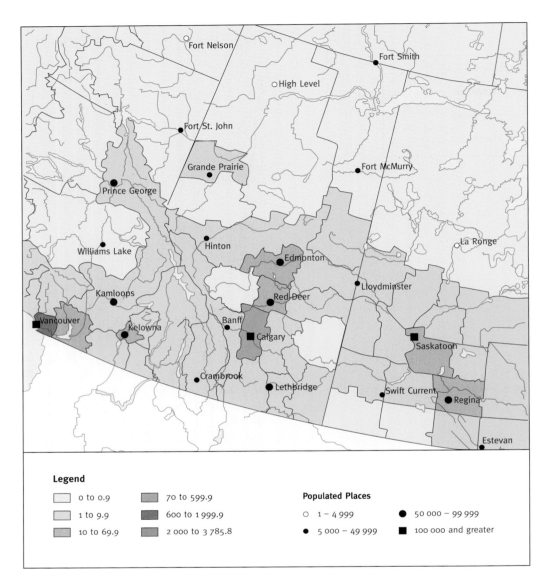

FIGURE 3.10 Population density by census division (persons/km²) in 1996 Alberta, an example of a choropleth map (area symbol mapping technique).

it is easy to read the contour map and understand how this cartographic technique portrays the configuration of the Earth's surface relief accurately. The land surface of the United States, except for Alaska, has been completely mapped at the fairly detailed scale of 1:24,000. Approximately 55,000 topographic quadrangle maps at this scale have been published by the U.S. Geological Survey and can now be purchased in both printed and digital formats. The latter is fully computer-accessible, and its recent availability is but one product of the technological revolution that is transforming cartography in the twenty-first century.

Evolving Cartographic Technology

The late twentieth century saw rapid advances in computer power and speed. Cartographers quickly applied

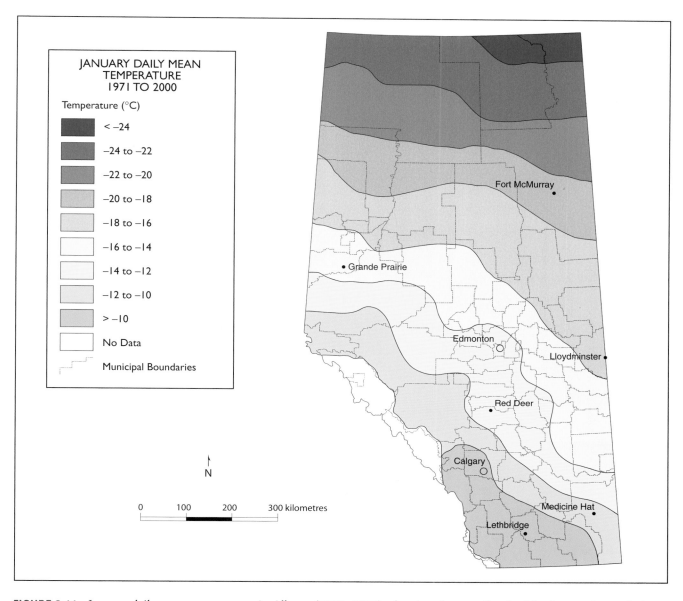

FIGURE 3.11 January daily mean temperature in Alberta (1971–2000), showing the use of an isarithmic mapping technique.

the new technology to mapmaking, and today virtually all maps are compiled digitally. As sophisticated mapping software was being pioneered, closely related breakthroughs were simultaneously occurring in airborne and satellite remote sensing (see Perspective: Remote Sensing of the Environment). This led to an explosion of new data about the Earth's surface, and propelled the rapid development of geographic information systems to analyze and interpret them.

A **geographic information system—GIS** for short—is an assemblage of computer hardware and software that enables spatial data to be collected, recorded, stored, retrieved, manipulated, analyzed, and displayed to the user. Especially when linked to remotely sensed data from high-altitude observation platforms, this approach allows for the simultaneous collection of several layers of information pertaining to the same study area. These layers can then be integrated by multiple map overlays (Fig. 3.14) in

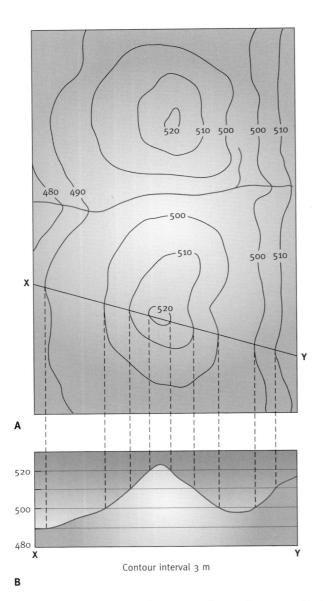

A

B

Contour interval 3 m

FIGURE 3.12 In topographic contouring, each contour line's points have the identical height above sea level. The surface relief described by the contour map (A) can be linked to a cross-sectional profile of the terrain. (In diagram B this is done for line **X–Y** on map A.) Note how contour spacing corresponds to slope patterns: the wider the spacing, the gentler the slope, and vice versa.

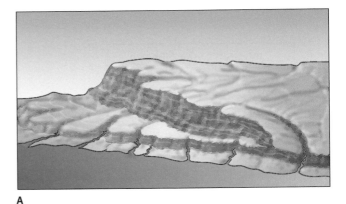

A

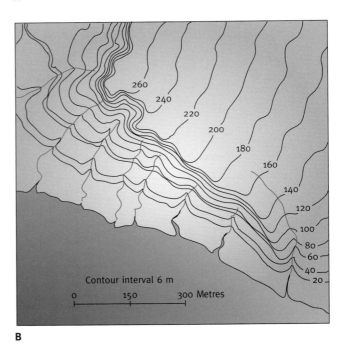

Contour interval 6 m

0   150   300 Metres

B

FIGURE 3.13 Perspective sketch of a coastal landscape (A) and its corresponding topographic map (B), adapted from U.S. Geological Survey sources. Note that the contour interval—most appropriate for this map—is 6 m.

order to assemble the components of the complex real-world pattern, a powerful analytical tool.

For cartographers, GIS technology is particularly valuable because all digital data are geo-referenced with respect to the Earth's latitude/longitude grid. This enables the data to be mapped within the framework of any map projection, and to move easily from one projection to another. It also allows the collating of digital data from diverse sources, even if the original source material exists in different map projections and/or at different scales. Another highly advantageous capability is the conversion of digital data from point-based format to line- or area-based formats, and vice versa.

Perhaps the most revolutionary aspect of GIS cartography is its break with the static map of the past. The use of GIS methodology involves a constant dialogue, via computer commands and feedback to queries, be-

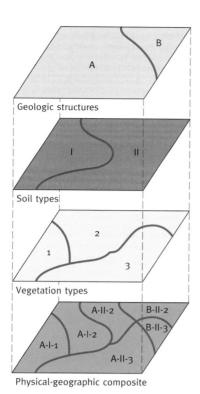

Geologic structures

Soil types

Vegetation types

Physical-geographic composite

FIGURE 3.14 GIS processing of overlays to produce map composite.

tween the map and the map user. This instantaneous two-way communication is known as **interactive mapping**, and it is expected to become the cornerstone of cartography in the future. Just one of the many possibilities of this technique is the use of video-disk maps displayed on automobile dashboards, allowing the driver to ask questions that elicit immediate map directions showing the best route to the desired destination.

PERSPECTIVES ON THE HUMAN ENVIRONMENT

Remote Sensing of the Environment

Maps have been used for centuries to graphically communicate information about the Earth's surface. The Greek legend of Icarus, who flew too close to the Sun and melted his wax-and-feather wings, shows how badly the scientific ancestors of modern geographers wanted to view the Earth from the sky. Today this is possible, and the work of mapmakers and spatial analysts is greatly facilitated and enhanced by powerful new tools and techniques. The most important of these is remote-sensing technology, the ability to scan the Earth from airborne and satellite observation platforms.

Remote sensing has been defined by Benjamin Richason as *any technique of imaging objects*
without the sensor being in direct contact with the object or scene itself. He goes on to point out that geographers who use this method normally *collect* data via an appropriate imaging system, *interpret* that spatial information (which is stored in the system, usually on film or computer tape), and *display* and *communicate* the results on a map.

Aerial photography is a remote-sensing technique that has been used since the advent of cameras early in the nineteenth century. Even though the Wright brothers did not take off until 1903, hot-air balloons and even trained birds were able to carry cameras aloft before 1850. With the rapid proliferation of aircraft over the past century, several methods were developed (many by the military to improve its advantages in ground warfare) that permitted maps to be produced directly from series of photographs taken from survey aircraft.

At the same time, photographic technology was being perfected to expand this capability. Along with improved camera systems came ever more sensitive black-and-white and then colour films. Moreover, by World War II, ultrasensitive film breakthroughs extended the use of photography into the *infrared radiation* (*IR*) range beyond the visible capacities of the human eye. By directly "seeing" reflected and radiated solar energy, aerial infrared photography could, for the first time, penetrate clouds, haze, and smoke—and even obtain clear images of the ground at night. The U.S. Air Force further pioneered the use of IR colour imagery, although the "colours" obtained—known as *false-colour images*—bore no resemblance to the natural colours of the objects photographed (but could readily be decoded by analysts).

During the late twentieth century, nonphotographic remote sensing developed swiftly as new techniques and instruments opened up a much wider portion of the *electromagnetic spectrum*. This spectrum, diagrammed in Fig. 3.15, consists of a continuum of energy as measured by wavelength, from the high-energy *shortwave radiation* of cosmic rays (whose waves are calibrated in billionths of a metre) to the low-energy *longwave radiation* of radio and electric power (with waves measured in units as large as kilometres).

Figure 3.15 also shows the discrete *spectral bands* within the electromagnetic spectrum, which can be picked up by radio, radar, thermal IR sensors, and other instruments. As remote sensing matured, scientists and engineers learned more about those parts of the spectrum and which types of equipment are best suited to studying various categories of environmental phenomena. This is important because each surface feature or object emits and reflects a unique pattern of electromagnetic energy—its *spectral signature*—which can be used to identify it, much like a fingerprint can identify any human individual.

Access to the nonvisible-light wavelengths of the electromagnetic spectrum is a significant technological achievement that is now paying rich dividends. Before this breakthrough, our perception was narrowly limited to the visible portion of the spectrum (the "optical window" shown in Fig. 3.15), which one scientist has likened to the width of a pencil in comparison to the Earth's circumference (40,000 km).

Two kinds of remote-sensing systems have been devised to collect and record electromagnetic pulses. *Passive systems* measure energy radiated and/or reflected by an object, such as the IR photography method described above. Also common today are *active systems,* which transmit their own pulsations of energy, thereby "illuminating" target objects that "backscatter," or reflect, some of that energy to receiving sensors that "see" the image (*radar* is a good example of such a system). Many remote-sensing platforms now employ both active and passive systems. In fact, they increasingly utilize *multispectral systems,* arrays of scanners attuned simultaneously to several different spectral

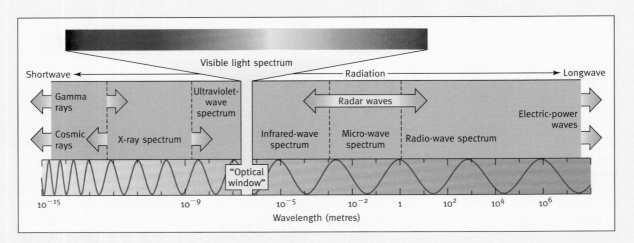

FIGURE 3.15 The complete (electromagnetic) radiation spectrum.

bands, which greatly enhances the quality of observations and their interpretations.

Although remote sensors can be ground-based, most systems that facilitate our understanding of physical geography need to collect data at high altitudes. Aircraft have been and continue to be useful, but they are limited by how high they can fly (approximately 20 km) and the weather conditions in which they can operate. With planes unable to reach the very high altitudes required to obtain the small-scale imagery for seeing large areas of the surface in a single view, the opening of the space age in 1957 soon provided the needed alternative in Earth-orbiting satellites.

By the 1980s, dozens of special-purpose satellites were circling the Earth at appropriate altitudes and providing remotely sensed data to aid in assembling the "big picture." Canada has had an important role in the development and application of aerial photography and photogrammetry. Originating from strategic and military uses and applications, the field of remote sensing in Canada evolved to focus on applications in the Canadian Arctic. Examples include the study of floating ice and information in aid of safe surface navigation through the North West Passage. Among the most important satellites in operation in Canada today is the RADARSAT series. In 1979 the Canadian Interagency Committee on Remote Sensing approved the development of Canada's first radar satellite. RADARSAT-1 was successfully launched in November 1995 (Fig. 3.16). Since then there have been numerous Canadian applications, including studies of glacier motion, oil-spill detection, snow mapping, forestlands management, ice-type identification and reconnaissance, geological mapping, and flood monitoring. RADARSAT-2, set to launch in 2005, will open up even more application opportunities, including agricultural remote sensing, improved ocean-wave measurement, wetland hydrology, and refined Arctic and Antarctic missions, among many others.

FIGURE 3.16 The first RADARSAT image ever produced was of the Cape Breton Highlands of Nova Scotia. The fact that the image was acquired through darkness, cloudy skies, rain, and strong winds (5:41 p.m. AST on the evening of November 28, 1995) illustrates the advantages of the Synthetic Aperture Radar (SAR).

KEY TERMS

REVIEW QUESTIONS

1. What is the difference between latitude and longitude? What are the reference lines and/or points for each measurement system?

2. Describe how the properties of *scale, area,* and *shape* relate to a map projection.

3. What are the differences between cylindrical, conical, and planar map projections?

4. What is an equal-area projection, and what mapping task(s) is it well suited to?

5. Define and give examples of point, line, area, and volume map symbols.

6. What are the distinguishing features of the geographic information system (GIS) and remote-sensing techniques?

REFERENCES AND FURTHER READINGS

CAMPBELL, J. B.   *Map Use and Analysis* (Dubuque, Iowa: WCB/McGraw-Hill, 3rd ed., 1998).

CAMPBELL, J. B.   *Introduction to Remote Sensing* (New York: Guilford Press, 3rd ed., 2002).

CHRISMAN, N.   *Exploring Geographic Information Systems* (New York: Wiley, 2nd ed., 2002).

DENT, B. D.   *Cartography: Thematic Map Design, with USGS Map Projection Poster* (Dubuque, Iowa: WCB/McGraw-Hill, 4th ed., 1996).

GOODCHILD, M. F.   "Geographic Information Systems," in Susan Hanson, Ed., *Ten Geographic Ideas That Changed the World* (New Brunswick, N.J.: Rutgers Univ. Press, 1997), 60–83.

GREENHOOD, D.   *Mapping* (Chicago: Univ. of Chicago Press, 1964).

JONES, C. B.   *Geographical Information Systems and Computer Cartography* (London/New York: Longman, 1997).

KEATES, J. S.   *Understanding Maps* (London/New York: Longman, 2nd ed., 1996).

JENSEN, J. R.   *Remote Sensing of the Environment: An Earth Resource Perspective* (New Jersey: Prentice Hall, 2000).

LILLESAND, T. M., KIEFER, R. W., and CHIPMAN, J. W. *Remote Sensing and Image Interpretation* (New York: Wiley, 5th ed., 2004).

LONGLEY, P. A., GOODCHILD, M. F., MAGUIRE, D. J., and RHIND, D. W.   *Geographic Information Systems and Science* (New York: Wiley, 2001).

MUEHRCKE, P. C., and MUEHRCKE, J. O.   *Map Use: Reading–Analysis–Interpretation* (Madison, Wis.: JP Publ., 4th ed., 1997).

PARKINSON, C. L.   *Earth from Above: Using Color-Coded Satellite Images to Examine the Global Environment* (New York: University Science Press, 1997).

RICHASON, B. F., Jr.   "Remote Sensing: An Overview," in B. F. Richason, Jr., Ed., *Introduction to Remote Sensing of the Environment* (Dubuque, Iowa: Kendall/Hunt, 2nd ed., 1983), 3–15 (definition of remote sensing on p. 5).

ROBINSON, A. H., MORRISON, J. L., MUEHRCKE, P. C., KIMERLING, A. J., and GUPTILL, S. C.   *Elements of Cartography* (New York: Wiley, 6th ed., 1995).

SNYDER, J. P.   *Flattening the Earth: Two Thousand Years of Map Projections* (Chicago: Univ. of Chicago Press, 1993).

THROWER, N. J. W.   *Maps and Civilization: Cartography in Culture and Society* (Chicago: Univ. of Chicago Press, 1996).

WEB RESOURCES

http://atlas.gc.ca The Atlas of Canada site includes many examples of thematic Canadian maps.

http://everest.hunter.cuny.edu/mp Background information and detailed graphics of map projections, as well as how cartographers choose an appropriate projection.

http://www.ccrs.nrcan.gc.ca The Canada Centre for Remote Sensing provides historical and contemporary perspectives on remote sensing in Canada with many examples of research applications.

http://www.rsi.ca The official RADARSAT International website.

http://www.sfei.org./ecoatlas/GIS/MapInterpretation/MapsandScales.html A guide to calculating map scales and mapping techniques.

The Earth in the Universe

The Blue Planet as seen from the Moon—swirls of cloud and expanses of ocean as the Earth rises above the lunar horizon.

OBJECTIVES

- To introduce the basic structure of the universe, speculations about its origin, and the position of our home galaxy and star within it

- To describe the functions of the Sun as the dominant body of the solar system

- To briefly survey each of the Sun's planets and the lesser orbiting bodies that constitute the remainder of the solar system

It was pointed out in Unit 2 that we live on a small, fragile planet. Even from the vantage point of the Moon—our nearest neighbour in outer space, only 390,000 km away—the Earth appears greatly shrunken in size (see photo above). If we were to view the Earth from the vicinity of the Sun, from a distance of 150 million km, it would only be a tiny speck. But these perspectives do not even begin to suggest the unimaginable vastness of the universe. How big is the universe? What is its structure? How do our Sun and its family of planets (including

Earth) fit into the overall scheme of things? These are some of the key questions to be considered in this unit.

The Universe

The **universe** may be defined as the entity that contains all of the matter and energy that exists anywhere in space and time. As for its size, to understand the enormity of the universe it must be considered in both space and time. The fastest thing that moves in the universe is light, a form of radiant energy that travels at a speed of 300,000 km per second. Thus, in a single second, a ray of light travels a distance equal to 7½ times the Earth's circumference. Even at this speed, however, it takes about eight minutes for light to travel from the Sun to the Earth. Light from the nearest star takes *more than four years* to get here. If that star exploded today, we would not know it for another four-plus years; our telescopes, therefore, only show us history.

Given the untold billions of stars that populate the universe (Fig. 4.1) and the fact that years are required for the light to reach us even from the nearest star beyond our own Sun, astronomers calibrate interstellar distances in light-years. A **light-year** is the distance travelled by a pulse of light in one year: 9.46 trillion (9.46×10^{12}) kilometres. To travel that distance aboard an airplane at 800 km per hour would require a journey of almost 1,350,000 years.

In terms of "deep space", our planetary system belongs to a **galaxy** (an organized, disk-like assemblage of billions of stars) called the *Milky Way*, which is about 120,000 light-years in diameter. As recently as the 1920s, this was believed to be the entire universe, but newer astronomical discoveries have drastically transformed that perception. We now know that the Milky Way galaxy itself is merely one of about 30 loosely bound galaxies that have clustered to form what astronomers call the *local galaxy group*, which measures about 4 million light-years across its longest dimension. This local group, in turn, is but a small component of the *local supercluster* (a supercluster is a conglomeration of galaxies, comprising the largest of all celestial formations), measuring approximately 100 million light-years in diameter.

To this point three time–space levels have been discussed—galaxy, galaxy cluster, galaxy supercluster—but only now are we ready to tackle the full dimensions of the known universe. That ultimate level is now under intense investigation by astrophysicists around the world, and research frontiers continue to expand. Today astronomers record images from the Hubble Space Telescope that have travelled almost 13 billion light-years from what are believed to be the outer edges of the universe. Since our local supercluster lies near the universe's centre, the *radius* of the universe is now estimated to be 13.7 billion light-years, and the *diameter* should be no less than 27.4 billion light-years.

The hierarchical organization of the universe's various time–space levels is seen in the "cones of resolution" diagrammed in Fig. 4.2. Each level is highly complex in its internal structure. For instance, the Milky Way galaxy alone consists of more than 100 billion stars, of which our Sun is only one—and a middle-sized and most ordinary star at that. In all, there are billions of galaxies. Their sheer numbers are beyond our comprehension, and most lie beyond the view of our most powerful telescopes. Then how many of those huge balls of glowing gas that we call stars does the total universe actually contain? The current estimate is more than *200 billion-billion* (200×10^{18}), about 50 billion stars for every human now alive. Where did all these celestial bodies and the other diverse matter and energy of the universe come from, and how was everything scattered across such an immense space?

The answers to these questions rest with theories concerning the origin of the universe, which a consensus

FIGURE 4.1 A tiny slice of the nighttime sky (featuring the constellation Orion near the centre of the photo), which can only suggest the enormous number of stars contained in the universe.

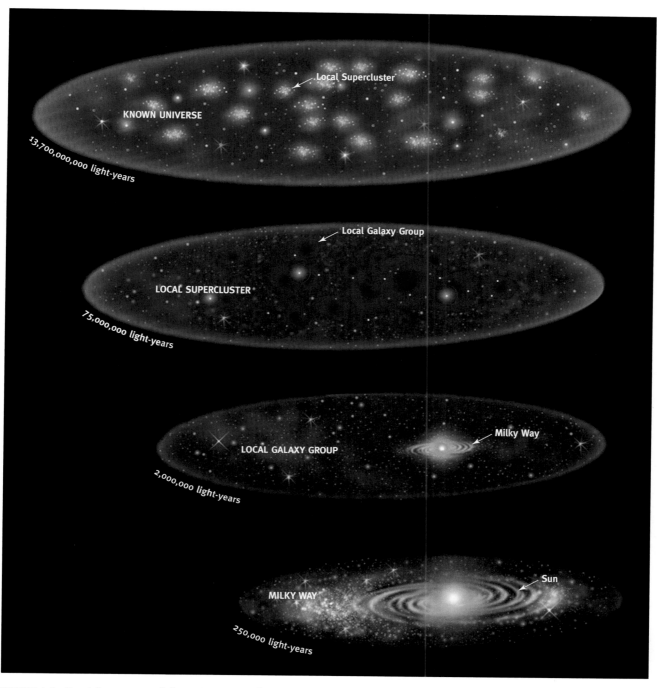

FIGURE 4.2 Spatial structure of the universe—and our place within it. All dimensions shown are radial measurements with respect to the centre of each disk.

of scientists believe to be the result of the so-called *Big Bang*. The Big Bang was a massive explosion of truly cosmic proportions, in which all the primordial matter and energy that existed before the formation of the universe was compressed together at almost infinite density, heated to trillions of degrees, and blown apart. This stupendous blast propelled matter and energy outward in a rapidly expanding fireball, which has been cooling and slowing ever since. In the wake of this violent advancing wave lay an amorphous cloud of debris, from which the contents of the universe gradually formed. Galaxies and larger star clusters slowly took shape from the condensation and consolidation of cooling gas and dust clouds. A key force in binding them together was

gravity, the force of attraction acting among all physical objects due to their *mass,* the quantity of material of which they are composed. Indeed, gravitational forces shape the structure of every one of the universe's time–space levels, bonding enormous interstellar clusters as well as the superheated gases of individual stars.

The Big Bang, which is based on Albert Einstein's general theory of relativity, took place approximately 13.7 billion years ago. As was noted in the preceding, the farthest objects in the universe appear to be located at a distance of about 13 billion light-years from Earth. If the universe is still expanding in the wake of the Big Bang, then the matter and energy at the outermost extremities of the universe represent the leading edge of that advance. The matter that exists at these extremities has been formed into mysterious, starlike objects; these brightly glowing masses are called *quasars,* shorthand for "quasi-stellar objects." Interestingly, quasars are embedded in a uniform glow of radio-wave-frequency radiation, an energy environment consistent with the hypothesis that this cosmic radiation (confirmed to exist everywhere in space) is the faint "echo" of the Big Bang that occurred so long ago.

Many scientists are also studying the consequences of these recent revelations for the future evolution of the universe. If the universe should turn out to be a finite or closed system, then gravity will inevitably reverse the expanding edge, force an implosion leading to another Big Bang, and spawn infinite expansion–contraction cycles beyond it. However, should the universe prove to be an open system, then it may end with a whimper rather than a bang as galaxies inexorably overcome the pull of gravity and eventually drift away from one another. In the search for answers, some researchers now subscribe to even more complex outcomes.

The Solar System

Our home galaxy, the Milky Way, began to form more than 12 billion years ago. The star we know as the Sun, however, was a relatively late addition and did not appear until about 4.6 billion years ago. The processes that formed the Sun mirrored the forces at work throughout the universe. One particular rotating cloud of gas and dust began to cool, and soon its centre condensed to form a star. Simultaneously, the remaining materials in the swirling cloud around this new star formed a disk and began to sort themselves out as the consolidating mass of the Sun exerted an ever stronger gravitational pull. Millions of eddies within this disk now began to condense as well and formed sizeable conglomerations of solid matter called *planetesimals.* As these objects grew

in mass, gravity began to draw them together. Soon these planetesimals were travelling in swarms, and it was not long before they were compressed together to form nine planets that began to circle the Sun in regular orbits. (**Planets** are dark solid or gaseous bodies, much smaller in size than stars, whose movements are controlled by the gravitational effects of nearby stars.)

Most of the larger residual planetesimals were captured by the gravitational fields of the evolving planets and began to orbit them as satellites or *moons.* A large belt of smaller planetesimal-like materials (known as *asteroids*) congregated between the fourth and fifth planets, and remain in orbit today. The Sun's gravitational field also contains small bodies of frozen gases and related materials called *comets,* tiny clusters of rock known as *meteoroids,* and vast quantities of *dust* that may be remnants of the system's formation.

The Sun, its planets, and related residual materials were born together some 4.6 billion years ago and collectively constitute the **solar system** (Fig. 4.3A). The Sun is located at the centre of the solar system and is the source of light, heat, and the overall gravitational field that sustains the planets. The nine planets may be grouped as follows. Mercury, Venus, Earth, and Mars comprise the four terrestrial or *inner planets,* which are rather small in size (see Fig. 4.3B). The next four—Jupiter, Saturn, Uranus, and Neptune—constitute the major or *outer planets* and are much larger in size. The outermost ninth planet, Pluto, was only discovered in 1930. Although it seemed to be more like the inner planets, astronomers knew so little about it that Pluto was not classified within either group. (That proved to be a wise step, as we shall see, because in 2002 evidence was discovered that could well result in Pluto's demotion from planetary status altogether.) Let us now examine the major components of the solar system.

The Sun

The Sun is the dominant body of the solar system. Its size relative to the planets and lesser orbiting materials is so great that the Sun accounts for 99.8 percent of the mass of the entire solar system, more than 750 times the mass of all the planets combined. (The Sun's diameter alone is 109 times larger than the Earth's.) This, of course, enables the Sun to extend its gravitational field far out into space. The effect of that gravity on the planets does weaken with distance, but at a rather slow rate. Earth, the third planet, is located at an average distance of 150 million km. The orbit of outermost Pluto, however, is about 40 times that distance from the centre of the solar system, demonstrating that the Sun's gravitational pull is powerful enough to control the movements

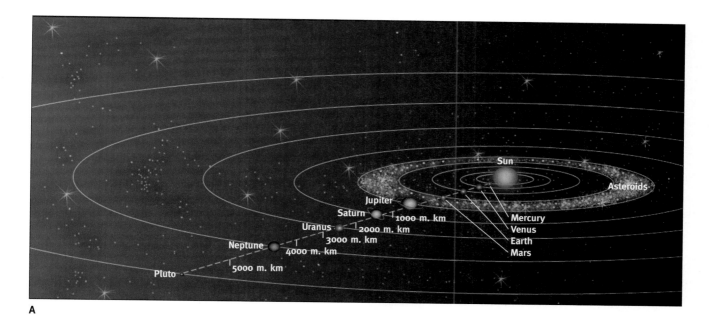

A

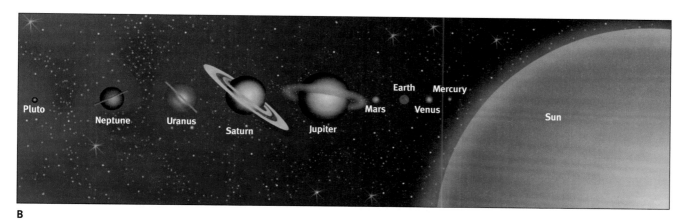

B

FIGURE 4.3   Solar system (A) and the relative sizes of the nine planets with respect to one another and the Sun (B). In diagram A the planets are aligned for demonstration purposes only; distances are given in millions of kilometres.

of a planet nearly 6 billion km away. Remember, too, that the largest planets are the fifth through eighth, located in a zone roughly 1 to 5 billion km distant from the Sun.

As with most stars, the Sun is a churning thermonuclear furnace, composed mainly of superheated hydrogen and helium gases mixed in a ratio of approximately 3:1. Surface temperatures average 6900°C. The enormous quantities of light and heat given off by the Sun, in the form of a stream of rapidly moving atomic particles, come from its surface and atmosphere (Fig. 4.4). Most of that gaseous flow of energy, which radiates outward in every direction and is known as the *solar wind,* is lost in space. (The Earth receives less than

one-billionth of the light and heat that are expelled by the Sun.) Although the solar wind "blows" at a fairly steady speed, disturbances originating deep inside the Sun occasionally rise to the surface and modify the outflow of solar energy. Solar scientists are particularly familiar with an 11-year cycle of magnetic stormlike activity that is associated with large, dark "spots" on the Sun's surface (see photo, p. 262). At their peak, *sunspots* can affect the Earth by triggering magnetic storms here that interfere with radio communications, cause powerline surges, and produce especially brilliant auroras in the night skies of the polar and subpolar regions. The last sunspot activity cycle peaked in 2001; the next midcycle minimum is expected to occur in 2006.

FIGURE 4.4 A total eclipse of the Sun, such as this one seen from Chisamba, Zambia, on June 21, 2001, reveals its large, luminous corona. The corona consists of a belt of fast-moving free electrons, at temperatures of about 2 million degrees Celsius, rising to about 75,000 km above the Sun's surface. A cloud of cosmic dust particles augments the corona far beyond.

The Planets

All the planets except Neptune and Pluto are bright enough to be seen in the night skies without a telescope, and they have been observed by humans for thousands of years. The ancient Greeks were particularly fascinated by these moving celestial bodies and coined the word *planet* (meaning wanderer). The arrangement of the nine planets in the solar system is shown in Fig. 4.3, which highlights their concentric orbits (only Pluto deviates from this pattern, as we shall see). The farther a planet is located from the Sun, the greater the length of its orbit. One complete circling of the Sun within such an orbital path is called a **revolution**. The closest planet to the Sun, Mercury, needs only 88 Earth-days to complete one revolution. The Earth, of course, requires exactly one year (365¼ days). The outer planets take far longer to revolve around the Sun. (Saturn requires almost 30 years, whereas outermost Pluto requires more than 247 years.) Information on revolution times is presented in column 3 of Table 4.1, which also displays six other categories of vital planetary data.

The Inner Planets The four planets nearest the Sun—Mercury, Venus, Earth, and Mars—are classified as *terrestrial* or Earth-like. All are much smaller than the four outer planets (see columns 5 and 6 in Table 4.1). Each is a solid sphere, composed largely of iron and rock, built around a dense metallic core. The surface layer of each inner planet received vast quantities of gases that were exhaled by volcanoes as the planet gradually cooled. In each case an atmosphere formed. Only Mercury no longer possesses one; its atmospheric envelope quickly boiled away because of its proximity to the searing heat of the Sun. All of these planets experienced considerable volcanic and seismic (earthquake) activity. Again, only Mercury no longer exhibits those geologic disturbances, whereas the other three planets remain quite active. Another characteristic of the terrestrial planets is the paucity of moons. While the four outer planets claim a total of 90 moons, only three are found in the inner solar system. Earth's Moon is the largest of these, with the remaining two tiny moons in orbit around Mars. Let us now take a closer look at each planet, proceeding in order away from the Sun.

Mercury, as is clear from the preceding discussion, is a dead planet. It could not hold on to its atmosphere, and volcanism and seismic activity appear to have ceased more than 3 billion years ago. Every aspect of Mercury is overshadowed by its innermost position in the solar system, which brings the planet's orbit to within 46 million km of the Sun at its closest point. Surprisingly, Mercury is not the hottest of the planetary surfaces: Venus, because of its very dense atmosphere, averages about 300°C higher (see Table 4.1, column 8). Moreover, Mercury's surface temperature on the side facing away from the Sun dips as low as −173°C. It should be noted (see column 4 of the table) that this planet spins or **rotates** on its axis approximately once every 59 days (a complete rotation of the Earth occurs once every [24-hour] day). Astronomers have assembled a fairly detailed picture of Mercury, thanks to the close-up imagery obtained during the 1974–1975 flyby of NASA's Mariner 10 space probe. The surface is like that of our Moon—lifeless and heavily cratered from severe meteorite impacts that could not be cushioned by the frictional effects of an overlying atmosphere.

Venus is often called the Earth's twin because the two planets are so close in size and mass, but they really have very little else in common. The extremely high temperatures of the Venusian surface (averaging 464°C), the hottest of any planet, have already been noted. These are undoubtedly heightened by the weight of an oppressive atmosphere that is 90 times as dense as the Earth's. Thick layers of yellowish-white sulfuric acid clouds constantly obscure Venus (Fig. 4.5). But the space explorations of the past three decades, particularly the U.S. Magellan mission that mapped Venus from an orbiting

Table 4.1 Characteristics of the Planets of the Solar System

Planet	Mean Orbital Distance from the Sun (Millions km)	Period of One Revolution (Days/Years)	Period of Rotation on Axis	Diameter at Equator	Mass (Earth = 1)	Main Atmospheric Components	Surface Temperature	Number of Moons
Mercury	57.9	88 (0.24 yrs)	58.7 days	4,879 km	0.06	Sodium Potassium Helium	−173°C to 427°C	0
Venus	108.2	224.7 (0.62 yrs)	243 days	12,104 km	0.82	Carbon dioxide Carbon monoxide Hydrogen chloride	464°C	0
Earth	149.6	365.3 (1.0 yrs)	23 hrs, 56 mins	12,756 km	1.00	Nitrogen Oxygen Water vapor	−88°C to 58°C	1
Mars	227.9	687 (1.9 yrs)	24 hrs, 37 mins	6,794 km	0.11	Carbon dioxide Carbon monoxide Water vapor	−63°C to 27°C	2
Jupiter	778.6	4,331 (11.9 yrs)	9 hrs, 51 mins	142,984 km	317.8	Hydrogen Helium Methane	−163°C to −123°C	28
Saturn	1,433.5	10,747 (29.5 yrs)	10 hrs, 14 mins	120,536 km	95.1	Hydrogen Helium Methane	−140°C	30
Uranus	2,872.5	30,589 (84.0 yrs)	17 hrs, 14 mins	51,118 km	14.54	Hydrogen Helium Methane	−195°C	21
Neptune	4,495.1	59,800 (164.8 yrs)	16 hrs, 3 mins	49,528 km	17.15	Hydrogen Helium Methane	−200°C	11
Pluto	5,869.7	90,588 (247.7 yrs)	6.4 days	2,930 km	0.002	Nitrogen Carbon dioxide Methane	−225°C	1

satellite in 1990–1991, have provided detailed images of its forbidding surface. Violent volcanism is widespread, and there are highly varied landforms all across the planet's relatively flat face. To earthlings, Venus has always been the third brightest object in the sky (after the Sun and Moon). It is often observed as the "evening star" or "morning star" as its position alternates while both planets revolve around the Sun. At its closest point, Venus comes within 40 million km of the Earth, a distance about 100 times greater than that between the Earth and the Moon. Even though it is the second closest planet to the Sun, Venus rotates on its axis much more slowly than any of the other eight planets. This oddity results from its aberrant rotational behaviour, with Venus being the only planet to rotate in the direction *opposite* to that of its orbital revolution.

Earth, the third planet, possesses a physical environment that is significantly shaped by its rotational and orbital behaviour (Earth–Sun relationships are the subject of Unit 5). At this point the Earth should be compared to its planetary cousins by referring to the data displayed in Table 4.1. Perusal of this table immediately reveals that the Earth and the conditions necessary to support terrestrial life are unique. They simply do not exist anywhere else in the solar system (though they could occur on planets elsewhere in the universe). Columns 7 and 8 in Table 4.1 are especially important because they illustrate the range of atmospheric compositions and surface temperatures, and underscore how different our planet is from all the others in these environmental variables that are so critical to the survival of Earth's plants and animals.

Named after the Roman god of war because of its reddish colour, **Mars** is the fourth planet from the Sun and thus Earth's neighbour. The Red Planet's diameter is only about half that of Earth's, but its structure has similarities, including a metallic core and a crust that varies in thickness from about 15 km to some 130 km. Because Mars rotates on an oblique axis and has an atmosphere consisting mainly of carbon dioxide, the planet experiences seasons—and wild daily surface temperature swings ranging from nighttime lows

FIGURE 4.5 Close-up view of Venus, taken from the Pioneer Orbiter in 1979 at a distance of 59,000 km. While thick clouds unrelentingly shroud this mysterious planet, more recent space probes have successfully penetrated that barrier to map the hellish Venusian surface.

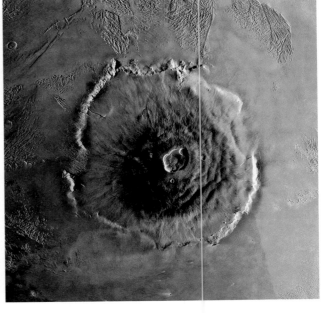

FIGURE 4.6 Olympus Mons (Mount Olympus) soaring skyward from the surface of Mars. The largest and tallest known volcano in the solar system, its summit rises 27 km above the surrounding plain, three times as high as Mount Everest. The base of Olympus Mons is 600 km wide.

below −73°C to daytime highs above 15°C. The United States put two Viking landers on Mars in 1976, and the images they sent back revealed a rocky arid desert. But high-altitude photography showed what appeared to be basins with water-sculpted margins, as well as gigantic canyons and a volcano at least three times as high as the tallest mountain on Earth. Named Olympus Mons, that volcano is the highest ever observed in the solar system (Fig. 4.6). NASA scored a remarkable success in 1997 when the U.S. Space Program landed Pathfinder on Mars, and the world watched on television as its "rover," the six-wheeled Sojourner Truth, transmitted live pictures of the terrain it crossed as it gathered data on the Red Planet's subsurface and atmosphere. To the question whether there is (or was) life on Mars there is as yet no final answer, but the accumulating evidence is increasing the probability. Scientists in 2001 concluded that Mars may have had oceans comparable (in terms of volume and extent) to those of Earth; in 2002, NASA's Mars Odyssey spacecraft yielded data indicating that, early in its history, the Red Planet was wet and warm—the ingredients for life. And Mars, while arid at the surface today, has not lost all of its water. In its polar regions, below about 60 cm of soil and rocky debris, lies a reservoir of frozen water; its volume at the North Pole is estimated to amount to about twice that of Lake Michigan. If life did get a start on Mars in its distant past, there may be survivors in the form of microbes, deep below that ice where the planet's interior heat may keep water in the liquid form. (See Fig. 4.7.) The next step is to drill a borehole through that frozen polar crust.

Canada hopes to play a major role in a scientific mission to Mars in this decade. The Canadian Space Agency

FIGURE 4.7 The "Columbia Hills" in colour. On May 16, 2004, NASA's Mars Exploration Rover Spirit used its panoramic camera to take the images that make up this mosaic of the "Columbia Hills." Scientists hope to find ancient rock outcroppings from this region that will hold clues to the water history of Mars.

(CSA) has undertaken consultation with the science and industry sectors and international partners to determine how Canadian technology and expertise can be applied to the exploration of Mars. Canada's expertise in space robotics and mining technologies could contribute to future Mars missions. The Canadian Space Agency is working toward the creation of a new "Canadian Concept" mission to Mars for the year 2011. The research frontier on this planetary neighbour is one of the most exciting prospects in all of science.

The Outer Planets The outer planets—Jupiter, Saturn, Uranus, Neptune—differ radically from their inner solar system counterparts. They are known as the *major planets* (or the *Jovian planets*—they all resemble giant, prototypical Jupiter), because they account for over 99 percent of all the matter of the solar system exclusive of the Sun itself. Each of these planets is a huge sphere composed largely of gases (hydrogen and helium dominate, as column 7 of Table 4.1 indicates), and each possesses a deep atmosphere with clouds. All except Uranus give off more heat than they absorb from the distant Sun. This heat is a residue from the formation of these planets, a physical property that can be likened to still-warm pieces of coal long after their fires have gone out. Perhaps the single most striking feature in this outer part

of the solar system is the planet Saturn surrounded by its spectacular rings. Space scientists have recently discovered that Jupiter, Uranus, and Neptune also possess rings, but these are far less prominent and dramatic than Saturn's.

Jupiter, the biggest planet in the Sun's family, is one-tenth the size of the Sun and so large that more than a thousand Earths would be needed to fill its volume. Jupiter is also the solar system's most rapidly spinning planet, requiring less than 10 hours to complete one full rotation. This rapid rotation produces a decided bulge at the Equator and the corresponding flattening of the polar regions. It also shapes the formation of latitudinal belts across the gaseous face of Jupiter. These horizontal bands, together with the Great Red Spot (Fig. 4.8), are the planet's most prominent features. They suggest an incredibly violent atmosphere and "surface" (no sharp boundary marks the contact between the atmosphere and the liquid interior). In fact, the Red Spot is a slow-moving, raging, hurricane-like storm that has been observed by astronomers since its discovery in 1630. Of Jupiter's 28 moons, four are large enough to be of planetary dimensions. Jupiter also possesses a system of thin, essentially transparent rings that consist, quite literally, of millions of additional tiny moons.

Saturn, the second largest planet, also is the second fastest in rotation (about 10¼ hours) and, like Jupiter, also exhibits equatorial bulging and polar flattening. Saturn's rings have fascinated skywatchers for centuries, but it was not until the 1980s that NASA's Voyager 1 and 2

FIGURE 4.8 Jupiter photographed from a distance of 28 million km by Voyager 1 in 1979. Clearly visible are the banded surface, the Great Red Spot (lower left), and two inner moons (Io and Europa).

FIGURE 4.9 One of the solar system's most spectacular sights—the intricate patterns and dazzling colours of Saturn's ring system, as photographed here by Voyager 2 in 1981. It has since been estimated that more than 100,000 individual rings and ringlets may exist.

space probes flew through them and sent back detailed information (Fig. 4.9). Now we know that there are seven major rings, which consist of literally thousands of tiny ringlets. The rings themselves (which do not touch Saturn) are composed of icy particles of water or rock that orbit above Saturn's equator like a pulverized moon. Although the rings extend outward into space for at least 400,000 km, they are quite flat, with an average thickness of less than 15 km. Beyond its ring system, Saturn has 30 moons, the most of any planet. The largest, Titan, is the only moon in the solar system with an atmosphere, composed mainly of nitrogen.

Uranus and **Neptune** have frequently been called twins because, at least from a distance, they were seen to share many characteristics (see Table 4.1). But the close-up data transmitted back to Earth by the Voyager 2 flyby (Uranus in 1986; Neptune in 1989) revealed major structural and atmospheric differences that have forced planetary scientists to revise their perceptions. Among the new discoveries: Uranus spins on its side and possesses a system of at least 11 rings, whereas Neptune gives off internal heat that helps drive a much more active atmosphere and was found to have spawned a five-ring system.

The Lesser Bodies of the Solar System   Pluto, the ninth and outermost planet, is treated separately from the other planets because of its small size and the fact that so little is known about it (no space probe has yet ventured to its vicinity). Perhaps its most notable characteristic is its highly eccentric orbit, which passes inside Neptune's orbital path for 20 of the 247½ years of the Plutonic revolution and is also inclined at an angle of more than 17° to the geometric plane in which Earth and the other planets circle the Sun (Fig. 4.3). Pluto has a single large moon, Charon, about half its size. Many astronomers have always been skeptical of Pluto's planetary status, and their case was greatly strengthened in 2002 by the discovery of a similar celestial body in the debris belt beyond the orbit of Neptune that serves as a reservoir of comets and other frozen objects. Named Quaoar, this newly discovered body is more than half the size of Pluto and also exhibits an orbit inclined at an angle to the plane in which the other eight planets revolve around the Sun. Thus Pluto's size and orbital path no longer make it an oddity in the solar system's outer debris belt. Moreover, actively looking researchers are confident that other large objects (perhaps as large as Mars) exist in this region—and the day may soon come when students will learn that our solar system consists of eight, not nine, planets.

FIGURE 4.10   Crater-studded surface of the Moon in the vicinity of the lunar equator's western segment (as seen from Earth). This photo was taken during the final manned (Apollo 17) mission to the Moon in 1972. Most appropriate for a physical geography textbook, the large crater left of centre is named Eratosthenes (see Unit 1). On the horizon at the right is the rim of Copernicus, the lunar surface's largest crater.

Moons are satellites that orbit every planet except Mercury and Venus. Moons probably originated as planetesimals that were subsequently captured by the gravitational pull of the emerging planets. The best known satellite to us on Earth is our own Moon, on whose surface American astronauts first landed in 1969. The Moon revolves around the Earth once every 27.3 days and is located at an average distance of 385,000 km—a spacecraft journey of about six days. The comparative sizes of the two bodies can best be visualized by reference to an often used analogy: if the Earth is imagined to be a basketball, then the relative size of the Moon would equal that of a tennis ball. Following a violent beginning from the time of the birth of the solar system (ca. 4.6 billion years ago) until about 3 billion years ago, the Moon has been a lifeless body during the most recent two-thirds of its existence. The lunar surface can be broadly divided into three physiographic categories: plains, highlands, and craters. The plains and highlands were created by volcanic activity during the Moon's early active stage, the lowlands originating as sheetlike lava flows and the hilly uplands shaped by eruptions. Superimposed across most of the Moon's face are billions of impact craters

(Fig. 4.10), with more than 300,000 measuring at least 1 km across.

We have already identified the remaining smaller objects of the solar system—asteroids, comets, meteoroids, and dust. However, as we saw in the case of the cratering of the Moon (a process that also occurs on many planets and every other moon), these objects make up in quantity what they lack in size, and their presence is continuously and ubiquitously felt. Moreover, astronomers are increasingly concerned that asteroids and *meteorites* (meteoroids that penetrate the atmosphere and reach the surface) pose a significant threat to Earth (see Perspective: Collision!).

This unit has discussed the overall context of the Earth, focusing on its place in the tiny corner of the universe it travels through and making comparisons with the other major bodies of the solar system. The next unit elaborates the special relationships between Planet Earth and the life-giving Sun, and forms the foundation for understanding the seasonal rhythms that are so important to the Earth's physical geography.

PERSPECTIVES ON THE HUMAN ENVIRONMENT

Collision!

Sketches of the solar system such as Fig. 4.3 suggest that our corner of the universe is now stable and steady, with the planets in fixed and predictable orbits and space a challenging frontier of empty distance. But space is not empty. Literally countless comets, asteroids, and meteors travel in orbits not nearly as predictable as those of the planets themselves. Most of these extraterrestrial fellow travellers are small and harmless, treating us to "meteor showers" when they burn up in the Earth's upper atmosphere. Many are well known to astronomers, who not only tell us to watch for the near-passage of familiar comets but who are able to tell us when, in centuries to come, the spectacle will repeat. But some are dangerous and unpredictable, and these pose a threat whose dimensions are becoming clearer and causing concern.

Numerous objects, large and small, are known to have struck the Earth over its 4.6-billion-year history. The largest of all—it may have been the size of Mars—struck at a low angle when our planet was only about 100 million years old, briefly burying itself in the molten mass of the Earth's primordial shell. So great was its speed, so huge the collision, that much of it bounced outward again into space, weighted down by a clump of earthly matter. Too heavy now to escape the Earth's gravitational field, the slowed-down planetoid was trapped in earthly orbit. Our planet had acquired its Moon.

Looking up at the Moon today, we can see what happened next. For more than 4 billion years, objects from space have intermittently crashed onto its surface, leaving numerous craters large and small. The lifeless Moon had no atmosphere to cushion the blows; everything from meteors to asteroids struck its crust at full speed. That bombardment left not a single square metre of the Moon's surface unaffected.

The Earth, too, was subject to such collisions, but the results are less obvious. The Earth acquired oceans that eventually covered more than 70 percent of its surface, obscuring the record of a similar percentage of impacts. The Earth also acquired an atmosphere that provided protection against smaller objects and partial relief against larger ones. And for reasons we will explain later, much of the impact record was erased through geologic and geomorphic processes.

Nevertheless, it is becoming clearer by the day that our planet has suffered devastating damage from asteroid and comet impacts throughout its history. It is now clear that the sudden demise of most dinosaur species at the end of the Cretaceous period 65 million years ago (see geologic time scale on p. 471), resulted from the impact of what is technically known as a carbonaceous meteorite, about 10 km in diameter and travelling at 90,000 km/h in the area that is today the northwestern edge of

Caribbean Mexico's Yucatán Peninsula. The crater, buried under subsequent sediments, was found, named Chicxulub, and mapped; it is not impossible that other objects struck the Earth elsewhere at the same time. The effect was to kill off the long-dominant dinosaurs, giving smaller, surviving mammals their chance and leading, eventually, to the rise of humanity.

If the demise of the dinosaurs is attributable to an impact, might earlier extinctions have similar causes? In its May 17, 2002, issue, the journal *Science* carried an article by Paul Olsen and his colleagues proposing that the sudden emergence of the large dinosaurs, just over 200 million years ago, might also have resulted from a collision. During the first period of the Mesozoic, Olsen reminds us, dinosaurs were small and just part of a huge assemblage of reptiles. Then, perhaps 202 million years ago, an asteroid or comet struck, killing the majority of the dinosaurs' larger competitors and changing the planet to their advantage. In a geologic instant, perhaps over a mere 10,000 years, the dinosaurs emerged to dominate the Jurassic and Cretaceous periods—until their reign ended with another bang. If Olsen's theory turns out to be correct, the search will be on for other impacts,

and the question of just how safe we are will acquire new urgency. Meanwhile, physical geographers point to the event at remote Tunguska, in Russia, as recently as June 30, 1908, when an asteroid perhaps 80 m in diameter penetrated the atmosphere far enough to explode just above the surface, levelling trees and triggering fires over a more than 2500-km^2 area. Had that impact occurred over a densely populated zone, casualties might have run into the millions.

Can humankind take measures to protect itself? A number of scientists think we can and should, first by creating a vastly improved monitoring system to trace the paths of potentially dangerous objects and second by developing technology to destroy or at least deflect incoming asteroids or comets.

But not every extraterrestrial object that hits the Earth's surface causes such dramatic reversals. How often do we get hit, and what are the risks? Ongoing research on the still-incomplete inventory of impact craters is beginning to provide some answers, but in truth we do not yet know. Some scientists are suggesting that a catastrophic impact could happen, on average, once every 100,000 years.

KEY TERMS

galaxy *page 46*

gravity *page 48*

light-year *page 46*

moon *page 54*

planet *page 48*

revolution *page 50*

rotation *page 50*

solar system *page 48*

Mercury *page 50*

Venus *page 50*

Earth *page 51*

Mars *page 51*

Jupiter *page 53*

Saturn *page 53*

Uranus *page 54*

Neptune *page 54*

Pluto *page 54*

universe *page 46*

REVIEW QUESTIONS

1. Describe the hierarchical organization of the universe's time–space levels.

2. Define the term *planet* and describe how the solar system's planets formed.

3. Define the term *revolution* and discuss its application to the orbital patterns of the Sun's planets.

4. Name the *inner planets* and list the major characteristics they share.

5. Name the *outer planets* and list the major characteristics they share.

6. What are the differences between *moons, comets, asteroids,* and *meteoroids?*

REFERENCES AND FURTHER READINGS

ALVAREZ, W. *T. Rex and the Crater of Doom* (Princeton, N.J.: Princeton Univ. Press, 1997).

AUDOUZE, J., and ISRAEL, G., Eds. *The Cambridge Atlas of Astronomy* (New York: Cambridge Univ. Press, 2nd ed., 1988).

BEATTY, J. K., et al., Eds. *The New Solar System* (New York: Cambridge Univ. Press, 4th ed., 1999).

BOOTH, N. *Exploring the Solar System* (New York: Cambridge Univ. Press, 1996).

CLOUD, P. *Cosmos, Earth, and Man* (New Haven, Conn.: Yale Univ. Press, 1978).

HAWKING, S. W. *A Brief History of Time: From the Big Bang to Black Holes* (New York: Bantam Books, 1988).

LEWIS, J. S. *Rain of Iron and Ice: The Very Real Threat of Comet and Asteroid Bombardment* (Reading, Mass.: Addison-Wesley, 1996).

LIGHTMAN, A. *Ancient Light: Our Changing View of the Universe* (Cambridge, Mass.: Harvard Univ. Press, 1993).

LODDERS, K., and FEGLEY, B., Jr. *The Planetary Scientist's Companion* (New York: Oxford Univ. Press, 1998).

McNAB, D., and YOUNGER, J. *The Planets* (New Haven, Conn.: Yale Univ. Press, 1999).

MOORE, P., Ed. *Astronomy Encyclopedia: An A-Z Guide to the Universe* (New York: Oxford University Press, 2002).

MOORE, P. *Atlas of the Universe* (New York: Cambridge Univ. Press, 1998).

SAGAN, C. *Cosmos* (New York: Random House, 1980).

TAYLOR, F. W. *The Cambridge Photographic Guide to the Planets* (New York: Cambridge Univ. Press, 2002).

ZEILIK, M. *Astronomy: The Evolving Universe* (New York: Wiley, 8th ed., 1997).

WEB RESOURCES

http://seds.lpl.arizona.edu/nineplanets/nineplanets/nineplanets.html An up-to-date multimedia presentation of the solar system, with links to more information.

http://ssd.jpl.nasa.gov A comprehensive guide to all planets, natural satellites, asteroids, and comets of the solar system, presented by NASA's Jet Propulsion Laboratory and Caltech.

http://www.space.gc.ca The Canadian Space Agency includes details about the RADARSAT, the International Space Station, Canadian astronauts, and future Canadian missions.

Earth—Sun Relationships

An astronaut's view of sunrise over a clouded Earth.

OBJECTIVES

- To examine the Earth's motions relative to the Sun

- To demonstrate the consequences of the Earth's axis tilt for the annual march of the seasons

- To introduce the time and spatial variations in solar radiation received at surface locations

arth is a small, fragile planet. As the third planet of the solar system it orbits the Sun—the source of light, heat, and the gravitational field that sustains all nine planets (see Fig. 4.3). Among the planets, however, only the Earth exhibits the unique physical conditions that are essential for the support of life as we know it. Conceivably these conditions could exist on planets elsewhere in the vast universe. The Earth's natural environment, particularly its vital heating, is significantly shaped by the movements of our planet relative to the Sun. In this unit we explore basic Earth—Sun relationships and their profound consequences for the temperature patterns that occur on the Earth's surface.

Earth's Planetary Motions

Unit 4 introduced two basic concepts of planetary motion—revolution and rotation. A revolution is one complete circling of the Sun by a planet within its orbital path. The Earth requires exactly one year to revolve around the Sun. As it revolves, each planet also exhibits a second simultaneous motion—rotation, or spinning on its axis. It takes the Earth almost one calendar day to complete one full rotation on its **axis**, the imaginary line that extends from the North Pole to the South Pole through the centre of the Earth.

As the Earth revolves around the Sun and rotates on its axis, the Sun's most intense rays constantly strike a different patch of its surface. Thus at any given moment, the Sun's heating (or solar energy) is unevenly distributed, always varying in geographic space and time. By time we mean not only the hour of the day, but also the time of the year—the major rhythms of Earth time for all living things as measured in the annual march of the seasons. Before examining seasonality, we need to know more about the concepts of revolution and rotation.

Revolution

The Earth revolves around the Sun in an orbit that is almost circular. Its annual revolution around the Sun takes 365¼ days, which determines the length of our year. Rather than starting the New Year at a time other than midnight, one full day is added to the calendar every fourth year, when February has 29 days instead of 28. Such a year (occurring in 2004 and 2008, for example) is called a *leap year*.

Like the Earth itself, which is *nearly* a sphere, the Earth's orbital path is *nearly* circular around the Sun. In fact, the Earth is slightly closer to the Sun in early January than it is in early July. This makes its orbital trajectory slightly elliptical. The average distance from the Earth to the Sun is approximately 150 million km. But on January 3, when the Earth is closest to the Sun, the distance is about 147.3 million km. This position is called the moment of **perihelion** (from the ancient Greek *peri*, meaning near; *helios*, meaning sun). From that time onward, the Earth–Sun distance increases slowly until July 4, half a year later, when it reaches about 152.1 million km. This position is called **aphelion** (*ap* means away from). Thus the Earth is farthest from the Sun during the Northern Hemisphere summer and closest during the northern winter (or Southern Hemisphere summer). But the total difference is only about 5 million km, not enough to produce a significant variation in the amount of solar energy received by our planet.

Rotation

Our planet ranks among the solar system's fast-spinning bodies, which produces equatorial bulging and polar-area flattening. Accordingly, geophysicists have discovered that the Earth's diameter when measured pole to pole (12,715 km) is slightly less than it is at the Equator (12,760 km). Thus the Earth is not a perfect sphere; it is an *oblate spheroid,* the technical term used to describe the departure from a sphere that is induced by the bulging/flattening phenomenon just described. The Earth's deviation from a true sphere, however, is a minor one. In fact, the difference between the equatorial and polar diameters is so small (just 45 km, or 0.35 percent) that it matters only to Earth scientists and other specialists involved in activities that demand exactness—for example, in space flight, detailed cartography, or *geodesy* (precise planetary measurement).

As the Earth rotates on its axis—which occurs in a west-to-east direction—this motion creates the alternations of day and night, as (a constantly changing) one-half of the planet is always turned toward the Sun whereas its other half always faces away. One complete rotation takes roughly 24 hours (23 hours, 56 minutes, to be exact), or one calendar day. During one full revolution around the Sun, the Earth makes 365¼ rotations. Consider this: the Earth's circumference at the Equator is slightly less than 40,000 km. Thus a place on or near the Equator, say the city of Quito, Ecuador, rotates at a speed of 1666 km per hour—continuously! But the distance travelled during a complete rotation diminishes northward and southward from the Equator, until it becomes zero at the poles. A person standing on the North or South Pole would merely make one full turn in place every 24 hours. This contrast between the force of rotation at or near the poles (known as angular momentum) on the one hand, and at or near the Equator on the other, causes the Earth to develop that slight bulge at the Equator.

Actually, the person standing at the pole does not feel any effect different from someone standing on the Equator. We do not notice the effect of the Earth's rotation, because everything on the planet—land, water, air—moves along at the same rate of speed. And the rate of rotation does not vary, so no slowing down or speeding up is sensed. But look up into the sky and watch the stars or moon rise, and the reality of the Earth's rotation soon presents itself. This is especially true concerning the stationary Sun. To us, it appears to "rise" in the east (the direction of rotation) as the leading edge of the unlit half of the Earth turns back toward the Sun. Similarly, the Sun appears to "set" in the west as the trailing edge of the sunlit half of the Earth moves off toward the east.

Note that reference was made to a person *standing* at certain places on the Earth's surface. The fact is that a person or object not in motion does not experience any effect from our planet's rotation. But *moving* people and objects do. Moving currents of water and streams of air are affected by a force that tends to deflect them away from their original direction of movement. This force was not known until it was identified by the French scientist Gustave Gaspard de Coriolis in the 1830s. Everything that moves under the influence of our rotating Earth is affected by this force, which is appropriately named the *Coriolis force* after its discoverer. The Coriolis force is an important factor in the Earth's climate and weather, ocean currents, and related parts of other environmental systems (see Unit 9).

The Earth rotates eastward, so that sunrise is always observed on the eastern horizon. The Sun then traverses the sky to "set" in the west. But, of course, it is not the Sun but the *Earth* whose movement causes this illusion. Looking down on a model globe, viewing it from directly above the North Pole (as in Fig. 3.6), we see that rotation occurs in a counterclockwise direction. This might seem to be a rather simple exercise. But several years ago, in one of the great bloopers of television history, a major TV network opened its nightly national news program with a large model globe turning the wrong way!

Seasonality

If on a flat piece of paper you draw the orbital path of the Earth around the Sun, the paper could be described as a geometric plane. The actual plane in space, which contains the line traced by the Earth's slightly elliptical orbit and the stationary Sun, is called the **plane of the ecliptic**. The seasons occur because the Earth is *tilted* with respect to the plane of the ecliptic.

Axis Tilt

The Earth's axis is always tilted at an angle of 66½ degrees to the plane of the ecliptic and is always tilted in the same direction no matter where the Earth is in its orbit. The constant tilt of the axis is the key to these seasonal changes. Sometimes the term *parallelism* is used to describe this axial phenomenon, meaning that the Earth's axis remains parallel to itself at every position in its orbital revolution. Thus at one point in its revolution, around June 22, the northern half of the Earth, the Northern Hemisphere, is maximally tilted toward the Sun. At this time, the Northern Hemisphere receives a much greater amount of solar energy than the Southern Hemisphere does. When the Earth has moved to the opposite point in its orbit six months later, around December 22, the Northern Hemisphere is maximally tilted away from the Sun and receives the least energy. This accounts for the seasons of heat and cold, summer and winter. Figure 5.1 summarizes these Earth–Sun relationships and shows how these seasons occur at opposite times of the year in the Northern and Southern Hemispheres.

Now consider Fig. 5.2, which shows that, on or about June 22, parallel rays from the Sun fall vertically at noon on the Earth at latitude 23½°N. This latitude, where the Sun's rays strike the surface at an angle of 90 degrees, is given the name **Tropic of Cancer**—the most northerly latitude where the Sun's noontime rays strike vertically. All areas north of latitude 66½°N, which is called the **Arctic Circle**, remain totally in sunlight during the

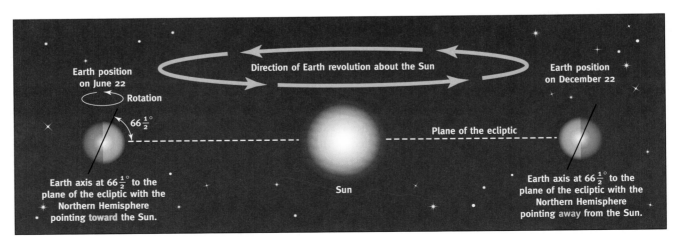

FIGURE 5.1 Extreme summer and winter positions of the Earth with regard to the Sun. The Earth's axis is tilted at the same angle to the plane of the ecliptic throughout the year.

FIGURE 5.2 Relative positions of Earth and Sun on June 22 and December 22. Points on Earth receive the Sun's rays at different angles throughout the year.

FIGURE 5.3 The sky above the Canadian Arctic with the silhouette of an Inukshuk. In late July, just poleward of the Arctic Circle, the Sun never sets.

Earth's 24-hour rotation (Fig. 5.3). If a vertical pole were placed at the Equator at noon on this day of the year, the Sun should appear to be northward of the pole, making an angle of 23½ degrees with the pole and an angle of 66½ degrees with the ground (Fig. 5.4). Note that the summation of these two angles equals 90 degrees.

Precisely six months later, on December 22, the position of the Earth relative to the Sun causes the Sun's rays to strike vertically at noon at 23½°S, the latitude called the **Tropic of Capricorn** (the southernmost latitude

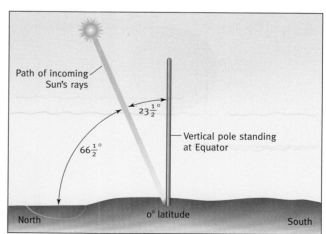

FIGURE 5.4 Angular relationships of incoming solar rays with the ground and a vertical pole standing at the Equator at noon on June 22.

where the Sun's noon rays can strike the surface at 90 degrees). The other relationships between the Earth and the Sun for June 22 as described are exactly reversed (see Fig. 5.2). Accordingly, the entire area south of the **Antarctic Circle**, located at latitude 66½°S, receives 24 hours of sunlight. Simultaneously, the area north of the Arctic Circle is in complete darkness. (Note that in Fig. 5.2, the area south of the Antarctic Circle was similarly darkened on June 22.)

Solstices and Equinoxes

To us on Earth it appears that the highest daily position of the Sun at noontime gets lower in the sky as the seasons progress from summer to fall to winter. If you were to plot the position of the noontime Sun throughout the year at a location in the middle latitudes of the Northern Hemisphere, it would seem to climb higher and higher until June 22, when it would appear to stop. Then it would move lower and lower, until it stopped again at December 22, before once more beginning to climb. South of the Equator the dates are reversed, but the phenomenon is identical. The ancient Greeks plotted the apparent movement of the Sun and called the points at which the stops occurred **solstices** (Sun stands still). Today we continue to use their word, calling the

Earth–Sun position of June 22 the **summer solstice** and that of December 22 the **winter solstice**. In the Southern Hemisphere, of course, these dates are reversed.

Exactly halfway between the two solstice dates there are two positions where the rotating globe receives 12 hours of sunlight and 12 of darkness at all latitudes. These positions occur on or about March 21 and September 23. Because of the equal lengths of night at every latitude, these special positions are called **equinoxes**, which in Latin means equal nights. On these two occasions the Sun's rays fall vertically over the surface at the Equator, and the Sun rises and sets due east and west. The equinox of March 21 is known as the **spring** or **vernal equinox**, and that of September 23 as the **fall** or **autumnal equinox**.

The Four Seasons

You can achieve a clear idea of the causes of the seasons if you imagine you are looking down on the Earth's orbit around the Sun (the plane of the ecliptic) from a point high above the solar system, a perspective diagrammed in Fig. 5.5. The North Pole always points to your right. At the summer solstice, the Arctic Circle receives sunlight during the entire daily rotation of the Earth, and all parts of the Northern Hemisphere have more than

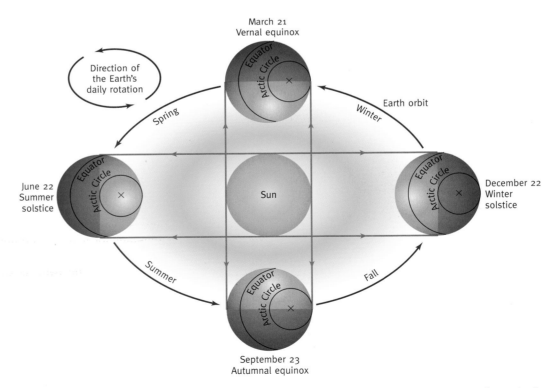

FIGURE 5.5 March of the seasons as viewed from a position above the solar system. Seasonal terminology here applies to the Northern Hemisphere. (The Southern Hemisphere seasonal cycle is the exact opposite.)

12 hours of daylight. These areas receive a large amount of solar energy in the summer season. At the winter solstice, the area inside the Arctic Circle receives no sunlight at all, and every part of the Northern Hemisphere receives less than 12 hours of sunlight. Thus winter is a time of cooling, when solar energy levels are at a minimum. However, at both the spring and fall equinoxes, the Arctic Circle and the Equator are equally divided into day and night. Both hemispheres receive an equal amount of sunlight and darkness, and energy from the Sun is equally distributed.

The annual revolution of the Earth around the Sun and the constant tilt of its axis give our planet its different seasons of relative warmth and coldness. The yearly cycle of the four seasons may be traced using Fig. 5.5. *Spring* begins at the vernal equinox on March 21 and ends at the summer solstice on June 22; *summer* runs from that date through the autumnal equinox on September 23; *autumn* occurs from then until the arrival of the winter solstice on December 22; *winter* then follows and lasts until the vernal equinox is again reached on March 21. This cycle, of course, applies only to the Northern Hemisphere; the Southern Hemisphere's seasonal march is the mirror image, with spring commencing on the date of the northern autumnal equinox (September 23).

Throughout human history, the passage of the seasons has been used as a basis for establishing secure reference points for measuring time (see Perspective: Measuring Time on Our Rotating Earth). The changing spatial relationships between Earth and Sun, produced by the planetary motions of revolution and rotation on a constantly tilted axis, cause important variations in the amount of solar energy received at the Earth's surface.

PERSPECTIVES ON THE HUMAN ENVIRONMENT

Measuring Time on Our Rotating Earth

The measurement of time on the Earth's surface is important in the study of our planet. One of the most obvious ways to start dealing with time is to use the periods of light and darkness resulting from the daily rotation of the Earth. One rotation of the Earth, one cycle of daylight and nighttime hours, constitutes one full day. The idea of dividing the day into 24 equal hours dates from the fourteenth century.

With each place keeping track of its own time by the Sun, this system worked well as long as human movements were confined to local areas. But by the sixteenth century, when sailing ships began to undertake transoceanic voyages, problems arose because the sun is always rising in one part of the world as it sets in another. On a sea voyage, such as that of Columbus in the *Santa Maria,* it was always relatively simple to establish the latitude of the ship. Columbus's navigator had only to find the angle of the Sun at its highest point during the day. Then, by knowing what day of the year it was, he could calculate his latitude from a set of previously prepared tables giving the angle of the Sun at any latitude on a particular day.

It was impossible, however, for him to calculate his longitude. In order to do that, he would have to know precisely the difference between the time at some agreed meridian, such as the Prime Meridian (zero degrees longitude), and the time at the meridian where his ship was located. Until about 1750, no portable mechanical clock or chronometer was accurate enough to keep track of that time difference.

With the perfection of the chronometer in the late eighteenth century, the problem of timekeeping came under control. A new problem, however, emerged in the nineteenth century. A standardized time system became increasingly necessary as railway travel expanded, serving communities that used hundreds of different local times. Confused scheduling was the inevitable result. The need for a standard time was felt in Europe (with England adopting the first regional standard time) but even more so in North America, where railway routes passed through places that had several hours difference in local time. Sir Sandford Fleming, a Canadian civil and railway engineer, initiated efforts to establish time zones. He played an important role in the convening of an *International Prime Meridian*

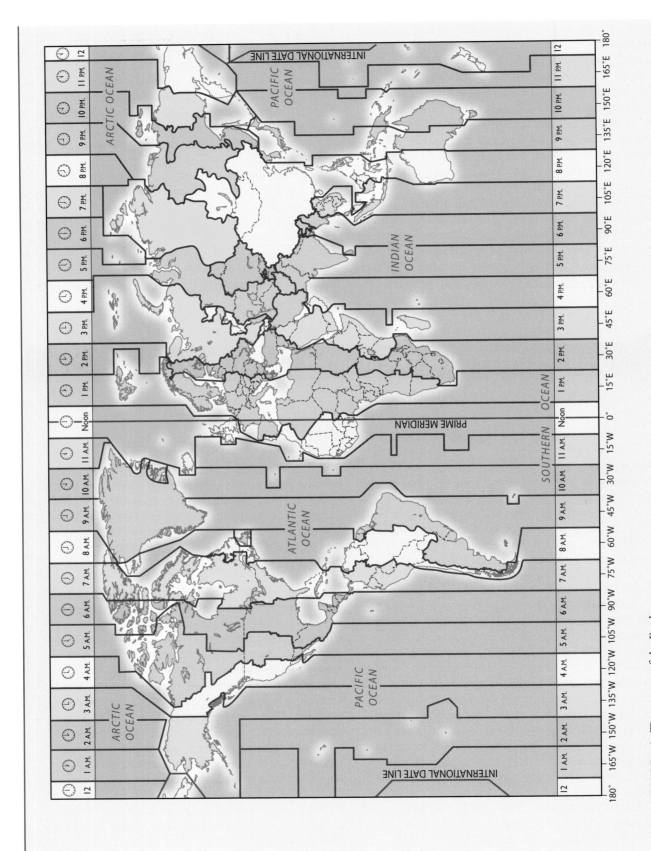

FIGURE 5.6 Time zones of the Earth.

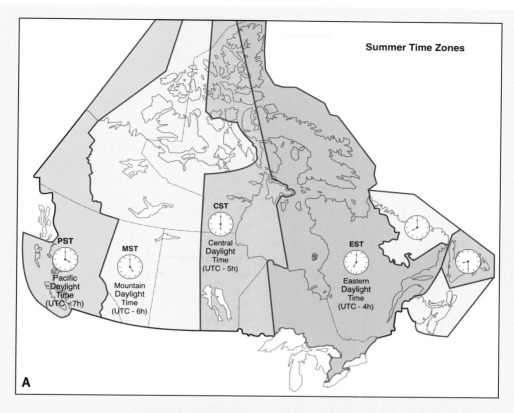

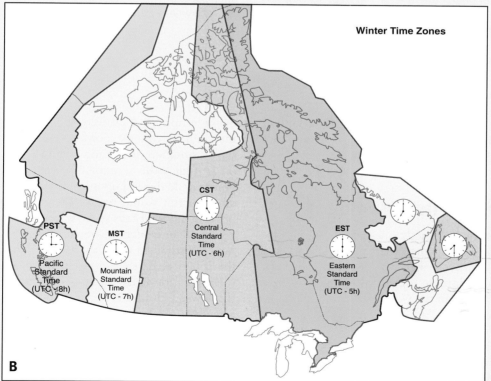

FIGURE 5.7 Canadian time zone maps—(A) summer and (B) winter.

Conference in Washington, D.C., in 1884, where 27 nations adopted the system of international standard time that is still in use today. The Earth was divided into the 24 time zones shown in Fig. 5.6, each using the time at standard meridians located at intervals of 15 degrees of longitude with respect to the Prime Meridian (24 × 15° = 360°). Each time zone differs by one hour from the next, and the time within each zone can be related in one-hour units to the time at Greenwich. When the Sun rises at Greenwich, it has already risen in places east of the observatory. Thus the time zones to the east are designated as *fast;* time zones west of Greenwich are called *slow.*

This solution led to a peculiar problem. At noon at Greenwich on January 2, 2004, it is midnight on January 2 at 180°E longitude (12 time zones ahead) and midnight on January 1 at 180°W (12 time zones behind). However, 180°E and 180°W are the *same* line. This meridian was named the **international date line** by the Washington conference. It was agreed that travellers crossing the date line in an eastward direction, toward the Americas, should repeat a calendar day; those travelling west across it, toward Asia and Australia, should skip a day. The international date line did not pass through many land areas (it lies mainly in the middle of the Pacific Ocean), thereby avoiding severe date problems for people living near it. Where the 180th meridian did cross land, the date line was arbitrarily shifted to pass only over ocean areas.

Similarly, some flexibility is allowed in the boundaries of other time zones to allow for international borders and even for state borders in such countries as Australia and the United States (see Fig. 5.6). Some countries, such as India, choose to have standard times differing by half or a quarter of an hour from the major time zones. Others, such as China, insist that the *entire country* adhere to a single time zone. In Canada, Newfoundland's standard time differs from its neighbours' by a half hour.

A further arbitrary modification of time zones is the adoption in some areas of **daylight saving time**, whereby all clocks in a time zone are set forward by one hour from standard time for at least part of the year. The reason for this practice is that many human activities start well after sunrise and continue long after sunset, using considerable energy for lighting and heating. Energy can be conserved by setting the clocks ahead of the standard time. In Canada today, most provinces (with the exception of Saskatchewan) begin daylight-saving time during the first weekend in April and end it on the last weekend in October (Fig. 5.7).

Those patterns are explored at some length in Unit 7, but certain basic ideas are introduced here because they follow directly from the preceding discussion.

Insolation and Its Variation

At any given moment, exactly one-half of the rotating Earth is in sunlight and the other half is in darkness. The boundary between the two halves is called the **circle of illumination**, an ever shifting line of sunrise in the east and sunset in the west. The sunlit half of the Earth is exposed to the Sun's radiant energy, which is transformed into heat at the planetary surface and, to a lesser extent, in the atmospheric envelope above it. There is, however, considerable variation in the surface receipt of **insolation** (a contraction of the term *in*com-ing *sol*ar radi*ation*).

Let us imagine for a moment that the Earth's axis had no tilt, that it was always perpendicular to the plane of the ecliptic. If that were the case, our planet would maintain its equinox position throughout the year. In such a situation, insolation would strictly be dependent on latitude—the amount of solar energy received at a point would depend upon its distance from the Equator. The Equator would receive the greatest solar radiation because the Sun's rays strike it most directly.

This can be demonstrated in Fig. 5.8, which shows how the parallel rays of the Sun fall on various parts of the spherical Earth. Note that three equal columns of solar radiation strike the curved surface differently, with the lower latitudes receiving more insolation per unit area than the higher latitudes. At the Equator, all the solar rays in column A are concentrated on a small square box; in the midlatitudes, at 35°N, an equal number of rays in column B are diffused across a surface area about twice as large; and in the polar zone, at 75°N latitude, that same number of rays in column C are scattered across an area more than three times the size of the box illuminated by column A.

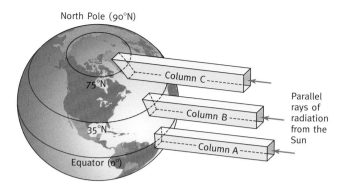

North Pole (90°N)

75°N

35°N

Equator (0°)

Column C

Column B

Column A

Parallel rays of radiation from the Sun

FIGURE 5.8 Reception of solar radiation, with the Earth in the equinox position. A surface at a higher latitude receives less radiation than a surface of equal area at a lower latitude.

In this particular instance, the Equator receives the most intense insolation because the midday Sun's rays strike it vertically, from the point directly overhead (known as the **zenith**), 90 degrees above the horizon. Thus if one travels north or south from the Equator, the solar radiation received decreases with progressively higher latitude as the angle of the Sun's noontime rays declines from the zenith point in the sky. However, that angle of **solar elevation** above the horizon, also known as the *angle of incidence,* is not the only determinant of annual insolation received at a point on the Earth's surface. The duration of daily sunlight is an equally important factor.

The axis of the real Earth, as we already know, is tilted at an angle of 23½ degrees from a straight line perpendicular to the plane of the ecliptic (or 66½ degrees with reference to the plane itself). This causes considerable variation in the length of a day at most latitudes during the course of a year. If you look at the weather page in today's newspaper or the weather segment of this evening's local television news program, you will quickly realize that today's sunrise and sunset times are slightly different from yesterday's or tomorrow's. This reflects the constant change of the latitude where the midday Sun shines on the Earth from the zenith point. From our earlier discussion of the seasons, you should be aware that the variation in this latitude occurs between 23½°N (on the day of the Northern Hemisphere summer solstice) and 23½°S (the winter solstice). The equatorial position illustrated in Fig. 5.8 occurs only on the days of the spring and fall equinoxes.

The combined effects of solar elevation and daily sunlight duration are graphed in Fig. 5.9. It should be stressed that this graph is a model of a much more complicated real world. Whereas its main purpose is to show

how insolation varies on our planet, the patterns in Fig. 5.9 depict solar radiation received at the top of the atmosphere (or at the surface if we assumed the Earth had no atmosphere at all).

In Fig. 5.9 the vertical axis represents the complete range of latitudes whereas the horizontal axis represents the months of the calendar year, with the solstices and equinoxes specially drawn in. The units of solar radiation measurement are not important for understanding this graph (insolation here is calibrated in megajoules per square metre per day). However, variations of insolation can readily be interpreted by looking at the isoline pattern (isolines are explained on p. 37): the higher the value, the greater the amount of radiation received.

Thus if we wanted to trace the global latitudinal profile of insolation for the summer solstice, we would simply follow the vertical line labelled June 22 from pole to pole. Starting at the top at the North Pole, we begin with some of the highest recorded values on the graph (greater than 44), which are equalled or slightly surpassed only in the high latitudes of the Southern Hemisphere around the time of the winter solstice. (Remember, that date is only 12 days before perihelion, when the Earth's orbit makes its closest approach to the Sun; hence the higher values at the start of the southern summer.) The polar-area values on June 22 are high because the length of a day north of the Arctic Circle is 24 hours. Even though the Sun is at a fairly low angle there (23½ degrees or less above the horizon), the many extra hours of sunlight are sufficient to raise the polar radiation-receipt level beyond the highest value ever recorded for the Equator (above 44 versus an equatorial range from about 33 to 38).

As we descend in latitude from the Arctic Circle, the June 22 line does not fall but rather levels off across the middle latitudes all the way to the Tropic of Cancer, near where the value of 40 is finally reached. This high, stable radiation value is maintained because, despite the decrease in daylight length as we move south, insolation is increasingly reinforced by the rising angle of the Sun in the sky as we approach zenith at 23½°N latitude. (Note that the zenithal position of the Sun across the year is denoted by the bell-shaped curve drawn in red.) Once we proceed south of the Tropic of Cancer on the June 22 line, insolation values exhibit a very different trend: they begin to decline swiftly, and south of the Equator they also fall off regularly (about seven to eight units every 10 degrees of latitude) until zero is reached at the Antarctic Circle. From here to the South Pole, of course, we enter the zone of seasonal darkness, which is illustrated in Fig. 5.2.

A great deal more could be said about the latitudinal distribution of incoming solar radiation shown in Fig. 5.9, which in many ways summarizes the Earth–Sun relationships we have covered here in Unit 5. You are

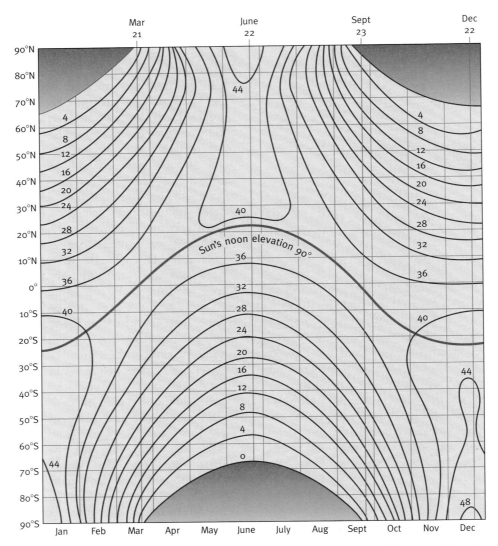

FIGURE 5.9 Spatial distribution of solar radiation falling on the top of the atmosphere (in megajoules per square metre per day). The annual variations you see are the result of the combined effects of solar elevation and the duration of daily sunlight.

encouraged to study this graph, and by tracing patterns along various latitudes or for specific times of the year, you should find the exercise a useful application of the concepts associated with revolution, rotation, axis tilt, seasonality, solstices, equinoxes, and insolation. Even though this graph is a simplification of reality, it is a useful preface to the study of the atmosphere (which commences in Unit 6) because it marks the point of transition from astronomic controls to the terrestrial forces that shape weather and climate across the face of the Earth.

KEY TERMS

Antarctic Circle *page 62*

aphelion *page 59*

Arctic Circle *page 60*

axis *page 59*

circle of illumination *page 66*

daylight saving time *page 65*

equinox *page 62*

fall (autumnal) equinox *page 62*

insolation *page 66*

international date line *page 66*

perihelion *page 59*

plane of the ecliptic *page 60*

solar elevation *page 67*

solstice *page 62*

spring (vernal) equinox *page 62*

summer solstice *page 62*

Tropic of Cancer *page 60*

Tropic of Capricorn *page 61*

winter solstice *page 62*

zenith *page 67*

REVIEW QUESTIONS

1. Describe the motions of the Earth in its revolution around the Sun and its rotation on its axis.

2. Describe the seasonal variation in the latitude of the vertical, noontime Sun during the course of the year.

3. Differentiate between the spring and autumnal equinoxes and between the summer and winter solstices.

4. What is an oblate spheroid, and why is the Earth an example of this phenomenon?

5. What is the international date line, and why is it a necessary part of the Earth's meridional system?

6. Why is insolation at the North Pole on the day of the summer solstice greater than that received at the Equator on the equinoxes?

REFERENCES AND FURTHER READINGS

BARTKY, I. R., and HARRISON, E. "Standard and Daylight-Saving Time," *Scientific American* (May 1979), 46–53.

GEDZELMAN, S. D. *The Science and Wonders of the Atmosphere* (New York: Wiley, 1980), chapters 4 and 6.

HARRISON, L. C. *Sun, Earth, Time and Man* (Chicago: Rand McNally, 1960).

HOYT, D. V., and SCATTEN, K. H. *The Role of the Sun in Climate Change* (New York: Oxford Univ. Press, 1997).

JOHNSON, W. E. *Mathematical Geography* (New York: American Book Co., 1907).

NEIBURGER, M., et al. *Understanding Our Atmospheric Environment* (San Francisco: Freeman, 2nd ed., 1982), chapter 3.

SOBEL, D. *Longitude: The True Story of a Lone Genius Who Solved the Greatest Scientific Problem of His Time* (New York: Walker, 1995).

U.S. NAVAL OBSERVATORY. *The Air Almanac* (Washington, D.C.: U.S. Government Printing Office, annual).

ZEILIK, M. *Astronomy: The Evolving Universe* (New York: Wiley, 8th ed., 1997).

WEB RESOURCES

http://www.canadiangeographic.ca/Magazine/SO98/geomap.asp An article from *Canadian Geographic* describing Canada's time zone irregularities.

http://www.canadiangeographic.ca/specialfeatures/Dst/dst.asp An article from *Canadian Geographic* describing the origin of Canada's legislated daylight savings time.

http://vortex.plymouth.edu/sun.html Tutorial site covering insolation and seasonality.

http://windows.arc.nasa.gov/cgi-bin/tour_def/the_universe/uts/ seasons1.html Explanation of Earth's planetary motions, Earth–Sun relationships, insolation, and seasonality; with three varying difficulty levels.

PART TWO

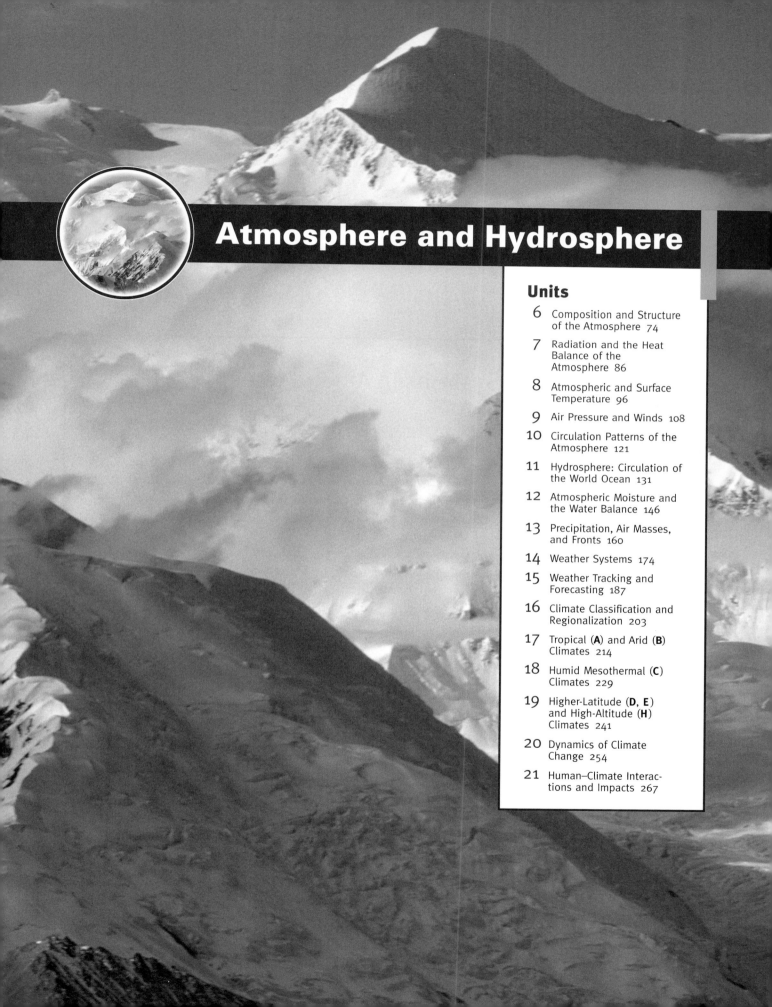

Atmosphere and Hydrosphere

Circulation Systems in Air and Ocean

The Sun's energy, combined with forces arising from the Earth's rotation, drives the hydrosphere and atmosphere into giant circulation systems that carry warmth from equatorial latitudes toward the poles and from sea level to high continental interiors. Giant cells of circular movement occupy entire ocean basins as water moves in slow drifts and faster currents from warm tropical environs to cooler mid-latitudes and beyond, returning toward the tropics with infusions of polar cold. In the atmosphere, equatorial warmth convects upward, generating a set of subsystems that move air vertically as well as horizontally. At and near the surface, huge air-circulation cells are the scenes of competition between low-latitude warmth and high-latitude cold, producing weather-making collisions that can spawn storms and tornadoes. Embedded in these systems are other, powerful subsystems ranging from hurricanes (see bottom photograph) to blizzards. The Earth's rotation influences the direction of circulation in water and air, the movement of weather systems, even the prevalence of persistent winds. Remember the interaction principle: conditions in the hydrosphere (warmth) under certain circumstances can promote the formation of hurricanes in the atmosphere; when a hurricane strikes land, it has an impact on the lithosphere (erosion) as well as the biosphere (destruction of natural vegetation and wildlife). Environmental systems are open systems.

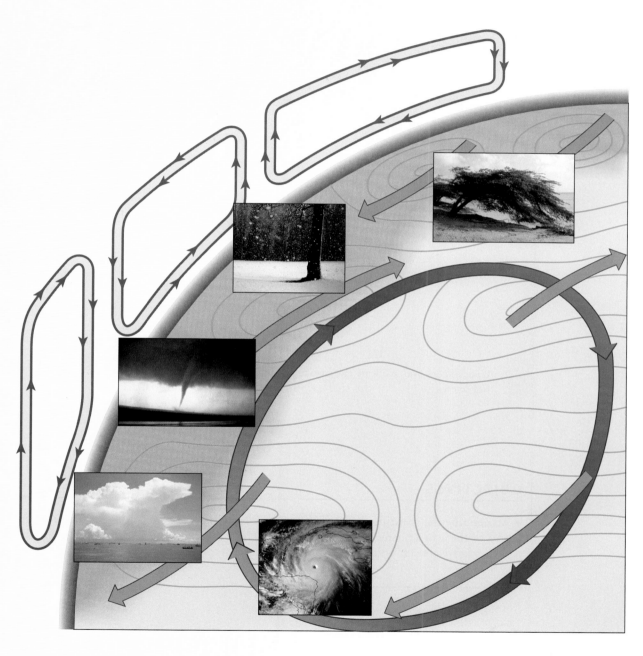

Composition and Structure of the Atmosphere

Cross-sectional view of the atmosphere, which occupies the narrow zone between the blue of the surface and the blackness of outer space.

OBJECTIVES

- To describe the constituents of the atmosphere and their relative concentrations

- To survey the four layers of the atmosphere together with their major properties

- To discuss the problem of ozone depletion and its consequences

Our atmosphere, one of our most precious natural resources, constitutes a vital component in the systematic study of our planet. This thin, shell-like envelope of life-sustaining air that surrounds the Earth (see photo above) is a place of incredible activity—as the units of Part Two will demonstrate. It has been called the working fluid of our planetary heat engine, and its constant motions shape the course of environmental conditions at every moment in every locality on the surface. The short-term conditions of the restless atmospheric system that impinge on daily human activities are called **weather**; the long-term conditions of aggregate weather over a region, summarized by averages and measures of variability, constitute a region's **climate**.

The atmosphere extends from a few metres below the ground on land, or at the water's surface in oceanic areas, to its outermost edge at a height of about 60,000 km. Most of the mass of the atmosphere is concentrated near the planetary surface (see graph on p. 109). Physical geographers are especially interested in the lower parts of the atmosphere, those below 50 km and, in particular, below 10 km. Important flows of energy and matter occur within these lower layers, which constitute the effective atmosphere for all life forms at the surface. Here, too, great currents of air redistribute heat across the Earth. These currents are part of the systems that produce our daily weather. Over time, weather and the flows of heat and water across the Earth are eventually translated into our surface patterns of climate. We are affected by both the local climate and the larger atmosphere, and we have the power to influence both to some degree. In the past, climatic changes have occurred without human intervention; but in the future, and even today, humankind may be playing a more active role.

Contents of the Atmosphere

The atmosphere may be broadly divided into two vertical regions (Fig. 6.1). The lower region, called the *homosphere,* extends from the surface to 80 to 100 km

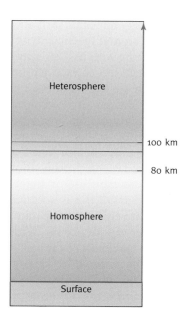

FIGURE 6.1 Two main vertical regions of the atmosphere.

above the Earth and has a more or less uniform chemical composition. Beyond this level, the chemical composition of the atmosphere changes in the upper region, known as the *heterosphere*. The homosphere is the more important of the two atmospheric regions for human beings because we live in it. If you experimented by collecting numerous air samples of the homosphere, you would find that it contains three major groups of components—**constant gases**, **variable gases**, and **impurities**. The constant gases are always found in the same proportions, but the variable gases are present in differing quantities at different times and places. Impurities are solid particles floating in the atmosphere, whose quantities also vary in time and space.

Constant Gases

Two major constant gases make up 99 percent of the air by volume, and both are crucial to sustaining human and other forms of terrestrial life. They are nitrogen, which constitutes 78 percent of the air, and oxygen, which accounts for another 21 percent. Thus the bulk of the atmosphere that we breathe consists of nitrogen. Atmospheric nitrogen is relatively inactive. Indirectly, however, it is important because bacteria convert it into other nitrogen compounds essential for plant growth.

Immediately necessary to our survival, of course, is oxygen. We absorb oxygen into our bodies through our lungs and into our blood. One of its vital functions there is to "burn" our food so that its energy can be released. Such burning actually involves the chemical combination of oxygen and other materials to create new products. The biological name for this process is *respiration*, and the chemical name is *oxidation*. An example of rapid oxidation is the burning of *fossil fuels* (coal, oil, and natural gas). Without oxygen, this convenient way of releasing the energy stored in these fuels would be lost to us. Slow oxidation can also occur, as in the rusting of iron. Therefore, oxygen is essential not only for respiration but also for its role in many other chemical processes.

In 1894, when scientists first removed oxygen and nitrogen from a sample of air, they noticed that another gas remained that seemed completely inactive: it would not combine chemically with other compounds, thereby making it an *inert gas*. The discoverers named this gas argon and found that it makes up almost 1 percent of the volume of dry air. Although this inert gas has some commercial uses (Fig. 6.2), it plays only a very minor role in the workings of environmental systems.

Variable Gases

Although they collectively constitute only a tiny proportion of the air, we must also recognize the importance of

FIGURE 6.2   Commercial use of atmospheric argon—the "neon" lights of such places as Yonge Street in downtown Toronto.

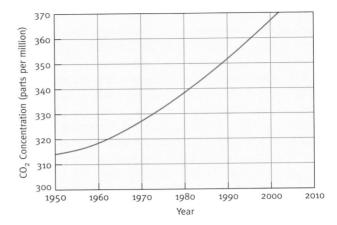

FIGURE 6.3   Changes in the carbon dioxide content of the Earth's atmosphere, 1950–2002. These data were collected at Mauna Loa Observatory on the island of Hawaii, far from the world's industrial and urban areas.

certain atmospheric gases that are present in varying quantities. Three of these variable gases are essential to human well-being—carbon dioxide, water vapour, and ozone.

Carbon Dioxide   Carbon dioxide (CO_2), which on average comprises only 0.04 percent of dry air, is a significant constituent of the atmosphere in terms of its climatic influence. Despite the comparatively small amounts present, carbon dioxide fulfills two vital functions for the Earth. The first is in the process of *photosynthesis,* in which plants use carbon dioxide and other substances to form carbohydrates, which are an essential part of the food and tissue of both plants and animals. The second function of carbon dioxide is to absorb and re-emit some of the energy transferred to the atmosphere from the Earth's surface (a process discussed in Unit 7). Because most of the other atmospheric constituents are such poor absorbers of this energy, carbon dioxide helps to keep the atmosphere at temperatures that permit life (which globally now average just over 15°C).

Carbon dioxide plays still other environmental roles. It helps dissolve limestone, which leads to the intriguing features of certain limestone-based landscapes (see Unit 44). Furthermore, a number of scientists believe that carbon dioxide plays a role in both major and minor climatic change. It has been estimated that over the past two centuries the total quantity of this gas in the atmosphere has risen by as much as 25 percent. The primary cause is believed to be increased industrialization and the associated burning of fossil fuels. The rise in the atmospheric carbon dioxide level since 1960 has

occurred at a faster rate (Fig. 6.3), accounting for just about half the total increase since the onset of the Industrial Revolution more than 200 years ago. Because carbon dioxide is a factor in the warming of the atmosphere, many researchers are concerned that its continued prodigious production could significantly affect the future climate of the Earth.

Water Vapour   The ability to absorb and re-emit energy from the Earth's surface and atmosphere is also found in the most widely distributed variable atmospheric gas—**water vapour**—the invisible gaseous form of water (H_2O). Water vapour is more efficient than carbon dioxide in capturing this radiant energy because it not only can absorb energy but can *store* it as well. When water vapour is moved around by currents of air, stored energy is transported along with it. This is part of an essential process by which the surface temperatures of most parts of the Earth are kept moderate enough for human habitation. In deserts or cold regions, water vapour makes up only a minute fraction of 1 percent of the air. But over warm oceans or moist tropical land areas it may make up as much as 3 or 4 percent.

In general, as Unit 12 will further illustrate, the warmer the air, the more moisture or water vapour it can hold. Because the parts of the atmosphere near the Earth's surface have relatively high temperatures, that is where most of the water vapour occurs. Without water vapour, there would be no clouds or rainfall. Thus most portions of the land surface would be too dry to permit agriculture. Without the great cycle in which water moves from the surface into the atmosphere and back again, little life of any kind would be found on our planet.

Ozone   The other variable gases in the lower parts of the atmosphere are found in much smaller quantities than water vapour. The most important of these is ozone, the rarer type of oxygen molecule composed of three oxygen atoms (O_3) instead of two (O_2). Ozone is confined mainly to the so-called **ozone layer** (or *ozonosphere*), lying between 15 and 50 km above the Earth, which is part of the vertically more extensive atmospheric layer known as the stratosphere, to be discussed later in this unit. The greatest concentrations of ozone, however, are found between about 20 and 25 km, although this gas is usually formed at higher levels and transported downward. Even where it is most highly concentrated, ozone often constitutes less than six parts per 100,000 of the atmosphere. But like carbon dioxide, it is very important. It, too, has the ability to absorb radiant energy, in particular the *ultraviolet radiation* associated with incoming solar energy. Ultraviolet radiation can give us a suntan, but large doses cause severe sunburn, blindness, and skin cancers. The ozone layer shields us from excessive quantities of this high-energy radiation.

Other Variable Gases   Minute quantities of many other variable gases are also present in the atmosphere. The most noteworthy are hydrogen, helium, sulphur dioxide, oxides of nitrogen, ammonia, methane, and carbon monoxide. Some of these are *air pollutants* (substances that impact organisms negatively) derived from manufacturing, transportation, and other human activities. They can produce harmful effects even when the concentrations are one part per million or less. (Interestingly, when found at or near the surface, ozone loses its beneficial qualities and becomes just another pollutant.) Other pollutants are found in the form of solid particles that can be classified as the impurities of the atmosphere.

Impurities

If you were to collect air samples, particularly near a city, they would likely contain a great number of impurities in the form of **aerosols** (tiny floating particles suspended in the atmosphere). Typical rural air might contain about four particles of dust per cubic millimetre, whereas city parks often have four times that density. A business district in a metropolitan area might have 200 particles per cubic millimetre, and an industrial zone over 4000. Both smoke and dust particles are common in urban air, but dust particles are the most prevalent type in rural air. Bacteria and plant spores are found in all parts of the lower atmosphere. Salt crystals are another major impurity, with large quantities usually formed by evaporation above breaking ocean waves.

Collectively, the impurities play an active role in the atmosphere. Many of them help in the development of clouds and raindrops (see Unit 12). Moreover, the small particles can affect the colour of the sky. Air and the smallest impurities scatter more blue light from the Sun than any other colour. This is why the fair-weather sky looks blue. But when low-angle sunlight travels a longer distance through the atmosphere to the surface, as at sunrise or sundown, most of the blue light has been scattered. We see only the remaining yellow and red light, which, of course, produces colourful sunrises and sunsets. Occasionally, when there is an abnormally large amount of impurities in the atmosphere, such as after a major volcanic eruption, this process is carried to some spectacular extremes.

Atmospheric Cycles

As the new planet Earth cooled following its birth about 4.6 billion years ago, the atmosphere was formed from gases expelled by volcanoes and the hot surface itself. During this formation, the atmospheric constituents achieved a state of dynamic equilibrium (a systems concept discussed in Unit 1), a condition that is still maintained today—as long as the air is not significantly altered by pollutants. The prevailing composition of the atmosphere we have just described is not static but is the result of constant gains and losses of its major and minor components. A critical part of this component exchange takes place because the boundary or surface layer of the atmosphere adjoins the lithosphere, hydrosphere, and biosphere. Four vital cycles have developed at this interface, involving the transfer of water, oxygen, nitrogen, and carbon dioxide.

The **hydrologic cycle** is a complex system of exchange involving water as it circulates within and between the atmosphere, lithosphere, hydrosphere, and biosphere. This cycle is so important that much of Unit 12 is devoted to it.

In the **oxygen cycle**, oxygen is put back into the atmosphere as a by-product of photosynthesis. It is extracted from the atmosphere when it is inhaled by animals or chemically combined with other materials during oxidation.

The **nitrogen cycle** is maintained by plants, whose roots contain bacteria that can extract nitrogen from the air or soil. These *nitrogen-fixing bacteria* convert atmospheric nitrogen into the organic compounds of the plants, especially organic protein. Some of this organic material is transferred to animals, including human beings, when the plants are eaten. When the plants and animals die, the nitrogen is transformed by other bacteria and micro-organisms first into ammonia, urea, and nitrates, and then eventually back into the gaseous form of nitrogen, which returns to the atmosphere.

FROM THE FIELDNOTES

FIGURE 6.4 "The apartment in Honolulu, high on the slope of the Punch Bowl, afforded great daytime views over the city. But what was most remarkable, even here in the middle of the Pacific Ocean, was the daily vivid sunset, proof of the presence of volcanic and desert dust, high in the atmosphere."

The **carbon dioxide cycle** is dominated by exchanges that occur between the air and the oceans. This atmospheric gas enters the sea by direct absorption from the air, by plant and animal respiration, and by the oxidation of organic matter. Alternatively, carbon dioxide is released from the ocean following the decomposition of countless millions of small organisms known as *plankton*. Another major carbon dioxide exchange takes place between the atmosphere and land plants of the biosphere, with the gas taken from the air by plants during photosynthesis and released by them during respiration and decay. In addition, carbon dioxide is released in the burning of fossil fuels, with possible consequences for climatic change.

The Layered Structure of the Atmosphere

Earlier we noted that the atmosphere consists of two broad regions: a lower homosphere and an upper heterosphere (Fig. 6.1). A more detailed picture of the structure

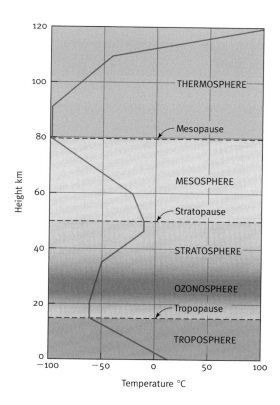

FIGURE 6.5   Variation of atmospheric temperature (red line) with height.

called the **stratopause**, and is topped by a layer known as the **mesosphere**. In the mesosphere temperatures again fall with height, as they did in the troposphere. Eventually the decline in temperature stops, at a boundary you might rightly guess to be called the **mesopause**. This occurs at about 80 km above the Earth's surface. Not far beyond the mesopause, temperatures once more increase with height in a layer called the **thermosphere**.

The Troposphere

Because the troposphere is the atmospheric zone in which we live and the layer where almost all weather happens, we need to know quite a bit about it. That survey of its processes is undertaken in Units 7 through 10, with Unit 8 focusing on temperature relationships. Before that detailed treatment, let us summarize the most significant interactions across the tropopause and the nature of the layers that lie above it.

The tropopause, as Fig. 6.5 indicates, is positioned at an average height of about 12 km. Actually, this altitude varies with latitude: it is lowest over the poles (about 8 km) and highest above the Equator (about 16 km). There are usually two distinct breaks in the tropopause, which are characterized by areas of variable lapse rates. These breaks are generally found at latitudes of about 25° and 50°N and S. The breaks, associated with fast-flowing winds in the upper atmosphere, are important because, through them, the troposphere and the stratosphere exchange materials and energy. Small amounts of water vapour may find their way up into the stratosphere at these breaks, whereas ozone-rich air may be carried downward into the troposphere through them.

The Stratosphere

Above the tropopause is the calmer, thinner, clear air of the stratosphere. Jet aircraft mainly fly through the lower stratosphere because it provides the most favourable flying conditions. The nearly total absence of water vapour in this layer prevents the formation of clouds, thus providing pilots with fine visibility. And temperature inversion prohibits vertical winds, so the horizontal winds in the stratosphere are almost always parallel to the Earth's surface, ensuring smoother flights than in the troposphere.

The *ozone layer* (ozonosphere) lies within the stratosphere (Fig. 6.5). Here ozone is produced naturally by the action of ultraviolet sunlight on oxygen, and destroyed naturally when it is turned back into oxygen. Ozone is also transported by natural processes from one part of the stratosphere to another. These chemical and transport processes create a constant balance of stratospheric ozone. The critical importance of the ozone layer

of the atmosphere emerges if we subdivide it into a number of vertical layers according to temperature characteristics. Altitude has a major influence on temperature, and the overall variation of atmospheric temperature with height above the surface is shown in Fig. 6.5.

The bottom layer of the atmosphere, where temperature usually decreases with an increase in altitude, is called the **troposphere**. The rate of a decline in temperature is known as the **lapse rate**, and in the troposphere the average lapse rate is 6.5°C/1000 m. The upper boundary of the troposphere, along which temperatures stop decreasing with height, is called the **tropopause**.

Beyond this discontinuity, in a layer called the **stratosphere**, temperatures either stay the same or start increasing with altitude. Layers in which the temperature increases with altitude exhibit positive lapse rates. These are called **temperature inversions** because they invert or reverse what we on the surface believe to be the normal state of temperature change with elevation—a decrease with height.

As the top of the stratosphere is approached, beyond about 52 km above the Earth, temperatures remain constant with increasing altitude. This boundary zone is

FROM THE FIELDNOTES

FIGURE 6.6 "On my way to Los Angeles on a 707 (October 17, 1962!). The advent of jet travel not only shortened flight times, it also allowed aircraft to fly near the stratosphere and thus avoid much of the bumpier air and obscuring cloud layers in the troposphere below."

in shielding the surface of the Earth from ultraviolet radiation has already been noted. At the same time, the absorption of ultraviolet radiation heats the stratosphere, giving it the positive temperature lapse rate we noted earlier. Thus it is vitally important to maintain the proper ozone balance. Not surprisingly, increasing reports of *ozone holes* in the atmosphere have raised concerns among environmental scientists (see Perspective: Ozone Holes in the Stratosphere).

The Mesosphere

Above the stratosphere, in the altitudinal zone between about 50 and 80 km, lies the layer of decreasing temperatures called the mesosphere. Over high latitudes in summer, the mesosphere at night sometimes displays high, wispy clouds, which are presumed to be sunlight reflected from meteoric dust particles that become coated with ice crystals. Another common phenomenon in this layer occurs when sunlight reduces molecules

PERSPECTIVES ON THE HUMAN ENVIRONMENT

Ozone Holes in the Stratosphere

In 1982 a British environmental research team in Antarctica made a startling discovery: its instruments could not detect the ozone layer in the stratosphere overhead. Atmospheric scientists had never before encountered this phenomenon, but artificial satellites and high-flying aircraft by 1985 confirmed the readings of ground-based spectrophotometers and established that a large "ozone hole" existed over most of the southern polar continent. Concerned investigators soon learned that this was a seasonal occurrence that peaked in the spring (Fig. 6.7); but it was also clear that the overall level of ozone was declining.

By the end of the 1980s, scientists had reached a consensus as to the causes of stratospheric ozone destruction. During the southern winter (late June through late September), Antarctic air is isolated from the rest of the Southern Hemisphere by a strong circumpolar windflow above the surrounding Southern Ocean. With warmer air walled off and daylight reduced to a minimum (which inhibits the creation of ozone), the intense cold of Antarctica's surface gradually penetrates the overlying atmosphere. This supercold air even affects the stratosphere, where icy cloud layers form.

The surfaces of the ice particles that constitute these clouds are sites of chemical reactions involving chlorine that are triggered by ultraviolet radiation as soon as sunlight returns near the end of the long Antarctic winter. The chlorine atoms released by these reactions swiftly destroy ozone molecules by breaking them down into other forms of oxygen. Moreover, each single freed atom of chlorine can trigger hundreds of destructive ozone reactions. Thus the ozone depletion process spreads rapidly, slowing only as rising temperatures evaporate the stratospheric clouds. By midsummer, ozone levels are again on the rise; they will peak in winter, but with the return of spring another cycle of destruction will be spawned.

This scenario should not necessarily suggest that the summer-through-winter buildup replenishes all the ozone lost in the spring. As Fig. 6.7

indicates, large holes in the ozone layer—shown by the blue-to-black colour sequence—appeared above Antarctica in every year. The 1998 ozone hole was the largest ever observed, at one point (shortly after this image was taken) covering 24.3 million km², an area almost twice the size of the Antarctic continent itself. Events such as these make it quite likely that a net overall depletion of ozone is taking place.

The villain, of course, is the chlorine, most of which is not of natural origin but a by-product of modern technology that adversely impacts our fragile atmosphere. The evidence today is overwhelming that artificial compounds, called **chlorofluorocarbons (CFCs)**, are at fault. Before the 1990s these chemicals were widely used in everyday life for a variety of purposes, such as coolants in refrigerators and air-conditioning systems, propellants in aerosol sprays, cleaning solvents for computer components, and plastic foam in hundreds of products. Thus vast quantities of CFCs entered the atmosphere for many years. Only recently, however, did scientists ascertain that these compounds can rise easily into the stratosphere and disperse themselves across the entire globe.

Even though initial research on the ozone hole in the 1980s tentatively concluded that the phenomenon was limited to Antarctica, the world scientific community was concerned enough to call for action. That resulted in a 1987 conference in Montreal, where more than 30 countries took the first steps to limit their CFC production. The Montreal Protocol established a scientific assessment panel, whose recommendations would be followed as part of an ongoing process to counteract the depletion of atmospheric ozone. A second conference took place in 1990, at which nearly 100 countries agreed to phase out the manufacturing of CFCs by 2000. In 1991 that deadline was advanced to 1996 (developing countries have received dispensations to delay implementation), when the panel reported an intensification in global ozone loss; in 1992 additional CFC-type chemicals were added to the list of products to be phased out (by 2030). By the

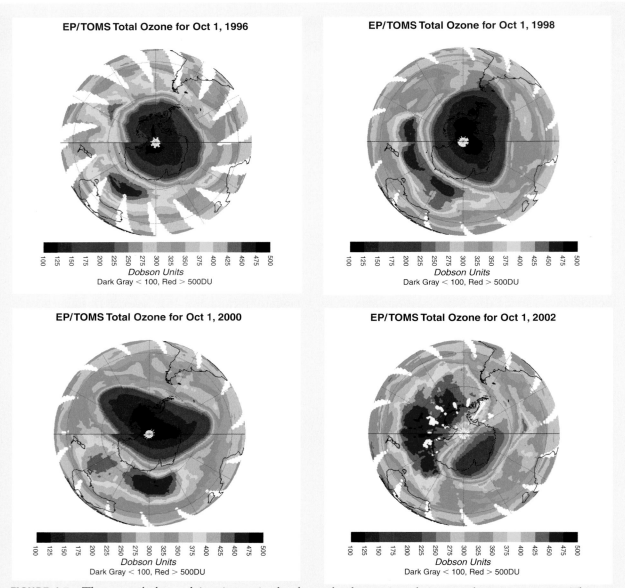

FIGURE 6.7 The ozone hole overlying Antarctica has been closely monitored since its detection in 1982. This sequence of remotely sensed satellite imagery, centred on the South Pole, shows the average distribution of ozone above the entire Southern Hemisphere for the same early spring month for the 1996–2002 period.

mid-1990s these measures appeared to be paying off because the annual rise in atmospheric CFC concentration was half of what it had been at the end of the 1980s. Moreover, the number of treaty signatories had risen to 132 countries, which contain almost 85 percent of the world's population.

Nonetheless, new research findings underscore the environmental damage that has already taken place. We now know that as much as 10 percent of the Earth's ozone layer has disappeared since

1970. A great deal also has been learned about the spatial variation of ozone depletion, which now extends far beyond the southern polar latitudes. Antarctica continues to be the leading region, but elsewhere in the Southern Hemisphere, particularly in southern South America, there is growing evidence of ozone depletion; and many scientists are also concerned about the Northern Hemisphere.

Ozone destruction in recent years has reached serious levels in the higher latitudes of the

Northern Hemisphere. Fortunately no ozone hole has yet opened above the northern polar region, whose winters are warmer and shorter than those of Antarctica (with its isolating windflows, higher-lying terrain, and thick ice sheet). But an Arctic ozone hole remains a possibility and would undoubtedly have more immediate human consequences because almost 90 percent of the world's population resides in the Northern Hemisphere.

Perhaps most sobering of all is the realization that humans have set off a sequence of atmospheric processes that cannot quickly be reversed. It takes about 10 years for rising CFC gases to reach the stratosphere; thus we have witnessed the effects of CFC usage only through the early 1990s. And when CFCs reach the ozone layer, they do not dissipate but remain in place as active chemicals for perhaps as long as another 140 years. Given these interpretations, we should not be surprised at the rapidity of ozone depletion because a new view of human-induced environmental modification is now emerging. Instead of slow change, pollutants may build up for years without noticeable effect; quietly, a critical mass is approached and surpassed, and then sudden change occurs with far-reaching consequences.

The global depletion of atmospheric ozone ranks among the most serious problems of potential environmental change. In view of the current situation, predictions have been made that the quantity of ultraviolet radiation reaching the Earth's surface will increase 5 to 20 percent over the next three decades. Even if the lower estimate is correct, at least 1 million new cases of skin cancer can be expected to materialize annually; other medical problems that would intensify include cataracts and the weakening of the immune system. Many animal and plant species would be threatened as well. One study has reported that a 10 percent increase in ultraviolet radiation could eliminate most forms of plankton, the biological cornerstone of food chains in the oceans. Land plants would undoubtedly be adversely affected too, and crop yields could drop by as much as 25 percent. This would present a disaster of unparalleled magnitude for a rapidly growing human population that can barely feed itself today.

to individual electrically charged particles called ions in a process known as *ionization*. Ionized particles concentrate in a zone called the **D**-layer, which reflects radio waves sent from the Earth's surface. "Blackouts" in communications between the ground and astronauts occur as the **D**-layer is crossed by space vehicles during re-entry.

The Thermosphere

The thermosphere is found above 80 km and continues to the edge of space, about 60,000 km above the surface. The temperature rises spectacularly in this layer and likely reaches 900°C at 350 km. However, because the air molecules are so far apart at this altitude, these temperatures really apply only to individual molecules and do not have the same kind of environmental significance they would in the vicinity of the Earth's surface.

Ionization also takes place in the thermosphere, producing two more belts (known as the **E**- and **F**-layers) that reflect radio waves. Intermittently, ionized particles penetrate the thermosphere, creating vivid sheetlike displays of light, called the *aurora borealis* in the Northern

Hemisphere and the *aurora australis* in the Southern Hemisphere (Fig. 6.8). In the upper thermosphere there are further concentrations of ions, which comprise the Van Allen radiation belts. This outermost layer is sometimes referred to as the *magnetosphere* because here the Earth's magnetic field is frequently more influential in the movement of particles than its gravitational field is. The thermosphere has no definable outer boundary and gradually blends into interplanetary space.

Research Frontiers

Scientists still understand relatively little about the layers above the effective atmosphere. These outer regions beyond the troposphere, which consist of concentrated ozone, electrically charged particles, bitter cold and extreme heat, meteoric dust, and weirdly illuminated clouds, lie at the frontiers of our knowledge. The ozone-depletion crisis, however, is now unleashing an unprecedented scientific effort to learn more about these higher layers, because it is increasingly evident that what happens along the fragile outer fringes of our

FIGURE 6.8 Aurora Borealis ("Northern Lights") over snow and forest near Yellowknife, N.W.T. Such a curtain of light results from the collision of energy-charged particles from the Sun with gas molecules in the Earth's atmosphere near the poles.

planetary domain is of significance to atmospheric and related processes in the surface layer. With human technology demonstrating a greater capacity to influence the chemistry of the air, much research is focusing on the nature of such change, its rates in various parts of the world, and the long-term consequences of its intensification.

As this work proceeds, a heightening sense of urgency prevails in certain quarters because climate and other environmental changes tend not to occur gradually and incrementally. Rather, they often seem to exhibit sharp jumps in response to the subtle but steady reorganization of the Earth's atmospheric system. The challenge lies not only in identifying the problems, but also in reversing the sequence of events that produce them (as in the attempt to halt human-induced ozone destruction). Such concerns—which also apply to the biosphere, the hydrosphere, and even the lithosphere—are becoming an integral part of physical geography in the twenty-first century.

KEY TERMS

aerosol *page 77*

carbon dioxide cycle *page 78*

chlorofluorocarbons (CFCs) *page 81*

climate *page 75*

constant gases *page 75*

hydrologic cycle *page 77*

impurities *page 75*

lapse rate *page 77*

mesopause *page 79*

mesosphere *page 79*

nitrogen cycle *page 77*

oxygen cycle *page 77*

ozone layer *page 77*

stratopause *page 79*

stratosphere *page 79*

temperature inversion *page 79*

thermosphere *page 79*

tropopause *page 79*

troposphere *page 79*

variable gases *page 75*

water vapour *page 76*

weather *page 75*

REVIEW QUESTIONS

1. What are the constituents of dry air in the atmosphere?
2. Discuss the role of ozone in absorbing incoming solar radiation. Where does this absorption take place?
3. Give the approximate altitudinal extents of each of the atmosphere's layers, and describe the temperature structure of each.
4. Define and describe the basic function of the oxygen, nitrogen, carbon dioxide, and hydrologic cycles.
5. What is the extent of the world's *ozone hole* problem, and what are its likely causes?

REFERENCES AND FURTHER READINGS

AMATO, J. A.   *Dust: A History of the Small and the Invisible* (Berkeley, Calif.: Univ. of California Press, 2000).

BRIMBLECOMBE, P.   *Air: Composition and Chemistry* (New York: Cambridge Univ. Press, 2nd ed., 1995).

GRAEDEL, T. E., and CRUTZEN, P. J.   "The Changing Atmosphere," *Scientific American* (September 1989), 58–68.

GRIBBIN, J.   "The Ozone Layer," *New Scientist,* "Inside-Science" Supplement 9 (May 5, 1988).

INGERSOLL, A. P.   "The Atmosphere," *Scientific American* (September 1983), 162–174.

McELROY, M. B., and SALAWITCH, J. B.   "Changing Composition of the Global Stratosphere," *Science,* 243 (February 10, 1989), 763–770.

MESZAROS, E.   *Global and Regional Changes in Atmospheric Composition* (Boca Raton, Fla.: CRC Press, 1993).

MINNAERT, M.   *The Nature of Light and Color in the Open Air* (New York: Dover, 1954).

SCHAEFER, V. J., and DAY, J.   *A Field Guide to the Atmosphere* (Boston: Houghton Mifflin, 1981).

SCHNEIDER, S. H., Ed.   *Encyclopedia of Climate and Weather,* 2 vols. (New York: Oxford Univ. Press, 1996).

STOLARSKI, R. S.   "The Antarctic Ozone Hole," *Scientific American* (January 1988), 30–37.

TOON, O. B., and TURCO, R. P.   "Polar Stratosphere Clouds and Ozone Depletion," *Scientific American* (June 1991), 68–74.

"Vanishing Ozone: The Danger Moves Closer to Home" (cover story), *Time* (February 17, 1992), 60–68.

YOUNG, L. B.   *Earth's Aura* (New York: Avon, 1979).

YOUNG, L. B.   *Sowing the Wind: Reflections on the Earth's Atmosphere* (Englewood Cliffs, N.J.: Prentice-Hall, 1990).

WEB RESOURCES

http://jwocky.gsfc.nasa.gov Information about the ozone hole in the stratosphere.

http://liftoff.msfc.nasa.gov/academy/space/atmosphere.html Description of components and layering of the atmosphere.

http://www.infoplease.com/ce6/sci/A0856759.html Explanation of the structure of the atmosphere, as well as related links to the role of the atmosphere and its components and characteristics.

Radiation and the Heat Balance of the Atmosphere

Mirrors concentrate the Sun's radiation at the Solar Electric Generating System near the town of Daggett in California's Mojave Desert.

OBJECTIVES

- To understand the Sun-generated flows of energy that affect the Earth and its atmosphere

- To link the greenhouse effect to the Earth's habitability and climatic variation

- To introduce the Earth's heat flows and their spatial patterns

To understand the workings of weather and climate, one needs to become familiar with the atmospheric processes that shape them. In Unit 6 the atmosphere is described as a dynamic, constantly churning component of a gigantic heat engine. In this unit, focus is placed on the functioning of that engine, which is fuelled by incoming solar radiation (*insolation*). Its main operations coordinate and distribute this radiant heat energy between the Earth's surface and the envelope of air that surrounds it. As the Earth is heated by the Sun's rays, the air in contact with the surface becomes warmer. That air begins to rise, cooler air descends to replace it, and the atmosphere has been set into motion. On a global scale, as insolation constantly changes, there is always considerable variation in heat energy across the planetary surface. To maintain equilibrium, large amounts of that energy must be moved from place to place to balance heat surpluses and deficits.

The Radiation Balance

The Sun provides 99.97 percent of the energy required for all the physical processes that take place on the Earth and in its atmosphere. As a result of absorbed insolation, different types of radiant heat or radiation flow throughout the Earth–atmosphere system, and inputs and outputs of radiation are balanced at the planetary surface.

Radiation may be regarded as a transmission of energy in the form of electromagnetic waves. The *wavelength* of the radiation is the distance between two successive wave crests. This wavelength varies in different types of radiation and is inversely proportional to the temperature of the body that sent it out: the higher the temperature at which the radiation is emitted, the shorter the wavelength of the radiation. The Sun has a surface temperature of about 6900°C, whereas the average surface temperature of the Earth is approximately 15°C. Thus radiation coming from the Sun is **shortwave radiation**, and that emitted from the Earth is **longwave radiation**. There is, in fact, a wide spectrum of radiation of different wavelengths, which is depicted in Fig. 3.15. This *electromagnetic spectrum* ranges from very short waves, such as cosmic rays and gamma rays, to very long waves, such as radio- and electric-power waves.

Radiation from the Sun

Measurements indicate that, on average, 1.95 calories* of energy per square centimetre are received every minute at the top of the Earth's atmosphere. This value, called the *solar constant,* would equal in one day all the world's industrial and domestic energy requirements for the next 100 years based on current rates of consumption.

---

* One *calorie* is the amount of heat energy required to raise the temperature of 1 gram of water by 1°C. (This should not be confused with the calories associated with the energy value of food, which are 1000 times larger than the calories mentioned here.) Another metric unit used to measure energy is the joule (one calorie equals 4.184 joules); power, or energy per unit time, is often measured in watts (one watt equals one joule per second).

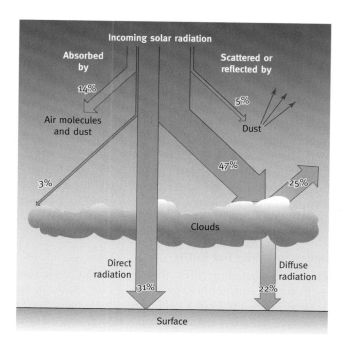

FIGURE 7.1 Solar radiation flows in the atmosphere.

When radiation travels through the atmosphere, several things can happen to it (Fig. 7.1). According to estimates based on available data and global averages, of all the incoming solar energy only 31 percent travels directly to the Earth's surface; this energy flow is called **direct radiation**. An almost equal amount, 30 percent, is reflected and scattered back into space by clouds (25 percent) and dust particles in the atmosphere (5 percent). Another 17 percent of the incoming solar rays is absorbed by clouds (3 percent) and dust and other components of the atmosphere (14 percent). Some of the scattered rays, 22 percent in all, eventually find their way down to the Earth's surface and are collectively known as **diffuse radiation**. Altogether, just over half (53 percent) of the solar energy arriving at the outer edge of the atmosphere reaches the surface as either direct or diffuse radiation. The rest is either absorbed by the atmosphere (17 percent) or scattered and/or reflected back into space (30 percent).

No matter where radiation strikes the Earth, one of two things can happen to it. It can either be *absorbed* by—and thereby heat—the Earth's surface, or it can be *reflected* by the surface, in which case there is no heating effect. The amount of radiation reflected by the surface depends mainly on the colour, composition, and slope of the surface. A ray of solar energy falling on the Equator on the day of the equinox, because it strikes perpendicularly, is less likely to be reflected than one falling on the same day at 35°N (see Fig. 5.8). And if the surface is a dark colour, such as black soil or asphalt, the energy is more likely to be absorbed than if the object has a light colour, such as a white building.

The proportion of incoming radiation that is reflected by a surface is called its **albedo**, a term derived from the Latin word *albus,* meaning white. The albedo of a snowy surface, which reflects most of the incoming radiation, might be 80 percent, whereas the albedo of a dark-green-coloured rainforest, which reflects very little radiation, might be as low as 10 percent. Not surprisingly, albedo varies markedly from place to place. Of all the solar radiation entering the atmosphere, only about half is absorbed by the Earth's surface. We now turn to the other side of the coin—the radiation from the Earth itself.

Radiation from the Earth

The Earth does more than absorb or reflect shortwave insolation: it constantly gives off longwave radiation on its own. When the Earth's landmasses and oceans absorb shortwave radiation from the Sun, it is transformed into longwave radiation. This process is triggered by rising temperature, and the heated surface now emits longwave radiation. One of two things can happen to this radiation leaving the planetary surface: either it is absorbed by the atmosphere or it escapes into space (Fig. 7.2).

The major atmospheric constituents that absorb the Earth's longwave radiation are carbon dioxide, water vapour, and ozone (see Unit 6). Each of these variable gases absorbs radiation at certain wavelengths but allows other wavelengths to escape through an atmospheric "window." Up to 9 percent of all terrestrial radiation is thereby lost to space, except when the window is shut by clouds. Clouds absorb or reflect back to Earth almost all the outgoing longwave radiation. Therefore a cloudy winter night is likely to be warmer than a clear one.

The atmosphere is heated by the longwave radiation it absorbs. Most of this radiation is absorbed at the lower, denser levels of the atmosphere, a fact that helps account for the air's higher temperatures near the Earth's surface. *Thus our atmosphere is actually heated from below, not directly by the Sun above.* The atmosphere itself, being warm, can also emit longwave radiation. Some goes off into space, but some, known as **counterradiation**, is reradiated back to the Earth (Fig. 7.2). Without this counterradiation from the atmosphere, the Earth's mean surface temperature would be about −20°C, 35°C colder than its current average of approximately 15°C. The atmosphere, therefore, acts as a blanket.

The blanket effect of the atmosphere is similar to the action of radiation and heat in a garden greenhouse. Shortwave radiation from the Sun is absorbed and transmitted through the greenhouse glass windows, strikes the interior surface, and is converted to heat energy. The longwave radiation generated by the surface heats the inside of the greenhouse. But the same glass that let the shortwave radiation in now acts as a trap to prevent that heat from being transmitted to the outside environment, thereby raising the temperature of the air inside the greenhouse. Another example of this same principle is the heating of a closed automobile parked in direct sunlight (Fig. 7.3).

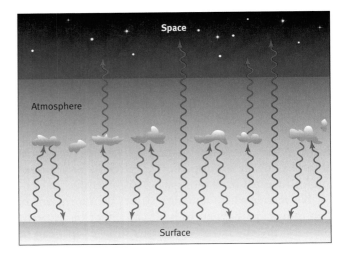

FIGURE 7.2   Longwave radiation emitted by the Earth (red arrows) and atmosphere (green arrows). Most of the terrestrial radiation is reflected back to the surface or absorbed by the atmosphere. The latter process simultaneously warms the atmosphere, which can now emit its own longwave radiation both downward toward the Earth (counterradiation, which is critically important in heating the planetary surface) and upward into space.

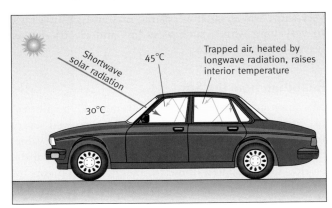

FIGURE 7.3   A parked automobile demonstrates the greenhouse effect. Shortwave radiation from the Sun enters through the glass windows and strikes interior surfaces. Now transformed into longwave radiation, that energy heats the interior air. But this air cannot pass through the glass and is trapped inside the car—at a temperature 15°C higher than the air outside.

A similar process takes place on the Earth, with the atmosphere replacing the glass. Not surprisingly, we call this basic natural process of atmospheric heating the **greenhouse effect**. As explained in the discussion of ozone depletion in the stratosphere in Unit 6, human beings may be influencing the atmosphere's delicate natural processes. The greenhouse effect is now under intensive scrutiny because many scientists have voiced concern that human activities are triggering a sequence of events that could heighten a **global warming** trend, with possibly dire consequences for near-future environmental change (see Perspective: The Greenhouse Effect and Global Warming).

Net Radiation

The annual radiation balance for the Earth is given in Table 7.1. We can see that similar quantities of shortwave and longwave radiation arrive at our planet's surface, but that the outgoing radiation is dominated by

Table 7.1 Estimated Annual Radiation Balance (Net Radiation*) of the Earth's Surface

Incoming	
Shortwave radiation (insolation) reaching the top of the atmosphere	263
Longwave counterradiation from the atmosphere absorbed at the Earth's surface	206
	469

Outgoing	
Longwave radiation emitted by the Earth	258
Shortwave radiation reflected into space by the atmosphere and the Earth's surface	94
Shortwave radiation absorbed by the atmosphere	45
	397

Net Radiation Balance	
(incoming minus outgoing)	**72**

*In thousands of calories per square centimetre.

Source: Adapted from W. D. Sellers, *Physical Climatology* (Chicago: Univ. of Chicago Press, 1965), 32, 47.

PERSPECTIVES ON THE HUMAN ENVIRONMENT

The Greenhouse Effect and Global Warming

The greenhouse effect makes our planet habitable. Just as warmth is trapped beneath the glass of a greenhouse, the atmosphere retains heat emitted by the Earth's Sun-radiated surface. This longwave radiation is absorbed by various constituents of the atmosphere, chief among them carbon dioxide (CO_2), water vapour, and ozone. Without this absorption, the Earth's surface heat would escape into space and our planet would be frigid.

Water vapour is important in this retention of warmth, but carbon dioxide, often called the key "greenhouse gas," is crucial because it is one of the atmosphere's variable gases. If there is more of it in the atmosphere, the Earth should warm up; when there is less, temperatures should cool down. The amount of CO_2 in the atmosphere is not constant. Carbon dioxide enters and leaves the atmosphere through several complex, interrelated cycles. Land plants remove CO_2 from the atmosphere during photosynthesis, but when they die and decay, the gas is returned to the air. Carbon dioxide also is absorbed directly from the atmosphere by ocean

water, to be used by plankton floating on the ocean surface. When plankton die, they sink to the ocean floor and release CO_2. That CO_2 eventually comes back to the surface and is released into the atmosphere. All this makes it difficult to assess long-term trends in the CO_2 content of the atmosphere.

Enter now the human factor. During the more than 200 years since the onset of the Industrial Revolution, the burning of coal, oil, and natural gas—the fossil fuels—has produced enormous quantities of carbon dioxide. As a result, the CO_2 content of the atmosphere has increased substantially. No reliable data exist to tell us what the atmosphere's CO_2 content was two centuries ago, but scientists report that its concentration has increased from about 315 parts per million (ppm) to almost 370 ppm over the past 50 years, an increase of approximately 15 percent (see Fig. 6.3).

Simultaneously, scientists reported an increase in average global temperatures. By the mid-1980s there were warnings that the continued pollution of the atmosphere by human industrial activity would lead to an enhanced greenhouse effect that would melt glaciers, raise sea levels by as much as 3 m, and inundate coastal cities and lands. As if to confirm these predictions, the 1980s produced four of the warmest years ever recorded in North America and Western Europe. As people sweltered in New York, London, and Paris, the prospect of an overheated world seemed real.

For some time the evidence appeared overwhelming, and a majority of scientists concurred that human-made greenhouse gases (not only CO_2, but also trace gases such as methane produced by crop farming and livestock herding) were responsible for observed temperature increases. But not all climatologists were convinced. One unresolved issue, for example, had to do with the relative amounts of the CO_2 increase contributed by nature and by human activity. We have no long-term baseline from which to measure natural fluctuations in the atmosphere's CO_2 content; how can we therefore be sure that part of the observed increase does not represent a natural cycle?

Doubt also was cast on the twentieth-century temperature record (see Unit 20). According to some interpretations of available data, the Earth actually underwent a *cooling* phase from about 1940 to 1970. But there was no corresponding reduction in the measured amount of CO_2 in the atmosphere, which appears to contradict the axiom that increased CO_2 inescapably equals enhanced greenhouse warming.

Another argument centred on nature's capacity to sustain or recover its equilibrium, as it has done after massive volcanic eruptions, impacts by extraterrestrial objects such as comets, and other disturbances. Might the current excess CO_2 also prove to constitute a lesser imbalance than some scientists have suggested? When the post-1970 warming trend was interrupted by the effects of the 1991 eruption of the Philippine volcano Pinatubo, its ash and dust causing global cooling for several years, the strength of CO_2-induced warming seemed to come into question.

Geographers also noted regional imbalances in warming trends that seemed to render the term "global warming" invalid. While annual temperature averages unquestionably continued to rise through the late 1990s and early 2000s, overheated areas in the Northern Hemisphere often were matched by excessively cool regions in the Southern Hemisphere. Moreover, contradictions abounded. One study found that Antarctica's central ice sheet was cooling; others reported the breakup of marginal ice shelves and the separation of huge icebergs, one approximately the size of P.E.I., an apparent sign of warming (Fig. 7.4).

As we will note in later units, our planet has undergone periods of warming and cooling for as long as it has had an atmosphere. The key question is not whether the greenhouse effect waxes and wanes over time—it does. The crucial issue is the degree to which human intervention, through the emanation of artificial greenhouse-enhancing gases, is affecting the natural cycle currently in progress.

FIGURE 7.4 Antarctic ice breaking up in the warmer temperatures of summer. This mountain, called Sharp Peak, lies on the Graham Coast, where the Antarctic Circle intersects the western shore of the Antarctic Peninsula.

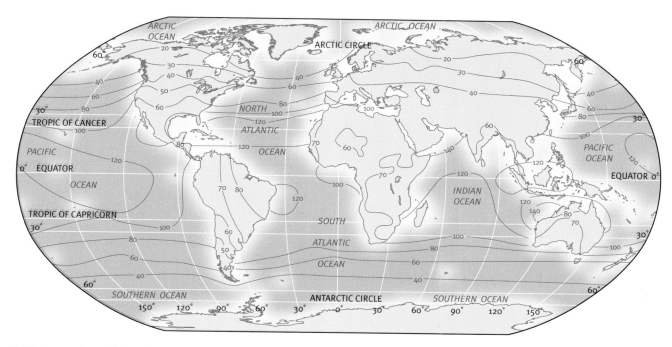

FIGURE 7.5 Annual distribution of net radiation at the surface of the Earth. Values are in thousands of calories per square centimetre. Red isolines show the pattern over land, blue isolines over the oceans.

the longwave radiation emitted by the Earth. The amount left over, when all the incoming and outgoing radiation flows have been tallied, is the **net radiation**. This net radiation balance totals about one-fourth of the shortwave radiation that originally arrives at the atmosphere's uppermost layer.

The reflectivity (albedo) of the Earth's surface and its temperature play particularly important roles in determining the final value of global net radiation. For instance, there is usually a difference in albedo and surface temperature between an area of land and one of sea at the same latitude (a topic treated in Unit 8). As is shown in Fig. 7.5, this variation results in a difference in net radiation values over the land and the ocean (represented by the red and blue isolines, respectively). That difference is greatest in the low latitudes and diminishes toward the poles. Overall, net radiation is greatest at low latitudes and smallest, or even negative (especially above ice-covered surfaces), at high latitudes.

Net radiation, moreover, may well be the single most important factor affecting the Earth's climates. It is certainly basic to the majority of physical processes that take place on the Earth because it provides their initial driving energy. For example, net radiation is by far the most significant factor determining the evaporation of water. The amount of water evaporated and the quantity of available net radiation together can largely explain the distribution of vegetation across the land surfaces of the Earth, from the dense forests of the equatorial tropics to the sparse mosses and lichens of the subarctic environmental zones. Furthermore, net radiation is vital in shaping the *heat energy balance* of the Earth.

The Heat Balance

Climate is often considered to be something derived from the atmosphere, and it is true that the climate of a place is essentially the result of the redistribution of heat energy across the face of the Earth. However, the events of the atmosphere are greatly affected by the processes that operate on the Earth's surface itself. Flows of heat energy to and from the surface are as much a part of the climate of an area as the winter snow or summer thunderstorm—more so, in fact, because these heat flows operate continuously.

The heat energy balance of the Earth's surface is composed, in its simplest form, of four different kinds of flows. One of these—the composite flows of *radiant heat* that make up net radiation—is already familiar to us. The second—*latent heat* (which causes evaporating liquids to change into gases)—is treated in Unit 12. The remaining two—*sensible heat flow* and *ground heat flow*—are introduced here.

All air molecules contain heat energy, the heat that we feel on our skin, and this sensed heat is termed **sensible heat flow**. Usually, during the day, the ground warms the air above it. Warmed air rises, and parcels of air move upward in a vertical heat-transfer process known as **convection**—thereby causing a sensible heat flow. We can occasionally see the results of this process, as in the case of shimmering air above a parking lot on a very hot day. Sometimes, when the ground surface is colder than the overlying air, sensible heat flows downward. This often happens at night or during the severe winters of cold climates.

Whereas sensible heat flow depends on convection, the heat that flows into and out of the ground depends on **conduction**, the transport of heat energy from one molecule to the next. The heat that is conducted into and out of the Earth's surface is collectively called **ground heat flow** or *soil heat flow*. These terms are used for convenience, even though this heat sometimes travels into plants, buildings, or the ocean. Ground heat flow is the smallest of the four heat balance components. Generally, the heat that passes into the ground during the day is approximately equal to that flowing out at night. Thus, over a 24-hour period, the balance of ground heat flow often is so small that it can be disregarded.

Except for the usually small amount of energy used by plants in photosynthesis, the total heat balance of any part of the Earth, say the part just outside your window, is made up of the flows of radiant heat (comprising net radiation), latent heat, sensible heat, and ground (soil) heat. One could examine the heat balance of a single leaf or football stadium or continent, but first the initial explanation of climates through the heat balance should be explored.

Climates and the Heat Balance

At any location, the temperature of the atmosphere depends on how much heat is involved in local radiant, latent, and sensible (as well as ground) heat flows. Net radiation is usually a source of heat for the Earth, and the heat gained in this way is used mainly for evaporation (in which case it is termed *latent heat*) or in a sensible heat flow into the air. But there are significant variations on this theme across the Earth's surface, and these lead to significant variations in climate. With that in mind, let us examine and compare the heat balance characteristics of four locations at widely separated latitudes.

Deep in the equatorial rainforest of South America at latitude 3°S, 1100 km inland from the mouth of the Amazon River, lies the northern Brazilian city of Manaus. Its hot humid climate is explained by the high amount of net radiation it receives, which in turn evaporates much of its large annual quantity (1800 mm) of rainfall. If we examine the heat balance diagram for Manaus, shown in Fig. 7.6A, we can see that most of the heat received in net radiation (**NR**) is lost through the latent (evaporative) heat flow (**LH**). A rather small amount is left over for the passage of sensible heat (**SH**) into the air. These conditions are almost constant throughout the year.

In contrast, at the subtropical latitude of Aswan, Egypt (located astride the Tropic of Cancer [23½°N]), net radiation varies with the season of the year, being highest in summer (Fig. 7.6B). There is little surface water to be evaporated, so the loss by latent heat is virtually nil (**LH** values are too small to appear on the graph). But Aswan's scorching temperatures—it lies in the heart of the huge North African desert zone—would be even higher if most of the heat gained by net radiation did not pass, via sensible flow, higher into the atmosphere.

Paris, the capital of France, lies within the middle latitudes near 50°N and exhibits another type of heat balance, as Fig. 7.6C indicates. The seasonal variation of net radiation is again a factor, but in Paris the loss of latent heat is only somewhat greater than the loss of sensible heat. However, a rather curious pattern occurs in Paris during the winter months. The net radiation becomes negative—more radiant heat is lost than is gained. Net radiation is no longer a heat source. Fortunately for the Parisians, this loss is offset: air that has been warmed in its journey across the North Atlantic Ocean can now provide heat to warm the Earth. Accordingly, during the winter months the sensible heat flow is directed toward the Earth's surface, as is shown by its negative values in Fig. 7.6C. The sensible heat flow, therefore, is responsible for keeping Parisian winter air temperatures relatively mild.

In central Siberia, deep inside the northern Asian component of Russia, this does not happen. Turukhansk, located at latitude 66°N, is typical, and air coming to this town in the winter has not travelled over a warm ocean but across a cold continent. Although the air passes some sensible heat toward the ground, it does not pass enough to offset the large net radiation deficit experienced in winter near the Arctic Circle (Fig. 7.6D). The result is bone-chilling temperatures. Yet here the seasonal change of climate is extreme. Paradoxically, the balance of heat in the summer months is rather like that in tropical Brazil! There are many such variations of heat balance across the ever-changing face of the Earth.

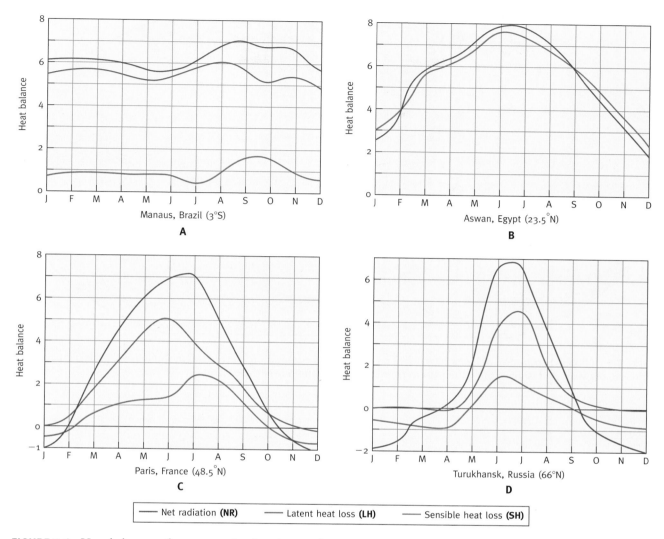

FIGURE 7.6 Heat balance at four contrasting locations. Values are in thousands of calories per square centimetre per month.

Global Distribution of Heat Flows

We have already examined the geographic variation of net radiation (Fig. 7.5). Now we will consider the disposal of net radiation through latent and sensible heat, losses that are necessary to keep the totality of radiation in balance for the Earth's surface as a whole. To find the amount of heat lost as latent heat, we multiply the amount of water evaporated by the value of the *latent heat of vaporization* (the amount of energy required to evaporate water). The global distribution of latent heat loss is mapped in Fig. 7.7. Over land surfaces (red isolines), the largest amount of latent heat loss occurs in the tropics on both sides of the Equator. Latent heat loss generally declines across subtropical latitudes, increases in the middle latitudes, and then further

declines in the higher latitudes. Over ocean surfaces (blue isolines), where water is always available for evaporation, latent heat loss is greatest in the subtropics. Here there are fewer clouds, on average, to reduce radiant heat input. Because of the effect of cloud cover, latent heat loss over oceans is not as great in the equatorial latitudes as in the subtropical latitudes. As over the land surfaces, latent heat loss is least above oceans at high latitudes.

Sensible heat loss over the land surface is greatest in the subtropics; from there it decreases toward the poles and the Equator. This is shown by the red isolines in Fig. 7.8, mapped in the same units as the world latent-heat-loss map (Fig. 7.7). Above the oceans (blue isolines), however, the amount of sensible heat loss generally tends to increase with latitude.

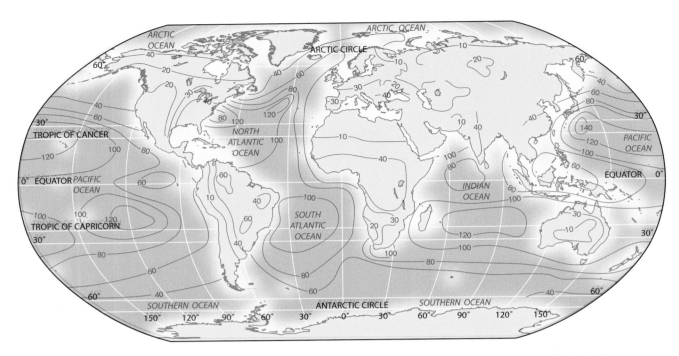

FIGURE 7.7   Global distribution of latent heat loss. The heat used in evaporation is expressed in thousands of calories per square centimetre per year. Red isolines show the pattern over land, blue isolines over the oceans.

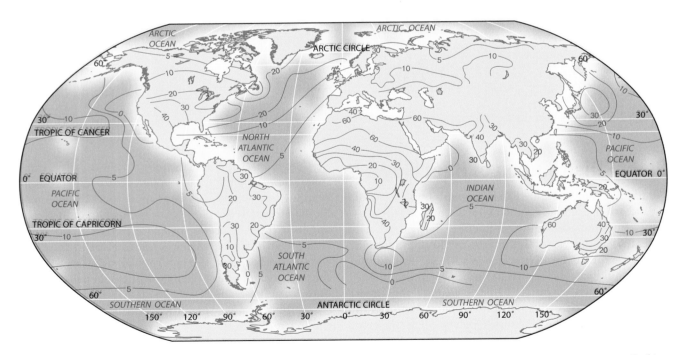

FIGURE 7.8   Global distribution of sensible heat loss. Values are in thousands of calories per square centimetre per year. Red isolines show the pattern over land, blue isolines over the oceans.

Over the Earth's surface as a whole, the net radiation heat gain is itself balanced by 70 percent of that heat being lost in the latent form and 30 percent being used to heat the air as sensible heat. But at any single point on our planet's surface, there is a unique interaction between the values of net radiation and latent and sensible heat flows. Temperature is the result of these heat flows, and its properties and variations are the subject of Unit 8. In Unit 9, global heat flows are discussed further, especially their linkage to atmospheric circulation patterns.

KEY TERMS

albedo *page 88*

conduction *page 92*

convection *page 92*

counterradiation *page 88*

diffuse radiation *page 87*

direct radiation *page 87*

global warming *page 89*

greenhouse effect *page 89*

ground heat flow *page 92*

longwave radiation *page 87*

net radiation *page 91*

radiation *page 87*

sensible heat flow *page 92*

shortwave radiation *page 87*

REVIEW QUESTIONS

1. What are the differences between solar and terrestrial radiation?

2. How much of the solar energy entering the atmosphere is absorbed by the atmosphere and how much by the Earth's surface? How much is reflected by the atmosphere and by the surface?

3. Describe in your own words the meaning of the term *greenhouse effect.*

4. Differentiate among the flows of radiant heat, latent heat, sensible heat, and ground heat.

5. What is meant by the term *albedo?* Give some examples of its application in your daily life.

6. What is meant by the popular term *global warming?* Can a strong case be made for it based on current evidence?

REFERENCES AND FURTHER READINGS

BENARDE, M. A. *Global Warming . . . Global Warming* (New York: Wiley, 1992).

CALVIN, W. H. "The Great Climate Flip-Flop: Global Warming Could, Paradoxically, Cause a Sudden and Catastrophic Cooling," *Atlantic Monthly* (January 1998), 47–64.

DRAKE, F. *Global Warming: The Science of Climate Change* (New York: Oxford Univ. Press, 2000).

FRÖHLICH, C., and LONDON, J. *Radiation Manual* (Geneva: World Meteorological Organziation, 1985).

"Global Warming" (cover story), *Time* (April 9, 2001), 22–29.

HOUGHTON, J. T. *Global Warming* (New York: Cambridge Univ. Press, 2nd ed., 1997).

JOYCE, T. "The Heat before the Cold," *New York Times* (April 18, 2002), A29.

KONDRATYEV, K. *Radiation in the Atmosphere* (New York: Academic Press, 1969).

LIOU, K.-N. *An Introduction to Atmospheric Radiation* (New York: Academic Press, 1980).

PHILANDER, S. G. *Is the Temperature Rising?: The Uncertain Science of Global Warming* (Princeton, N.J.: Princeton Univ. Press, 1998).

REVKIN, A. C. "The Devil Is in the Details: Efforts to Predict the Effects of Global Warming Hinge on Gaps in Climate Models," *New York Times* (July 3, 2001), D1, D2.

SCHNEIDER, D. "Trends in Climate Research: The Rising Seas," *Scientific American* (March 1997), 112–117.

STEVENS, W. K. "Global Warming: The Contrarian View," *New York Times* (February 29, 2000), D1, D6.

WEB RESOURCES

http://climate.gsfc.nasa.gov/~cahalan/Radiation/RadiativeBalance.html Discussion of Earth's radiative balance with accompanying graphics.

http://lwf.ncdc.noaa.gov/oa/climate/globalwarming.html NOAA's guide to global warming and the greenhouse effect.

http://www.earthobservatory.nasa.gov/Observatory/Datasets/lwflux.erbe.html User can build false colour animations of longwave radiation emitted by Earth for any given month from 1990 to present, in order to compare heat received and transmitted for different time periods.

http://www.ec.gc.ca/climate/home-e.htm Environment Canada's climate change site, including action plans for Canada.

Atmospheric and Surface Temperature

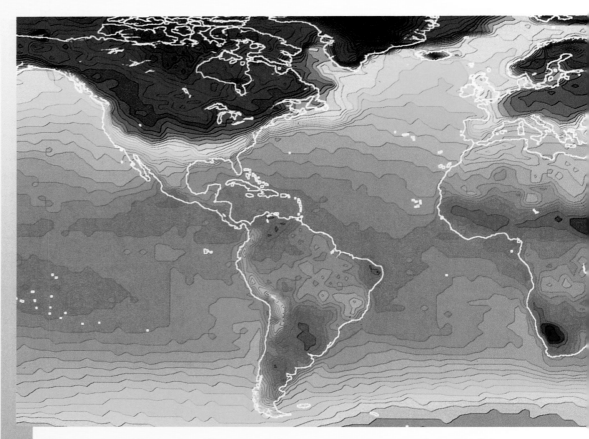

Enhanced satellite image of January surface temperatures across the part of the world centred on the Atlantic Ocean. Temperatures range from 40°C in southwestern Africa to −40°C in the Russian Arctic.

OBJECTIVES

- To discuss the measurement and characteristics of temperature and heat

- To explain the adiabatic process whereby vertically moving air heats and cools

- To discuss the global distribution of temperatures and their variation in time and space

On the rather cloudy day of June 26, 1863, British scientist James Glaisher and his assistant climbed into the basket of a balloon in Wolverton, England. This flight, one of their 28 flights between 1862 and 1866 (Fig. 8.1), lasted an hour and a half. They ascended to 7050 m and travelled 80 km before descending at Ely. En route they encountered rain, snow, and fog. One of the main purposes of this flight was to note the temperatures along the way.

FIGURE 8.1 James Glaisher and his assistant, Coxwell, during a balloon flight on September 5, 1862.

inquire more explicitly about what is meant by the concept of temperature.

What Is Temperature?

Imagine an enclosed box containing only molecules of air. They are likely to be moving constantly in all directions, in what is called *random motion*. The molecules move because they possess the energy of movement, known as **kinetic energy**. The more kinetic energy molecules possess, the faster they move. The index we use to measure their kinetic energy is called **temperature**. Thus temperature is an abstract term describing the energy, and therefore the speed of movement, of molecules. In a gas such as air, the molecules actually change their location when they move. But in a solid, like ice, they only vibrate in place. Nonetheless, the speed of this vibration is described by their temperature.

It is almost impossible to examine individual molecules, so we usually use an indirect method to measure temperature. We know that changes of temperature make gases, liquids, and solids expand and contract. Therefore temperature is most commonly measured by observing the expansion and contraction of mercury in a glass tube. Such an instrument is called a **thermometer**, and you are probably familiar with the medical and weather varieties. The mercury thermometer is placed in the mouth, air, or some other place where it can come into thermal equilibrium with the medium whose temperature it is measuring.

A thermometer is calibrated according to one of three scales. The scale used throughout most of the world is the **Celsius scale** (formerly centigrade scale), the metric measurement of temperature we have routinely been using in this book. On this scale, the *boiling point* of water is set at 100°C and its *freezing point* at 0°C. Scientists also employ an *absolute scale*—the **Kelvin scale**—which is based on the temperature of *absolute zero* (−273°C). (Scientists theorize that a gas at absolute zero would have no volume, no molecular motion, and no pressure.) The kelvin is identical in size to the Celsius degree, except that water freezes at 273 K and boils at 373 K. We will not mention kelvins again in this book, but will continue to use Celsius degrees.

It is important to distinguish temperature from heat. Temperature merely measures the kinetic energy of molecules. It does not measure the number of molecules in a substance or its *density* (the amount of mass per unit of volume). But the heat of a substance depends on its volume, its temperature, and its capacity to hold heat. Thus a bowl of soup, with a high heat capacity, might burn your tongue at the same temperature at which you could

In Glaisher's own words, these varied from the "extreme heat of summer" to the "cold of winter." In fact, however, the temperatures varied from 19°C at the ground to −8.3°C at 7050 m. The pair had good reason to be wary of the hazards of high altitudes: on a flight the previous year, Glaisher had fainted at 8700 m from lack of oxygen. His assistant, arms paralyzed with cold, climbed the rigging of the balloon to release the gas control with his teeth. Those flights firmly established that temperature typically decreases with an increase in altitude, at least as far as 8700 m above the surface.

These findings of vertical temperature changes were an important addition to existing knowledge. Together with what was already known about heating patterns of the planetary surface, they reinforced the notion that temperatures could be highly variable in any direction. Before we further examine those vertical and horizontal temperature relationships, we must briefly digress to comfortably drink a glass of hot water. Because it contains many more molecules, a large lake with a water temperature of 10°C contains much more heat than a cup of hot coffee at 70°C. Now that we know something about temperature, let us return to discussing the temperatures of the atmosphere.

The Vertical Distribution of Temperature

Glaisher's observations for the lower part of the atmosphere were indeed correct—temperature typically does decline with an increase in altitude. However, subsequent unmanned balloon observations showed that, above about 12 km, the temperature stops decreasing with height and begins to increase. Nobody believed this at first, and only after several hundred balloon ascents was it finally accepted. Later ascents during the twentieth century to still higher altitudes revealed an even more complex temperature pattern. These upper atmospheric layers are discussed in Unit 6, and their temperature characteristics are graphed in Fig. 6.5. Our focus here is on the lowest atmospheric layer, the troposphere.

Tropospheric Temperature and Air Stability

The troposphere is the layer of the atmosphere we live in, and it is here that the weather events and climates affecting humans occur. As shown in Fig. 6.5, its temperature typically decreases with increasing altitude until the tropopause is reached. Another distinctive feature of the troposphere is the possibility and frequency of vertical, as well as horizontal, movement of air. Any long continuation of vertical movement depends on the rate of change of temperature with height—the *lapse rate*. As we note in Unit 6, the average tropospheric lapse rate is 0.65°C/100 m of elevation.

The lapse rate determines the **stability** of the air, a concept illustrated in Fig. 8.2 by a wedge of wood. When it is resting on its side (A), a small push at the top may move it horizontally, but its vertical position remains the same. It is therefore *stable*. When the wood rests on its curved base (B), a similar push might rock it, but it will still return to its original position; it is still stable. But if we balance the wedge of wood on its pointed edge (C), a small push at the top knocks it over. It does not return to its original position; hence it is *unstable*.

We use the same terminology to refer to the vertical movement of a small parcel of air. If it returns to its original position after receiving some upward force, we say it is stable. But if it keeps moving upward after re-

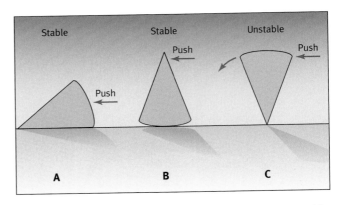

FIGURE 8.2   Concept of stability. The block of wood, like parcels of air, is considered stable as long as it returns to its original position after a small push.

ceiving the force, then we say it is unstable. In order to understand air stability, we must first consider that air is a poor conductor of heat. Without any air movement, it takes a long time for heat to pass from one air molecule to the next. Therefore a parcel of air of one temperature that is surrounded by a mass of air at another temperature will neither gain nor lose heat energy in a short period of time. When heat is neither gained from nor lost to the surrounding air, the process is called **adiabatic**.

Adiabatic Lapse Rates

If you have ever used a bicycle pump, you know that when the air is compressed at the bottom of the pump the air's temperature rises and the bottom of the pump becomes hot. The opposite occurs when the volume of a given mass of air is forced to expand: the temperature of the air decreases. A similar thing happens in the atmosphere. If a parcel of air rises to a higher altitude, it expands and cools (as if it were contained inside an expanding balloon). This is an adiabatic process because that air parcel neither gains heat from nor loses heat to its surroundings. Hence such air-parcel lapse rates in the troposphere are called **adiabatic lapse rates**.

Dry Adiabatic Lapse Rate (DALR)   When an air parcel is not saturated with water vapour, it cools with an increase in altitude at a constant rate of 1°C/100 m. This is the **dry adiabatic lapse rate (DALR)**. But because air sometimes is saturated, and because mechanisms (especially radiant energy exchange) are involved in heating and cooling the atmosphere, any particular atmospheric lapse rate may not be the same as the DALR. The lapse rate at any particular time or location is called the **environmental lapse rate (ELR)**, which may be thought of as the vertical temperature profile of the atmosphere (as would be measured from an ascending balloon), which changes from day to day and from place to place. In the context of our example, the ELR is the temperature decline with height in the stationary mass of air in the atmosphere that surrounds our cooling parcel of air. The troposphere's (nonadiabatic) normal lapse rate—which we have now more specifically defined as the ELR—averages 0.65°C/100 m.

What happens to a parcel of air in two different environments with two different ELRs. In Fig. 8.3A, the parcel of air rises from the ground (because it is either warmed by the surface or forced upward mechanically). Because it neither gains heat from nor loses it to the surrounding air mass, it cools at the DALR, decreasing its temperature 1°C for each 100 m of ascent. But in this case the ELR is 0.5°C/100 m, so after rising 100 m, the air parcel has a temperature 0.5°C lower than its surroundings. The colder the air, the more dense it is. Therefore the air parcel is now denser and heavier than the surrounding air and tends to fall back to Earth. This would happen even if the parcel rose to 300 m, where it would be 1.5°C colder than its surroundings. The cooled parcel thus returns to its original position on the surface. We would say the whole of the air in that environment is stable, meaning *it resists vertical displacement.* In contrast, Fig. 8.3B shows the ELR to be 1.5°C/100 m. Under these conditions, an air parcel rising and cooling at the DALR would be warmer than its surroundings. The warmer the air, the less dense it is, so the air parcel that is lighter and less dense than the surrounding air continues to rise. We would call the air in this environment unstable, because it does not return to its original position.

One can often tell whether or not a portion of the atmosphere is stable by looking at it. A stable atmosphere is marked by clear skies or by flat, layerlike clouds. An unstable atmosphere is typified by puffy, vertical clouds, which sometimes develop to great heights. A photograph of Florida taken from a spacecraft, shown in Fig. 8.4, illustrates the two conditions. Over the Atlantic Ocean to the east and the Gulf of Mexico to the west, the ELR is less than the DALR, so parcels of air remain near the sea surface. But the higher temperatures of the land surface in daytime make the ELR higher than the DALR. The resulting instability allows parcels of hot air to rise in the atmosphere, forming those puffy clouds as they cool.

Saturated Adiabatic Lapse Rate (SALR)   The situation is somewhat different when the air contains water vapour that is changing to water droplets as it cools. Latent heat (a concept introduced in Unit 7) is given off when the state of water changes from a gas to a liquid, a process called *condensation.* The resultant lapse rate when condensation is occurring is less than the DALR. This lapse rate is called the *wet* or **saturated adiabatic lapse rate (SALR)**.

Unlike the DALR, the value of the SALR is variable, depending on the amount of water condensed and latent heat released. A typical value for the SALR at 20°C is 0.44°C/100 m, compared with 1°C/100 m for the DALR. As a rule, we may assume that the atmosphere will be stable if the ELR is less than the SALR, and unstable if the ELR is greater than the DALR. If the ELR lies between the SALR and DALR, the atmosphere is said to be *conditionally unstable.* The conditions depend

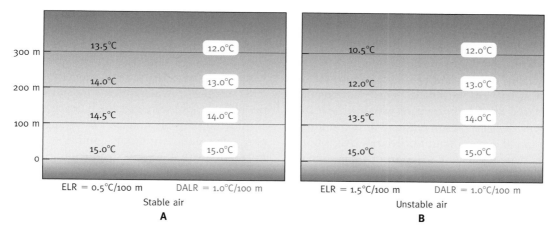

FIGURE 8.3 Environmental lapse rate conditions for a mass of stationary air (shown in blue) that surrounds an individual parcel of air (shown in white) rising through it. When the ELR is less than the DALR, an air parcel is stable (A). When the ELR is greater than the DALR, an air parcel is unstable (B).

FIGURE 8.4 Looking southward at the Florida peninsula and surrounding waters from the NASA's ill-fated space shuttle Columbia passing over the Jacksonville area. In this classic summertime view, the land area of southern Florida is almost perfectly defined by its cloak of puffy clouds, the signature of atmospheric instability associated with rising hot air.

on whether the gaseous water vapour in the air changes into liquid water and thereby adds heat to the air.

Temperature Inversions and Air Pollution

In dealing with the stability of the troposphere, we are really considering the possibility—and vigour—of the vertical mixing of air within it. This has practical implications, the most important of which is how well pollutants will disperse when released into the atmosphere. The initial vertical (and horizontal) distribution of pollutants depends on the location of their sources. Any further spread of air pollution is associated with two main factors: (1) the stability of the air and its propensity to allow vertical mixing, and (2) how well air stability combines with the flushing effect of horizontal winds. Both are related to the temperature structure of the lower troposphere, particularly the influence of temperature inversions.

Under usual conditions, the tropospheric temperature decreases with height as ground-warmed air rises, expands, and cools (see Fig. 6.5). Thus any pollutants contained in that surface layer of air would disperse along with it. At times, however, this vertical cleansing mechanism does not operate because the usual negative lapse rate is replaced by a positive one. Such an increase in temperature with height is defined in Unit 6 as a **temperature inversion** because it inverts what we, on the surface, believe to be the "normal" behaviour of temperature change with altitude.

Because of the nightly cooling of the Earth's surface and the atmosphere near the ground, it is common for a temperature inversion—warm air lying above cold air—to develop in early morning over both city and countryside. These inversions, which form an atmospheric "lid," can be broken down by rapid heating of the surface or by windy conditions. Without these conditions, air pollution is trapped and intensifies beneath the inversion layer (Fig. 8.5). This is especially true in certain urban areas, where *dust domes* frequently build up (see Perspective: Urban Dust Domes and Heating Patterns).

The subsidence (vertical downflow) of air from higher in the troposphere can also contribute to the trapping of pollutants, as residents of downtown Toronto know only too well (Fig. 8.7). This airflow is usually quite cool and is reinforced by onshore surface winds that blow across the cold waters of the adjacent Pacific Ocean. Moreover, the cooling effect is heightened by the nighttime drainage of cold air into the Los Angeles Basin from the mountains that form its inland perimeter. These air movements often produce and sustain temperature inversions at an altitude of approximately 1000 m, resulting in poor-quality surface-level air that is popularly known as *smog* (a contraction of "smoke" and "fog").

Horizontal flushing by winds can help to relieve air pollution. Air pollution potential may be estimated by calculating the vertical range of well-mixed pollutants and the average wind speed through the mixing layer. Figure 8.8 shows the average number of days (between 1987 and 1992) when ozone concentrations of 82 parts per billion (ppb) were exceeded. Levels above 65 ppb are considered poor air quality. On average it appears that air-quality and ventilation conditions are best in the northern, central, and western regions of Canada, with the poorest air-quality conditions occurring in southern Ontario and Atlantic Canada. The role of topographic factors is important in determining the fate of air pathways, a factor that does not show up at the scale of the map in Fig. 8.8. The region from Windsor, Ontario, to Quebec City has the worst air quality in Canada. Approximately half of the smog in this region originates in

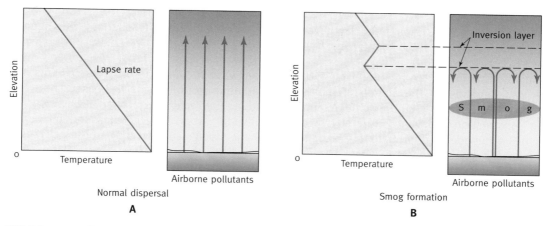

FIGURE 8.5 Effect of a temperature inversion on the vertical dispersal of atmospheric pollutants. (A) Normal dispersal; (B) smog formation.

PERSPECTIVES ON THE HUMAN ENVIRONMENT

Urban Dust Domes and Heating Patterns

Many North American metropolitan areas lie beneath a **dust dome**. A high concentration of fuel combustion and heat from concrete can cause the air in urban areas to be warmer than surrounding areas (see *urban heat islands*, p. 270). This can result in dust domes, which trap particulates in a dome over a city, lowering air quality in those regions. The brownish haze of a dust dome can stand out against the blue sky (see Fig. 8.7). Torontonians have become increasingly concerned about the quality of their air. Ground-level ozone and inhalable particles (the main ingredients of smog) are believed to be leading to increased rates of respiratory and cardiovascular illness and even premature death. Air temperatures have been rising and air quality has been declining over the past half-century. Lower temperatures and smog levels can be found only a short distance outside of the urban core. The situation is similar in many other large cities in North America. Why don't these effluents simply just blow away?

Studies of the movement of dust and gaseous pollutants over cities show that heat generated in many urban areas forms a local circulation cell. Air currents capture the dust and mould it into a dome (Fig. 8.6). Dust and pollution particles rise in air currents around the centre of the city where the temperature is warmest. As they move upward, the air cools and diverges. The particles gradually drift toward the edges of the city and settle downward. Near the ground they are drawn into the centre of the city to complete the circular motion. Frequent temperature inversions above the city prevent upward escape, and the particles tend to remain trapped in this continuous cycle of air movement.

All parts of the radiation balance discussed in Unit 7 (see pp. 87–91) are altered in the urban environment. In London, England, researchers have discovered that the city centre has an average of 3.6 hours of sunshine per day. Outside the city, it

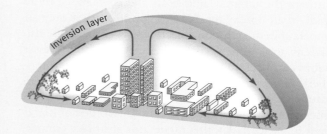

FIGURE 8.6 Air circulation within an urban dust dome.

is sunny an average of 4.3 hours per day because of the absence of a dust dome to intercept the incoming shortwave radiation.

The amount of insolation absorbed by a city's surface also depends on the albedo of that surface. This, in turn, depends on the actual materials used in construction and varies from city to city. Many cities are made of dark materials or materials that have been blackened by smoke (the industrial cities in Britain, for example). They have a lower albedo (17 percent) than agricultural land does (approximately 23 percent), and therefore they absorb more radiation. In contrast, some cities (like the central areas of Los Angeles) have construction materials with lighter colours and therefore exhibit a higher albedo than the more vegetated residential zones.

Scientists know less about the behaviour of longwave radiation in cities, but many studies show increases in both upward and downward longwave radiation in urban areas. This increased radiation can offset the decreased shortwave radiation. The result is a net radiation that is not very different from that in surrounding rural areas. Some studies suggest that, of the net radiation arriving at the city surface, about 80 percent is lost as sensible heat warming the city air and that the rest acts mainly as ground heat flow to warm the materials constituting the urban landscape. Very little heat appears to be used in evaporative cooling.

the Ohio Valley and Cleveland and Detroit areas of the United States. Canada is now engaged in negotiations with the United States to reduce the trans-border issue of air pollution. The geographical location and tendency for hot, stagnant summer weather is the perfect scenario for the formation of ground-level ozone. In Atlantic Canada, 50 to 80 percent of the smog originates in the United States or central Canada (see Fig. 8.9).

The Horizontal Distribution of Temperature

The spatial distribution of temperatures across the landmasses, oceans, and icecaps that constitute the Earth's surface represents the response to a number of factors. Certainly insolation is one such factor, and the amount of solar radiation received depends on the length of daylight and the angle of the Sun's rays (both a function of the latitudinal position). A second major factor is the nature of the surface. Land heats and cools much more rapidly than water, and this strongly affects not only air temperatures directly above each type of surface, but also adjacent areas influenced by them. A number of lesser factors can be locally important as well. Since tropospheric temperatures usually decrease with an increase in altitude, places located at higher elevations tend to experience temperatures lower than those recorded at places closer to sea level. Another moderator of surface temperatures is cloudiness, and places with more extensive cloud cover generally experience lower daytime high temperatures than similar places with clearer skies. (This may also

be true in areas where pollution haze plays a role identical to that of clouds.) And for coastal locations and islands, air temperatures can be influenced to a surprising extent by the warmth or coolness of local ocean currents.

Daily and Yearly Cycles

The pattern of temperature change during a day is called the **diurnal cycle**. Shortly after dawn, radiation from the Sun begins to exceed the radiant loss from the Earth's surface. The Earth begins to heat the air, so the air temperature rises. It continues to rise as the net radiation rises. But the heating of the ground and the flow of sensible heat take some time to develop fully. Thus maximum air temperatures usually do not occur simultaneously with the maximum net radiation peaks at solar noon, but an hour or more later. In late afternoon, net radiation and sensible heat flow decline markedly, and temperatures begin to fall. After the Sun has set, more radiation leaves the Earth than arrives at the surface, which produces a negative net radiation. The surface and the air above it enter a cooling period that lasts all through the night. Temperatures are lowest near dawn; with sunrise, the diurnal cycle starts again.

The pattern of temperature change during a year is called the **annual cycle** of temperature, which in the middle and high latitudes is rather similar to the diurnal cycle. In the spring, net radiation becomes positive and air temperatures begin to rise. The highest average temperatures do not occur at the time of the greatest net radiation, the summer solstice, but usually about a month later. In autumn, decreasing net radiation leads to progressively lower temperatures. The lowest winter

FIGURE 8.7   Downtown Toronto under a thick blanket of smog (7:08 a.m., June 27, 2001). The public has become increasingly aware of and concerned with high levels of ground-level ozone and inhalable particulates (the main ingredients of smog) in the city.

temperatures occur toward the end of the period of lowest (and often negative) net radiation and when the ground has lost most of the heat it gained during summer. Then it is spring again, and net radiation once more begins its cyclical increase.

Land/Water Heating Differences

The time it takes to heat the surface at any particular location determines when the highest air temperatures will occur. The difference between land and ocean is particularly noteworthy. Dry land heats and cools relatively rapidly because radiation cannot penetrate the solid surface to any meaningful extent.

Unlike solid surfaces, water requires far more time to heat up and cool down. For one thing, compared to land, radiation can penetrate the surface layer of water to a relatively greater depth. There is also considerable vertical mixing—driven by waves, currents, and other water movements—that constantly takes place between newly warmed (or cooled) surface water and cooler (or warmer)

layers below. Moreover, the energy required to raise the land temperature by a given number of degrees would have to be tripled in order to increase the surface temperature of a body of water by an equivalent amount.

Not surprisingly, the ocean surface exhibits a decidedly smaller annual temperature range—from −2°C to about 32°C, as opposed to the land-surface extremes of −88°C and 58°C. In addition, seasonal ocean temperature change is particularly moderate. In the tropics this variation averages 1 to 4°C, and even the upper middle latitudes record only a modest 5 to 8°C swing between seasonal extremes. On a diurnal basis, the ocean-surface range is almost always less than 1°C.

As a consequence of this heating differential, the air above an ocean remains cooler in summer and warmer in winter than does the air over a land surface at the same latitude. This can be seen in Table 8.1, which displays data on the annual range of temperatures, at 15-degree latitudinal intervals, for each hemisphere. Note that the Southern Hemisphere, which is only about 20 percent land, consistently exhibits smaller yearly

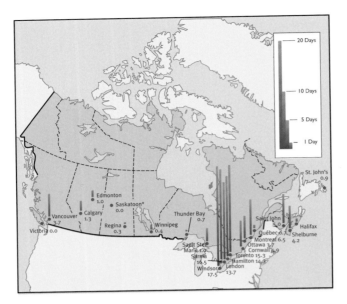

FIGURE 8.8   Average number of days (1987-1992) when one-hour average concentrations of ozone surpassed 82 parts per billion (ppb). An excess of 65 ppb is indicative of relatively poor air-quality conditions.

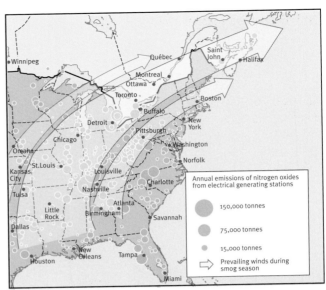

FIGURE 8.9   Annual emission of nitrogen oxides from electrical generating stations in eastern North America, indicating predominant flow of atmospheric transport of effluents.

temperature ranges than the Northern Hemisphere, whose surface is approximately 40 percent land.

In places where the oceanic air is transported onto the continents (as in our discussion of Paris in Unit 7), air temperatures are ameliorated accordingly, that is, they do not become extremely hot or cold. As the distance from the coast increases, however, this moderating effect diminishes (it terminates more abruptly if high mountain ranges parallel to the shore block the inland movement of oceanic air). This is illustrated in Fig. 8.10, which graphs the annual temperature regimes for Victoria, British Columbia, and Winnipeg, Manitoba, both located at approximately the same latitude. Interior Winnipeg, located in the heart of the North American continent, experiences both a warmer summer and a much colder winter, whereas Victoria, located on the Pacific coast, enjoys a temperature regime that is free of extremes in both summer and winter.

This moderating influence of the ocean on air temperatures is called the **maritime effect** on climate. In the opposite case, where the ocean has a minimal ameliorating influence on air temperatures well inland, there is a **continental effect**. This property of **continentality** is strongly suggested in the case of Winnipeg (Fig. 8.10), but the most dramatic examples are found deep inside Eurasia, in the heart of the world's largest landmass. The Russian town of Verkhoyansk, located in far northeastern Siberia, is well known to climatologists in this regard, and its annual temperature regime is plotted in Fig. 8.11.

Sometimes air from outside an area has more influence on air temperatures than do local radiation and sensible and latent heat flows. For instance, there might be quite a large amount of net radiation at midday during a Nebraska winter, but the air temperatures may still be very low. This is because the overlying air may have come from the Arctic, thousands of kilometres to the north, where a completely different heat balance prevailed. Thus, although the air temperature is a function of the amount of heat that makes up the local heat balance, it can also be affected by the **advection** (horizontal transport through the atmosphere via wind) of air from a region exhibiting a different heat energy balance. The results of different heat balances and the large-scale advection of air can be seen in the worldwide distribution of surface air temperatures.

Table 8.1 Variation in Average Annual Temperature Range by Latitude, °C

Latitude	Northern Hemisphere	Southern Hemisphere
0	0	0
15	3	4
30	13	7
45	23	6
60	30	11
75	32	26
90	40	31

Source: Information from F. K. Lutgens and E. J. Tarbuck, *The Atmosphere: An Introduction to Meteorology* (Upper Saddle River, N.J.: Prentice-Hall, 8th ed., 2001), 64.

Global Temperature Variations

The global distribution of air temperatures is mapped in Fig. 8.12. In order to avoid the distorting effects of altitude, all temperatures have been converted to their averages at sea level. Insolation, which is determined by the angle of the Sun's rays striking the Earth and the length of daylight, can change significantly in most places over a period of weeks. Thus physical geographers have always faced a problem in trying to capture the dynamic patterns of global temperatures on a map. For our purposes, the worldwide shifting of air temperatures, or their *seasonal march,* is best visualized by comparing the patterns of the two extreme months of the year—January and July—which immediately follow the solstices. The cartographic technique of isarithmic mapping (defined in Unit 3) is used in Fig. 8.12, whose January and July distributions employ **isotherms**—lines connecting all points having the same temperature.

Both maps reveal a series of latitudinal temperature belts that are shifted toward the "high-Sun" hemisphere (Northern Hemisphere in July, Southern Hemisphere in January). The tropical zone on both sides of the Equator experiences the least change between January and July, because higher total amounts of net radiation at low latitudes (see Fig. 7.5) lead to higher air temperatures.

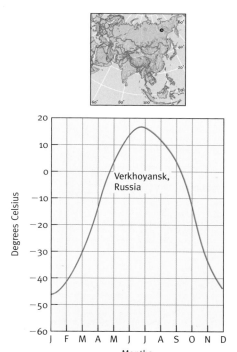

FIGURE 8.11   Annual temperature regime in Verkhoyansk (68°N, 133°E) in Russia's far northeastern Siberia, demonstrating the extremes of continentality.

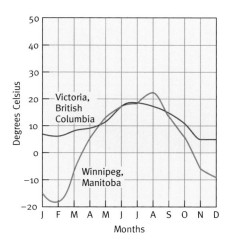

FIGURE 8.10   Annual temperature regimes in Victoria, British Columbia, and Winnipeg, Manitoba. Note the contrast between interior continental and coastal locations.

The middle and upper latitudes, particularly in the hemisphere experiencing winter, exhibit quite a different pattern. Here the horizontal rate of temperature change over distance—or **temperature gradient**—is much more pronounced, as shown by the "packing" or bunching of the isotherms. (Note that the isotherms are much farther apart in the tropical latitudes.)

Another major feature of Fig. 8.12 is the contrast between temperatures overlying land and sea. There is no mistaking the effects of continentality on either map: the Northern Hemisphere landmasses vividly display their substantial interior annual temperature ranges. Clearly visible, too, are the moderating influence of the oceans and the maritime effect on the air temperatures over land surfaces near them. Where warm ocean currents flow, as in the North Atlantic just west and northwest of Europe, the onshore movement of air across them can decidedly ameliorate winter temperatures; note that northern Britain, close to 60°N, lies on the 5°C January isotherm, the same isotherm that passes through North Carolina at about 35°N, the northern edge of the U.S. Sunbelt! In general, we observe a poleward bending of the isotherms over all the oceans, an indicator of their relative warmth with respect to land at the same latitude. The only notable exceptions occur in conjunction with cold ocean cur-

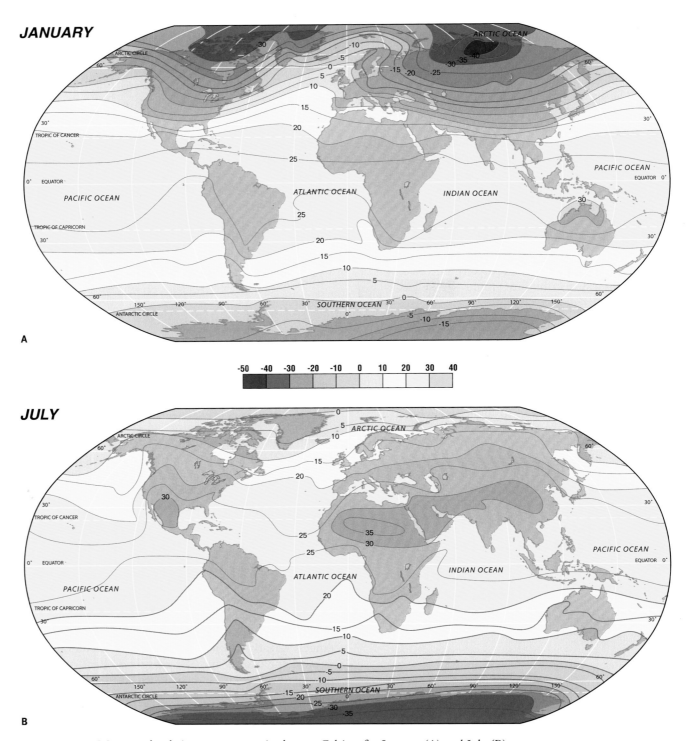

FIGURE 8.12   Mean sea-level air temperatures, in degrees Celsius, for January (A) and July (B).

rents, such as off the western coasts of Africa and South America south of the Equator, or off the northwestern coast of Africa north of the Equator.

The flow patterns associated with ocean currents and the movement of air above them remind us that the atmosphere and hydrosphere are highly dynamic entities.

Indeed, both contain global-scale circulation systems that are vital to understanding weather and climate. Now that we are familiar with the temperature structure of the atmosphere, we are ready to examine the forces that shape these regularly recurring currents of air and water.

KEY TERMS

adiabatic   *page 98*

adiabatic lapse
  rate   *page 98*

advection   *page 104*

annual cycle   *page 102*

Celsius scale   *page 97*

continentality (continental
  effect)   *page 104*

diurnal cycle   *page 102*

dry adiabatic lapse
  rate (DALR)   *page 98*

dust dome   *page 101*

environmental lapse
  rate (ELR)   *page 98*

isotherms   *page 105*

Kelvin scale   *page 97*

kinetic energy   *page 97*

maritime effect   *page 104*

saturated adiabatic lapse
  rate (SALR)   *page 99*

stability   *page 98*

temperature   *page 97*

temperature gradient   *page 105*

temperature inversion   *page 100*

thermometer   *page 97*

urban heat islands   *page 99*

REVIEW QUESTIONS

1. Discuss the major differences between the Celsius and Kelvin temperature scales.

2. What is the difference between stable and unstable air?

3. What is the *adiabatic* process? Define *DALR* and *SALR*.

4. What is a *temperature inversion,* and what are the negative consequences for an urban area affected by this atmospheric condition? How does it influence the ventilation of air pollution?

5. What are the factors that shape the spatial distribution of temperature across the Earth's surface?

6. What are the main differences in annual temperature regimes between maritime and interior continental locations?

REFERENCES AND FURTHER READINGS

AMATO, J. A.   *Dust: A History of the Small and the Invisible* (Berkeley, Calif.: Univ. of California Press, 2000).

ELSOM, D.   *Atmospheric Pollution: A Global Problem* (Cambridge, Mass.: Blackwell, 2nd ed., 1992).

GEIGER, R.   *The Climate Near the Ground* (Cambridge, Mass.: Harvard Univ. Press, 1965).

GOUDIE, A.   *The Human Impact on the Natural Environment* (Cambridge, Mass.: MIT Press, 5th ed., 2000).

HENDERSON-SELLERS, A., and ROBINSON, P. J.   *Contemporary Climatology* (London/New York: Longman, 1986), chapter 2.

KONDRATYEV, K.   *Radiation in the Atmosphere* (New York: Academic Press, 1969).

MATHER, J. R.   *Climatology: Fundamentals and Applications* (New York: McGraw-Hill, 1974), chapter 2.

MIDDLETON, W.   *A History of the Thermometer and Its Use in Meteorology* (Baltimore, Md.: Johns Hopkins Univ. Press, 1966).

OKE, T. R.   *Boundary Layer Climates* (New York: Methuen, 2nd ed., 1987).

THOMPSON, R., and PERRY, A., Eds.   *Applied Climatology: Principles and Practice* (London/New York: Routledge, 1997).

TREWARTHA, G. T., and HORN, L. H.   *An Introduction to Climate* (New York: McGraw-Hill, 5th ed., 1980), chapters 2, 8–12.

WEB RESOURCES

http://www.atl.ec.gc.ca/airquality/query/   Atlantic Region interactive air-quality data (past 24 hours, daily and monthly), indicating the type of pollutant.

http://www.city.toronto.on.ca/environment/moving_toward.htm Toronto's "Moving towards Cleaner Air" reports on how the city can move forward in addressing air emissions.

http://www.cpc.ncep.noaa.gov/products/tanalaccesspage.html NOAA's climate prediction centre displays daily U.S. temperature analyses, as well as long-term temperature and precipitation plots for U.S. cities.

http://www.ec.gc.ca/air/   Environment Canada's air-quality and pollution website.

http://www.ec.gc.ca/air/qual/2002/appendixb_e.html Canada–United States Air Quality Agreement, Ozone Annex.

http://www.epa.gov/airnow/Canada   View an animation of current or previous levels of ozone in different regions of Canada.

Air Pressure and Winds

Fast-moving air in persistent directional flow shapes many features on the Earth's surface, including this divi-divi tree on Aruba in the Caribbean. (Authors' photo)

OBJECTIVES

- To explain atmospheric pressure and its altitudinal variation

- To relate atmospheric pressure to windflow at the surface and aloft

- To apply these relationships to the operation of local wind systems

I n our previous discussions, the atmosphere has been likened to a blanket and a protective shield. Yet another analogy can now be added: an ocean of air surrounding the Earth. Such imagery is often used in physical geography because the atmosphere resembles the world ocean in its circulation patterns. This unit is about atmospheric pressure and winds, the dynamic forces that shape the regularly recurring global movements of air (and water). Units 10 and 11 focus on the patterns that result—the atmospheric and oceanic currents that constitute the general circulation systems affecting our planetary surface and form the framework for weather and climate.

The leading function of the general circulation of the atmosphere is to redistribute heat and moisture across the Earth's surface. Were it not for the transport of heat from the Equator to the poles, most of the Earth's surface would be uninhabitable because it would be either too hot, too cold, or too dry. Atmospheric circulation accounts for approximately 87 percent of this heat redistribution, and oceanic circulation accounts for the remainder. The atmosphere moves the way it does primarily because of the variation in the amount of net radiation received at the surface of the Earth. The resulting temperature differences produce the global wind system. We will begin to examine this system by detailing the relationships between air pressure, heat imbalances, winds, and the rotational effects of the Earth.

Atmospheric Pressure

Wind, the movement of air relative to the Earth's surface, is a response to an imbalance of forces acting on air molecules. This is true whether the air is moving horizontally or vertically, and indeed these two movement dimensions are related via the concept of atmospheric pressure. First we consider the concept of atmospheric pressure, its fundamental cause and the resultant vertical distribution produced. We then link atmospheric pressure to windflow by considering both the additional forces that come into play once motion begins and the patterns of air circulation within the atmosphere that result.

The Concept of Pressure

The primary force exerting an influence on air molecules is *gravity*. The atmosphere is "held" against the Earth by gravitational attraction. The combined weight of all the air molecules in a column of atmosphere exerts a force on the surface of the Earth. Over a given area of the surface, say 1 cm², this force produces a **pressure**. Although several different units are used to measure atmospheric pressure, the standard unit of pressure in atmospheric studies is the *millibar (mb)*. The average weight of the atmospheric column pressing down on the Earth's surface (or *standard sea-level air pressure*) is 1013.25 mb.

Atmospheric pressure is commonly measured as the length of a column of liquid it will support. In 1643 the Italian scientist Evangelista Torricelli performed an experiment in which he filled a glass tube with mercury and then placed the tube upside down in a dish of mercury. Figure 9.1 depicts his experiment. Instead of the mercury in the tube rushing out into the dish, the atmospheric pressure pushing down on the mercury in the surrounding dish supported the liquid still in the

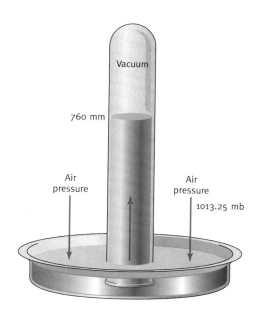

FIGURE 9.1   Mercury barometer invented by Torricelli. The greater the atmospheric pressure, the higher the column of mercury. These data exhibit the reading when standard sea-level pressure exists.

tube. The height of the column in the tube was directly proportional to the atmospheric pressure—the greater the pressure, the higher the column in the tube. (Note that standard sea-level air pressure produces a reading of 760 mm in the height of the mercury column.) Torricelli had invented the world's first pressure-measuring instrument, known as a **barometer**.

Atmospheric Pressure and Altitude

Once scientists found they could measure atmospheric pressure, they set about investigating its properties. They soon discovered that atmospheric pressure does not vary all that much horizontally but does decrease very rapidly with increasing altitude. Measurements of atmospheric pressure from both higher land elevations and balloons showed dramatic results. The standard pressure at sea level (1013 mb) decreases to about 848 mb at Banff, Alberta, whose elevation is 1476 m. At the highest elevations at adjacent Lake Louise (2637 m), the air pressure is approximately 750 mb. On top of the world's tallest peak—Mount Everest in South Asia's Himalayas, elevation 8850 m—the pressure is only 320 mb.

Because air pressure depends on the number of molecules in motion and is highest in the lower atmospheric layers, we may deduce that most of the molecules are concentrated near the Earth's surface. This is confirmed in Fig. 9.2, which graphs the percentage of the total mass of the atmosphere below certain elevations. For example, 50 percent of the air of the atmosphere is

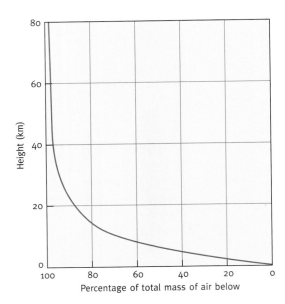

FIGURE 9.2 Mass of the atmosphere as a function of height. A greater proportion of the atmosphere is concentrated near the Earth's surface. Atmospheric pressure depends on mass, so it also decreases with altitude.

found below 5 km, and 85 percent lies within 16 km of the surface.

Air Movement in the Atmosphere

Since the days when it became common for sailing ships to make transoceanic voyages, people have known that the large-scale winds of the planet flow in certain generalized patterns. This information was vital in planning the routes of voyages that might take two or three

years. However, it was often of little assistance in guiding the ships through the more localized, smaller-scale winds that fluctuate from day to day and place to place. It is therefore useful to separate large-scale air movement from smaller-scale movement, even though the two are related to the same phenomenon—atmospheric pressure. We begin by considering the causes, and resultant patterns, of the large-scale movement of air that is in contact with the surface of the Earth.

Causes of Atmospheric Circulation

Two basic factors explain the circulation of air in the atmosphere: (1) the Earth receives an unequal amount of heat energy at different latitudes, and (2) it rotates on its axis. If we examine the amount of incoming and outgoing radiation by latitude, as shown in Fig. 9.3 for the Northern Hemisphere (the Southern Hemisphere's general pattern is identical), we find that there is a marked surplus of net radiation between the Equator and the 35th parallel. At latitudes poleward of 35°N, outgoing radiation exceeds incoming radiation. The main reason for this is that rays of energy from the Sun strike the Earth's surface at higher angles, and therefore at greater intensity, in the lower latitudes than in the higher latitudes (see Fig. 5.8). As a result, the Equator receives about two and one-half times as much annual solar radiation as the poles do.

If this latitudinal imbalance of energy were not somehow balanced, the low-latitude regions would be continually heating up and the polar regions cooling down. Energy, in the form of heat, is transferred toward the poles, and the amount of heat transferred by atmospheric circulation (and to a much lesser extent, oceanic circulation) is also indicated in Fig. 9.3. We can

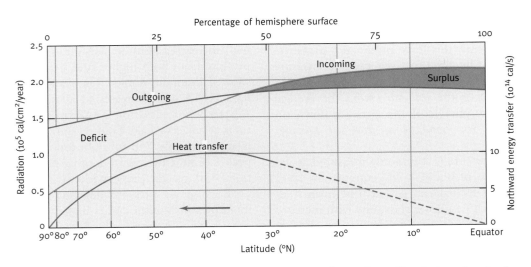

FIGURE 9.3 Latitudinal radiation balance averaged over all Northern Hemisphere longitudes and the consequent poleward transfer of heat.

see from the heat-transfer curve that the maximum transfer occurs in the middle latitudes. Thus the weather at these latitudes is characterized by frequent north–south movements of air masses.

Imagine for a moment that the Earth is stationary and that there are no thermal differences between land-masses and oceans. Under these circumstances, heat transfer could occur by a simple cellular movement: warm air would rise at low latitudes, travel toward the poles at a high altitude, descend as it cools, and then return to the low latitudes as a surface wind. This type of circulation, however, is prohibited by the rotation of the Earth and the differing energy-absorbing characteristics of land and water.

Strange as it may seem, the simple rotation of the Earth complicates the operation of the general atmospheric circulation. The most important effect is expressed as an apparent deflective force. An understanding of the nature of this force is best approached by an analogy. Suppose you are riding on a moving merry-go-round and try to throw a ball to a friend riding across from you; but when you throw the ball straight at your friend, it travels toward the outside of the merry-go-round. This happens because between the time you release the ball and the time it would have reached your friend, your friend is no longer where he or she was when you released the ball. To you, it appeared that the ball was deflected to the right of its intended path (assuming that the merry-go-round was spinning counterclockwise when viewed from above). But to an observer standing next to the merry-go-round, the ball travelled in a straight path.

This deflective force affecting movement on a rotating body is called the **Coriolis force**. As noted in Unit 5, anything that moves over the surface of our spinning planet—from stream currents to missiles to air particles—is subjected to the Coriolis force. In the absence of any other forces, moving objects are deflected to their *right* in the Northern Hemisphere and to their *left* in the Southern Hemisphere. Thus if a wind is blowing from the North Pole, it would be deflected to the right and become an easterly wind (Fig. 9.4). (Note that this easterly wind blows toward the west: *winds are always named according to the direction from which they come.*) A little later we will see how the Coriolis force plays a major role in determining the general pattern of atmospheric circulation. First, the actual forces involved in windflow will be described.

Forces on an Air Molecule

The Earth's energy imbalance and its rotation may be regarded as the foremost causes of the general circulation of the atmosphere. However, specific wind speed and

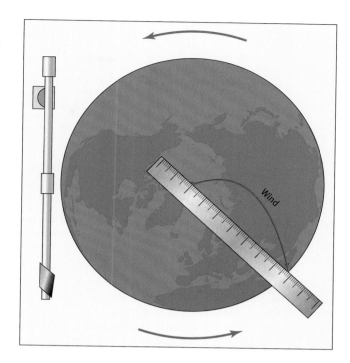

FIGURE 9.4 Coriolis force in action. The North Pole on a map of the Northern Hemisphere is placed over the spindle of a record turntable, which is spun in a counterclockwise direction to simulate the Earth's rotation. A line starting from the pole and drawn along the edge of a stationary ruler (on the Earth rotating beneath the ruler) describes an arc and ends up travelling toward the west.

direction are determined by three forces: (1) the pressure-gradient force, (2) the Coriolis force, and (3) the frictional force.

The **pressure-gradient force** is the actual trigger for the movement of air. Gravity causes the air to press down against the surface of the Earth; this is atmospheric pressure. The pressure, however, may be different at two locations. The difference in surface pressure over a given distance between two locations is called the *pressure gradient*. When there is a pressure gradient, it acts as a force that causes air to move from the place of higher pressure to that of lower pressure. This force, called the pressure-gradient force, increases as the difference in air pressure across a specified distance increases. The most common cause of the differences in air pressure is differences in air temperature, which, in turn, cause differences in air density. Warm air is less dense and tends to rise, lowering surface pressure as the the inflow of air near the surface exceeds the outflow of air at higher altitudes. On the other hand, cold air tends to sink, reinforcing and raising surface pressure as the inflow aloft exceeds the outflow near the surface (Fig. 9.5).

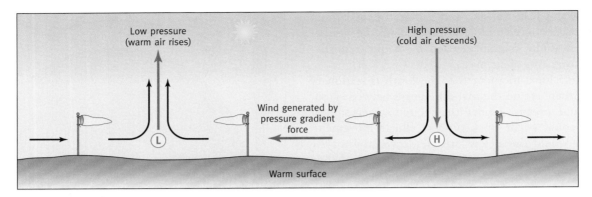

FIGURE 9.5 Air movement at the surface is always from areas of higher pressure (**H**) toward areas of lower pressure (**L**). The greater the pressure difference between **H** and **L**, the higher the pressure gradient and the stronger the wind.

We are already familiar with the *Coriolis force,* which acts to deflect moving air to the right (Northern Hemisphere) or left (Southern Hemisphere). Here we need only to note two further observations. First, the Coriolis force is not constant, but is greatest at the poles and decreases as one approaches the Equator (Fig. 9.6). Second, we can deduce that it will be significant only over fairly large distances, since it is dependent on the rotation of the Earth.

Finally some of the motion of the air in the atmosphere takes place very near the Earth's surface. Thus, the closer individual air molecules are to the surface, the more they are slowed by drag, or a **frictional force**.

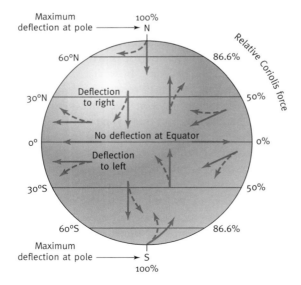

FIGURE 9.6 Latitudinal variation in the Coriolis force. Deflection is zero at the Equator, increases with latitude, and is most pronounced at each pole. (Note the percentages along the right of the globe.)

The magnitude of the frictional force depends primarily on the "roughness" of the surface. There is less friction with movement across a smooth snow or water surface than across mountainous terrain or the ragged skyline of a metropolitan area.

How do these three forces act together in the atmosphere? Collectively, they determine the pattern of windflow within any area—something that impinges upon a wide range of human activities (see Perspective: Air Pressure and Wind in Our Daily Lives).

Large- and Smaller-Scale Wind Systems

Except for local winds (which affect only relatively small areas) and those near the Equator, the wind never blows in a straight path from an area of higher pressure to an area of lower pressure. Once motion begins, the pressure-gradient, Coriolis, and frictional forces come into play and heavily influence the direction of windflow.

Geostrophic Winds

Once a molecule of air starts moving under the influence of a pressure-gradient force, the Coriolis force deflects it to the right if it is in the Northern Hemisphere. Fig. 9.7 diagrams the path that results: eventually, the pressure-gradient force and the Coriolis force acting on the wind balance each other out. The resultant wind, called a **geostrophic wind**, follows a relatively straight path that minimizes deflection. Geostrophic windflow is common in the "free" atmosphere, that is, above the contact layer where friction with the surface occurs. Because of the balancing of forces, a geostrophic wind always

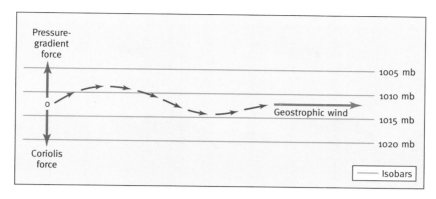

FIGURE 9.7 Formation of a geostrophic wind in the Northern Hemisphere, looking directly down toward the surface.

PERSPECTIVES ON THE HUMAN ENVIRONMENT

Air Pressure and Wind in Our Daily Lives

We all bear the weight of the atmosphere pressing down on us. At sea level, the air pressure can be from 9 to 18 metric tons, depending on our size. Like the deep-sea creatures who live their entire lives with the weight of hundreds of metres of water above them, we have adapted to functioning and moving efficiently in our particular environmental pressure zone. Only a sharp change—such as a Prince Edward Island sea-level flatlander taking a vacation trip high in British Columbia's Rocky Mountains—reminds us of our adjustment to, and dependence on, a specific atmospheric environment. Two factors influence this sensitivity to altitude.

The first is the density of air molecules, particularly oxygen, at any altitude. At higher elevations the air is "thinner"; that is, there is more space between the oxygen molecules, and consequently there are fewer of them in any given air space. We have to do more breathing to get the oxygen necessary to maintain our activity levels. When the Olympic Games were held in Mexico City in 1968, the low density of oxygen at that elevation (2240 m) was a decisive factor in the unimpressive competition times recorded by most of the participating athletes.

The second factor is the response of our internal organs to changes in atmospheric pressure. Our ears may react first as we climb to higher

elevations. The "pop" we hear is actually the clearing of a tiny tube that allows pressure between the inner and middle ear to equalize, thereby preventing our eardrums from rupturing. At very high altitudes we travel in pressurized aircraft. Astronauts also use pressurized cabins, and when they leave their vehicles for walks in atmosphere-less space, they require spacesuits to maintain a safe pressurized (and breathing) environment.

Winds play a constant role in our lives as well because they are a major element of local weather and climate. In coastal areas or on islands, atmospheric conditions can vary considerably over short distances. Oceanfront zones facing the direction of oncoming wind experience more air movement, cloudiness, and moisture than nearby locations protected from this airflow by hills or mountains. Places exposed to wind are called **windward** locations; areas in the "shadow" of protecting topographic barriers are known as **leeward** locations.

The west coast of Canada provides an excellent example to illustrate these differences. There is a distinct difference in the climates of Vancouver Island in the region of Victoria and the city of Vancouver. As wind rises over the Olympic Mountains and the ridge of hills and mountains over Vancouver Island, the air cools and moisture condenses. As the air descends on the leeward (east) side of the ranges, it warms and clouds dissipate, result-

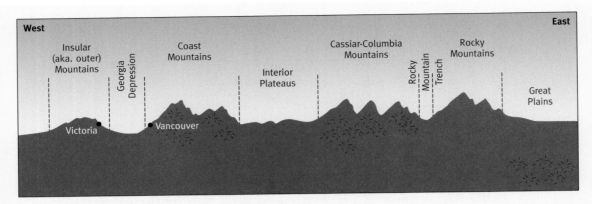

FIGURE 9.8   West coast of British Columbia, in profile. The windward slope facing the Pacific experiences more moisture and cloudiness than the leeward slope.

ing in less precipitation. The city of Vancouver is located at the base of the Coast Range. Air flows over the Olympic Range and Vancouver Island, descends over the Georgia Basin, and then rises again to flow over the Coast Range. The second rise squeezes more precipitation from the air and gives Vancouver more annual precipitation than Victoria (Fig.9.8). Moving further inland to Kamloops (258 km from the Pacific Ocean), one finds

an even greater extreme. Movement over the Coastal Mountain barrier further condenses water vapour from the moist Westerlies, resulting in the area that extends up the Thompson River Valley being one of the driest in Southern Canada. The climate in this region is semi-arid and borders on desert.

At another place and time, a similar windward/leeward relationship helped shape the locational

Table 9.1 Wind Chill Temperature Index

Temperature (°C)

T air	5	0	−5	−10	−15	−20	−25	−30	−35	−40	−45	−50
5	4	−2	−7	−13	−19	−24	−30	−36	−41	−47	−53	−58
10	3	−3	−9	−15	−21	−27	−33	−39	−45	−51	−57	−63
15	2	−4	−11	−17	−23	−29	−35	−41	−48	−54	−60	−66
20	1	−5	−12	−18	−24	−30	−37	−43	−49	−56	−62	−68
25	1	−6	−12	−19	−25	−32	−38	−44	−51	−57	−64	−70
30	0	−6	−13	−20	−26	−33	−39	−46	−52	−59	−65	−72
35	0	−7	−14	−20	−27	−33	−40	−47	−53	−60	−66	−73
40	−1	−7	−14	−21	−27	−34	−41	−48	−54	−61	−68	−74
45	−1	−8	−15	−21	−28	−35	−42	−48	−55	−62	−69	−75
50	−1	−8	−15	−22	−29	−35	−42	−49	−56	−63	−69	−76
55	−2	−8	−15	−22	−29	−36	−43	−50	−57	−63	−70	−77
60	−2	−9	−16	−23	−30	−36	−43	−50	−57	−64	−71	−78
65	−2	−9	−16	−23	−30	−37	−44	−51	−58	−65	−72	−79
70	−2	−9	−16	−23	−30	−37	−44	−51	−58	−65	−72	−80
75	−3	−10	−17	−24	−31	−38	−45	−52	−59	−66	−73	−80
80	−3	−10	−17	−24	−31	−38	−45	−52	−60	−67	−74	−81

V10 (row label axis, left side)

☐ Low risk of frostbite for most people

☐ Increasing risk of frostbite for most people in 10 to 30 minutes of exposure

☐ High risk for most people in 5 to 10 minutes of exposure

☐ High risk for most people in 2 to 5 minutes of exposure

☐ High risk for most people in 2 minutes of exposure or less

Frostbite Guide

Source: Environment Canada, June 10, 2004. (website URL given at end of this Perspective box)

pattern of the textile industry in nineteenth-century Britain. West of England's "backbone" of the Pennine Mountains, in Lancashire, the humid air transported in from the Atlantic Ocean by westerly winds was ideal for cotton-textile manufacturing. Woollen-textile manufacturing, however, required a drier environment, which was readily available to the east in Yorkshire on the leeward side of the moisture-screening Pennines.

There are countless other examples of associations between wind and human activities. As we note in Unit 8, the horizontal flushing effects of wind are vital to maintaining acceptable air quality in urban areas, where large quantities of pollutants are dumped into the local atmosphere. Many outdoor sporting events are affected by wind conditions during games. For example, certain baseball stadiums are infamous for their unpredictable wind currents. San Francisco's now retired Candlestick Park (located in the lee of the peninsula alongside the Bay) was notorious in this regard; and in the "Windy City" of Chicago, Cubs games are constantly subject to wind influences at venerable Wrigley Field. Canadian football fans will also be aware of the potential problems at the Saskatchewan Roughriders' Taylor Field. Some CFL players say it is the worst place to kick because of the often strong and unpredictable winds.

The reinforcing effects of wind on cold winter temperatures continue to be an unpleasant fact of life. To give us a precise idea of how cold we would feel under given combinations of wind speed and air temperature, scientists have developed the **wind chill temperature (WCT) index**, which is displayed in Table 9.1. Although it does not take into account evaporative heat loss and the amount of protective clothing we wear, this index is closely related to the occurrence of frostbite. The WCT index, therefore, applies mainly to sensible heat loss. It is also based on the latest research findings and was introduced in late 2001 to replace an older, less precise index. The new wind chill index approximates how the temperature of the human skin (especially the face) changes with various temperature and wind conditions. The index was verified at a Department of Defence lab in Toronto when 12 volunteers (six men and six women) underwent clinical trials in a refrigerated wind tunnel. Wind chill can have serious effects on the human body, especially as temperatures fall below approximately 17°C. According to Statistics Canada, 111 Canadians died in 1997 from the effects of cold weather. The coldest wind chill ever recorded in Canada was at Pelly Bay, Nunavut, on January 13, 1975. Fifty-six km/h winds made the temperature of −51°C feel closer to −92°C! Additional information, including a wind chill calculator for any given temperature and wind speed, can be found at http://www.msc.ec.gc.ca/education/windchill/index_e.cfm.

flows *parallel* to the **isobars**—lines that join points of equal atmospheric pressure (Fig. 9.7). If we have a map showing the distribution of atmospheric pressure well above the surface, we can get a rather good idea of where these winds are blowing (as we shall see in Unit 15). We can, moreover, predict the wind speed if we also know the pressure-gradient force, the air density, and the latitude (which determines the strength of the Coriolis force; see Fig. 9.6).

Frictional Surface Winds

Near the surface of the Earth, below an elevation of about 1000 m, frictional force comes into play and disrupts the balance represented by the geostrophic wind. Friction both reduces the speed and alters the direction of a geostrophic wind. The frictional force acts in such a way as to cause the pressure-gradient force to overpower the Coriolis force, so that the (no-longer-geostrophic)

wind at the surface blows *across* the isobars instead of parallel to them. This produces a flow of air out of high-pressure areas and into low-pressure areas, but at an angle to the isobars rather than straight across them.

Since surface pressure systems are often roughly circular when viewed from above, we can deduce the general circulation around cells of low and high pressure (Fig. 9.9). Surface winds converge toward a **cyclone** (a low-pressure cell—**L** in Fig. 9.9A); this converging air has to go somewhere, so it rises vertically in the centre of the low-pressure cell. The reverse is true in the centre of an **anticyclone** (a high-pressure cell—**H** in Fig. 9.9B); diverging air moves outward and draws air down in the centre of the high-pressure cell (see also Fig. 9.5). Thus cyclones are associated with *rising air* at their centres, and anticyclones are associated with *subsiding air* at their centres. This simple vertical motion produces very different weather associated with each type of pressure system.

CANADIAN GEOGRAPHERS IN THE FIELD

"This photo shows *Nothofagus*, near Harberton, Tierra del Fuego, Argentina. *Nothofagus* is the only tree genus present in Tierra del Fuego. The forms of the tree vary greatly with the local climate conditions that they are exposed to, including temperature, snow loading, and prevailing wind speed and direction. This tree was shaped by the prevailing westerly winds in southern Tierra del Fuego, causing it to grow eastward over time. In the local Spanish vernacular, these are referred to as 'flag trees'. By sampling the rings of the tree using a small-diameter borer (which doesn't harm it), the changing climate conditions during the lifetime of the tree can be studied."

Norm Catto is Professor of Geography,
Memorial University of Newfoundland.

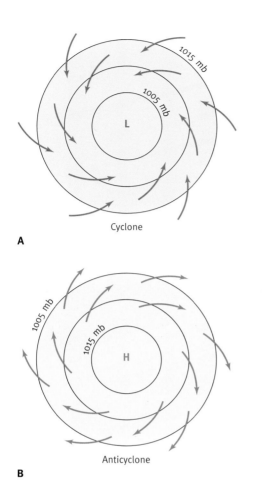

FIGURE 9.9 Air circulation patterns associated with a cyclonic low-pressure cell (A) and an anticyclonic high-pressure cell (B) in the Northern Hemisphere. In the Southern Hemisphere the windflows move in the opposite direction (clockwise toward cyclones and counterclockwise away from anticyclones).

Local Wind Systems

Although one cannot overlook the forces outlined in the preceding when attention is focused on small-scale airflows, local wind systems are often more significant in day-to-day weather because they respond to much more subtle variations in atmospheric pressure than are depicted in Fig. 9.9. Moreover, because smaller distances are involved, the effect of the Coriolis force can usually be disregarded. A number of common local wind systems serve to illustrate how topography and surface type can influence the pressure gradient and its resultant windflow.

Sea/Land Breeze Systems

In coastal zones and on islands, two different surface types are in close proximity—land and water. As we have noted before, land surfaces and water bodies display sharply contrasting thermal responses to energy input.

Land surfaces heat and cool rapidly, whereas water bodies exhibit a more moderate temperature regime.

During the day a land surface heats up quickly, and the air layer in contact with it rises in response to the increased air temperature. This rising air produces a low-pressure cell over the coastal land or island. Since the air over the adjacent water is cooler, it subsides to produce a surface high-pressure cell. A pressure gradient is thereby produced, and air in contact with the surface now moves from high pressure to low pressure. Thus during the day, shore-zone areas generally experience air moving from water to land—a **sea breeze** (Fig. 9.10A). At night, when the temperature above the land surface has dropped sufficiently, the circulation reverses because the warmer air (and lower pressure) is now over the water. This results in air moving from land to water—a **land breeze** (Fig. 9.10B).

Note that when generated, sea and land breezes produce a circulation cell composed of the surface breeze, rising and subsiding air associated with the lower- and higher-pressure areas, respectively, and an airflow aloft in the direction opposite to that of the surface (Fig. 9.10). Although it modifies the wind and temperature conditions at the coast, the effect of this circulation diminishes rapidly as one moves inland. Note also that we use the word *breeze*. This accurately depicts a rather gentle circulation in response to a fairly weak pressure gradient. The sea breeze/land breeze phenomenon can easily be overpowered if stronger pressure systems are nearby. Figure 9.11 illustrates the distribution of wind speeds in Canada (1971–2000), indicating the influence of the coastal environment on higher winds.

Mountain/Valley Breeze Systems

Mountain slopes, too, are subject to the reversal of day and night local circulation systems. This wind circulation is also thermal, meaning that it is driven by temperature differences between adjacent topographic features. During the day, mountain terrain facing the Sun tends to heat up more rapidly than do shadowed, surrounding slopes. This causes low pressure to develop, spawning an upsloping *valley breeze*. At night, greater radiative loss from the mountain slopes cools them more sharply, high pressure develops, and a downsloping *mountain breeze* results. Figure 9.12 shows the operation of this type of oscillating, diurnal wind system in a highland valley that gently rises away from the front of the diagram.

Other Local Wind Systems

Another category of local wind systems involves **cold-air drainage**, the steady downward oozing of heavy,

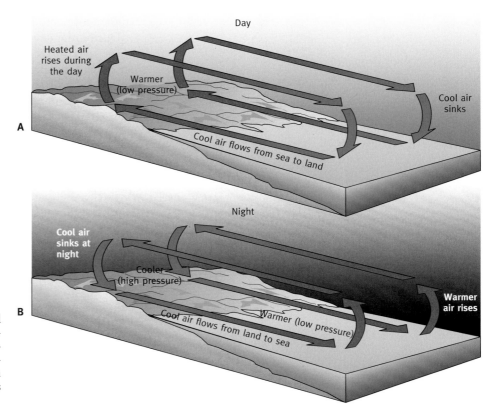

FIGURE 9.10 Sea breeze/land breeze local air circulation systems. These reversing, cell-like airflows develop in response to pressure differentials associated with day/night temperature variations at the land and water surfaces.

dense, cold air along steep slopes under the influence of gravity. The winds that result are known as **katabatic winds** and are especially prominent under calm, clear conditions where the edges of highlands plunge sharply toward lower-lying terrain. These winds are fed by large pools of very cold air that collect above highland zones. They are also common around major ice sheets, such as the huge, continental-scale glaciers that cover most of Antarctica and Greenland.

Katabatic winds can attain destructive intensities when the regional windflow steers the cold air over the steep edges of uplands, producing a cascade of air much like water in a waterfall. The most damaging winds of this type occur where local topography channels the downward surge of cold air into narrow, steep-sided valleys. The Rhône Valley of southeastern France is a notable example: each winter it experiences icy, high-velocity winds (known locally as the *mistral* winds) that drain the massive pool of cold air that develops atop the snowy French and Swiss Alps to the valley's northeast.

Yet another type of local wind system is associated with the forced passage of air across mountainous terrain (which is discussed in detail in Unit 13). Briefly, this transmontane movement wrings out most of the moisture contained in the original mass of air, and it also warms the air adiabatically as it plunges downward after

its passage across the upland. Thus the area that extends away from the base of the mountain's backslope experiences dry and relatively warm winds, which taper off with increasing distance from the highland. Occasionally such winds can exceed hurricane-force intensity (greater than 120 km/h). This happens when they are reinforced by an anticyclone upwind from the mountains that feeds air into a cyclone located on the downwind side of the upland.

Surprisingly, atmospheric scientists have yet to provide a generic name for such wind systems, which still go only by their local names. The best known Canadian example is the **chinook wind**, which occurs on the (eastern) downwind side of the Rocky Mountains along the western edge of the Prairies. Chinook is a Native American word meaning "snow eater," in reference to its ability to melt winter snow over a short time. The chinook is a type of *foehn* wind, which means that it has been warmed and dried by its descent off a slope. The chinook effects are most strongly felt in southwestern Alberta, where the chinooks funnel through the Crowsnest Pass, subsequently moving out across southern Alberta and Saskatchewan. There are approximately 30 chinook days each winter in the Crowsnest Pass, 25 in Calgary, and 20 in Medicine Hat. Another well-known example is the **Santa Ana wind** of coastal South-

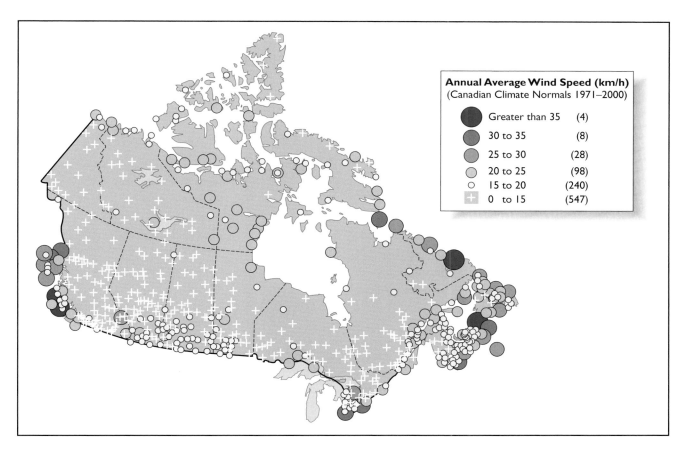

FIGURE 9.11   The distribution of wind speeds in Canada (1971–2000), indicating the influence of the coastal environment on higher winds.

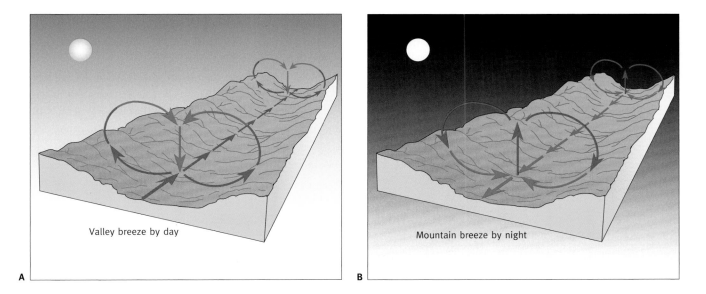

FIGURE 9.12   Formation of valley (daytime) and mountain (nighttime) breezes. Red arrows represent warm winds; blue arrows indicate colder winds.

ern California, an occasional hot, dry airflow whose unpleasantness is heightened by the downward funnelling of this wind from the high inland desert (where it is generated by an anticyclone) through narrow passes in the mountains that line the coast. Such winds can also exacerbate wildfires during the dry season.

In many locations, as we have just seen, local winds can at times become more prominent than larger-scale airflows. But the regional expressions of the global system of wind currents still play a far more important role overall. That is the subject of Unit 10, which investigates the general circulation of the atmosphere.

KEY TERMS

anticyclone *page 115*

barometer *page 109*

chinook wind *page 118*

cold-air drainage *page 117*

Coriolis force *page 111*

cyclone *page 115*

frictional force *page 112*

geostrophic wind *page 112*

isobar *page 115*

katabatic wind *page 118*

land breeze *page 117*

leeward *page 113*

pressure *page 109*

pressure-gradient force *page 111*

Santa Ana wind *page 118*

sea breeze *page 117*

wind *page 109*

wind chill temperature (WCT) index *page 115*

windward *page 113*

REVIEW QUESTIONS

1. Define atmospheric pressure, and describe its vertical structuring within the atmospheric column.

2. What are the forces that determine wind speed and direction?

3. Define the Coriolis force and describe its operations in both the Northern and Southern Hemispheres.

4. What is a *geostrophic* wind? Where does it occur and why?

5. Describe the air circulation patterns associated with cyclones and anticyclones.

6. Describe the operation of the sea breeze/land breeze local wind system.

REFERENCES AND FURTHER READINGS

ATKINSON, B. W. *Meso-Scale Atmospheric Circulations* (New York: Academic Press, 1981).

DUTTON, J. A. *The Ceaseless Wind: An Introduction to the Theory of Atmospheric Motion* (New York: McGraw-Hill, 1976).

DUTTON, J. A. *Dynamics of Atmospheric Motion* (New York: Dover, 1995).

EDINGER, J. G. *Watching for the Wind* (Garden City, N.Y.: Doubleday, 1967).

GEDZELMAN, S. D. *The Science and Wonders of the Atmosphere* (New York: Wiley, 1980), chapter 15.

GLANZ, J. "Wind Chill: Cheer Up, It Used to Be Even Colder," *New York Times* (November 25, 2001), WK3.

GROSS, J. "When the Fog Rolls In, the Bay Area Hears Music," *New York Times* (June 22, 1988), 10.

HIDY, G. M. *The Winds* (New York: Van Nostrand-Reinhold, 1967).

MIDDLETON, W. K. *The History of the Barometer* (Baltimore, Md.: Johns Hopkins Univ. Press, 1964).

PALMÉN, E., and NEWTON, C. W. *Atmospheric Circulation Systems* (New York: Academic Press, 1969).

SIMPSON, J. E. *Sea Breeze and Local Winds* (New York: Cambridge Univ. Press, 1994).

"The Santa Ana Winds," *New York Times* (October 29, 1993), A10.

"Where the Wind Blows," *Scientific American* (December 1996), 44.

WHITEMAN, C. D. *Mountain Meteorology: Fundamentals and Applications* (New York: Oxford Univ. Press, 2000).

"Wind Chill," *CBC News* (January 20, 2004) Online (http://www.cbc.ca/news/background/forcesofnature/windchill.htm).

WEB RESOURCES

http://nasaui.ited.uidaho.edu/nasaspark/safety/weather/atmosphere.html   Explanation of driving forces in the atmosphere that create air movement.

http://www.cmc.ec.gc.ca/rpn/modcom/eole/CanadianAtlas.htm   Environment Canada's Canadian Wind Atlas.

http://www.doc.mmu.ac.uk/aric/eae/Weather/Older/Pressure.html   General description of atmospheric pressure measurement, global movement of air masses, and links to other weather-related topics.

http://www.on.gc.ca/weather/winners/intro-e.html   How does your city or town rank among the rainiest, sunniest, windiest, or snowiest?

Circulation Patterns of the Atmosphere

Action in the atmosphere—cloud formation over Easter Island in the South Pacific Ocean. (Authors' photo)

OBJECTIVES

- To develop a simple model of the global atmospheric circulation
- To discuss the pressure systems and wind belts that constitute that model
- circulation and the complications that arise when the model is compared to the actual atmospheric circulation
- To introduce the basic workings of the upper atmosphere's circulation

Unit 9 introduced the basic causes of air movements in the atmosphere. In this unit focus is placed on the global air currents that constitute the general atmospheric circulation. In the short run these air currents carry along, and to a certain extent cause, the weather systems that affect us daily. The longer-term operation of this general circulation, in conjunction with atmospheric energy flows, produces the climates of the Earth.

To be sure, the workings of the general atmospheric circulation are very complex, and scientists still do not understand the exact nature of some of these circulation features. Nonetheless, we can deduce many of these features using our knowledge of the basic causes of air movement, which can be used to develop a model to describe and explain the major processes. Let us begin by considering the atmosphere's near-surface circulation, and then make some observations regarding windflow in the upper atmosphere.

A Model of the Surface Circulation

Unit 9 illustrated the probable arrangement of the global atmospheric circulation on a uniform, nonrotating Earth: a single, girdling cell of low pressure around the Equator, where air would rise, and a cell of high pressure at each pole, where air would subside. The surface winds on such a planet would be northerly in the Northern Hemisphere and southerly in the Southern Hemisphere, moving directly from high pressure to low pressure across the pressure gradient, as shown in Fig. 10.1.

We might further speculate that adding the rotation of the Earth to this simple model would produce surface northeasterly winds in the Northern Hemisphere (as the air moving toward the Equator was deflected to the right) and southeasterly winds in the Southern Hemisphere. In fact, such a model would be "unstable," breaking down because of one simple problem: achievement of this scenario would require slowing down the Earth's rate of spin, since everywhere on the planet the atmosphere would be moving *against* the direction of Earth rotation. As it turns out, there are areas of low pressure at the Equator and high pressure at the poles, but the situation in the midlatitudes is more complex.

We will now introduce the actual effects of rotation on our hypothetical planet but, for the time being, will ignore seasonal heating differences and the land/water contrast at the surface. The model that results is an idealized but reasonable generalization of the surface circulation pattern, and its elaboration that follows is keyed to Fig. 10.2.

The Equatorial Low and Subtropical High

Year-round heating in the equatorial region produces a thermal low-pressure belt in this latitudinal zone.

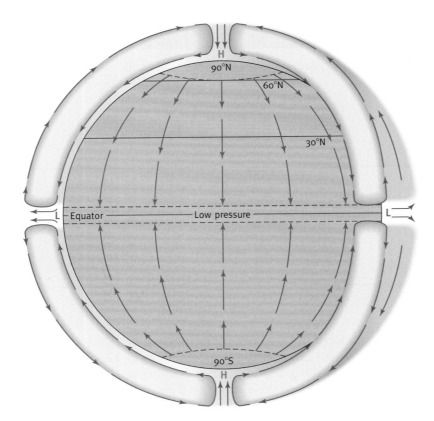

FIGURE 10.1 Hypothetical atmospheric circulation on a featureless, nonrotating Earth. Polar high pressure and equatorial low pressure would result in northerly surface winds in the Northern Hemisphere and southerly surface winds in the Southern Hemisphere. The rotation of the Earth, the variation in the latitude of the vertical Sun position, and land/water heating contrasts at the surface prevent this simple general circulation from developing.

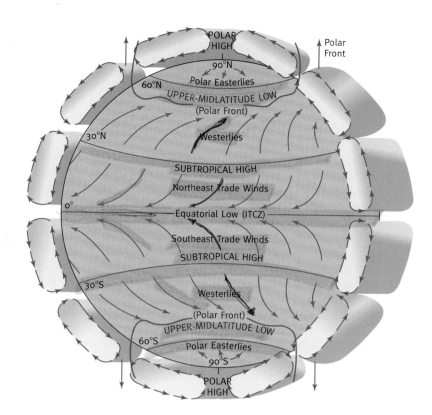

FIGURE 10.2 Idealized version of the global atmospheric circulation pattern showing the major pressure belts, the cell-like airflows that develop between them, and the Coriolis deflection of surface winds.

That belt of rising air is called the **Equatorial Low** or **Inter-Tropical Convergence Zone (ITCZ)**. (The reason for this latter terminology will become evident shortly.) The air rises from the surface to the tropopause and flows poleward in both the Northern and Southern Hemispheres.

Much of this now-cooled, poleward-moving air descends at approximately latitudes 30°N and 30°S. (Subsidence here is most likely associated with the "piling up" of air aloft because of its increased westerly flow, a directional curvature caused by the strengthening Coriolis force; see Fig. 9.6.) The descending air produces a belt of high pressure at the surface near both these latitudes; the two high-pressure belts, understandably, are termed the **Subtropical Highs**.

The Trade Winds and the Westerlies

Remembering that surface airflows diverge out of areas of high pressure, we can easily deduce the nature of the wind movement, both equatorward and poleward, of this high-pressure belt. Air returning toward the Equator in the Northern Hemisphere is deflected to the right and forms a belt of northeasterly winds, called the **Northeast Trades** (see Perspective: The Sailor's Legacy—Naming the Winds). Air returning toward the Equator from the Subtropical High in the Southern Hemisphere is deflected to its left to form the **Southeast**

Trades. As you can see in Fig. 10.2, these two wind belts converge—hence the rationale for calling this low-latitude area the *Inter-Tropical Convergence Zone*.

Air moving poleward from the two Subtropical Highs acquires the appropriate Coriolis deflection and forms two belts of generally west-to-east–flowing winds (one in the Northern Hemisphere, one in the Southern Hemisphere) known as the **Westerlies**. These prevailing winds form broad midlatitude belts from about 30 to 60°N and 30 to 60°S.

The Polar High, Polar Easterlies, and Polar Front

Windflows emanate from the **Polar Highs**, large cells of high pressure centred over each pole. Here, air moving toward the Equator is sharply deflected to become the **Polar Easterlies**. You can see in Fig. 10.2 that the Polar Easterlies flowing out of the Polar Highs will meet the Westerlies flowing out of the Subtropical Highs.

The atmospheric boundary along which these wind systems converge is called the **Polar Front**. Along the Polar Front in each hemisphere (located equatorward of 60°N and 60°S, respectively), the warmer air from the Subtropical High is forced to rise over the colder, and thus denser, polar air. This rising air produces a belt of low pressure at the surface called the **Upper-Midlatitude Low**.

Overall, the now completed model of the surface circulation for a uniform, rotating planet has seven pressure

PERSPECTIVES ON THE HUMAN ENVIRONMENT

The Sailor's Legacy—Naming the Winds

Spanish sea captains headed to the Caribbean and the Philippines in search of gold, spices, and new colonial territory for the crown. They depended on a band of steady winds to fill the sails of their galleons as they journeyed westward in the tropics. Those winds were named the trade winds, or the *trades*. These were the winds that first blew Christopher Columbus and his flotilla to North America in 1492.

In the vicinity of the Equator, the Northern and Southern Hemisphere Trades converge in a zone of unpredictable breezes and calm seas. Sailors dreaded being caught in these so-called *doldrums*. A ship stranded here might drift aimlessly for days. That was the fate of the ship described in these famous lines from Samuel Taylor Coleridge's *The Rime of the Ancient Mariner*:

Day after day, day after day,
We stuck, nor breath nor motion;
As idle as a painted ship
Upon a painted ocean.

Ships also were becalmed by the light and variable winds in the subtropics at about latitudes 30°N and 30°S. Spanish explorers who ran afoul of the breezes in these hot regions threw their horses overboard to lighten their loads and save water for the crew. The trail of floating corpses caused navigators of the seventeenth century to label this zone the *horse latitudes*.

In the middle latitudes of the Southern Hemisphere, ships heading eastward followed the strong westerly winds between 40 and 60°S. These winds were powerful but stormier than the trades to the north; so, depending on their approximate latitude, they became known as the *Roaring Forties*, the *Furious Fifties*, and the *Screaming Sixties*. Thus some important terminology that is still applied to wind belts dates from the early days of transoceanic sailing.

---

features (an Equatorial Low, two Subtropical Highs, two Upper-Midlatitude Lows, and two Polar Highs) and six intervening wind belts (the Northeast and Southeast Trades plus the Westerlies and Polar Easterlies of each hemisphere). Note that the circulation patterns of the Northern and Southern Hemispheres are identical except for the opposite Coriolis deflection (Fig. 10.2).

The Actual Surface Circulation Pattern

In contrast to the idealized pattern of the surface circulation model, the actual pattern (Fig. 10.3) is considerably more complex because it incorporates two influences ignored in the model. Remember that the location of maximum solar heating shifts throughout the year as the latitude of the (noonday) vertical Sun changes from 23½°N at the Northern Hemisphere's summer solstice to 23½°S at its winter solstice. Of great significance is that the continents respond more

dramatically to this latitudinal variation in heating than do the oceans (as we note in Unit 8). This has the effect of producing individual pressure cells (which we can call *semipermanent highs and lows*) rather than uniform, globe-girdling belts of low and high pressure. Moreover, because the Northern Hemisphere contains two large landmasses whereas the Southern Hemisphere is mostly water, the two hemispheres exhibit somewhat different atmospheric circulations. Nonetheless, they are similar enough to be considered together.

Climates are governed by complex interactions between atmospheric circulations and the movement and properties of oceanic waters. The Southern Oscillation, a variable pressure gradient in the equatorial zone of the Pacific Ocean, influences the formation and intensity of *El Niños* (both are discussed on pp. 140–141). Other pressure systems elsewhere also affect climate and weather. To understand these links, one must examine the prevailing global pressure patterns and then look more closely at embedded systems that govern climate as well as weather across the planet.

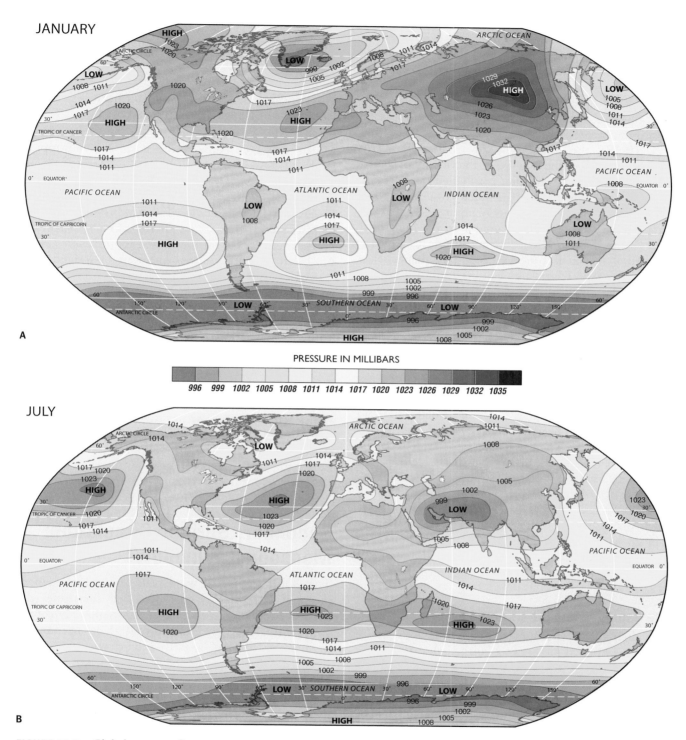

FIGURE 10.3   Global mean surface pressure patterns in January (A) and July (B). Maps adapted from *Goode's World Atlas,* 19th edition. © 1995 by Rand McNally R.L.

The Equatorial Low (ITCZ)

Careful inspection of Fig. 10.3 reveals the following modifications to the simplified picture seen in Fig. 10.2. The Equatorial Low, or ITCZ, migrates into the "summer" hemisphere (the Northern Hemisphere during July, the Southern Hemisphere during January), a shift most prominent over landmasses. Note that in July (Fig. 10.3B), the Equatorial Low is located nearly 25 degrees north of the Equator in the vicinity of southern Asia. But ITCZ migration is subdued over oceanic areas because bodies of water are much slower to respond to seasonal changes in solar energy input received at the surface. Note, too, that the migration of the Equatorial Low into the Southern Hemisphere in January (Fig. 10.3A) is far less pronounced. This makes sense because there are fewer large landmasses in the tropics south of the Equator; the Equatorial Low is, however, considerably displaced poleward over Africa and Australia, and to a lesser extent above South America.

The Bermuda and Pacific Highs

In contrast to our model's Subtropical High pressure belts (straddling 30°N and 30°S), the actual semipermanent highs at these latitudes are more cellular. There are five such cells on the map, one above each subtropical ocean (Fig. 10.3). These cells are most evident in the "summer" hemisphere. In the Northern Hemisphere, the North Atlantic's high-pressure cell is called the *Bermuda* (or Azores [Azoric]) *High,* and the North Pacific cell is referred to as the *Pacific* (or Hawaiian) *High.* These cells also shift north and south with the Sun, but to a much lesser extent, latitudinally, than the Equatorial Low. This again is due to the more subdued response of water to seasonal changes in solar energy receipt.

The Canadian and Siberian Highs

Now directing our attention to the polar regions, we see that the simplified picture of a Polar High centred over each pole needs considerable revision, particularly in the Northern Hemisphere, where the large landmasses of Eurasia and North America markedly protrude into the high latitudes. It is here that the seasonal cooling will be most extreme, rather than over the more northerly Arctic Ocean with its floating polar icecap. As a result, the Polar High in the Northern Hemisphere is actually two separate cells, a weaker cell centred above northwestern Canada (the *Canadian High*) and a much more powerful cell covering all of northern Asia (the *Siberian High*). Note, too, that these features are much stronger in winter and at their weakest during the summer (Fig. 10.3). In the Southern Hemisphere, because of

the dominance of the Antarctic landmass in the high latitudes, the model's single cell of high pressure over the pole is reasonably accurate.

The Aleutian, Icelandic, and Southern Hemisphere Upper-Midlatitude Lows

Finally, the actual configuration of the Upper-Midlatitude Low between the Polar and Subtropical Highs needs to be re-examined. In the Northern Hemisphere in January (Fig. 10.3A), when both the Polar and Subtropical Highs are apparent, the Upper-Midlatitude Low is well defined as two cells of low pressure, one over each subarctic ocean. These are the *Aleutian Low* in the northeastern Pacific off Alaska and the *Icelandic Low* in the North Atlantic centred just west of Iceland. The convergence and ascent of air within these cells are more complex than this still rather generalized map suggests. Therefore these features are covered in greater depth in the discussion of air masses and storm systems of the midlatitudes in Unit 14. For the time being we also note that these cells, too, weaken to the point of disintegration during the summer (Fig. 10.3B).

As for the Southern Hemisphere, note again on the map that the Upper-Midlatitude Low is evident in both winter and summer. The persistence of the Polar High over Antarctica makes this possible. Moreover, the absence of landmasses in this subpolar latitudinal zone causes the Upper-Midlatitude Low to remain beltlike rather than forming distinct cells over each ocean.

Secondary Surface Circulation: Monsoonal Windflows

The global scheme of wind belts and semipermanent pressure cells we have just described constitutes the **general circulation** (or *primary circulation*) system of the atmosphere. At a more localized scale, there are countless instances of "shifting" surface wind belts that create pronounced winter/summer contrasts in weather patterns. Here, to illustrate such regional (or *secondary*) circulation systems, one of the most spectacular examples—the Asian monsoon—will be described.

A **monsoon** (derived from *mawsim,* the Arabic word for season) is a regional wind that blows onto and off of certain landmasses on a seasonal basis. Monsoonal circulation occurs most prominently across much of southern and eastern Asia, where seasonal wind reversals produced by the shifting systems cause alternating wet and dry seasons. Specifically, the moist onshore winds of summer bring the *wet monsoon,* whereas the offshore winds of winter are associated with the *dry monsoon.*

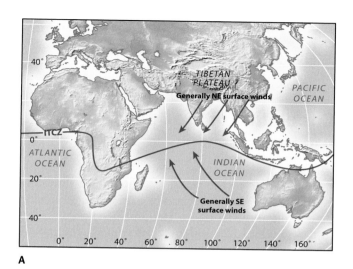

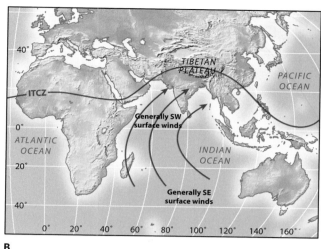

A

B

FIGURE 10.4 Wind reversals associated with the dry winter monsoon (A) and wet summer monsoon (B) in southern Asia. This phenomenon is usually most pronounced on the Indian subcontinent, one of the world's greatest concentrations of human settlement.

These reversing wind systems override the expected pattern of the general atmospheric circulation—and yet, as we are about to see, are still a part of it.

In January, high pressure over the interior of southern Asia (particularly the Indian subcontinent) produces northeasterly surface winds for much of the region (Fig. 10.4A). This cool continental air contains very little moisture, so precipitation during winter is at a minimum. But as spring gives way to summer, the high-pressure cell dissipates, and the ITCZ (Equatorial Low) shifts far northward to a position over the Tibetan Plateau. As a result, the airflow from the Southeast Trades now crosses the Equator and is recurved—by the opposite Coriolis deflection of the Northern Hemisphere—into a southwesterly flow (Fig. 10.4B).

This air has passed above most of the warm tropical Indian Ocean and therefore now possesses a very high moisture content. The arrival of this saturated air over the Indian subcontinent (further induced by a deepening low-pressure cell as the land surface heats during the spring) marks the onset of the wet summer monsoon, and precipitation is frequent and heavy. As a matter of fact, the world record one-month precipitation total is held by the town of Cherrapunji in the hills of northeastern India (see p. 239), where, in July 1861, 930 cm of rain fell. During the winter months of the dry monsoon, however, average precipitation values at Cherrapunji are normally on the order of 1 to 2 cm.

The southwestern wet monsoon consists of two main branches, as Fig. 10.5 shows. One branch penetrates the Bay of Bengal to Bangladesh and northeastern India, where it is pushed westward into the densely populated Ganges Plain of northern India by the Himalayan

mountain wall (Fig. 10.6). A second branch to the west of the subcontinent, with a tendency to split into two airflows, arrives from the Arabian Sea arm of the Indian Ocean. The rains from both branches gradually spread across much of the subcontinent, soak the farm fields, and replenish the wells.

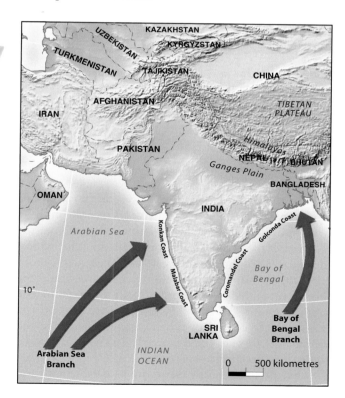

FIGURE 10.5 The main branches of the southwestern wet-monsoon windflow over South Asia.

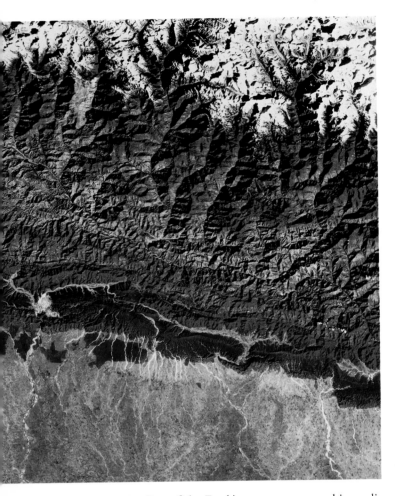

FIGURE 10.6 One of the Earth's steepest topographic gradients links the ice-capped Himalayas (top) to the plain of the Ganges River (bottom). This gigantic mountain barrier blocks the onshore windflow of the summer monsoon, steering it westward onto the Gangetic lowland, where its torrential rains nourish one of humanity's largest and most heavily populated agricultural regions.

These wet-monsoon rains, however, are not continuous, even during the wettest of years. Once the onshore wind movement is established, they depend on the recurrence of smaller-scale low-pressure cells within the prevailing southwesterly airflow. These depressions reinforce the lifting of the moist air, and enhance the formation and continuation of rain throughout the summer months. When they fail to materialize, disastrous drought can result. Their dramatic failure in the summer of 1987 triggered one of India's worst dry spells and crop losses of the past century.

This peculiar South Asian monsoonal circulation also owes its identity to subtle seasonal variations in the windflows of the upper atmosphere, especially the behaviour of the tropical, subtropical, and Polar Front

jet streams (which are introduced in the following section). In fact, the same is true everywhere: airflow patterns in the upper atmospheric circulation exert a decisive influence on what happens at the surface.

Circulation of the Upper Atmosphere

Windflow in the upper atmosphere is geostrophic (perpendicular to the pressure gradient, as shown in Fig. 9.7), with the higher pressure on the right looking downwind in the Northern Hemisphere and on the left in the Southern Hemisphere. Furthermore, the general circulation aloft is much simpler, since we lose the effects of the land/water contrast that made the surface pattern decidedly cellular. However, the specific nature of the upper atmospheric circulation is complex, and we will not attempt to explain how it is maintained, but rather will note some relevant generalizations.

First and foremost, the upper atmospheric circulation is dominated by **zonal flow**, meaning *westerly* in its configuration. Thus the winds of the upper atmosphere generally blow from west to east throughout a broad latitudinal band in both hemispheres; essentially, windflow is westerly poleward of 15°N and 15°S. But the pressure gradient in the upper atmosphere is not uniform, and two zones of concentrated westerly flow occur in each hemisphere: one in the subtropics and one along the Polar Front. These concentrated, high-altitude, tubelike "rivers" of air are called **jet streams**.

A cross-sectional profile of the atmosphere between the Equator and the North Pole (Fig. 10.7) reveals that these two jet streams—appropriately called the *subtropical jet stream* and the *Polar Front jet stream*—are located near the altitude of the tropopause (12 to 17 km). The diagram also shows the existence of a third jet stream, the *tropical easterly jet stream,* which is a major feature of the opposite, east-to-west flow in the upper atmosphere of the equatorial zone south of 15°N. Interestingly, the tropical easterly jet stream occurs in the Northern Hemisphere only, whereas the subtropical and Polar Front jet streams exist in both hemispheres. The two latter jet streams are instrumental in moving large quantities of heated air from the equatorial to higher latitudes. They usually flow at extremely high rates of speed (occasionally reaching 350 km/h), and can thus achieve the heat and volume transfers that could not be accomplished at the far more moderate velocities associated with the cell circulations depicted in Fig. 10.2. It should also be pointed out that the subtropical and Polar Front jet streams are at their strongest during the half-year centred on winter. You would be correct in presuming that the Polar Front

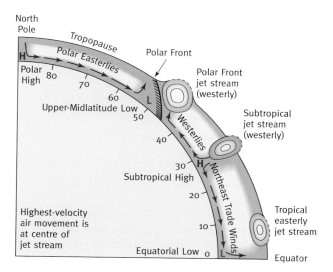

FIGURE 10.7   Atmosphere of the Northern Hemisphere in cross-section, with its three jet streams highlighted.

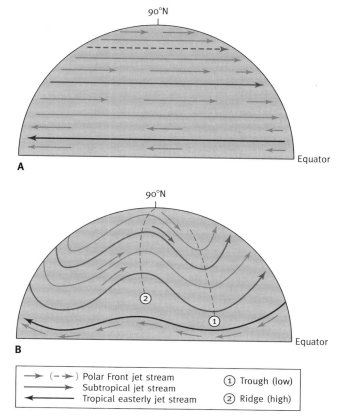

FIGURE 10.8   Zonal (westerly) flow dominates in the upper atmosphere of the Northern Hemisphere (A). Azonal (meridional) flow (B) is characterized by pronounced troughs and ridges, and a generally stronger Polar Front jet stream. Azonal flow promotes warm-air movement to the north beneath the ridges and cold-air movement to the south beneath the troughs.

jet stream must be related to the Polar High semipermanent pressure cell, but the details need not concern us here.

Another important generalization concerns the frequency of deviations from zonal windflow in the midlatitudes, particularly above the heart of North America. For a variety of rather complicated reasons, waves develop in the upper atmospheric pressure pattern. These alternating sequences of *troughs* (areas of low pressure) and *ridges* (areas of high pressure) cause the geostrophic wind to flow northwesterly and southwesterly around them (Fig. 10.8). Those deviations from westerly airflow are important because they reflect substantial *meridional* (north–south) air exchange. As you are aware, the fundamental cause of atmospheric circulation is a heat imbalance between the polar and tropical regions. These periods of meridional or **azonal flow** help correct that heat imbalance (Fig. 10.8). It is also worth noting that episodes of pronounced azonal flow produce unusual weather for the surface areas they affect. The next time you notice an unseasonable weather event, it is likely to be a result of waves developing in the upper atmospheric pressure pattern.

In a sense, it is misleading to treat the surface and upper atmospheric pressure patterns and their resultant windflows separately because they must always be interrelated. Indeed, strong surface pressure gradients are invariably reinforced by strong upper atmospheric pressure gradients. In truth, they are both the cause and effect of each other. But keep in mind that there is another component of this cause–effect relationship: the circulation of the world ocean. Although the effects of the ocean surface on the general circulation of the atmosphere have been discussed, the enormous influence of the circulating atmosphere on the ocean surface has yet to be examined and will be described in Unit 11.

KEY TERMS

azonal flow *page 129*

Equatorial Low *page 123*

general circulation *page 126*

Inter-Tropical Convergence Zone (ITCZ) *page 123*

jet stream *page 128*

monsoon *page 126*

Northeast Trades *page 123*

Polar Easterlies *page 123*

Polar Front *page 123*

Polar High *page 123*

Southeast Trades *page 123*

Subtropical High *page 123*

Upper-Midlatitude Low *page 123*

Westerlies *page 123*

zonal flow *page 128*

REVIEW QUESTIONS

1. List the seven semipermanent pressure belts of the surface atmospheric circulation and give their approximate locations.

2. List the six wind belts that connect these semipermanent highs and lows.

3. Discuss the shifting of these wind and pressure systems with the seasons of the year.

4. What are some of the main differences between the ideal model and the actual pattern of surface atmospheric circulation?

5. Describe the mechanisms of the monsoonal circulation of South Asia.

6. Describe the zonal circulation pattern of the upper atmosphere, its relation to the jet streams and why azonal flow occurs.

REFERENCES AND FURTHER READINGS

ATKINSON, B. W. *Meso-Scale Atmospheric Circulations* (Orlando, Fla.: Academic Press, 1981).

CHANG, J. *Atmospheric Circulation Systems and Climates* (Honolulu, Haw.: Oriental Publishing Co., 1972).

FEIN, J. S., and STEPHENS, P. L., Eds. *Monsoons* (New York: Wiley, 1987).

JAMES, I. N. *Introduction to Circulating Atmospheres* (New York: Cambridge Univ. Press, 1994).

LORENZ, E. *The Nature and Theory of the General Circulation of the Atmosphere* (Geneva: World Meteorological Organization, 1967).

PALMÉN, E., and NEWTON, C. W. *Atmospheric Circulation Systems: Their Structure and Physical Interpretation* (New York: Academic Press, 1969).

PERRY, A. H., and WALKER, J. M. *The Ocean–Atmosphere System* (London/New York: Longman, 1977).

REITER, E. R. *Jet Streams* (Garden City, N.Y.: Anchor/Doubleday, 1967).

SCHNEIDER, S. H., Ed. *Encyclopedia of Climate and Weather* (New York: Oxford Univ. Press, 2 vols., 1996).

WEBSTER, P. J. "Monsoons," *Scientific American* (August 1981), 109–118.

WEISMAN, S. R. "Worst Drought in Decades Hits Vast Area of India," *New York Times* (August 16, 1987), 8.

WELLS, N. *The Atmosphere and Ocean: A Physical Introduction* (New York: Wiley, 2nd ed., 1997).

WEB RESOURCES

http://daac.gsfc.nasa.gov/CAMPAIGN_DOCS/atmospheric_dynamics/ad_images_dao_animations.html Description of Asian monsoon with 2D and 3D animations.

http://pubs.usgs.gov/gip/deserts/atmosphere Article relating the effects of the atmosphere on aridity, including a discussion of the major global wind belts.

http://www.ucar.ecu/communications/quarterly/winter99/TIME.html A discussion of the general model of upper air circulation and of new models being developed by researchers.

Hydrosphere: Circulation of the World Ocean

Hydrosphere meets lithosphere on the north shore of Oahu, Hawaii. (Authors' photo)

OBJECTIVES

- To relate the surface oceanic circulation to the general circulation of the atmosphere

- To describe the major currents that constitute the oceanic circulation

- To demonstrate the role of oceanic circulation in the transport of heat at the Earth's surface

In this unit we focus on the large-scale movements of water, known as **ocean currents**, that form the oceanic counterpart to the atmospheric system of wind belts and semipermanent pressure cells treated in Unit 10. The two systems are closely integrated, and we will be examining that relationship in some detail. Ocean currents affect not only the 71 percent of the face of the Earth covered by the world ocean, but the continental landmasses as well. We must become familiar with the oceanic circulation on a global basis, as it is vital to our understanding of the weather and climate of each part of the planet's surface.

Surface Currents

Like the global atmospheric circulation above it, the world ocean is a significant transporter of heat from equatorial to polar regions. The oceans account for approximately 13 percent of the total movement of heat from low to high latitudes; the atmosphere is responsible for the other 87 percent. But in the broad zone between the tropics and the upper midlatitudes, both north and south of the Equator, the oceans are estimated to

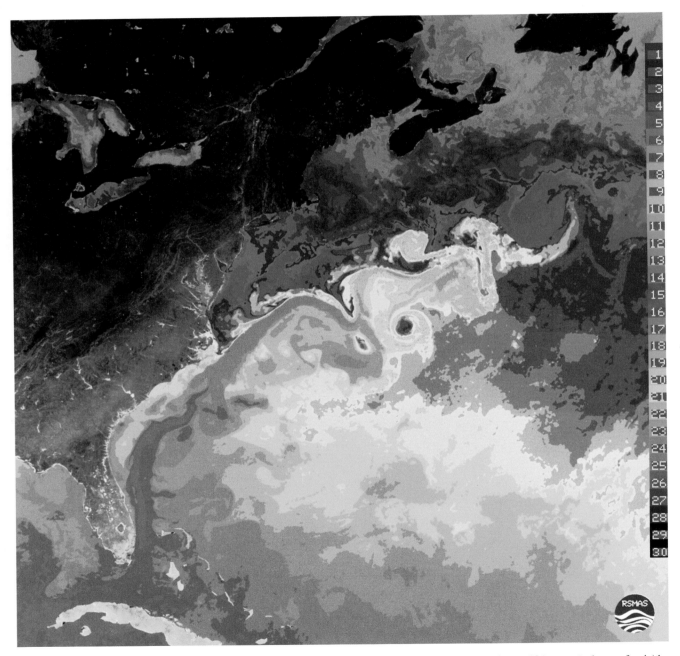

FIGURE 11.1 This sea-surface temperature image of the western North Atlantic Ocean shows the Gulf Stream in hues of red (denoting warmth) as it skirts the North American coast from Florida to North Carolina, whence it flows northeastward into the open ocean and becomes the less clearly defined North Atlantic Drift. The warmth carried north- and northeastward into the middle latitudes has a major influence on atmospheric environments in Western Europe. The colour chart at right indicates approximate temperatures in degrees Celsius. Note that even though the Gulf Stream turns eastward, its influence on coastal North America is recorded as far north as Massachusetts.

account for up to 25 percent of the poleward heat movement (Fig. 11.1).

Specifically, it is through the circulation of water masses in large-scale currents that the world ocean plays its vital role in constantly adjusting the Earth's surface heat imbalance. Although the sea contains numerous horizontal, vertical, and even diagonal currents at various depths, almost all of the oceanic heat-transfer activity takes place via the operation of horizontal currents in the uppermost 100 m of water. Thus most of the attention in this unit is directed toward the 10 percent of the total volume of the world ocean that constitutes this surface layer.

Although they transport massive volumes of water, most global-scale ocean currents differ only slightly from the surface waters through which they flow. So-called "warm" currents, which travel from the tropics toward the poles, and "cold" currents, which move toward the Equator, usually exhibit temperatures that deviate by only a few degrees from those of the surrounding sea. Yet these temperature differences are often sufficient to markedly affect atmospheric conditions over a wide area. As demonstrated in our discussion of the *maritime effect* (p. 104), onshore winds blowing across warm currents pick up substantial moisture from the heightened evaporation of seawater, whose latent heat (p. 91) can generate rising currents of air.

In their rates of movement, too, most currents are barely distinguishable from their marine surroundings. Currents tend to move slowly and steadily, averaging only about 8 km per hour. They are often called **drifts** because they lag far behind the average speeds of surface winds blowing in the same general direction. Faster-moving currents are usually found only where narrow straits squeeze the flow of water, such as between Florida and Cuba or in the Bering Sea between Alaska and northeasternmost Russia. Slower-moving currents exist as well but are mainly confined to the deeper oceanic layers below 100 m, where the friction caused by the high pressure of overlying water is much greater.

Generation of Ocean Currents

Ocean currents can be generated in several ways. Sometimes water piles up along a coastline, yielding a slightly higher sea level than in the surrounding ocean. A good example is the tropical South Atlantic Ocean just south of the Equator, where the landmass of northeastern Brazil protrudes well out to sea. When westward-flowing water piles up against this shore, gravity forces it back, forming an eastward-moving current along the Equator (Fig. 11.2). The eastward rotation of the Earth reinforces this piling-up phenomenon, which occurs to some degree along the western edge of every ocean basin. Alternatively, surface waters do not experience such squeezing along the eastern margins of an ocean, and water movement there is more diffuse.

Another source of oceanic circulation, which largely affects deeper zones below the surface layer, is variation in the density of seawater. Density differences can arise from temperature differences, as when the chilled sur-

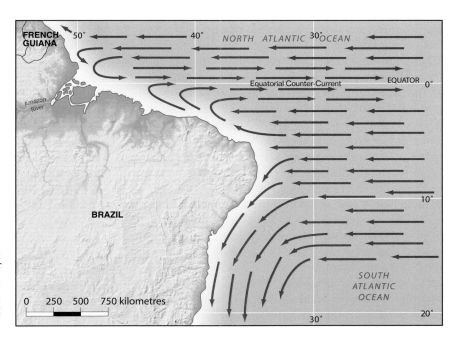

FIGURE 11.2 The pile-up of ocean water against the northeastern coast of Brazil forces a return flow, generating the Equatorial Counter-Current, which moves eastward against the surrounding dominant westward current.

face water of the high latitudes sinks and spreads toward the Equator, or from salinity differences. The ocean beneath a dry subtropical high-pressure zone is more saline than under an equatorial rain belt. The saltier water, being denser than the less saline water, tends to sink and give way to a surface current of lower salinity.

These influences notwithstanding, the leading generator of ocean currents is the frictional drag on the water surface set up by prevailing winds. Frictional drag transfers kinetic energy, the energy of movement, from the air to the water. Once set in motion, as is the case with moving air, the water is subjected to the deflective Coriolis force. As a rule, when the prevailing wind blows over the ocean surface of the rotating Earth, the Coriolis force steers the surface current to flow at an angle of about 45 degrees to the right of the wind in the Northern Hemisphere (and at approximately 45 degrees to the left in the Southern Hemisphere). This surface motion also influences the waters below to a depth of around 100 m. Within this column, the motion in each underlying water layer is increasingly to the right (or left in the Southern Hemisphere) as depth increases, and exhibits a decreasing speed of flow.

Flow Behaviour of Ocean Currents

In our discussion of oceanic circulation so far, we have for the most part been dealing with models that describe ideal situations. By this point in the book, of course, we are well aware that in nature things are more complex, and the currents of the world ocean are no exception. It would, therefore, be erroneous to presume that a large-scale ocean current is an unswerving river of water that follows the same exact path and exhibits constant movement characteristics. Deviations from the "norm" occur all the time. With the rapid expansion of oceanographic research based on satellite data over the past three decades, much has been learned about the detailed dynamics of surface currents. In many ways, their flow patterns (if not their speeds) resemble those of the Polar Front jet stream discussed in Unit 10.

Most ocean currents develop riverlike *meanders,* or curving bends, which can become so pronounced (especially after the passage of storms) that many detach and form localized *eddies,* or loops, that move along with the general flow of water. These phenomena are most common along the boundaries of currents, where opposing water movements heighten the opportunities for developing whorl-like local circulation cells. Figure 11.3 diagrams such a situation, involving the western edge of

the warm Gulf Stream current off the Middle Atlantic coast of North America.

Gyre Circulations

Prevailing winds, the Coriolis force, and sometimes the configuration of bordering landmasses frequently combine to channel ocean currents into cell-like circulations that resemble large cyclones and anticyclones. In the ocean basins these continuously moving loops are called **gyres**, a term used for both clockwise and counterclockwise circulations. Gyres, in fact, are so large that they can encompass an entire ocean. Since ocean basins are usually more extensive in width than in length, most gyres assume the shape of elliptical cells elongated in an east–west direction.

The ideal model of gyre circulation in the world ocean, shown in Fig. 11.4, displays a general uniformity in both the Northern and Southern Hemispheres. As with the model of the general circulation of the atmosphere, these hemispheric flow patterns are essentially mirror images of one another. Each hemisphere contains tropical and subtropical gyres. Differences in high-latitude land/water configurations give rise to a fifth (subpolar) gyre in the Northern Hemisphere that is not matched in the Southern.

Subtropical Gyres   The **subtropical gyre** dominates the oceanic circulation of both hemispheres. In each case, the subtropical gyre circulates around the Subtropical High that is stationed above the centre of the ocean basin (see Fig. 10.3). The two clockwise-circulating gyres of the Northern Hemisphere are found beneath two such high-pressure cells: the Pacific (Hawaiian) High over the North Pacific Ocean and the Bermuda (Azores) High centred above the North Atlantic Ocean. In the Southern Hemisphere, there are three subtropical gyres that each exhibit a counterclockwise flow trajectory; these are located beneath the three semipermanent zones of subtropical high pressure, respectively centred over the South Pacific Ocean, the South Atlantic Ocean, and the southern portion of the Indian Ocean.

The broad centres of each of these five gyres are associated with subsiding air and generally calm wind conditions, and are therefore devoid of large-scale ocean currents. The currents are decidedly concentrated along the peripheries of the major ocean basins, where they constitute the various segments or *limbs* of the subtropical gyre. Along their equatorward margins, the subtropical gyres in each hemisphere carry warm water toward the west. These currents diverge as they approach land. Some of the water is reversed and transported eastward along the Equator as the Equatorial Counter-Current,

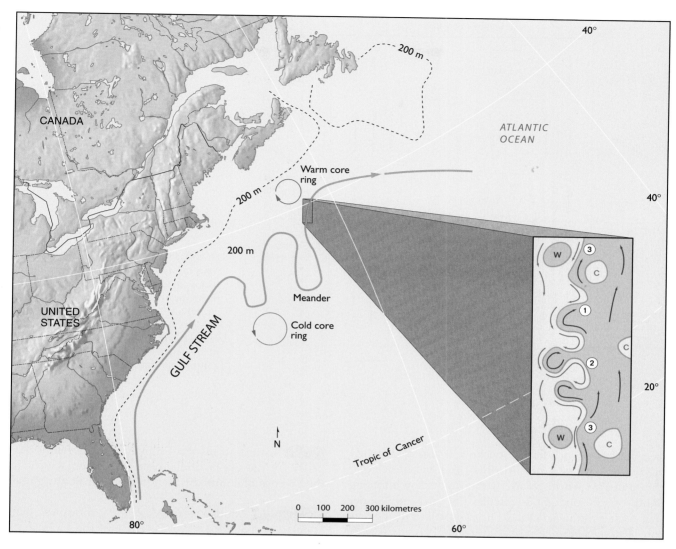

FIGURE 11.3   When ocean currents consisting of waters with contrasting temperatures make contact as they move in opposite directions, their boundaries become masses of swirling eddies. As the northward-moving Gulf Stream begins to move off the North American east coast, colder waters moving southward create such a situation. In this sketch of the Middle Atlantic coastline, a section of the contact zone is enlarged (inset). At ① the contact surface between the contrasting waters becomes indented. At ② the swirling eddies create balloon-like protrusions of cold and warm water. At ③ these warm and cold masses are separated from the main bodies on the opposite sides of the boundary.

but most of the flow splits and is propelled poleward as warm currents along the western edges of each ocean basin (Fig. 11.2).

As Fig. 11.4 indicates, when polar waters are encountered in the upper midlatitudes, the currents swing eastward across the ocean. In the Northern Hemisphere, these eastward drifts remain relatively warm currents because the colder waters of the subpolar gyre to their north are largely blocked by landmasses from mixing with this flow. When they reach the eastern edge of the ocean, the now somewhat cooled waters of the subtropical gyre turn toward the Equator and move southward

along the continental coasts. These cool currents parallel the eastern margins of the ocean basins and finally converge with the equatorial currents to complete the circuit and once again form the westward-moving (and now rapidly warming) equatorial stream.

Gyres and Windflow   The side panels in Fig. 11.4 remind us that a subtropical gyre circulation is continuously maintained by the operation of the wind belts above it. The trade winds in the tropical segments of the eastern margin of an ocean work together with the Westerlies in the midlatitude segments of the western

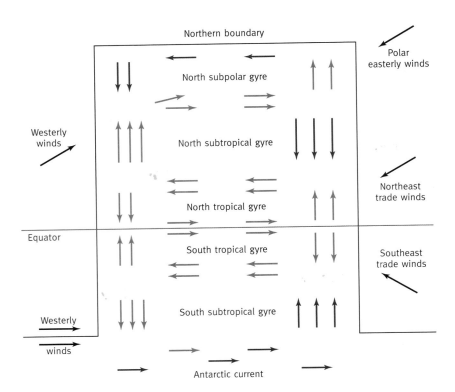

FIGURE 11.4 Generalized pattern of currents in a typical ocean basin, showing the major circulation cells (gyres) and their influencing wind systems. Relatively warm currents are shown in red; relatively cool currents in blue. Note that the Northern Hemisphere differs from the Southern Hemisphere because of the variation in continental landmass configurations.

periphery to propel the circular flow. If you blow lightly across the edge of a cup of coffee, you will notice that the liquid begins to rotate; with two such reinforcing wind sources to maintain circular flow, it is no wonder that these gyres never cease. The circulations of the narrow **tropical gyres**, composed of the equatorial currents and returning countercurrents, are also reinforced by winds—the converging Northeast and Southeast Trades.

The circulatory interaction between the sea and the overlying windflows is more complicated in the case of the Northern Hemisphere **subpolar gyres**, where landmasses and sea ice interrupt surface ocean flows. Along the southern limbs of these gyres, westerly winds drive a warm current across the entire ocean basin. This flow remains relatively warm because, as indicated before, the southward penetration of cold Arctic waters is largely blocked by continents, squeezing through only via the narrow Bering Strait in the northernmost Pacific and the slender channel separating Canada and Greenland in the northwestern North Atlantic. In the more open northeastern Atlantic between Greenland and Europe, a branch of the warm eastward-moving drift enters the subpolar gyre (Fig. 11.4), frequently driven across the Arctic Circle by a reinforcing southwesterly tail wind associated with storm activity along the Polar Front. The subpolar gyres are nonexistent in the Southern Hemisphere. Instead, an eastward-moving cold current is propelled by the upper midlatitude Westerlies, which, in the absence of continental landmasses, girdle the globe.

Upwelling   Another feature of the subtropical gyre circulation is represented in Fig. 11.4 by the wider spacing of arrows representing currents along the eastern sides of ocean basins. This wide spacing indicates that surface waters are not squeezed against the eastern edge of the basins, as they are against the west. It also suggests the presence of an additional influence that reinforces the actions of prevailing winds—upwelling. **Upwelling** involves the rising of cold water from the ocean depths to the surface where the Coriolis force prompts ocean currents to diverge from continental coastlines. As warmer surface waters are transported out to sea, they are replaced by this cold water, which lowers the surface air temperatures and the local rate of evaporation. Not surprisingly, some of the driest coastal areas on Earth are associated with upwelling, particularly in latitudes under the influence of the semipermanent subtropical high-pressure cells.

Figure 11.5 maps four such upwelling zones in the Pacific and Atlantic Oceans. Each subtropical west coast on the continent adjacent to the shaded upwelling zone experiences aridity. Much of coastal northwestern

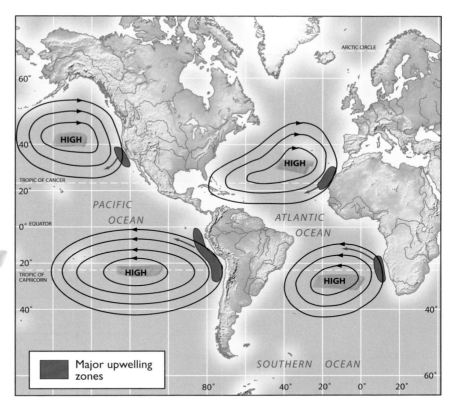

FIGURE 11.5 Four major cold-water up-welling zones, all adjacent to west coasts in the subtropical latitudes of the eastern Atlantic and Pacific ocean basins. The Coriolis force and high-pressure atmospheric systems drive waters offshore (red arrows), to be replaced by nutrient-rich, upwelling waters near the coast (indicated in dark blue). In each such location coastlines are arid, but offshore fishing industries are very productive.

Mexico as well as northern Chile and Peru bordering the Pacific exhibit desert conditions. Moreover, in the areas of northwestern and southwestern Africa bordering the Atlantic upwelling zones, we find two of the driest deserts in the world—the Sahara and the Namib, respectively. Although it can result in desiccation on nearby coasts, upwelling does produce one important benefit for humans: it carries to the surface nutrients that support some of the most productive fishing grounds in the world ocean.

The Geography of Ocean Currents

The basic principles of oceanic circulation are now familiar to us, and they can be applied at this point to the actual distribution of global-scale surface currents mapped in Fig. 11.6. As we know, these currents do respond to seasonal shifts in the wind belts and semipermanent highs and lows. However, those responses are minimal because seawater motion changes quite slowly and usually lags weeks or even months behind shifts in the atmospheric circulation above. The geographic pattern of ocean currents shown in Fig. 11.6, therefore, is based on the average annual position of these flows. But most currents deviate only slightly from these positions. On the world map, the only noteworthy departures involve the reversal of smaller-scale currents under the

influence of monsoonal air circulations near the coasts of southern and southeastern Asia (see Fig. 10.4). Now let us briefly survey the currents of each major ocean basin.

Pacific Ocean Currents The Pacific Ocean's currents closely match the model of gyre circulations displayed in Fig. 11.4. In both the Northern and Southern Hemispheres components of this immense ocean basin, surface flows are dominated by the subtropical gyres. In the North Pacific, the limbs of this gyre are constituted by the clockwise flow of the North Equatorial, Japan (Kuroshio), North Pacific, and California Currents. Because the Bering Strait to the north admits only a tiny flow of Arctic seawater to the circulation, all of this gyre's currents are warm except for the California Current. That current is relatively cold as a result of upwelling and its distance from the tropical source of warm water. The lesser circulations of the tropical and subpolar gyres are also evident in the North Pacific. The tropical gyre encompasses the low-latitude Equatorial Counter-Current and the North Equatorial Current. The subpolar gyre consists of the upper-midlatitude loop of the North Pacific, Alaska, and Kamchatka (Oyashio) Currents.

The South Pacific Ocean is a mirror image of the Northern Hemisphere flow pattern, except for the fully

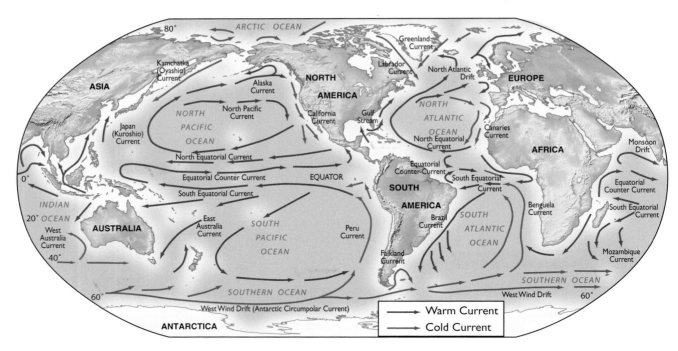

FIGURE 11.6   World distribution of ocean currents, showing average positions and relative temperatures in each of the ocean basins.

expected replacement of the subpolar gyre by the globe-encircling movement of the West Wind Drift (Antarctic Circumpolar Current), where the Pacific gives way to the Southern Ocean at approximately 45°S. The strong subtropical gyre that dominates the circulation of the South Pacific includes the South Equatorial, East Australian, West Wind Drift, and Peru Currents. The South Pacific's tropical gyre is comprised of the Equatorial Counter-Current and the South Equatorial Current.

Atlantic Ocean Currents   The Atlantic really consists of two ocean basins because of the hourglass-like narrowing between South America and Africa in the vicinity of the Equator. Nevertheless, the overall pattern of Atlantic currents is quite similar to that of the Pacific. The subtropical gyre—composed of the North Equatorial Current, Gulf Stream, North Atlantic Drift, and Canaries Current—dominates circulation in the North Atlantic Ocean. The subpolar gyre, as noted before, is modified by sea ice and high-latitude land bodies, but the rudiments of circular flow are apparent on the map. In the equatorial latitudes, despite the east–west proximity of continents, both tropical gyres have enough space to develop their expected circulations.

Proceeding into the South Atlantic Ocean, the subtropical gyre is again dominant, with the warm waters of the Brazil Current bathing the eastern shore of South America and the cold waters of the Benguela Current,

reinforced by upwelling, paralleling the dry southwestern African coast. South of 35°S the transition to the Southern Ocean and its West Wind Drift is identical to the pattern of the South Pacific.

Indian Ocean Currents   The Indian Ocean's circulatory system is complicated by the configuration of the surrounding continents, with an eastward opening to the Pacific in the southerly low latitudes and the closure of the northern part of the ocean by the South Asian coast. Still, we can observe some definite signs of subtropical gyre circulation in the Indian Ocean's Southern Hemisphere component. Moreover, a fully developed pair of tropical gyres in the latitudinal zone straddling the Equator operates for a good part of the year. During the remaining months, as is explained in the discussion of the wet monsoon in Unit 10, the Inter-Tropical Convergence Zone (ITCZ) is pulled far northward onto the Asian mainland. This temporarily disrupts the air and even the oceanic circulations that prevail north of the Equator between October and June (see Fig. 10.4).

Deep-Sea Currents

As noted earlier in this unit, significant water movements occur below the surface layer of the sea, which extends to a depth of about 100 m. In fact, another complete global system of currents exists below that level, where the bulk (approximately 90 percent) of the world ocean's water lies. This deep-sea system of oceanic circulation operates in sharp contrast to the surface system, which interfaces with the atmosphere and is largely driven by prevailing winds in tandem with the Coriolis force.

The deep-sea system of oceanic movement can be categorized as a **thermohaline circulation**, because it is controlled by differences in the temperature and/or salinity of water masses. Thermohaline circulation involves the flow of currents driven by differences in water density. Because of the greater pressure of overlying water below 100 m, increased frictional resistance acts to slow the speed of currents substantially. Another factor that makes deep-sea currents much slower than their surface-layer counterparts is that the latter are strictly horizontal whereas the former are much more likely to exhibit vertical motion.

The temperature and salinity differences that trigger thermohaline circulation are generated at the ocean surface in the high-latitude wind belts. Water density gradients high enough to spawn deep-sea currents are developed by the actions of two related processes. One process entails the sinking of surface water, which gets colder, and therefore denser, when it is in contact with polar-area air temperatures. The other is the freezing of surface seawater, which increases the salinity—and density—of the water just under the ice (which consists mainly of nonsaline freshwater).

Recent research has established that thermohaline circulation is part of a **global conveyor belt** that moves masses of cold, deep-sea water from high to lower latitudes (Fig. 11.7). Note that each ocean basin has its own deep-water circulation, with the only interoceanic exchanges occurring in the depths of the Southern Ocean. Note, too, that cold bottom water from each polar oceanic zone flows into different oceans: the deep-sea currents of the North and South Atlantic emanate from the Arctic Ocean, whereas those of the Pacific and Indian Oceans are generated in the waters surrounding Antarctica. Figure 11.7 also shows that the deep-sea limb of the global conveyor belt is connected to a surface-layer limb of warm water that transports vast amounts of heat energy among the same ocean basins. A growing number of researchers believe that the total conveyor system varies its rate of flow over time, and

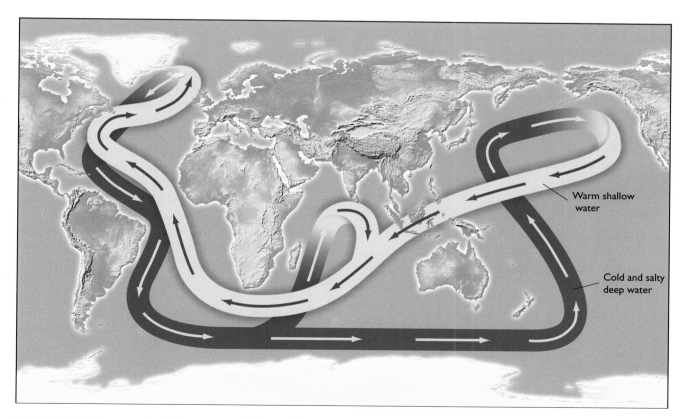

FIGURE 11.7 Deep-sea circulation system of the world ocean, which is part of the larger global conveyor belt that links thermohaline currents to a warm surface-layer flow among the same ocean basins.

they are studying the implications of these oscillations for both short- and long-term climate change.

The Coupled Ocean–Atmosphere System

This unit has discussed numerous interactions between the world ocean and the atmosphere. It should be evident by now that a *coupled*, two-way relationship exists between atmospheric and hydrospheric processes. Windflow patterns in the atmosphere create surface currents and, through cold temperatures at higher latitudes, deep-sea circulation. The ocean also affects the atmosphere in several ways. Two of the most important of those influences are the transport of heat from low to higher latitudes and the capacity of the world ocean to store huge amounts of heat energy.

Table 11.1 indicates that approximately 87 percent of the movement of heat away from the Equator toward the poles is accounted for by the atmosphere and the remaining 13 percent by the sea. However, the breakdown shown in the table reveals that the oceans transport considerably more heat at certain latitudes, and it has been estimated that the sea is responsible for as much as 25 percent of the global heat movement in the low and middle latitudes. With the excess heat of the tropical oceans systematically dissipated by its poleward transport, the world ocean exhibits a general pattern of temperature decline as the latitude increases (see Fig. 8.12).

Many climatologists assert that the single most important influence of the world ocean on the atmosphere is its heat storage capacity. Unlike the atmosphere, which is far less capable of storing heat for any length of time, the sea is known to act as a vast heat reservoir. Scientists are now closely investigating this component of the ocean–atmosphere system, and some are concerned that if this excess heat were to be released

rapidly, it could have a significant warming effect on the global climate. A related concern is the warming of the world ocean itself, which produces an increase in water volume that can lead to a eustatic (global) rise in sea level. (Researchers now estimate that about one-third of the 10-cm rise in global sea level during the twentieth century was caused by warming in the upper layers of the oceans.)

El Niño–Southern Oscillation

A vital component in the general circulation of the atmosphere is the rising motion of air in the warm tropics near the Equator. Since nearly 80 percent of the surface that the Equator traverses is ocean, significant fluctuations in the temperature of that sea surface could temporarily modify the pattern of semipermanent low-pressure cells that mark the ITCZ in these latitudes. This in turn could produce short-term, global-scale changes in weather patterns capable of disrupting human activities.

Such linkages within the coupled ocean–atmosphere system are now the subject of intensive climatological research. Much of this work has focused on sea-surface warming in the largest stretch of equatorial water—the vast central Pacific that sprawls across 160 degrees of longitude between Indonesia and South America.

Intermittent anomalies in seawater temperature off the coasts of Peru and Ecuador in northwestern South America have long been known, but their larger significance became apparent only during the 1980s. The warming of coastal Pacific waters there by about 2°C is, in fact, a yearly occurrence, which reduces the fish catch temporarily when a local southward-drifting warm current suppresses the usually present upwelling (see Fig. 11.5) that transports nutrients crucial to the surface-layer food chain. Because this three-month-long phenomenon usually arrives around Christmas time, it is called **El Niño** ("the child") in honour of the Christ Child. But once every two to seven years—most recently in 1982–1983, 1986–1987, 1992–1994, and 1997–1998—a much more pronounced El Niño develops.

This abnormal El Niño—which can linger up to three years—is accompanied by an expanded zone of warm coastal waters. The upwelling of cold water associated with the Peru Current ceases, and the absence of nutrients results in massive fish kills and the decimation of the bird population (which feeds on the fish). In addition, Ecuador and Peru experience increases in rainfall that can result in crop losses as well as severe flooding in the heavily populated valleys of the nearby

Table 11.1 Average Annual Heat Flow at the Earth's Surface in Units of 10^{14} Calories per Second

Latitude	Total	Ocean (%)		Atmosphere (%)	
60°	7.6	0.7	(9.2)	6.9	(90.8)
50°	8.2	1.3	(15.9)	6.9	(84.1)
40°	12.0	1.8	(15.0)	10.2	(85.0)
30°	11.0	2.1	(19.1)	8.9	(80.9)
20°	8.4	1.3	(15.5)	7.1	(84.5)
10°	4.6	−0.3	—	4.9	(106.5)
Totals	51.8	6.9	(13.3)	44.9	(86.7)

Source: Information from M. I. Budyko (1958).

Andes Mountains. These localized El Niño effects, in fact, are but one symptom of a geographically much wider anomaly in the relationship between the equatorial ocean and the atmosphere. The cause of this abnormal El Niño is rooted in the temporary reversal of surface sea currents and airflows throughout the Pacific's equatorial zone.

The eastern portion of that oceanic zone is normally an area of high atmospheric pressure, because the upwelling Peru and California Currents converge (Figs. 11.5 and 11.6), and the cool surface water creates a condition of stability that inhibits the air from rising to form the equatorial low-pressure trough. These cool waters then move westward into the Pacific as the Equatorial Current, propelled not only by the converging trade winds but also by a strong surface airflow from the eastern Pacific high toward the semipermanent low in the western equatorial Pacific, which is positioned over Indonesia and northern Australia. As Fig. 11.8A shows, a cell of air circulation forms above the Equator, with air rising above the western low, flowing eastward at high altitude, and subsiding over the eastern Pacific.

For reasons that are still not fully understood, during pronounced El Niño episodes there is a collapsing of both this pressure difference (between the eastern Pacific high and the western Pacific low) and the resultant westward surface windflow. (These corresponding atmospheric events are called the **Southern Oscillation**.) What then occurs is a swift reversal in the flow of equatorial water and wind—known in combination as **ENSO** (El Niño–Southern Oscillation)—as the mid-oceanic circulation cell now operates in the opposite direction (Fig. 11.8B). Most importantly, the piled-up warm water in the western Pacific surges back to the east as the greatly enhanced Equatorial Counter-Current, and the eastern Pacific equatorial zone is now overwhelmed by water whose temperatures can be as much as 8°C higher than normal. Moreover, as Fig. 11.8B shows, these events are accompanied by a subsurface infusion of warm water, which makes the Peruvian upwelling flow warm and reinforces the anomalous heating of the ocean surface.

The effects of ENSO are now believed to spread so far beyond the equatorial Pacific that climatologists today rank the phenomenon as a leading cause of disturbance in global weather patterns. The El Niño of 1997–1998 was the strongest ever observed, with sea-surface warming between Indonesia and Peru more than double the expected ENSO temperature anomaly. Reports of severe weather abnormalities soon flowed in from around the world and fell into two categories. Heavy rains and disastrous flooding occurred in Ecuador and Peru, eastern China, and parts of the U.S.

Pacific coast. The other abnormality caused by El Niño was drought, which affected interior Australia, Indonesia, northern India, southern Africa, and northeastern South America.

ENSO research efforts have multiplied in recent years, and much has been learned. Among the more important findings is that extratropical Pacific sea-surface temperatures can remain elevated long after an El Niño event has ended. Satellite imagery has demonstrated that the 1982–1983 El Niño produced so much eastward-moving warm water that a sizeable mass of it in the northern tropics ricocheted off the North American landmass. Subsequently this huge pool of water migrated slowly northwestward and was still evident a decade later, thousands of miles away in the midlatitudes east of Japan. Since that part of the northern Pacific is a spawning ground for North American weather systems, there may be a linkage between this pool and some of the extreme weather events that have plagued the United States over the past decade.

Today many ENSO-related studies are focusing on **La Niña**. This term, which refers to the female counterpart of El Niño, was originally coined to indicate the lull between ENSO episodes. But further investigation has revealed that these interims of supposedly "normal" conditions can be marked by sea-surface *cold events,* which, in essence, represent an opposite extreme to a fully developed El Niño. Researchers are now turning to examine the atmospheric implications of this discovery, particularly the impact of La Niña on distant weather patterns. They are also beginning to redesign their models to reflect what may well be three distinctly different states of air–sea interaction in the Pacific's tropical latitudes (an effort discussed in several chapters in Glantz, 2002).

Intensive studies of ENSO have also prompted scientists to search for other large-scale anomalies of this type that may affect global weather patterns. They are particularly interested in such influences on the climate of heavily populated regions in the middle latitudes (see Perspective: The North Atlantic Oscillation). This work continues today on a number of fronts, and is forging a new subfield of climatology known as *teleconnections*— the study of long-distance linkages between weather patterns (a subject explored further in the Perspective box in Unit 20).

On a normal day-to-day basis, the latent heat released in the evaporation of seawater helps to power the general circulation of the atmosphere. That evaporative process simultaneously adds vital moisture to the air, a topic explored in Unit 12.

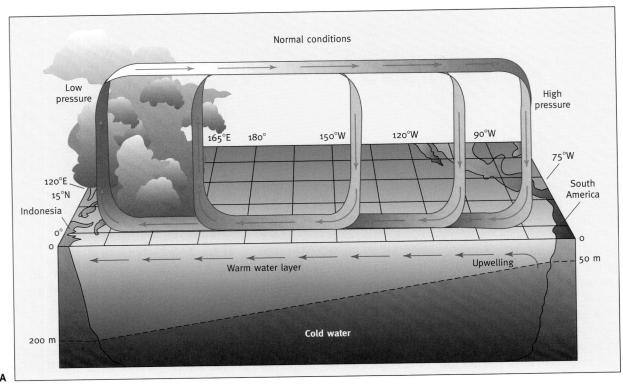

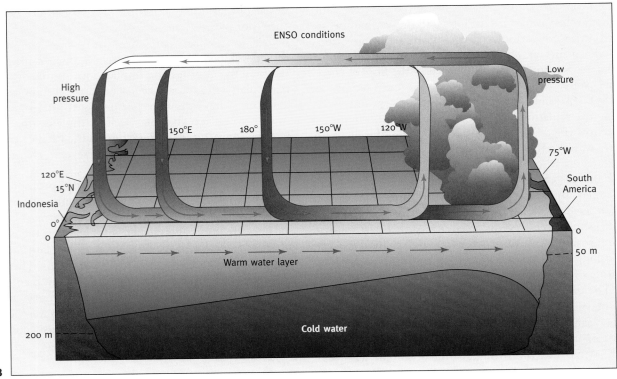

FIGURE 11.8 Equatorial Pacific waters and overlying airflows during normal (A) and El Niño–Southern Oscillation (B) conditions. Adapted from Ramage, "El Niño." Copyright 1986 by Scientific American, Inc. All rights reserved.

PERSPECTIVES ON THE HUMAN ENVIRONMENT

The North Atlantic Oscillation

The Southern Oscillation of the Pacific equatorial zone governs recurrent El Niños and affects tropical climate and weather far beyond its limits. When ENSO came to be better understood, questions soon arose about possible "oscillations" elsewhere over the global ocean, perhaps with similar influence over climate outside the tropics.

The **North Atlantic Oscillation (NAO)** is now known to do just that. This is an alternating pressure gradient between that semipermanent, upper midlatitude low-pressure system we identified in Unit 10 as the Icelandic Low and the subtropical high-pressure system known as the Bermuda High, especially its eastern segment, which is usually centred above the Azores Islands and referred to as the Azoric High. When the situation shown in Fig. 11.9 prevails in the eastern North Atlantic, westerly surface winds are strengthened,

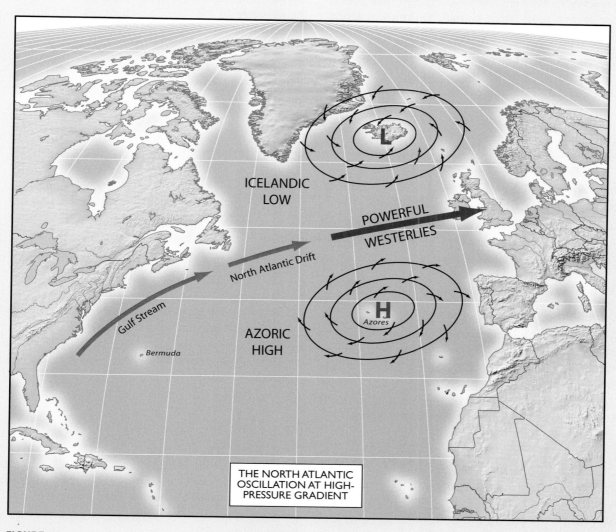

FIGURE 11.9

sending oceanic warmth and rain deep into densely populated Europe. But as the name of the NAO implies, there are times when the situation is reversed, and a persistent high-pressure system forms over Iceland and a low near the Azores. This reduces the pressure gradient that propels the Westerlies, slowing them down and allowing cold air from Arctic and Siberian sources to push into Europe.

We might conclude that the conditions shown in Fig. 11.9 represent the normal summer situation, and that their reversal is typical of winter. But things are more complicated than that. Such seasonal seesawing does occur, but there are also times when the Icelandic Low develops late, or not at all, so that the Westerlies are all but stopped and cold air has free reign over Europe, even in summer. Conversely, the Icelandic Low may persist for several years, right through the winters, giving Europe warm, moist winters and stormy summers. Ongoing research is showing that these oscillations can last as long as 20 years or more. Several

centuries ago, long-term failure of the Icelandic Low led to frigid conditions in Europe (see Unit 20).

The NAO involves more than pressure gradients and windflows. It is a complex, dynamic system that incorporates (1) the Gulf Stream and its outflow, the North Atlantic Drift current; (2) the sinking of warm water southwest of Greenland and north of Iceland, starting these salt-laden waters on an ocean-floor path to the Southern Hemisphere (Fig. 11.7) and creating a heat-pump effect that draws more warm water northward; (3) the upwelling of cold water off northwest Africa (Fig. 11.5); and (4) several additional components. As more becomes known about the NAO and its intricate mechanisms, one wonders what would happen if some crucial component (such as the heat pump) were to fail. The consequences for Europe would be far worse than the known devastations El Niños can cause.

KEY TERMS

drift *page 133*

El Niño *page 140*

ENSO *page 141*

global conveyor belt *page 139*

gyre *page 134*

La Niña *page 141*

North Atlantic Oscillation
(NAO) *page 143*

ocean current *page 131*

Southern Oscillation *page 141*

subpolar gyre *page 136*

subtropical gyre *page 134*

thermohaline circulation *page 139*

tropical gyre *page 136*

upwelling *page 136*

REVIEW QUESTIONS

1. Describe the ways in which ocean currents develop.

2. What is the relationship between the subtropical gyres and the overlying atmospheric circulation?

3. Name the major currents of the Pacific Ocean and their general flow patterns.

4. Name the major currents of the North and South Atlantic Oceans and their general flow patterns.

5. Describe the general pattern of deep-sea currents. What factors influence those currents?

6. Briefly describe what is meant by El Niño–Southern Oscillation, and discuss this phenomenon's major mechanisms.

REFERENCES AND FURTHER READINGS

BIGG, G. R.   *The Oceans and Climate* (New York: Cambridge Univ. Press, 1996).

BROAD, W. J.   *The Universe Below: Discovering the Secrets of the Deep Sea* (New York: Simon & Schuster, 1997).

BUDYKO, M. I.   *The heat balance of the earth's surface.* Trans. Nina A. Stepanova from *Teplovi balans zemnoi poverkhnost* (Washington, D.C.: U.S. Department of Defense, 1958).

CHANGNON, S., Ed.   *El Niño, 1997–1998: The Climate Event of the Century* (New York: Oxford Univ. Press, 2000).

COUPER, A. D., Ed.   *Atlas and Encyclopedia of the Sea* (New York: Harper & Row, 1989).

GLANTZ, M. H.   *Currents of Change: El Niño's Impact on Climate and Society* (New York: Cambridge Univ. Press, 1996).

GLANTZ, M. H., Ed. *La Niña and Its Impacts: Facts and Speculation* (Tokyo: United Nations Univ. Press, 2002).

KRAUS, E. B., and BUSINGER, J. A. *Atmosphere–Ocean Interaction* (New York: Oxford Univ. Press, 2nd ed., 1994).

PEDLOSKY, J. *Ocean Circulation Theory* (New York: Springer Verlag, 1996).

PHILANDER, G. *El Niño, La Niña and the Southern Oscillation* (Orlando, Fla.: Academic Press, 1989).

PRAGER, E. J., and EARLE, S. *The Oceans* (New York: McGraw-Hill, 2000).

RAMAGE, C. S. "El Niño," *Scientific American* (June 1986), 76–85.

STEINBERG, P. E., Guest Ed. "Focus: Geography of Ocean-Space," *The Professional Geographer,* 51 (1999), 366–450.

STEVENS, W. K. "Scientists Studying Deep Ocean Currents for Clues to Climates," *New York Times* (November 9, 1999), D5.

"The Oceans," *Scientific American Presents* (Fall, 1998).

WELLS, N. *The Atmosphere and Ocean: A Physical Introduction* (New York: Wiley, 2nd ed., 1997).

WEB RESOURCES

http://seawifs.gsfc.nasa.gov/OCEAN_PLANET/HTML/oceanography_currents_1.html Discussion of movement of ocean currents, including Dynamic Ocean Topography data from the TOPEX/POSEIDON mission.

http://www.acl.lanl.gov/Grand Chal/GCM/currents.hml A graphical representation of the major oceanic surface currents.

http://www.elnino.noaa.gov Comprehensive site for El Niño information with forecasts, observations, research data, La Niña information, and links to animations, graphics, and other educational sites.

http://www.factmonster.com/ce6/sci/A0860100.html A fact sheet describing the relationship between the atmosphere and the ocean, with links to information about currents and ocean circulation.

UNIT 12

Atmospheric Moisture and the Water Balance

The hydrologic cycle in action—looking across Vermillion Lakes toward Mount Rundle (left) and Sulphur Mountain (right), Banff National Park, May 1998.

OBJECTIVES

- To discuss the various forms of water and to understand the important heat transfers that accompany changes of these physical states
- To explain the various measures of atmospheric humidity, how they are related, and the processes responsible for condensation
- To outline the hydrologic cycle and the relative amounts of water that flow within this cycle
- To introduce the concept of precipitation
- To describe the Earth's surface water balance and its variations

Our physical world is characterized by energy flows and mass transfers. Energy and matter are never destroyed; they continually pass from one place to another. One of the best examples of such cyclical motion is the flow of water on the Earth. The *hydrosphere* encompasses the global water system, whose flows occur in the world ocean, on and within the land surface, and in the atmosphere. Unit 11 treats the oceans, and in Part Five water movements on and beneath the ground are explored.

In this unit we focus on water in the atmosphere and its relationships with the Earth's surface. Our survey considers the continual movement of water among various Earth spheres that leads to a balance of water at the planetary surface. This circulation of water is powered by radiant energy from the Sun, a form of heat whose inflows and outflows also balance at the Earth's surface.

The Physical Properties of Water

Human bodies are 70 percent water. Each of us requires 1.4 litres of water a day in order to survive, and our food could not grow without it. Water is everywhere. It constitutes 71 percent of our planet's surface. We breathe it, drink it, bathe in it, travel on it, and enjoy the beauty of it. We use it as a raw material, a source of electric power, a coolant in industrial processes, and a medium for waste disposal.

The single greatest factor underlying water's widespread importance is its ability to exist in three physical states (shown in Fig. 12.1) within the temperature ranges encountered near the Earth's surface. The solid form of water, ice, is composed of molecules linked together in a uniform manner. The bonds that link molecules of ice can be broken by heat energy. When enough heat is applied, ice changes its state and becomes the liquid form we know as water. The molecules in the

liquid are not arranged in an evenly spaced pattern but exist together in a random form. In the liquid state, the individual molecules are freer to move around. The introduction of additional heat completely frees individual molecules from their liquid state, and they move into the air. These airborne molecules constitute a gas known as **water vapour**.

Water is so common and consistent in its physical behaviour that we use it as a reliable measure of heat. We say that 1 *calorie* (cal) is the amount of heat energy required to raise the temperature of 1 gram (g) of water by 1°C. It takes about 80 cal to change 1 g of water from the solid state to the liquid state, a process we call **melting**. When it was first discovered that 80 cal of heat was needed to break the molecular bonds in solid water, the required heat appeared to be hidden, or *latent*. Thus the heat involved in melting is called the **latent heat of fusion**. Similarly, it takes 597 cal to change the state of 1 g of water at 0°C from a liquid to a gas. This change is called **evaporation** or *vaporization,* and the heat associated with it is known as the **latent heat of vaporization**. Sometimes ice can change directly into water vapour. In this process, called **sublimation**, the heat required (677 cal) is the sum of the latent heats of fusion and vaporization.

One of the beauties of these physical processes is that they are completely reversible. Water vapour can change back into water in the **condensation** process; water can change into ice through **freezing**; and water vapour can change directly into ice as well, a process that is also called sublimation (or *deposition*). In reversing these processes, the identical quantities of latent heat are given off.

Measuring Water Vapour

Lord Kelvin, the inventor of the absolute temperature scale, once said that we do not know anything about anything until we can measure it. How, then, do we measure water in its three physical states? The measurement of solid ice and liquid water is quite straightforward—we simply weigh them. We also employ this method indirectly when we measure the vapour pressure of water vapour in a column of air. (*Vapour pressure* is the pressure exerted by the molecules of water vapour.) Other atmospheric measurements of water vapour are also of value, the most useful ones being relative humidity, specific humidity, and the mixing ratio.

To use any of these methods of measurement, water vapour must first be condensed into liquid water. One way of condensing water vapour is to cool it together with the surrounding air. *Saturated air* is air that is holding all the water vapour molecules it can possibly contain at a

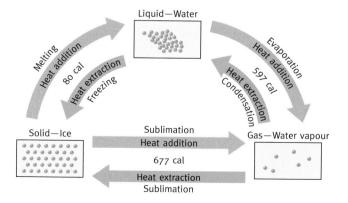

FIGURE 12.1 Schematic view of the molecular structure of water in its three physical states and heat-energy exchange among those states. The latent heat-exchange numbers between the arrows are explained in the text.

given temperature. Condensation takes place when a parcel of saturated air is cooled further, or when more water vapour is transferred from the surface to the atmosphere.

Condensation often happens around the surface of a cold soft-drink bottle or can. The air in contact with the container is cooled. Because cooler air holds less water vapour than warmer air, the saturation level is soon reached, and the excess vapour in the cooled air condenses into liquid water droplets on the container. The same process occurs when the Earth cools at night, subsequently cooling and saturating the air next to it. The excess water vapour beyond the saturation level contained in such a layer of air condenses into fine water droplets, on surfaces at and near the ground, that we call **dew**. Accordingly, the temperature at which air becomes saturated, and below which condensation occurs, is called the **dew point**.

Relative Humidity

Relative humidity tells us how close a given parcel of air is to its dew-point temperature, or saturation level. Consequently, we can define **relative humidity** as the proportion of water vapour present in a parcel of air relative to the maximum amount of water vapour that air could hold at the same temperature. Relative humidity is expressed as a percentage, so that air of 100 percent relative humidity is saturated and air of 0 percent relative humidity is completely dry. Relative humidity, which is dependent on the air temperature, often varies in opposition to that temperature. Relative humidity is usually lower in early and midafternoon when the diurnal temperature reaches its high, because the warmer the air, the more water vapour it can hold. At night, when the temperature falls, the colder air holds less water vapour, and so the air approaches its dew point and the relative humidity is higher.

Specific Humidity and the Mixing Ratio

The other measurements used to assess the amount of water vapour in the air need less explanation. *Specific humidity* is the ratio of the weight (mass) of water vapour in the air to the combined weight (mass) of the water vapour plus the air itself. The *mixing ratio* is the ratio of the mass of water vapour to the total mass of the dry air containing the water vapour.

The relative humidity, the mixing ratio, and the specific humidity may be found by using a psychrometer, an instrument with two thermometers. The bulb of one thermometer is surrounded by a wet cloth; water from the cloth evaporates into the air until the air surrounding the bulb is saturated. The evaporation process results in cooling, and that thermometer reaches a temperature called the wet-bulb temperature. The other thermometer, not swaddled in cloth, indicates the dry-bulb temperature. The difference in temperature between the wet-bulb and dry-bulb thermometers is computed, and the relative humidity and/or the mixing ratio is then determined by referring to the appropriate set of published humidity tables.

Now that we are armed with some basic terminology and an understanding of the ways in which water changes from one physical state to another, we can proceed to find out how water circulates through the Earth System. The natural cycle describing this circulation is called the hydrologic cycle.

The Hydrologic Cycle

Early scientists believed that the wind blew water from the sea through underground channels and caverns and into the atmosphere, removing the salt from the water in the process. Today's scientists talk in terms of the **hydrologic cycle**, whereby water continuously moves from the atmosphere to the land, plants, oceans, and freshwater bodies and then back into the atmosphere. The hydrologic cycle model consists of a number of stages, with Fig. 12.2 showing the relative amounts of water involved in each:

1. The largest amounts of water transferred in any component of the total cycle are those involved in the direct evaporation from the sea to the atmosphere and in precipitation back to the sea. As noted previously, evaporation is the process by which water changes from the liquid to the gaseous (water vapour) form. **Precipitation** includes any liquid water or ice that falls to the surface through the atmosphere.

2. The passage of water to the atmosphere through leaf pores is called *transpiration,* and the term *evapotranspiration* encompasses the joint processes by which water evaporates from the land surface and transpires from plants. Evapotranspiration combines with the precipitation of water onto the land surface to play a quantitatively smaller, but possibly more important, part in the hydrologic cycle.

3. If surplus precipitation at the land surface does not evaporate, it is removed via the surface network of streams and rivers, a phenomenon called **runoff**. In Fig. 12.2 the runoff value includes some water that *infiltrates* (penetrates) the soil and flows beneath the surface, eventually finding its way to rivers and the ocean.

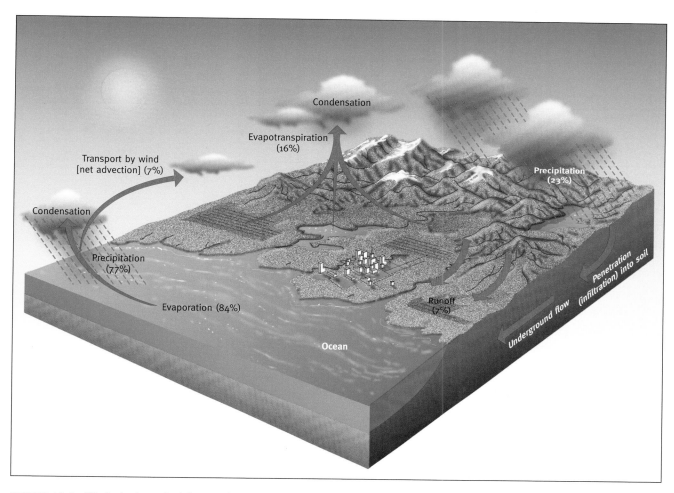

FIGURE 12.2 Hydrologic cycle. The numbers attached to each stage of the cycle show the percentage of the total water annually circulating in the system that is involved in any single stage. Surface flow and underground flow are considered as land runoff.

The hydrologic cycle can readily be viewed as a closed system, in which water is continuously moved among the component spheres of the Earth System. For example, the values in Fig. 12.2 indicate that the amount of water transported in the atmosphere over the continents equals the amount transported by surface runoff back to the ocean. Water circulates between the lower atmosphere, the upper lithosphere, the plants of the biosphere, and the oceans and freshwater bodies of the hydrosphere—or is sequestered in the ice, snow, and permafrost of the cryosphere for varying lengths of time. The system can also be split into two subsystems, one consisting of the precipitation and evaporation over the oceans and the other involving evapotranspiration and precipitation over land areas. The two subsystems are linked by horizontal movement in the atmosphere (known as *advection*) and by surface runoff flows.

The time required for water to traverse the full hydrologic cycle can be quite brief. A molecule of water can pass from the ocean to the atmosphere and back again within a matter of days. Over land, the cycle is less rapid. Groundwater goes into the soil or subsurface and can remain there for weeks, months, or years. The circulation is even slower where water in the form of ice in the cryosphere is concerned. Significant water has been locked up in the major ice sheets and glaciers of the world for many thousands (and in some cases, millions) of years.

Water is quite unequally distributed within the hydrosphere, as Fig. 12.3 reminds us. The world ocean contains 97 percent of all terrestrial water, but the high salt content makes it of little direct use to people. Of the remaining 3 percent, which constitutes the world's freshwater supply, three-quarters is locked up in ice sheets and glaciers. The next largest proportion of freshwater, about one-seventh, is accessible only with difficulty because it is groundwater located below 750 m.

Therefore the freshwater needed most urgently for our domestic, agricultural, and industrial uses must be

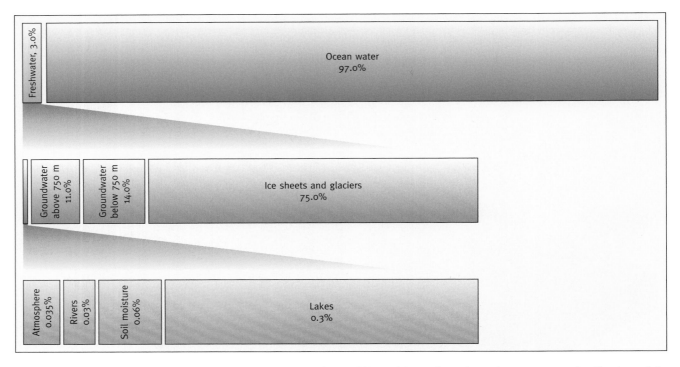

FIGURE 12.3 Distribution of water in the hydrosphere. The middle and lower bars show the percentage distribution of the 3 percent of total hydrospheric water that is fresh. Of that freshwater component, only about one-tenth is easily available to humans.

taken from the relatively small quantities found at or near the surface—in the rivers, lakes, soil layer, and atmosphere. These storage areas contain less than two-hundredths of the 3 percent of freshwater in the hydrosphere, and that finite supply is increasingly taxed by growing human consumption and abuse (see Perspective: Water Usage in Canada). Moreover, this very modest amount of freshwater must keep circulating within the hydrologic cycle through evaporation, condensation, and precipitation.

Evaporation

We cannot see evaporation occurring, but its results are sometimes visible. When you see mist rising from a lake that is warm in comparison to the cold air above it, you are seeing liquid water droplets that have already condensed. It is not too hard to imagine molecules of invisible water vapour rising upward in the same way.

Conditions of Evaporation

Evaporation occurs when two conditions are met. First, heat energy must be available at the water surface to change the liquid water to a vapour. This heat is sometimes provided by the moving water molecules, but

most often the radiant heat of the Sun, or both sources together, provides the necessary heat energy.

The second condition is that the air must not be saturated—it must be able to absorb the evaporated water molecules. Air near a water surface normally contains a large number of vapour molecules. Thus the *vapour pressure,* caused by the density and movement of the vapour molecules, is high. But air at some distance from the water surface has fewer molecules of vapour and, consequently, a lower vapour pressure. In this case we say there is a *vapour-pressure gradient* between the two locations. A vapour-pressure gradient exists above a water surface as long as the air has not reached its saturation level (dew point). Just as people tend to move from a very crowded room to a less crowded one, molecules of water vapour tend to move along the vapour-pressure gradient to areas of less pressure, which usually means moving higher in the atmosphere.

Knowing the requirements for evaporation—a heat source and a vapour-pressure gradient—we can infer the kinds of situations that would yield maximum evaporation. Because radiation from the Sun is a leading heat source, large amounts of evaporation can be expected where there is a great deal of sunlight. This is particularly true of the tropical oceans. Water molecules also move most easily into dry air because of the sizeable

PERSPECTIVES ON THE HUMAN ENVIRONMENT

Water Usage in Canada

In Canada today, freshwater—drawn from lakes, rivers, and subsurface deposits—is consumed in prodigious quantities at a daily rate of more than 340 l per household, or more than 1400 m³ of water per household per year. And, according to Statistics Canada reports, Canadians are the world's second largest consumers of water, second only to the United States (Fig. 12.4). This may not seem like a particularly worrying statistic, given the fact that about 9 percent of Canada's total area (or approximately 891,863 km²) is covered by freshwater lakes, ponds, and rivers. Canada is therefore a water-rich country, compared to most other nations. So why should there be any concerns regarding the quantities of water consumption in Canada? The answer is that our vast water use may, in fact, be threatening the country's freshwater resources. Lower levels on rivers and lakes can affect navigation, water quality is affected by

lowered water levels, and on the economic side, high levels of water consumption require expensive investments in water-system infrastructure to maintain high extraction levels. Even though efforts have been made to conserve water usage in Canada, our consumption is still several times higher than that of many Western European nations and hundreds of times higher than that of most developing nations. Given this massive rate of consumption, there is the potential for further environmental and economic consequences. A geographic and sectoral breakdown of the problem sheds light on where further changes will be necessary.

Even though Canada is a relatively water-wealthy country, the majority of our water flows north, while the majority of our population lives closer to the southern border. The spatial distribution of the proportion of the population that relies

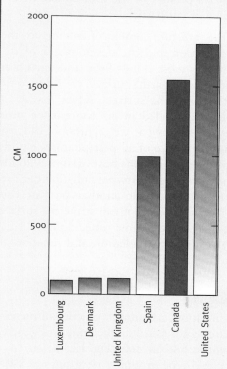

FIGURE 12.4 Average daily domestic water use (per capita).

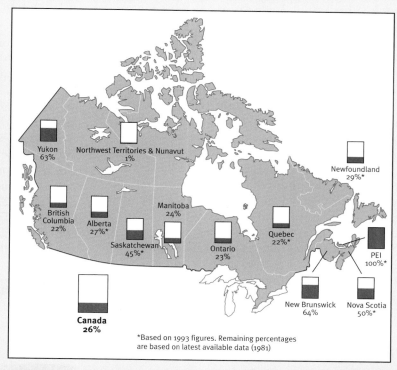

FIGURE 12.5 Percentage of Canadian population reliant on groundwater (based on 1993 Figures)

heavily on the use of groundwater as a source of freshwater illustrates that at least one-fifth of the population in every province and territory is dependent on groundwater. The provinces with higher rural populations (Saskatchewan, Atlantic provinces) have a higher reliance on groundwater resources (Fig. 12.5). The main use of water in Canada by sector is hydroelectric power generation. Although this is a non-consumptive use, Canada, to generate hydroelectric power, has diverted more water by damming rivers than any other country. Of the users that withdraw water,

the primary sectors by consumption are (1) thermal power generation (64 percent), (2) manufacturing (14 percent), (3) municipal (10 percent), (4) agricultural (9 percent), and (5) mining (1 percent). When factoring in the efficiency of these uses as a function of the percentage of water returned to the system, we find that agriculture is worst, with only a 30 percent return, which makes it the largest consumer of water. Alberta accounts for most of the water withdrawn for agricultural uses in Canada. The highest domestic consumers are in southern Alberta and British Columbia.

vapour-pressure gradient. So the drier the air, the more evaporation will occur, as can be seen by the high values associated with the subsiding air of the subtropical high-pressure zones on the world map of latent heat loss (see Fig. 7.7). Evaporation is even faster in windy conditions, when the air containing new vapour molecules can be continually replaced.

Evapotranspiration

Most of the evaporation into the atmosphere occurs over the ocean. Over land, water evaporates from lakes, rivers, damp soil, and other moist surfaces. The water that plants lose to the air during photosynthesis (transpiration) is another major source. As we know, **evapotranspiration** is the passage of moisture from the land surface to the atmosphere through the combined processes of evaporation and transpiration.

Physical geographers draw a distinction between potential evapotranspiration and actual evapotranspiration. **Potential evapotranspiration (PE)** is the maximum amount of water that can be lost to the atmosphere from a land surface with abundant available water. **Actual evapotranspiration (AE)** is the amount of water that can be lost to the atmosphere from a land surface with any particular soil-moisture conditions. AE can equal PE when the land surface is saturated, but when the soil moisture is less than its maximum value, AE is usually less than PE.

Now that water has entered the atmosphere, let us see how it makes its way through this component of the hydrologic cycle and moves back to the surface. We begin with the formation of clouds and then trace the development of precipitation.

Condensation and Clouds

Clouds are visible masses of suspended, minute water droplets and/or ice crystals. Two conditions are necessary for the formation of clouds:

1. The air must be saturated, either by cooling below the dew point (causing water vapour to condense) or by evaporating enough water to fill the air to its maximum water-holding capacity. Parcels of air may cool enough to produce condensation when they rise to the higher, cooler parts of the atmosphere, or when they come into contact with colder air or a colder surface.

2. There must exist a substantial quantity of small airborne particles called **condensation nuclei**, around which liquid droplets can form when water vapour condenses. Condensation nuclei are almost always present in the atmosphere in the form of dust or salt particles.

The greater the moisture content of cooling air, the greater the condensation and the development of the cloud mass. Although most clouds form and remain at some elevation above the Earth's surface, they can come into direct contact with the surface. When masses of fine water droplets suspended in air concentrate near the ground, they produce what we commonly call *fog*.

Besides being the source of all precipitation, clouds play a key role in the atmosphere's heat balance. Clouds both reflect some incoming shortwave radiation back to space at their tops and scatter another part of this incoming solar radiation before it can strike the surface directly (see Fig. 7.1). At the same time, clouds absorb part of the Earth's longwave radiation and reradiate it back toward the land and the sea.

Cloud Classification

Cloud-type classification, a common practice in meteorology and climatology, is based on the criteria of general structure, appearance, and altitude (Fig. 12.7).

One major cloud-type grouping encompasses **stratus clouds**. As this term implies, stratus clouds are layerlike in appearance. They also are fairly thin and normally cover a wide geographic area. Stratus clouds

FROM THE FIELDNOTES

FIGURE 12.6 "When you are in the Maasai Mara to study wildlife, you get up early—before sunrise. Here, not far from the Kenya–Tanzania border, the elevation is enough to make for some chilly nights, and you start the day in a sweater (later the sun will make you wish for a patch of shade). So cool does the ground surface become that, even in this arid environment, the slight amount of moisture in the air will condense and a ground fog develops. It is an unusual sight here in tropical Africa, and it does not last long after sunrise. But it moistens the grass just enough to enhance its vigor and to make it more palatable to the grazers of the morning."

are classified according to their altitude. Below 3 km, they are simply called *stratus* clouds—or *nimbostratus* if precipitation is occurring. Between 3 and 6 km, they are designated *altostratus* clouds, and above 6 km, *cirrostratus* clouds.

A second major cloud-type category involves **cumulus clouds**, which are thick, puffy, billowing masses that often develop to great heights (Fig. 12.7). These clouds are also subclassified into the same lower, middle, and upper altitudinal levels, proceeding in ascending order through *cumulus* or *stratocumulus, altocumulus,* and *cirrocumulus.* Very tall cumulus clouds, extending from 500 m at the base to about 12 km at their anvil-shaped heads, are called *cumulonimbus.* These are often associated with violent weather, including heavy rain, high winds, lightning, and thunder.

A third cloud-type category consists of **cirrus clouds**. These are thin, wispy, streak-like clouds that consist of ice particles rather than water droplets. They invariably occur at altitudes higher than 6 km and are signalled by the prefix *cirro* (Fig. 12.7, upper left).

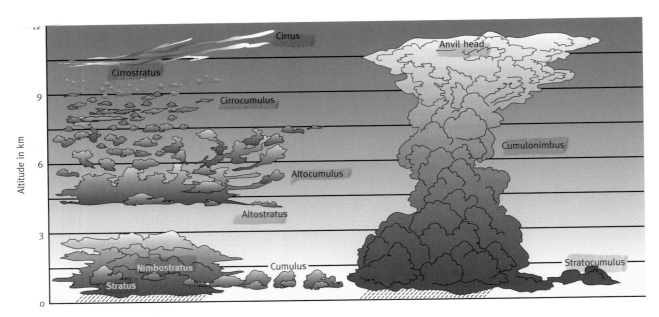

FIGURE 12.7 Schematic diagram of the different cloud types—stratus, cumulus, and cirrus.

Precipitation

Clouds are a necessary prerequisite for precipitation to fall to Earth. However, not all clouds produce precipitation because water droplets and ice crystals first must undergo some intermediate transformations before they are ready to fall to the surface. When water droplets within clouds first form, they are so small that the slightest upward air current keeps them airborne for long periods. We now examine the processes by which these droplets grow large enough to fall out of a cloud as precipitation.

The Ice-Crystal Process

Probably the most common process, the *ice-crystal process* was first identified in the 1930s by meteorologists Tor Bergeron and Von Findeisen. This process requires both liquid droplets and ice particles in a cloud. Ice particles are normally present if the temperature is below 0°C and if there are small particles called *freezing nuclei*. Freezing nuclei perform the same function for ice particles that condensation nuclei perform for water droplets.

When a cloud contains both ice particles and water droplets, the water droplets tend to evaporate, and then the resultant water vapour sublimates (changes from a vapour to a solid) directly onto the ice crystals. The ice crystal attracts more of the water vapour because the vapour pressure over the ice crystal is lower than that over the water droplet. Thus the ice crystal grows at the expense of the liquid droplet.

The ice crystals become larger and often join together to form a snowflake. When the snowflake is heavy enough, it drops out of the cloud. On its way down it usually encounters higher temperatures and melts, eventually reaching the surface as a liquid raindrop. Most rainfall and snowfall in the midlatitudes are formed by the ice-crystal process, but in the tropics the temperature of many clouds does not necessarily drop below the freezing point. Therefore, a second process—coalescence—is thought to make raindrops large enough to fall from clouds.

The Coalescence Process

The *coalescence process* (sometimes called the collision-coalescence process) requires some liquid droplets to be larger than others, which happens when there are giant condensation nuclei. As they fall, the larger droplets collide and join with the smaller ones. But narrowly missed smaller droplets may still be caught up in the wake of the larger ones and drawn to them. In either case, the larger droplets grow at the expense of the smaller ones and soon become heavy enough to fall to Earth.

Forms of Precipitation

Precipitation reaches the Earth's surface in several forms, as the photographic display in Fig. 12.8 indicates. Large liquid water droplets form *rain*. If the ice crystals in the ice-crystal process do not have time to melt before reaching the Earth's surface, the result is *snow*. *Sleet* refers to pellets of ice produced by the

A

B

C

D

FIGURE 12.8 Four major forms of precipitation. (A) A rainstorm approaching Muncho Lake, B.C. (B) Fresh snowfall on the trees in Banff National Park, Alberta. (C) A heavy, icy coating formed by freezing rain on tree branches frames the Peace Tower on Parliament Hill in Ottawa. (D) A woman huddles under her umbrella at the University of Western Ontario during a heavy hailstorm.

freezing of rain before it hits the surface. If the rain freezes after reaching the ground, it is called *freezing rain* (or *glaze*). Soft *hail* pellets (sometimes called snow pellets) can form in a cloud that has more ice crystals than water droplets, and eventually fall to the surface. True *hailstones* result when falling ice crystals are blown upward from the lower, warmer part of a cloud, where they gain a water surface, to the higher, freezing part, where the outer water turns to ice. This process, which often occurs in the vertical air circulation of thunderstorms, may be repeated over and over to form ever larger hailstones (see Fig. 12.8D).

The Surface Water Balance

As far as humans are concerned, the most crucial segment of the hydrologic cycle occurs at the planetary surface. Here, at the interface between Earth and atmosphere, evaporation and transpiration help plants grow, and precipitation provides the water needed for that evapotranspiration. And it is here at the surface that we may measure the **water balance**. An accountant keeps a record of financial income and expenditures and ends up with a bottom-line balance. The balance is positive when profits have been earned and negative when excess debts have been incurred. The balance of water at the Earth's surface can be described in similar terms, using methods devised by climatologist C. Warren Thornthwaite and his colleagues.

Water can be gained at the surface by precipitation or, more rarely, by horizontal transport in rivers, soil, or groundwater. Water may be lost by evapotranspiration or through runoff along or beneath the ground. The water balance at a location is calculated by matching the gains from precipitation with the losses through runoff and evapotranspiration. When actual evapotranspiration is used for the computation, the balance (in the absence of such human intervention as importing irrigation water) is always zero because no more water can run off or evaporate than is gained from precipitation. However, when potential evapotranspiration is taken into account, the balance may range from a constant surplus of water at the Earth's surface to a continual deficit. Figure 12.9 illustrates this range.

The Range of Water Balance Conditions

Bellary, located in the centre of southern India, exemplifies the water balance at a deficit (Fig. 12.9A). Through-out the year, the potential evapotranspiration exceeds the water gained in precipitation. On average, even during the time of the late-summer rains, the soil contains less water than it could hold. Because plants depend on water, the vegetation in this region is sparse, except where irrigation is possible.

At Bogor, on the most heavily populated Indonesian island of Jawa, the situation is reversed (Fig. 12.9B). During every month of the year, rainfall, sometimes as much as 45 cm in a single month, exceeds the amount of water that can be lost through evapotranspiration. The surplus water provides all that is needed for luxuriant vegetation, and still leaves copious quantities to run off the land surface.

An intermediate situation exists in Berkeley, California, adjacent to San Francisco (Fig. 12.9C). From November to March precipitation exceeds the potential evapotranspiration, but from April through October there is a water deficit. Starting in April, when potential evapotranspiration surpasses precipitation, soil moisture from below the ground is used in evaporation. Most of it is drawn up through the roots of plants and evaporates from their leaves. This process continues until the end of October, when rainfall once more exceeds potential evapotranspiration and the stock of available soil water is recharged. During this time runoff is more plentiful from California's winter storms.

The amount of runoff in any location cannot exceed the amount of precipitation, and usually there is much less runoff than precipitation. This is because some water almost always evaporates and/or infiltrates the soil. In 2004 the Government of Canada (with partners from Natural Resources Canada [NRCan], Statistics Canada, and Environment Canada) established "The Canada Water Accounts" as the first-ever attempt to

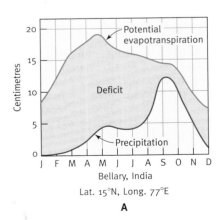

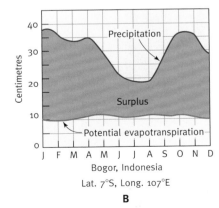

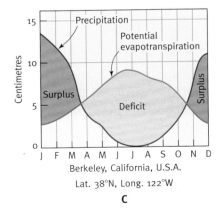

FIGURE 12.9   Range of water balance conditions. (A) Bellary, India, experiences a constant deficit because potential evapotranspiration always exceeds precipitation. (B) At Bogor, Indonesia, the situation is reversed, and a constant water surplus is recorded. (C) At Berkeley, California, across the bay from San Francisco, the intermediate situation occurs, with a combination of surplus and deficit at different times of the year.

produce a "budget" of Canada's water resources. These "accounts" reconcile supply from stream flow and precipitation with natural losses owing to evaporation, runoff, and water use. The water balance accounts can then be used to identify which areas are near water limitation, and therefore help us develop adaptation strategies to reduce vulnerability.

Water Balance Variations and Latitude

Across the globe as a whole, the values of precipitation, evaporation, and runoff vary greatly with latitude. As Fig. 12.10 shows, annual precipitation and runoff are highest near the Equator. Evaporation is also high in this low-latitude zone, but it is greatest in the subtropical latitudes (20 to 35 degrees). The upper midlatitudes (45 to 60 degrees) exhibit water surpluses. Precipitation, runoff, and evaporation are lowest in the highest latitudes. All the forces underlying this distribution of the three variables graphed in Fig. 12.10 are discussed in Units 7 to 11.

On this graph we are mainly looking at the results of differences in the radiant energy that reaches different latitudinal zones, and at global-scale currents of atmospheric and oceanic circulation. Near the Equator, stronger radiant energy from the Sun leads to high evaporation rates. It also causes air to rise, cool, and thereby yield large quantities of precipitation. In subtropical areas descending and warming air, in association with semipermanent high-pressure cells, produces clear weather. Here there are high rates of evaporation over the oceans, but little evaporation over the land surfaces because of the scarcity of moisture to be evaporated.

In the higher midlatitudes, eastward-moving storms (driven by the Westerlies and the Polar Front jet stream) provide moderate amounts of precipitation in most areas, but smaller quantities of radiant energy evaporate less of that water than would be the case in the low latitudes. In the high latitudes, the cold air can hold little water vapour. Consequently there is little precipitation, and given the low amounts of radiant energy received here, rates of evaporation are minimal. These relationships should be kept in mind as we now consider and compare the world distributions of evapotranspiration (Fig. 12.11) and precipitation (Fig. 12.12).

Population and the Water Balance

As a final exercise in this unit, let us reconsider the distribution of the Earth's population (see Fig. 2.5) in the context of the global patterns of evapotranspiration (Fig. 12.11) and precipitation (Fig. 12.12). This comparison will reveal that most people live in areas where there are neither great surpluses nor great deficits in the water balance.

For example, the great fertile zones of North America, Europe, and much of China are concentrated in midlatitude areas, which, year in and year out, do not usually experience excessive conditions of precipitation or evapotranspiration. Thus 75 cm of annual rainfall in the U.S. Corn Belt or the North China Plain may be far more effective for crop raising than the 200 cm received at a tropical location, where much of the moisture is removed by evapotranspiration.

The variability of precipitation is a phenomenon that concerns farmers around the world. In general, variability increases as the yearly precipitation total decreases. We pursue this matter in our survey of the dry climates in Unit 17, which features a map of the global distribution of annual precipitation variability (see Fig. 17.11).

Weather systems play a major role in shaping the temperature and moisture regimes of many climate types. Unit 13 relates the atmospheric moisture flows we have just learned about to the formation of weather systems.

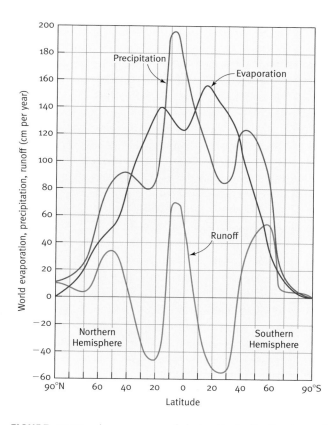

FIGURE 12.10 Average annual latitudinal distribution of precipitation, evaporation, and runoff for the entire surface of the Earth.

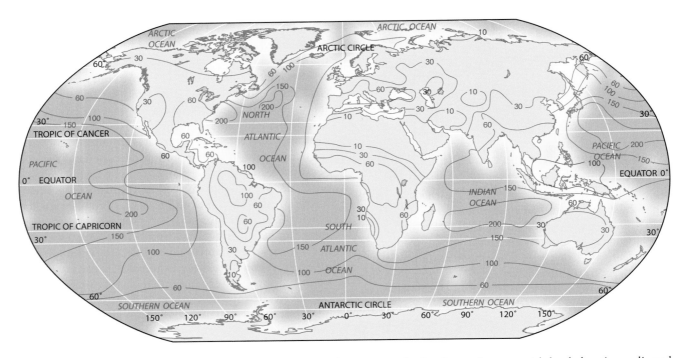

FIGURE 12.11   Global distribution of annual evaporation and evapotranspiration in centimetres, with land elevations adjusted to sea level. Red isolines show the pattern over land; blue isolines over the oceans.

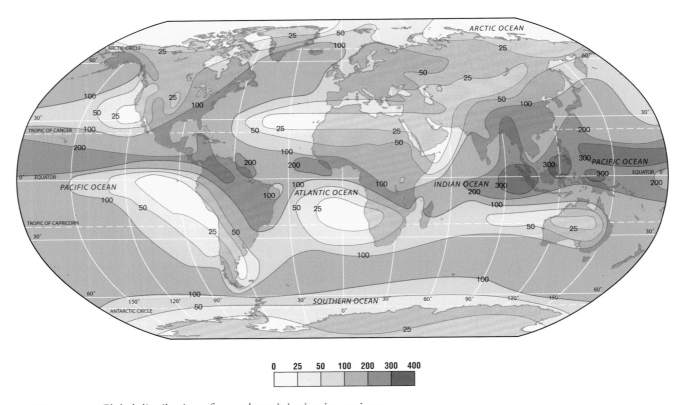

FIGURE 12.12   Global distribution of annual precipitation in centimetres.

KEY TERMS

actual evapotranspiration *page 152*	evaporation *page 147*	precipitation *page 148*
cirrus clouds *page 153*	evapotranspiration *page 152*	relative humidity *page 148*
cloud *page 152*	freezing *page 147*	runoff *page 148*
condensation *page 147*	hydrologic cycle *page 148*	stratus clouds *page 152*
condensation nuclei *page 152*	latent heat of fusion *page 147*	sublimation *page 147*
cumulus clouds *page 153*	latent heat of vaporization *page 147*	water balance *page 156*
dew *page 148*	melting *page 147*	water vapour *page 147*
dew point *page 148*	potential evapotranspiration *page 152*	

REVIEW QUESTIONS

1. Describe the energy requirements for the melting of ice and the evaporation of water.

2. Describe the various measures of atmospheric humidity and their relation to one another.

3. How does evaporation differ from evapotranspiration?

4. How does potential evapotranspiration differ from actual evapotranspiration?

5. Describe the two processes of raindrop formation.

6. Describe the necessary conditions for surface runoff within the context of the water balance.

REFERENCES AND FURTHER READINGS

BAUMGARTNER, A., and REICHEL, E. *The World Water Balance: Mean Annual Global, Continental, and Maritime Precipitation, Evaporation, and Runoff* (Amsterdam: Elsevier, 1975).

BIGG, G. R. *The Oceans and Climate* (New York: Cambridge Univ. Press, 1996).

GLEICK, P. H. *The World's Water 2000–2001: The Biennial Report on Freshwater Resources* (Washington, D.C.: Island Press, 2000).

HOUZE, R. A., Jr. *Cloud Dynamics* (San Diego, Calif.: Academic Press, 1993).

LEGATES, D. R., and MATHER, J. R. "An Evaluation of the Average Annual Global Water Balance," *Geographical Review,* 82 (1992), 253–267.

LEOPOLD, L. B. *Water: A Primer* (San Francisco: Freeman, 1974).

MASON, B. J. *Clouds, Rain and Rainmaking* (New York: Cambridge Univ. Press, 1975).

MATHER, J. R. *The Climate Water Budget in Environmental Analysis* (Lexington, Mass.: Heath, 1978).

MATHER, J. R. "Water Budget Climatology," in Susan Hanson, Ed., *Ten Geographic Ideas That Changed the World* (New Brunswick, N.J.: Rutgers Univ. Press, 1997), 108–124.

MATHER, J. R., and SANDERSON, M. *The Genius of C. Warren Thornthwaite, Climatologist-Geographer* (Norman, Okla.: Univ. of Oklahoma Press, 1996).

MILLER, D. H. *Water at the Surface of the Earth* (New York: Academic Press, 1977).

PIELOU, E. C. *Fresh Water* (Chicago: Univ. of Chicago Press, 1998).

STEVENS, W. K. "Expectation Aside, Water Use in U.S. Is Showing Decline," *New York Times* (November 10, 1998), A1, A16.

SUMNER, G. *Precipitation: Process and Analysis* (New York: Wiley, 1988).

THORNTHWAITE, C. W., and MATHER, J. R. *The Water Balance* (Centerton, N.J.: Drexel Institute of Technology, Laboratory of Climatology, Publications in Climatology, vol. 8, 1955).

"Water: The Power, Promise, and Turmoil of North America's Fresh Water," *National Geographic,* special ed. (November 1993).

WEB RESOURCES

http://atlas.gc.ca/site/english/maps/freshwater/consumption/ This Natural Resources Canada site provides maps of water consumption in Canada as well as a discussion of sectoral water uses.

http://observe.arc.nasa.gov/nasa/earth/hydrocycle/hydro1.html Overview of the components of the hydrologic cycle with graphics and animations.

http://www.ec.gc.ca/water/e_main.html Environment Canada's freshwater website.

http://wwwga.usgs.gov/edu/waterproperties.html A discussion of the physical and chemical properties of water, with links to information about capillary action and a self-quiz.

Precipitation, Air Masses, and Fronts

Dry air mass meets moist air over the northern Pacific Ocean near the Kurile Islands—a front in the making. (Authors' photo)

OBJECTIVES

- To discuss the four basic mechanisms for producing precipitation
- To develop the concept of air masses—their character, origin, movement patterns, and influence on precipitation
- To distinguish between cold fronts and warm fronts, and to describe their structure and behaviour as they advance

On a day-to-day basis, the atmosphere is organized into numerous weather systems that blanket the Earth. In this unit the connection is made between the atmospheric moisture flows covered in Unit 12 and the formation of those weather systems. Much of our attention is directed at the forces that cause the atmospheric lifting of moist air, thereby producing precipitation. This unit also introduces the concept of air masses—large uniform bodies of air that move across the surface as an organized whole—and the weather contrasts that occur along their advancing edges.

Lifting Mechanisms That Produce Precipitation

All precipitation originates from parcels of moist air that have been adiabatically cooled below their condensation level (dew-point temperature). This is accomplished through the lifting of air from the vicinity of the surface to higher levels in the atmosphere. The occurrence of at least one of four processes is necessary to induce the rising of moist air that will result in significant precipitation. On many occasions more than one process occurs, which may enhance the production of precipitation. These four precipitation-producing mechanisms involve (1) the forced lifting of air where low-level windflows converge; (2) the spontaneous rise of air, or convection; (3) the forced uplift of moving air that encounters mountains; and (4) the forced uplift of air at the edges of colliding air masses associated with cyclonic storms.

Convergent-Lifting Precipitation

Where warm, moist airflows converge at or very near the surface, particularly in the tropical latitudes, their molecules are forced to crowd together. This increases molecular kinetic energy, warms the combining windstreams, and induces the air to rise. Because the equatorial zone of convergence is already an area of relatively low atmospheric pressure (having pulled those winds toward it in the first place), the lifting of air here becomes more pronounced. The cooling of large quantities of water vapour in the uplifted air causes the rainfall that is so common in the wet tropics. As we would expect, the most prominent and durable tropical weather systems marked by this process of **convergent-lifting precipitation** lie where the trade winds from the Northern and Southern Hemispheres come together at the ITCZ.

The Inter-Tropical Convergence Zone

In the discussion of global wind belts and semipermanent pressure zones in Unit 10, it was noted that the Northeast and Southeast Trade Winds converge in the equatorial trough of low pressure. The rising air that results is responsible for the cloudiness and precipitation that mark the Inter-Tropical Convergence Zone (ITCZ). The ITCZ occurs at low latitudes all around the Earth, most notably above the oceans, particularly the equatorial Pacific. But the rainfall that its clouds deliver over the intervening continents and islands is vital to millions of inhabitants of tropical lowlands and hillsides, especially in the Indonesian archipelago of Southeast Asia and the Congo Basin in western equatorial Africa.

The ITCZ changes its location throughout the year, generally following the latitudinal corridor of maximum solar heating. Accordingly, as Fig. 13.1 demonstrates, the average July position of the ITCZ lies at about 10°N, whereas in January, at the opposite seasonal extreme, it is found hundreds of kilometres to the south. Although the ITCZ owes its origin to the position of the overhead Sun, this is not the only factor that determines its location. The distribution of land and sea, as well as the flows of the tropical atmosphere, is also important. Therefore, at any given moment the ITCZ may not be where generalized theory tells us it ought to be.

Closer inspection of Fig. 13.1 shows that in July the ITCZ is entirely absent in the Southern Hemisphere, when it is drawn northward to a latitudinal position beyond 20°N over southern Asia—as was pointed out in

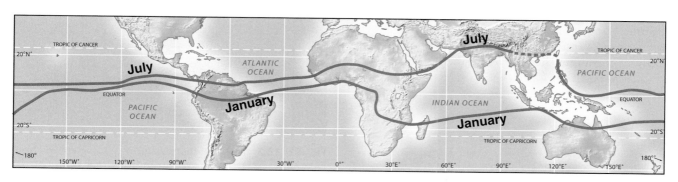

FIGURE 13.1 Average positions of the ITCZ in January and July. The wide annual swing over the northern Indian Ocean is associated with the regional-scale atmospheric circulations that produce the dry and wet monsoons in southern Asia, a topic treated in Unit 10.

the discussion of the wet monsoon in Unit 10. Yet in January the ITCZ ranges from a southernmost extreme of 20°S, above northern Australia, to a northernmost position within the Northern Hemisphere tropics in the oceans adjoining South America. Not unexpectedly, the moisture regimes of areas lying inside the broad latitudinal band mapped in Fig. 13.1 are decidedly boosted as the ITCZ continually shifts across this region.

Convectional Precipitation

Convection denotes spontaneous vertical air movement in the atmosphere, and **convectional precipitation** occurs after condensation of the upward-moving air. The process of convection is generally localized, usually covering only a few square kilometres of the surface. Convection begins when this relatively small area is heated steadily and intensely by insolation and the parcel of overlying air is rapidly warmed through its contact with the now hot surface.

A rising column of air, known as a *convection cell,* develops quickly. The temperature of this upward-flowing air cools at the dry adiabatic lapse rate (DALR) of 1°C per 100 m. (As noted in Unit 8, the DALR is the cooling rate of rising unsaturated air.) This cooling rate continues as long as the relative humidity of the rising air remains below 100 percent. When the dew point is reached, condensation commences and a small cumulus cloud forms. That cloud soon mushrooms as the added energy of the latent heat released by the condensing water vapour converts the original convection cell into an ever more powerful updraft.

Very large cumulus clouds of the towering cumulonimbus type can now develop if three conditions are met. First, there must be sufficient water vapour in the updraft to sustain the formation of the cloud. Second, the immediate atmosphere must be unstable, so that the upward airflow originally triggered in the surface-layer convection cell is able to persist to a very high altitude. And third, there must be relatively weak winds aloft. With these conditions satisfied, we are likely to encounter the type of weather associated with *thunderstorms.**

---

* Although thunderstorms are discussed here in conjunction with convectional precipitation, it should be noted that this type of severe weather can also be produced by other lifting mechanisms. All thunderstorms are triggered by the uplifting of moist, unstable air and the release of enough latent heat to fuel continuing uplift. Some of the most severe are squall-line thunderstorms generated by particularly abrupt uplifting in advance of a rapidly moving cold front, which we discuss in the section on frontal precipitation on page 169.

Thunderstorms

Thunderstorms are common in both the low and middle latitudes, especially during afternoon hours in the warmest months of the year. Like the larger-scale storm systems discussed in Unit 14, thunderstorms have a distinct life cycle. Although that cycle rarely lasts longer than a few hours, these smaller-scale weather systems can attain sizeable dimensions. For example, the massive thunderclouds shown in Fig. 13.2 were easily discerned by astronauts as they orbited above the tropical Indian Ocean to the east of the African continent.

The **life cycle of a thunderstorm** begins with the onset of the convection process in an unstable atmosphere as moist heated air rises, undergoes condensation, and releases large quantities of latent heat. This heat energy makes the air much warmer than its surroundings, and the resulting updrafts of warm air attain speeds of about 10 m per second. They can sometimes move as fast as 30 m per second in this *developing stage,* as Fig. 13.3A indicates. Raindrops and ice crystals may form at

FIGURE 13.2 Massive thunderstorm photographed from an orbiting space vehicle over the Indian Ocean east of Madagascar. With a diameter of nearly 100 km and an anvil cloud reaching 16 km in height, a storm of this type generates powerful windflow at the surface and strong vertical currents resulting in heavy rains.

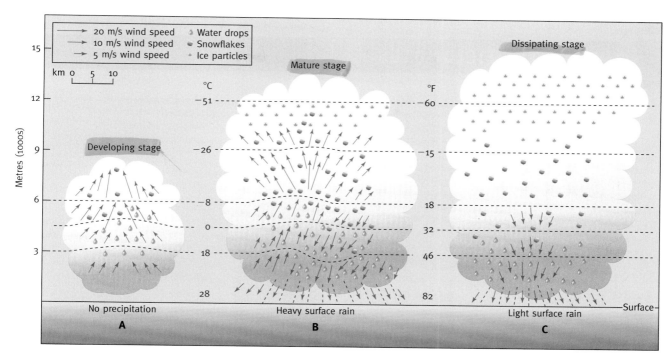

FIGURE 13.3 Life cycle of a thunderstorm. The developing stage (A) involves increasingly rapid updrafts, the mature stage (B) is associated with both updrafts and downdrafts, and the dissipating stage (C) is largely one of cool downdrafts. The arrows indicate the direction and speed of the vertical air currents.

this stage, but they do not reach the ground because of the updrafts.

When the middle, *mature stage* is reached, the updrafts continue, producing towering cumulonimbus clouds. More significantly, however, enough raindrops fall to also cause downdrafts of cold air. Evaporation from the falling drops accentuates the cooling. Heavy rain now begins to fall from the bottom of the cloud (Fig. 13.3B), and cold air at that level spreads out in a wedge formation. At the same time, the top of the cloud is often drawn out by upper-air winds to form an *anvil top,* so named because it resembles the shape of a blacksmith's anvil.

Within a few hours, the moisture in the storm is used up. The final, *dissipating stage* occurs when the latent heat source starts to fail. Downdrafts gradually predominate over updrafts, and this situation continues until the storm dies away (Fig. 13.3C).

Thunderstorm-Related Phenomena

A precipitation phenomenon associated with thunderstorms in the midlatitudes is the formation of *hail.* Figure 13.3B shows that, in the mature stage of the storm, an ice crystal might be caught in a circulation that continually moves it above and below the freezing level. This circulation pattern can create concentric shells of ice in

the hailstone. In some storms, such as a *squall-line storm,* these circulations can be exaggerated. Figure 13.5 demonstrates how falling hailstones can be scooped back into the main cloud by the intense circulation around such a storm system. Thus hailstones may experience several journeys through the freezing level before falling to Earth. Many a farmer's crop has been destroyed because of these conditions, when hailstones as large as softballs can bombard the ground (see Fig. 12.8D). Figure 13.5 also indicates that squall-line storms can generate even more severe weather in the form of *tornadoes* (see Perspective: Tornadoes and Their Consequences).

Lightning and *thunder* are related phenomena, and both are a result of the thunderstorm's powerful vertical air currents. Although the exact mechanism is not fully understood, cloud droplets and ice crystals acquire electrical charges. This electric energy, in the form of lightning strokes, makes intermittent contact with the ground. These lightning strokes also rapidly heat the surrounding air, which expands explosively—producing thunder.

Thunderstorms do not usually exist as a single cell such as in the simplified storm in Fig. 13.3. Radar studies have shown that thunderstorms actually consist of several cells organized into clusters, ranging from 2 to 8 km in diameter. Occasionally these clusters expand over a much wider area and assume their own rotation, thereby forming *supercells* and even larger *mesoscale con-*

FROM THE FIELDNOTES

FIGURE 13.4 "The city of Singapore lies as close to the Equator as any major city in the world—and it lies on an island as well. On most days of the year you can look southward over the warm, island-studded waters between the Malay Peninsula and the Indonesian island of Sumatera and watch the cumulonimbus clouds build to 10,000 m and higher, developing windswept anvils and generating powerful thunderstorms."

vective complexes. As the storms advance, new cells develop to replace old ones that dissipate. If the downdrafts of two cells meet at the surface, a new updraft and a new cell can form.

Convectional thunderstorms are the dominant type of precipitation in the equatorial zone and are especially active in the vicinity of the ITCZ (where the convergence of the trade winds accentuates the uplifting of air). Heat is a constant feature of the surface environment in the low latitudes. That heat, coupled with the generally high water-vapour content of tropical equatorial air, produces impressive convectional storms of the type seen in Fig. 13.2.

Orographic Precipitation

Mountains, and highlands in general, strongly influence air and moisture flows in the atmosphere. During *orographic uplift* (*oros* is the Greek word for mountain), a moving mass of air encounters a mountain range or other

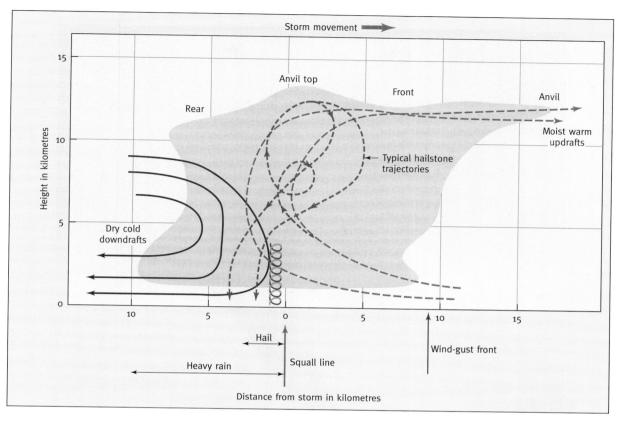

FIGURE 13.5 Model of a thunderstorm producing sizeable hailstones. This squall-line storm is advancing from left to right.

PERSPECTIVES ON THE HUMAN ENVIRONMENT

Tornadoes and Their Consequences

The interiors of large continents, especially in the spring and early summer, experience severe thunderstorms, which can produce tornadoes, nature's most vicious weather. A **tornado** is a small vortex of air, averaging 100 to 500 m in diameter, that descends to the ground from rotating clouds at the base of a violent thunderstorm. If the twister forms over a water surface, it is called a *waterspout*.

The pressure in the centre of such a spinning funnel cloud may be 100 to 200 mb below the pressure of the surrounding air. This triggers highly destructive winds, whose speeds can range from

50 to 130 m per second. Tornadoes tend to follow rather straight paths that can leave swaths of destruction up to 160 km long and 900 m wide. Their awesome, often dark colour is accentuated by the vegetation, loose soil, and other objects sucked into the centre tube of this gigantic vacuum cleaner (Fig. 13.6).

Most people are aware of the havoc that tornadoes wreak in parts of the United States, but few are aware of how frequently and severely Canada is struck by tornadoes. In an average year, approximately 80 tornadoes strike Canada, resulting in an

FIGURE 13.6   Nature's most violent weather is associated with tornadoes. At least 80 of these twisters strike Canada in any given year, most commonly during the spring and summer months of May to September.

average of two deaths in addition to tens of millions of dollars in property damage. Numerous others may go undetected in more remote or rural areas. This still contrasts sharply with the United States, which experiences more severe thunderstorms than any other landmass on Earth. Each year these 10,000-plus storms spawn more than 1000 tornadoes, resulting in an average of 90 deaths per year. About 20 percent of these tornadoes are classified as "strong," and even those that are categorized as "weak" can exhibit winds in excess of 45 m per second. These tornadoes typically develop over the Great Plains and the Midwest, particularly in the north–south corridor known as "Tornado Alley," which extends through central Texas, Oklahoma, Kansas, and eastern Nebraska. Here dry air from the high western plateaus moves eastward into the Plains, where it meets warm, moist, low-level air swept northward from the Gulf of Mexico. When this maritime tropical Gulf air collides with the drier air, the different temperature and humidity characteristics of these air masses create a volatile mixture that can unleash especially violent thunderstorms. Canada's "Tornado Alleys" are located in southern Ontario, Alberta, and southeastern Quebec, as well as in a band that stretches from southern Saskatchewan and Manitoba through to Thunder Bay. The interior of British Columbia and western New Brunswick also have tornado zones.

The deadliest twister on record in the United States was the so-called Tri-State Tornado, which on March 18, 1925, barrelled across parts of Missouri, Illinois, and Indiana, killing 689 people and injuring another 1980 in less than 45 minutes. The deadliest tornado to strike Canada occurred on June 30, 1912, slashing through six city blocks in Regina. The twister killed 28 people, injured hundreds, and destroyed 500 buildings in only three minutes. The largest outbreak of tornadoes in a 24-hour period occurred on April 3,1974, when 148 twisters killed 315 people in the American Midwest and Southeast. One of the worst single disasters in recent Canadian history occurred when a tornado ripped through the Green Acres campground at Pine Lake, Alberta, on July 14, 2000 (Fig. 13.7). The popular vacation site was crowded with over 1000 campers, resulting in 11 people killed and 136 injured.

The conditions that triggered the Green Acres tornado were detected by Environment Canada and reported as a severe thunderstorm watch. The warning also included a reminder that some severe thunderstorms can produce tornadoes. In Canada and the United States, tornado warnings are usually issued on visual confirmation of funnel clouds having touched down or with Doppler radar evidence. At 7:05 p.m. MDT the RCMP notified Environment Canada's Prairie Storm Prediction Centre that a tornado had just been reported at Pine Lake. The severe thunderstorm warning was immediately upgraded to a tornado warning. Warnings and watches were continued through the evening hours of July 14. More than 40 watches and warnings were issued for Alberta and Saskatchewan. Although the alert came too late for those at Pine Lake, forecasters continue to improve their predictions with Doppler radar and more-advanced weather-tracking equipment. Meteorologists today are integrating radar, satellite, and computer technology to make tornado detection and warning more precise than ever, and the occurrence of unpredicted tornadoes is becoming a rare event.

Tornado warnings do not always require high technology, however. Across Canada, volunteer "weather watchers" have done what technology may have failed to do. When weather watchers spot tornadoes, thunderstorms, or other severe weather, they report it to Environment Canada. On July 31, 1987, a deadly tornado heading toward Edmonton was spotted by a volunteer observer, Tom Taylor, a pharmacist in Leduc, Alberta, 24 km away. He immediately called Environment Canada, which promptly issued a life-saving warning to thousands of Canadians.

FIGURE 13.7   Tornado damage at Pine Lake, 2000.

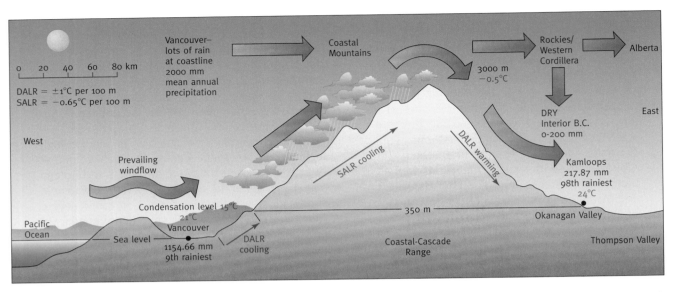

FIGURE 13.8   Orographic precipitation on the upper windward slope of the Coastal-Cascade Mountains in western British Columbia. Note the significant temperature and moisture differences between the windward and leeward sides of this major mountain barrier. (Horizontal scale is not exact.)

upland zone over which it is forced to rise, propelled by surface winds and the push of air piling up behind it. When a mountain range is close to and parallels the coast, and when prevailing onshore winds carry maritime air laden with moisture, not much cooling is needed to trigger condensation during the forced ascent of this airflow. The rain (and often snow) that results from this lifting process is called **orographic precipitation**.

This precipitation on the range's windward slopes, however, is not matched on the inland-facing leeward slopes. Quite to the contrary, the lee side of the range is marked by dryness because much of the water vapour gained over the ocean has been precipitated out during the windward-slope ascent. Once the mass of air crests the range in a stable atmosphere that does not force it to continue to rise, the air immediately descends to lower altitudes, thereby warming rapidly and reducing its relative humidity (i.e., increasing its capacity to hold whatever moisture remains).

Stages of Orographic Uplift

A classic example of this orographic effect exists along most of the west coast of North America, where the Sierra Nevada, the Cascade Mountains, and the coastal mountains form a north–south wall extending from Southern California well into Canada. Figure 13.8 illustrates the eastward-moving passage of moist Pacific air across the Coastal and Cascade Mountains of southwestern British Columbia, specifically between Vancou-

ver at the edge of the southern Strait of Georgia and Kamloops in the Thompson Valley, located in south-central British Columbia. Between these two cities lies the Stein Valley Provincial Park, with peaks rising to 2925 m at the summit of Skihist Mountain.

Let us assume that a parcel of air with a temperature of 21°C arrives at the near-sea-level western base of the coastal mountains in Vancouver. This parcel of air begins its forced ascent of the mountain range and starts to cool at the DALR (1°C/100 m). At this rate, the air parcel cools to 15°C by the time it reaches 600 m. Now assume that the air reaches its dew point at this temperature and condensation begins. Clouds quickly form, and continued cooling soon leads to heavy rainfall as the air parcel continues to make its way up the windward slope.

Because saturation has occurred and condensation has begun, however, the air above 600 m cools more slowly at the saturated adiabatic lapse rate (SALR)—here assumed to average 0.65°C/100 m. By the time the uplifted air reaches the mountaintop at an altitude of 3000 m, its temperature is some 15.5°C lower, or −0.5°C. Since this temperature is below the freezing point, precipitation near the summit will fall as snow. (In winter, of course, freezing and snowfall will commence at a lower elevation on the mountainside.)

Now having crested the range in an atmospheric environment presumed to be stable, the air parcel seeks to return to its original level and swiftly descends to the warmer layer of the lower atmosphere. The air is now no

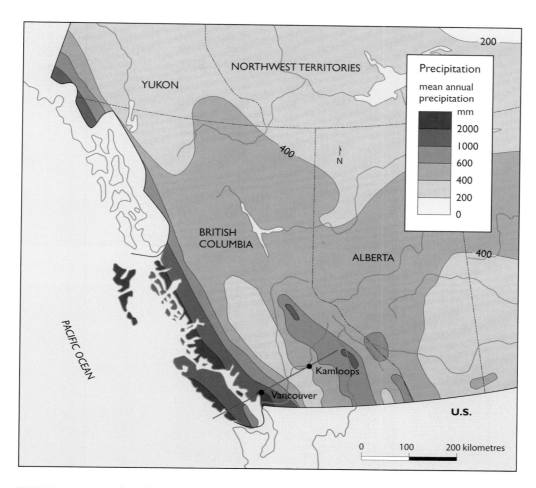

FIGURE 13.9   British Columbia's precipitation pattern, with the distribution of isohyets exhibiting the results of the orographic effect as westerly winds off the Pacific are forced across the north–south-trending Coastal-Cascade Mountains. The transect across the Coastal-Cascades between Vancouver and Kamloops, diagrammed in Fig. 13.8, is marked by a red line.

longer saturated, so the air parcel warms at the DALR. When it reaches the bottom of the 2400-m leeward slope, its temperature will have risen by 24.5°C to 24°C. Thus our air parcel is now noticeably warmer on the lee side of the range, even though the elevation around Kamloops is 300 m higher than at Vancouver. It is also much drier, as explained before, and the generally dry conditions caused by this orographic process is termed the **rain shadow effect**.

In the absence of new moisture sources, rain shadows can extend for hundreds of kilometres. This is the case throughout most of far western North America, because once Pacific moisture is removed from the atmosphere, it cannot be locally replenished. Figure 13.9 vividly illustrates the rain shadow covering the central region of British Columbia. Secondary orographic precipitation occurs as air rises over the Rocky Mountains in the province's eastern border with Alberta.

Leeward areas also frequently experience the rapid movement of warm, dry air known as a *foehn* (pronounced *fern* with the "r" silent) wind. Above the western plateaus of Canada and the United States, these airflows are called *chinook* winds and can sometimes reach sustained speeds approaching 50 m per second.

Frontal (Cyclonic) Precipitation

A fourth process that generates precipitation is associated with the collision of air masses of significantly different temperatures. Such activity is a common occurrence in the middle and upper-middle latitudes, where the general atmospheric circulation causes poleward-flowing tropical air to collide with polar air moving toward the Equator. Because converging warm and cold air masses possess different densities, they do not

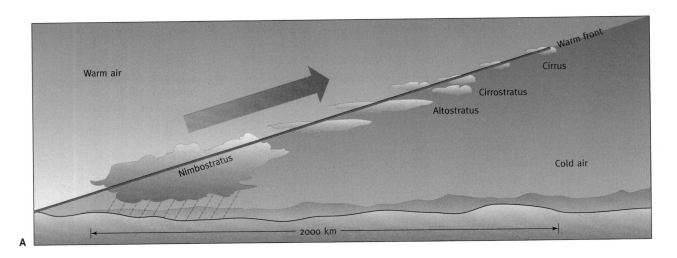

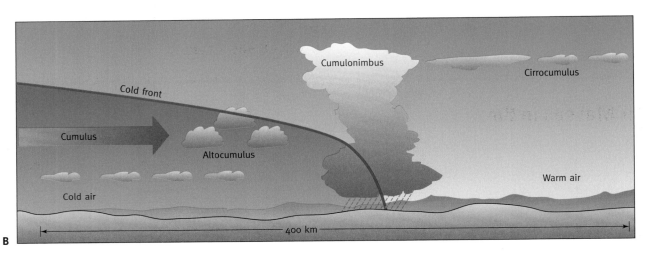

FIGURE 13.10 Warm front (A) and cold front (B) in cross-sectional profile, showing their associated cloud types.

readily mix. Rather, the denser cold air will inject itself beneath and push the lighter warm air upward. And if the warmer air approaches a stationary mass of cooler air, it will ride up over the cooler air. In both situations we have the lifting of warm, often moist air, the cooling of which soon produces condensation, clouds, and precipitation.

Air masses are bounded by surfaces along which contact occurs with neighbouring air masses possessing different characteristics. Therefore such narrow boundary zones mark sharp transitions in density, humidity, and especially temperature. Whenever warm and cool air are in contact like this, the boundary zone is called a **front**. Although fronts can be stationary, they usually advance. Thus a moving front is the leading edge of the air mass built up behind it. When warm air is lifted, cooled, and its water vapour condensed as a result of frontal movement, **frontal precipitation** is produced.

When a warm air mass infringes upon a cooler one, the lighter warmer air overrides the cooler air. This produces a boundary called a **warm front** (Fig. 13.10A). Warm fronts, because of their gentle upward slope, are associated with wide areas of light to moderate precipitation that extend out well ahead of the actual surface passage of the front. As indicated in the diagram, warm fronts involve the entire sequence of stratus clouds, ranging from upper-level cirrostratus down through altostratus and nimbostratus layers (see Fig. 12.7).

The behaviour of a cold front is far more dramatic. A **cold front** is produced when the cold air, often acting like a bulldozer, hugs the surface and pushes all other air upward as it wedges itself beneath the pre-existing warmer air (Fig. 13.10B). A cold front also assumes a steeper slope than a warm front, causing more abrupt cooling and condensation in the warm air that is uplifted just ahead of it. This produces a smaller but much more intense zone of precipitation, which usually exhibits the kind of stormy weather associated with the convectional precipitation process discussed earlier. Not surprisingly, cold fronts exhibit a variety of cumulus-type clouds, particularly the clusters of cumulonimbus clouds that are the signature of squall-line thunderstorms. But once the swiftly passing violent weather ends, the cool air mass behind the front produces generally fair and dry weather.

Frontal precipitation is frequently called *cyclonic precipitation* because it is closely identified with the passage of the warm and cold fronts that are essential components of the cyclones that shape the weather patterns of the midlatitudes. In Unit 14, which treats weather systems, we examine the life cycle of these storm cells and their fronts, extending the discussion developed here. The rest of this unit takes a closer look at air masses (whose movement triggers these weather systems) and introduces a geographic classification based on the source regions of air masses.

Air Masses in the Atmosphere

In large, relatively uniform expanses of the world, such as the snow-covered Arctic wastes or the warm tropical oceans, masses of air in contact with the surface may remain stationary for several days. As the air hovers over these areas, it takes on the properties of the underlying surface, such as the icy coldness of the polar zones or the warmth and high humidity of the maritime tropics. Extensive geographic areas with relatively uniform characteristics of temperature and moisture form the **source regions** where air masses can be produced.

The air above a source region will reach an equilibrium with the temperature and moisture conditions of the surface. An **air mass** can thus be defined as a very large parcel of air in the boundary layer of the troposphere that possesses relatively uniform qualities of temperature, density, and humidity in the horizontal dimension. In addition to its large size, which is regarded by meteorologists to be at least 1600 km across, an air mass must be bound together as a cohesive unit. This is necessary because air masses travel as distinct entities, covering hundreds of kilometres as they are steered away from their source regions by the airflows of the general atmospheric circulation.

Classifying Air Masses

To keep track of their identities as they migrate, air masses are given letter codes that reflect the type of surface and the general location of their source region. These codes

are as follows: maritime (**m**) or continental (**c**) and tropical (**T**) or polar (**P**). In a warm source region, such as the Caribbean Sea, the equilibrium of temperature and moisture in an overlying air mass is established in two or three days. Unstable air in either a maritime tropical (**mT**) air mass or a continental tropical (**cT**) air mass is warmed to a height of about 3000 m.

In contrast, within cold source regions air masses can take a week or more to achieve equilibrium with their underlying surfaces. Only a relatively shallow layer of air, up to about 900 m, cools in continental polar (**cP**) or maritime polar (**mP**) air masses. Of course, the air above that level is cold as well, but for reasons other than contact with the surface. It takes such a relatively long time for a cold air mass to become established because cooling at its base stabilizes lapse rates, thereby preventing vertical mixing and prohibiting efficient heat exchange.

In addition to the four leading types of air masses (**mT, cT, mP,** and **cP**) already discussed, three more can be recognized. The first is found in the highest latitudes and is called continental Arctic (**cA**) (or continental Antarctic [**cAA**] in the Southern Hemisphere); paradoxically, these form at higher latitudes than the polar air masses do. The final two are found in the lowest latitudes astride the Equator and are labelled continental equatorial (**cE**) and maritime equatorial (**mE**). The letter pairs used to label air masses are sometimes supplemented by letters that indicate whether the mass is colder (**k**) or warmer (**w**) than the underlying surface, and whether the air is stable (**s**) or unstable (**u**). Thus a maritime tropical air mass that is warmer than the ocean below it and unstable is designated as **mTwu.**

Movements of Air Masses

If you live in the midwestern United States, you can testify to the bitterness of the polar air that streams southward from Canada in the winter and the oppressiveness of the warm humid air that flows northward from the Gulf of Mexico in the summer. Air masses affect not only their source areas, but also the regions across which they migrate. As an air mass moves, it may become somewhat modified by contact with the surface or by changes within the air, but many of its original characteristics remain identifiable far from its source region. This is a boon to weather forecasters, because they can predict weather conditions more accurately if they know the persisting characteristics of a moving air mass as well as its rate and direction of movement.

The principal air masses affecting North America are shown in Fig. 13.11. The arrows represent the most common paths of movement away from the various source regions indicated on the map. If the contents of this map look like a military battle plan, that may be because opposing air masses fight for supremacy throughout the year. Losses and gains of territory in this battle are controlled by one important factor: the Polar Front and its associated jet stream. The main current of a river does not let eddies pass from one bank to another, and so it is with the Polar Front jet stream, which provides an unseen barrier to advancing air masses. This is a key to understanding weather in most of Canada, and our discussion of the Polar Front jet stream, begun in Unit 10, is developed further in Unit 14.

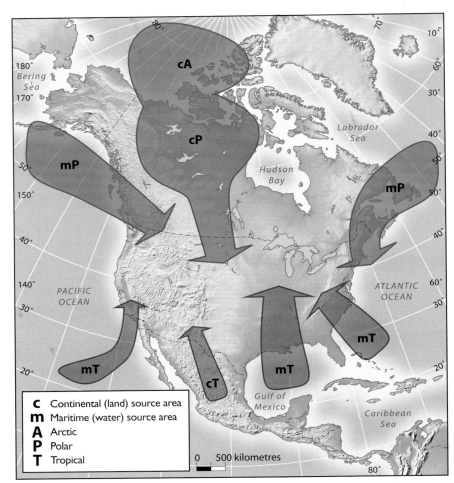

FIGURE 13.11   Source regions and the most likely paths of the principal air masses that affect North America.

KEY TERMS

REVIEW QUESTIONS

1. What are the necessary conditions for convectional precipitation? What are some of the more severe types of weather associated with this type of precipitation?
2. Describe the geographic pattern of precipitation on the windward and leeward flanks of a mountain range.
3. Describe the general precipitation characteristics associated with a warm front.
4. Describe the general precipitation characteristics associated with a cold front.
5. Describe the characteristics of the four major air mass types: **mT, cT, mP,** and **cP.**
6. Describe the internal structure of a tornado and explain why these twisters are capable of so much destruction.

REFERENCES AND FURTHER READINGS

APPLEBOME, P.   "After a Twister [in Saragosa, Texas]: Coping in a Town That Isn't There," *New York Times* (May 24, 1987), 1, 18.

BATTAN, L. J.   *Fundamentals of Meteorology* (Englewood Cliffs, N.J.: Prentice-Hall, 2nd ed., 1984), chapters 6 and 7.

BLUESTEIN, H. B.   *Tornado Alley: Monster Storms of the Great Plains* (New York: Oxford Univ. Press, 1999).

DAVIES-JONES, R.   "Tornadoes," *Scientific American* (August 1995), 49–57.

DE BLIJ, H. J., Ed.   *Nature on the Rampage* (Washington, D.C.: Smithsonian Institution Press, 1994).

FEW, A. A.   "Thunder," *Scientific American* (July 1975), 80–90.

GRAZULIS, T. P.   *The Tornado: Nature's Ultimate Windstorm* (Norman, Okla.: Univ. of Oklahoma Press, 2001).

KESSLER, E., Ed.   *Thunderstorm Morphology and Dynamics* (Norman, Okla.: Univ. of Oklahoma Press, 2nd ed., 1986).

MIDDLETON, W.   *History of Theories of Rain and Other Forms of Precipitation* (Chicago: Univ. of Chicago Press, 1968).

PAUL, A.   "Prairie Tornadoes," *Atmosphere-Ocean,* 19 (1981), 66–70.

PAUL, A.   "The Thunderstorm Hazard on the Canadian Prairies," *Geoforum,* 13 (1982), 275–288.

ROBINSON, A.   *Earth Shock: Hurricanes, Volcanoes, Earthquakes, Tornadoes and Other Forces of Nature* (New York: Thames and Hudson, 1993).

Significant Tornadoes: 1871–1991 (St. Johnsbury, Vt.: Tornado Project, 1993).

SNOW, J. T.   "The Tornado," *Scientific American* (April 1984), 86–96.

Tornado Terror: (CBC News Report, July 14, 2000), http://www.cbc.ca/news/indepth/facts/tornado.html.

WHITEMAN, C. D.   *Mountain Meteorology: Fundamentals and Applications* (New York: Oxford Univ. Press, 2000).

WILLIAMS, E. R.   "The Electrification of Thunderstorms," *Scientific American* (November 1988), 88–99.

WEB RESOURCES

http://archive.greenpeace.org/~climate/flood_report/1-3.html
An explanation of the geographic distribution of precipitation, as well as descriptions of the different types of precipitation.

http://www.pnr-rpn.ec.gc.ca/air/summersevere/ae00s02.en.html
Environment Canada's tornado website.

http://www.spc.noaa.gov/faq/tornado   Guide to general tornado information, including real-time monitoring.

http://www.tpub.com/weather1/4c.htm   A description of cloud and precipitation features of warm and cold fronts, with satellite imagery of frontal systems.

Weather Systems

Swirling clouds mark the approach of a cyclonic weather system as Western Europe still enjoys the clear skies of an anticyclone. In a few hours the front will strike Ireland, then move across Britain and the mainland.

OBJECTIVES

- To demonstrate the importance of migrating weather systems in the global weather picture

- To discuss the significant tropical weather systems, particularly hurricanes
- To explain how midlatitude cyclones are formed,

and to describe the weather patterns associated with them

Weather systems are organized phenomena of the atmosphere—with inputs and outputs and changes of energy and moisture. Unlike the semipermanent pressure cells and windflows of the general circulation, these transient weather systems are secondary features of the atmosphere that are far more limited in their magnitude and duration. Such recurring weather systems, together with the constant flows of moisture, radiation, and heat energy, make up our daily weather. This unit focuses on the migrating atmospheric disturbances we call **storms**. We begin by looking at the storm systems of the tropics, which are typically associated with heavy precipitation. We then shift our focus from the low latitudes to the storm systems that punctuate the weather patterns of the middle and higher latitudes.

Low-Latitude Weather Systems

The equatorial and tropical latitudes are marked by a surplus of heat, which provides the energy to propel winds and to evaporate the large quantities of seawater that are often carried by them. The abundance of water vapour, convergence of the trade winds, and frequent convection produce the heavy rains that are observed in the tropics. Two of the major low-latitude weather systems are covered in other units. In Unit 13 we discuss the largest system, the Inter-Tropical Convergence Zone (ITCZ), and in Unit 10 we examine the related monsoonal circulation of coastal Asia. Here we investigate the smaller-scale, moving weather systems that recur in tropical regions—easterly waves and hurricanes.

Easterly Waves

For centuries, people have known about the trade winds, the constant easterly surface flow of tropical air between 30°N and 30°S latitude. But only within the past four decades has it been discovered that this flow is frequently modified by wavelike phenomena that give rise to distinctive weather systems. Unit 9 explains that geostrophic winds parallel isobars. If we apply this relationship to Fig. 14.1, we see that the isobars indicate the easterly trade winds blowing across the tropical North Atlantic Ocean. The **easterly wave** depicted represents a vertical perturbation within the general flow of these winds.

Through fairly complex mechanisms, this easterly wave produces both uplift and descent of air. Westward-moving air is forced to rise on the upwind side of the wave and descend on the downwind side. Thus on the eastern side of such a wave, we can expect to find towering cumulus clouds and often heavy rainfall. But clear weather occurs on the leading western side of the low-pressure wave trough because the air column decreases in depth, and atmospheric subsidence prevails.

Weather systems associated with easterly waves (which also go by their more popular name, *tropical waves*) are most frequently observed in the Caribbean Basin. Similar phenomena are also common in the west-central Pacific and in the seas off China's central east coast. These systems travel toward the west at about 18 to 26 km/h and are relatively predictable in their movement. But for reasons that are not well understood, each

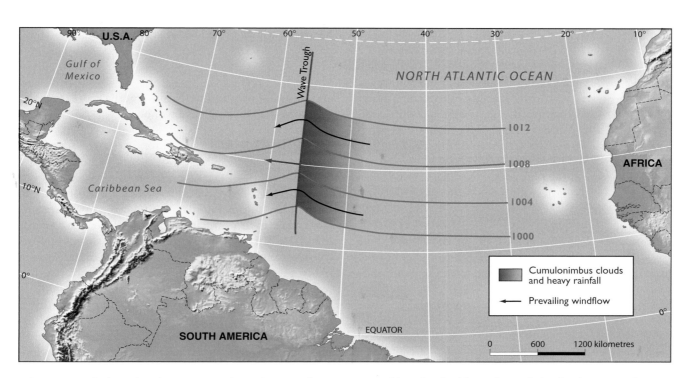

FIGURE 14.1   Isobars showing a westward-moving easterly wave approaching the Caribbean Sea and the development of towering rain clouds along its trailing limb.

year certain easterly waves increase their intensity. As these weak low-pressure troughs deepen, they begin to assume a rotating, cyclonic organization. Such a disturbance is called a *tropical depression.* If the low intensifies and sustained wind speeds surpass 63 km/h, the weather system becomes a *tropical storm.* Further development is possible, and if the now fully formed tropical cyclone exhibits sustained winds in excess of 119 km/h, a hurricane is born.

Hurricanes

An intensely developed tropical cyclone is one of the most fascinating and potentially destructive features of the atmosphere. These severe storms go by different names in different regions of the world. In the western Atlantic and eastern Pacific Oceans they are called **hurricanes,** the term we employ here. Elsewhere they are known as *typhoons* (western North Pacific) or *tropical cyclones* (Indian Ocean).

The tropical cyclone is a tightly organized, moving low-pressure system, normally originating at sea in the warm, moist air of the low-latitude atmosphere. As with all cyclonic storms, it has distinctly circular wind and pressure fields (see Fig. 9.9A). In Fig. 14.2, a satellite image of Hurricane Mitch, which ravaged parts of Central America in 1998, the circular windflow extends vertically, and the pinwheel-like cloud pattern associated with the centre of the system reminds us of its cyclonic origin.

The World Meteorological Organization describes a hurricane as having wind speeds greater than 119 km/h and a central surface pressure below 900 mb. However, in the most severe storms, such as Hurricane Gilbert (which in 1988 exhibited the lowest pressure ever recorded in the Western Hemisphere as it smashed its way westward across the Caribbean Sea), wind speeds can exceed 320 km/h and cause massive destruction.

The hurricane's structure is diagrammed in Fig. 14.3. A striking feature is the open **eye** that dominates the middle of the cyclonic system, the "hole in the doughnut" from which spiral bands of cloud extend outward, often reaching an altitude of 16 km. The strongest winds and heaviest rainfall (up to 50 cm per day) are found in the **eye wall,** the towering cloud tube that marks the rim of the eye. Within the eye itself, which extends vertically through the full height of the storm, winds are light and there is little rain as dry cool air descends down the entire length of the central column. Temperatures vary little throughout the area of a tropical cyclone, which has an average diameter of about 500 km. But the diameter can vary from 80 km to about 2500 km. In general, the greater the amounts of energy

FIGURE 14.2 The eye of Hurricane Mitch is still over water, but this 1998 storm is poised to strike Central America and will become the costliest natural disaster in the modern history of the Western Hemisphere. Honduras will be hit hardest, with nearly 10,000 deaths and the loss of over 150,000 homes, 34,000 km of roads, and 335 bridges. When it is over, nearly one-quarter of the country's 6.4 million people will be homeless, and most of the agricultural economy will be ruined. Honduras and adjacent areas of neighbouring Nicaragua will carry Mitch's scars for generations to come.

and moisture involved in the system, the more extensive and powerful the hurricane will be.

Hurricane Development   Hurricanes are efficient machines for drawing large quantities of excess heat away from the ocean surface and transporting them into the upper atmosphere. Accordingly, they are most likely to form in late summer and autumn when tropical sea surfaces reach their peak annual temperatures (i.e., greater than 27°C). The origin of these tropical storms appears to be related to easterly waves and the equatorial trough of low pressure. However, many aspects of hurricane formation are still only partially understood, particularly the exact triggering mechanism that transforms fewer than one of every 10 easterly waves into a tropical cyclone. Nonetheless, meteorologists are making progress in their efforts to forecast these storms, and the development of new predictive tools has improved the accuracy of hurricane-track forecasting by more than 25 percent since 1990.

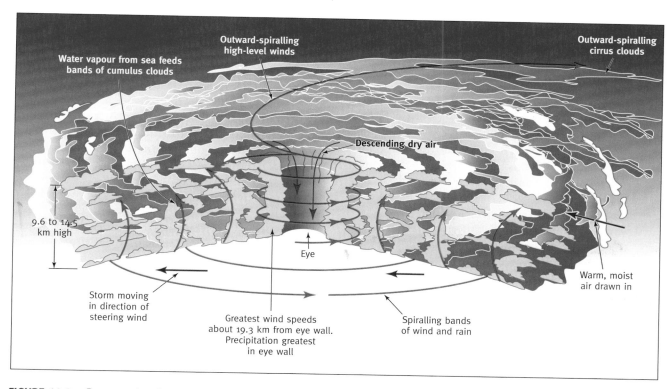

FIGURE 14.3 Cross-sectional view of a hurricane showing its mechanics and component parts.

From studies of past storms it is known that hurricanes form when latent heat warms the centre of a pre-existing storm and helps to intensify an anticyclone present in the upper troposphere. Once the tropical cyclone has developed, it becomes self-sustaining. Vast quantities of heat energy are siphoned from the warm ocean below and transported aloft as latent heat. This energy is released as sensible heat when clouds form. The sensible heat provides the system with potential energy, which is partially converted into kinetic energy, thereby causing the hurricane's violent winds.

Hurricanes originate between 5 and 25 degrees latitude in all tropical oceans except the South Atlantic and the southeastern Pacific, where the ITCZ seldom occurs. These latitudinal limits are determined by the general conditions necessary for hurricane formation: equatorward of 5 degrees the Coriolis force is too weak to generate rotary air motion, whereas poleward of 25 degrees sea-surface temperatures are too cool. Once hurricanes are formed, their movement is controlled by the steering effects of larger-scale air currents in the surrounding atmosphere; these can be erratic, and a hurricane is often likened to a block of wood floating in a river with complicated currents.

In the Northern Hemisphere, hurricanes usually travel first westward and then to the northwest before curving around to the north and east, where they come under the influence of the westerly winds of the middle latitudes. The paths of typical Atlantic hurricanes are mapped in Fig. 14.4, and they underscore the vulnerability of the U.S. southeastern coast, the entire rim of the Gulf of Mexico and eastern Canada. Hurri-

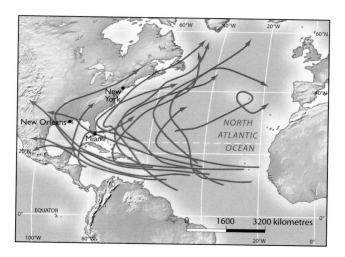

FIGURE 14.4 Typical hurricane tracks in the North Atlantic Ocean. The path of every storm in this part of the world since 1871 is mapped in the National Hurricane Center's "track book," which is updated annually.

canes usually advance with forward speeds of 16 to 24 km/h. If they pass over a large body of land or cooler waters, their energy source—the warm ocean—is cut off, and they gradually weaken and die.

Hurricane Destruction   Before these tropical cyclones die, normally within a week of their formation, they can cause considerable damage on land. The Saffir–Simpson Scale, which ranks hurricane intensity from 1 to 5 (Table 14.1), is used to estimate the potential property damage and flooding expected from a hurricane landfall. Much of this damage is done by high winds and torrential rains. However, near coastlines, waves and tides rise to destructive levels, particularly when wind-driven water known as the **storm surge** (which can surpass normal high-tide levels by more than 5 m) is hurled ashore. The destructive potential can be imagined when you consider that the amount of energy unleashed by a hurricane in one hour equals the total electric power generated in the United States in an entire year. With the exception of tornadoes—which sometimes are spawned in the inner spiral rain bands of the strongest hurricanes—tropical cyclones are the most dangerous of all atmospheric weather systems.

Not surprisingly, the most powerful hurricanes to strike the United States and Canada have ranked among the landmark weather events of the past century. Before World War II (and the development of sophisticated weather tracking), hurricanes in 1900 and 1935 caused enormous destruction on the coasts of Texas and the Florida Keys, respectively; in 1938, much of southern New England was devastated. In eastern Canada in 1891, two Category 1 hurricanes and one Category 2 hurricane hit Nova Scotia within a two-month period, one of which resulted in the collapse of the first bridge that spanned the Halifax Harbour. After 1945, hurricanes were named in alphabetical order of their occurrences each year. Among the most destructive of these have been Hazel (1954), Camille (1969), Agnes (1972), and Hugo (1989). Overall, since 1900, hurricanes have cost more than 1500 lives and untold billions of dollars in damage.

The costliest hurricane to strike eastern Canadian in recent history was Hurricane Juan, which struck on September 28–29, 2003 (Fig. 14.5). In its path across Nova Scotia and Prince Edward Island, this Category 2 hurricane was the first to hit one of the nation's larger metropolitan areas—Halifax—with its full force (wind speeds up to 158 km/h). The hurricane's impact took many by surprise: eight lives lost, hundreds of thousands without power (lasting up to two weeks in some locations), physical damage to homes and property, and widespread tree blow-downs. Estimates of the final economic costs are still being tallied, but property losses exceeded $100 million with insurable losses at over $80 million. However, many comparatively worse hurricanes have hit metropolitan areas in the United States. The costliest hurricane to strike the United States (and the third most expensive natural disaster in American history) was Hurricane Andrew in 1992. In its path across southernmost Florida, this relatively small but ferocious hurricane was the first to directly hit one of the United States' largest metropolitan areas—Miami—with average winds of 267 km/h. The final accounting was truly staggering: 95,400 private homes completely destroyed; a total of $16.04 billion paid to settle 795,912 property insurance claims; more than 125,000 people left homeless and 86,000 jobless; and a cleanup effort involving the removal of 35 million tons of debris at a cost of $600 million.

Although 26 people were killed in the United States as Hurricane Andrew tracked across Florida and Louisiana, in other countries it is not unusual for the death toll in a single storm of that strength to be in the thousands. In fact, the second greatest natural disaster of the twentieth century was the tropical cyclone that smashed into Bangladesh in 1970, killing upward of 300,000 people (and perhaps as many as half that number perished when another cyclone struck the country in 1991). Beyond the toll in human lives, hurricanes can also cause catastrophic disruptions in the social and economic life of a nation. In recent years, no country

Table 14.1 Saffir–Simpson Scale of Hurricane Intensity

Intensity Category	Wind Speed	Description of Effects
1	119–153 km/h	Damage primarily to unanchored mobile homes, shrubbery, tree branches; power lines blown down
2	154–177 km/h	Damage to roofing material, doors and windows; small trees blown down; unprotected marine craft break moorings
3	178–209 km/h	Damage to small buildings; large trees blown down; mobile homes destroyed; flooding near coast destroys many structures
4	210–249 km/h	Extensive roof failures on houses and smaller commercial buildings; major damage to doors and windows, and lower floors of near-shore structures; flooding up to 9 km inland from coast
5	>249 km/h	Widespread roof failures and destruction of many smaller-sized buildings; major damage to all structures less than 4.5 m above sea level; flooding up to 16 km inland from coast

Source: Information from NOAA, National Hurricane Center.

FIGURE 14.5   Some of the worst damage caused by Hurricane Juan was to trees (September 28–29, 2003). On some streets, such as this one in Dartmouth, Nova Scotia, every tree lining the street was blown over, giving an immediate impression of the direction the wind had been blowing.

has suffered more than Honduras, which since late 1998 has been struggling to recover from taking the brunt of the most powerful hurricane to make landfall in the recorded history of Central America (see Perspective: Honduras after Hurricane Mitch).

Although the tropics are generally marked by monotonous daily weather regimes, violence and drama accompany the occasional storms that are spawned in the energy-laden air of the low latitudes. Weather systems in the middle and higher latitudes are often less dramatic, but are usually more frequent, involve wider areas, and affect much larger populations.

Weather Systems of the Middle and Higher Latitudes

The general atmospheric circulation of the middle and higher latitudes exhibits some basic differences from that of the tropical latitudes. The principal difference is the frequent interaction of dissimilar air masses. In the

higher latitudes, high-pressure and low-pressure systems moving eastward are carried along by the westerly winds of the upper air. In the middle latitudes, air of different origins—cold, warm, moist, dry—constantly comes together, and fast-flowing jet streams are associated with sharp differences in temperature. Therefore the weather is much more changeable than in the tropics.

The Polar Front Jet Stream

Unit 10 explains how the fast-flowing upper air currents of the jet streams are related to the process of moving warm air from the tropics and cold air from the high latitudes. Unit 13 points out that jet streams may also be thought of as boundaries between large areas of cold and warm air. One of them, the Polar Front jet stream, although not in itself a weather system, controls the most important midlatitude weather systems.

Figure 14.7 shows the upper-air isotherms (dashed lines of constant temperature) sloping away from the tropics toward the polar regions. In the middle latitudes these temperatures drop abruptly, and warm and cold air

PERSPECTIVES ON THE HUMAN ENVIRONMENT

Honduras after Hurricane Mitch

A Category 5 hurricane (see Table 14.1) making landfall in the western North Atlantic Basin is always an extremely dangerous event. But even the most pessimistic forecasters did not envision the scope of the disaster that was about to unfold as Hurricane Mitch took aim on the Caribbean shore of Honduras on the evening of October 28, 1998. Mitch had surfaced as a tropical depression six days earlier off the north coast of Colombia, and began drifting generally northwestward through the southwestern corner of the Caribbean Sea (Fig. 14.6). By the 24th, even though it was late in the season, Mitch had blossomed into a minimal hurricane. Then, suddenly, amid reports of no expected further

strengthening, Mitch caught forecasters totally by surprise on the night of October 26 as it exploded into a Category 5 monster, packing sustained winds of 290 km/h. At the same time the storm shifted to a southwesterly track and began heading for the beaches of Honduras, now less than 160 km away (see Fig. 14.2).

Drawing one final intake of energy from the tropical sea, the hurricane's eye wall slammed ashore near the midpoint of the northern Honduran coast on the morning of October 29 (Fig. 14.6). What followed over the next two days, as the ferocious storm crawled across the heart of the country, was a disaster of such magnitude that Mitch was

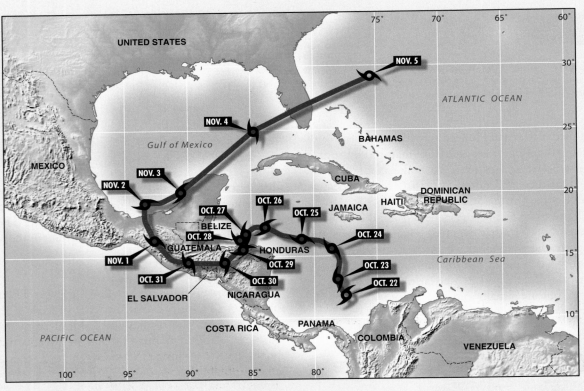

FIGURE 14.6   Mitch's 4500-km track, from its birth in the western Caribbean off Colombia to its demise, 15 days later, in the Atlantic east of Florida. Honduras took the worst beating as the storm made landfall there as a Category 5 hurricane and then took more than 48 hours to traverse the full length of the country.

immediately classified as the deadliest hurricane to strike in the Western Hemisphere since the great storm of 1780 killed an estimated 22,000 people in the islands of the eastern Caribbean. Although wind speeds gradually abated as Mitch moved inland, massive quantities of rainfall were produced as the storm's feeder bands swirled into the eye from both the Caribbean and the Pacific—precipitation significantly enhanced by orographic effects as the weather system encountered the highlands of central and southern Honduras. These uplands received as much as 190 cm of rain overall, triggering unprecedented floods and mudslides that effectively destroyed almost all of Honduras's infrastructure.

The staggering consequences of Mitch's rampage across Honduras, which underscore the wide range of impacts a major hurricane can generate, are summarized in this assessment by the U.S. National Climatic Data Center:

Human Toll: An estimated 9200 dead. More than 150,000 homes demolished, leaving up to 1.5 million displaced and homeless. Critical food, medicine, and water shortages. Hunger and near-starvation conditions affected countless villages. Fever and respiratory illness widespread, as was the threat of outbreaks of cholera, dengue, and malaria.

Structural Damage: Infrastructure devastated. Whole communities washed away. Upwards of 70 percent of transportation facilities washed away, including 335 bridges and 21,000 mi (34,000 km) of roadway. Communications disrupted. Fuel, electricity, and safe drinking water

rare commodities. Damage so severe it may take up to years to rebuild.

Crop Damage: Upwards of 70 percent of crops destroyed, including 80 percent of the banana crop. Warehouses and storage facilities for coffee flooded. Total agricultural losses estimated to be close to $1 billion.

Although the struggle to repair daily social life has largely been accomplished, the economic aftereffects of Mitch continue to bedevil Honduras. Keep in mind that Honduras was already the third poorest country in the Americas, so the pronouncement of its president that Mitch had destroyed 50 years of national progress is ominous indeed. The key to economic recovery is the agricultural sector, which in 1998 employed two-thirds of Honduras's labour force, accounted for nearly a third of its gross domestic product, and earned more than 70 percent of its foreign revenues. Bananas constitute the leading commercial crop, an industry all but ruined by Mitch. Rebuilding it depends heavily on reinvestment by the large (foreign-based) companies that control banana plantations. So far, many damaged fields have been replanted, but this was often accompanied by the installation of more modern irrigation and packing equipment, which has reduced the number of jobs substantially. With few other opportunities available in chronically disadvantaged Honduras, this is but one example of Mitch's heavy price this nation will continue to pay for decades to come.

Much of this box is based on material found in *Mitch: The Deadliest Atlantic Hurricane since 1780*, a report posted on the website of the National Climatic Data Center (http://lwf.ncdc.noaa.gov/oa/reports/mitch/mitch.html).

face each other horizontally. As we know, such a narrow zone of contact constitutes a front. The *Polar Front*, therefore, separates relatively cold polar air from relatively warm tropical air, and the jet stream associated with this temperature divide is called the **Polar Front jet stream** (Fig. 14.7). As noted in Unit 10, at the core of the wavelike westerly winds of the upper troposphere, the Polar Front jet stream snakes its way around the globe in large meanders (Fig. 14.8).

These meanders develop in response to fairly complex physical laws that govern the movement of high-velocity air currents in the upper atmosphere. The important thing to remember is that they cause airflows to converge and diverge strongly in the vicinity of the meander bends. The upper atmospheric convergence and divergence causes the air to subside (under the area of convergence) or ascend (under the area of divergence). As a result, these zones have important implications for the surface pressure pattern and attendant weather. The significance of the Polar Front jet stream can be demonstrated by considering the process of **cyclogenesis**—the formation, evolution, and movement of midlatitude cyclones.

Midlatitude Cyclones

The weather at the Earth's surface in the midlatitudes is largely determined by the position of the Polar Front jet

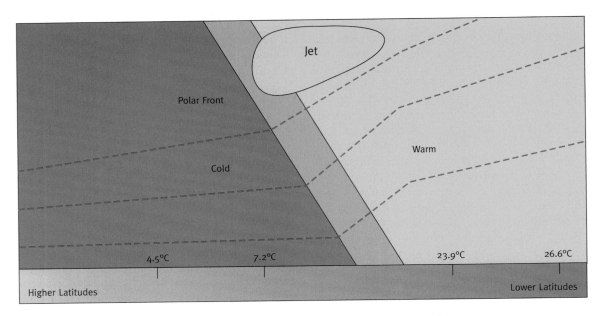

FIGURE 14.7   The Polar Front jet stream positioned above the Polar Front, near the tropopause.

stream. In Fig. 14.9A, the jet stream passes across North America 9000 m above the ground. The air in the jet stream converges at point **X**, as shown in cross-section (Fig. 14.9B). The converging air undergoes an increase in density, and so it descends. The descending air causes high pressure at the surface, as shown in Fig. 14.9C, and spreads out or diverges from the surface anticyclone. At point **X**, therefore, we could expect fair weather because of the descending air.

Meanwhile, farther downwind in the eastward-flowing jet stream, at point **Y**, the air in the jet stream diverges. The diverging air aloft must be replaced, and air is drawn up from below. As air is drawn up the column, a converging cyclonic circulation develops at the surface, exhibiting its characteristic low pressure. The rising air cools, forming clouds that soon produce pre-cipitation. In this manner, the jet stream becomes the primary cause of fair weather when it generates upper atmospheric convergence, and stormy weather when it produces divergence.

Life Cycle of a Midlatitude Cyclone   On most days, spiral cloud bands can be observed in the mid-latitude atmosphere. The unit-opening satellite image (p. 174) shows a huge, spiralling midlatitude cyclone over the North Atlantic Ocean northwest of the British Isles. These are the most common large-scale weather systems found outside the tropics. The midlatitude cyclone, like its low-latitude counterpart, goes by several names. It is often called a *depression* or an *extrat-ropical* (meaning outside the tropics) *cyclone*. A midlati-tude cyclone is characterized by its circular windflow and low-pressure field as well as the interaction of air of different properties. As with many atmospheric weather systems, it possesses a definite life cycle.

Figure 14.10A shows the early stage in the develop-ment of a midlatitude cyclone. A mass of cold air and a mass of warm air lie side by side, with the boundary be-tween them called a **stationary front**. Divergent upper airflow causes a slight cyclonic motion at the surface, and a small kink appears in the stationary front. As the surface cyclonic motion develops, the kink grows larger and becomes an **open wave**, as indicated in Fig. 14.10B. In this open-wave stage, the warm and cold air interact in distinct ways. On the eastern side of the cyclone, warm air now glides up over the colder air mass along a surface that has become a warm front. To the west, the

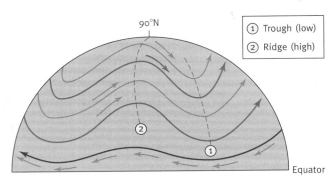

FIGURE 14.8   Spatial context of the Polar Front jet stream, represented by a solid red line, in this generalization of the upper atmosphere of the Northern Hemisphere.

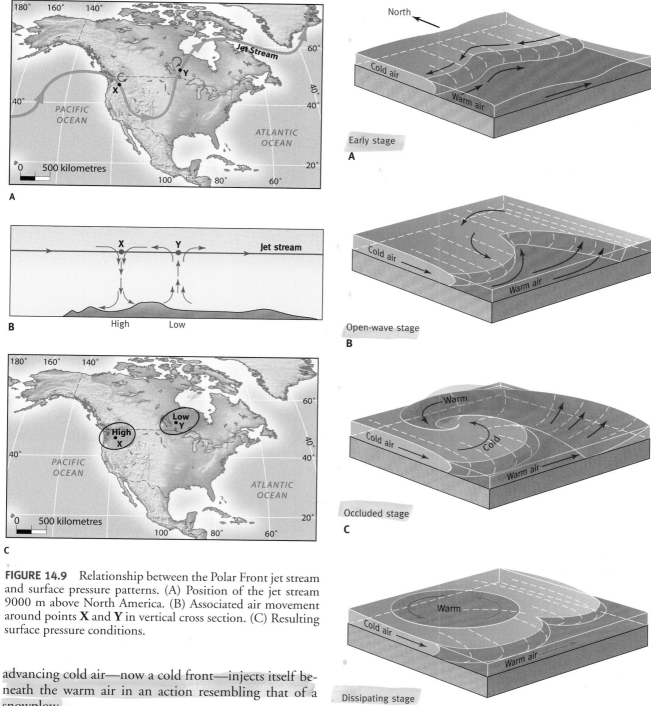

FIGURE 14.9   Relationship between the Polar Front jet stream and surface pressure patterns. (A) Position of the jet stream 9000 m above North America. (B) Associated air movement around points **X** and **Y** in vertical cross section. (C) Resulting surface pressure conditions.

advancing cold air—now a cold front—injects itself beneath the warm air in an action resembling that of a snowplow.

The open-wave stage represents maturity in the life cycle of a midlatitude cyclone, but generally the energy of the circulation is spent within a few days. Figure 14.10C shows how the better-defined cold front travels faster than the warm front, overtaking it first at the centre of the cyclone. When this happens, the snubnosed cold front lifts the warm air entirely off the ground, causing an **occluded front**—the surface boundary between the

FIGURE 14.10   Four stages in the life cycle of a midlatitude cyclone: (A) early, (B) open wave, (C) occlusion, and (D) dissipation. After Arthur N. Strahler, copyright Arthur N. Strahler.

cold and cool air—to form. In time the entire wedge of surface warm air is lifted to the colder altitudes aloft, and the cyclone dissipates (Fig. 14.10D). This weather system, however, does not die where it was born: the Polar Front jet stream has continually steered the cyclone eastward during its lifespan.

This wave model of the midlatitude cyclone was first proposed by Norwegian weather forecasters more than 75 years ago. It has turned out to be a good forecasting tool, and we can see why if we look more closely at the open-wave stage.

Weather Forecasting and the Open-Wave Stage   The most obvious features of Fig. 14.11A, which shows a series of midlatitude cyclones forming along the Polar Front, are the roughly circular configuration of the isobars and the positions of the fronts. Although the isobars are generally circular, they tend to be straight within the area enclosed by the cold and warm fronts. This wedge of warm air is called the *warm sector*. Also noteworthy is the *kinking*, or sharp angle, the isobars form at the fronts themselves.

The wind arrows tend to cross the isobars at a slight angle—just as they should when friction at the Earth's surface partially upsets the geostrophic balance. The wind arrows indicate a large whirl of air gradually accumulating at the centre of the low-pressure cell. This converging air rises and cools, especially when it lifts at the fronts, and its water vapour condenses to produce a significant amount of precipitation. Maritime tropical air (**mTw**), warmer than the surface below it, forms the warm sector, and cold continental polar air (**cPk**) advances from the northwest.

In the cross-sectional view in Fig. 14.11B, the warm front has the expected gentle slope. As the warm air moves up this slope, it cools and condenses to produce the characteristic sequence of stratus clouds. The cold front, however, is much steeper than the warm front. This forces the warm air to rise much more rapidly, creating towering cumulus clouds, which can yield thunderstorms and heavy rains.

Although no two wave cyclones are identical, there are enough similarities for an observer on the ground to predict the pattern and sequence of the atmospheric events as outlined above. These events are summarized in Fig. 14.11C and are as follows:

1. As the midlatitude cyclone approaches along the line of cross-section shown in Fig. 14.11A, clouds thicken, steady rain falls, and the pressure drops.
2. As the warm front passes, the temperature rises, the wind direction shifts, pressure remains steady, and the rain lets up or turns to occasional showers with the arrival of the warm sector.

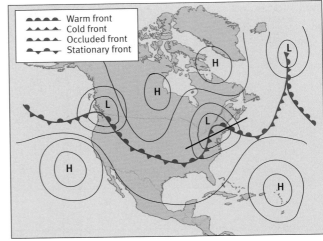

			Warm front
			Cold front
			Occluded front
			Stationary front

A

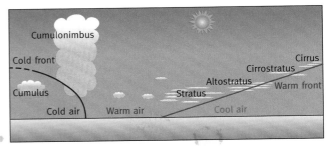

B

Post Cold Front	Warm Sector	Pre Warm Front	Sector \ Weather Condition
Heavy rain, then clearing	Showers	Rain and fog	**Precipitation**
↘ ↘	↗ ↗	↖ ↖	**Surface Wind Direction**
Rising	Low steady	Falling	**Pressure**
Lower	Higher	Lower	**Temperature**

C

FIGURE 14.11 Midlatitude cyclones over North America. (A) Pressure fields, windflows, and fronts. (B) Cross-sectional view along the dashed line mapped in (A). (C) Summary of surface weather conditions along the cross-sectional transect.

3. Then comes the frequently turbulent cold front, with its high-intensity but short-duration rain, another wind shift, and an abrupt drop in temperature.

The whole system usually moves eastward, roughly parallel to the steering upper-air jet stream. Thus a weather forecaster must predict how fast the system will move and when it will occlude. But those two predictions are often difficult and account for most of the forecasts that go awry.

Because it is so influential and prevalent, the midlatitude cyclone is a dominant climatic control outside the tropics. These weather systems follow paths that move toward the poles in the summer and toward the Equator in the winter, always under the influence of the Polar Front and its jet stream. Their general eastward movement varies in speed from 0 to 60 km/h in winter; in summer, the velocities range from 0 to 40 km/h. These wave cyclones may be anywhere from 300 to 3000 km in diameter and range from 8 to 11 km in height. They provide the greatest source of rain in the midlatitudes, and as we are about to see, they generate kinetic energy that helps power the primary circulation of the atmosphere.

Energy and Moisture within Weather Systems

As can be seen in satellite images and as your own experiences probably confirm, every day a multitude of weather systems parade across the planetary surface. These systems entail the large-scale atmospheric disturbances of the tropical, middle, and higher latitudes discussed in this unit, which are fundamental to an understanding of the climates of those zones. They also involve the meso- (medium-) and small-scale systems that make up the daily texture of the atmosphere, such as monsoonal circulations (covered in Unit 10) and thunderstorms (Unit 13). Each weather system, though distinctive in detail, has a characteristic internal organization. In each, warm air is transformed into faster-moving air, and moisture becomes precipitation.

The processes of such transformations form a unique system, which is diagrammed in Fig. 14.12. There are

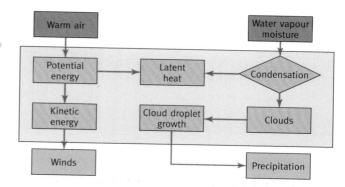

FIGURE 14.12 Schematic representation of the energy and moisture transformations within a weather system.

two inputs into this system: (1) warm air carrying the energy of heat, and (2) moisture in the form of water vapour. The heat energy of the rising warm air adds potential energy to the system, and the system's centre of gravity lifts higher off the ground. At the same time, the moisture condenses, which has two effects. First, the latent heat that is released helps to swell the store of potential energy; and second, the condensed moisture appears as clouds. There are, of course, outputs from the system as well. The growing store of potential energy changes to kinetic energy, and air movement increases. This kinetic energy leaves the system in the form of winds. Meanwhile the droplets in the clouds grow to precipitable size. They, too, are exported from the system, via the various forms of precipitation that fall to Earth.

These events occur in clouds of the ITCZ, in tropical easterly waves, and in the wet monsoons. You may be able to envision them best in the more dramatic weather produced by tropical cyclones and thunderstorms. Yet whether in a tornado or in a midlatitude cyclone, these events take place in a similar way. Because of the inputs and outputs of energy and moisture to many of these phenomena, we have considerable justification for calling them weather *systems*. Unit 15 looks at how we track and forecast weather systems such as these, and Units 16 to 19 demonstrate how these systems combine together with the general atmospheric circulation to form the climates of the Earth.

KEY TERMS

REVIEW QUESTIONS

1. Describe the general conditions necessary for the formation of a hurricane.
2. Describe the internal structure of a fully developed hurricane.
3. How does the Polar Front jet stream contribute to the formation of a midlatitude cyclone?
4. Describe the internal structure of a midlatitude cyclone.
5. What is an occluded front, and what sort of weather is associated with it?
6. Describe the general weather changes at a location experiencing the complete passage of a midlatitude cyclone.

REFERENCES AND FURTHER READINGS

CARLSON, T.   *Mid-Latitude Weather Systems* (London/New York: Routledge, 1991).

DE BLIJ, H. J., Ed.   *Nature on the Rampage* (Washington, D.C.: Smithsonian Institution Press, 1994).

DIAZ, H. F., and PULWARTY, R. S., Eds.   *Hurricanes: Climate and Socioeconomic Impacts* (New York: Springer Verlag, 1997).

DRYE, W.   *Storm of the Century: The Labor Day Hurricane of 1935* (Washington, D.C.: National Geographic Society, 2002).

EAGLEMAN, J. R.   *Severe and Unusual Weather* (Lenexa, Kan.: Trimedia, 2nd ed., 1990).

ELSNER, J. B., and KARA, A. B.   *Hurricanes of the North Atlantic: Climate and Society* (New York: Oxford Univ. Press, 1999).

HARMAN, J. R.   *Tropospheric Waves, Jet Streams, and United States Weather Patterns* (Washington, D.C.: Association of American Geographers, Commission on College Geography, Resource Paper No. 11, 1971).

HASTENRATH, S.   *Climate Dynamics of the Tropics* (Dordrecht, Netherlands: Kluwer, 1991).

McGREGOR, G. R., and NIEUWOLT, S.   *Tropical Climatology* (Chichester, U.K.: Wiley, 2nd ed., 1998).

MUSK, L. F., and BAKER, S.   *Weather Systems* (New York: Cambridge Univ. Press, 1988).

REITER, E. R.   *Jet Streams* (Garden City, N.Y.: Anchor/Doubleday, 1966).

RIEHL, H.   *Climate and Weather in the Tropics* (New York: Academic Press, 1979).

ROBINSON, A.   *Earth Shock: Hurricanes, Volcanoes, Earthquakes, Tornadoes and Other Forces of Nature* (New York: Thames and Hudson, 1993).

SCHNEIDER, S. H., Ed.   *Encyclopedia of Climate and Weather* (New York: Oxford Univ. Press, 2 vols., 1996).

SIMPSON, R. H., and RIEHL, H.   *The Hurricane and Its Impact* (Baton Rouge, La.: Louisiana State Univ. Press, 1981).

WEB RESOURCES

http://www.atl.ec.gc.ca/weather/hurricane/index_e.htm   The Canadian Hurricane Centre provides information to Canadians on storms of tropical origin that affect Canada or its territorial waters. This site includes forecasts, storm summaries, and a range of information related to the science of hurricanes.

http://www.nhc.noaa.gov/index.shtml   The National Weather Service's Tropical Prediction Center, which tracks all hurricane activity in the Atlantic-Caribbean and Eastern Pacific zones that border the U.S.

http://www.usatoday.com/weather/wstorm0.htm   A page of links covering the topics of air pressure and weather, storm formation, fronts, and types of weather systems.

Weather Tracking and Forecasting

To better detect and predict severe weather and identify potential transportation hazards, radar and satellite systems are now being more frequently used, in conjunction with ground-based monitoring sites. The King Weather Radar Research Station in King City, Ontario, provides data for regional weather forecasting.

OBJECTIVES

- To discuss the general network of weather stations and the types of data collected from each

- To illustrate typical weather maps compiled from weather data and to provide some elementary interpretations of them

- To outline weather forecasting methods and comment on their formulation and reliability

It is New Year's Eve, 2001, in Rio de Janeiro, and citizens are looking forward to a night of celebration after a period of particularly deadly floods in Brazil. Heavy rains had triggered mudslides in the greater Rio area, in southeastern Brazil, killing more than 60 people. The public had perhaps been disappointed to hear the forecast for this particular New Year's Eve. A veteran local meteorologist, with over 35 years of experience, predicted rain, and as a result only 2 million people have come to the city to celebrate (much less than in previous years). The cold front that was anticipated to bring the rain breaks up earlier than expected, however, and the rain does not come. Perhaps the unfortunate but true story might end there, simply another example of how quickly the weather can change. In this case, however, the mayor of Rio decides that the forecaster should be held accountable for the inaccurate forecast, which could have caused panic in a city that had very recently been hammered by devastating rains. The charge is punishable by up to six months in prison. One might argue better to be safe than sorry, or can a case be made against the meteorologist for making a bad weather forecast?

This case is a reminder that, even with today's sophisticated knowledge of the atmosphere and high-technology equipment to monitor its every murmur, weather forecasting very much remains an art as well as a science. In this unit we explore the forecasting process by discussing the collection of weather data, the manipulation and mapping of these data, and the critical interpretations made by analysts that lead to weather predictions.

The Canadian public today is probably more aware of weather conditions than ever before (witness the stampede to supermarkets and hardware stores when a snowstorm is forecast). This is due, in no small part, to the improvement in the news media's weather coverage in recent years. On television, the inarticulate little bow-tied man, with his broken car antenna pointing at a messy, postage-stamp-sized map, is long gone. Today we are far more likely to see weather reporters with meteorology degrees who use animated maps, satellite imagery, and colour radar (Fig. 15.1). Moreover, with millions of Canadian households now wired to receive the *Weather Network* on cable TV and such websites as *wunderground.com* and *weather.com* via computer, viewers and Internet surfers are better informed than ever.

Weather Data Acquisition

The World Meteorological Organization, an agency of the United Nations, supervises the World Weather Watch, a global network of about 20,000 weather stations and moving vehicles. More than 130 nations participate in this monitoring system, which coordinates and distributes weather information from its processing centres in Washington, D.C., Moscow, and Melbourne, Australia. Every six hours, beginning at midnight GMT,

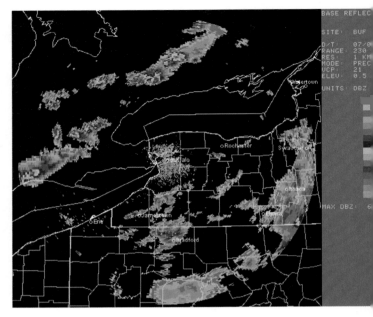

FIGURE 15.1   Radar reveals a squall line of thunderstorms in southwestern Ontario (July 4, 2001). Thunderstorms (shown in red and orange) may produce damaging winds and hail, conditions that may favour the development of tornadoes. This squall line unfortunately spawned four confirmed tornadoes and several floods throughout the region.

or Greenwich Mean Time (also known as Universal Coordinated Time [UTC]), a set of standard observations on the local state of the atmosphere are taken around the globe and reported to those centres from about 10,000 land-based stations, more than 1000 upper-air observation stations, and at least 9000 ships, buoys, aircraft, and satellites in transit. High-powered computers then rapidly record, manipulate, and assemble these data to produce **synoptic weather charts**, which map meteorological conditions at that moment in time across wide geographic areas.

Although reliable weather instruments have been available since about 1700, comprehensive simultaneous observation could not begin before the invention of long-distance communications. The arrival of the telegraph in the 1840s provided the initial breakthrough. The Meteorological Service of Canada was established in 1871 as a national program for the official recording and observation of climate in Canada. Forecasting services have been consistently provided to Canadians since that time, with a brief interruption of services during World War II, when the Canadian and American governments banned publishing and broadcasting weather information for fear that it might aid the enemy. The program was renamed the Atmospheric Environment

Service in 1970. Today, Environment Canada oversees a number of divisions that relate to weather and climate, including the Canadian Meteorological Centre (CMC) and the present-day Meteorological Service of Canada (MSC), Canada's source for meteorological information. Environment Canada's weather forecasting services include a weather-warning service and five-day forecasts that are available 24 hours a day, 365 days a year. The Canadian weather forecasting service oversees 14 regional weather centres across the country; these centres provide Canadians with toll-free and pay-telephone services that cover their own and surrounding communities. A series of Weatheradio transmitters across southern Canada reaches 85 percent of Canadians, and forecasts are also made for inland and coastal waters as well as the Arctic. In addition, forecasts of ice conditions are prepared on a seasonal basis for Arctic and coastal waters, the Great Lakes, and the St. Lawrence Seaway. This information utilizes data from Canada's surface weather stations, marine buoys (Canada's Marine Network overseas 45 moored and six drifting buoys in addition to vessel-based monitoring on approximately 300 vessels), and a network of upper-air stations, together with satellite technology.

Weather Stations

Within Canada, more than 2000 observation stations report surface weather conditions. Each station deploys a number of instruments and obtains their readings. These include thermometers, barometers, rain gauges, hygrometers (to measure the moisture of the air), weather vanes (to indicate wind direction), and anemometers (to measure wind speed). The following data are then reported to the synoptic network: air temperature, dew-point temperature, air pressure and its direction of change, precipitation (if any), wind speed and direction, visibility, relative amount of cloudiness, cloud types present, estimated height of cloud base, and any significant weather that might be occurring. This data cluster for each station is then processed by the central facility for placement in shorthand, symbolic form on the synoptic weather chart, as shown in Fig. 15.2. Of the several hundred surface weather stations in Canada, 290 have been designated as Reference Climate Stations, which are weather stations that have more than 30 years of continuous record, with no significant gaps, and are of high quality. This network of surface stations may provide invaluable data regarding the trends in surface weather conditions in Canada, as well as an insight into climate trends.

Surface conditions, however, represent only a single dimension of the overall weather picture. To gain a fuller

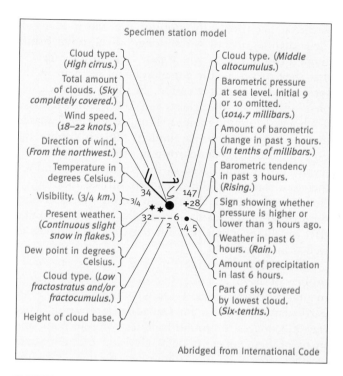

FIGURE 15.2 Data cluster for each weather station, which is entered in this shorthand form on the synoptic weather chart. This diagram, which represents a specimen station, is the key to interpreting the weather data for the cities shown in the daily surface weather map produced by the Meteorological Service of Canada (see Fig. 15.4).

understanding, meteorologists must go beyond this bottom slice of the atmosphere and acquire a more complete profile of its current vertical structuring. One way this is accomplished is through the use of **radiosondes**, radio-equipped instrument packages that are carried aloft by balloon. Canada has 37 radiosonde stations, part of a worldwide network that transmits readings to receiving facilities on the ground every 12 hours (noon and midnight GMT). Whereas most of these upper-air observations of temperature, humidity, and pressure are obtained for altitudes up to 32 km above the surface, a number of radiosonde stations now release more powerful balloons that can reach heights well beyond 32 km. High-altitude radar is also a useful tool for acquiring information about the upper atmosphere, and equipped stations regularly make *rawinsonde* observations (radar trackings of radiosonde balloons) that provide information about wind speed and directions at various vertical levels.

Weather Satellites

Perhaps the most important source of three-dimensional atmospheric data today are the dozens of orbiting weather satellites that constantly monitor the Earth. Many of these satellites operate within longitudinal, **polar orbits** about 1100 km high, which pass close to the poles, so that they survey a different meridional segment of the surface during each revolution. In this manner a complete picture of the globe can be assembled every few hours. More and more satellites are now being placed in much higher orbits (around 35,000 km) above the Equator, called **geosynchronous orbits**—that is, they revolve at the same speed as the planet rotates and are therefore stationary above a given surface location. A "fixed" satellite at this altitude can monitor the same one-third or so of the Earth continually, and with infrared (IR) capability it can perform that task in darkness as well as in daylight.

Particularly important are the U.S. geostationary orbiters of the GOES (Geostationary Orbiting Environmental Satellite) series. GOES-10 and GOES-12 are particularly important for Canadian forecasting. They transmit images to ground facilities twice an hour, and many of them appear in daily television and newspaper weather reports. GOES-10 monitors portions of central and western North America and the eastern Pacific Ocean from its vantage point above the Equator at longitude 135°W (Fig.15.3B). GOES-12 monitors the central and eastern provinces and western Atlantic Basin from its fixed position above the Equator at longitude 90°W (Fig.15.3A). Both of these satellites transmit visible, IR, and water vapour images, which can be viewed at http://www.goes.noaa.gov. As useful as this imagery is, however, weather-satellite technology is constantly being upgraded. NOAA is keeping pace by planning to launch, over the next few years, additional GOES orbiters equipped with the most advanced weather observation systems available.

Mapping Weather Data

The massive quantity of surface and upper-air weather data reported by thousands of stations around the globe are collected and organized by various international and national processing centres so that forecasters may begin their never-ending work. Synoptic weather charts are crucial to this task, and the meteorological services of most of the world's countries prepare and publish these maps at frequent intervals (with many increasingly available on the Internet). In Canada, the Canadian Meteorological Centre supplies the Meteorological Service of Canada with daily data so that the MSC can produce maps that include surface weather and corresponding upper-air conditions (as shown by the 250-mb, 500-mb,

700-mb, and 850-mb height contours). The analyses are made available four times a day, enabling those interested to see the latest snapshots of the state of the atmosphere over Canada and the Northern Hemisphere (http://weatheroffice.ec.gc.ca/analysis/index_e.html). Because the surface and 500-mb maps are fundamental tools in learning about the geography of Canadian weather, each will be reviewed in detail. The maps of July 28, 2004, were selected for presentation here (Fig. 15.4).

The Surface Weather Map

The map of surface weather conditions for Wednesday, July 28, 2004, is shown in Fig. 15.4. But before we proceed to interpret its contents, it is necessary to become familiar with the map's point, line, and area symbols.

Each weather station is represented by a point symbol that shows up on the map as a data cluster arranged around a central circle—an application of the specimen station model displayed in Fig. 15.2. In the central circle, the percentage of blackening indicates the proportion of the sky covered by clouds; on the July 28 map, for instance, the skies above Cape Breton, Nova Scotia, are completely covered, while the area around Dawson City (toward the western border of the Yukon Territory) are completely cloudless. Among the numbers distributed around the central circle, the most noteworthy are current temperature in degrees Celsius (shown at the 10 o'clock position with respect to the circle), dew-point temperature (8 o'clock), and air pressure (1 o'clock). Thus, on the map, Vancouver reports a temperature of 22°C, a dew point of 15°C, and a pressure of 1014.9 mb.

Among these symbols, most important are wind direction and speed. Wind direction (always indicated by where the wind comes *from*) is represented as the line extending outward from the central circle; wind speed is indicated by the number of hash marks attached to the end of that line. Thus Calgary's wind is from the north-northwest at about 14 to 19 km/hr, whereas the wind in Eureka, Ellesmere Island, is from the south-southeast at about 33 to 40 km/hr. The line symbols in Fig. 15.5 represent the jet stream and the fronts, and are calculated on the basis of the surface station weather and upper-air analysis chart information in Fig.15.4. Thunderstorms are expected across the low-pressure regions of central North America, the western Atlantic and northern portions of Alberta, British Columbia, and the Yukon Territory, with generally clear conditions for the remaining portions of the continent.

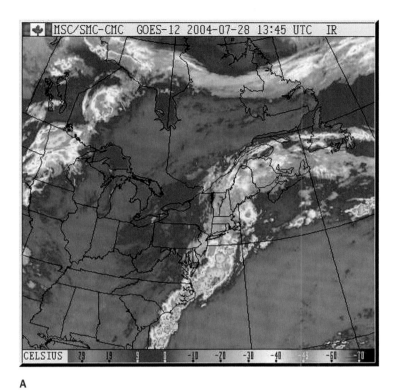

A

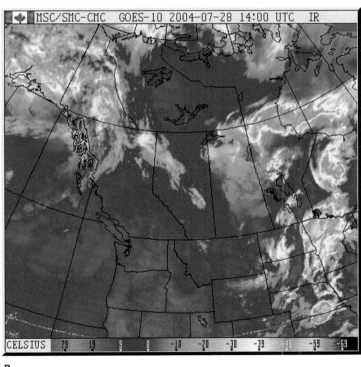

B

FIGURE 15.3   A pair of simultaneous GOES satellite images taken on Wednesday, July 28, 2004. (A) The GOES-12 fixed image scans the atmosphere of the entire Northern Hemisphere between the central North Atlantic Ocean in the east and the western regions of North America in the west. (B) The scanning field of the GOES-10 is constantly trained on an area that covers the same latitudinal range but extends longitudinally from eastern North America to the west-central Pacific. In tandem, these overlapping perspectives provide continuous observation of the evolution and progress of weather systems that affect the North American continent.

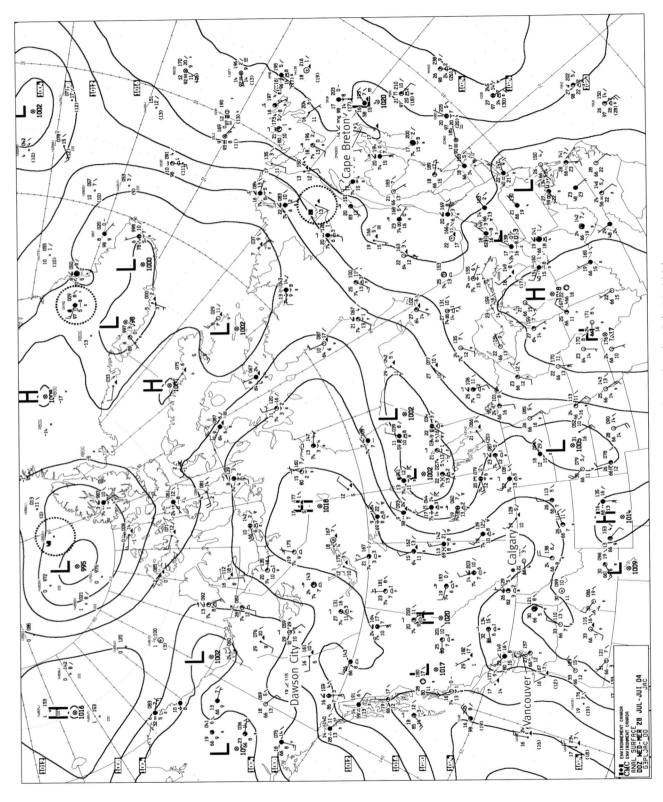

FIGURE 15.4   The Meteorological Service of Canada surface weather map for Wednesday, July 28, 2004.

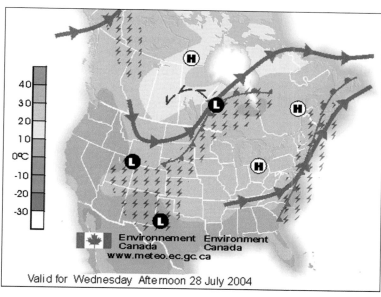

Valid for Wednesday Afternoon 28 July 2004

FIGURE 15.5   North American weather systems (jet stream, fronts, low- and high-pressure systems) for Wednesday, July 28, 2004.

The Upper-Air Weather Map

The significance of vertical atmospheric data for weather forecasting has already been established. Accordingly, the Meteorological Service of Canada's Canadian Meteorological Centre, based on radiosonde and rawinsonde observations, issues a 500-mb height contours map as part of its daily synoptic chart package. In addition, it produces 250-mb, 700-mb, and 850-mb height contours maps. The 500-mb chart is particularly useful in the analysis of the upper atmosphere. In reading a 500-mb chart, one should remember that the higher the altitude of the 500-mb level, the warmer the surface temperature of the air beneath it; therefore the gradient of the 500-mb surface should always dip in the general direction of the higher latitudes. Winds on the 500-mb chart are geostrophic, flowing parallel to the isobars (or, in this case, height contour lines), with high pressure on the right looking downwind. Extreme curvature signifies upper-air cyclonic and anticyclonic circulations.

The 500-mb chart for July 28, 2004, compiled at the same moment as the surface weather map (Fig. 15.4), is shown in Fig. 15.6. Symbolization here should be quite easy to interpret. The height contours on this map are calibrated in 10-m units, called decametres. Wind speeds and directions are represented by the same symbols used for surface weather stations. A departure in wind-speed depiction is the triangular pennant (which equals five hash marks in the style of Fig. 15.2), indicating velocities in excess of 88 km/h.

The configuration of the 500-mb surface resembles the ground-level pressure pattern (Fig. 15.4) in a number of ways. Most prominent is the upper-air trough that dips out of north-central Canada to cover much of interior Canada. Around this trough is the fast-flowing jet stream, which can be seen by the presence of the number of hash marks on the wind line symbol. A second stream can be picked out around the low centred on southwestern Ontario and extending up the eastern seaboard of North America. Bad weather in the form of frontal precipitation and patches of thunderstorms occur in areas where the jet stream flows toward the North Pole (compare with Fig. 15.5). Conversely, fair weather is observed along the western interior of British Columbia, where the jet stream moves toward the Equator.

Weather Forecasting

Unlike weather forecasters who must make projections into an unknown future, we have the luxury of being able to check the outcome of our prediction by simply consulting the next daily weather map (July 29, 2004). That surface map is shown in Fig. 15.7. Note that the frontal system along the eastern seaboard of North America has moved off the map (having moved offshore). The low-pressure system that was centred on western Ontario has since moved further north and east toward north-central Ontario and the western boundary of Quebec and Ontario. Showers are now moving into areas that were to the immediate east of the system on July 28, 2004.

Although it is safe to say that those who issued the actual forecast on July 28, 2004, had more data and experience on which to base their predictions, much of the salient information they needed was indeed summarized in the surface and 500-mb synoptic charts we have discussed. Whereas the 7:00 a.m. EST maps represent "freeze frames," forecasters had access to the "motion picture" of the dynamic atmosphere, as satellites, radar, and other instruments constantly monitored its every change. Yet even these data, when run through highly sophisticated computers, could provide only small additional clues as to what was about to happen. Thus weather prediction, especially in North America, remains an art as well as a science, because forecasters oversee a geographic domain that experiences some of the most variable weather on Earth, which frequently swings from one extreme to another (see Perspective: Weather Extremes).

The Forecasting Industry

Environment Canada's Meteorological Service of Canada (MSC) provides weather forecasts and warnings of extreme weather events and hazardous air quality. The MSC is one of the most automated weather services in the world, with infrastructure ranging from traditional (thermometers and rain gauges) to high-tech (radar and satellite technology). Forecasts are issued from 14 regional weather centres distributed across the country, as well as from specialized service offices, such as the Canadian Hurricane Centre, which is part of Halifax's Maritimes Weather Centre. The Canadian Meteorological Centre is located in Montreal and serves as the hub of the national telecommunications, weather modelling, and emergency-preparedness services.

This computer forecasting method is called **numerical weather prediction** and is based on projections by small increments of time. For example, a forecast is prepared for the weather 15 minutes from now.

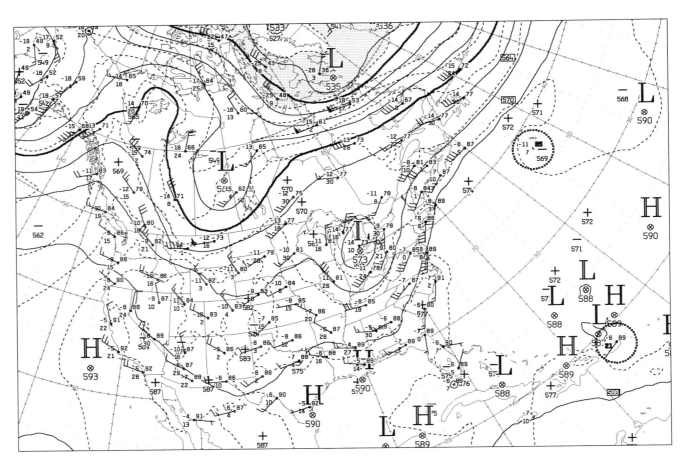

FIGURE 15.6   A 500-mb chart for July 28, 2004, compiled at the same moment as the surface weather map in Fig. 15.4. Heights are given in 10-m units, known as decametres.

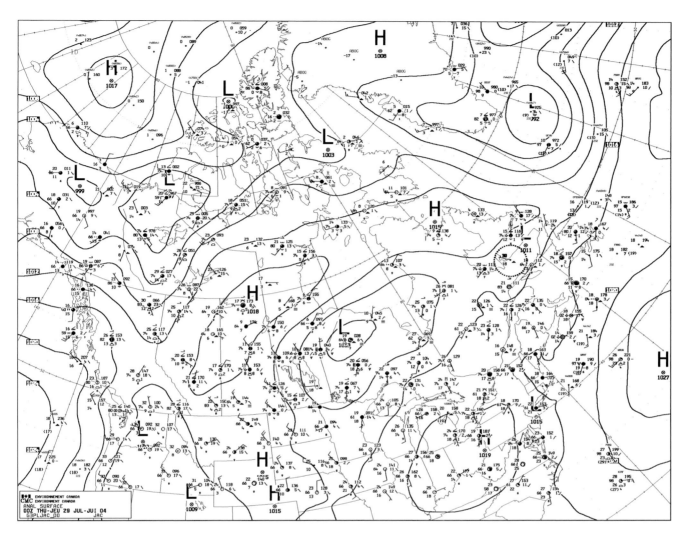

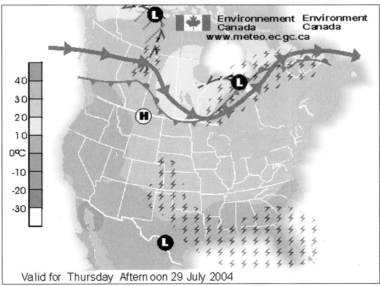

FIGURE 15.7   The Meteorological Service of Canada surface weather map for Thursday, July 29, 2004.

Once those conditions are determined, the computer repeats the process by using them to make predictions for 15 minutes after that and so forth until the desired future time of the forecast is reached. Obviously, unavoidable errors begin to creep in immediately, and they are magnified as the length of the forecast period increases. The American Meteorological Society has pronounced that the accuracy of forecasts up to 48 hours ahead is now "considerable." While that may be true nationally, your local experiences may not always fit that designation!

It has been pointed out that northeastern North America is a region of particularly changeable weather. Thus over the years, more forecasts have gone wrong there than in any other part of the nation. Winter storms have proven especially difficult to predict even a few hours ahead, and the need for better snow and ice warnings in this heavily urbanized region has prompted the intensification of research efforts. Meteorologists are most interested in learning more about the sudden genesis of the fierce snowstorms they call "bombs."

[A "bomb" is a] relatively mild winter weather disturbance that drifts northward in the Atlantic from the Cape Hatteras area off North Carolina and then, when it is off New York or Cape Cod, the "bombing range," suddenly and inexplicably explodes within six hours or so into a surprising, freezing fury that threatens unsuspecting shipping and paralyzes unprepared coastal cities and towns with heavy sheets of snow and ice (Ayres, 1988).

Over the past half-century, dozens of these storms have caught the Northeast off guard, and forecasters are still unable to do much more than closely watch the area when conditions are ripe and report a storm as it swiftly materializes. Meteorologists suspect that "bombs" are the product of a collision of Arctic and moist tropical air. This contrast is heightened along the Mid-Atlantic seaboard by the trapping of large quantities of cold air in the nearby Appalachian Mountains and the infusion of warm-surface seawater by the Gulf Stream (see Fig. 11.3). During the 1990s, a data-gathering network of sea buoys and monitoring instruments was put in place offshore, and researchers are hopeful that this technology will enable them to better understand and predict these dangerous storms.

Because the predictions of Environment Canada are for broad regions and are occasionally unreliable, the needs of businesses whose activities are closely related to weather conditions have given rise to a private forecasting industry. This is particularly prevalent in the United States, where hundreds of companies concentrate on tailoring forecasts to the special needs of their corporate clients. Agricultural concerns comprise the biggest single-user category. Private forecasters can prepare surprisingly specific predictions, particularly with respect to moisture conditions, and the recent growth of their clientele demonstrates that an important need is being met. Many subscribers, such as electrical utilities and fuel oil distributors, require hour-by-hour information in order to be ready to meet customer demands as temperatures rise or fall. A whole host of firms engaged in

PERSPECTIVES ON THE HUMAN ENVIRONMENT

Weather Extremes

Since climatologists no longer concentrate their work on average figures, a brief consideration of the extreme weather conditions that increasingly concern them is a worthwhile exercise. In early 1987, Athens, Greece experienced its first recorded snowfall and then, a few months later, its hottest summer ever—only to learn the following December that the average yearly temperature came out almost exactly "normal." On August 11, 1984, residents of Miami, Florida experienced both the highest (35.5°C) and lowest (21°C) temperatures

ever recorded on that day—only to see it noted that the mean temperature for the day came very close to the normal daily average of 28°C. These are only two isolated cases, but they underscore how averages can misrepresent actual weather conditions and the accompanying human adjustments to the physical environment of a particular place.

Figure 15.8 illustrates some of the noteworthy global weather extremes, while Fig. 15.9 shows weather extremes in Canada. With some of the

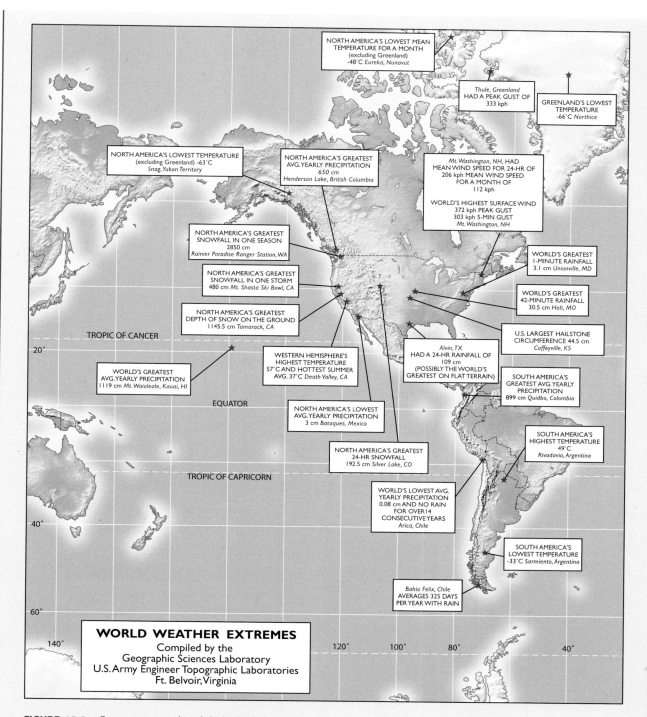

FIGURE 15.8   Some noteworthy global weather extremes.

most changeable weather occurring in the midlatitudes, North America has a number of record-breakers. Among the world weather records held in places throughout North America are greatest yearly average precipitation and highest surface wind speed. The interaction between the polar and tropical air masses in North America, together with the volatile twistings of the Polar Front jet stream,

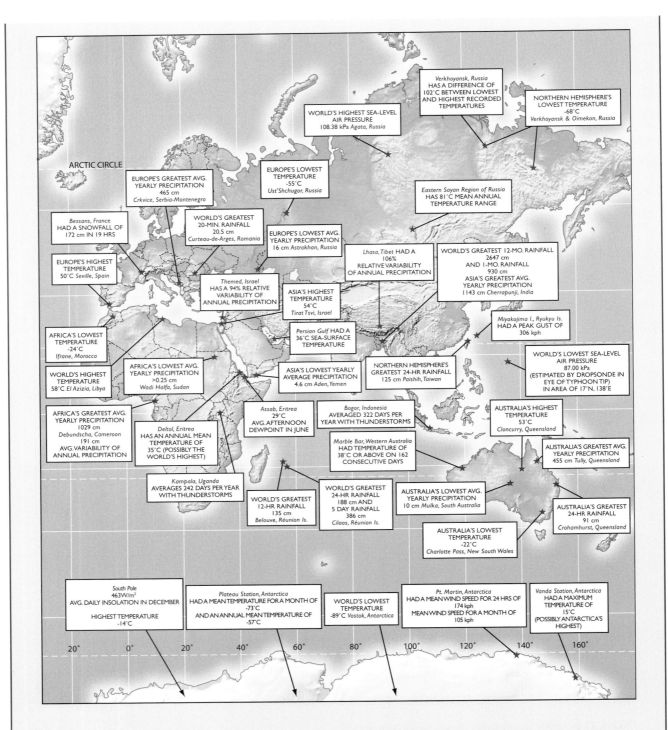

helps to produce many more weather extremes in North America than in the continental heart of Eurasia. (Note how, in Fig.15.8, Siberia records only a handful of weather extremes in temperature and air-pressure readings.) And as we learn more about global temperature trends (Unit 7) and phenomena of the El Niño type (Unit 11), atmospheric scientists may well discover additional explanations for the many still-puzzling occurrences of extreme weather that mark the world map.

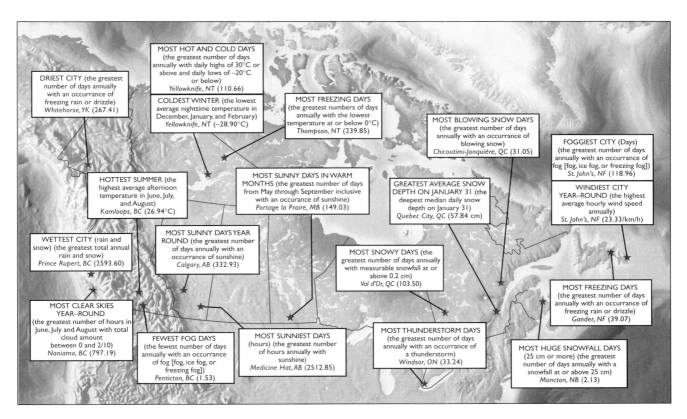

FIGURE 15.9 Canadian Weather Extremes.

FIGURE 15.10 NOAA's special-purpose forecasting facilities utilize state-of-the-art computer and imaging systems to study and track storms. This facility, located in Tucson, Arizona, is the control centre of the National Lightning Detection Network.

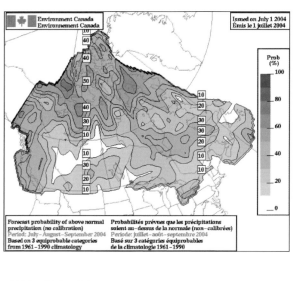

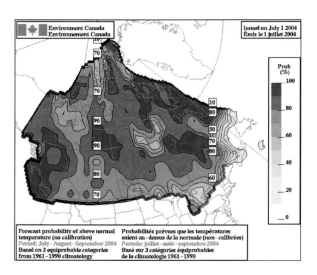

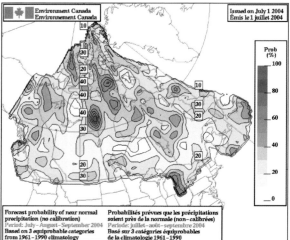

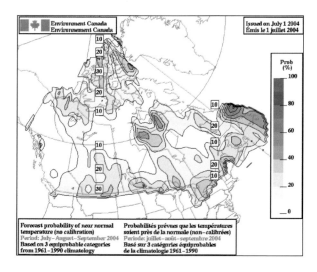

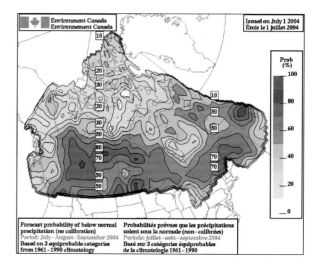

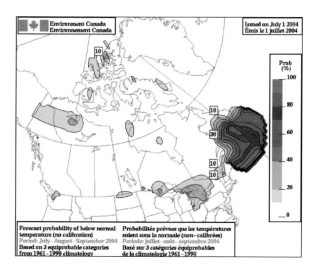

FIGURE 15.11   State-of-the-art long-range weather forecasting by the Meteorological Service of Canada. More examples can be obtained from their website at http://weatheroffice.ec.gc.ca/saisons/index_e.html.

outdoor activities, from airline companies to motion picture producers to construction contractors, are also frequent customers of private forecasting services. In Canada the general public is probably most familiar with the news media's use of private forecasts. The Weather Network's patented Pelmorex Forecast Engine (PFE) technology, for example, allows their meteorologists to issue weather forecasts for the entire country down to a 10-km^2 grid.

Long-Range Forecasting

Long-range forecasting constitutes a lively new frontier for weather scientists and poses some of the toughest research challenges they face today. In response to the need and desire for longer-term outlooks, the Canadian Meteorological Centre began producing, through the Meteorological Service of Canada, seasonal temperature and precipitation anomaly forecasts, starting in 1995. The seasonal forecasts are issued four times a year, on the first day in December, March, June, and September. Temperature and precipitation forecasts are made for 0–3-month, 3–6-month, 6–9-month, and 9–12-month

periods. The maps represent air temperature and precipitation that is expected to be below normal, near normal, and above normal (deterministic forecasts). In addition, probabilistic forecasts are produced; these indicate the respective probability of the temperature and precipitation being below, near, or above normal. The Meteorological Service of Canada's seasonal forecast web page (http://weatheroffice.ec.gc.ca/saisons/index_e. html) includes forecast maps, details of how the maps are produced, and reliability results. A series of examples are illustrated in Fig. 15.11.

Units 13, 14, and 15 have focused on the moving weather systems that blanket the Earth at any given moment. These recurring systems, together with the constant flows of radiation, heat energy, and moisture, make up our daily weather. Over time, a region's weather conditions exhibit regular rhythms and patterns that are characteristic of a certain type of climate. Unit 16 provides a basis for the classification and regionalization of climate types, which is subsequently applied (in Units 17–19) to all of the Earth's land areas.

KEY TERMS

geosynchronous orbit *page 190*

numerical weather prediction *page 194*

polar orbit *page 190*

radiosonde *page 189*

synoptic weather chart *page 188*

REVIEW QUESTIONS

1. Describe the basic weather elements whose variations are observed and recorded at weather stations.

2. What is a radiosonde station and what kinds of atmospheric data does it provide?

3. How does the 500-mb chart aid in the forecasting of surface weather?

4. Why is long-range weather forecasting still such a tenuous science?

REFERENCES AND FURTHER READINGS

AYRES, B. D., Jr. "Volatile Weather 'Bomb' Is Tracked," *New York Times* (March 14, 1988), 8.

BADER, M. J., et al., Eds. *Images in Weather Forecasting: A Practical Guide for Interpreting Satellite and Radar Imagery* (New York: Cambridge Univ. Press, 1995).

BURROUGHS, W. *Watching the World's Weather* (New York: Cambridge Univ. Press, 1991).

CARLETON, A. M. *Satellite Remote Sensing in Climatology* (London: Belhaven, 1991).

COX, J. D. *Storm Watchers: The Turbulent History of Weather Prediction from Franklin's Kite to El Niño* (New York: Wiley, 2002).

CHASTON, P. R. *Weather Maps: How to Read and Interpret All the Basic Weather Charts* (Kearney, Mo.: Chaston Scientific, 1997).

EAGLEMAN, J. R. *Severe and Unusual Weather* (Lenexa, Kan.: Trimedia, 2nd ed., 1990).

FEDER, B. J. "Highs and Lows Are Their Business: More Companies Are Relying on Private Weather Forecasters," *New York Times* (October 22, 1996), C1, C3.

FISHMAN, J., and KALISH, R.   *The Weather Revolution: Innovations and Imminent Breakthroughs in Accurate Forecasting* (New York: Plenum, 1994).

KIDDER, S. Q., and VONDER HAAR, T. H.   *Satellite Meteorology: An Introduction* (San Diego, Calif.: Academic Press, 1995).

KRISHNAMURTI, T. N., and BOUNOUA, L.   *An Introduction to Numerical Weather Prediction Techniques* (Boca Raton, Fla.: CRC Press, 1996).

MONMONIER, M.   *Air Apparent: How Meteorologists Learned to Map, Predict, and Dramatize Weather* (Chicago: Univ. of Chicago Press, 1999).

PEARCE, E. A., and SMITH, C. G.   *World Weather Guide* (New York: Random House, 1990).

RILEY, D., and SPALTON, L.   *World Weather and Climate* (New York: Cambridge Univ. Press, 2nd ed., 1981).

THOMAS, M. K.   *Beginnings of Canadian Meteorology* (Chicago: Independent Publishers Group, 1991).

WAGNER, R. L., and ADLER, B., Jr.   *The Weather Sourcebook: Your One-Stop Resource for Everything You Need to Feed Your Weather Habit* (Guilford, Conn.: Globe Pequot, 1994).

WEB RESOURCES

http://lwf.ncdc.noaa.gov/oa/reports/weather-events.htm   Worldwide weather and climate events with links to many extreme weather-event sites.

http://wunderground.com   Weather Underground is one of the most common Internet sites for obtaining international weather data.

http://www.msc.ec.gc.ca/education/severe_weather/page02_e.cfm   Environment Canada's volunteer weather watchers site, with the "Severe Weather Watcher Handbook."

http://www.msc-smc.ec.gc.ca/msc/brochure_e.html   The Meteorological Service of Canada.

http://www.theweathernetwork.com   Canada's Weather Network.

http://www2010.atmos.uiuc.edu/(Gh)/guides/maps/home.rxml   "Reading Weather Maps" from the University of Illinois.

Climate Classification and Regionalization

At the Sahara's southern margin, a zone of climatic transition, the arid desert gives way to the semi-arid grassland.

OBJECTIVES

- To define climate and discuss the general problems of climate classification based on dynamic phenomena
- To outline a useful climate classification scheme

devised by Köppen, based on temperatures and precipitation amounts and timing
- To apply the modified Köppen classification system to the Earth and

briefly describe appropriate climate regions as they appear on a hypothetical continent and the world map

Climatology is the study of the Earth's regional climates, whereas meteorology is the study of short-term atmospheric phenomena that constitute weather. To understand this distinction, we may use the rule that weather happens now but climate goes on all the time. Thus climate involves the day-to-day, aggregate weather conditions each of us expects to experience in a particular place. If we live in Florida or Hawaii, we expect to wear light clothes for most of the year; if we live in Nunavut, we expect to wear heavy jackets. Climate, therefore, is a synthesis of the succession of weather events we have learned to expect in any particular location.

Because there is a degree of regularity in the heat and water exchanges at the Earth's surface and in the general circulation of the atmosphere, there is a broad and predictable pattern of climates across the globe. But this pattern is altered in detail by such additional *climatic controls* as the location of land and water bodies, ocean currents, and mountain ranges and other highlands. More specifically, the **climate** of a place may be defined as the average values of weather elements, such as temperature and precipitation, over at least a 30-year period and the important variations from those average values. Units 17 to 19 we examine the ways in which broad patterns and fine details create distinctly different climates across the Earth. This unit provides a framework for that investigation by discussing the classification of climate types and their global spatial distribution.

Classifying Climates

Because of the great variety and complexity of recurring weather patterns across the Earth's surface, it is necessary for atmospheric scientists to reduce countless local climates to a relative few that possess important unifying characteristics. Such classification, of course, is the organizational foundation of all the modern sciences. Where would chemistry be without its periodic table of the elements, geology without its time scale of past eras and epochs, and biology without its Linnaean system of naming plant and animal species?

The ideal climate classification system would achieve five objectives:

1. It should clearly differentiate among all the major types of climates that occur on Earth.
2. It should show the relationships among these climate types.
3. It should apply to the whole world.
4. It should provide a framework for further subdivision to cover specific locales.
5. It should demonstrate the controls that cause any particular climate.

Unfortunately, in the same way that no map projection can simultaneously satisfy all of our requirements (see Unit 3), no climate classification system can simul-

taneously achieve all five of these objectives. There are two reasons. First, so many factors contribute to climate that we must compromise between simplicity and complexity. We have values for radiation, temperature, precipitation, evapotranspiration, wind direction, and so forth. We could use one variable—as the Greeks used latitude to differentiate "torrid," "temperate," and "frigid" zones—and have a classification system that would be too simple to be useful. Or, on the other hand, we could use all the values to gain infinite detail—but overwhelming complexity.

The second reason is that the Earth's climates form a spatial continuum. Sharp areal breaks between the major types of climate are rarely found, because both daily and generalized weather patterns change from place to place gradually, not abruptly. Yet any classificatory map forces climatologists to draw lines separating a given climate type from its neighbours, thereby giving the impression that such a boundary is a sharp dividing line rather than the middle of a broad transition zone.

When confronted with these problems, climatologists focus their compromises on a single rule: the development or choice of a climatic classification must be determined by the particular use for which the scheme is intended. With so many potential uses, it is not surprising that many different classification systems have been devised. Whereas qualitative and/or subjective criteria could be used to distinguish climates (see Perspective: Climate in Daily Human Terms), the practicalities of contemporary physical geography demand an objective, quantitative approach. Moreover, for our purposes, the classification system must be reasonably simple and yet reflect the full diversity of global climatic variation. The **Köppen climate classification system** provides us with that balanced approach, offering a descriptive classification of world climates that brilliantly negotiates the tightrope between simplicity and complexity. To Wladimir P. Köppen (1846–1940), the key to classifying climate was plant life.

The Köppen Climate Classification System

In 1874 the Swiss botanist Alphonse de Candolle produced the first comprehensive classification and regionalization of world vegetation based on the internal functions of plant organs. It is to Wladimir Köppen's everlasting credit that he recognized that a plant, or assemblage of plants, at a particular place represents a

PERSPECTIVES ON THE HUMAN ENVIRONMENT

Climate in Daily Human Terms

1. "The butter, when stabbed with a knife, flew like very brittle toffee. The lower skirts of the inner tent are solid with ice. All our [sleeping] bags were so saturated with water that they froze too stiff to bend with safety, so we packed them one on the other full length, like coffins, on the sledge."

2. "The rain poured steadily down, turning the little patch of reclaimed ground on which his house stood back into swamp again. The window of this room blew to and fro: at some time during the night, the catch had been broken by a squall of wind. Now the rain had blown in, his dressing table was soaking wet, and there was a pool of water on the floor."

3. "It was a breathless wind, with the furnace taste sometimes known in Egypt when a *khamsin* came, and, as the day went on and the sun rose in the sky it grew stronger, more filled with the dust of Nefudh, the great sand desert of Northern Arabia, close by us over there, but invisible through the haze."

4. "The spring came richly, and the hills lay asleep in grass—emerald green, the rank thick grass; the slopes were sleek and fat with it. The stock, sensing a great quantity of food shooting up on the sidehills, increased the bearing of the young. When April came, and warm grass-scented days, the flowers burdened the hills with color, the poppies gold and the lupines blue, in spreads and comforters."

5. "The east wind that had blown coldly across the [English] Channel that morning had brought a dusting of snow to Picardy. Snow in April! It lay in a thin covering on hillsides, like long, torn bed sheets, the earth showing through in black streaks. It made the ordinary-looking landscape seem dramatic, the way New Jersey looks in bad weather, made houses and fences emphatic, and brought a sort of cubism to villages that would otherwise have been unmemorable. Each place became a little frozen portrait in black and white."

What do these rather poetic excerpted selections have in common? They attempt to convey a sense of climate, the impact a particular climate—especially a demanding and harsh climate—has on people who attempt to explore and live in it. Description of climate is one of the cornerstones of the literature of exploration and travel. Perhaps nothing conveys a sense of an environment as efficiently and dramatically as notation of its winds, precipitation, and temperatures. And, as these skillful writers show, climate tells you a great deal about the "feel" of a place.

Now to relieve your curiosity. Selection 1 is from Robert Falcon Scott's memoirs of his explorations in the Arctic, published posthumously in 1914. Selection 2 is by Graham Greene, who, after being stationed in West Africa during World War II, wrote *The Heart of the Matter*. Selection 3 is by Thomas Edward Lawrence ("Lawrence of Arabia"), the British soldier who organized the Arab nations against the Turks during World War I. Selection 4 is by John Steinbeck, writing in *To a God Unknown* during the 1930s about the Mediterranean climate of central California. Selection 5 is from travel writer Paul Theroux, who, in *Riding the Iron Rooster*, recorded his mid-1980s train-window impression of northern France en route from London to a year of journeying on China's railroads.

synthesis of the many variations of the weather experienced there. He therefore looked to de Candolle's classification of vegetation to solve the puzzle of the global spatial organization of climates.

Köppen (pronounced "KER-pin" with the "r" silent) compared the global distribution of vegetation mapped by de Candolle with his own maps of the world distribution of temperature and precipitation. He soon identified several correlations between the atmosphere and biosphere and used them to distinguish one climate from another. For example, he observed that in the high latitudes the boundary marking the presence or absence of trees closely coincided with the presence or absence of at least one month in the year with an average temperature of 10°C. He noted many other such correlations, and in 1900 he published the first version of his classification system. This regionalization scheme, subsequently modified by Köppen and other researchers (notably Rudolf Geiger), was to become the most widely used climatic classification system.

Figure 16.1 presents a simplified version of the Köppen system, which will be used in this book. Just as code letters are used to describe air masses, the Köppen classification uses a shorthand notation of letter symbols to distinguish different characteristics of the major climates. The six major climate groups (column 1) are labeled **A**, **B**, **C**, **D**, **E**, and **H**. The major tropical (**A**), mesothermal (**C**), microthermal (**D**), and polar (**E**) climates are differentiated according to temperature. (*Mesothermal* implies a moderate amount of heat, and *microthermal* implies a small amount—as the temperature criteria in their respective boxes in Fig. 16.1 indicate.) The major dry (**B**) climates are distinguished by potential evapotranspiration exceeding precipitation. The variable highland climates (**H**) are grouped into a separate major category.

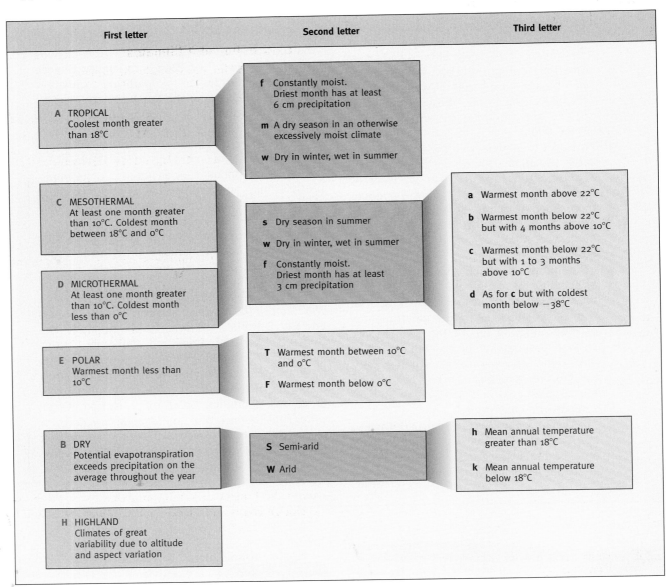

FIGURE 16.1   Simplified version of the modern Köppen climate classification system.

As Fig. 16.1 shows, these major climate groups are further subdivided in terms of heat or moisture by the use of a second letter (column 2) and in some cases a third letter (column 3). In the second column, the lowercase letters **f, m, w,** and **s** tell us when precipitation occurs during the year, and are applicable to **A, C,** and **D** climates. Capital letters **S** and **W** indicate the degree of aridity in dry (**B**) climates, with **S** designating semi-arid conditions and **W** full aridity. Letters referring to moisture conditions are shown in the green-coloured boxes in Fig. 16.1; letters referring to heat are shown in the peach-coloured boxes. The heat modifiers of the third column—lowercase letters **a, b, c,** and **d**—provide details on the temperatures of **C** and **D** climates. The third letters **h** and **k** do the same for the **B** climates, and the second letters **T** and **F** subdivide the temperatures in polar (**E**) climates.

Many different climates can be defined with this shorthand code, including all that can be represented and mapped at the world regional scale. As we proceed through each major climate type in the next three units, you will be able to decode any combination of Köppen letter symbols by referring back to Fig. 16.1. For instance, an **Af** climate is a tropical climate in which the average temperature of every month exceeds 18°C and total monthly precipitation always exceeds 6 cm. Before considering each of the six major climate groups, we need to establish their spatial dimensions, both in general terms and on the world map.

The Regional Distribution of Climate Types

The easiest way to picture the distribution of world climates is first to imagine how they would be spatially arranged on a **hypothetical continent** of uniform low elevation. Such a model is shown in Fig. 16.2 and represents a generalization of the world's landmasses. A comparison with the actual global map reveals that this hypothetical continent tapers from north to south in close correspondence with the overall narrowing of land areas between 50°N and 40°S. Note that on the world map the bulk of both Eurasia and North America is greatest in the latitudinal zone lying between 50° and 70°N. Conversely, at 40°S the only land interrupting the world ocean is the slender cone of southern South America and small parts of Australia and New Zealand.

Five of the six major climate groups—**A, B, C, D,** and **E**—are mapped on the hypothetical continent in Fig. 16.2. (**H** climates are not shown beyond a token presence because this model de-emphasizes upland areas.) The hypothetical continent model, of course, represents an abstraction of the more complex *empirical* or actual distribution of climate regions (shown in Fig. 16.3), which, like all regional schemes, is itself a simplification of the still greater complexity that exists across the Earth's surface.

The following discussion of world climate regions is based upon a side-by-side consideration of Figs. 16.2 and 16.3. The hypothetical continent is useful for gaining a general understanding of the latitudinal extent and continental position of each climate type; the empirical Köppen climate map makes the connections to the specific regions that blanket the continental landmasses. The emphasis in the remainder of this unit is on broad patterns. Units 17, 18, and 19 consider each major climate type in greater detail.

The Distribution of A Climates

The tropical **A** climates straddle the Equator, extending to approximately 25 degrees latitude in both the Northern and Southern Hemispheres (Fig. 16.2). The heart of the **A** climate region is constituted by its wet subtype, the *tropical rainforest* climate (**Af**), named for the vegetation it nurtures. On the poleward margins of the tropical rainforest, forming transitional belts between the **A** and **B** climates, lies the **Aw** climate, which exhibits a distinct winter dry season. This is called the *savanna* climate because of the tall grasses that grow there, dominating the vegetational spaces between clumps of trees and/or thorny bushes. A third **A** climate, the **Am**, or *monsoon*, variety of the rainforest climate, is often found at coastal corners of the **Af** region and is subject to even more pronounced seasonal fluctuations in rainfall.

Closer inspection of the tropical climate zone on the hypothetical continent will also reveal that areas of **A** climate are widest on the eastern side of the world island. This occurs because the trade winds blow onshore from the northeast and southeast, and the difference in overall latitudinal extent of the **A** region is about 20 degrees greater on the east coast of a continent than on the west coast.

The world Köppen map (Fig. 16.3) displays a more intricate pattern but is consistent with the generalizations we have just made with respect to the distribution of **A** climates. In the Americas, the **A** climates are centred around the Equator, reaching to about 25°N and S on the eastern coasts and islands, and to about 20°N and S in western Central and South America, respectively. The African pattern is similar south of the Equator, but to the north the **A** climates are compressed because the moist northeast trades are blocked by the landmass of southern Asia. For reasons identified in Unit 10, the Asian tropical climates are dominated by the monsoon effect. The

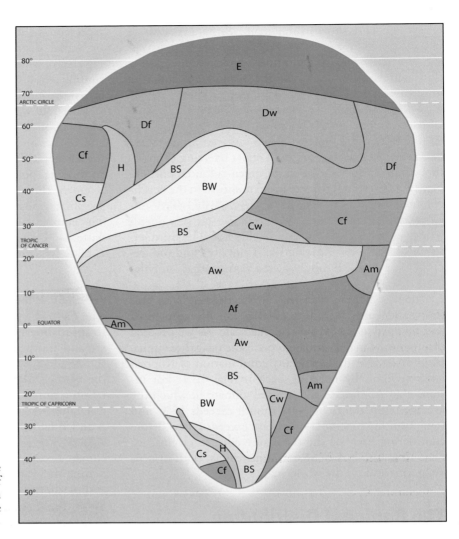

FIGURE 16.2 Distribution of climate types across a hypothetical continent of low, uniform elevation. Climate types on this world-island are identified in the legend of Fig. 16.3.

prevalence of oceans and seas between Southeast Asia and northern Australia has sharply reduced the areal extent of tropical climates over land, but many of the islands of the lengthy Indonesian archipelago still exhibit rainforest climates over most of their surfaces.

The Distribution of B Climates

The dry **B** climates are located poleward of the **A** climates on the western sides of continents. These climates are associated with the subsiding air of the subtropical high-pressure zones, whose influence is greatest on the eastern side of the oceans. This leads to a major intrusion of arid climates onto neighbouring continents in both the Northern and Southern Hemispheres. As the hypothetical continent model shows (Fig. 16.2), this occurs at the average latitudes of the Subtropical High between 20° and 30°N and S. Once inland from the west coast of the continent, however, the **B** climate region curves poleward, following the airflows of the

Westerlies in each hemisphere and reaching to about 55°N and 45°S, respectively. As shown in Unit 17, continentality also plays a significant role in the occurrence of **B** climates, particularly on the Eurasian landmass.

The heart of the **B** climate region contains the driest climatic variety, true *desert* (**BW**—with **W** standing for *wüste*, the German word for desert). It is surrounded by the semi-arid short-grass prairie, or *steppe* (**BS**), which is a moister transitional climate that lies between the **BW** core and the more humid **A, C,** and **D** climates bordering the dry-climate zone.

On the world map (Fig. 16.3) consistencies between model and reality can again be observed. The most striking similarity occurs with respect to the vast bulk of subtropical-latitude land that stretches east–west across northern Africa and then curves northeastward through southwestern and central Asia. The desert climate (**BW**) dominates here and forms a more or less continuous belt between northwestern Africa and Mongolia, interrupted only by narrow seas, mountain corridors, and a handful of well-watered river valleys. Included among these vast arid basins are North Africa's Sahara, the deserts of the Arabian Peninsula and nearby Iran, and China's Takla Makan and Gobi Deserts. Note that these **BW** climates become colder north of 35°N (as indicated by the third Köppen letter **k** replacing **h**) and that all the deserts are framed by narrow semi-arid or steppe (**BS**) zones that also change from **h** to **k** in the vicinity of the 35th parallel.

In North America the arid climates occur on a smaller scale, but in about the same proportion and relative areal extent vis-à-vis this smaller continental landmass. The rain shadow effect (see Unit 13) plays an important role in the dryness of the western United States and Canada, where high mountains parallel the Pacific coast and block much of the moisture brought onshore by prevailing westerly winds. In the Southern Hemisphere, only Australia is reminiscent of the **B** climate distributions north of the Equator because this island continent comprises the only large body of land within the subtropical latitudes. On the tapering landmasses of South America and southern Africa, the arid climate zones are compressed but still correspond roughly to the regional patterns of the hypothetical continent.

The Distribution of C Climates

As Fig. 16.2 reveals, the mesothermal (moderate-temperature) **C** climates are situated in the middle latitudes. The land/water differential between the Northern and Southern Hemispheres, however, becomes more pronounced poleward of the subtropics, and the hypothetical continent no longer exhibits regional patterns that mirror each other. North of the Equator, as the world island's greatest bulk is approached, the absence of oceanic-derived moisture in the continental interior produces an arid climate zone that interrupts the east–west belt of **C** climates lying approximately between the latitudes of 25° and 45°N. In the Southern Hemisphere, where the mesothermal climatic belt is severely pinched by the tapering model continent, **C** climates reach nearly across the remaining landmass south of 40°S.

The subtypes of the **C** climate group reflect the hemispheric differences just discussed, but some noteworthy similarities exist as well. On the western coast, adjacent to the **B** climate region, small but important zones of *Mediterranean* (**Cs**) climate occur where the subtropical high-pressure belt has a drying influence during the summer. Poleward of these zones, *humid climates with moist winters* (**Cf**) are encountered and owe their existence, especially on the western side of the continent, to the

storms carried by the midlatitude westerly winds. **Cf** climates are also found on the eastern side of the continent, where they obtain moisture from humid air on the western side of the adjoining ocean's subtropical high-pressure zone. Another mesothermal subtype, sometimes called the *subtropical monsoon* (**Cw**) climate, is found in the interior of the **C** climate region and represents a cooler version of the savanna climate, where the **Aw** regime spills across the poleward margin of the tropics.

The world Köppen map (Fig. 16.3) again demonstrates the applicability of the distributional generalizations of the model continent. Both Eurasia and North America exhibit the central **B** climate interruption of the mesothermal climatic belt, with the **C** climates less prominent on the Eurasian landmass where distances from maritime moisture sources are much greater. Southern Hemisphere patterns are also generally consistent with the model, although the **C** climates are often confined to narrow coastal strips that result from rain shadow effects produced by South America's Andes Mountains, South Africa's Great Escarpment, and Australia's east-coast Great Dividing Range.

The individual **C** climates further underscore the linkages between the hypothetical continent and the real world. Mediterranean (**Cs**) climates are located on every west coast in the expected latitudinal position (around 35 degrees), and even penetrate to Asia's "west coast," where the eastern Mediterranean Sea reaches the Middle East.

The west-coast marine variety of the **Cf** climate is generally observed on the poleward flank of the **Cs** region, but mountains paralleling the ocean often restrict its inland penetration; the obvious exception is Europe, where blocking highlands are absent and onshore Westerlies flow across warm ocean waters to bring mild weather conditions hundreds of kilometres inland. The **Cf** climates on the eastern sides of continents are particularly apparent in the United States (thanks to the moderating effects of the Gulf of Mexico), South America, and the Pacific rim of Australia. In East Asia, this **Cf** subtype is limited by the more powerful regional effects of monsoonal reversals, but where it does occur in eastern China and Japan, it is associated with a massive population concentration that contains over one-eighth of humankind.

The **Cw** climates of the Northern Hemisphere are confined mainly to the subtropical portions of southern and eastern Asia, and, of course, are closely related to the monsoonal weather regime. The Southern Hemisphere **Cw** climate regions function as transitional zones, in both Africa and South America, between the equatorial-area savannas to the north and the subtropical arid and humid climates to the south.

WORLD CLIMATES
After Köppen–Geiger

A   Humid Equatorial Climate

Af	No dry season
Am	Short dry season
Aw	Dry winter

B   Dry Climate

| BS | Semi-arid |
| BW | Arid |

h = hot
k = cold

C   Humid Temperate Climate

Cf	No dry season
Cw	Dry winter
Cs	Dry summer

a = hot summer
b = cool summer
c = short, cool summer
d = very cold winter

D   Humid Cold Climate

| Df | No dry season |
| Dw | Dry winter |

E   Cold Polar Climate

| E | Tundra and ice |

F   Highland Climate

| H | Unclassified highlands |

0   1000   2000   3000 kilometres

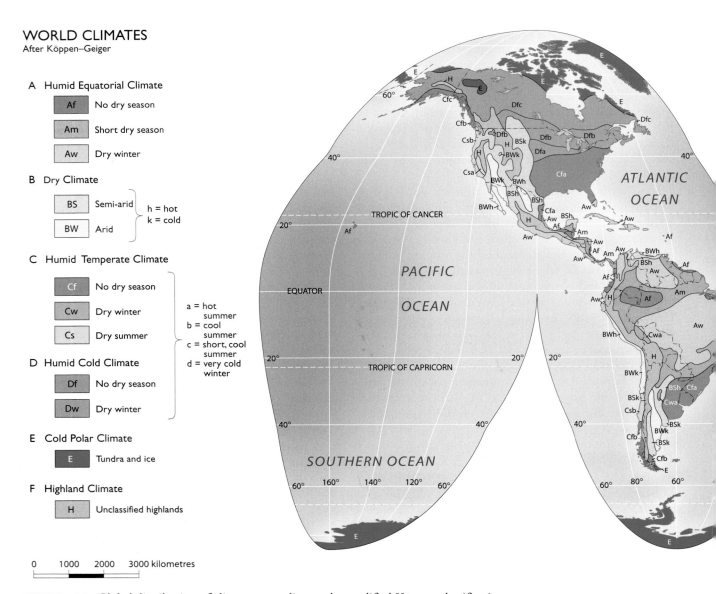

FIGURE 16.3   Global distribution of climates according to the modified Köppen classification system.

The Distribution of D Climates

The microthermal **D** climates, which receive relatively small amounts of heat, are found exclusively in the Northern Hemisphere. There are no large landmasses in the Southern Hemisphere between 50° and 70°S, so here latitude and the effect of continentality do not support the cold winters of the **D** climates. On the world island (Fig. 16.2) the microthermal climates are associated with the large landmasses in the upper-middle and subpolar latitudes, and occupy an east–west belt between approximately 45° and 65°N. This climatic band of severe winters is at its widest in the interior of the hypothetical continent, moderating only near the coasts (particularly the west coast), where the ameliorating influences of maritime air penetrate inland.

Two subtypes of the **D** climate group can be observed. The **Df** variety experiences precipitation throughout the year; it can exhibit a fairly warm summer near the **C** climate boundary and certain coastal zones, but in the interior and toward the higher latitudes the summers are shorter and much cooler. The other subtype—**Dw**—is encountered where the effects of continentality are most pronounced. Annual moisture totals there are lower, and the harsh winters are characterized by dryness. The extreme cooling of the ground in midwinter is associated with a large anticyclone that persists throughout the

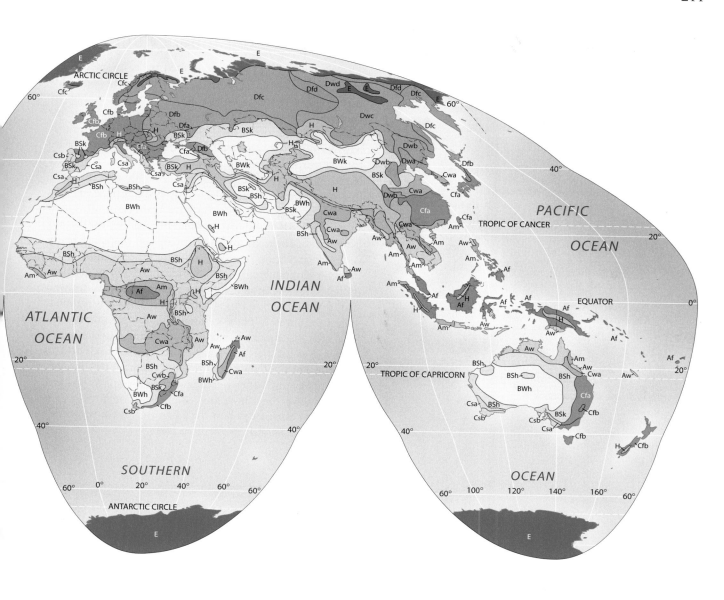

cold season and blocks all surface winds that might bring in moisture from other areas.

The actual distribution of **D** climates (Fig. 16.3) accords quite well with the model continent. The greatest east–west extents of both Eurasia and North America are indeed the heart of the **D** climate region, which dominates the latitudes lying between 50° and 65°N. The only exceptions occur along the western coasts, where the warm North Atlantic Drift and Alaskan Current bathe the subpolar coastal zone with moderating temperatures. In the Eurasian interior, extreme continentality pushes the microthermal climates to a higher average latitude, a pattern not matched in eastern Canada, where the colder polar climates to the north penetrate farther south.

As for the **D** subtypes, they correspond closely to the model. However, note that North America, wide as it is, does not contain sufficient bulk to support the **Dw** climate or even the coldest variant of the **Df** climate (**Dfd**). Only Eurasia exhibits these extreme microthermal climates, which are concentrated on the eastern side of that enormous landmass. Two reasons underlie the eastward deflection: (1) the overall altitude of the land surface is much higher in the mountainous Russian Far East and northeastern China, and (2) northeastern Asia lies farthest from the warm waters off western Eurasia that pump moisture into the prevailing westerly winds that sweep around the globe within this latitudinal zone.

The Distribution of E Climates

In both hemispheres, land areas poleward of the Arctic and Antarctic Circles (66½°N and S, respectively), with deficits of net radiation, exhibit polar **E** climates. The hypothetical continent and world Köppen maps both display similar patterns, with **E** climates dominant in Antarctica, Greenland, and the poleward fringes of northernmost Eurasia and North America. As for subtypes, the *tundra* climate (**ET**), where the warmest month records an average temperature between 0°C and 10°C, borders the warmer climates on the equatorward margins of each polar region. The highest latitudes in the vicinity of the poles themselves—as well as most of interior Greenland and high-lying Antarctica—experience the *icecap* or *frost* climate (**EF**), in which the average temperature of the warmest month fails to reach 0°C.

The **E** climates are also often associated with the high-altitude areas of lower latitudes, particularly in the upper reaches of mountainous zones that are too cold to support vegetation. In these situations, they are labelled **H** or *highland* climates, which are surveyed together with the **E** climates in Unit 19.

Boundaries of Climate Regions

The classification system developed by Köppen and his associates has been criticized because it does not consider the causes of climate and because some of its climate–vegetation links are not very strong. Yet it remains the most often used classification scheme, and it has obviously proven itself both useful and appropriate for the purpose of introducing students to the complexity of global climatic patterns. Earlier in this unit, we discussed the shortcomings of any geographical classification of climate. We conclude by again reminding you that what look like sharp regional boundaries on the hypothetical continent and world Köppen maps are really zones of transition from one climate type to another.

The Köppen regional scheme, therefore, which was designed for the broad global or regional scale, is not well suited for microclimatological studies. Thus it is not possible to accurately place a climate-region boundary in a local area, because only a few places in any city or county have compiled the necessary weather data for climatic analysis. Think of your local weather report. The "official" temperature and other weather statistics are obtained at a single site for the whole area, such as at the airport or a downtown park, or at best for a handful of communities scattered across your immediate area.

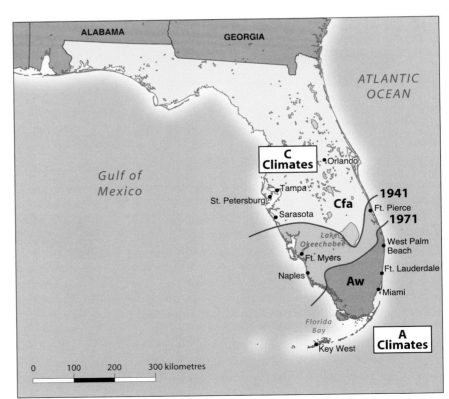

FIGURE 16.4 Changing location of the January 18°C isotherm in southern Florida, 1941–1979.

Another problem in applying Köppen boundaries at the microscale is that these boundaries change over time. Climates, as we will see, are highly dynamic, and substantial change can occur over long periods. And even over shorter time spans, such change can be seen on the map. A good example is shown in Fig. 16.4, which maps the poleward boundary of the **Aw** climate in tropical South Florida. Note that in 1941 the January 18°C isotherm was located between 40 km and 120 km to the northwest of its 1979 position. Thus over at least those four decades, the tropical zone contracted, and cities such as Ft. Myers, Naples, and Ft. Pierce "shifted" into the mesothermal (**Cfa**) climatic zone. These "changes," of course, are very subtle, and even a resident of Ft. Myers who has lived there since 1940 would almost certainly not be aware of any meaningful change. But this little exercise about boundaries is instructive and should interject a little healthy skepticism in preparation for the more detailed overview of climate regions covered in Units 17 to 19.

KEY TERMS

climate *page 204*

hypothetical continent *page 207*

Köppen climate classification system *page 204*

REVIEW QUESTIONS

1. How is a location's climate determined from weather data?

2. What are the thermal criteria for tropical, mesothermal, microthermal, and polar climates in the Köppen system?

3. Outline the interpretation of the second and third letters of the codes used in the Köppen system. For example, how does an **Af** climate differ from an **Aw** climate?

4. Describe two advantages of the Köppen climate classification system.

5. Describe two problems or shortcomings of the Köppen climate classification system.

6. Why should Köppen regional-scale boundaries not be used to ascertain climate-zone boundaries at the local scale?

REFERENCES AND FURTHER READINGS

CRITCHFIELD, H. J.   *General Climatology* (Englewood Cliffs, N.J.: Prentice-Hall, 4th ed., 1983).

EAGLEMAN, J. R.   *The Visualization of Climate* (Lexington, Mass.: Heath, 1976).

HAURWITZ, B., and AUSTIN, J. M.   *Climatology* (New York: McGraw-Hill, 1944).

HOUGHTON, J. T., Ed.   *The Global Climate* (New York: Cambridge Univ. Press, 1984).

KENDREW, W. G.   *The Climates of the Continents* (New York: Oxford Univ. Press, 5th ed., 1961).

LINACRE, E.   *Climate Data and Resources: A Reference and Guide* (London/New York: Routledge, 1992).

LOCKWOOD, J.   *World Climatic Systems* (London: Edward Arnold, 1985).

LYDOLPH, P. E.   *The Climate of the Earth* (Totowa, N.J.: Rowman & Allanheld, 1985).

OKE, T. R.   *Boundary Layer Climates* (London/New York: Methuen, 2nd ed., 1987).

RILEY, D., and SPALTON, L.   *World Weather and Climate* (New York: Cambridge Univ. Press, 2nd ed., 1981).

TREWARTHA, G. T.   *The Earth's Problem Climates* (Madison, Wis.: Univ. of Wisconsin Press, 2nd ed., 1981).

TREWARTHA, G. T., and HORN, L. H.   *An Introduction to Climate* (New York: McGraw-Hill, 5th ed., 1980).

WILCOCK, A. A.   "Köppen after Fifty Years," *Annals of the Association of American Geographers*, 58 (1968), 12–28.

WEB RESOURCES

http://geography.about.com/library/weekly/aa011700a.htm   An overview of the Köppen climate classification system with links to a Köppen climate chart and other climate websites.

http://www.worldclimate.com   Page that gives average climate data for any city name entered.

Tropical (A) and Arid (B) Climates

A **BW** climatic zone expands: desertification in the Somali borderland of Kenya, East Africa. (Authors' photo)

OBJECTIVES

- To expand the discussion of tropical (**A**) and arid (**B**) climates using climographs developed for actual weather stations

- To highlight climate-related environmental problems within tropical and arid climate zones

- To examine the causes and consequences of tropical deforestation and desertification

U nit 16 set the stage for a global survey of the principal climate types based on the Köppen classification and regionalization system. An overview begins in this unit with the **A** (tropical) and **B** (dry or arid) climates, and you should use Figs. 16.2 (p. 208) and 16.3 (pp. 210–211) as a guide to the spatial distribution of all the world's major climate types.

In addition to providing greater detail about each of the principal subdivisions of the tropical and arid climates, we focus on the leading environmental problem of each major climate group. For the **A** climates, *deforestation* is an intensifying crisis that could have far-reaching environmental consequences in the foreseeable future. For the **B** climates, our concern is with *desertification,* the spread of desert conditions engendered by human abuse of dryland environments. Based on a similar approach, the rest of the major climate types are treated in Units 18 and 19.

The Major Tropical (A) Climates

Contained within a continuous east–west belt astride the Equator, varying latitudinally from 30 to 50 degrees wide, is the warmth and moisture of the **A or tropical climates**. Warmth is derived from proximity to the Equator (**A** climate temperatures must average higher than 18°C in the coolest month); moisture comes from the rains of the ITCZ (Inter-Tropical Convergence Zone), wet-monsoon systems, easterly waves, and hurri-

canes. The tropical climates can be subdivided into three major types: the *tropical rainforest*, the *monsoon rainforest,* and the *savanna.*

The Tropical Rainforest (Af) Climate

The **Af** or tropical rainforest zone exhibits the greatest effects of heat and moisture. In areas undisturbed by human intervention, tall evergreen trees completely cover the land surface. This dense forest has very little undergrowth, however, because the trees let through only a small amount of sunlight. But any serious discussion of this environment today must take into consideration the appalling rush toward the destruction of rainforests throughout the tropical latitudes (see Perspective: Deforestation of the Tropics).

The climatic characteristics of the tropical rainforest are illustrated in Fig. 17.2, which uses three graphic displays for a typical weather station in the **Af** zone. The place chosen for such a presentation is São Gabriel de Cachoeira, a Brazilian village situated almost exactly on the Equator deep within the heart of the Amazon Basin. Of the three graphs, the most important for our purposes is the first—the climograph, a device employed

PERSPECTIVES ON THE HUMAN ENVIRONMENT

Deforestation of the Tropics

Only a generation ago, lush rainforests clothed most of the land surfaces of the equatorial tropics and accounted for 10 percent of the Earth's vegetation cover. Since 1980, however, industries and millions of residents of low-latitude countries have been destroying billions of those trees through rapid **tropical deforestation**—the clearing and destruction of rainforests to make way for expanding settlement frontiers and the exploitation of new economic opportunities. In Brazil's Amazon Basin, an area about the size of New Jersey is now being burned annually, half of it virgin forest and the other half jungly regrowth, to briefly replenish the infertile soil. If this prodigious removal rate endures, the planet's tropical rainforests—already effectively reduced to two large patches in west-equatorial Africa and the central Amazon Basin—will disappear by the middle of this century.

As rainforests are eradicated, they do not just leave behind the ugly wastelands seen in Fig. 17.1. The smoke from their burning releases particles and gases that rise thousands of metres into the atmosphere and are then transported thousands of kilometres around the world. A number of atmospheric scientists believe that the effects of such fires, together with the removal of massive stands of carbon-dioxide-absorbing trees, could have an increasingly harmful effect on global climate. Let us quickly review the causes and climatic consequences of this deepening environmental crisis.

The causes of deforestation in tropical countries lie in the swift reversal of perceptions about tropical woodlands in recent years. Long regarded as useless resources and obstacles to settlement, rainforested areas suddenly assumed new importance as rapidly growing populations ran out of

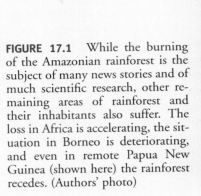

FIGURE 17.1 While the burning of the Amazonian rainforest is the subject of many news stories and of much scientific research, other remaining areas of rainforest and their inhabitants also suffer. The loss in Africa is accelerating, the situation in Borneo is deteriorating, and even in remote Papua New Guinea (shown here) the rainforest recedes. (Authors' photo)

living space in the late twentieth century. In Brazil in particular, the government began to build roads and subsidize huge colonization schemes, instantaneously attracting millions of peasants who were now able to buy land cheaply for the first time in their lives. Even though the deforested soil soon proved infertile, enough affordable land was available locally to allow these farmers to relocate to newly cleared plots every few years and begin the cycle over again.

In addition to this shifting-cultivation subsistence economy, many commercial opportunities arose as well. Cattle ranchers were only too happy to buy up the abandoned farmlands and replace them with pasture grasses, and a large industry has mushroomed in Amazonia, Central America's Costa Rica, and elsewhere. At the same time, lumbering became a leading activity as developed countries, especially Japan and South Korea, turned from their exhausted midlatitude forests to the less expensive and much more desirable trees of the tropics as sources for paper, building materials, and furniture. By the mid-1990s, hundreds of millions of workers in developing countries had come to depend on the rainforests for their livelihoods, and the total steadily mounts each year.

There are many serious threats to the global environment as well, not the least of which are mass extinctions of plant and animal life (now estimated to be 100 species per day), because the tropical rainforest is home to as many as 80 percent of the planet's species (see box, pp. 286–287). As mentioned before, rainforest destruction may also be linked to the Earth's climatic patterns. Researchers continue to explore possible connections and longer-term consequences. Two major climatic problems associated with the wholesale burning of tropical woodlands have been identified, and both are likely to reach global proportions as deforestation continues to intensify.

The first of these problems involves the loss of the rainforest over large areas, thereby modifying regional climates, particularly in the direction of dryness. This occurs because approximately 80 percent of the rainfall in areas covered by tropical rainforests comes from transpiration and evaporation. Transpired water vapour rises in the atmosphere and is precipitated back as rainfall. But in deforested regions this cycle is broken, and most of the rainfall is lost to runoff.

The second climatic problem is that the trees of the tropical rainforest have always absorbed large quantities of atmospheric carbon dioxide, thereby helping to maintain a stable global balance of this greenhouse gas. With the destruction of this important reservoir for removing CO_2 from the atmosphere and storing it, climatologists are actively studying the long-term implications. Some predict a rapid rise in atmospheric concentrations of CO_2. Others see a worldwide intensification of pollution, because rainforests have been known to function as large-scale cleansing mechanisms for effluents that enter its ecosystems via the atmosphere and hydrosphere.

FROM THE FIELDNOTES

FIGURE 17.2 "Traversing the Panama Canal turned out to have several geographic benefits, in addition to learning about the history of the project and understanding better the changing relationship between Panama and the United States. I was unaware that the forests flanking the Canal had been used to train U.S. military forces in advance of their assignment to Vietnam in the Indochina War. Nor did I expect to see pristine rainforest of the kind shown here, on Barro Colorado Island. I was reminded that the Köppen map shows this part of Panama as an **Am** climate, and the vegetation reflects it."

repeatedly in Units 17, 18, and 19. A **climograph** for a given location simultaneously displays its key climatic variables of average temperature and precipitation, showing how they change month by month through the year.

The climograph in Fig. 17.3 reveals that average monthly temperatures in São Gabriel are remarkably constant, hovering consistently around 26°C throughout the year. In fact, the diurnal (daily) temperature may vary as

much as 6°C, an amount greater than the annual range of 1.6°C. Rainfall also tends to occur in a diurnal rather than seasonal rhythm. A normal daily pattern consists of relatively clear skies in the morning, followed by a steady buildup of convectional clouds from the vertical movement of air with the increasing heat of the day. By early afternoon, thunderstorms burst forth (see Fig. 13.2) with torrential rains. After several hours, these stationary storms play themselves out as temperatures decline a few

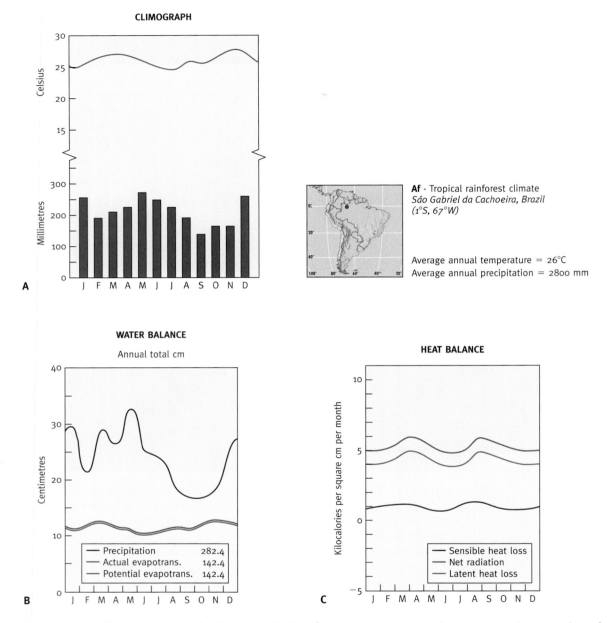

FIGURE 17.3   Climograph and related graphic displays for a representative weather station in the tropical rainforest (**Af**) climate zone.

degrees with the approach of night. This pattern monotonously repeats itself day after day.

In São Gabriel, no month receives less than 130 mm of rain, and in May about 10 mm of rain falls per day. The average total rainfall for the year is 2800 mm. Such large amounts of rain keep the water balance in perpetual surplus, as Fig. 17.3B indicates. Evapotranspiration in this area constantly occurs at its potential rate; much of the surplus water runs off into the Rio Negro (on which the village is located) and from this tributary di-

rectly into the Amazon itself. As a result, most of the net radiation is used in latent heat (Fig. 17.3C), and so the moisture in the highly humid air is continuously replaced. When the moisture condenses, latent heat adds to the monotonous warmth of the atmosphere. When the Sun passes directly overhead at the equinoxes, the rainfall values are not noticeably affected because they are always high. But the heat balance is markedly affected, as demonstrated by the relatively higher values of net radiation and latent heat loss in the graph.

CANADIAN GEOGRAPHERS IN THE FIELD

"On a field trip to the southwest United States and Mexico, our group of geology students from Queen's University stopped to examine a large salt flat formed by the evaporation of sea water at the north end of the Gulf of California in Baja California, Mexico. Put a group of Canadians on a large, flat, white surface, however hot it may be, and naturally a hockey game broke out. Here we are 'cooling' down with a post-game round of hacky sac."

Blair Hrabi has a B.Sc. (McMaster University) and M.Sc. (Queen's University) in geology and studies the geochemical composition of volcanic rocks and the structural evolution of Precambrian rocks in the Canadian Shield.

The Monsoon Rainforest (Am) Climate

The monsoon rainforest (**Am**) climate is restricted to tropical coasts that are often backed by highlands. It has a distinct dry season in the part of the year when the Sun is lower, but almost always a short one; a compensating longer season of heavy rainfall generally prevents any soil-moisture deficits. These characteristics are seen in the representative climograph for this climate type (Fig. 17.4), the city of Trivandrum located near India's southern tip on the narrow Malabar Coast at the base of the Cardamom Uplands.

In some places, such as the hills leading up to the Himalayas in northeastern India, the highlands add an orographic effect to the wet-monsoon rains. The station of Cherrapunji (see Fig. 18.12) in this hilly region averages an annual total of 11,450 mm of rain—most of it occurring during the three summer months! (Until the 1950s this was believed to be the rainiest place on Earth, but that distinction now belongs to Mount Waialeale on the Hawaiian island of Kauai, where 11,990 mm of rain falls in an average year.) The vegetation of the monsoon rainforest zone consists mainly of evergreen trees, with occasional grasslands interspersed. The trees, however, are not as dense as those found in the remaining areas of true tropical rainforest.

The Savanna (Aw) Climate

The savanna (**Aw**) climates are found in the transitional, still-tropical latitudes between the subtropical high-pressure and equatorial low-pressure belts. Although these areas often receive between 750 and 1750 mm of rain per year, there is an extended dry season in the months when the angle of the Sun is at its lowest. Moisture deficits in the soil can occur during the dry season, whose length and severity are proportional to a given savanna area's distance from the Equator. The climograph for Nkhata Bay, Malawi, in southeastern Africa (Fig. 17.5) shows the typical march of temperatures and precipitation totals in a normal year. Do not be misled, however, by the decline of both variables in the middle months of the year, because on this occasion we deliberately selected a Southern Hemisphere station to remind you of the opposite seasonal patterns that exist south of the Equator.

In the region of East Africa to the north of Malawi, the pastoral Maasai people traditionally move their

CLIMOGRAPH

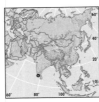

Am - Tropical monsoon climate
Trivandrum, India
(8°N, 77°E)

Annual average
temperature = 27°C

Annual average
precipitation = 1835 mm

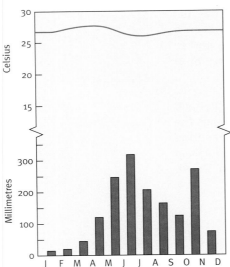

FIGURE 17.4   Climograph of a monsoon rainforest (**Am**) weather station.

CLIMOGRAPH

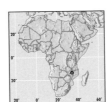

Aw - Tropical savanna climate
Nkhata Bay, Malawi
(15°S, 35°E)

Average annual
temperature = 23°C

Annual average
precipitation = 1676 mm

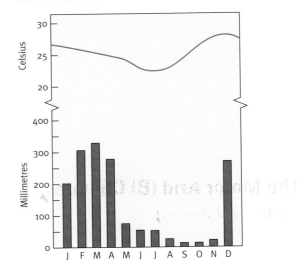

FIGURE 17.5   Climograph of a tropical savanna (**Aw**) weather station.

FIGURE 17.6   Tree-dotted savanna of Kenya's Maasai Mara game reserve. (Authors' photo)

herds of cattle north and south in search of new grass sprouted in the wake of the shifting rains that correspond to the high Sun. The vegetation of this region, besides its tall, coarse seasonal grasses, also includes clumps of trees or individual trees and thorn bushes (Fig. 17.6). There are extensive areas of savanna climate in the world, most prominently covering parts of tropical South America, South Asia, and Africa (see Fig. 16.3). Along the poleward margins of this climate zone, however, rainfall is so unreliable that these peripheral areas are considered too risky for agricultural development in the absence of irrigation systems.

The Major Arid (B) Climates

The **B** or **arid climates** provide a striking visual contrast to the **A** climates (Fig. 17.7) because in these areas potential evapotranspiration exceeds the moisture supplied by precipitation. Dry climates are found in two general locations (see Fig. 16.3). The first group consists of two interrupted bands near 30°N and 30°S,

FIGURE 17.7   One of the world's driest landscapes—a rocky desert in the western Sahara near the border between Morocco and Algeria.

where the semipermanent subtropical high-pressure cells are dominant. The largest areas of this type are the African-Eurasian desert belt (stretching from the vast Sahara northeastward to Mongolia) and the arid interior of Australia. The driest of these climates are often located near the western coasts of continents. Weather stations in northern Chile's Atacama Desert, for instance, can go 10 years or more without recording precipitation.

The second group of dry climates can be attributed to two different factors. First, a continental interior remote from any moisture source and experiencing cold high-pressure air masses in winter can have an arid climate (the central Asian countries east of the Caspian Sea are a good case in point). And second, rain shadow zones in the lee of coast-paralleling mountain ranges often give rise to cold deserts, as in the interior far west of North America and southern Argentina's Patagonia.

Average annual temperatures in arid climates are usually typical of those that might be expected at any given latitude—high in the low latitudes and low in the higher latitudes. However, the annual *range* of temperature is often greater than might be expected. In North Africa's central Sahara, for example, a range of 17°C at 25°N is partly the result of a continental effect. The diurnal range of temperature can also be quite large, averaging between 14° and 25°C. On one unforgettable day in the Libyan capital city of Tripoli, the temperature went from below freezing (−0.5°C) at dawn to 37°C in midafternoon! Rocks expanding through such extreme changes of heat sometimes break with a sharp crack; North African soldiers in World War II occasionally mistook these breaking rocks for rifle shots.

The **B** climates are not necessarily dry all year round. Their precipitation can range from near 0 to about 625 mm per year, with averages as high as 750 mm in the more tropical latitudes. In summer, these equatorward margins of the **B** climates are sometimes affected by the rains of the ITCZ as they reach their poleward extremes. In winter, the margins of the arid areas nearest the poles may be subject to midlatitude-cyclone rains. There also are rare thunderstorms, which occasionally lead to flash floods. At Hulwan, just south of Cairo, Egypt, seven of these storms in 20 years yielded a total of 780 mm of rain. Moreover, along coasts bathed by cold ocean currents, rather frequent fogs provide some moisture; Swakopmund, in southwestern Africa's Namibia, adjacent to the Benguela Current (see Fig. 11.6), experiences about 150 days of such fog each year.

The Desert (BW) Climate

For the most part, however, considerable dryness is the rule in **B** areas. This aridity is exemplified by Yuma, Arizona, where the average annual temperature is 23.5°C, with an annual range of some 23°C. The climate here is **BWh**—a hot, dry desert. The small amount of rainfall shown in Fig. 17.8 (89 mm) comes either from occasional winter storms or from the convectional clouds of summer. The water balance diagram below the climograph shows a marked deficit throughout the year: potential evapotranspiration greatly exceeds precipitation. Most water that falls quickly evaporates back into the dry atmosphere. But as the heat balance diagram for Yuma indicates, there is little water for evaporation, so latent heat loss is negligible. Consequently most of the heat input from net radiation, which is markedly seasonal, is expended as sensible heat—adding even more warmth to the already hot air. (Daily highs between May and October almost always exceed 38°C.)

The Steppe (BS) Climate

As the world climate map (Fig. 16.3) shows, the most arid areas—deserts (**BW**)—are always framed by semi-arid zones. This is the domain of the *steppe* (also known in western North America as the *short-grass prairie*) or **BS** climate, which can be regarded as a transitional type between fully developed desert conditions and the subhumid margins of the **A, C,** and **D** climates that border **B** climate zones. The maximum and minimum amounts of annual rainfall that characterize semi-arid climates tend to vary somewhat by latitude. In general, lower-latitude **BS** climates range from 375 to 750 mm yearly; in the middle latitudes, a lower range (from 250 to 625 mm) prevails. Astana, the capital of the central Asian republic of Kazakhstan, which lies at the heart of the Eurasian landmass, is a classic example of the cold subtype of the steppe climate (**BSk**). The climograph for this city (Fig. 17.9) shows its proximity to the Turkestan Desert, which lies just to the south: rainfall totals only 279 mm per year. As for the monthly temperature curve, an enormous range of 39°C is recorded, reflecting one of the most pronounced areas of continentality on the Earth's surface.

Human Activities in B Climates

During the late 1950s and early 1960s, Astana (then called Tselinograd) was the headquarters for the so-called Virgin and Idle Lands Program, one of the most ambitious agricultural development schemes in the history of what until 1991 was the Soviet Union. In an attempt

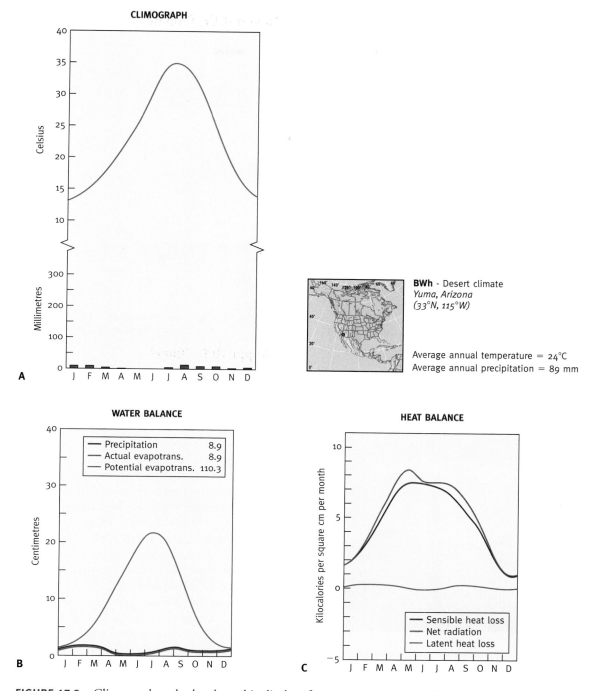

FIGURE 17.8 Climograph and related graphic displays for a representative weather station in the hot, dry desert (**BWh**) climate zone.

to emulate the highly mechanized, large-scale wheat farming of a similar climatic zone in the northern Great Plains of the United States (Fig. 17.10), Moscow's planners invested heavily in the Kazakh Soviet Socialist Republic, hoping to substantially boost food produc-

tion, which had been a troublesome problem since the Communist Revolution of 1917. For a few years the gamble of expanding agriculture into this risky region appeared to be paying off. But those turned out to be wetter than normal years, and by the mid-1960s it

CLIMOGRAPH

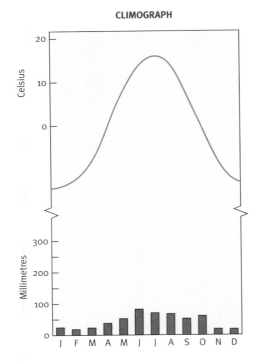

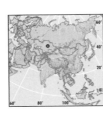

BSk - Steppe climate
Astana, Kazakhstan
(51°N, 71°E)

Average annual temperature = 2°C
Average annual precipitation = 279 mm

FIGURE 17.9 Climograph of a midlatitude steppe (**BSk**) weather station.

FIGURE 17.10 A pair of combines (left) harvesting ripe wheat in the heart of the Great Plains region. This is one of the world's most mechanized farmscapes, a model of large-scale agricultural productivity.

became evident that the plan was doomed to failure because extreme continentality worked against the accumulation of sufficient moisture to support the massive wheat raising that the Soviet leaders had in mind.

The problem of drought, which is examined in Unit 18, is an ever-present environmental hazard in all semi-arid areas, and the Great Plains region has suffered many severe dry spells since it was settled by farmers during the late nineteenth century. The global distribution of precipitation variability is mapped in Fig. 17.11 and underscores this dilemma. Perversely, for human purposes, rain falls most reliably where it is abundant, whereas the arid areas experience the greatest variations from year to year (as even a cursory comparison of Figs. 16.3 and 17.11 reveals).

Throughout the human experience on this planet, dry climates have proven inhospitable, restricting settlement to the rare water sources of oases or to the valleys of rivers that originate outside a given zone of aridity. In certain cases, such as Egypt's Nile Valley, irrigation can maximize these scarce water resources, but the practice often tends to wash important minerals from the soil. Over the past quarter-century, environmental abuse has been a growing problem at the margins of arid zones, and *desertification* (see Perspective: Desertification) now constitutes a serious crisis in many such places. This, however, is only the latest reminder that the balance among the Earth's natural systems in dryland areas is particularly fragile.

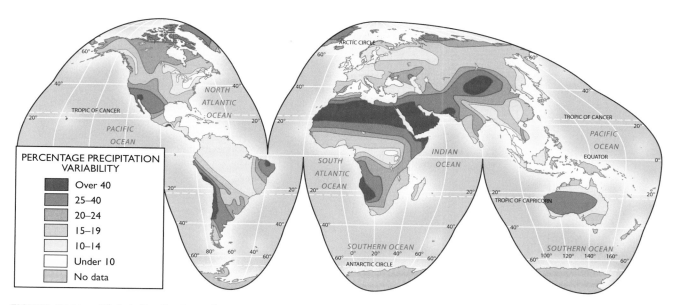

FIGURE 17.11   Global distribution of annual precipitation variability, shown as percentage departures from normal. Map adapted from *Goode's World Atlas,* 19th edition. ©1995 by Rand McNally R.L. 92-S-82-renewal 95.

PERSPECTIVES ON THE HUMAN ENVIRONMENT

Desertification

Desertification may be an awkward word, but it is on target in what it defines—the process of desert expansion into steppelands, largely as a result of human degradation of fragile semi-arid environments (Fig. 17.12). This term was added to the physical geographer's lexicon in the 1970s following the disastrous famine, caused by rapid and unforeseen desiccation, that struck the north-central African region known as the *Sahel*. This name means "shore" in Arabic—specifically the southern shore of the Sahara, an east–west semi-arid (**BSh**) belt straddling latitude 15°N, ranging in width from 320 to 1120 km, which stretches across the entire continent of Africa (see Fig. 16.3). During the height of the tragic starvation episode from 1968 to 1973, as paralyzing drought destroyed both croplands and pasturelands, the Sahel suffered a loss of at least 250,000 human lives and 3.5 million head of cattle.

This catastrophe prompted an international research effort, and one of its products was a world map of spreading deserts (Fig. 17.13), whose most hazardous zones coincided closely with the semi-arid regions mapped in Fig. 16.3. Another accomplishment was the creation of a global desertification monitoring network, which has provided some alarming data. At least 15 million km² of the world's arid and semi-arid drylands—an area almost the size of South America—have now become severely desertified, thereby losing over 50 percent of their potential productivity. Another 34.8 million km²—an area greater than the size of Africa—has become at least moderately desertified, losing in excess of 25 percent of its potential productivity. Moreover, it is estimated that an area half the size of New York State (64,800 km²) is being added to the total of severely desertified land each year. In the process, more than a billion people (over one-sixth of humankind) are already affected by desertification—and the world's arid-land population is growing at a rate 50 percent faster than in adequately watered areas.

FIGURE 17.12   The desert encroaches on human settlement near Nouakchott, the capital of Mauritania in West Africa. A dune-stabilization effort in the foreground gives temporary protection to the poorest of the city's inhabitants, who live in the squatter settlement just beyond.

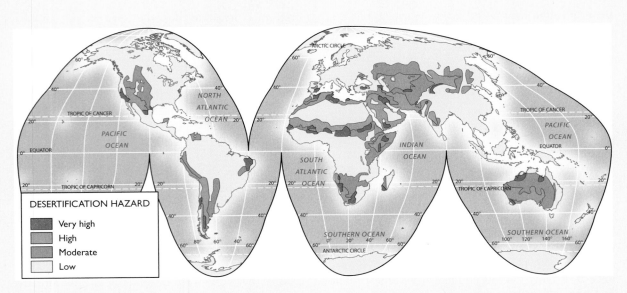

FIGURE 17.13   Degree of desertification hazard according to the scientists of the United States Nations Environmental Program. The red-brick–coloured areas indicate a critical situation; the orange-coloured zones experience serious effects; the tan-coloured areas represent a significant problem.

When desertification was first studied, it was believed that climate change played a significant role. Today, however, we have learned enough to know that the process is more heavily controlled by human actions, whose consequences are accentuated in years of lower than normal precipitation. The British geographer Andrew Goudie has noted the particular susceptibility of semi-arid areas, because rainfall there is sufficient to swiftly erode carelessly used soils and because farmers often misinterpret short-term success during wetter than normal years as a sign of long-term crop-raising stability (as the Soviets did before they cancelled Kazakhstan's Virgin and Idle Lands Program).

Desperate for more food-producing, income-earning space, farmers in developing countries readily expand their cash cropping and cattle herding into these marginal lands during wet years, ploughing furiously and introducing more grazing animals than the limited grass/shrub vegetation can support in dry years. Once these bad land-use practices are established,

. . . a depletion of vegetation occurs which sets in [motion] such insidious processes as [soil erosion and the blowing away of loosened topsoil by the wind]. The vegetation is removed by clearance for cultivation, by the cutting and uprooting of woody species for fuel, by overgrazing [cattle], and by the burning of vegetation for pasture and charcoal (Goudie, 2000, p. 75).

As suggested in Fig. 17.12, the final stage of the desertification process is nothing less than the total denudation of once-productive land. In the more extreme cases, the cultural landscape may even be obliterated by the encroaching desert sands. In the western Sahel, for instance, encroachment is now so far advanced that some predict that much of the upper West African country of Mali will soon become uninhabitable (most of its permanently settled adult residents already shovel sand to keep daily life from grinding to a halt).

With desertification heavily tied to artificial causes, planners and policymakers are focusing on human activities in their search for solutions to the crisis. One highly promising avenue is the new technology of *fertigation,* now being perfected by the Israelis in their recent large-scale development of the Negev Desert. Here plants have been genetically engineered to be irrigated by the brackish underground water that is available throughout the region. (Most semi-arid areas are underlain by similar water resources.) To avoid evaporation, the water is pumped through plastic pipes directly to the roots of plants, where it combines with specially mixed fertilizers to provide exactly the right blend of moisture and nutrients. Today more than half a million people are thriving in the Negev's agricultural settlements and producing enormous quantities of high-quality fruits and vegetables for domestic and foreign markets.

KEY TERMS

arid climate *page 221*
climograph *page 217*

desertification *page 225*
tropical climate *page 215*

tropical deforestation *page 215*

REVIEW QUESTIONS

1. Describe the general latitudinal extent of **A** climates.
2. Describe the general latitudinal extent of **B** climates.
3. Contrast the rainfall regimes of **Af, Aw,** and **Am** climates.
4. What is the primary difference between **BS** and **BW** climates?

5. Why is ongoing tropical deforestation regarded as a catastrophe by so many natural scientists?
6. Describe the circumstances leading to desertification.

REFERENCES AND FURTHER READINGS

ALLAN, T., and WARREN, A. *Deserts: The Encroaching Wilderness* (New York: Oxford Univ. Press, 1993).

BEAUMONT, P. *Drylands: Environmental Management and Development* (London/New York: Routledge, 1993).

CAUFIELD, C. *In the Rainforest* (New York: Knopf, 1985).

COLE, M. M. *The Savannas: Biogeography and Geobotany* (Orlando, Fla.: Academic Press, 1986).

COUPLAND, R. T., Ed. *Grassland Ecosystems of the World* (New York: Cambridge Univ. Press, 1979).

GOODALL, D. W., et al. *Arid Land Ecosystems* (New York: Cambridge Univ. Press, 1979).

GOUDIE, A. S. *The Human Impact on the Natural Environment* (Cambridge, Mass.: MIT Press, 5th ed., 2000).

GOUDIE, A. S., and WILKINSON, J. C. *The Warm Desert Environment* (New York: Cambridge Univ. Press, 1977).

GOUROU, P. *The Tropical World: Its Social and Economic Conditions and Its Future Status* (London/New York: Longman, S. H. Beaver, Trans., 5th ed., 1980).

HARE, F. K. *Climate and Desertification: A Revised Analysis* (Geneva: World Meteorological Organization/UNEP, World Climate Program, vol. 44, 1983).

HEATHCOTE, R. L. *The Arid Lands: Their Use and Abuse* (London/New York: Longman, 1983).

KELLMAN, M., and TACKABERRY, R. *Tropical Environments: The Functioning and Management of Tropical Ecosystems* (London/New York: Routledge, 1997).

McCLARAN, M. P., and VAN DEVENDER, T. R., Eds. *The Desert Grassland* (Tucson, Ariz.: Univ. of Arizona Press, 1995).

MIDDLETON, N. J., and THOMAS, D. S. G. *World Atlas of Desertification* (London: Edward Arnold, 2nd rev. ed., 1997).

NIEUWOLT, S. *Tropical Climatology: An Introduction to the Climates of the Low Latitudes* (New York: Wiley, 1977).

RAVEN, P. H. "The Cause and Impact of Deforestation," in H. J. de Blij, Ed., *Earth '88: Changing Geographic Perspectives* (Washington, D.C.: National Geographic Society, 1988), 212–229.

READING, A. J., et al. *Humid Tropical Environments* (Cambridge, Mass.: Blackwell, 1994).

REPETTO, R. "Deforestation in the Tropics," *Scientific American* (April 1990), 36–42.

RICHARDS, J. F., and TUCKER, R. P., Eds. *World Deforestation in the Twentieth Century* (Durham, N.C.: Duke Univ. Press, 1988).

THOMAS, D. S. G., and MIDDLETON, N. J. *Desertification: Exploding the Myth* (New York: Wiley, 1994).

WILLIAMS, M. A. J., and BALLING, R. C. *Interactions of Desertification and Climate* (New York: Wiley, 1995).

WEB RESOURCES

http://earthobservatory.nasa.gov/Library/Deforestation The causes of deforestation are explored, as well as deforestation rates and processes.

http://pubs.usgs.gov/gip/deserts/desertification Review of the causes of desertification, global monitoring techniques, and remediation strategies.

http://www.squ1.com/index.php?http://www.squ1.com/climate/koppenA.html An overview of **A** climates, with photographs of typical dwellings for each climatic subtype.

Humid Mesothermal (C) Climates

Mediterranean vegetation drapes the countryside on the Greek island of Crete. (Authors' photo)

OBJECTIVES

- To expand our understanding of the various **C** climates

- To interpret representative climographs depicting actual conditions in these **C** climate areas

- To highlight a major environmental-climatic problem of many **C** climate areas—drought

he moderately heated **C or mesothermal climates** are dominant on the equatorward sides of the middle latitudes, where they are generally aligned as interrupted east–west belts (see Figs. 16.2 and 16.3). On a global scale, mesothermal climates may be viewed as transitional between those of the tropics and those of the upper midlatitude zone, where polar influences begin to produce climates marked by harsh winters. The specific limiting criteria are (1) an average temperature below 18°C but above 0°C in the coolest month, and (2) an average temperature of not less than 10°C for at least one month of the year. Such limits tell us that temperature is now a more important climatic indicator than in the lower latitudes, and that the annual rhythms of the **C** climates are more likely to involve cyclical shifts between warm and cool seasons rather than rainy and dry seasons.

Humid mesothermal climates are also associated with that great lower atmosphere battleground, the latitudinal belt where polar and tropical air masses collide and mix. As a result, changeable weather patterns are the rule as meandering jet streams periodically steer a parade of anticyclones and cyclonic storms across the midlatitudes from west to east. Because so many of the world's large population concentrations lie in the **C** climate zone (see Fig. 2.5), these swings are of considerable importance. In daily human terms, the episodes of extreme weather frequently experienced in **C** climates are of particular concern. These departures from average conditions can also occur over longer time periods, as we see in our focus on drought as a major environmental problem of the mesothermal climates.

Three major subtypes of humid mesothermal climate can be distinguished according to their pattern of precipitation occurrence. The **Cf** climate is perpetually moist; the **Cs** climate has a dry season in the summer; and the **Cw** climate is dry in the winter.

The Perpetually Moist (Cf) Climates

The perpetually moist mesothermal climates (**Cf**) are found in two major regional groupings, both of which are near a major source of water.

The Humid Subtropical (Cfa) Climate

The first such group is the warmer, perpetually moist mesothermal climate, usually called the *humid subtropical* (**Cfa**) climate, which is situated in the southeastern portions of the five major continents. It owes its existence to the effects of the warm moist air travelling northwestward (in the Northern Hemisphere) around the western margins of the oceanic subtropical high-pressure zones. Additional moisture comes from the movement of midlatitude cyclones toward the Equator in winter and from tropical cyclones in summer and autumn.

Miyazaki, located on the east coast of the southern Japanese island of Kyushu, exhibits the strong seasonal effects of the humid subtropical climate (Fig. 18.1). Average monthly temperatures there range from 6.8°C

in mildly cold January to 26.7°C in hot humid August; the mean annual temperature is 16.7°C. Rainfall for the year almost totals that of the tropical rainforest—2560 mm, peaking in early summer. The water balance at Miyazaki is never at a deficit, not even during the relatively dry winter. Throughout the year, actual evapotranspiration always equals the potential evapotranspiration. The heat balance diagram also demonstrates the humid nature of this climate. Most of the net radiation is used to evaporate water, and a relatively small proportion passes into the air as sensible heat.

The similarities of the humid subtropical climate in diverse parts of the world are underscored in the climographs for Charleston, South Carolina (Fig. 18.2), and Shanghai, China (Fig. 18.3). Both cities lie on the southeastern seaboard of a large landmass (North America and Asia, respectively) near latitude 32°N. Compared to Miyazaki (Fig. 18.1), Charleston and Shanghai exhibit significantly lower annual precipitation totals—undoubtedly a function of stronger windflows off the continent lying to their west—whereas offshore Kyushu is more constantly bathed by the moist southeasterly winds generated by the North Pacific's Subtropical High.

Slight differences can also be detected in a comparison of all three **Cfa** stations. For example, whereas summer temperatures are strikingly alike, Charleston has a noticeably milder winter because of the smaller bulk of North America (which does not develop as cold and durable a winter high-pressure cell as interior Asia) and the proximity of the warm Gulf of Mexico to the southwest. The overall congruence of climatic characteristics between Charleston and Shanghai, however, is not observed in the cultural landscapes of the southeastern United States and east-central China. In fact, these are about as different as any two on Earth (Fig. 18.4), demonstrating the completely different uses that human societies can make of nearly identical natural environments.

The Marine West Coast (Cfb, Cfc) Climate

The second group of perpetually moist mesothermal climates, with coasts caressed by the prevailing Westerlies year-round, is usually called the *marine west coast* (**Cfb, Cfc**) climate. One such area is in Western Europe; others are found in the Pacific Northwest of the United States, the adjacent west coast of Canada, southern Chile, southeastern Australia, and New Zealand. In all these places, storms generated by midlatitude cyclones bring a steady flow of moist, temperate, maritime air from the ocean onto nearby land surfaces. The extent of inland penetration depends on topography. Where few

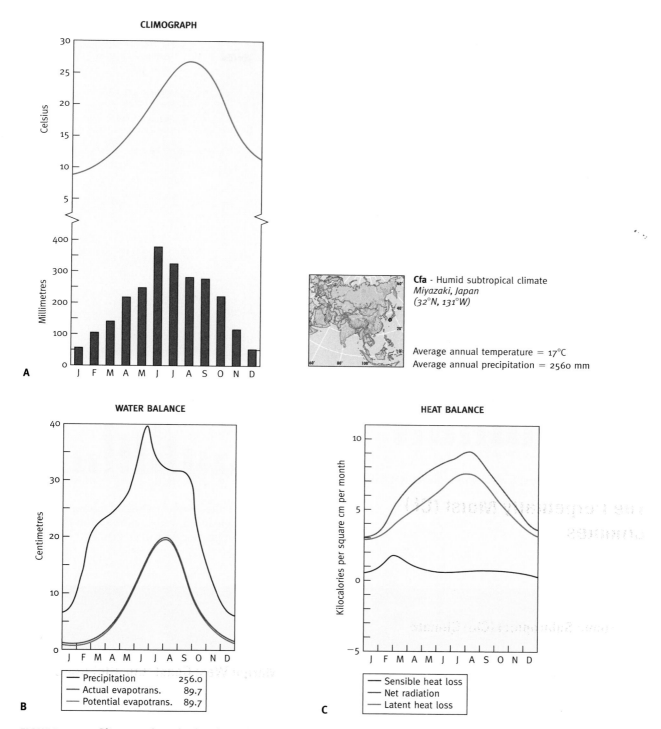

FIGURE 18.1 Climograph and related graphic displays for a representative weather station in the humid subtropical (**Cfa**) climate zone.

orographic barriers exist, such as in Europe north of the Alps, the **Cfb** climate reaches several hundred kilometres eastward from the North Atlantic; but where mountains block the moist onshore winds, such as in western North America and Chile in southernmost South America, these climates are confined to coastal and near-coastal areas.

There are rarely any extremes of temperature in

CLIMOGRAPH

Cfa - Humid subtropical climate
*Charleston, South Carolina
(33°N, 80°W)*

Average annual
temperature = 18°C

Average annual
precipitation = 1247 mm

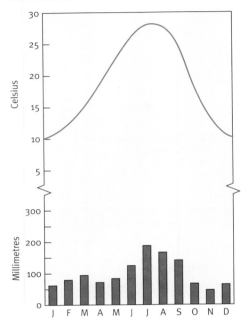

FIGURE 18.2 Climograph of a humid subtropical (**Cfa**) location with a particularly mild winter.

CLIMOGRAPH

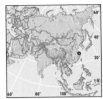

Cfa - Humid subtropical climate
*Shanghai, China
(32°N, 122°E)*

Average annual
temperature = 16°C

Average annual
precipitation = 1135 mm

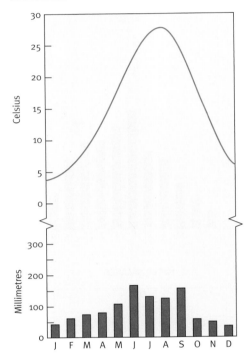

FIGURE 18.3 Climograph of a humid subtropical (**Cfa**) location with a pronounced winter, enhanced in this case by the dry monsoon of interior Asia.

A

B

FIGURE 18.4 A pair of farming areas in similar **Cfa** climatic zones, but these agricultural landscapes could not be more different. (A) In the southeastern United States large fields, independent farmsteads, and highway transport prevail. (B) In east-central China small rectangular plots, clustered villages, and water transport dominate.

FROM THE FIELDNOTES

FIGURE 18.5 "The name Ireland is practically synonymous with **Cfb** climate. I was reminded of this while sailing the Irish coast in day after day of dreary, rainy weather. When the sun broke through as we approached the little harbor of Dunmore East near Waterford in the southeast, you could see why this is known as the Emerald Isle. All was bright green as far as the eye could see; grass grew even atop the cliffs."

marine west coast climates. Average monthly temperatures never exceed 22°C, and at least four months record mean temperatures above 10°C in the **Cfb** zones (the cooler **Cfc** subtype experiences less than four months of mean temperatures above 10°C). The **Cfb** patterns are seen in the climographs for Vancouver and London, England (Figs. 18.6 and 18.7). In your comparisons you will note that despite its popular image as a rainy city, London receives on average only 583 mm of precipitation annually, equivalent to the yearly total in the moistest semi-arid climate. But London does indeed experience a great number of cloudy and/or rainy days each year (the hallmark of many a marine west coast climate location), with much of its precipitation occurring as light drizzle. The cooler **Cfc** pattern is shown in the climograph for Reykjavik, Iceland (Fig. 18.7), which

records only three months with mean temperatures at or above 10°C.

The **Cfb** climates are situated precisely in the middle of the midlatitude, prevailing westerly wind belts. The cooler **Cfc** climates are found only in the Northern Hemisphere at higher latitudes, where strong warm ocean currents sweep poleward along western continental shores (such as off Iceland, Norway, and Alaska). Western civilization moved to the **Cfb** climates of northwestern Europe after leaving its Mediterranean hearth. The adequate year-round precipitation naturally produces a forest of evergreen conifers and broadleaf trees that shed their leaves in winter. Although dry spells are not unknown in these areas, the soil rarely has a moisture deficit for a long period of time.

CLIMOGRAPH

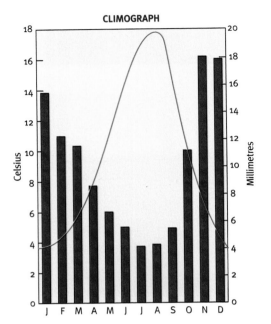

Cfb - Marine west coast climate
Vancouver, Canada
(48°N, 122°W)

Average annual
temperature = 12°C

Average annual
precipitation = 1013 mm

FIGURE 18.6 Climograph of a marine west coast (**Cfb**) weather station in the Canadian Pacific northwest.

CLIMOGRAPH

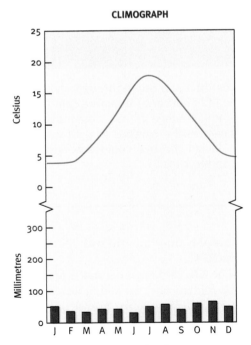

Cfb - Marine west coast climate
London, United Kingdom
(52°N, 0°)

Average annual
temperature = 10°C

Average annual
precipitation = 583 mm

FIGURE 18.7 Climograph of a marine west coast (**Cfb**) location in maritime Europe. Despite its image as a rainy city, note that London annually receives only about half the precipitation of Vancouver (Fig. 18.5).

The Dry-Summer (Cs) Climates

The second major mesothermal subtype is the dry subtropical or *Mediterranean* (**Cs**) climate. It is frequently described, particularly by people of European descent, as the most desirable climate on Earth. This is the climate that attracted filmmakers to Southern California, so famous for its clear light and dependable sunshine. The

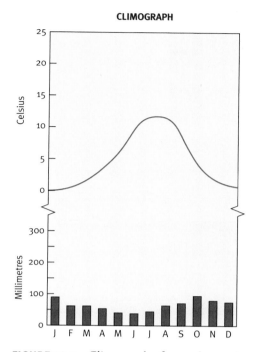

Cfc - Marine west coast climate
Reykjavik, Iceland
(64°N, 22°W)

Average annual
temperature = 5°C

Average annual
precipitation = 805 mm

FIGURE 18.8 Climograph of a weather station that experiences the cooler variety of the marine west coast (**Cfc**) climate.

warmer variety of Mediterranean climate, **Csa,** is found in the Mediterranean Basin itself as well as in other interior locations. The cooler variety, **Csb,** is found on coasts near cool offshore ocean currents, most notably in coastal areas of California, central Chile, southern and southwestern Australia, South Africa, and Europe's Iberian Peninsula (northern Portugal and northwestern Spain).

In the **Cs** climate, rainfall arrives in the cool season, largely as a result of the winter storms produced by mid-latitude cyclones. Annual precipitation totals are moderate, ranging from approximately 400 to 650 mm. The long dry summers are associated with the temporary poleward shift of the wind belts, specifically the warm-season dominance of subsiding air on the eastern side of the oceanic subtropical high-pressure zone. Thus, extended rainless periods are quite common in Mediterranean climates. But when they occur in the more widely distributed (and more heavily populated) **Cf** climates, they can lead to serious *droughts* that disrupt human–environmental relationships (see Perspective: The Drought of 2001).

Some aspects of the "perfect" climate can be observed for San Francisco in Fig. 18.9. The cool offshore California Current, with its frequent fogs, keeps average monthly temperatures almost constant throughout the

year, with a range of only 6.6°C around an annual mean of 13.6°C. The water balance values for San Francisco indicate an average annual rainfall total of 551 mm, with the rains mostly emanating from winter storms steered southward by the Polar Front jet stream. Although in winter actual evapotranspiration reaches the potential amount, in summer it falls well short.

The effect of the dry summer is reflected in the heat balance diagram for nearby Sacramento, located about 150 km northeast of San Francisco. During winter much of the net radiation is expended as latent heat loss. But in the summer soil-moisture deficits require that a large proportion of the net radiation be used in the form of sensible heat to warm the air; with intensive fruit and vegetable agriculture dominating California's Central Valley south of Sacramento, widespread irrigation is an absolute necessity (Fig. 18.11). For purposes of comparison, Fig. 18.12 shows the climograph for Athens, Greece, a classic example of the warmer **Csa** Mediterranean climate variety. Note the similarities to the San Francisco temperature and precipitation pattern (Fig. 18.9). The only noteworthy difference is the greater annual range of temperatures produced by the more continental location of Athens.

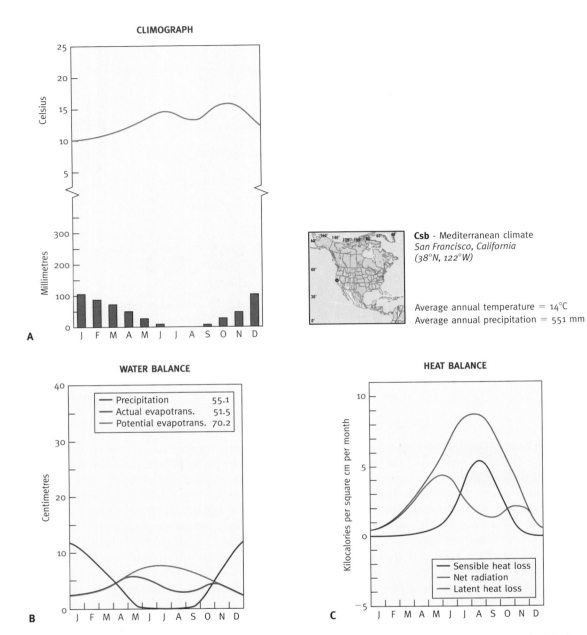

FIGURE 18.9   Climograph and related graphic displays for a representative weather station in the Mediterranean (**Csb**) climate zone. The heat balance graph is based on data from Sacramento, located 150 km inland from San Francisco.

The Dry-Winter (Cw) Climates

The **Cw** climate, the third major subtype of humid mesothermal climate, is little different from the tropical savanna (**Aw**) climate discussed in Unit 17. The only departures are the amounts of rainfall and a distinct cool season, with the average temperature of at least one month falling below 18°C. The **Cw** climate, therefore, is the only subdivision of the **C** climates found extensively in the tropics. For this reason it often shares with the **Aw** climate the designation *tropical wet-and-dry* climate.

In many cases the winter dry season of **Cw** climates is a result of offshore-flowing winds that accompany a winter monsoon. (Indeed, the **Cw** climate is sometimes called the *subtropical monsoon* climate.) In South and Southeast Asia as well as in northeastern Australia, rainfall is provided by the wet summer monsoon. In other cases, such as in south-central Africa, the winter dry sea-

PERSPECTIVES ON THE HUMAN ENVIRONMENT

The Drought of 2001

The drought that plagued so much of Canada in 2001, one of the worst since the dust bowl of the 1930s, was a classic example of this major environmental problem. At its peak in late summer, extreme and severe drought conditions extended across southern and western Canada. As severe as the 2001 drought was, with economic losses estimated at $5 billion, the 1961 drought remains the single most severe growing-season drought to occur on the Canadian Prairies (Fig.18.10). These dry spells have always been part of the gamble of living and farming in the **B** climate areas of the Canadian Prairies and interior British Columbia. Southern parts of the Prairies usually have a moisture deficit and have highly variable precipitation, and western Canada has experienced at least 40 severe droughts in recorded history. The 2001 drought was particularly unusual because it tended to extend almost coast to coast, into **D** climate areas. In Ontario (a **Dfb** climate), corn and soybean farmers reported substantially reduced crop yields. Arid conditions extended into other

Dfb climates, such as Moncton, New Brunswick, which received 17.3 mm of rain in July 2001, compared to the normal 102 mm it receives during July. Forest fires broke out in extensive parts of British Columbia and in pockets of Newfoundland, and in Nova Scotia, blueberries, the province's biggest farm export, shrivelled in the scorched conditions. In the Prairie provinces, however, conditions were most critical, as farmers had to cope with the extreme drought in addition to swarms of grasshoppers in some locations. The dry weather created perfect egg-laying conditions, and consequently the crops were affected by both dry weather and an infestation of insects.

Unlike desertification, which is largely a process of human degradation that affects many **B** climate environments (see Unit 17), **drought** is a natural hazard that recurs in seemingly irregular cycles. In general, a drought involves the below-average availability of water in a given area over a period of at least several months. Specifically, there are three types of drought that may occur separately

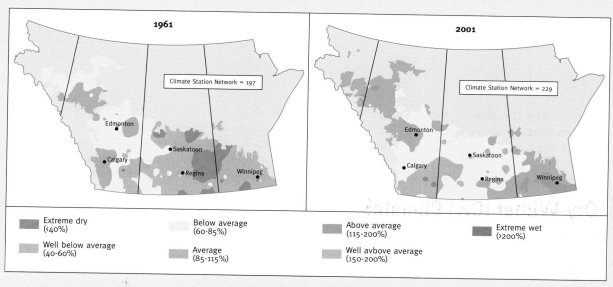

Extreme dry (<40%)

Well below average (40-60%)

Below average (60-85%)

Average (85-115%)

Above average (115-200%)

Well avbove average (150-200%)

Extreme wet (>200%)

FIGURE 18.10   Drought conditions on the Canadian Prairies in 1961 and 2001, expressed as a percent of average precipitation.

or simultaneously: *meteorological* (precipitation is below normal for a prolonged period of time), *agricultural* (low soil moisture and scarce water supplies stunt crop growth, reduce yields, and threaten livestock), and *hydrological* (a prolonged meteorological drought that causes reduced levels of the groundwater table, rivers, and lakes). The conditions that constitute a drought are clear enough: a decrease in precipitation accompanied by warmer than normal temperatures (2001 was the third warmest year on record at that time) and the shrinkage of surface- and soil-water supplies. If the drought reaches an extreme stage of development, all of these conditions intensify further and may result in the spreading of grass and/or forest fires as well as in the blowing away of significant quantities of topsoil by hot dry winds.

However dramatic it may become at its height, a drought has no clear beginning or end. It develops slowly until it becomes recognized as a crisis, and it tends to fade away as more normal moisture patterns return. Because droughts encompass no spectacular meteorological phenomena, they were not intensively studied before the 1970s. But the Sahel disaster of that decade in northern Africa (see Unit 17) finally aroused the interest of climatologists, whose subsequent research is providing a clearer understanding of droughts and their often far-reaching consequences.

As these studies proceeded, it quickly became evident that a drought was not simply a meteorological/hydrological aberration but a complex phenomenon that also encompassed economic, socio-logical, and even political dimensions. In 2001 and during the subsequent drought in 2002, the worsening water shortage in vast regions of the Prairies and abnormal weather conditions throughout much of Canada became national news, dominating newscasts and headlines daily from May through September. As the heavily publicized plight of farmers and the disruptions of their lives reached unprecedented levels, the federal government invested $60 million in a prairie water development program and a new farm-aid package to help farmers cope through the hard, dry summers. The "Say Hay" initiative raised over $1.5 million through two benefit concerts in Edmonton and Calgary (with more than 30 Canadian country singers performing), in addition to money raised through silent auctions, radio pledges, and a national telethon. The origins of the name of the fundraising initiative stemmed from the shortage of hay across western Canada that resulted from the drought. Without hay, farmers were being forced to sell their cattle and livestock for fear that the animals would starve over the winter. The money raised through Say Hay was used to pay for the transportation of hay donated from Ontario and Atlantic Canada, as well as to establish the Say Hay Farm Assistance Program. Any definition of drought, therefore, must now go well beyond the physical-geographic aspects of a prolonged water shortage. As the 2001–2002 experience demonstrated, drought is no longer strictly an agricultural disaster.

---

son occurs because the rains of the ITCZ migrate into the Northern Hemisphere with the Sun.

The **Cw** climates are also associated with higher elevations in the tropical latitudes, which produce winter temperatures too cool to classify these areas as **A**. Cherrapunji, in the Khasi Hills of northeastern India, is a good example (Fig. 18.13). Because of its location near the subtropics at latitude 25°N, combined with its alti-tude of 1313 m, this highland town exhibits the characteristics of the cooler variety of this climatic subtype (**Cwb**). Cherrapunji's enormous annual rainfall (which averages 11,437 mm), as explained in the discussion of the **Am** climate in Unit 17, is the result of wet-monsoon winds that encounter particularly abrupt orographic lifting on their way inland from the Bay of Bengal to the blocking Himalayan mountain wall not far to the north.

FIGURE 18.11 California's agriculturally rich San Joaquin Valley (the southern component of the Central Valley) is highly dependent on irrigation for its productivity. These lush cotton fields border the dry foothills that lead up to the Sierra Nevada on the valley's eastern margin.

CLIMOGRAPH

Csa - Mediterranean climate
Athens, Greece
(38°N, 24°E)

Average annual
temperature = 18°C

Average annual
precipitation = 402 mm

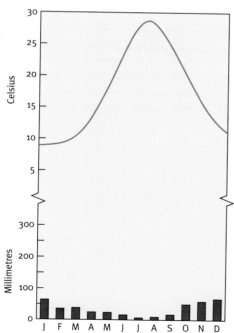

FIGURE 18.12 Climograph of a weather station that experiences the warmer variety of the Mediterranean (**Csa**) climate.

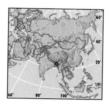

CLIMOGRAPH

Cwb - Subtropical monsoon climate
Cherrapunji, India
(25°N, 92°E)

Average annual
temperature = 17°C

Average annual
precipitation = 11,437 mm

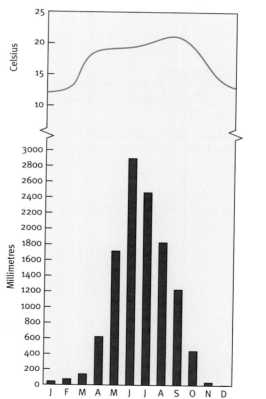

FIGURE 18.13 Climograph of a weather station in the **Cwb** zone, sometimes called the subtropical monsoon climate.

KEY TERMS

drought *page 237*   mesothermal climate *page 229*

REVIEW QUESTIONS

1. What distinguishes **Cfa** from **Cfb** and **Cfc** climates?
2. How do **Cw** climates differ from **Aw** climates?
3. What are the major precipitation patterns associated with Mediterranean (**Cs**) climates?

4. What is meant by the term *drought*?

REFERENCES AND FURTHER READINGS

ARAKAWA, H., Ed. *Climates of Northern and Eastern Asia* (Amsterdam: Elsevier, World Survey of Climatology, vol. 8, 1969).

BRYSON, R. A., and HARE, F. K., Eds. *Climates of North America* (Amsterdam: Elsevier, World Survey of Climatology, vol. 11, 1974).

DI CASTRI, F., and MOONEY, H. A., Eds. *Mediterranean-Type Ecosystems: Origin and Structure* (New York: Springer-Verlag, 1973).

HOUSTON, J. M. *The Western Mediterranean World: An Introduction to Its Regional Landscapes* (New York: Praeger, 1964).

"The Long, Hot Summer of '88," *Natural History* (January 1989, special issue).

MATHER, J. R. *Water Resources: Distribution, Use, and Management* (New York: Wiley/V.H. Winston, 1984), 362–382.

PALMER, W. C. *Meteorological Drought: Its Measurement and Classification* (Washington, D.C.: U.S. Weather Bureau, Research Paper No. 45, 1965).

STEWART, G. R. *Storm* (New York: Modern Library, 1947).

WALLEN, C. C., Ed. *Climates of Northern and Western Europe* (Amsterdam: Elsevier, World Survey of Climatology, vol. 5, 1970).

WALLEN, C. C., Ed. *Climates of Central and Southern Europe* (Amsterdam: Elsevier, World Survey of Climatology, vol. 6, 1977).

WEB RESOURCES

http://www.cgr.gc.ca/pfra/drought/ Agriculture and Agri-Food Canada's "Drought Watch."

http://www.canadainfolink.ca/climate.htm Canadian climate data and climate graphs. Part of the Teaching and Learning about Canada website.

http://www.cpc.ncep.noaa.gov/products/expert_assessment/drought_assessment.html U.S. seasonal drought outlook, as well as precipitation and temperature data and soil moisture data.

http://www.drought.noaa.gov Background information about cause of droughts, U.S. drought outlook, and many links to water resource websites.

Higher-Latitude (D, E) and High-Altitude (H) Climates

Climatic boundary on the ground. The moist **H** (highland) region of the Kenya Highlands, foreground, meets the **BS** (steppe) climate on the Rift Valley floor west of Nairobi. (Authors' photo)

OBJECTIVES

- To expand the discussion of typical **D, E,** and **H** climates and to interpret representative climographs for these zones

- To highlight a major environmental-climatic problem of many **D** climate regions—acid precipitation

- To characterize the general influence of altitude on climatic conditions

I n this unit we survey the remaining climates in the Köppen global classification and regionalization system, which range from the upper middle to the polar latitudes and into the highest elevations capable of supporting permanent human settlement. We begin with the microthermal (**D**) climates that dominate the Northern Hemisphere continents poleward of the mesothermal (**C**) climates. Some large population clusters are located within the milder portions of the microthermal climate zone. The major environmental problem we consider here is associated with the effluents of urban-industrial concentrations—*acid precipitation.* Our attention next turns to the polar (**E**) climates that blanket the highest latitudes. Finally, we treat the highland (**H**) climates, which are often reminiscent of **E**-type temperature and precipitation regimes because they lie at altitudes high enough to produce Arctic-like conditions regardless of latitude.

The Major Humid Microthermal (D) Climates

Northern Hemisphere continental landmasses extend in an east–west direction for thousands of kilometres. In northern Eurasia, for instance, the distance along 60°N between Bergen on Norway's Atlantic coast and Okhotsk on Russia's Pacific shore is almost 9000 km. Indeed, Russia alone is so broad that the summer Sun rises above the eastern Pacific shoreline before it has set over the Baltic Sea in the west—10 time zones away! Consequently vast areas of land in the middle and upper latitudes are far away from the moderating influence of the oceans. The resulting continentality shapes a climate in which the seasonal rhythms of the higher latitudes are carried to extremes, one of distinctly warm summers balanced by harsh frigid winters. These are the **D** or **humid microthermal climates**, distinguished by a warm month—or months—when the mean temperature is above 10°C, and a period averaging longer than a month when the mean temperature is below freezing (0°C). The people who live in **D** climates have acquired lifestyles as varied as their wardrobes to cope with such conditions.

The cold-winter **D** climates are found mainly in the middle- and upper-latitude continental expanses of Eurasia and North America (see Fig. 16.3). As the world map shows, these areas are sometimes punctuated by regions of the entirely summerless **E** climates, especially in northeastern Asia and the Canadian Arctic. The **D** climates are also found in certain Northern Hemisphere midlatitude uplands and on the eastern sides of continental landmasses. These microthermal climates represent the epitome of the continentality effect—although they cover only 7 percent of the Earth's surface overall, they cover no less than 21 percent of its land area.

The Humid Continental (Dfa/Dwa, Dfb/Dwb) and Taiga (Dfc/Dwc, Dfd/Dwd) Climates

The humid microthermal climates are usually subdivided into two groups. In the upper middle latitudes, where more heat is available, we observe the *humid continental* (**Dfa/Dwa** and **Dfb/Dwb**) climates. Farther north toward the Arctic, where the summer net radiation cannot raise average monthly temperatures above 22°C , lie the subarctic *taiga* (**Dfc/Dwc** and **Dfd/Dwd**) climates. (Taiga means "snowforest" in Russian.) Both groups of climates usually receive enough precipitation to be classified as moist all year round (**Df**). But in eastern Asia, the cold air of winter cannot hold enough moisture, so a dry-winter season (**Dw**) results.

All **D** climates show singular extremes of temperature throughout the year. In Unit 7 we observe the heat balance for the northern Siberian town of Turukhansk (see Fig. 7.6D). In July the temperature there averages a pleasant 14.7°C, but the January mean plunges to −31°C. However, brutal as the latter reading might be, Turukhansk is only an example of the **Dfc** climatic subtype, which is not the most extreme category. The harshest subtype, **Dwd**, is exemplified by Verkhoyansk, a remote far northeastern Russian village 2100 km northeast of Turukhansk, whose particularly extreme temperatures are discussed in Unit 8 (see Fig. 8.11). As the climograph in Fig. 19.1 shows, the *average* January temperature in Verkhoyansk is an astonishing −46.8°C. Also fascinating are the *ranges* of temperature, the difference between the highest and lowest monthly averages: 45.7°C for Turukhansk and 62.5°C for Verkhoyansk. These are among the greatest annual temperature ranges found anywhere on our planet's surface.

Such temperatures have a far-reaching impact. There is a short, intense growing season, because the long summer days at these high latitudes permit large quantities of heat and light to fall on the Earth. Special quick-growing strains of vegetables and wheat have been developed to make full use of this brief period of warmth and moisture (Fig. 19.2). On the Chukotskiy Peninsula, the northeasternmost extension of Asia where Russia faces Alaska's western extremity across the narrow Bering Strait, one variety of cucumber usually grows to full size within 40 days. But agriculture is severely hampered by the thin soil (most was removed by the passing of extensive ice sheets thousands of years ago) and permafrost. **Permafrost**, discussed at length in Unit 48, is a permanently frozen layer of the subsoil that sometimes exceeds 300 m in depth.

Although the top layer of soil thaws in summer, the ice beneath presents a barrier that water cannot permeate.

CLIMOGRAPH

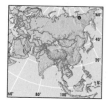

Dwd - Taiga climate
*Verkhoyansk, Russia
(68°N, 133°E)*

Average annual
temperature = −15°C

Average annual
precipitation = 155 mm

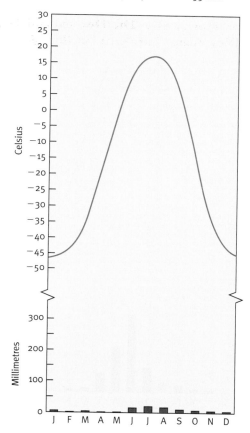

FIGURE 19.2 Short growing season, luxuriant growth. These giant cabbages are among many varieties of vegetables grown during the brief summer in a typical **D** climate.

FIGURE 19.1 Climograph of a weather station in the **Dwd** zone, the harshest extreme of the humid microthermal climate regions.

Thus the surface is often poorly drained. Moreover, the yearly freeze–thaw cycle expands and contracts the soil, making construction of any kind difficult, as Fig. 19.3 demonstrates. Because of the soil's instability, the trans-Alaska oil pipeline built during the 1970s must be elevated above ground on pedestals for much of its 1300-km length. This prevents the heated oil in the pipeline from melting the permafrost and causing land instability that might damage the pipe.

Long-lasting snow cover has other effects. It reflects most of the small amount of radiation that reaches it, so that little is absorbed. It cools the air and contributes to the production of areas of high atmospheric pressure. It

presents difficulties for human transport and other activities, but, paradoxically, it does keep the soil and dormant plants warm because snow is a poor conductor of heat. Measurements in St. Petersburg, Russia's second largest city, have shown that ground temperatures below a layer of snow can be as high as −2.8°C when the air overlying the cover is a bitter −40°C.

In the humid microthermal climates, most of the precipitation comes in the warmer months. This is not just because the warmer air can hold more moisture. In winter, large anticyclones develop in the lower layers of the atmosphere. Within the anticyclones the air is stable, and these high-pressure cells tend to block midlatitude cyclones. In summer, convection in the unstable warmer air creates storms, so midlatitude cyclones can pass through **D**-climate areas more frequently during that time of year. In some places there is also a summer monsoon season. China's capital city of Beijing (**Dwa**)

FIGURE 19.3 A once straight-standing historic building in Dawson City, Yukon, is now tilted by the annual cycles of freezing and thawing in the underlying surface layer of soil.

experiences a pronounced wet monsoon (Fig. 19.4), which is typical of upper midlatitude coastal areas on the East Asian mainland.

The more detailed features of the microthermal climate type are seen in the temperature, precipitation, water balance, and heat balance data displayed in Fig. 19.5. These graphs are for the southern Siberian city of Barnaul, located in a **Dfb** region within the heart of Eurasia at 53°N near the intersection of Russia and China with the western tip of Mongolia. The extreme seasonal change of Barnaul's climate is apparent everywhere in Fig. 19.5. Average monthly temperatures range from 20°C in July to −17.7°C in January; the annual mean temperature is 1.4°C. Most of the precipitation falls during summer, but it is not enough to satisfy the potential evapotranspiration rate.

The heat balance diagram shows the large amount of net radiation that supports Barnaul's intense summer growing season. The lack of naturally available surface water means that only a little of this energy is used in evaporation in summer; thus most of it warms the air as sensible heat. As in Turukhansk and Verkhoyansk, the low winter temperatures are the result of net radiation deficits that are not balanced by a significant flow of sensible heat to the surface. Barnaul, a manufacturing centre, is also located near the Kuznetsk Basin, one of the largest heavy-industrial complexes in Russia. Such regions are important features of the economic geography of the middle latitudes, and they involve physical geography as well because industrial areas

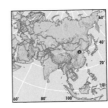

Dwa - Humid continental climate
*Beijing, China
(40°N, 117°E)*

Average annual
temperature = 12°C

Average annual
precipitation = 623 mm

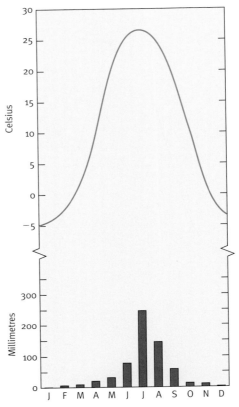

FIGURE 19.4 Climograph of a weather station in the **Dwa** climate zone, which also experiences a marked summer monsoon.

are the sources of pollutants that produce **acid precipitation**—abnormally acidic rain, snow, or fog resulting from high levels of the oxides of sulfur and nitrogen in the air. This is a serious environmental problem that plagues many a **D**-climate zone (see Perspective: Acid Precipitation).

Canada is dominated by **D** climates (primarily **Dfb** and **Dfc** climates). Dfc winters tend to be long and severe, and summers are relatively short and cool. This climate type is the most widespread in Canada, occupying the northern half of the country, with its southern boundary coinciding approximately with the northern limit of cultivation. The humid continental type (**Dfb**), second in spatial extent, corresponds roughly with the

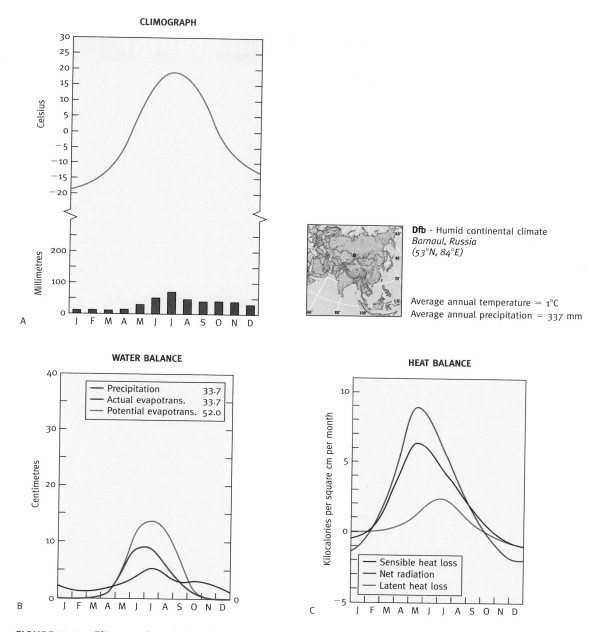

CLIMOGRAPH

Dfb - Humid continental climate
*Barnaul, Russia
(53°N, 84°E)*

Average annual temperature = 1°C
Average annual precipitation = 337 mm

WATER BALANCE

Precipitation	33.7
Actual evapotrans.	33.7
Potential evapotrans.	52.0

HEAT BALANCE

Sensible heat loss
Net radiation
Latent heat loss

FIGURE 19.5 Climograph and related graphic displays for a representative weather station in the **Dfb** climate zone.

aspen parkland and mixed forest regions. Winters are long and cold, but summers are rather warm and pleasant. As discussed in Unit 16 (p. 209), these climate boundaries are not fixed, but rather evolve and fluctuate over time. For example, during the 1930s, a boundary shift toward the north was indicative of a dry and warm decade, while the 1920s showed a shift to the south, a result of wetter and colder conditions. With global warming, it would be expected that climate boundaries could shift significantly.

The Polar (E) Climates

Beyond the Arctic and Antarctic Circles (66½°N and S, respectively), summer and winter become synonymous with day and night. Near the poles there are six months of daylight in summer, when the monthly average temperature might "soar" to −22°C. In winter, six months of darkness and continual outgoing radiation lead to the lowest temperatures and most extensive icefields on the planetary surface. The lowest temperature ever recorded

PERSPECTIVES ON THE HUMAN ENVIRONMENT

Acid Precipitation

Acid precipitation has been a major environmental problem since the mid-twentieth century. Acid rain is the most common form of this phenomenon, but the effects of acid precipitation are also associated with snow, fog, clouds, and even dust particles contained in the boundary layer of the atmosphere.

When fossil fuels (oil, coal, and natural gas) are burned, they release sizeable quantities of sulphur dioxide (SO_2) and nitrogen oxides (NO_x) into the surrounding air. These effluent gases then react chemically with water vapour in the atmosphere and are transformed into precipitable solutions of both sulphuric and nitric acid. When these gaseous pollutants are present in sufficient quantity, they can produce acid concentrations in precipitation that are capable of causing significant damage to vegetation as well as to animal and aquatic life.

Acidity is measured by the **pH scale**, which ranges from 0 to 14. Above the neutral level of 7, *alkalinity* is observed (which strengthens as the pH rises toward 14); below 7, a solution becomes increasingly *acidic* as its pH approaches zero. In most humid environments, the slightly acidic pH of 6.5 is considered normal in standing bodies of freshwater (by way of comparison, the salty seawater of the oceans exhibits an average pH of 7.8). Researchers have demonstrated that significant environmental damage occurs with increasing acidification. For instance, even a relatively small drop in pH from 6.5 to 5.9 changes a lake's phytoplankton composition so that certain fish species are eliminated from the food chain and disappear. When a pH of 5.6 is reached, large patches of slimy algae appear on the surface, begin to choke off the lake's oxygen supply, and block sunlight from filtering down into lower water layers. These effects would climax should the pH drop to 5.0 (about 30 times the normal acidity level), a point at which no fish species would be able to survive.

Besides freshwater lakes, there is considerable evidence that acid precipitation can also devastate marine life near heavily industrialized coastal zones. Forests are another major casualty of waterborne acid pollution, and vast areas of the upper middle latitudes have experienced damage to once healthy woodlands over the past three decades. Even human endeavours are being increasingly affected: in rural areas acid-sensitive crops are threatened constantly, whereas in the cities the deterioration of older buildings and concrete is noticeably hastened.

The sources of sulphur dioxide and nitrogen oxides are most closely linked to major urban-industrial areas containing the highest densities of fossil-fuel combustion. Sources within Canada are primarily from industrial sources (74 percent), while electric power plants are the leading polluters originating in the United States (67 percent). Other sources include transportation and fuel combustion.

The geography of acid rain in North America, however, corresponds decreasingly to the spatial distribution of sulphur dioxide and nitrogen oxide sources because of measures taken since the 1960s to reduce atmospheric pollution. In an effort to improve the air quality of industrial areas, much higher smokestacks (often in excess of 300 m) were constructed to disperse the effluents released by fossil-fuel burning. These measures did achieve their local goals, but instead of dispersing, the pollutants entered higher-level, longer-distance windflows, which tended to channel and transport them in still-high concentrations. Thus, in effect, certain distant areas now became the new dumping grounds for these emissions. In the case of the U.S. Midwest, the largest North American regional source of sulphur and nitrogen oxides, prevailing winds steered these acid-precipitation-producing wastes hundreds of kilometres toward the northeast (and eventually south as well). Over half of the acid rain received in eastern Canada originates in emissions in the United States. Areas of Ontario, like the Muskoka-Haliburton region, and Quebec City receive three-quarters of their acid deposition from the United States. According to Environment

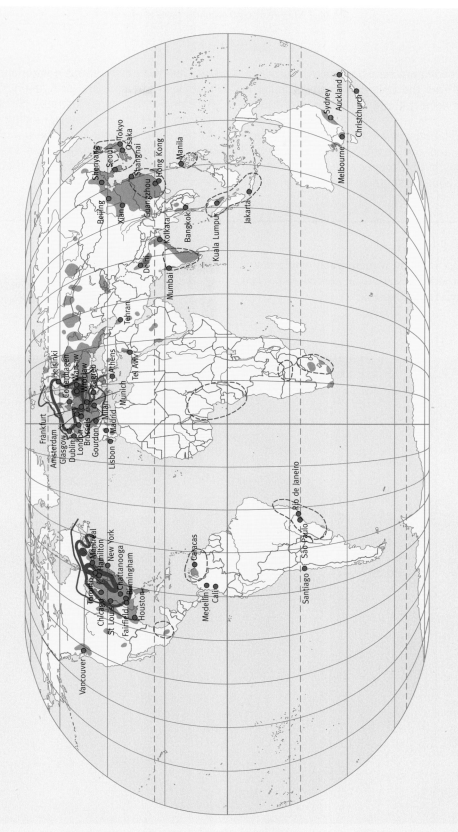

FIGURE 19.6 Global regions of acid rain, showing areas of elevated levels of fossil-fuel burning and consequent areas of high acid rain deposition.

Canada, the estimated transboundary flow of sulphur dioxide from the United States to Canada in 1995 was between 3.5 and 4.2 millions of tonnes per year.

A strong relationship exists between pollutant-laden winds and the spatial distribution of acid rain. The crisis is particularly acute in the heavily wooded **Dfb** zone of southeastern Canada, where fish kills and other serious environmental damage have been widespread. North America, however, is not alone as Fig. 19.6 illustrates. Similar effects of acid precipitation are now spreading across Eurasia too, most notably in Northern and Eastern Europe as well as in many of the vast wilderness areas that blanket Siberia and the Russian Far East.

on Earth——89°C—was on a memorably chilly day at one of the highest-altitude stations in central Antarctica, the Russian research facility Vostok.

The Tundra (ET) Climate

E or **polar climates** are defined as those climates in which the mean temperature of the warmest month is less than 10°C. There are two major subtypes of polar

FIGURE 19.7   Snowcapped Mount McKinley, the highest mountain in North America (6194 m), is located near the centre of the Alaska Range. Known to Native Americans as Denali (the High One), the mountain is flanked by tundra (foreground). The boundary between **ET** and **EF** climates lies along the foothills between the snowy peak and the lower plain.

CLIMOGRAPH

ET - Tundra climate
Resolute, N.W.T.
(74°N, 95°W)

Average annual
temperature = −20°C

Average annual
precipitation = 139.6 mm

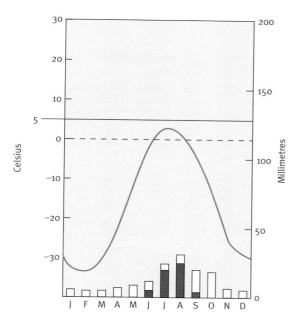

FIGURE 19.8 Climograph of a high-latitude tundra (**ET**) weather station.

The Icecap (EF) Climate

In *icecap* (**EF**) climates, the second major polar subtype, we find the lowest annual temperatures on Earth. In a given year about 90 mm of precipitation, usually in the form of snow, falls onto the barren icy surface. The inhospitable climate has made it difficult to collect data from these areas, which lie mainly in Antarctica and interior Greenland as well as atop the Arctic Ocean's floating icecap.

The Russian station, Mirnyy, is located in Antarctica just inside the Antarctic Circle. Its relatively low latitude hosts temperatures that are rather moderate for an icecap climate, but the mean annual temperature of −11°C is not high, and the warmest monthly average does not rise above the freezing point—the hallmark of an **EF** climate (Fig. 19.9). Year-round snow makes it almost impossible to obtain accurate water balance data, but the Russians have measured the heat balance components, which vividly characterize the frigid **EF** climate. There is significant positive net radiation at Mirnyy for only about four months of the year; more radiation leaves the Earth than enters during the other months. Sensible heat flow throughout the year is directed from the air toward the ground, the final result of the general circulation of the atmosphere moving heat toward the poles. Sensible heat and net radiation can provide energy for some evaporation in the warmer months, but in the winter condensation of moisture onto the surface provides only a minor source of heat.

These extreme conditions notwithstanding, a number of scientists now live and work in icecap climates, studying the environment or searching for oil and other secrets of the Earth. But every one of them depends for survival on artificial heating and food supplies flown in from the outside world, without which human life could not exist in the coldest climate on the planet.

High-Altitude (H) Climates

Our overview of the mosaic of climates covering the Earth's land surface would not be complete without some mention of the climates of highland regions. The mountains of the highest uplands reach into the lower temperatures and pressures of the troposphere. Thus as one moves steadily upward into a highland zone, the corresponding changes in climate with increasing elevation mimic those observed in a horizontal passage from equatorial to progressively higher latitudes.

One of the outstanding features of **H** or **highland climates** is their distinct **vertical zonation** according to

climate. If the warmest average monthly temperature is between 0° and 10°C, the climate is called *tundra* (**ET**), after its associated vegetation of mosses, lichens, and stunted trees (Fig. 19.7). Practically all of the **ET** climates are found in the Northern Hemisphere, where the continentality effect yields particularly long and bitter winters. Furthermore, many of the **ET** areas border the Arctic Ocean, which provides a moisture source for frequent fogs when it is not frozen. In summer, poor drainage leads to stagnant water, the breeding grounds for enormous swarms of flies and mosquitoes. Precipitation, mainly from frontal midlatitude depressions in the warmer months, seldom exceeds 300 mm for the year. The climograph for Resolute, on Cornwallis Island in the Northwest Territories (Fig.19.8), displays the typical **ET** regimes of temperature and moisture.

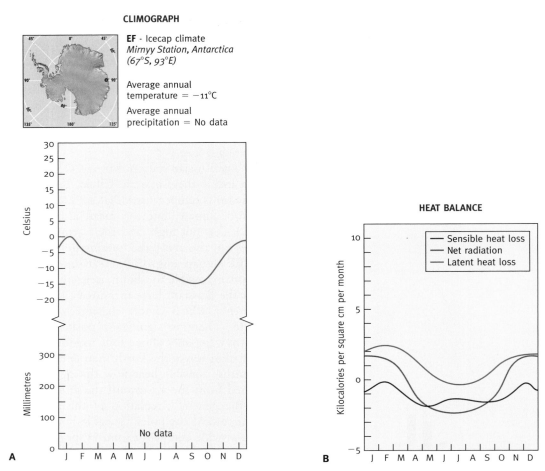

FIGURE 19.9   Climograph and heat balance diagram for a representative weather station in the ice-cap (**EF**) climate zone. There are no precipitation data available for this remote Antarctic location.

altitude. Nowhere has this been better demonstrated than in the tropical Andes mountain ranges of north-western South America. Figure 19.10 combines the characteristics of many of these highlands into a single model. The foothills of the Andes lie in a tropical rain-forest climate in the Amazon Basin in the east and in arid climates tempered by a cool Pacific Ocean current in the west. Above 1200 m, tropical climates give way to the subtropical zone. At 2400 m the mesothermal climates appear, with vegetation reminiscent of that found in Mediterranean climatic regions. These in turn give way to microthermal climates at 3600 m, and above 4800 m permanent ice and snow create a climate like that of polar areas. It is sometimes said that if one misses a bend at the top of an Andean highway, the car and driver will plunge through four different climates before hitting bottom!

These altitudinal zones mainly reflect the decrease of temperatures with rising elevation. But wind speeds tend to increase with height, as can rainfall (and snowfall), fog, and cloud cover. Moreover, the radiation balance is markedly altered by altitude. Because less shortwave radiation is absorbed by the atmosphere at higher elevations, greater values are recorded at the surface. This is especially true of the ultraviolet radiation responsible for snow blindness as well as the suntans of mountaineers and skiers. Where there are snow-covered surfaces, much of the incoming radiation is reflected and not absorbed, which further acts to keep the temperatures low.

Mountainous areas are often characterized by steep slopes, and these slopes have different orientations or *aspects* (they may face in any compass direction). In the Northern Hemisphere, southerly aspects receive far more solar radiation than do north-facing slopes, which

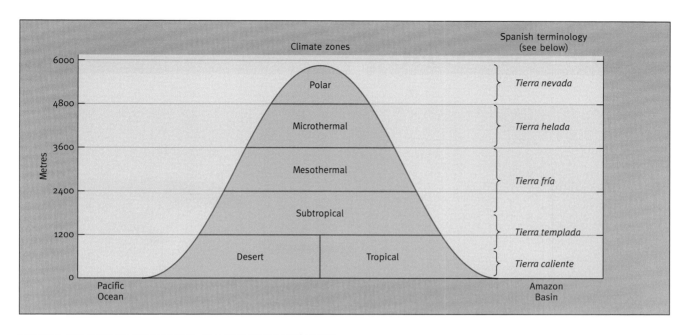

Vertical zone	Elevation range	Average annual temperature range
Tierra nevada	4800+ m	<−7°C
Tierra helada	3600–4800 m	−7°–13°C
Tierra fría	1800–3600 m	13°–18°C
Tierra templada	750–1800 m	18°–24°C
Tierra caliente	0–750 m	24°–27°C

FIGURE 19.10 Highly generalized west-to-east cross-section of the Andes in equatorial South America. The vertical climatic zonation shown on the mountain corresponds to the Spanish terminology at its right, which is interpreted in the table at left.

may receive no direct solar radiation for much of the winter season. These differences in radiation receipt are often manifested as vegetation contrasts on different slope aspects. South-facing slopes are commonly drier and exhibit a sparser vegetation cover. North-facing slopes are typically more lush, since temperatures, and hence evaporation rates, are lower. Rugged terrain also influences local windflow patterns that may have an effect on climatic conditions. Finally, the climate of a particular upland area depends on its location with respect to the global-scale factors of climate, such as the general circulation of the atmosphere.

A broadly simple pattern of climates occurs because of the heat and water exchanges at the Earth's surface and because of the spatial organization of the general circulation of the atmosphere. This pattern is altered in detail by the specific location of land and water bodies, ocean currents, and upland regions. The resulting mosaic of climates may be classified in different ways. We have mainly followed the system first devised by Köppen, who divided the climates of the Earth into six major types and a number of additional subtypes.

In Units 20 and 21, respectively, two additional aspects of the geography of climate are explored: (1) climatic variations over time and what these changes may portend for the future distribution of climate regions, and (2) the interactions between humans and their climatic environment.

FROM THE FIELDNOTES

FIGURE 19.11 "Watching the sun rise over Kilimanjaro and its ice-capped peak, Kibo, is one of the most memorable experiences a traveller in East Africa can have, and I am here as often as I can. In the far distance to the left (east, since we are in Kenya and viewing from the north) you can see Mawensi, the eroded peak that once looked like Kibo does today. Up there beyond 5800 m, the climate is frigid and polar, although we are within sight of the Equator. Two German geographers were the first Europeans to reach the summits: Hans Meyer climbed Kilimanjaro (5895 m) in 1889 and Fritz Klute scaled Mawensi (5355 m) in 1912. Global warming is in the process of shrinking the permanent ice and snow on Kibo."

KEY TERMS

acid precipitation *page 244*

highland climate *page 249*

humid microthermal climate *page 242*

permafrost *page 242*

pH scale *page 246*

polar climate *page 248*

vertical zonation *page 249*

REVIEW QUESTIONS

1. How do humid continental climates differ from taiga climates?

2. What is permafrost and how does it form?

3. What is acid precipitation, and why is it often found so far from its source areas?

4. Why do polar climates invariably exhibit low precipitation values?

5. Describe the effects of increasing altitude on temperature, precipitation (types and amounts), and wind speeds.

REFERENCES AND FURTHER READINGS

BARRY, R. G. *Mountain Weather and Climate* (London/New York: Routledge, 2nd ed., 1992).

BENISTON, M., Ed. *Mountain Environments in Changing Climates* (London/New York: Routledge, 1994).

BLISS, R. G. *Tundra Ecosystems: A Comparative Analysis* (New York: Cambridge Univ. Press, 1981).

BRYSON, R. A., and HARE, F. K., Eds. *Climates of North America* (Amsterdam: Elsevier, World Survey of Climatology, vol. 11, 1974).

Environment Canada. *2001 Annual Progress Report on the Canada-Wide Acid Rain Strategy for Post-2000* (Ottawa: Environment Canada, 2001).

FRENCH, H. M., and SLAYMAKER, O., Eds. *Canada's Cold Environments* (Montreal/Kingston: McGill-Queen's Univ. Press, 1993).

GERRARD, A. J. *Mountain Environments: An Examination of the Physical Geography of Mountains* (Cambridge, Mass.: MIT Press, 1990).

HARRIS, S. A. *The Permafrost Environment* (Totowa, N.J.: Rowman & Littlefield, 1986).

IVES, J. D., and BARRY, R. G., Eds. *Arctic and Alpine Environments* (London: Methuen, 1974).

LUOMA, J. R. "Bold Experiment in Lakes Tracks the Relentless Toll of Acid Rain," *New York Times* (September 13, 1988), 21, 24.

LYDOLPH, P. E., Ed. *Climates of the Soviet Union* (Amsterdam: Elsevier, World Survey of Climatology, vol. 7, 1977).

PIELOU, E. C. *A Naturalist's Guide to the Arctic* (Chicago: Univ. of Chicago Press, 1994).

PRICE, L. W. *Mountains and Man: A Study of Process and Environment* (Berkeley, Calif.: Univ. of California Press, 1981).

SCHWARTZ, S. E. "Acid Deposition: Unraveling a Regional Phenomenon," *Science,* 243 (February 10, 1989), 753–763.

SUGDEN, D. E. *Arctic and Antarctic: A Modern Geographical Synthesis* (Totowa, N.J.: Barnes & Noble, 1982).

WHITEMAN, C. D. *Mountain Meteorology: Fundamentals and Applications* (New York: Oxford Univ. Press, 2000).

WEB RESOURCES

http://www.ec.gc.ca/acidrain Environment Canada's Acid Rain site, including case studies and information about what's being done about the acid rain problem.

http://www.epa.gov/airmarkets/acidrain Overview of the chemical components of acid precipitation, its formation, its effects, and how it can be reduced. Glossary of terms is provided.

Dynamics of Climate Change

A glacier melts back as climate warms: you can walk and drive where the Franz Josef Glacier of New Zealand's Southern Alps stood less than 50 years ago. (Authors' photo)

OBJECTIVES

- To examine various lines of evidence for climate change

- To trace the history of climatic change on Planet Earth, focusing on the past 2 million years

- To discuss mechanisms that can cause climatic variations

Planet Earth, as was noted in Unit 4, has turbulent origins. For hundreds of millions of years following its birth, geochemical processes generated such surface heat that life as we know it was precluded. The gigantic collision that led to the formation of the Moon was only one incident in a series of impacts that cratered the surface even as volcanoes poured out molten rock from below. Slowly the Earth's crust cooled enough for slabs of solid rock to form and endure, and eventually almost all of the planet's outer skin solidified. Now the global ocean began to fill the basins and a primitive atmosphere, loaded with such gases as methane, ammonia, and helium, and later carbon dioxide and nitrogen, formed. Oxygen, the atmospheric gas upon which we depend for life, was but a trace 4 billion years ago, but a few hundred million years later photosynthesis had begun and the abundance of oxygen in the atmosphere started its slow but uninterrupted rise. Not only did the still young Earth have an atmosphere, it also had climates, seasons, and daily weather variations. And global climates have been changing ever since.

It would seem reasonable to assume that the Earth continued to cool throughout its geologic history, eventually experiencing ice ages that pushed glaciers far from the frigid poles into the middle latitudes. But recent research is yielding data that suggest something quite different. About 800 million years ago, when the atmosphere's oxygen content was about one-twentieth of its present level or just 1 percent of total volume, the first single-celled animals (the protozoa) had emerged, and nothing much was changing in the world of evolution. But then something dramatic happened. Land and sea were frozen over, and according to the *Snowball Earth hypothesis,* the planet went into a deep freeze. What might have caused this is unknown; perhaps the Sun's radiation output fell sharply for some reason. The Earth was in a full-scale ice age, and the protozoa responded by developing into multicelled metazoa, many of which acquired protective shells using the plentiful calcium carbonate being precipitated on the ocean floor. When the ice age ended and the planet warmed up again, the stage was set for life's *Cambrian explosion,* the burgeoning of marine organisms in unprecedented diversity.

Whether or not the Snowball Earth hypothesis turns out to be verified, we know that the Earth's climatic environments change continuously. In the approximately 570 million years since the opening of the Cambrian period (the geological time scale is shown on p. 471), our planet has been repeatedly warmed to tropical levels, only to be cooled to ice-age conditions, although no later ice age was as frigid as the Snowball Earth. Always there were mild refuges where many life forms could survive.

The two most recent ice ages are quite well known, because the evidence is well preserved. An ice age started during the Pennsylvanian (late Carboniferous) period and lasted tens of millions of years into the Permian. After that ice age ended, tropical warmth replaced Arctic cold, luxuriant vegetation spread poleward, and life took on the exuberance of Jurassic Park. The dinosaurs ruled, and much smaller mammals survived in protected settings (Fig. 20.1). But then, as we report in Unit 4, the age of the dinosaurs ended with an impact from space, and among the survivors were those small mammals whose descendants would inherit the Earth. The Cretaceous/Tertiary (K/T) boundary, some 65 million years ago, marked the beginning of the Cenozoic Era, and in

FIGURE 20.1 Information derived from fossils, such as this dinosaur skeleton exposed at Dinosaur National Monument on the Colorado–Utah border, can reveal much about the environment that prevailed during their lifetimes. During the Jurassic, climates over much of the Earth were warmer and more moist than today, creating vast forests and swamps, which supported numerous species of large herbivores (plant eaters) and carnivores.

its early period nothing suggested what lay ahead. But by about 35 million years ago, it would have been clear to any weather forecaster: the Earth was headed for another ice age. The Antarctic landmass acquired permanent ice; glaciers formed on the world's highest mountains; tree lines dropped to lower elevations; vegetation shifted equatorward; mammals everywhere, including primates, migrated and evolved in response to the climatic challenge.

Unlike what happened during the Snowball Earth episode, more recent ice ages have been less extreme and less pervasive. Warm periods have interrupted the cooling, allowing for the recovery of plants and animals; glaciers have expanded and then receded again. The Earth today is experiencing such a warm phase, and in recent years we have actually worried more about global warming than about global cooling. But the *Late Cenozoic Ice Age* has not ended, and over the long term our descendants, like our ancestors, will cope with the rigours of a cooling world.

Evidence of Climate Change

Climate change is the norm, not the exception, on our planet. But how is it possible to reconstruct climates of millions, even hundreds of millions, of years ago? The evidence exists in various forms. When glaciers expand, they scour the surface, breaking off, grinding up, and carrying away part of the bedrock below. Later, when they melt away, they leave behind their telltale work in the form of deposits that leave no doubt as to their former presence (see Units 45 to 47). Particular types of soils form under certain environmental conditions (such as thick tropical soils and thin desert soils). When such soils are buried by subsequent geologic events, they form a durable record of climatic conditions at the time of their formation. Occasionally entire diagnostic landforms are buried and preserved, for example, fossilized sand dunes, which may tell us more than just the fact that it was dry when and where they formed: from their morphology we may even be able to determine the prevailing winds at the time, millions of years ago.

Animal and plant fossils provide compelling evidence as well. Specific kinds of marine fauna formed under cold or warm conditions, and certain types of plants grow under warm, moist as opposed to cool, dry environments. From a combination of fossil data it has been determined that much of the Earth was warm and moist during the heyday of the dinosaurs, with luxuriant tropical vegetation, swamps, and marshes providing an environment that supported a profusion of many forms of life. But before the era of the dinosaurs opened, the cold of an ice age kept animals small, thick-shelled, and relatively sparse, and much of the planet was not only cool but also dry.

Evidence from sediments deposited over long periods on ocean floors and lake bottoms is also crucial in this scientific detective work. Samples ("cores") of these deposits are tested for accumulations of the fossils of tiny sea creatures, for mineral composition, even for ash (Fig. 20.2). The ash from volcanic eruptions that occurred hundreds of thousands of years ago dropped from the atmosphere and sank to the ocean floor, forming thin layers that can be correlated against other evidence and provide valuable time lines. Most valuable of all is information derived from nuclear particles embedded in the seafloor deposits, because these differ in significant ways. The nucleus of an atom is made up of positively charged protons and uncharged neutrons. Two separate atoms of one element, for example oxygen, may have different numbers of neutrons, but they will always have the same number of protons. These related but different forms of the same element are called *isotopes,* and their differences reveal variations in the environmental conditions prevailing during their formation.

By coring ocean-floor sediments in higher latitudes as well as thick ice sheets in Greenland and Antarctica, scientists have been able to reconstruct the climatic record for hundreds of thousands of years past. Obviously, the closer we come to the present, the more detailed the information, which is why the Snowball Earth idea is still a hypothesis, but the Late Cenozoic Ice Age is beyond doubt, although the picture we have is still very general. Climate swings violently even over the short term, and pieces of the environmental puzzle for even the past several thousand years are still being put into place.

Evidence for Recent Climatic Variation

The Earth in the twenty-first century does not seem to be in the thrall of an ice age. Glaciers are confined to high latitudes and high-mountain elevations, and in many parts of the world they are melting, showing little sign of any advance. The planet has been warm for about 11,000 years, and with some minor variations the world climate map (Fig. 16.3) represents the pattern that has prevailed for most (though not all) of the past 6000 years. During that period, humanity has expanded numerically and spatially to fill almost every niche, inhabit virtually every environment, exploit practically every resource on land and at sea.

But the climate has indeed fluctuated even as humankind expanded, and the fluctuations have sometimes had significant, even disastrous consequences. Compared to the geologic advent of ice ages, these variations have been but minor. Yet they reveal how, in our huge numbers, we are now at risk from even modest perturbations.

How do we know what has happened over the past several thousand years? Here the evidence is rather different from that discussed in the preceding section,

FIGURE 20.2 Cataloguing of core samples of ocean-floor sediments, showing their careful positional calibration, at the laboratory aboard the famous drilling vessel *Glomar Challenger.*

although ice cores do play a role in the reconstruction. But other data come from tree rings, fossil pollen, paired annual lake sediments known as *varves*, fruit harvests (winegrowers' harvest dockets are especially valuable), historical narratives, farmers' trade records, and even the work of artists. Over the past 150 years, scientific instruments have made their appearance, and today huge quantities of data on every aspect of the planet's environments are being recorded.

Each bit of evidence, corroborated from a second and possibly third source, helps us build a picture of past climates. But each piece of the puzzle usually tells us only about conditions in one area and in one limited span of time. It is therefore risky to generalize about global climate except in the most indefinite terms. With that in mind, let us examine climate change from recent to distant history.

The Climatic History of the Earth

Most history books start with the oldest times and work their way forward. In contrast, most descriptions of past climates start with the most recent times and work backward. To begin with, much more information is available on recent times, which allows statements to be made with greater certainty. Another advantage of such an approach is that it allows investigators to use certain climatic events as landmarks as they delve farther into the increasingly obscure past. The following account also begins with the more recent time periods, and we use certain events for guides as we shift time scales within our examination of the climatic past.

The Past 150 Years

Although there is much evidence of past climate change and weather variability, accurate record-keeping based on reliable instruments began only during the last 150 years. Weather records spanning a century or more still are rare, and come from weather stations mostly in Western Europe and North America. Many crucial areas of the world have climate records less than a half-century old. Political upheavals have interrupted record-keeping in other areas. In West Africa, for example, good records from weather stations established by the French and the British ended, or were interrupted, during the instabilities of the 1960s. Moreover, satellite observations of global weather conditions are just a few decades old, and to this day surface verification is inadequate over large parts of the Earth's landmasses and oceans. Undeniably, the absence of dependable long-term data is a major obstacle in our efforts to gauge climate change.

Nevertheless, the available record indicates considerable temperature variations over the past 140 years (Fig. 20.3). The most notable features of the average annual temperature of the world's landmasses over the past century and a half are a warming trend beginning in the 1880s, a cooling trend from 1940 into the 1960s, and another warming trend since then.

Different parts of the world have experienced these changes to a greater or lesser degree. For instance, the 1940–1975 cooling trend was most strongly felt in the Atlantic sector of the Arctic region, where average winter temperatures in some locations dropped almost 3°C. On the other hand, no cooling at all was detected

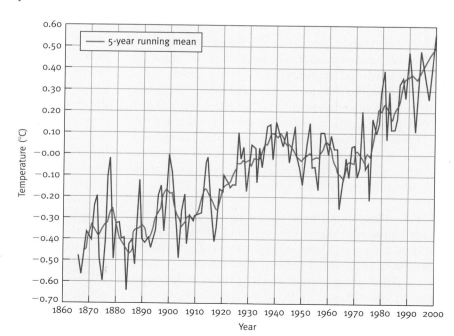

FIGURE 20.3 Variation of annual mean surface temperatures for the world's land areas, 1866–2000. Because this graph incorporates data from many different places, annual mean temperatures are expressed as a deviation from the average annual mean temperature for the 1951–1980 period.

during that 35-year period in parts of the Southern Hemisphere (such as New Zealand), where the warming trend launched in the 1880s continued.

Recent research indicates that this regional variation in warming and cooling is a hallmark of climate change. Computer models that project global warming during the twenty-first century, for example, indicate that any such warming will be felt most strongly in the higher latitudes—not evenly around the world. *Global* warming (or cooling) may, therefore, turn out to be a misnomer—while certain regions experience one trend, others may record the opposite.

The Past 1500 Years

To gauge climate and weather over the past 1500 years, we must depend on less-exact information. Tree rings, lake sediments, ice cores, cave deposits, harvest records, diaries, and other sources produce a picture of considerable variation and even quite sudden change.

Apparently the Earth was warm and becoming warmer during the centuries prior to 1000 C.E.—a trend not unlike the one we are experiencing today. Sea level was high, low-lying coastal countries coped with rising water (in Holland the Dutch learned to build dikes and polders during this period), and high-latitude environs, even Greenland and Iceland, proved amenable to permanent settlement. The Romans had planted grapevines in Britain, and the wine industry thrived there under the mild conditions of what climatologists have come to call the *Medieval Optimum*.

In her 1988 book entitled *The Little Ice Age,* Jean Grove describes conditions thus:

> For several hundred years climatic conditions in Europe had been kind; there were few poor harvests and famines were infrequent. The pack ice in the Arctic lay to the north and long sea voyages could be made in the small craft then in use . . . Icelanders made their first trip to Greenland about A.D. 982 and later they reached the Canadian Arctic and may even have penetrated the North West Passage. Grain was grown in Iceland and even in Greenland; the northern fisheries flourished and in mainland Europe vineyards were in production (500 km) north of their present limits.

Were these conditions representative only of the higher latitudes of the Northern Hemisphere or of the world as a whole? There are clues from the Southern Hemisphere that the Medieval Optimum may have been a global phenomenon. Even as the Scandinavians traversed the Atlantic and, led by Leif Eriksson (the son of Eric the Red), reached northern North America,

Polynesians in the Southern Hemisphere for the first time managed to land in (upper-midlatitude) New Zealand. Was it a coincidence? Perhaps. On the other hand, this group of Polynesians (the Maori) had been sailing the South Pacific for centuries, never having reached the largest islands in their realm. The warmth and tranquility of the Medieval Optimum may have given them the same opportunity the Scandinavians seized in the far north.

The Medieval Optimum seems to bear some resemblance to the current warming trend. Many glaciers were in retreat, winters were generally mild, crops were plentiful. The frontiers of human settlement pushed into higher latitudes. But then, as Grove tells us, things changed quite suddenly:

> The beneficent times came to an end. Sea ice and stormier seas made the passages between Norway, Iceland, and Greenland more difficult after A.D. 1200; the last report of a voyage to Vinland [North America] was made in 1347. Life in Greenland became harder; the people were cut off from Iceland and eventually disappeared from history toward the end of the fifteenth century. Grain would no longer ripen in Iceland, first in the north and later in the south and east . . . life became tougher for fishermen as well as for farmers. In mainland Europe, disastrous harvests were experienced in the latter part of the thirteenth and in the early fourteenth century . . . extremes of weather were greater, with severe winters and unusually hot or wet summers.

From the late thirteenth century onward, Europe was in the grip of climatic extremes as the Medieval Optimum gave way to the *Little Ice Age*. Britain's wine industry was extinguished in a few years; the limit of agriculture was driven southward by hundreds of kilometres. Nor was only Europe affected. In China, the rulers of the Ming Dynasty found themselves facing drought and famine as the northern wheat fields lay bare. Having just embarked on a series of explorations of the Indian Ocean and beyond by large fleets carrying thousands of men, the emperors called these adventures to a halt, ordered the ships (then the most advanced ever built) burned, and directed the shipbuilding industry to construct only barges that could carry rice from warmer central China to the starving north.

Not until the fifteenth century did the Little Ice Age moderate somewhat (it may be no coincidence that this marked the revival of Atlantic navigation, including Columbus's crossings). But in the midsixteenth century the cold returned, not to yield again until the midnineteenth—marking the start of the warming trend to which we may now be contributing through our industrial pollution of the atmosphere.

Is the Little Ice Age over? At the moment we have no more evidence to suggest that it is than we have to conclude that it is not. The current warming phase may be just a prelude to the return of the conditions of the thirteenth century, the time of weather extremes that threw Europe into disorder.

The Past 15,000 Years

By going back 15,000 years, we must rely on even less dependable evidence for our reconstruction of climate. There is no written human record of the weather, although archaeologists draw useful conclusions from the seeds, tools, and other artifacts recovered from ancient inhabited sites. And now another line of evidence becomes critical—the geologic record. Just 15,000 years ago, the world was a very different place, and its geology bears witness.

Fifteen thousand years ago, the Earth still was in the grip of a major **glaciation**, which had lasted about 80,000 years. Great ice sheets covered most of northern North America; ice stood as far south as the Ohio River and New York City. Virtually all of what is today Canada was buried under thousands of metres of ice. Much of the United States resembled Siberia. In Europe the ice covered Scandinavia and nearly all of Britain and Ireland. Most of northern Asia was under glaciers, and the higher mountains of the Earth (the Rockies, Andes, Alps, and Himalayas among them) lay under icecaps.

Yet there were signs, 15,000 years ago, that this glaciation—known as the Wisconsinan—was coming to an end. The ice had reached its maximum extent just 3000 years earlier, and the margins were melting. Vast amounts of meltwater poured into the U.S. Midwest and flowed into the oceans. Pulverized rock, pebbles, and boulders carried by the ice were deposited by these meltwaters. Landmarks such as the Great Lakes and Cape Cod were in the making.

But the warming phase would not continue without a hiccup. Those melting and thinning ice sheets still covering much of present-day Canada became unstable. Not only were they less heavy now, but they became liquified at their bases even as they melted around their margins and upper surfaces. About 12,000 years ago, one of those ice sheets slid into the North Atlantic, causing disastrous waves along its coasts and chilling the ocean right back to glaciation-like temperatures. This event, named the *Younger Dryas* after a tundra wildflower, must have been catastrophic for thousands of people living in coastal zones at ever-higher latitudes. Those who survived the flooding were confronted with glacial conditions not felt for several thousand years. But as it happened, the Younger Dryas was a short-lived event. Within a thousand years, the post-Wisconsinan warming had resumed and the remaining glaciers had resumed their recession. The end of this Younger Dryas episode, about 11,000 years ago, therefore marks the start of the *Holocene* epoch on most geologic calendars (see ours on p. 471).

By about 10,000 years ago, therefore, it would have been clear to modern scientists that this was no ordinary, brief interlude of the kind experienced so many times during the Wisconsinan glaciation. This would be a new epoch of sustained warmth lasting thousands of years, a true **interglacial** (the term for a prolonged warm period between glaciations). By about 7000 years ago, the great ice sheets had melted away approximately to their present dimensions, and for about 2000 years the Earth was even warmer than it is today. Since then, the global climate appears to have been not only warm but also relatively stable. Even the fluctuations of the Little Ice Age are merely mild aberrations against the background of a full-scale glaciation.

One lesson learned from research into the Holocene (the epoch that has witnessed the entire drama of the emergence of human civilization) is that reversals of temperature are sudden and seem to be preceded by opposite trends. For example, the warmest period of the Holocene was preceded by the temporary but severe cooling of the Younger Dryas. As in the case of the Little Ice Age, trends in one direction seem to presage sudden reversals to the other. This is one concern arising from the current "greenhouse warming" phenomenon—that this global warming, far from foreshadowing an overheated world, portends a precipitous return to full-scale glaciation.

The Past 150,000 Years

One hundred and fifty thousand years ago, the Earth was locked in another great glaciation, which preceded the one just discussed. We have the geologic evidence to confirm that this glaciation, too, was experienced worldwide and spread its ice sheets deep into the heart of the present-day United States. Of particular interest is the warm spell that separated this glaciation from its successor, because this interglacial is similar to the Holocene epoch of today.

This warm spell, called the Eemian interglacial, began about 130,000 years ago and lasted about 10,000 years. Evidence from ice cores taken from the Greenland Ice Sheet, which has survived the interglacials and thus carries valuable information, indicates that the Eemian resembled the Holocene in some ways but differed in others. One similarity lies in the timing of maximum warmth: like the Holocene, the Eemian began with

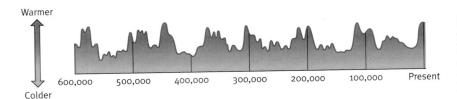

Warmer

Colder

600,000   500,000   400,000   300,000   200,000   100,000   Present

FIGURE 20.4 Graph of surface temperature changes over the past 600,000 years, based on a composite of seven independent estimates, demonstrating the repeated alternation between cold and warm conditions.

nearly 3000 years of high temperatures, but even higher than those of the early Holocene. Then, however, the Eemian's equable climate was frequently interrupted by cold episodes much more severe than those we have known during the Holocene.

The well-defined length of the Eemian—just 10,000 years—gives rise to concern. The Holocene already has lasted longer, and the question is, how long will our interglacial continue? When the Eemian ended, one last surge of rising temperatures was summarily terminated by a massive onset of severe cold. That cold marked the beginning of 110,000 years of global glaciation, interrupted only by a comparatively slight warming (about halfway through), which was not intense enough to be called a true interglacial.

We should also take note of a cataclysmic event that occurred during the period under discussion. About 73,000 years ago, a huge volcanic eruption took place on the Indonesian island of Sumbawa, where the volcano named Toba exploded and spewed vast quantities of ash and dust high into the atmosphere. The Earth already was in the grip of a glaciation. Now the crucial tropical latitudes were deprived of sunlight as these airborne ejected materials were carried around the globe by high-altitude winds. Anthropologists and archaeologists report that humankind came very close to extinction during this twin assault by nature. When the skies finally cleared, there was little to suggest that the next interglacial would witness the rise of modern civilization.

The Past 1,500,000 Years

The sequence just described—of long-lasting glaciations separated by relatively brief interglacials—has marked the last 1.5 million years and beyond. The past 1.5 million years constitute almost all of an intensified phase of the Late Cenozoic Ice Age, which began about 1.8 million years ago. The word "intensified" is appropriate, because the cooling that foreshadowed this period began more than 30 million years ago and followed a significant drop in global temperatures during the Pliocene epoch around 6 million years ago. By the time this subsequent *Pleistocene* epoch began, primates and hominids that had survived the Pliocene cooling were those best able to accommodate sudden swings in climate.

The Pleistocene is sometimes misnamed an ice age, but in fact it is only the most recent phase of the Late Cenozoic Ice Age, which has witnessed the rise of mammals and of humanity. It is an epoch marked by repeated glacial advances and recessions—perhaps as many as 20 over its 1.8-million-year time span. The last four of these advances are the best known, and the latest, the Wisconsinan, is the one whose end led to the warmth we enjoy today. In turn, the start of the Wisconsinan glaciation marked the end of the previous warm phase, the Eemian.

It has become clear that the Pleistocene epoch marked the depth of the Late Cenozoic Ice Age: for most of its nearly 2 million years the Earth has been frigid, with only brief warm interglacials. Figure 20.4 suggests what conditions may have been like over the past approximately 600,000 years—glaciations last around 100,000 years; warm interglacials average about 10,000 years. It is a datum that should give us pause. Temperatures fluctuate somewhat during interglacials (witness the Little Ice Age and the Medieval Optimum). What would happen if the current warming phase ended as suddenly as the Eemian did, and nearly 7 billion people faced the prospect of a rapidly cooling, drying Earth?

Issues relating to ice ages and glaciations will be examined in Part Five, but the foregoing raises a general question: what is "normal" for our planet? Ice ages are known to last for tens of millions of years, but the Earth is 4.6 billion years old, and all the known ice ages together span no more than 10 percent of this lifetime. Indeed, scientists report that most evidence points to an overall warm planetary climate, with temperatures about 5°C higher than those of the Late Cenozoic. Such balmy conditions, familiar to the dinosaurs if not to us, seem to have prevailed ever since the Snowball Earth episode, and possibly longer than that.

The Mechanisms of Climate Change

The picture of past climates and their variations that we have just sketched is still a hazy one. It does become clearer as we focus on more recent times, but there is still

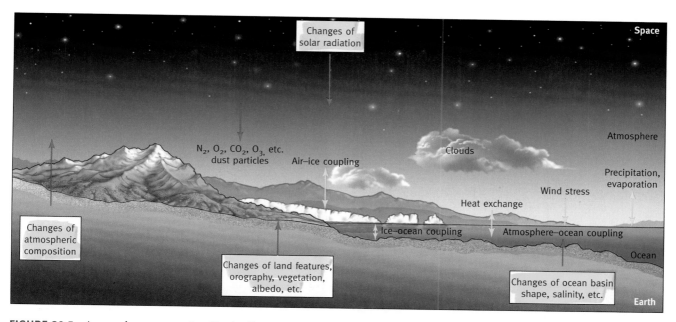

FIGURE 20.5 Atmosphere–ocean–ice–Earth climatic system. Red arrows denote external processes; yellow arrows indicate internal processes.

a need for more factual information. One fact, however, will be apparent to you by now—climates certainly do change. But how?

One of the issues related to climate change is that there are many probable causes, all acting at different scales in time and geographic space. A further complicating factor is that many forces shaping climate are linked and interact with one another, so that changes in one trigger changes in others. As if this were not enough, there are still gaps in our knowledge of the exact way the atmosphere and the oceans operate, both separately and in tandem. And there may even be additional major variables that have not yet been considered.

Given these difficulties, a framework for ideas and facts concerning the causes of climatic change can nonetheless be compiled. But first the parameters of the system within which climate changes take place must be specified. This system cannot deal with the atmosphere alone: it must also account for the ice of the cryosphere as well as the oceanic component of the hydrosphere. Such an interlinked atmosphere–ocean–ice–Earth system is shown in Fig. 20.5. Within this system, both the heat-energy system and the hydrologic cycle are at work; moreover, the diagram models the interactions of wind, ice, and ocean characteristics (including surface currents). Outside the climatic system, a number of boxes list forces, such as a change in radiation coming from the Sun, that have the power to alter the system externally. The important thing to remember is that a change in any one or more of these processes creates a climatic change.

External Processes

At night any particular Earth location receives far less radiation from the Sun than during the day. In a similar way, solar radiation changing over a longer period of time affects the Earth's climate. There are both short-term and long-term variations in the behaviour of the Sun. Short-term changes take place when storm areas occur on the surface of the Sun; these are called *sunspots* and occur in cycles that peak about every 11 years (Fig. 20.6 shows sunspots at their maximum and minimum development). Sunspots may also affect terrestrial weather, but research findings are still inconclusive as to whether they significantly influence the amount of solar radiation received at the Earth's surface.

Longer-term changes also occur because of three cyclical peculiarities in the orientation of the Earth's orbit and axis. One is a periodic variation in the shape of the Earth's orbit around the Sun (Fig. 20.7A). During cycles lasting about 100,000 years, the Earth's orbit "stretches" from nearly circular to markedly elliptical and back to nearly circular. The resulting fluctuation in the distance between the Earth and Sun is as much as 17.5 million km. Another variation in the Earth–Sun relationship, which follows an approximately 41,000-year cycle, is due to the

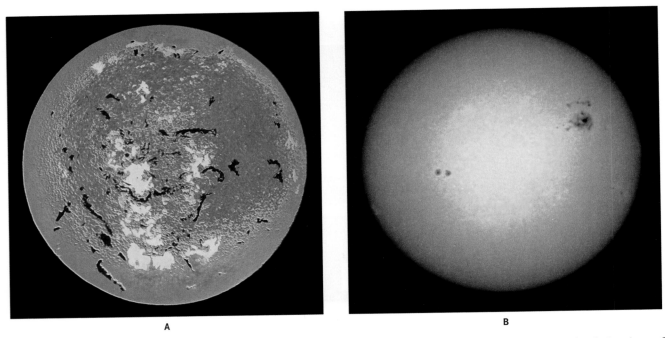

A

B

FIGURE 20.6 Two views of the Sun, showing an occurrence of sunspots (A) and intervening normalcy (B). The dark colour of the sunspots reflects the reduced temperatures in these areas on the Sun's surface. Scientists theorize that intense localized magnetic fields interfere with the convection process that brings hot material to the surface. Sunspots develop in cycles that peak approximately every 11 years, and their occurrence brings an increase in the solar wind, resulting in enhanced auroras (see p. 81) and interference in radio transmissions on and from Earth.

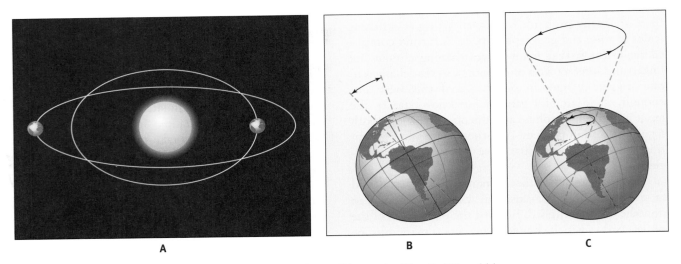

A

B

C

FIGURE 20.7 Long-term changes in the Earth's orbit and axis: (A) stretch, (B) roll, (C) wobble.

obliqueness of the Earth's axis. In other words, the Earth "rolls" like a ship (Fig. 20.7B), so that the angle between our planet's axis and the plane of the ecliptic (see Unit 5) changes from 65.6 to 68.2 degrees (the present angle of 66.5 degrees is therefore not constant). The major effect of this axial shifting is to alter the annual distribution of solar radiation received at the surface. The third variation might best be described as a "wobble" because, like a spinning top, the Earth's axis swivels once every 21,000 years or so (Fig. 20.7C). This affects the distance between the Earth and the Sun during any given season, which gradually changes as the cycle proceeds.

These variations individually produce episodes of some cooling and warming. But when the cooling periods of all three cycles coincide, the variation in solar radiation estimated to reach the Earth is strikingly parallel to the waxing and waning of the global ice cover over the past 1.5 million years. However, these orbital and axial variations presumably also took place during the 90 percent of Earth history when ice ages did not occur.

Other external processes that might lead to climatic change are considered elsewhere in this book (start with the Perspective box in Unit 45). They include volcanism (the subject of Unit 34), the uplifting and wearing away of the land surface (Units 32, 37, and 38), the shifting distribution of landmasses and oceans caused by plate tectonics (Unit 33), and the hypothesized intensification of the greenhouse effect (Unit 7).

Internal Processes

Units 7 through 14 describe the heat and water exchanges within the atmosphere, the way the general circulation distributes heat and moisture across wide areas of the Earth, and the weather systems forming the fine grain of atmospheric movement and operation. All these are internal processes, and many of them function as systems by themselves. Although changes in any one of them could lead to climatic variation, they are linked by feedback mechanisms (see Unit 1).

An increase in unusual variations in ocean temperature provides an example of *positive feedback*. A change in the temperature of the sea surface may modify the amount of sensible heat transferred to the overlying air, thereby altering atmospheric circulation and cloudiness. Variations in radiation, wind-driven mixing of ocean water, and other factors may, in turn, affect the temperature of the original ocean surface. In the tropical Pacific Ocean, the sea-surface temperature has increased for several years at a time because of positive feedback mechanisms such as those just described.

An example of *negative feedback* occurs when a snow-covered surface reduces atmospheric temperatures. The cooler atmosphere holds less water vapour, and thus less snow falls; Antarctica's low precipitation levels are partly a result of such negative feedback. Many other examples of both positive and negative feedback exist. Researchers today are particularly interested in *teleconnections,* newly discovered relationships between weather phenomena that involve distant parts of the globe (see Perspective: Weather Extremes and Teleconnections).

The Climatic Future

If we understand the mechanisms of climate, is it possible to predict the climatic future of the Earth? Unfortunately, despite the availability of better information than ever before and the advances in knowledge that have recently taken place, forecasting climates continues to be a supremely difficult challenge. These constraints notwithstanding, it is still possible to conjecture about what lies ahead. A particularly thoughtful statement is offered by a leading student of global climate change, Reid Bryson, former professor of meteorology, geography, and environmental studies at the University of Wisconsin:

> From the beginning of the atmosphere to the present the climate has been changing, on all time-scales and for many reasons. Paralleling the changes of climate, reacting to and interacting with it, has been the ever-changing pattern of life.... It can be said with some certainty that the climate will continue to change, and with great probability that there will be more periods of continental glaciation, and not in the far distant geological future. In a brief century the widespread use of meteorological instrumentation has replaced human memory and qualitative chronicles with a storehouse of quantitative information about the climate. At the same time, research has shown us how to read the clock and climatic record provided by nature. A belief in a constant climate has been replaced by a knowledge of how climate has changed, and how the changes of the past have affected the biota and cultures that embellish the Earth.... The problem now is to understand fully the meaning of this rich natural history in order to anticipate the coming climatic events and prepare for them. This is a very large order for humanity if it is going to last to and through the next ice age without losing the hard-won fruits of civilization.

As one draws conclusions about the tendencies of climate to undergo change, it is important also to keep in mind another force—human interference (a topic discussed in Unit 21). Modification of the ozone layer, increased atmospheric carbon dioxide, and other human-induced factors could alter the unknown natural pattern of climatic change. Only one thing is certain, as stated in a recent report from the U.S. National Academy of Sciences: "The clear need is for greatly increased research on both the nature and the causes of climatic variation."

PERSPECTIVES ON THE HUMAN ENVIRONMENT

Weather Extremes and Teleconnections

Severe and unusual weather episodes of the recent past are discussed in a number of places in this book (see, for example, the Perspective boxes in Units 13, 14, and 15). We were constantly reminded of such events by accounts of extreme-weather-punctuated newscasts on an almost daily basis: persistent drought, record high temperatures, unprecedented levels of rainfall, massive wildfires, and the worst floods ever seen (Fig. 20.8). The message of this incessant drumbeat of headlines is all too clear: in this time of obvious climatic transition, we had better get used to encountering episodes of extreme weather!

In the quest for a better understanding of the forces that shape severe weather—and climate change in general—one promising new avenue of research is focused on teleconnections. **Teleconnections** are long-distance linkages between weather patterns that occur in widely separated parts of the world. The most studied of these relationships is ENSO, the El Niño–Southern Oscillation discussed in Unit 11, which links midlatitude weather extremes to cyclical abnormalities in the warming of the tropical Pacific Ocean surface.

This line of research has also established teleconnections between ENSO and weather cycles in the lower latitudes, particularly variations in the wet monsoon of South Asia (a topic covered in Unit 10). The one-billion-plus residents of India and neighbouring Bangladesh are well aware of fluctuations in these torrential summer-monsoon rains. In some years this activity is mild and intermittent, but in other years it is much more active and often destructive. Even though the causal mechanism is not fully understood, evidence has accumulated that shows a relationship between warm-water El Niño peaks in the Pacific and mild wet monsoons on the Indian subcontinent. Conversely, when Pacific sea-surface temperatures reach a cool ebb between El Niños—the phenomenon now known as *La Niña**—South Asia is likely to experience its most violent summer rains. Moreover, researchers recently made an important discovery that strengthens these linkages: sea-surface temperatures warm and cool along the equatorial Indian

FIGURE 20.8 The Old City of Prague, capital of Central Europe's Czech Republic, at the height of the colossal flood of mid-August 2002. More than 40,000 people had to be evacuated from this area as the Vltava (Moldau) River overflowed its banks to an extent not seen since the late eighteenth century.

Ocean in lockstep with the El Niño and La Niña events in the Pacific Ocean to the east.

Teleconnection research is expanding today and concentrates on two related areas. The first is the search for mechanisms that control the evolution of meteorological conditions which, for months or even years at a time, spawn high- and low-pressure cells whose movements result in atypical weather patterns. The second concern is the specification and interpretation of additional ENSO-like systems. Three such large-scale relationships are now under investigation:

1. Linkages between the northern Pacific and North America involving weather cycles in Alaska's Aleutian Islands, western Canada, the U.S. Southeast, and the Caribbean.

2. The North Atlantic Oscillation (discussed in the Perspectives box in Unit 11), which is controlled by shifting pressure gradients between the subpolar Icelandic Low and the subtropical Azoric High.

3. The influence of the seasonal snow cover in northern Eurasia on Asia's monsoonal airflows and even the El Niño phenomenon itself.

Two goals propel teleconnection research in contemporary climatology: (1) the long-range prediction of weather patterns for the coming season (and perhaps even the coming year); and (2) the development of longer-term explanations that contribute to the unlocking of the remaining secrets of how and why the global climate changes.

*As discussed on p. 141 in Unit 11, new research is establishing that the "cool ebb" designated La Niña is very likely a third state in the atmosphere–ocean interaction of the equatorial Pacific, representing a cold extreme vis-à-vis "normal conditions" that can be as strong as the warm extreme exhibited by El Niño.

KEY TERMS

glaciation *page 259*   interglacial *page 259*   teleconnections *page 264*

REVIEW QUESTIONS

1. What are proxy climatic data, and why are they important in the reconstruction of past climates?

2. Describe the general climatic history of the past 1.5 million years.

3. What is the Late Cenozoic Ice Age?

4. Describe the primary external processes that might contribute to climatic fluctuations.

5. What are teleconnections? Give two examples of this phenomenon.

REFERENCES AND FURTHER READINGS

BALLING, R. C., Jr. *The Heated Debate: Greenhouse Predictions versus Climate Reality* (San Francisco: Pacific Research Institute for Public Policy, 1992).

BIGG, G. R. *The Oceans and Climate* (New York: Cambridge Univ. Press, 1996).

BRADLEY, R. S., and JONES, P., Eds. *Climate Since A.D. 1500* (London/New York: Routledge, 2nd ed., 1995).

BRYSON, R. A. "What the Climatic Past Tells Us about the Environmental Future," in H. J. de Blij, Ed., *Earth '88: Changing Geographic Perspectives* (Washington, D.C.: National Geographic Society, 1988), 230–246. Quotation taken from pp. 245–246.

BURROUGHS, W. *The Climate Revealed* (New York: Cambridge Univ. Press, 1999).

CRONIN, T. M. *Principles of Paleoclimatology* (New York: Columbia Univ. Press, 1999).

FAGAN, B. *The Little Ice Age: How Climate Made History, 1300–1850* (New York: Basic Books, 2000).

GLANTZ, M. H., Ed. *La Niña and Its Impacts: Facts and Speculation* (Tokyo: United Nations Univ. Press, 2002).

GLANTZ, M. H., et al., Eds. *Teleconnections Linking Worldwide Climate Anomalies* (New York: Cambridge Univ. Press, 1990).

GROVE, J. M. *The Little Ice Age* (London/New York: Methuen, 1988), 1–2.

HOYT, D. V., and SCATTEN, K. H. *The Role of the Sun in Climate Change* (New York: Oxford Univ. Press, 1997).

KONDRATYEV, K. Y., and CRACKNELL, A. P. *Observing Global Climate Change* (Bristol, Penn.: Taylor & Francis, 1998).

KRAUS, E. B., and BUSINGER, J. A. *Atmosphere–Ocean Interaction* (New York: Oxford Univ. Press, 2nd ed., 1994).

LAMB, H. H. *Climate, History, and the Modern World* (London/New York: Routledge, 2nd ed., 1995).

ROTBERG, R. I., and RABB, T. K. *Climate and History* (Princeton, N.J.: Princeton Univ. Press, 1981).

RUDDIMAN, W. F. *Earth's Climate: Past and Future* (New York: Freeman, 2000).

SILVER, C. S., and DE FRIES, R. S. *One Earth, One Future: Our Changing Global Environment* (Washington, D.C.: National Academy Press, 1990).

STEVENS, W. K. *The Change in the Weather: People, Weather, and the Science of Climate* (New York: Delacorte Press, 2000).

WILSON, R. C. L., DRURY, S. A., and CHAPMAN, J. A., Eds. *The Great Ice Age: Climate Change and Life* (London/New York: Routledge, 2000).

WRIGHT, H. E., et al. *Global Climates Since the Last Glacial Maximum* (Minneapolis, Minn.: Univ. of Minnesota Press, 1994).

WEB RESOURCES

http://lwf.ncdc.noaa.gov/oa/climate/severeweather/extremes.html A collection of extreme weather data, containing historical extreme weather data, satellite imagery, and a profile of billion-dollar weather disasters.

http://www.c-ciarn.ca/index_e.asp The Canadian Climate Impacts and Adaptation Research Network.

http://www.wildweather.com/gallery Photograph gallery of hurricanes, tornadoes, floods, and weather extremes, and their resulting damage.

Human—Climate Interactions and Impacts

Industrial complex on the shore of the Inland Sea near Kakogawa, Japan. Industries the world over pour pollutants into the atmosphere, affecting global climate. (Authors' photo)

OBJECTIVES

- To relate our understanding of atmospheric processes to the human environment

- To illustrate the utility of using energy balance concepts to characterize systems of the human environment

- To focus on several of the impacts humans have had, and may come to have, on our climatic environment

This closing unit on the physical geography of the atmosphere treats some key relationships between humans and their climatic environment, and highlights the impact of human activities on the functioning of climate at various scales. The unit begins by specifying the interaction of the human body with its immediate surroundings and shows how our comfort depends on access to adequate shelter. Most modern dwellings tend to be clustered in urban areas that exhibit **microclimates** (climate regions on a localized scale) of their own. The cities that anchor this metropolitan landscape usually contain concentrations of the wrong things in the wrong place at the wrong time—a phenomenon known as pollution. We examine those aspects of pollution that occur in the atmosphere and how urban air affects the surrounding countryside. Our inquiry then expands to the macroscale as we briefly discuss humankind as a possible agent of world climatic change. We therefore proceed from the level of the individual to that of the entire globe. A good way to start that progression is to consider the human body as a heating and cooling system.

The Heat Balance of the Human Body

Unit 7 describes the concept of heat balance with respect to the surface of the Earth. The idea of examining the flows of heat energy to and from an object can usefully be applied to the human body as well. It is essential that the internal temperature of our bodies remain at about 37°C. Depending on the person, temperature fluctuations exceeding 3° to 6°C result in death. The body, therefore, has to be kept within a very limited range of temperature by regulating the flows of heat to and from it. Four kinds of heat flows can be altered—radiant, metabolic, evaporative, and convectional—and they are diagrammed in Fig. 21.1.

To begin with, humans all live in a radiation environment. We receive shortwave radiation from the Sun and longwave radiation from our surroundings—clothing, walls, the planetary surface, and the like. Humans also emit longwave radiation. Our radiation balance, the sum of incoming and outgoing radiation, can be positive or negative, depending on the environment we are in. More often than not, the balance is a positive one. So net radiation is usually a heat gain for us, especially during daylight hours.

Another heat gain is the heat that our bodies produce, called *metabolic heat.* The body produces metabolic heat by converting the chemical energy in the food we assimilate into heat energy. The amount of metabolic heat we produce depends on, among other things, our age, activity level, and environmental temperature. An older person at rest produces metabolic heat equal to that used to power a 75-watt lightbulb. A five-year-old child produces the equivalent of 120 watts, and an active adult about 260 watts (this rate could double if the adult were playing tennis). We produce even more metabolic heat when exposed to colder temperatures. At 33°C an adult creates 3100 calories (cal) per day, whereas at 0°C an adult's metabolism creates 3930 cal per day.

Metabolic heat is always a heat source to the human body. But the evaporation of water from the skin

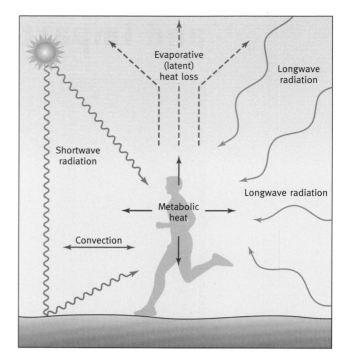

FIGURE 21.1 Heat-energy flows to and from the human body.

through perspiration is always a heat loss. Perspiring is a vital function, because some of the heat used in evaporating the perspired water is taken from the body and thereby cools it down. One of the factors determining how much evaporation can take place is the amount of water vapour already present in the surrounding air, as measured by relative humidity. As we all know, we can feel fairly comfortable on a hot day if the relative humidity is low, but we feel distinctly uncomfortable, even at a lower temperature, if the humidity is high. You can see in Fig. 21.2 that if other heat losses and gains are kept constant, relative humidity acts as an index of how efficient our evaporative cooling system is. It could even become a deciding factor between life and death.

Finally, a flow of sensible heat can act as either a cooling or a heating mechanism, depending on the relative temperatures of the body and the air, by means of a *convectional* heat flow. Hot air blowing onto our bodies makes us gain heat, whereas a cold wind leads to a rapid heat loss. When we breathe, we pass air into and out of our lungs; this air may be warmer or cooler than our lungs. For convenience, we can regard the loss or gain of heat through breathing as a convective heat flow.

Our bodies consciously and unconsciously regulate these four types of heat flows so that the body temperature stays within the narrow vital range. For example, if our environmental temperature changes over a short

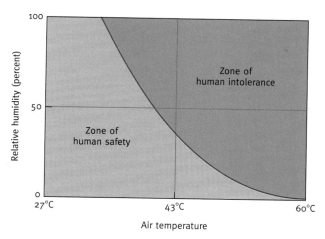

FIGURE 21.2 Limitation imposed on our evaporative cooling system by relative humidity.

period of time from 40°C to 10°C, the metabolic heat production might stay the same, as Fig. 21.3 shows. But radiant and convectional heat flows change from being a slight heat gain to being a marked heat loss. Evaporative cooling of the body moves from a high level to a relatively low level in the cooler environment. Many of our feelings of comfort or discomfort and almost all of our artificial adaptations to the environment, such as shelter and clothing, are related to the balance of these energy flows that maintain our constant internal temperature.

Shelter, Houses, and Climate

Ever since people first felt the effects of sensible heat loss by winds or an increased evaporative cooling when they were rained upon, they have sought some form of shelter.

The form of shelter depended on the most prevalent features of the climate and on the available building materials. Climate still plays a large role in some of the design features of our dwellings. In hot climates, for instance, where there is a need to promote convectional cooling, the nomads of the Saudi Arabian desert roll up the inside walls of their tents; in more humid (and more tropical) India, screens are aligned to catch any cooling breeze.

In our discussion of the human body we used the concept of heat balance, which may also be applied to the typical contemporary house. As with the body, there are four major types of flows to and from the roof and walls of a house. Instead of—but analogous to—metabolism, the house contains an artificial heating (and/or cooling) system. An artificial heating system usually channels heat from the central interior toward the walls and roof of the building. The evaporative cooling part of the house is normally designed with a sloping roof that removes surface water or snow as rapidly as possible. However, most houses have the important function of reducing the amount of convectional cooling by wind; they provide shelter from the wind and facilitate control of the inside climate via the heating system.

Radiant heating and cooling applies to the outside of a house much as it applies to the body, and architects take it into consideration in several ways. If they want to use radiation for heating the house by means of the greenhouse effect, they can ensure that the windows of the building are open to the direct rays of the Sun. Sometimes they use a partial shade to cut out direct rays coming from high Sun angles in the summer, when heating is not required; but rays from low Sun angles bypass the shade and supply winter heating. Thus, by

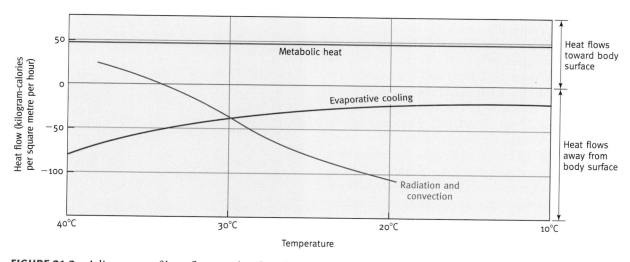

FIGURE 21.3 Adjustment of heat flows under changing environmental temperatures to maintain a constant internal body temperature.

adapting their designs to the operation of the four factors of the heat balance system, architects can provide our houses with a small environment capable of adjustment to the changing seasonal needs of our bodies.

Urban Microclimates

For the most part the marvels of modern architectural design and engineering work well as small, individual open systems. But in today's world, where close to 50 percent of humanity resides in metropolitan areas, individual buildings do not function as single entities but as a group.

Mass, Energy, and Heat in Metropolitan Areas

The metropolis is an extraordinary processor of mass and energy and has its own metabolism. A daily input of water, food, and energy of various kinds is matched by an output of sewage, solid refuse, air pollutants, energy, and materials that have been transformed in some way. The quantities involved can be enormous. Each day, directly or indirectly, the average Canadian urbanite consumes about 500 l of water, 2 kg of food, and 8 kg of fossil fuel. This is converted into roughly 400 l of sewage, 2 kg of refuse, and more than 1 kg of air pollution. Multiply these figures by the population of your metropolitan area, and you will get some idea of what a large processor it is, even without including its industrial activities and motor vehicle emissions. Many aspects of this energy use affect the atmosphere of the city, particularly in the production of heat.

In winter the values of heat produced by a central city and its suburban ring can equal or surpass the amount of heat available from the Sun. All the heat that warms a building eventually transfers to the surrounding air, a process that is quickest where houses are poorly insulated. But an automobile produces enough heat to warm an average house in winter; and if a house were perfectly insulated, one adult could also produce more than enough heat to warm it. Therefore, even without any industrial production of heat, an urban area tends to be warmer than the adjacent countryside.

The burning of fuel, such as by cars, is not the only source of this increased heat. Two other factors contribute to the higher overall temperatures in cities. The first is the heat capacity of the materials that constitute the cityscape, which is dominated by concrete and asphalt. During the day, heat from the Sun can be conducted into these materials and stored—to be released at night. But in the countryside, materials have a significantly lower heat capacity because a vegetative blanket prevents heat from easily

flowing into and out of the ground. The second factor is that radiant heat coming into the metropolis from the Sun is trapped in two ways: (1) by a continuing series of reflections among the numerous vertical surfaces that buildings present, and (2) by the **dust dome** (dome-shaped layer of polluted air) that most urban areas spawn. Just as in the greenhouse effect, shortwave radiation from the Sun passes through the pollution dome more easily than outgoing longwave radiation does; the latter is absorbed by the gaseous pollutants of the dome and reradiated back to the urban surface (Fig. 21.4).

Urban Heat Islands

The above are the reasons why the metropolis will be warmer than its surrounding rural areas, and together they produce the phenomenon known as the **urban heat island**. If we regard isotherms (lines of constant temperature) as analogous to contour lines of elevation on a map, then the distribution of temperatures within a metropolis gives the general impression of an area of higher land—or an island of higher temperatures—set above a more uniform plain. This effect is clearly seen in Fig. 21.5, which maps the distribution of average late-winter low (nighttime) temperatures in the heart of metropolitan Montreal.

Note that the mildest temperatures on this surface are recorded above the city centre. From central Montreal, temperatures drop with either elevation (as indicated by adjacent Mont Royal) or with increasing distance from the city centre. At the urban/rural boundary (located at Site 2 at the time this map was originally created in 1978), surface temperatures are 3°C cooler than in the downtown regions of Montreal.

FIGURE 21.4   View of Montreal's urban pollution dome.

Heat islands develop best under the light wind conditions associated with anticyclones, but in large cities they can form at almost any time. The precise configuration of a heat island depends on several factors. The island can be elongated away from the prevailing wind; pools of cold air can be found over unbuilt parkland and other open space within the metropolis; and sometimes tongues of warmer air follow the courses of rivers. When the heat island is well developed, microscale variations can be extreme. In winter, busy streets in cities can be 1.7°C warmer than the side streets; the areas near traffic lights can be similarly warmer than the areas between them because of the effect of idling cars.

The maximum difference in temperature between neighbouring urban and rural environments is called the **heat-island intensity** for that region. In general, the larger the metropolitan complex, the greater its heat-island intensity. The actual level of intensity depends on such factors as physical layout, population density, and the productive activities of a metropolis.

Recent studies have shown that some of the greatest heat-island intensities are found in rapidly urbanizing desert environments. For example, Phoenix, Arizona, which is located in the American Southwest, has had a dramatic rise in its summer nighttime temperatures. Average temperatures in the central city have soared by 5.5°C since 1960.

The consequences of higher temperatures in urban areas should not be overlooked. During the 2003 heat wave that extended across much of Europe, the city of Paris, France, was hit particularly hard. Of the 14,800 deaths across France attributed to the excessive heat, several hundred occurred in Paris. Within the urban core, the higher than average temperatures rose to 40°C. It has been estimated that in Paris up to 180 people died in one day alone—all linked directly or indirectly to the abnormally high temperatures. A contributing cause of the deaths was believed to be the lack of air conditioning in most European homes, simply because it was not needed before the summer of 2003. That the nation's health system could allow such a death toll became an obvious matter of controversy in France. The European heat wave of 2003 has been linked to unprecedented weather extremes in other parts of the world in the same general period (e.g., the worst drought in recorded history in Australia and massive floods in the United States) and attributed to global warming.

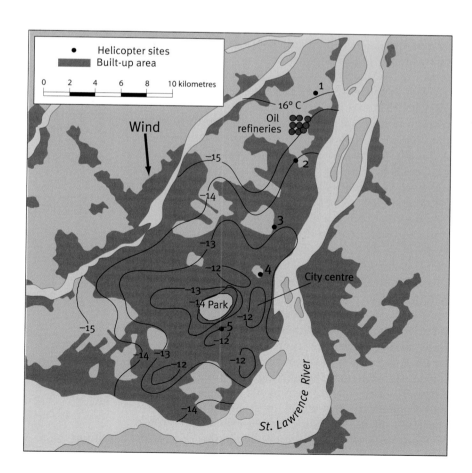

FIGURE 21.5 Urban heat island of Montreal, as represented by isotherms of mean late-winter low temperatures.

Peculiarities of Metropolitan Climates

The surface–atmosphere relationships inside metropolitan areas understandably produce a number of climatic peculiarities. For one thing, the presence or absence of moisture is affected by the special qualities of the urban surface. With much of the built-up landscape impenetrable by water, even gentle rain runs off almost immediately from rooftops, streets, and parking lots. Thus city surfaces, as well as the air above them, tend to be drier between precipitation episodes. With little water available for the cooling process of evaporation, relative humidities are usually lower.

Wind movements are also modified by the cityscape because buildings increase the friction on air flowing over and around them. This tends to slow the speed of winds (by as much as 80 percent at a height of 30 m), making them far less efficient at dispersing pollutants when they travel above large cities. At certain locations within the metropolis, on the other hand, air turbulence increases in association with high-velocity, skyscraper-channelled airflows and wind eddies on street corners. Other unique aspects of city climates originate in the artificially modified air over the urban landscape. As we know, a dust dome forms, which often gives rise to the wind circulation cells shown in Fig. 21.6. In the box on pp. 101–102 in Unit 8, we discuss the impact of dust domes on the urban radiation balance; here we examine the dome's effects on the atmospheric moisture of cities.

Within the dust dome there are far more airborne particles that can act as condensation nuclei than in corresponding rural areas, and this significantly modifies the moisture content of the urban atmosphere. Although little water vapour rises from the city surface, horizontal flow in the atmosphere brings just as much moisture to the city as to the nearby countryside. Because of the greater number of particles in the air above a city, there is a greater propensity for condensation and the formation of small droplets of liquid mist, fog, and cloud. As a result, fog is more frequent in cities than in surrounding areas, an effect heightened when there are local moisture sources such as lakes and rivers within the metropolitan area.

Not surprisingly, the presence of a metropolis also increases the amount of rainfall. Most cities seem to have about 10 percent more precipitation than the surrounding area. But some, such as the urban areas of Champaign-Urbana, Illinois (Fig. 21.7) and St. Louis, Missouri, exhibit larger increases. The cause appears in part to be greater turbulence in the urban atmosphere, the result of hot air rising from the built-up surface. However, as we will see in the following section, artificially produced pollution can also play a major role.

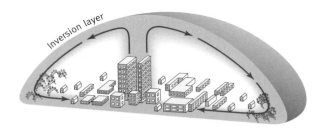

FIGURE 21.6   Wind circulation in an urban dust dome.

Air Pollution

The most important climate modifications of urban areas are summarized in Table 21.1, and many of them can be attributed to the pollutants that cities discharge into the air. We say that air is polluted when its composition departs significantly from its natural composition of such gases as nitrogen and oxygen. However, we might call cigarette smoke pollution but not the aroma of a charbroiled steak. We are therefore concerned with factors that are in some way detrimental to, or uncomfortable for, human life.

The Nature of Air Pollution

We can group airborne pollutants into two categories: primary and secondary. **Primary pollutants**, which may be gaseous or solid, come directly from industrial and domestic sources and the internal combustion engines of motor vehicles. The principal gaseous primary pollutants are carbon dioxide, water vapour, hydrocarbons, carbon monoxide, and oxides of sulfur and nitrogen—in particular sulfur dioxide and nitrogen dioxide. The effluents toward the end of this list are

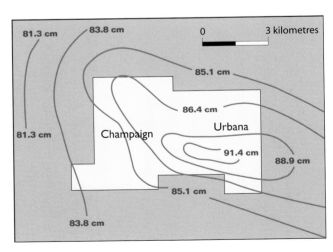

FIGURE 21.7   Average yearly precipitation in Champaign-Urbana, Illinois.

sometimes called "status-symbol" pollutants because they are especially associated with the industrially developed countries. The leading solid primary pollutants are iron, manganese, titanium, lead, benzene, nickel, copper, and suspended coal or smoke particles. Except where coal or wood is burned in homes, these pollutants also emanate mainly from industrial sources.

Secondary pollutants are produced in the air by the interaction of two or more primary pollutants or from reactions with normal atmospheric constituents. There also are two varieties of secondary pollution. The first is the *reducing type*. An example occurs when sulphur dioxide changes to sulfur trioxide during combustion or in the atmosphere. The sulfur trioxide then combines with atmospheric water to form droplets of sulfuric acid. This acid is corrosive, irritating, and attracts water, thereby enhancing the development of rain droplets— and acid precipitation (see Perspective: Acid Precipitation in Unit 19). The other kind of secondary pollution is called the *oxidation type*. Here the effects of sunlight— known as photochemical effects—play a role. An example is nitrogen dioxide, the source of the brown colour of urban dust domes (see Fig. 21.4) when it reacts with sunlight to form nitrogen monoxide and one odd oxygen atom. The freed oxygen atom can then combine with normal oxygen (O_2) to form ozone (O_3), which acts as an irritant.

Air pollution is an old, persistent, and costly problem. Indeed, a treatise on London's polluted air was published as long ago as the late seventeenth century. An oft-quoted death toll of 4000 during the infamous London smog episode of December 1952 (Fig. 21.8) is evidence enough of the dangerous effects of air pollution. More recent data, published in conjunction with every major smog outbreak, indicate that substantial increases in respiratory disease accompany the severely polluted air. The World Health Organization reports that 3 million people now die each year from the adverse effects of air pollution. This is three times the 1 million who die each year in automobile accidents. A large number of these deaths can be traced to air pollution from vehicle emissions. The financial costs of air pollution are difficult to gauge accurately, but they are surely astronomical. The Ontario Medical Association has estimated that air pollution costs Ontario citizens more than $1 billion a year in hospital admissions, emergency room visits, and absenteeism.

In Unit 8 we discuss the conditions that lead to the formation of smog and pollution domes over cities, particularly the influence of local *temperature inversions*. These inversions can prevent urban air from rising more than a few hundred metres, thereby acting as an atmospheric "lid," which traps airborne pollutants and greatly increases their concentration in the city's surface layer. Horizontal flushing by winds can play a significant role in relieving air pollution in an urban area. But this means that using the skies above a metropolis as a dumping ground quickly becomes someone else's problem as the effluents are transported downwind, often for considerable distances when pollutants are discharged via smokestacks taller than 300 m. We now turn to examine such impacts by considering the macroscale effects of airborne pollution.

Larger-Scale Air Pollution

The problem of air pollution is no longer a local one, and its effects are increasingly felt over wide areas. Just as individual houses tend to interact within a metropolis, urban regions have significant effects beyond their immediate vicinities, thereby contributing to pollution on a broader scale. We are already familiar with the concept of the urban dust dome (see Fig. 21.6). When the prevailing wind is greater than 13 km/h the dome begins to detach itself from the metropolis, and the airborne pol-

Table 21.1 The Effect of Cities on Climatic Elements

Element	Comparison with Rural Environment
Radiation	
Global	15–20% less
Ultraviolet, winter	30% less
Ultraviolet, summer	5% less
Sunshine duration	5–15% less
Temperature	
Annual average	0.5°–1.0°C more
Winter low (average)	1°–2°C more
Contaminants	
Condensation nuclei and particles	10 times more
Gaseous mixtures	5–25 times more
Wind speed	
Annual average	20–30% less
Extreme gusts	10–20% less
Calms	15–20% more
Precipitation	
Totals	5–10% more
Days <5 mm	10% more
Snowfall	5% less
Cloudiness	
Cover	5–10% more
Fog, winter	100% more
Fog, summer	30% more
Relative humidity	
Winter	2% less
Summer	8% less

Source: Information from H. E. Landsberg (1970), copyright World Meteorological Organization.

lutants stream out above the surrounding countryside as a **pollution plume**. As Fig. 21.9 shows, the plume emanating from Mexico City extends great distances vertically as well as horizontally into the atmosphere. Similarly, population clusters around the world are affected by pollution plumes that originate in industrial cities.

FIGURE 21.8 In one of the worst London-fog events on record (December 1952), a blanket of dense smog hides most of the city from view. Here Scots Guards march toward Buckingham Palace to take up sentry duty, but only the gates to the palace are visible. Traffic has slowed to a crawl, hospitals are filled with people suffering from respiratory problems, and the British capital is virtually paralyzed.

As it advances, the heat- and dust-bearing plume brings with it many of the climatic characteristics associated with cities. For instance, the amount of shortwave solar radiation received on a clear day in the countryside beyond the urban perimeter depends markedly on which way the wind is blowing out of the central city. Pollution plumes affect more than the particulate content and heat levels of the atmosphere. New research suggests that air pollution may have the tendency to mitigate rain and snow (see Perspective: Weather Modification). The abnormally small pollution particles allow cloud moisture to condense into smaller than usual droplet size. This, in turn, affects the collision and coalescence processes responsible for the production of rain droplets large enough to fall to the Earth.

Another factor reinforcing the problem of macroscale air pollution is that many industrial centres are concentrated in certain regions. For example, the metropolitan areas of the U.S. northeastern seaboard—as well as many in Western Europe and Japan—are geographically so close to one another that their pollution plumes merge and act together rather than individually. These coalesced, multimetropolitan regions (called *conurbations* by urban geographers) are now so large that they function as pollution sources on a continental scale. Thus the release of sulfur dioxide above western Germany's Rhine Valley can lead to an increase in the acidity of precipitation in Norway and Sweden (similar worldwide pollution flows are mapped in Fig. 19.6).

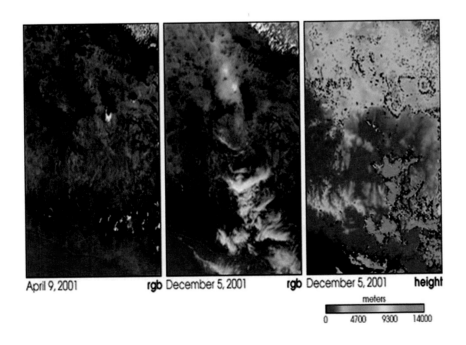

April 9, 2001   **rgb** December 5, 2001   **rgb** December 5, 2001   **height**

meters

0   4700   9300   14000

FIGURE 21.9 Pollution plume of Mexico City and the surrounding regions. The images at the far left and centre are natural colour views acquired by NASA's Terra satellite on April 9 and December 5, 2001, respectively. Mexico City can be identified in the centre panel by the large area of haze accumulation. The right image is an elevation field corresponding to the December 5 view.

PERSPECTIVES ON THE HUMAN ENVIRONMENT

Weather Modification

> "Everybody talks about the weather,
> but nobody does anything about it."
> – Mark Twain

Local and regional weather patterns have the potential to be significantly altered by human activities. Sometimes weather modification is intentional, sometimes inadvert. It has been well documented that human activities such as biomass burning, agriculture, and industry can modify local and regional weather conditions. Recent studies of urban areas in tropical regions, for example, have confirmed that significant modification of weather conditions can occur in this climatic zone leading to cloud and precipitation increases of 10 to 20 percent. Can we intentionally change the weather to create more favourable conditions?

Many nations have undertaken weather modification initiatives, beginning in the latter half of the twentieth century. *Weather modification* is the general term that refers to any human attempt to control some aspect of the weather. Scientists know that no one can "control" the weather and that perhaps the most we can do is change the weather in small ways, such as by squeezing a little more precipitation out of clouds than would have otherwise fallen. Today dozens of nations are undertaking more than 100 weather modification projects. Nations that are particularly arid and semi-arid, with scarce water resources, are at the forefront of those undertaking such projects, even though direct evidence that weather (such as precipitation, hail, lightning, or winds) can be significantly modified artificially is limited. Nevertheless, weather modification remains a big business both in North America and abroad. Commercial companies now exist that attempt to enhance rainfall by "seeding" clouds and assist farmers by firing "hail cannons" to shock summertime storms into reducing hail.

In Canada, both the federal and provincial governments have determined to closely monitor and limit the use of weather modification until it is shown conclusively that such modifications do not in any way affect or alter weather patterns and precipitation levels in non-target areas. Nonetheless, in 1996 a Hail Suppression Project was initiated and funded by insurers in Alberta. When a developing storm approaches, aircraft seed the clouds with silver iodide particles, a tactic intended to greatly reduce the size of hailstones and subsequently reduce the damage. In 1999 hail suppression aircraft flew more missions than ever before, and as a result, according to the insurance industry, no hailstorm cost more than $200,000. From 1988 through 1998 insurance losses attributed to hail in the province of Alberta exceeded $1 billion. During the 2001 and 2002 droughts (see pp. 237–238), farmers contended that hail suppression operations might be contributing to the reduced rainfall. The weather modification industry quickly set out to counter those contentions (see Krauss & Santos, 2003). Figure 21.10 illustrates the location of the Alberta Hail Suppression Project.

FIGURE 21.10 The Alberta Hail Suppression Project area.

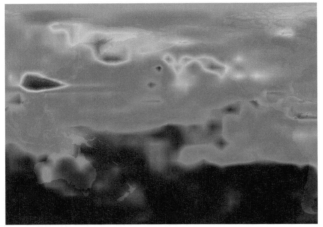

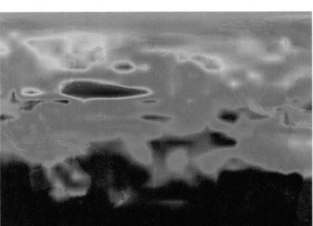

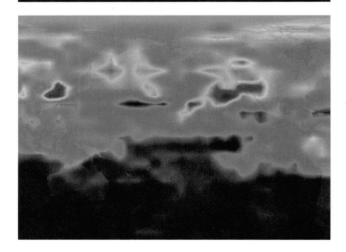

FIGURE 21.11 NASA images showing the long-range diffusion of pollutants from East Asia toward North America on March 10–15, 2000. Strong winds and convection carried the pollution particles high into the troposphere, where they increasingly mingled with smoke from industrial pollution in eastern Asia to spawn this trans-Pacific plume, seen here streaming across the Pacific Ocean.

The latest evidence reveals that certain plumes can extend for thousands of kilometres, thereby facilitating the intercontinental transfer of pollutants. Quite prominent among these is the pollution plume that carries industrial effluents, pesticides, and desert dust from northeastern China clear across the Pacific Ocean to western North America (Fig. 21.11). The connecting windflows are strongest during the springtime months, and require less than a week to transport their load of airborne particles. Studies in the mountains of the U.S. Pacific Northwest have shown that these pollutants include measurable quantities of potentially harmful heavy metals and are very likely contributing to the increasing acidity of the region's streams.

Human Activities and the Global Climate Machine

At the global scale, human climatic impacts may be reaching a level capable of interfering with certain natural processes of the atmosphere. We discuss such hypotheses in other units, particularly in the Perspectives boxes on ozone depletion (Unit 6), deforestation (Unit 17), desertification (Unit 17), and acid precipitation (Unit 19). Because little is being done worldwide to counteract these human-induced environmental problems, they are likely to persist well into the future.

Despite the advances of contemporary environmental science, we have only begun to develop an understanding of the longer-term consequences of atmospheric pollution and their possible linkage to the forces of climatic change. Recent experience has shown that monitoring and forecasting methods need to be improved, because instead of slow, incremental change, certain pollutants may build up silently for years. Then, only after they surpass a critical mass, do they produce rapid and potentially far-reaching environmental change.

With scenarios such as these to contend with, soon it may no longer be possible to regard the Earth's climate as a finely tuned natural machine in long-term equilibrium, constantly correcting itself to maintain exactly the right balance of warmth and moisture required to sustain the range of life on this planet. Today many scientists assert that humans have begun to disturb the delicate workings of that machine, and what that portends is becoming one of the leading pursuits of the atmospheric, life, and Earth sciences.

KEY TERMS

dust dome *page 270*

heat-island intensity *page 271*

microclimate *page 268*

pollution plume *page 274*

primary pollutants *page 273*

secondary pollutants *page 273*

urban heat island *page 270*

REVIEW QUESTIONS

1. Describe the various sources of energy and heat received by and lost from the human body.
2. Describe how an urban heat island develops and the meteorological consequences of this climatic modification.
3. What are primary pollutants? What are secondary pollutants? Give examples of both.
4. What is a pollution plume and how does it develop?

REFERENCES AND FURTHER READINGS

BRYSON, R. A., and ROSS, J. E. "The Climate of the City," in T. R. Detwyler et al. *Urbanization and the Environment: The Physical Geography of the City* (North Scituate, Mass.: Duxbury Press, 1972), 51–68.

BURNETT, R. T., CAKMAK, S., and BROOK, J. R. "The Effect of the Urban Ambient Air Pollution Mix on Daily Mortality Rates in 11 Canadian Cities," *Canadian Journal of Public Health*, 89 (1998), 152–156.

CHANG, K. "Scientists Watch Cities Make Their Own Weather," *New York Times* (August 15, 2000), D1, D2.

CHANGNON, S. A. "Inadvertent Weather Modification in Urban Areas: Lessons for Global Climate Change," *Bulletin of the American Meteorological Association*, 73 (1992), 6619–6627.

CONDELLA, V. "Climate Islands: Sprawling Cities Affect Air Patterns Overhead and Change the Weather around Them," *Earth Magazine* (February 1998), 54–56.

COTTON, W. R., and PIELKE, R. A. *Human Impacts on Weather and Climate* (New York: Cambridge Univ. Press, 1995).

DETWYLER, T. R., et al. *Urbanization and the Environment: The Physical Geography of the City* (North Scituate, Mass.: Duxbury Press, 1972).

ELSOM, D. *Atmospheric Pollution: A Global Problem* (Cambridge, Mass.: Blackwell, 2nd ed., 1992).

GOUDIE, A. S. *The Human Impact on the Natural Environment* (Cambridge, Mass.: MIT Press, 5th ed., 2000).

GOUDIE, A. S., Ed. *The Human Impact Reader: Readings and Case Studies* (Malden, Mass.: Blackwell, 1997).

GOUDIE, A. S., and VILES, H. *The Earth Transformed: An Introduction to Human Impacts on the Environment* (Malden, Mass.: Blackwell, 1997).

JACOBSON, M. Z. *Atmospheric Pollution: History, Science, and Regulation* (New York: Cambridge Univ. Press, 2002).

KASPERSON, J. X., KASPERSON, R. E., and TURNER, B. L., Eds. *Regions at Risk: Comparisons of Threatened Environments* (New York/Tokyo: United Nations Univ. Press, 1996).

KRAUSS, T., and SANTOS, J. R. "The Effect of Hail Suppression Operations on Precipitation in Alberta, Canada," *Proceedings, 8th WMO Scientific Conference on Weather Modification* (Casablanca, Morocco, 2003).

LANDSBERG, H. E. "Climates and Urban Planning," in *Urban Climates* (Geneva: World Meteorological Organization, no. 254, Technical Paper 141, Technical Note 108, 1970), 364–374.

MEYER, W. B. *Human Impact on the Earth* (New York: Cambridge Univ. Press, 1996).

OKE, T. R. *Boundary Layer Climates* (London: Methuen & Co. Ltd, 1978).

SMOYER, K. E., RAINHAM, D. G., and HEWKO, J. N. "Heat-Stress-Related Mortality in Five Cities in Southern Ontario: 1980–1996," *International Journal of Biometeorology*, 44 (2000), 190–197.

TURNER, B. L., Ed. *The Earth as Transformed by Human Action: Global and Regional Changes in the Biosphere over the Past 300 Years* (New York: Cambridge Univ. Press, 1990).

WINTERS, H. A., et al. *Battling the Elements: Weather and Terrain in the Conduct of War* (Baltimore, Md.: Johns Hopkins Univ. Press, 1998).

WEB RESOURCES

http://eetd.lbl.gov/HeatIsland Abstracts from the Canadian Heat Island Summit, as well as background information about strategies to prevent formation of urban heat islands.

http://www.gsfc.nasa.gov/gsfc/earth/terra/co.htm Data from the NASA/CSA global air pollution monitor are interpreted and presented in full colour as well as in three-dimensional animations.

PART THREE

The Biosphere

Biosphere

The biosphere is the most recent of the Earth's great environmental realms, where lithosphere, hydrosphere, atmosphere, and cryosphere converge and interact in the formation and sustenance of all forms of life. Numerous systems and subsystems, processes, and cycles link lithosphere and biosphere, beginning with the disintegration of rock and continuing through the evolution of terrestrial and marine ecosystems. The key component in this endless series is the development and deepening of soil, with its various properties reflecting the environmental regimes under which it evolved. Air, water, temperature, and other factors combine to transform rock into soil, and elements of the global climatic map are reflected in the soil regions now recognized. In turn, these soil regions support particular combinations of plants, generating biomes that sustain life in literally countless forms. But global environments change, and biomes formed over thousands of years can be swept away in short order by climatic changes. Advancing glaciers can scrape the bedrock bare of soils and plants, and only after the planet warms up again can the whole process start over. Like all environmental maps, those of soils and biomes are but still pictures of an ever-changing planet.

The Biosphere

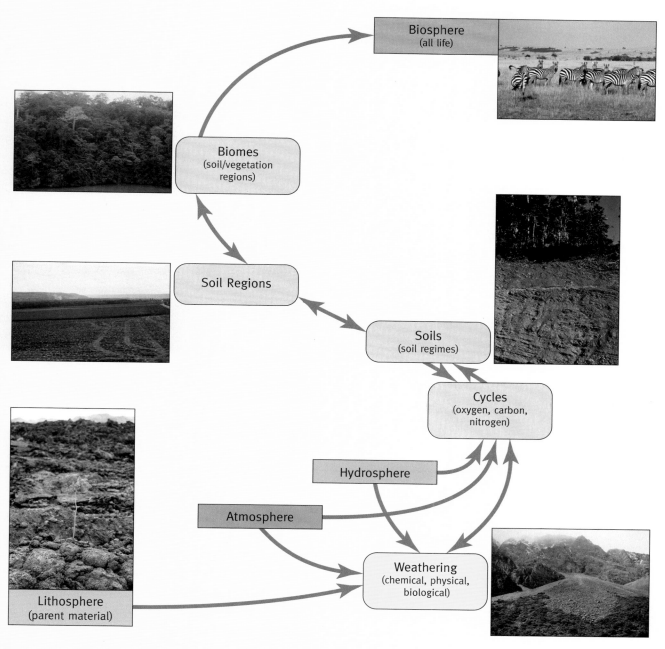

Biosphere
(all life)

Biomes
(soil/vegetation
regions)

Soil Regions

Soils
(soil regimes)

Cycles
(oxygen, carbon,
nitrogen)

Hydrosphere

Atmosphere

Weathering
(chemical, physical,
biological)

Lithosphere
(parent material)

Climate, Soil, Plants, and Animals

The effects of clear-cut logging, Clayoquot Sound Area, west coast of Vancouver Island north of Tofino, British Columbia. Such logging causes the destruction of coastal rainforest biomes, slope instability, soil erosion, and stream aggradation.

OBJECTIVES

- To expand our concept of physical geography by including biotic systems operating at the Earth's surface

- To relate biotic systems to our understanding of global climates

- To link physical geography to the more general topic of conservation

I n Part Two we focused on one major aspect of physical geography—climate. After having studied the processes that take place in the atmosphere, we then concentrated on a geographical interpretation of the results—the Earth's present climate regions. (Figure 16.3 summarizes the global distribution of macroclimatic regions.) Part Two concluded with a discussion of the dynamics and human interactions of climate.

As we delve further into the physical geography (and with it, the natural history) of our planet in Part Three, we should remember that processes and resulting patterns are always changing. Just a few thousand years ago, leafy forests and green pastures stood where desert conditions prevail today; animals now extinct roamed countrysides that are now empty and barren. A mere 10,000 years ago, glaciers were melting back after covering much of North America and the heart of Europe.

If you have been following the news lately, you have heard about other changes in our terrestrial environments. One such example is the depletion of the atmosphere's ozone layer, especially above Antarctica. As we note in the Perspectives box in Unit 6, this may portend a future of greater cancer risk and unforeseeable effects on plants and animals. In short, maps of climates—as well as other elements of the environment—are still pictures of a changing world.

In Part Three we discuss several aspects of the environment that are closely related to climate. Geographers are most interested in interrelationships—between climate and soils, soils and plants, natural environments and human societies, and many other ecological connections. More often than not, the prevailing climate, past or present, is a key to our understanding of such relationships. Again and again, when we study the distributions of natural phenomena such as soils, plants, and animals, we see the importance of climate patterns.

Natural Geography

The study of soils, plants (*flora*), and animals (*fauna*) in spatial perspective is a branch of physical geography (see Fig. 1.4), although this aspect of the discipline might be better designated *natural geography*—the geography of nature. The geography of soils is a part of the science of **pedology**, a term that derives from the ancient Greek word *pedon,* meaning ground. The geography of plants and animals defines the field of **biogeography**, a combination of biology and geography. Biogeography is further divided into two subfields: **phytogeography**, the geography of plants, and **zoogeography**, the geography of animals.

Geography of Soils

The next three units (23 to 25) examine the development, properties, classification, and regionalization of soils. On the landmasses, soils and vegetation lie at the *interface* between the lithosphere and the atmosphere, at the plane of interaction between rocks and their minerals on the one hand, and the air with its moisture

FIGURE 22.1 Leaf litter on the forest floor—source of vital nutrients for the living plants.

and heat on the other. Soil is the key to plant life, containing mineral nutrients and storing water. But the vegetation itself contributes to its own sustenance by adding decaying organic matter to the soil, which is absorbed and converted into reusable nutrients (Fig. 22.1). The processes that go on at this interface are intricate and complicated.

Life would not exist on this planet without the presence of water. One reason is that without water there would be no soil. The Moon's lifeless surface of rock fragments and pulverized rubble holds no water—and therefore no soil. Water is the key to the chemical and physical processes that break down rocks, thus triggering the process of soil formation. As the soil develops or matures, water sustains its circulatory system, promotes the necessary chemical reactions, transfers nutrients, helps decompose organic matter, and ensures the continued decay of rocks below the evolving soil layer. Some soils capable of supporting permanent vegetation can develop in a short period (between one and two centuries), but most soils require thousands of years to mature fully (Fig. 22.2). Over this period of time the soil absorbs and discharges water, inhales and exhales air through its pore spaces, takes in organic matter and dispenses nutrients, and is inhabited by organisms of many kinds. In every sense of the term, *the soil is a living entity*.

As with all living things, the soil's well-being can be threatened, and soils can actually die. When allowed to develop and mature, a soil will achieve a state of equilibrium with the prevailing climate, with the vegetation it supports (and that supports it), and with other elements

FIGURE 22.2 A soil profile of a well-developed soil whose structure has evolved over thousands of years.

of the surrounding environment. Many conditions can threaten a soil, some natural, others artificial. Climatic change may also lead to change in the natural vegetation, which, in turn, can expose a soil to increased erosion. Farming may overtax the soil, giving it insufficient time to recover from ploughing, planting, and harvesting year after year (Fig. 22.3). Domesticated animals may trample vegetation and compact topsoil, thereby weakening the soil and subjecting it to erosion by water and wind.

The geographical study of soils involves learning about the development and maturation of this critical "cloak of life," as well as about ways to protect and conserve it. When it comes to the components of the Earth's biosphere, the more we know about nature, the better prepared we are to help sustain it. In Part Three, therefore, we explore the development of a typical soil, view a mature soil in profile, and discuss the processes that go on within and between the layers of a soil. Next we

study ways of classifying soils, and from this classification emerges regionalization, the map of world soils (see Fig. 25.15). A comparison between this map and other global maps covered in this text (such as climate [Fig. 16.3], precipitation [Fig. 12.11], and vegetation [Fig. 27.1]), reveals some of the spatial relationships between soil regions and other elements of the natural environment. Moreover, comparing the soil map and a map of world population distribution (see Fig. 2.5) indicates the critical importance of certain soil types for food production.

Biogeography

Another major topic, addressed in Units 26 to 28, is biogeography, or the geography of flora and fauna. Several of the world's climates are named after the vegetation that characterizes them (e.g., savanna, steppe, and tundra). When climate, soil, vegetation, and animal life reach a stable adjustment, vegetation constitutes the most visible element of the ecosystem. When you fly southward in Africa from the central Sahara (25°N) to the equatorial heart of the Congo Basin, you cross over a series of ecosystems ranging from desert to rainforest. You cannot see the climate changing, nor can you clearly see the soil most of the way. But the vegetation tells the story: the barren desert gives way to shrub; the grasses gradually become denser; trees appear, widely spaced at first, then closer together; and finally, the closed canopies of the tropical rainforest come into view. The best indicator of the succession of prevailing ecosystems is vegetation (Fig. 22.4).

In Unit 27, we will learn that the Earth's great vegetation assemblages consist not of just one or two, but of literally millions of species. Biologists suggest that there may be as many as 30 million species alive today, of which only about *1.7 million* have been identified and classified (see Perspective: Biodiversity under Siege). Geographers are especially interested in the distribution of the known species, as well as in the relationships between plant and animal communities and their natural environments. Biogeographers seek explanations for the distributions the map reveals. For example, why are certain species found in certain areas but not in others that also seem suitable for them? And why do species exist cooperatively in some places but competitively in others? What is the effect of isolation on species and their interrelationships?

The founder of biogeography as a systematic field of study was Alexander von Humboldt (1769–1859), who travelled much of the world in search of plant specimens. When von Humboldt reached South America's Andes, he recognized that altitude, temperature, natural

FROM THE FIELDNOTES

FIGURE 22.3 "About 16 km from the Kenyan town of Meru the landscape showed signs of severe erosion. We stopped to talk with the people of these homesteads and asked them about their crops. Yes, they knew that farming on slopes as steep as these would lead to 'gullying,' but they saw no alternative. You get a crop one or two years, and that's better than nothing, they said. Some neighbours whose village had lost most of its land this way had gone to the city (Nairobi) we were told, and now the place where they had lived was like a desert."

vegetation, and crop cultivation were interrelated. After returning to Europe, he produced a monumental series of books that formed a basis not only for biogeography but also for many other fields of the natural sciences.

The separation of biogeography into phytogeography and zoogeography occurred after the appearance of von Humboldt's writings. Probably the most important book on zoogeography to appear during the nineteenth century was written by Alfred Russel Wallace and entitled *The Geographical Distribution of Animals* (1876). Wallace was particularly interested in the complicated distribution of animals in Southeast Asia and Australia. Australia is the last major refuge of the marsupials (animals whose young are born very early in their development and then carried in an abdominal pouch); the kangaroo, koala, and wombat are three Australian marsupials. While a few marsupials survive in other areas of the world, such as the Virginia opossum in North America and the yapok (or water opossum) of South America, Australia's fauna is unique, and Wallace wanted to establish the zoogeo-

FIGURE 22.4   Vegetation boundaries on the coastal mountains of British Columbia. Here the coniferous west coast rainforest gives way to the hardier tundra ecosystem above the treeline.

graphical boundary line between Southeast Asia's very different animal assemblage and that of Australia. When he did his fieldwork, he discovered that Australian fauna existed not only in Australia itself but also in New Guinea and even on some eastern islands of what is today Indonesia. So Wallace drew a line between Kalimantan (Indonesian Borneo) and Sulawesi, and between the first island (Bali) and the second island (Lombok) east of Jawa (Fig. 22.5). *Wallace's Line* soon became one of the most hotly debated zoogeographic boundaries ever drawn. The debate continues to this day (Unit 28).

Zoogeography is a field of many dimensions and challenges. Vegetation regions can be seen from the air and can be mapped from remotely sensed data. But animals move and migrate, their *range* (area of natural occurrence) changes over time and even seasonally, and detection can present problems as well. Mapping faunal distributions for large animals is difficult enough; for smaller species it is often far more complicated.

PERSPECTIVES ON THE HUMAN ENVIRONMENT

Biodiversity under Siege

Biodiversity, shorthand for *biological diversity*, refers to "the number, variety, and variability of living organisms" (MacDonald, 2003). The cataloguing of those life forms according to species has proven to be the most practical approach (spatial variations are discussed in the Perspectives box in Unit 26). A **species** may be defined as a population of physically and chemically similar organisms within which free gene flow takes place.

How many living species does the global environment contain? By 2003 approximately 1.7 million species had been identified and described. About 963,000 of these are insects, 270,000 are plants, 46,000 are vertebrate animals, and the remainder are accounted for by invertebrates, fungi, algae, and micro-organisms. However, biologists unanimously agree that these subtotals constitute only a small proportion of the total number of terrestrial species. The renowned biologist Edward O. Wilson estimates that the total far exceeds the number of known species and lies somewhere between 5 and 30 million.

Biodiversity may be regarded as one of our planet's most important resources, and it is a rising concern today because it is under siege. In Unit 17 it is noted that tropical rainforests are especially threatened by the mass burning and cutting of trees, which annually removes a woodland area just over three times the size of New Brunswick. These forests also are home to about 80 percent of all living species, and the rate of loss is now about 100 species per day (36,500 per year). Other fragile biological communities are besieged as well, particularly coastal zones and wetlands. The main source of these exterminations is loss of habitat caused by the expansion of such human activities as deforestation, agriculture, urbanization, and air and water pollution.

As these uses—and misuses—of the global environment multiply, there is growing evidence that decline in biodiversity may soon become a universal phenomenon. An ominous example is the decrease in field observation, since the mid-1980s, of more than 70 percent of the bird species that are known to summer in eastern North America. This decrease is consistent with Wilson's finding that perhaps 20 percent of all bird species have disappeared in modern times and another 10 percent are endangered.

Although biodiversity is one of the life sciences' newest research arenas, we already know enough to draw the following conclusion: as human technology continues to advance, it is increasingly accompanied by the largest extinction of natural species the world has undergone since the mass extinctions that occurred at the time the dinosaurs disappeared 65 million years ago.

Conservation and the Biosphere

The more that is learned about the Earth's biosphere, the more concern is voiced about the future. The overuse and erosion of soils are worsening global problems (Fig. 22.6). A large part of the sediment load carried oceanward by the world's great rivers comes from slopes where cultivators have loosened the topsoil, which is carried away by rainstorms. The destruction of tropical rainforests is accelerating in South and Central America, Subsaharan Africa, and southeastern Asia. Botanists estimate that as many as one-quarter of all the presently living plant species may become extinct during the next 50–100 years. Animals large and small are also facing extinction, from the great African elephant to tiny insects.

People pose many threats to animals, only one of which is their invasion of the last refuges of wildlife. The horn of the African rhinoceros, for instance, is prized in Saudi Arabia as a dagger handle, and in East Asia its powdered form is regarded as an aphrodisiac. As a result, rhinos have been killed by poachers so quickly that only comparatively few survive. Recently the price of powdered rhino horn on the Asian market has been four to five times higher by weight than that of gold! So Africa's rhinos are threatened less by competition from poor, land-hungry farmers than by the whims of the distant wealthy.

Whether we focus on soils, plants, or animals, our geographic perspective soon underscores the reality that the Earth's biosphere is under severe stress. All too often, the changes that take place are irreversible. Topsoil that has taken hundreds or thousands of years to develop is washed away in a few months. Plant species never even inventoried are lost forever, and it will never be known what role they might have played in combating disease. As Africa's elephant herds dwindle in the face of ivory poachers, we are witnessing the extinction of a legacy of hundreds of millions of years. The explosive growth of the Earth's human population and the profligate spending behaviour of consumers in the world's wealthiest countries have combined to put the biosphere under stress as never before. From fishing grounds to mountain pastures, from rainforest to desert margin, the evidence is everywhere (Fig. 22.7).

How can this tide of destruction be slowed or reversed? Knowledge and awareness are powerful allies in any such endeavour. For years after the Communists

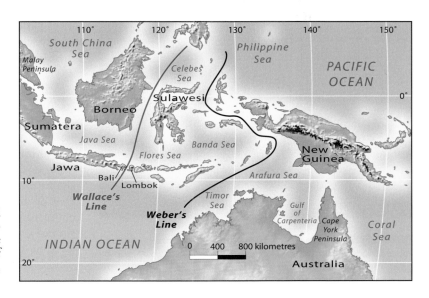

FIGURE 22.5 Wallace's Line, the presumed zoogeographic boundary between the faunal assemblages of Southeast Asia and Australia. One of Wallace's many challengers, the proposer of the alternative Weber's Line (see Unit 28), placed that boundary farther to the east.

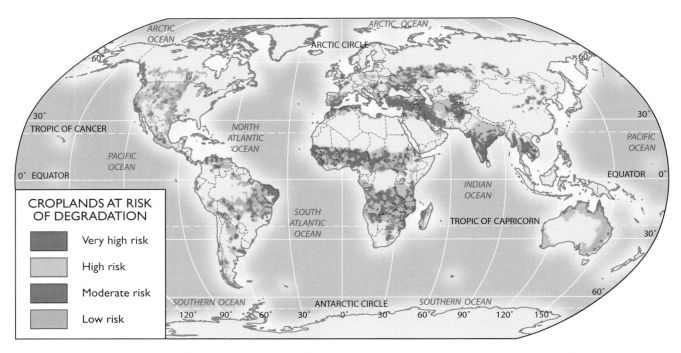

FIGURE 22.6   Croplands susceptible to degradation on the basis of climate, soil type, and human pressures. Such areas are most at risk where population densities are high. That risk is reduced, however, in countries where proactive measures to preserve soil resources are being pursued.

took power in China in 1949, Chinese leaders extolled the virtues of population expansion, at home and abroad, as a means of furthering their ideological objectives. Then China became aware that economic devel-

FIGURE 22.7   Signs of a forest in trouble. Three decades ago this section of forest in eastern Ontario was in good condition, but years of pollution from factories in the U.S. and Ontario and acid precipitation have done much damage.

opment would be stymied by the needs of so many millions of additional citizens, and its policies were changed (Fig. 22.8). In the summer of 2004 the Chinese government announced that the country was going to have millions more men than women because of this policy; the traditional cultural preference for male children has led to many abortions, the dumping of baby girls, and disregard of the law. Not only population control but also soil conservation and reforestation programs were made high priorities. But the People's Republic of China, unlike India and many other countries has a powerful, highly centralized government that can impose such measures rather effectively. Elsewhere, change must come through education and voluntary cooperation, which is far more difficult to achieve.

Although Part Three concentrates on the biosphere, it should be remembered that the principles and practices of conservation apply to more than soils, plants, and animals. **Conservation** entails the careful management and use of natural resources, the achievement of significant social benefits from them, and the preservation of the environment. For more than half a century, courses in conservation were a cornerstone of an education in geography.

One of the incentives behind this practice was the terrible experience of the 1930s, a phenomenon now known simply as the *dust bowl*. In the Great Plains and

FROM THE FIELDNOTES

FIGURE 22.8 "I walked from my hotel toward the main square of the city of Chengdu. On the opposite side of the square stood a huge billboard. At first I thought that it was merely an unusually large advertisement (of which in 1981 one sees rather more in southern China than in the north), but soon it became obvious that there was a message here, and it was clear enough. One child per couple is the official stipulation, and here that is proclaimed in Chinese as well as in English. A tough rule, but it will undoubtedly be enforced. Perhaps this will slow the land degradation and overuse we had observed on the way to Chengdu from Kunming."

Prairies of North America, where raising wheat was the mainstay of the region's farmers, below-average rainfall was recorded for several years running. Wheat had been sown on land that was only marginally suitable for grain cultivation, and when the rains failed, the loosened soil fell prey to the ever-present wind. Great clouds of dust soon blackened the skies as millions of tonnes of topsoil were blown away (Fig. 22.9). Dunes formed, some more than 3 m high, and the landscape was transformed. Thousands of farmers abandoned their land and moved westward, hoping to make a new start in British Columbia, Alberta, or California. Nearly 200,000 migrated from the Prairies and went further west during this period. The physical destruction of much of the Great Plains and Prairies and the social dislocation that accompanied it made an indelible mark on North

FIGURE 22.9 A massive dust storm southwest of Laken heath near Assiniboia, Saskatchewan during the height of the Dust Bowl of the 1930s.

soils, agriculture, and related topics, many students came to geography because of their interest in conservation.

The Roosevelt administration in the United States (1933–1945) launched large programs to counter future dust-bowl experiences. The U.S. Congress passed legislation in support of land-use planning and soil protection, and the federal government created several offices and agencies to implement these initiatives. The Soil Conservation Service was among these agencies, as were the Natural Resources Board and the Civilian Conservation Corps. One of the most important agencies to be founded during this period was the Tennessee Valley Authority (TVA), a massive regional project begun in 1933 to control destructive floods, assist farmers, improve navigation, and create electric power sources in the Tennessee River basin (Fig. 22.10). The TVA, still operating today, includes parts of seven states: Alabama, Georgia, Kentucky, Mississippi, North Carolina, Tennessee, and Virginia. It has transformed the physical and human geography of a large region. No such large programs were initiated in Canada. The Conservative government of R. B. Bennett (1930–1935)

America (a struggle immortalized in John Steinbeck's classic novel *The Grapes of Wrath*), and the idea of conservation took hold. Since geographers study climates,

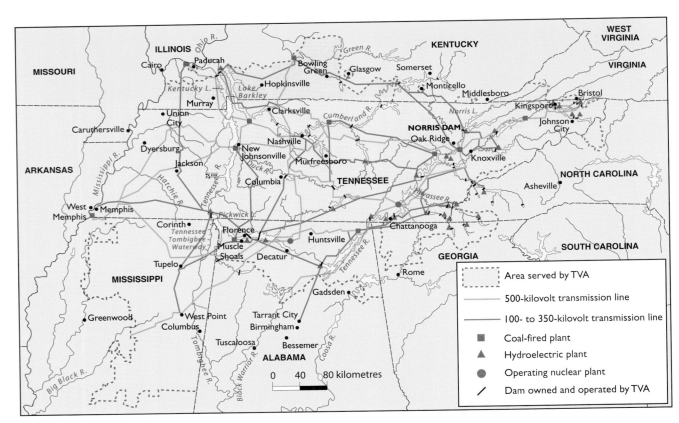

FIGURE 22.10 Region developed by the Tennessee Valley Authority (TVA), beginning in the mid-1930s.

was reluctant to spend money on massive public works or relief payments. The Mackenzie King government that followed (1935–1947) initiated the Prairie Farm Rehabilitation Administration (PFRA) in the latter 1930s. This agency had the authority to rehabilitate devastated land and develop sustainable dryland farming practices that it would then demonstrate to the remaining farmers. Such practices were essential to the farmers' ability to make a living. For nearly a decade the PFRA's soil and water conservation and development practices had positive results. New drought-resistant grasses were introduced and watering sites were supplied, transforming lifeless, wind-eroded land into productive pasture land.

The 1930s, which some have called the golden age of conservation in the United States, were followed by a period during which attention in the United States was diverted to other causes: war and global strategic competition. In the meantime, urbanization was increasing in North America, and many farmers, unable to afford mechanization and other new technologies required to compete in the postwar marketplace, were forced to sell their land. Fortunately some far-sighted people continued to support conservationist ideas and programs with their own money. Among privately funded conservation organizations were the U.S. Conservation Foundation (founded in 1948), U.S. Resources for the Future (1952), and the Canadian Audubon Society (1948), which is now called Nature Canada (2004). The Canadian Nature Conservancy was established in the early 1960s. Such organizations sponsored research and publications on conservation issues and practices and helped keep the conservation ethic before the North American people.

As environmental problems intensified not only at home but also abroad, the public interest in and concern over conservation matters was revived. The U.S. government finally responded in 1970 by creating the Environmental Protection Agency (EPA). The EPA soon became a high-profile agency that addressed a wider range of conservation and environmental concerns than any of its predecessors. After a number of scandals and exposures of lax enforcement during the 1980s, under the Clinton administration in the 1990s the EPA—along with a reinvigorated U.S. Department of the Interior—again played a major role in the conservation arena. Although that government-led effort has substantially diminished since 2000, the conservation movement continues in the twenty-first century—increasingly under the banner of **sustainable development**, which the World Commission on Environment and Development defines as "development that meets the needs of the present without compromising the ability of future generations to meet their own needs." The government of Canada has led the way in terms of the establishment of national parks and ecological reserves in all ecological zones of the country. The Department of the Environment has established a two-prong approach to conservation: (1) a landscape approach that provides for the ecologically sound use of resources and environmental protection of all Canadian landscapes (terrestrial and marine); and (2) a national network of representative protected areas (national parks and reserves) within each of the ecological and/or landscape areas of Canada. The protected areas now occupy approximately 20 million hectares or about 2 percent of Canada's territory. However, many of these protected areas are too small to be ecologically self-sustaining. In western Canada, only four national parks (in the Rockies) are large enough to sustain resident populations of predators, such as cougars and wolves. Canada also led the way in the international environmental movement with the establishment of Greenpeace in 1971 (founding members included Patrick Moore, Bob Hunter, David McTaggart, and Paul Watson) to protest nuclear weapons testing in Alaska. This organization is now working in nearly 30 countries, and its 2.5 million members champion environmental conservation of all types. Some of the original members of Greenpeace have gone on to form other conservation groups, such as the Sea Shepherd Society.

As you can see, the geographic study of the biosphere is not just a theoretical exercise. It involves science as well as policy, research as well as application. To make decisions we need basic information, and each of the next six units in Part Three contains essential background to help us do so.

KEY TERMS

biodiversity *page 286*

biogeography *page 283*

conservation *page 288*

pedology *page 283*

phytogeography *page 283*

species *page 286*

sustainable development *page 291*

zoogeography *page 283*

REVIEW QUESTIONS

1. Which subjects are encompassed by *pedology* and by *biogeography*?

2. What are the major functions of soil?

3. In what way does physical geography help us understand problems of conservation?

4. Why was the Tennessee Valley Authority created in the 1930s?

5. What was the Canadian government's response to the "Dust Bowl" of the 1930s?

REFERENCES AND FURTHER READINGS

BAILEY, R. G. *Ecosystem Geography* (New York: Springer Verlag, 1996).

BRADBURY, I. K. *The Biosphere* (New York: Wiley, 2nd ed., 1998).

CUTTER, S. L., and RENWICK, W. H. *Exploitation, Conservation, Preservation: A Geographic Perspective on Natural Resource Use* (New York: Wiley, 3rd ed., 1999).

EBLEN, R. A., and EBLEN, W. R., Eds. *The Encyclopedia of the Environment* (Boston: Houghton Mifflin, 1994).

HOLE, F. D., and CAMPBELL, J. B. *Soil Landscape Analysis* (Totowa, N.J.: Rowman & Allanheld, 1985).

HUGGETT, R. J. *Environmental Change: The Evolving Ecosphere* (London/New York: Routledge, 1997).

HUSTON, M. A. *Biological Diversity: The Coexistence of Species on Changing Landscapes* (New York: Cambridge Univ. Press, 1994).

JEFFERIES, M. *Biodiversity and Conservation* (London/New York: Routledge, 1997).

LOVELOCK, J. *The Ages of Gaia: A Biography of Our Living Earth* (New York: Norton, 1988).

MacDONALD, G. M. *Biogeography: Introduction to Space, Time and Life* (New York: Wiley, 2003).

McMICHAEL, A. J. *Planetary Overload: Global Environmental Change and the Health of the Human Species* (New York: Cambridge Univ. Press, 1993).

PEPPER, D. *Modern Environmentalism: An Introduction* (London/New York: Routledge, 1995).

RAVEN, P. H., and BERG, L. R. *Environment* (Hoboken, N.J.: Wiley, 4th ed., 2004).

REAKA-KUDLA, M. L., WILSON, D. E., and WILSON, E. O., Eds. *Biodiversity II: Understanding and Protecting Our Biological Resources* (Washington, D.C.: National Academy Press, 1997).

Scientific American. *The Biosphere: A Scientific American Book* (San Francisco: Freeman, 1970).

SPELLERBERG, I. F., and HARDES, S. *Biological Conservation* (New York: Cambridge Univ. Press, 1992).

STEINBECK, J. *The Grapes of Wrath* (New York: Viking Press, 1939).

TRUDGILL, S. A. *Soil and Vegetation Systems* (London/New York: Oxford Univ. Press, 2nd ed., 1988).

WALLACE, A. R. *The Geographical Distribution of Animals; With a Study of the Relations of Living and Extinct Faunas as Elucidating the Past Changes of the Earth's Surface* (New York: Hafner, 1962 [reprint of 1876 original]).

WILSON, E. O. "The Current State of Biological Diversity," in E. O. Wilson, Ed. *Biodiversity* (Washington, D.C.: National Academy Press, 1988), 3–18.

WILSON, E. O. *The Diversity of Life* (Cambridge, Mass.: Belknap/Harvard Univ. Press, 1992).

WEB RESOURCES

http://www.royal.okanagan.bc.ca/mpidwirn/agriculture/erosion.html Explanations of worldwide soil degradation and erosion, with links to many Canadian soil science websites. Lists of strategies for prevention of degradation.

http://www.sp2000.org/ A baseline data set is being created to outline all currently known species of plants, animals, fungi, and microbes to facilitate global biodiversity research. This project is still underway, and available species can be searched for in the growing catalogue for scientific name, status, and classification.

Formation of Soils

Massive, destructive erosion in the tropical rainforest of southeastern Nigeria. This erosional scar is largely the result of local misuse of the land. (Authors' photo)

OBJECTIVES

- To understand the components of soil

- To outline the factors affecting soil formation

- To describe and explain a typical soil profile and the processes responsible for the formation of soil horizons

Soil is regarded as a living system because it supports plants, the organisms responsible for plant decay, and a variety of other life forms. Using more formal terms, the Canadian System of Soil Classification defines **soil** as a "naturally occurring body of animal, mineral, and organic constituents at the Earth's surface that is capable of supporting plant growth. It is differentiated into horizons of variable depth which differ from the material below and the parent material in morphological makeup, chemical properties and composition, and biological characteristics." *Weathering,* the chemical decay and physical disintegration of earth materials by the action of air, water, and organisms, is more closely examined in Unit 24. The major controls governing soil formation are discussed in this unit.

The term *soil* actually means different things to different people. Agricultural scientists regard soil as the few top layers of weathered material in which plants root and grow. But geologists use the term to refer to all materials that are produced by weathering at a particular site. Using this definition, we can still consider as soil those soils that were produced thousands of years ago and are now covered by layers of other material, even though it is impossible to grow plants in them. Alternatively, civil engineers look upon soil as something to build on and, in general, as anything that does not have to be blasted away.

Soil is obviously located at the Earth's surface and in contact with the atmosphere. It is not, except in small quantities, found in the air, although when dry or unprotected, soil is subject to the action of wind. Nor is it naturally encountered in large quantities in rivers, although erosion and transportation by water may put it there. The general location of soil is at the interface of the atmosphere, hydrosphere, biosphere, and lithosphere. The soil layer, in fact, constitutes one of the most active interfaces among these spheres of the Earth System.

We may not normally think of it as such, but soil is one of our most precious natural resources. Geographers classify the Earth's resources into **renewable resources**, those that can regenerate as they are exploited, and **nonrenewable resources**, such as metallic ores and petroleum, which when consumed at a certain rate will ultimately be used up. Schools of fish, for example, form a renewable resource: harvested at a calculated rate, they will restore themselves continuously. But as all fishing people know, this balance can easily be disturbed by pollution or overfishing. And once a population has been overexploited, the fish may not return for many years, if ever (e.g., Atlantic Cod).

So it is with soil. Soil is a renewable resource—it can be used and depleted, but it continues to regenerate. Renewable resources, however, are not inexhaustible. Damaged beyond a certain level, a soil may be lost to erosion and perhaps destroyed permanently. Farmers know the risks involved in cultivating steep slopes by the wrong methods. Terraces must be created, but more importantly, they must be *maintained* (Fig. 23.1). Once neglected, a terraced slope is ripe for soil erosion; once gullies appear, the process may be irreversible (Fig. 23.2).

The Formation of Soil

When the Earth first formed and molten rock began to solidify, there was as yet no soil. The surface was barren, and not until an atmosphere and a biosphere evolved could any soil develop. Once the Earth acquired its layer of moisture-carrying and heat-transferring air and organisms of various kinds, soil formation progressed—as it continues to do today.

Soil Components

Soil contains four components (Fig. 23.3): the mineral component, organic matter, water, and air. A soil's minerals make up its tiny rock particles; the organic matter is of various types; water usually clings to the surfaces of the rock particles; and air fills the intervening gaps. Each component will now be considered more closely.

The *mineral component* is made up of primary minerals, weathered rock fragments, and secondary minerals—for example, oxides and clay minerals such as illite or kaolinite.

Another soil component is *organic matter,* the material that forms from living matter. Half of every handful of soil is made up of small animals, plants, and organic residues. In the upper layers of the soil, there is an accumulation of decaying and decayed remains of leaves, stems, and roots of plants. There are also the faeces and dead bodies of various types of animals. The decay processes are carried out by an astronomical number of micro-organisms, such as bacteria and fungi. All of these contribute to the organic content of the soil, the most important product of which is called *humus*. Humus is the most active form of organic matter in terms of soil formation and plant growth. It is a colloid (like clay). A colloidal state occurs when microscopic particles (about 1 micrometre in size) are dispersed evenly throughout a material, liquid, or air. Two common examples of colloids are milk (tiny particles of milk solids dispersed in liquid) and cloud (water droplets dispersed in air).

Soil also contains life-sustaining *water.* There is an electrical attraction between the mineral particles and the water molecules surrounding them. Normally after a rainstorm, fills much of the space between the minerals. But even in very dry soils, the attraction is so persistent that there may be a thin film of water, possibly one or two molecules thick, around the mineral particles. The water is not pure, but exists as a weak solution of the various chemicals found in the soil. Without water, the many chemical changes that must occur in the soil could not take place. Soil, water, and air have a reciprocal relationship.

FROM THE FIELDNOTES

FIGURE 23.1 "Driving upcountry from Colombo to Kandy in Sri Lanka, you see areas where the whole countryside is transformed by human hand into intricate, meticulously maintained terraces. It is the product of centuries of manipulation and maintenance, with long-term success depending on careful adjustment to nature's cycles and variations. Scenes like this (similar ones can be observed in Indonesia, the Philippines, and other rice-growing societies) reflect a harmonious human–environment relationship that evolved over countless generations."

Soil air fills the spaces among the mineral particles, organic matter, and water. It is not exactly the kind of air we know in the atmosphere. Soil air contains more carbon dioxide and less oxygen and nitrogen than atmospheric air does. As water enters the soil during a rainstorm, air is displaced as water fills the pores. As the water drains down-profile, air replaces it in the vacated pores.

It is simple enough to deduce that these four soil components came from the other spheres of the Earth System. The more interesting task is to discover how. Five important factors will direct us to that understanding.

Factors in the Formation of Soil

Some of the factors in soil formation are obvious, whereas others are not so apparent. Rocks and the deposits formed from them are called the **parent material**. The atmosphere provides the water and air for the soil layer (and in high latitudes the cryosphere also plays a role where soil ice dominates some permafrost soils).

FROM THE FIELDNOTES

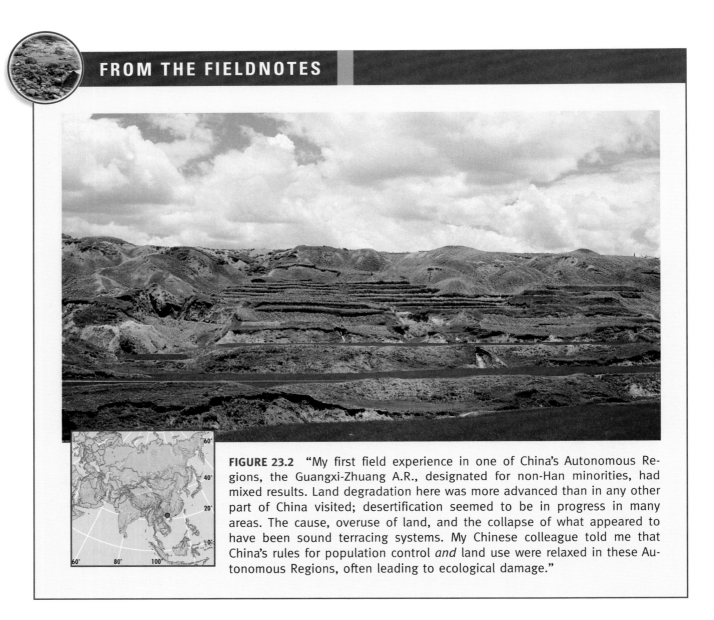

FIGURE 23.2 "My first field experience in one of China's Autonomous Regions, the Guangxi-Zhuang A.R., designated for non-Han minorities, had mixed results. Land degradation here was more advanced than in any other part of China visited; desertification seemed to be in progress in many areas. The cause, overuse of land, and the collapse of what appeared to have been sound terracing systems. My Chinese colleague told me that China's rules for population control *and* land use were relaxed in these Autonomous Regions, often leading to ecological damage."

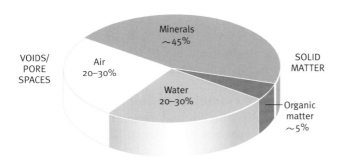

FIGURE 23.3 Four major components and their relative percantages.

But the processes of the atmosphere vary across the Earth's surface, and therefore *climate* is a distinct soil-forming factor. Because of the presence of organic matter, vegetation and other organisms will be factors. Only close observation tells us that soils seem to vary with *topography*. The last factor is not obvious, but the formation of soils depends on *time*. Once the soil has started to develop, its character will influence soil processes and development too. Thus, soil is a function of parent material, climate, organisms, topography, time, and soil. How do these factors come into play?

Parent Material   When a soil forms directly from underlying rock, the dominant soil minerals bear a direct relationship to the original rock. This, the simplest kind of soil formation, gives rise to what is known as a **residual soil**. Thus on the Canadian Shield, soils contain the insoluble residues of the iron oxides and aluminum silicates from the original rock. Such cases are quite common throughout the world. Yet even on the Shield there may also be soil differences resulting from the variation of climate.

In a second category of soil, known as **transported soil**, the soil may be totally independent of the underlying solid rock because the parent material has been transported and deposited by one or more of the gradational agents, often far from its original source. During the most recent ice age, large quantities of material were transported thousands of kilometres by ice and deposited. These materials then formed the parent material for new soil formation. Many soils in southern Ontario and the Prairies formed from such parent material.

Sediments deposited in stream valleys are another source of parent material. This type of parent material often creates fertile soils, as in the case of the lands bordering the Fraser River in southwest British Columbia. In still other instances, the wind carries and eventually deposits thick blankets of fine matter that form the parent materials of new soil. Such deposits of windblown material are called *coversands* and *loess.* Many areas of the Prairies and Southern Ontario are underlain by coversands and loess, sometimes reaching up to several metres in thickness.

Climate In parts of the Maritime provinces and Quebec, the soil has developed from granites. Yet the resulting soils are not the same because the two areas have different climates. The warmer, moister climate of the Maritimes has caused a much more complete pattern of chemical change in the soils. As far as the development of soils is concerned, the important elements of climate are moisture, temperature, and to a lesser degree, wind. The amount of soil moisture is determined by the amount of precipitation and evapotranspiration at a particular location. Both moisture and higher temperatures accelerate the chemical reactions of the soil. Thus thicker, well-developed soils should be found in the lower, warmer latitudes. Wind is another factor in the formation of some soils. In certain areas, wind action is responsible for the accumulation of sediment that may become the parent material of soil. Elsewhere, especially in areas with sparse vegetation cover, wind may be responsible for soil erosion by deflation.

Organisms Climate affects the types and amounts of vegetation and other organisms that are found in an

FIGURE 23.4 Humus in the blackish layer at the top of the soil, consists of decomposing organic matter.

area. Outside the tropics, usually the greater the amount of vegetation on the soil, the greater the amount of organic matter in the soil. Most of the organic activity takes place at or close to the surface in the *Rhizosphere* or root zone. Partially decomposed organic matter, called **humus**, forms a dark layer at the top of the soil (Fig. 23.4). The most fertile soils are rich in humus. In many respects, humus and vegetation form a closed system. The substances that circulate through this system are plant foods—such as nitrogen compounds, phosphates, and potassium—collectively known as *plant nutrients.*

There are a number of ways that organic matter can enter a soil as *litter* to form various types of humus. *Mor humus* is found under coniferous vegetation. It develops as a mat of twigs, cones, and so forth on top of the mineral soil. Because of the acidic conditions, earthworms are rare and there is not much mixing of organic and mineral layers. *Moder humus* is found under deciduous forest where the soil pH is less acidic. Conditions allow mixing of the organic and mineral components by various micro- and meso-fauna (especially earthworms).

A microscope would be needed to see the bacteria and fungi that are the key to this circulation. Decomposing micro-organisms continually change the nutrients into simpler compounds, which can enter plants through their roots. At the same time, other bacteria "fix" atmospheric nitrogen so that it too can be absorbed. Plants use these nutrients to grow, and when they die the decomposing bacteria return the nutrients to the soil to continue the cycle. This system turns into an open system when erosion, humans, or animals remove the vegetation. Then the soil must often be balanced with artificial nutrients (fertilizers).

Several macro- and meso-organisms living in the soil also act as biological agents of formation. While the most important animal in temperate-zone soils is the earthworm, the most important in the tropics is the termite. There are many different species of earthworm, but the most important in many areas is the dew worm or night crawler (also called the rainworm—*Lubricus terrestris*). The importance of the earthworm to the soil is threefold:

1. They burrow through the soil and create a *porosphere* which increases aeration and drainage.
2. They produce a *tilth*—a suitable habitat for micro-organisms. As earthworms move through the soil, they mix mineral and organic soil components in their digestive systems. In doing so, they add nitrogen, potassium, organic matter, and 11 trace elements to the soil. They also add $CaCo_3$ from a calcareous gland situated on their skin near their heads. Earthworms also produce a lot of urine each day (60 percent of body weight). They urinate through their skins. This adds ammonia to the soil.
3. They move soil around. Some species cast or defecate on the surface, while others defecate in the soil. Their castings can amount to 5000–10,000 kg/ha/yr. It is estimated that there are approximately 1.5 million earthworms per hectare in Southern Ontario (50 to 75 percent of the soil animal biomass).

Most of the earthworm species in many parts of North America were either intentionally or unintentionally imported. Many of the indigenous species were killed off by cold soil temperatures during the Late Cenozoic ice age.

Termites (often mistakenly called red ants) are part of the family *Isoptera*. The top 2–3 m of soil in the tropics are derived from the erosion of above-ground termite nests (*termitaria*). Some of the larger species—for example, *Macrotermes sp.*—build mounds reaching up to 15 m high in some areas of Africa, although generally only 6 m. Each mound contains 2–4 tonnes of fine soil material, termite saliva, and faeces. The soil material is less than 1 mm in diameter (limited by the strength of a termite). Termitaria are built to maintain an internal temperature of 31–32°C. Openings can be closed or opened to change airflow to maintain the temperature. Some mounds have roofs to divert precipitation away from the termitaria. Erosion usually occurs once a colony moves out or dies.

Termites are important to tropical soils for these reasons:

1. They create a stone-free top soil because the soil is derived from the erosion of the termitaria.
2. They bioturbate or mix the top 1.5 to 2 m of the soil as they tunnel through it.
3. They create a lack of vegetation and vegetable debris on the soil surface around their nests because they collect it and concentrate organic matter in their nests for their "gardens." They chew up organic matter to use to grow fungi (specific to termite gardens). They also "herd" aphids in these gardens, which they "milk" for nectar.
4. They speed up the breakdown of organic matter. Their digestive systems are more efficient than those of earthworms and have a symbiotic bacteria that can break down cellulose.

Topography   Another factor that affects the formation of a soil is its location with respect to the Earth's terrain. In the case of mountain climates, the aspect of a slope partially determines its receipt of radiation and moisture and therefore the amount of moisture evaporating from it. Windward and leeward slopes receive varying amounts of precipitation. Their steepness also affects runoff and thus the amount of moisture that penetrates to the lower layers of the soil. These phenomena, to a large degree, control the amounts of moisture and heat in a soil-forming area. A hillside might have a relatively thin layer of soil in part because of its efficient drainage and erosion. If the hillside faces away from the Sun, this is even more likely because both heat and moisture are minimized. In contrast, a less well drained valley bottom, receiving a large amount of heat and moisture, is an optimal location for the chemical processes of soil formation. We could therefore expect a deep soil layer in a valley because of this and because of deposition of eroded material from upslope. It is normal to find a sequence of different soils on a slope (a *catena*) related to erosion and moisture drainage.

Time Time is the only independent factor. Whether a soil is deep or shallow, it still may need a long time to form. The processes of soil formation are slow, and thus time becomes an important factor. An example of relatively rapid soil formation comes from the Indonesian volcanic island of Krakatau. In its tropical climate, 35 cm of soil developed on newly deposited lavas within 45 years. The same process often takes much longer in colder climates: some of the organic matter in Arctic soils in the Northwest Territories or the Yukon are still not thoroughly decomposed, even though it is nearly 3000 years old. Often the first evidence of a layered soil develops in as little as a century, but a fully mature soil requires thousands of years . This shows how serious any damage to a soil can be. The destruction caused in a few years of careless farming (such as by overgrazing) can take centuries to repair.

Soil The character of developing soil will influence the soil-forming processes and inevitably influence the long-term development of a certain type of soil.

A particular soil type at a specific location is a function of the dynamic interaction of the factors of soil formation. The factors can be divided into two groups based on their relation to energy:

1. Active (or energy-supplying) factors
   a) climate
   b) organisms
2. Passive (or energy-receiving) factors
   a) topography
   b) parent material
   c) time

The passive factors cannot form soil without the action of the active factors. Numerous combinations of factors are possible, hence the great many different soil types that are found.

Processes in the Soil

From the foregoing it may be concluded that soil formation results from a set of processes, all occurring simultaneously within the soil's developing layers. It is difficult to generalize about these processes. What goes on in evolving equatorial soils is very different from what happens in higher-latitude or high-altitude soils.

In 1959, the U.S. soil scientist Roy Simonson published a general theory of soil formation that provides a useful framework for understanding what takes place within a maturing soil. Simonson noted that certain processes occur in all soils during their formation, but that some very active processes present in some soils are nearly dormant in others. He further noted the lack of sharp boundaries between soils: soils tend to change gradually over space, and few *soil bodies* (geographical areas within which soil properties remain relatively constant) have distinct margins.

Soils also change vertically, but in a much more abrupt manner, so that we normally observe a sequence of layers or horizons. It was concluded that the development of such layers in soils can be ascribed to four sets of processes:

1. **Additions** refer to the gains made by the soil when solar energy, water, gases, and organic matter from plant growth are added, or sometimes when loose sediments move downslope and come to rest on the soil. Many soils have a dark-coloured upper layer whose appearance results from the addition of organic material. Some soils even develop an entirely organic uppermost layer consisting of decaying vegetative matter (e.g., Organic soils).

2. **Transformations** denote the weathering of rocks and minerals and the continuing decomposition (humification) of organic material in the soil. The breakdown of rocks and minerals proceeds throughout all the layers of a soil, but the processes of weathering tend to be more advanced in the upper layers. Near the base of the soil, chunks of yet unaltered rock still exist, but toward the top of the soil no trace of these can be found.

3. **Losses** result from the movement of dissolved soil components as they are carried downward by water (leached), plus the loss of other material in suspension as the water percolates through the soil from the upper toward the lower layers (lessivation). Some soil material is removed by water or wind at the soil surface. While the upper layers are thus depleted, the dissolved and suspended materials are redeposited lower down in the soil.

4. **Translocations** refer to the introduction of dissolved and suspended particles from the upper layers into the lower ones or vice versa. Nutrients are moved by plants and total soil by animals. In deep soils, for example, in equatorial and certain other tropical areas, the translocation processes redeposit these particles so deep into the soil that plant roots cannot reach them.

These fundamental processes take place within all soils, but not everywhere at the same rate or with the same degree of effectiveness. They depend on the soil-forming factors and on the conditions just discussed—parent material, climate, organisms, topography, and time. As they proceed, the soil is internally differentiated into discrete layers with particular properties (horizons).

Soil Profiles

Now that some information about the factors involved in soil formation and the major processes that go on within soils have been discussed, the time has come to dig a hole in the soil in a certain location to see what lies below the surface.

A hole or pit about 2 m deep has been excavated. Even before it was finished a major discovery was made: the soil consisted of a series of layers revealed by changes in colour and by the "feel" or texture of the materials of which they are made. Each of these soil layers is called a **soil horizon**, and the differentiation of soil into distinct layers is called *horizonation*. Some soils have quite sharply defined horizons; in others, horizons are difficult to identify. All the horizons, from top to bottom, are known as the **soil profile**. A soil profile is to a pedologist what a fingerprint is to a detective. Soil scientists, of course, cannot take the time to dig holes wherever they study soils, so they often use a device called a screw or bucket auger. The bucket auger is a hollow, sharp-edged pipe that is pushed into the soil and retrieves a sample of the upper horizons (or, in a shallow soil, the entire profile).

When looking at a 2-m profile of a well-developed soil, it is usually not difficult to identify the horizonation within it. Soil scientists for many years have used a logical scheme to designate each horizon in a model profile: they divided the profile into three sections designated alphabetically. Accordingly, the **A** horizon lies at the top (often darkened by organic material); the **B** horizon in the middle, often receiving dissolved and suspended particles from above; and the **C** horizon at the bottom, where the weathering of parent material proceeds.

This **A–B–C** designation has been in use for over a century, although it has undergone much modification. For instance, some soil profiles include an uppermost horizon—*above* the **A** horizon—consisting entirely of organic material in various stages of decomposition. Where this occurs, it is identified as a **L-F-H** horizon, an organic horizon separate from the **A** horizon on top of which it lies. Note that a soil with an **A** horizon coloured dark from vegetation growing in it is *not* an organic horizon; a **L-F-H** horizon consists exclusively of organic material.

As pedologists learned more about soil profiles, they found that individual horizons were themselves layered. Some upper **A** horizons, for example, are dark-coloured but turn light-coloured perhaps 30 cm down. Thus these are designated an **Ae** horizon (eluviated or leached). At the base of the soil, the horizon where the bedrock is breaking up and weathering into the particles from which soil is being formed is designated at the **C** horizon or an **R** horizon (**R** for *regolith*). A **W** horizon replaces the **C** or **R** horizons where the soil is fully saturated with water either because it is under water or because of impermeable layers that keep water in the soil. A **W** horizon is found in gleys, thawed cryosols, and organic soils.

A typical soil profile, representing a soil found in the moist coastal area of a Maritime province would look like the one shown in Fig. 23.5. Note that the major horizons (**A, B,** etc.) are sometimes given secondary designations, such as **Ae** and **Bt**. The significance of these combinations will be identified as this diagram is studied.

The profile shown in Fig. 23.5 contains master horizons marked by capital letters: **L-F-H, A, B, C,** and **R.** The organic matter at the soil surface is designated an **L-F-H** layer. These layers correspond to the degree of decomposition and humification of the organic matter. **L** stands for *litter*, **F** for *fermentation*, and **H** for *humus*. The litter layer is formed by largely un-rotted leaves, twigs, fruit, cones, conifer needles, animal faeces, and so on. The fermentation layer underlying it is undergoing decomposition. The humus layer contains the end product of the decomposition process, humus. Organic soils and gleys do not have the same kind of organic layers. In both of these types of soil there is water-logging, and they are generally found in areas with cooler temperatures. These conditions favour a greater production of decayable vegetation matter, and at the same time, inhibit the microbial breakdown, so that deep layers of decaying and decayed organic matter build up. This type of thick organic layer is designated an **O** horizon.

Immediately below this layer is the **A** horizon, the uppermost layer of the soil derived from the parent material below but coloured dark by the organic matter from above. Soon, however, the **A** horizon becomes lighter, and about 25 cm down it shows evidence of the removal by percolating water of particles in solution or suspension. It is now designated an **Ae** horizon (**e** standing for the process known as **eluviation**, the general term for removal; it means leached or "washed out").

Below the **Ae** horizon comes the **B** horizon. When a soil is developing, it may not yet possess a clearly developed **B** horizon. Figure 23.6 shows the possible development of soil horizons on a sedimentary parent material. Note that a **B** horizon develops only in the second stage of soil evolution. Also note that when the **B** horizon first develops, it is not yet enriched by particles carried down from the **A** horizon; eluviation, too, is just beginning. Such weakly developed **B** horizons are marked **Bw**. But after enough time has elapsed, the soil displays an **A** and an **Ae** horizon, translocation is in full force, and the **B** horizon matures. The symbol **Bt** (**t** stands for translocated) is used to identify such a mature **B** horizon, and the term **illuviation** signifies the deposition of particles carried downward by percolating water. Thus eluviation from the **A** and **E** horizons is matched by illuviation in the **B** horizon.

The **Bt** designation reflects the common presence of calcium carbonate ($CaCO_3$) in the soil. For instance, the sediments from which many soils of the Prairies are formed, consisting of rock pulverized by ice sheets, contain lime as do tills in southern Ontario. When rainwater percolates downward through such lime-containing soils, the $CaCO_3$ is dissolved in the water and carried away in a process called **leaching**. This eventually makes the topsoil acidic, which in turn stimulates mineral weathering. The result of this weathering is the release of ions of nutrients, which enter the soil solution and greatly contribute to soil fertility (see Perspective: Exchange of Cations).

Another effect is the formation of microscopic clay particles. These clay particles, translocated by eluviation (lessivation) and illuviation from the **A** horizon into the **B** horizon, signal the maturing of the **Bt** horizon. The illuvial accumulation of clay particles transforms a weakly developed **Bw** horizon into a more fully developed **Bt** horizon.

What happens when the parent material contains little or no clay and there is little lime to set the clay-producing process in motion? There will be little clay illuviation into the **B** horizon, and no **Bt** horizon will develop. However, the decaying organic materials in the **L-F-H** layer will acidify rainwater, causing chemical reactions with aluminum (Al) and iron (Fe) in the upper soil. Oxides of Al and Fe are then mobilized and illuviated into the **B** horizon, creating the red-coloured **Bhs** horizon of so many tropical and equatorial soils (**h** for humus; **s** for sesquioxides of aluminum and iron). In North America, soils with **Bhs** horizons occur in forested areas from Quebec to Florida, and they are common in the tropics. Soils with such **B** horizons tend to be of low fertility and low water-retention capacity.

The **C** horizon is the soil layer in which parent material is transformed by weathering into soil particles. The parent materials of soil range widely, of course,

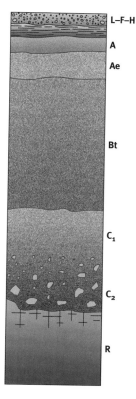

FIGURE 23.5   Soil profile typical of the humid midlatitudes, showing the various soil horizons.

from already pulverized glacial sediments and river-deposited alluvium to hard bedrock. Figure 23.5 assumes a hard-bedrock parent material. Accordingly, the **C** horizon is divided into a lower zone (C_2) where pieces of bedrock still lie interspersed with weathered soil material, and an upper zone (C_1) where the weathering process is more advanced.

The **R** horizon denotes the regolith, where solid rock is first affected by soil formation. Here cracks and other zones of weakness in the bedrock are weathered, loosened, and opened, and the transformation process is in its beginning stages.

Soil Regimes

The soil profile represented in Fig. 23.5 is only one of thousands of such profiles charted by soil scientists around the world. Imagine the range of possibilities: take the complex pattern of global geology, superimpose a map of climates much more intricate than the Köppen regionalization we studied, overlay this with the diversity of biogeography, add local variations of relief and slope, and insert the factor of time. The resulting soil

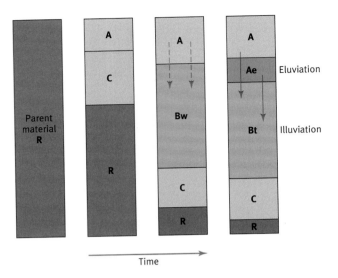

Time

FIGURE 23.6 Possible "stages" of soil horizon evolution on a sedimentary parent material.

map is infinitely complicated, and understanding it is quite a challenge.

The concept of **soil** or **pedogenetic regimes** is used to explain the special patterns of soil formation. Even if the parent material remained the same throughout the world, soils would differ because they would form under different temperature, moisture, biogeographical, and other conditions. It is possible to imagine some of these regimes by recalling some information from Part Two. Among other things, we learned that soils may form under various types of moisture and temperature conditions. Early in our study of soils we learned that certain soils with particular characteristics prevail under certain regimes: calcium-rich soils under arid conditions in lower latitudes; silica-rich soils under somewhat more moist and much more cooler environments in higher latitudes; and iron- and aluminum-rich soils under both warmer tropical and cooler temperate areas.

Different sets of factors can be grouped together, and the regimes can be divided according to these major controlling factors as follows:

1. Bioclimatic regimes (dominated by biogeographical and climatic factors)
   a) podzolization regime
   b) laterization regime
   c) calcification regime
2. Hydromorphic regime (dominated by water-logged conditions)
   a) gleization regime
3. Geomechanical regimes (dominated by specific clay minerals and their reaction to freeze–thaw or wetting–drying)
   a) vertisolization (cracking) regime

Bioclimatic Regimes

Podzolization Regime The podzolization regime is common in areas with a positive moisture balance in mid- and high latitudes and at high elevations. The characteristic climate in the northern parts of North America and Eurasia has long cold winters with considerable snowfall. The annual precipitation ranges from 250 to 1000 mm/yr. Soils may freeze in the winter to a depth of 2 m. The summers are short but have long day length and the average temperature of the warmest month is over 10°C. This regime also occurs on coarse granular materials and weathered acidic bedrock in a wide range of environments. *Podzols* are characteristic of the better-drained areas of the Canadian Shield, especially toward the top of slopes or on well-drained fluvioglacial materials. The temperatures are cold enough to inhibit the intense microbial breakdown of organic matter. The organic matter accumulates on the soil surface and forms a distinct mat of coniferous needles, cones, twigs, and so forth—mor humus). The climate is warm enough to support large coniferous or boreal forests. These forests require few bases, as they do not lose their leaves annually. The soil pH ranges from below 5 to 6. The most significant decomposing agents are fungi. The acidity of the plant litter and soil is not suitable for earthworms and most other soil organisms. Bases, colloids, and oxides are mobilized as the conditions become more and more acidic and are eluviated (leached), leaving a very diagnostic soil profile. As stated above, the organic litter forms a discrete mat on top of the mineral soil (mor humus with L[itter]-F[ermentation]-H[umus] layers). Organic acids from this layer are washed down into the top of the **A** horizon, which is dark brown to black in colour as a consequence. The lower part of the **A** horizon is eluviated, is ash-grey coloured (albic or podzolic [Fig. 23.7]), and has a sandy texture (an **Ae** horizon—**e** stands for eluviated). Many, if not most, of the bases and colloids have been leached out of this horizon, hence its pale colouration and sandy texture. Most of the materials that have been removed are flushed out of the soil column into the groundwater system. Some bases and colloids plus iron and/or aluminum oxides accumulate in the **B** horizon to form an illuviated or spodic horizon—**Bfe** (iron-rich), **Bt** (translocated), **Bh** (humic), etc.—which is characteristically reddish brown in colour because of staining by the oxides and organic matter. The illuviated material may be diffused throughout the horizon or occur as nodules, along root holes or as a pan (placic horizon—iron-pan). The development of an indurated pan may cause the soil-forming processes to change. Pans can stop water drainage downprofile, which will ultimately lead to a change in the character of the soil.

PERSPECTIVES ON THE HUMAN ENVIRONMENT

Exchange of Cations

Just how do mineral substances become nutrients for plants? How do mineral particles enter the water that percolates through the soil, and how do they leave these liquids to enter plant roots? We would need a powerful microscope to observe these exchanges in the soil. When minerals and humus break down, they disintegrate into tiny particles no larger than 0.1 micrometre (0.0000001 m) in diameter. Such tiny particles of humus and clay are called *colloids,* and they can be observed in suspension in the soil solution, making it look turbid.

The colloid surface is electrically charged, attracting other particles with an opposite charge. These other particles also result from the breakup of humus and minerals, but not into colloidal fragments. Rather, they result when mineral compounds dissolve in the soil water and form atoms or groups of atoms called *ions.* Calcite ($CaCO_3$), for example, breaks up into atoms of calcium and carbonate.

The ions resulting from the decomposition of minerals also are electrically charged. Positively charged ions, such as those of calcium (Ca^{2+}), are called *cations.* Negatively charged ions, such as the carbonates, nitrates, and phosphates, are known as *anions.*

A colloid particle with its negatively charged surface will attract (depending on its size) many positively charged ions. These cations come from plant nutrients such as calcium, potassium, magnesium, and sodium. The colloids hold these cations on their surfaces, but let them go when a stronger attraction pulls them into the roots of plants or downprofile. They are replaced by other cations in the soil solution (cation exchange). So the colloids function to make the nutrient-providing ions available to the plants growing in the soil. Without them, these nutrients would be quickly washed away.

The podzol profile becomes less distinct as the climate becomes warmer and the vegetation changes toward the Equator or downslope. In Canada the luvisolic soil order is distinguished from the true pozols. Luvisolic soils are lessivated rather than leached. Luvisols are not excessively leached and have bases retained in the profile, but they are characterized by the translocation of clay particles downprofile (the old name for these soils was grey-brown podzols).

To the north of the podzol zone (or at higher elevations) the podzolization processes are retarded by colder temperatures and a lack of freely drained sites in permafrost areas.

Laterization Regime (Oxisolization or Ironstone Formation) The term *laterite* is derived from the Latin word for brick. The name laterite was first used by Dr. Francis Buchanan in his 1807 publication *A Journey from Madras through the Countries of Mysore, Canara and Malabar.* He described the local people making adobe-like bricks out of a vesicular, mottled red-and-cream, iron-rich soil. The bricks were used for houses and road surfaces. Many of the large ceremonial buildings in parts of India and Southeast Asia are built of laterite (e.g., Ankor Wat in Cambodia).

Laterite occurs in areas with seasonally heavy rainfall and warm temperatures (e.g., tropical and equatorial areas with humid climates with a pronounced dry season). Precipitation ranges from 250 to 2000mm/yr. Laterites occur under savanna and tropical forests of various kinds. Tropical rainforests are characterized by their lateritic and podzolic soils rather than by true laterites.

Vegetation production is high because of the conditions, but there is intense microbial breakdown of the litter and hence organic matter rapidly turns back into biomass. Consequently, there are few minerals and little humus in the soil. The environmental conditions also cause intense deep weathering of the bedrock and the removal of the weatherable minerals. These processes have gone on uninterrupted by glaciations, or anything else, for tens or even hundreds of millions of years. The topsoil in these areas is washed in or blown in or is derived from the erosion of termite mounds (*Macrotermes sp.* mounds can reach more than 15 to 25 m high) and

FIGURE 23.7 The grey, ash-like colour of the **Ae** horizon is the signature of the podzolic soil type.

bears no relation to the laterite layers. Because of this long-continued weathering even silica derived from quartz and silicate minerals has been rotted and removed. The solubility of silica can be seen by the amount of silica carried in dissolved solid form by streams in these environments (e.g., the average amount of silica carried by all streams draining such deeply weathered etchplain areas is in the order of 50 percent of the dissolved solid load; this can be compared to the average silica content of all streams, which is 12 percent). The mobilization and leaching of all the bases and even silica leaves a residual iron-rich or oxic-rich horizon in kaolinite clay. Iron oxides are mobilized and are accumulated in the **B** horizon to form this layer. Once deposited, they are relatively insoluble because of the lack of organic acids. The iron-rich horizons can become vesicular, pisolitic, concretionary, slag-like, massive, or a mixture of more than one type. Some of these types may have been eroded and moved from one place to another. Sometimes two types of laterite can occur on top of each

other. On exposure, the iron-rich layer may become indured to form a laterite or plinthite cuirasse (duricrust or ferricrust). If aluminum is the main mineral left in the soil, this residual layer is called bauxite. Bauxite is the most important ore of aluminum, and this soil layer is mined in places such as Jamaica and Guyana for export to North America and elsewhere.

The major problem with respect to the lateritic layer is its scale. In places it can reach up to 30 or 40 m in depth. Some scientists have argued that this amount of iron can only be accounted for by the erosion of a former iron-rich rock bed, but there is little evidence for the existence of such beds in areas where laterite is found. Others have suggested that the iron was deposited by bacterial action. According to prevailing wisdom, laterite forms because of the recycling of minute iron particles by termites that descend through the laterite to get material to build or repair their termitaria, and by so doing, bring iron material up to the soil surface. It has also been suggested that seasonal variations in the depth of the groundwater table leads to the deposition of iron onto the laterite layer from below. Iron is deposited during periods with a high water table. There is a pallid *lithomarge* layer under the laterite that looks very much like the albic layer in podzols, but the thickness is much, much greater (more than 20 to 30 m in places).

The laterite cuirasses or duricrusts are very important protectants of the landscape and underlie many savanna plateaux. The indurated ends of the laterite are exposed at the edges of the plateaux and "breakaway" forest occurs on the eroded slopes of the lithomarge exposed on the slopes under the laterite, between different savanna levels.

In wetter and/or cooler areas the laterite layers are not as deep or as dominating, and the soils are called *lateritic* or *ferruginous soils*. Tropical or sub-tropical red soils developed on basalts or other mafic parent materials are called krasnozems (red earths) which do not generally exhibit strongly developed horizons.

Calcification Regime The calcification regime occurs in arid and semi-arid areas with negative water balances where the lack of moisture means that there is little vegetation cover and lots of bare, exposed surface (Fig. 23.8). These conditions supply little organic matter to the soil, and thus there is little humus available. Some minor leaching may occur down to approximately 1 to 1.5 m below the surface and is related to sporadic infiltration from the surface. Calcium, magnesium, halite, and other bases remain in the soil and may cement the soil into dense structures. Evapotranspiration from the surface causes the capillary rise of groundwater into the soil column. This brings more calcium, halite, and so on into

FIGURE 23.8 Calcified soils, characteristically light in colour, dominate California's Mojave Desert.

the soil as the water rises and is evapotranspired from the surface. Calcium and/or other salts may build up to form nodules in the **B** horizon or a diffuse layer. In some areas the salts form a surface crust or effluorescence. In very arid areas the calcium may reach the surface layer, and when exposed by erosion this layer becomes a deep, indurated calcium or calcium-magnesium-rich surface horizon called a *calcrete* or *caliche*. This, like laterite, can protect more easily erodable strata and tops many buttes, mesas, and columns in areas of the southwestern United States. Less extreme examples of calcification are found in areas of short-grass prairie of the Palliser Triangle in southern Alberta and Saskatchewan.

In more moist areas where grasses can grow more luxuriantly, organic debris can build up because of limited microbial activity. The buildup of grass-leaf debris and root debris tends to form a deep, dark-coloured *mollic* horizon (moder humus). This layer is essentially developed *in situ* and has not been subjected to mixing by soil organisms and micro-organisms such as earthworms. In many areas the major organisms found in this layer of the soil are arthropods (insects, spiders, centipedes, etc.). The calcium-rich horizon occurs deeper in the soil profile and is less well developed because there is more leaching and a shorter dry period. Instead of a calcium-rich horizon there may be calcium nodules, some shaped like dolls (*loess kinder*). There may also be rodent burrows (ground squirrels, gophers) that have been infilled by fine (wind-borne) material. These are called *krotovinas*. All these features are diagnostic of *chernozems*. These soils are very common in the moister areas to the north and east of the Palliser Triangle and

other more-humid parts of the Great Plains. Chernozems are associated with the long-grass prairie region of Manitoba.

Under very arid conditions with little vegetation, and therefore not much organic material, excessive evaporation from the surface may leave a salt crust or effluoressence and halite in the topsoil (salinization). This process occurs in extremely dry areas, such as parts of the American southwest, Australia, North Africa and the Middle East, and in the dry interior of British Columbia. In wetter areas the salt-rich horizon (salic horizon) occurs at greater depth. Salinization can also occur because of a saline parent material (e.g., saline soils developed on marine sedimentary rocks in the Peace country of northeastern British Columbia near Fort St. John).

It is quite easy to see changes of soil type along environmental gradients of temperature and moisture that influence vegetation cover and soil processes within this regime

Hydromorphic Regime

Gleization Gleization is related to topography and soil drainage. Gleys (gleis) occur in waterlogged conditions associated with bogs or wetlands and slope-foot areas in cool or cold environments. Climate is not the limiting factor, however, except that there must be sufficient precipitation for this type of regime. This regime is common in marine, tundra, and humid continental–cool summer zones, but it is also widespread in certain situations in the wet and dry tropics and monsoonal areas. It is often developed on a wide range of Pleistocene and Holocene sediments and usually forms where the water table approaches or breaks the surface—in flat areas, in depressions, or at the base of slopes where there are high rates of vegetation production and low rates of microbial breakdown because of anaerobic (waterlogged) conditions and fairly cool or cold temperatures. This means that there is a buildup of decaying organic matter and the development of a deep organic horizon (**O** horizon). Moisture is the dominant influence on soil development and hence it is called a hydromorphic regime.

The organic layer may well reach over 10 cm deep. Because of the type of vegetation and groundwater or surface water chemistry the sites are typically acidic. In time the organic matter may develop into a peat (organic soil). The gleying process occurs best with anaerobic bacterial activity in stagnant water. Over time a small amount of sticky blue-grey clay forms under the organic horizon. This material is derived from clays washed down through the organic layer.

This layer gives the regime its name. *Glei* is the Russian word for blue-grey. The colour of this horizon occurs because of internal weathering and the reduction of iron to the ferrous state in anaerobic conditions. Blue-grey mottling may occur in soils upslope from gley sites. The mottling is indicative of imperfect or seasonally imperfect drainage. Gleys form the lower wetter ends of many catenas in many areas.

Geomechanical Regime

Vetisolization (Cracking) Regime This soil regime is also known by the Australian term *gilgai* and as a *grumusol*. It is restricted to sites with a specific soil mineral content and is characterized by the mechanical mixing and inversion of the upper 1 to 2 m of the soil because of cracking caused by the wetting and swelling and the drying and shrinking of *montmorillonitic clays*— $Ca_{0.4}(Al_{0.3}Si_{7.7})Al_{2.6}(Fe^{3+}_{0.9}Mg_{0.3})O_{20}(OH)_4nH_2O$. Typically these soils occur on flat or gently sloping sites in arid and semi-arid areas beneath tall grass or thorn scrub (often fire disclimaxes). Their greatest extent is in tropical and midlatitude desert and steppe areas where leaching is minimal so that basic cations accumulate in the soil. This provides conditions favourable to the formation of this type of clay mineral. Drying and shrinkage occur in the dry season as the surface becomes dessicated. Cracks form and topsoil is blown and/or washed into the cracks. During the wet season the clays swell because of the presence of water, and the cracks close. The soil is inverted in this way. This type of regime is found in the arid and semi-arid areas of North America on montmorillonitic clay soils. In Canada these soils occur in the Palliser Triangle area of the southern Prairies.

In cold permafrost areas the same process of cracking and closure of the soil surface occurs, but here it is not related to the presence of specific clay minerals. As the surface freezes, cracking takes place and surface material is blown and/or washed into the cracks. The cracks close up as melting occurs. This process is associated with the development of ice wedges and patterned ground. This type of regime is common in the permafrost areas of northern Canada, Alaska, and northern Eurasia.

Before we try to make sense of the global and regional distribution of soils (Unit 25), we must examine the more important physical properties that mark them (Unit 24).

KEY TERMS

addition *page 299*

eluviation *page 300*

humus *page 297*

illuviation *page 301*

leaching *page 301*

loesses *page 299*

nonrenewable resources *page 294*

parent material *page 295*

renewable resources *page 294*

residual soil *page 297*

soil *page 293*

soil horizon *page 300*

soil profile *page 300*

soil (pedogenetic) regime *page 302*

transformation *page 299*

translocation *page 299*

transported soil *page 297*

REVIEW QUESTIONS

1. What are the four primary soil components?
2. What are the five major factors in soil formation?
3. What are the four processes of soil formation?

4. Describe the dominant characteristics of the **L-H-I, A, B, C,** and **R** soil horizons.

REFERENCES AND FURTHER READINGS

AMUNDSON, R., et al., Eds. *Factors of Soil Formation: A Fiftieth Anniversary Retrospective* (Madison, Wis.: Soil Science Society of America, 1994).

ASHMAN, M., and PURI, G. *Essential Soil Science* (Malden, Mass.: Blackwell, 2002).

BIRKELAND, P. W. *Soils and Geomorphology* (London/New York: Oxford Univ. Press, 3rd ed., 1999).

BRADY, N. C., and WEIL, R. R. *The Nature and Properties of Soil* (Upper Saddle River, N.J.: Prentice-Hall, 12th ed., 1999).

CHARMAN, P., and MURPHY, B., Eds. *Soils: Their Properties and Management* (New York: Oxford Univ. Press, 2nd ed., 2000).

DANIELS, R. B., and HAMMER, R. D. *Soil Geomorphology* (New York: Wiley, 1992).

ELLIS, S., and MELLOR, A.   *Soils and Environment* (London/New York: Routledge, 1995).

FANNING, D. S., and FANNING, M. C. B.   *Soil: Morphology, Genesis, and Classification* (New York: Wiley, 1989).

FITZPATRICK, E. A.   *Soils: Their Formation, Classification, and Distribution* (London/New York: Longman, 1983).

FOTH, H. D.   *Fundamentals of Soil Science* (New York: Wiley, 8th ed., 1990).

GERRARD, A. J.   *Fundamentals of Soils* (London/New York: Routledge, 2000).

JENNY, H.   *The Soil Resource: Origin and Behavior* (New York/Berlin: Springer Verlag, 1981).

PARTON, T. R., et al.   *Soils: A New Global View* (New Haven, Conn.: Yale Univ. Press, 1996).

ROWELL, D. L.   *Soil Science: Methods and Applications* (New York: Wiley/Longman, 1994).

SIMONSON, R. W.   "Outline of Generalized Theory of Soil Genesis," *Soil Science Society of America, Proceedings,* 23 (1959), 152–156.

Soil Science Society of America.   *Glossary of Soil Science Terms* (Madison, Wis.: Soil Science Society of America, 1984).

WEB RESOURCES

http://ltpwww.gsfc.nasa.gov/globe/forengeo/secret.htm   An overview of soil formation factors, a description of instruments used to study soil and of what forensic geologists do. Links to other soil science pages and research materials are provided.

http://www.soils.org   The Soil Science Society of America's website, with soil degradation information, glossary of terms, and links to soil science journals.

Physical Properties of Soil

Fertile luvisols in the agriculturally productive Paris Basin. (Authors' photo)

OBJECTIVES

- To introduce terminology used to describe soil characteristics

- To define some important properties that arise out of a soil's physical characteristics

- To illustrate the likely arrangement of soil characteristics in a hypothetical landscape

The next time you take a daytime highway trip of any substantial length, you can make it much more interesting by taking time to stop at some road cuts to examine the exposed rock and soil. In Parts Four and Five we discuss some of the rock types and structures you may be able to see; if you are lucky, you might even find an unusual mineral or fossil. But even the soil alone makes a stop worthwhile. Especially in relatively fresh road cuts, you may be able to see several soil horizons, regolith, humus, plant roots, even the imprints made by worms and other inhabitants of the soil. However, do not expect to be able to recognize all the soil properties the road cut reveals. It is one thing to understand a soil profile from a textbook, but in the field those well-defined horizons might not be so evident. But it does help to know some basic terminology, and you can measure some of the soil properties yourself.

If the road cuts through a hill, you may note that the soil's depth at the top of the hill is less (say, 1 m) than halfway down the slope. Much of the difference may come from the **A** horizon, which is especially exposed to erosion on top of the hill.

Sol and *Ped*

The terms *sol* and *ped* appear frequently in soil studies, either alone or in some combined form. We already have encountered both, as in brunisol and, of course, pedology, the science of soils. In examining the classification and regionalization of soils in Unit 25, it is possible to identify soil orders by means of a dominant characteristic followed by *sol* or *solic*. For example, soils forming in poorly drained areas are known as *gleysols* or *gleysolic*. Why sol? Russian scientists were among the world's leading experts in this area (the Russian word for soil is *sol*).

The **solum** of a soil consists of the **A** and **B** horizons, and constitutes that part of the soil in which plant roots are active and play a role in the soil's development. Below the solum, in the **C** horizon, parent material is being weathered. Therefore, when it is reported that "the solum is 1.5 m thick," the reference is to the zone where all the interacting processes of plant life and soil development are taking place.

The *ped* in pedology also appears in the term **pedon**, a column of soil drawn from a specific location, extending from the top of the surface horizon all the way down to the level where the bedrock shows signs of being transformed into **C** horizon material (Fig. 24.1). In other words, a pedon is a soil column representing the entire soil profile. The term *ped* also is used by itself to identify a naturally occurring aggregate or "clump" of soil and its properties. The discussion of this topic is deferred until later in the unit, when it is easier to understand why soils exhibit this property of forming natural peds.

Soil Texture

Descriptions of soils often contain terms such as sandy clay, loam, or silt. These terms are not just general descriptions of the character of soils. In fact, they have a very specific meaning and refer to the sizes of the individual particles that make up a soil (or one of its horizons). If you were to rub a tiny clump of soil between your thumb and forefinger, you would be left with the smallest grains that make up that part of the

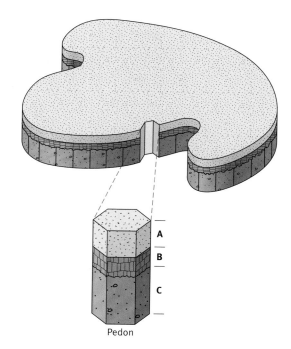

FIGURE 24.1   Complete soil column, or pedon.

soil from which the clump came. These grains may be quite coarse and look or feel like sand, or they may be very fine, like dust on your fingertip. The size of the particles in soil, or its *texture,* is very important, because it has to do with the closeness with which soil particles can be packed together, the amount of space there is in the soil for air and water, how easily roots can penetrate, and other aspects of its behaviour and performance.

Soils, of course, often exhibit several kinds of textures. For instance, that clump on your forefinger may contain some sandy and some much finer particles. In your fieldnotes, therefore, you might call it a *sandy clay*—a mostly fine-grained soil, but with some coarser particles in it. The coarsest grains in a soil are *sand* (not counting even larger gravel, which is sometimes found in soil as well). Sand particles range in size from 2 down to 0.05 mm. The next smaller particles are called *silt* (0.5 to 0.002 mm). There are still smaller grains than silt, namely, the *clay* particles (below 0.002 mm). The smallest of the clay particles are in the colloidal range and are less than a one hundred-thousandth of a millimetre in diameter.

A single soil may contain grains of all three size categories—sand, silt, and clay. Such a soil is called a **loam** if all three are present within specific proportions (Fig. 24.2). Unlike sand, silt, and clay, therefore, *loam* refers not to a size category but to a certain combination of variously sized particles. The Soil Survey of Canada has established a standard system to ensure that such

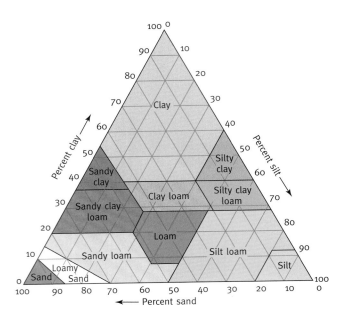

FIGURE 24.2 Soil texture categories, defined by the percentages of sand, silt, and clay found in a soil sample.

terms as sandy clay and silt loam have more than a subjective meaning.

When we rub some soil between thumb and forefinger, we can tell that there are particles of different sizes in the clump—but we can only estimate in what proportions. An accurate determination of these proportions requires additional analysis. Figure 24.2 is a triangular chart that shows the percentages of all three components. A soil that is about one-third sand, one-third silt, and one-third clay falls in the clay loam area. To be called a silty clay, a typical soil would have 45 percent silt, 45 percent clay, and 10 percent sand.

The soil texture is related to the parent material from which the soil was derived. Some types of bedrock yield sand-rich soils, whereas others give rise to clayey soils. Most soils contain some combination of various components. Texture is the critical factor determining the pore spaces in soil, and hence its capacity to hold (*porosity*) and to transmit (*permeability*) water. This is not difficult to imagine: the very term *clay* seems to imply a waterlogged soil, and sand is usually dry and light. Thus a sandy soil allows water to percolate downward under the influence of gravity, draining (and drying up) rapidly. Plants with roots in sandy soils do not have much opportunity to absorb water, because the soil is drained rapidly.

Clay, on the other hand, has a far greater **field capacity** (ability to hold water against the downward pull of gravity). But this characteristic produces a different problem for plants: the pore spaces in clay are so small that permeability (drainage) is poor, reducing the circulation of nutrient- and oxygen-carrying solutions. Furthermore, the close packing of clay particles may make it difficult for plant roots to penetrate deeply into the soil. Such texture-related properties must be considered when farmers plant crops. The potato plant, for example, handles the wetness and compactness of clayey soils well, but wheat should not be sown in these soils.

From the above, it would appear that loams present the best combination of textural properties. Indeed, that is the case. Loams do not stay waterlogged, nor do they yield their water content too rapidly. Pore spaces are large enough to let plant roots find their way downward. Good drainage, which is directly related to soil texture, is a key to successful crop cultivation. Indeed, many farmers say it is more important than nutrient content. Nutrients can be supplemented artificially, but soil texture cannot be easily changed.

Soil Structure

Earlier we referred to so-called peds, naturally occurring clumps of soil that tend to form and stay together unless they are purposely broken up. Again, you will discern this tendency in soil when you examine it: dislodge a bit of soil and notice that it does not disintegrate, like loose sand, but forms small clumps. Only when rubbed do these peds in break up into the individual grains described previously. Peds develop because soil particles are sometimes held together by a thin film of clay, which is deposited during soil formation by circulating solutions. Other peds may develop because of molecular attraction among the particles they contain. Either way, peds give soil its structure, and they are quite important because they affect the circulation of water and air throughout the soil. Soil structure—that is, the nature of its peds—affects the soil's vulnerability to erosion, its behaviour under cultivation, and its durability during dry periods when cohesive forces weaken.

Soils exhibit four basic structures: *platy, prismatic, blocky,* and *spheroidal* (see Figs. 24.3 through 24.6).

1. **Platy structure** (Fig. 24.3), as the term suggests, involves layered peds that look like flakes stacked horizontally. A soil with a platy structure is immediately recognizable because the individual plates often are as much as 1 to 2 cm across, and occasionally even larger.

2. **Prismatic structure** (Fig. 24.4) reveals peds arranged in columns, giving the soil vertical strength. In Unit 49 a wind-deposited material called *loess,* on which very fertile soils develop, is

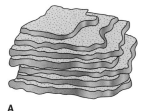

A

B

FIGURE 24.3   Platy soil structure.

A

B

FIGURE 24.4   Prismatic soil structure.

discussed. In their deep **B** horizons, loess soils have a well-developed prismatic structure and can form, without collapsing, bluffs many metres high. Individual peds in soils with prismatic structure range from 0.5 cm to as large as 10 cm.

3. **Blocky** (or **angular**) **structure** (Fig. 24.5) consists of irregularly shaped peds. These peds, however, have straight sides that fit against the flat surfaces of adjacent peds, giving the soil considerable strength.

4. **Spheroidal** (or **granular**) **structure** (Fig. 24.6) displays peds that are usually very small and often nearly round in shape, so that the soil looks like a layer of bread crumbs. Such soils are very porous, and with the peds so small and cohesion very weak, they are more susceptible to erosion.

As noted, not only the shape of the peds (i.e., the structure alone) but also their size is important. Descriptions of soil structure include observations on whether the peds are coarse, medium, or fine. There are no hard rules governing these size categories, but previously reference was made to dimensions that range from

a fraction of 1 cm to 10 cm (note the scale [the soil structure relative to the object shown] of each of the photographs in Figs. 24.3 through 24.6).

Another indicator of soil properties is what pedologists call *soil consistence*. This is a rather subjective measure of a moist or wet soil's stickiness, plasticity, cementation, and hardness. It is a test done in the field by rolling some moist soil in the hand and observing its behaviour. After a bit of soil has been subjected to this test, some of it will have stuck to the skin (indicating its stickiness). The rolled-up soil may form a small rope and then break up, or it may attain a thin, twinelike shape, as moist clay would. This reveals its plasticity. The greater the clay content, the more tightly the soil particles bind together because of the cohesiveness of clay, and the longer the rope- or worm-like roll will be. Conversely, the greater the sand content, the more likely the soil is to crumble and fall apart. Soil hardness often varies downprofile as well. The soil may crumble easily in the **A** horizon, but parts of the **B** horizon may resist even a knife. All these attributes relate to soil consistence.

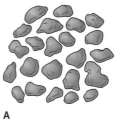

A

B

FIGURE 24.5   Blocky (angular) soil structure.

A

B

FIGURE 24.6   Spheroidal (granular) soil structure.

Soil Colour

Soils generally exhibit a range of colours. Only rarely are soils encountered that do not display some colour variation down their profile. Even a typical equatorial or tropical soil, dominated by the rusty redness of iron and aluminum oxides, exhibits lighter and darker shades of red and orange (see Fig. 25.13). Soil colour is a most useful indicator of the processes that prevail. A dark brown to black upper layer reflects the presence of an organic material, humus. A soil's colour may range from nearly black at the top of the profile to brown in the lower **A** and the **B** horizons to beige in the lower **B** horizon—indicating the decrease in humus content with depth.

The soil colour tends to change with the degree of wetness. Wetting causes soil colours to become much more vivid. Obviously the range of hues in soils is almost infinite, and soil scientists use the Munsell Soil Color Chart to describe soil colours objectively. This chart, which takes into account many possible conditions, contains hundreds of colours, each with a letter and number code. The colour of a sample of soil can therefore be codified. If we do job carefully, we can be certain that a coded soil from the **B** horizon of a Prairie pedon is exactly the same colour as one from the **B** horizon in Ukraine without having to put the samples side by side.

Soil Acidity and Alkalinity

Soil colloids are associated with the presence of cations in the soil (see Perspectives box in Unit 23). Hydrogen (H^+) cations are very common, and their dominance in the soil solution defines an *acid* condition. Conversely, a relative absence of H^+ cations and the presence of hydroxyl (OH^-) anions plus sodium (Na^+) and other associated cations make the soil *alkaline* (or basic) in nature. The acidity of soil is measured by its pH value. A pH value of 7.0 is considered neutral, which occurs when H^+ and OH^- ions are balanced and present at relatively low levels. Lower values (normally between 4.0 and 7.0) indicate acidic soils, whereas higher values (7.0 to 11.0) indicate alkaline soils.

The acidity of a soil is closely related to its fertility because acids are necessary to make nutrients available to plants. However, extreme acidity or alkalinity is detrimental to plant growth. In dry climate regimes, where

Fertilizer

The global population explosion raises a painful question—can we feed all of these 6+ billion people? Our limited amount of agricultural land must produce more and more food. One way to meet the challenge is to use fertilizer, which enriches the existing soil and produces much larger harvests. Some eastern Native Americans increased soil fertility by planting a fish with each seed. In other cultures, farmers apply organic fertilizer—primarily manure. But organic fertilizer cannot meet our needs. Today more than 50 million tonnes of nutrients are added to the soil each year. Chemical fertilizers supply the primary nutrients: nitrogen, phosphorus, and potassium.

Although pesticides, new hybrid seeds, and mechanization contribute to higher crop yields, fertilizers bring the most substantial rewards. For each kilogram of fertilizer a farmer spreads on the soil, 10 extra kilograms of grain may be harvested. By using the proper combination of nutrients to complement those available in the soil, a farmer may grow two or three times as many crops. At the start of the twenty-first century, 140 million tonnes of nitrogen was being used to support the world's 6.3 billion people. This means that a 23-kg bag of chemical fertilizer is being used for each person on Earth.

Understanding the composition of the soil will allow us to fertilize more efficiently, but there are some undesirable side effects. These include nitrate contamination of groundwater and accelerated *eutrophication* (excessive growth of organic matter through overfertilization) of water bodies, especially lakes, resulting from surface runoff containing nitrogen and phosphorus. Animal feedlot runoff, dairies, and sewage effluent also contribute to eutrophication. Overenrichment of nutrients and excessive algal blooms signal the rapid aging, ecological degradation, and eventual demise of affected water bodies.

---

alkaline soils often occur, one remedy is to treat them with compounds containing sulphur. Conversely, the most common treatment for too much acidity is to apply lime to the soil. (These artificial manipulations of the soil quality, of course, remind us that fertilizers have long been an integral part of the human use of the Earth [see Perspective: Fertilizer].) Different plants and microorganisms are adapted to varying degrees of acidity. The variation of acidity often bears a relationship to both climate and parent material, and is associated with the different soil-forming processes.

Soils of Hills and Valleys

Topography strongly influences soil formation. On gently undulating (rolling) countryside, soil profiles tend to develop fully and would look much like the profile examined in Fig. 23.5. When the landscape flattens out, the soil reflects this by developing a thick **B** horizon. A flat surface promotes leaching, and a dense clay layer in the **B** horizon may be encountered. When the landscape becomes hilly, soils tend to become thinner. As a rule, hilltop soils have a thin **A** horizon, and the **B** horizon will be shallow as well. Rapid draining and exposure to surface erosion inhibit the development of soils on the crests of slopes. Where the land is poorly drained, as in meadows and bogs, the soil profile may show a lack of contrast between **A** and **B** horizons. The regional landforms, therefore, are an important guide to what types of soils occur.

On hillsides in southern Sudan in Africa, as in many other parts of the world, soils have a characteristic arrangement from the top to the bottom of the slopes. As Fig. 24.7 shows, lateritic soils and a capping of hard *laterite* (the name sometimes given to a very hard iron or oxic horizon) are found on the top of the hill. Some of the soil particles washed downhill during overland flow (wash) come to rest farther down the slope. They form a material known as *colluvium,* and soils that develop

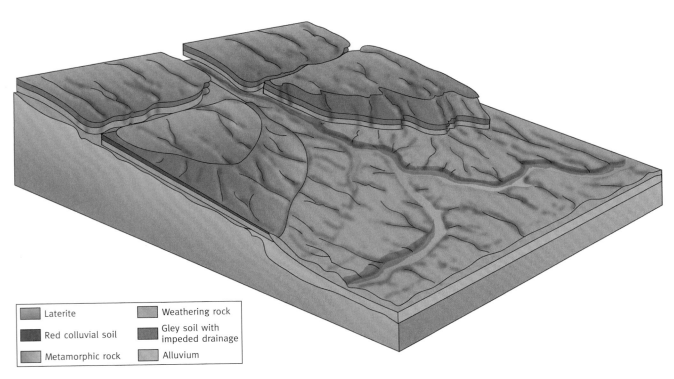

Laterite	Weathering rock
Red colluvial soil	Gley soil with impeded drainage
Metamorphic rock	Alluvium

FIGURE 24.7   Type of soil catena commonly found in southern Sudan.

from this are called colluvial soils. Most of the material brought down valleys by stream water ends up as *alluvium* on the valley floor, and alluvial soils may develop from it (these are often poorly drained). When the same parent material results in an arrangement of different soil types, say along a hillside, this is called a *catena*. This term comes from the Latin word meaning chain or series. A **soil catena** is usually defined as a sequence of soil profiles appearing in regular succession on landform features of uniform rock type.

The Soil-Development System

It is now possible to put together all the factors relating to soil development. They will come together to form a coherent picture if the total process and the soil profile are regarded as a system, as shown in Fig. 24.8. An overall view of this system reinforces the statement that the soil serves as an interface among the atmosphere, biosphere, lithosphere, and hydrosphere (plus the cryosphere in cold climates).

These main spheres of the Earth System are the starting point of the soil-development system. Atmosphere and hydrosphere provide heat and moisture, whereas lithosphere and biosphere furnish the materials. Then a variety of chemical and physical weathering processes

(enhanced by cryospheric processes at high latitudes and high altitudes) break down and transform the parent material and organic matter. The biosphere provides not only organic material, but also new chemicals, especially acids, resulting from the breakdown of this material. These can contribute to further weathering of the inorganic matter of the lithosphere. At the same time, the chemical and physical weathering processes can release nutrients to the plants of the biosphere. The interaction between the biosphere and the soil of the lithosphere is therefore both reciprocal and vital.

As a result of the weathering process and the decay of the plants of the biosphere, the soil system ends up with four ingredients. First there is *organic matter*. Second there is the *resistant residue* that cannot be altered in any way by the weathering processes; this often takes the form of silica, such as the quartz particles found in most soils, particularly sandy soils. Third there is a whole host of newly *altered chemical compounds*, such as oxides and carbonates. These include the various clay minerals, which by cation exchange react with the fourth component, the *soil solution* (water plus dissolved matter). The soil solution contains many of the minerals extracted from the original parent material.

These four components of the soil system are then subjected to various processes of dispersion, translocation, and aggregation. Some of the more important of

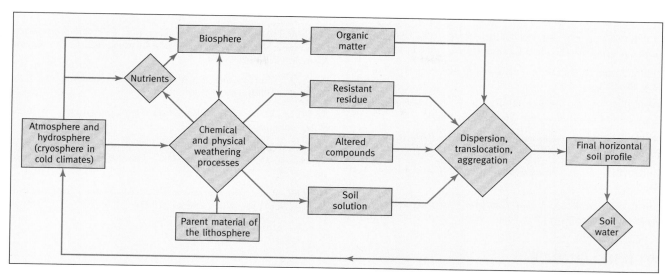

FIGURE 24.8 Structure and flows of the soil-development system.

these processes are the flow of water through the soil under the influence of gravity (leaching), the upward movement of water by capillary action, and the evapotranspiration of water from the soil surface. Water is clearly important. Although the diagram does not include such events as the carbon dioxide and nitrogen cycles (see Unit 6), the groundwater component of the hydrological cycle is illustrated. The final result of these

and many more processes is usually the soil profile, with its distinctive horizons.

All parts of the soil-development system often operate simultaneously. Soils are a particularly dynamic component of the physical world, and they also exhibit important spatial variations. These are considered in Unit 25, which focuses on the geography of soils.

KEY TERMS

blocky (angular)
   structure *page 311*
field capacity *page 310*
loam *page 309*

pedon *page 309*
platy structure *page 310*
prismatic structure *page 310*
soil catena *page 314*

solum *page 309*
spheroidal (granular)
   structure *page 312*

REVIEW QUESTIONS

1. What is meant by the terms *sol* and *ped?*
2. Identify the size ranges for grains of sand, silt, and clay.
3. Define *field capacity.*
4. What is the difference between an acid soil solution and an alkaline soil solution?

5. What is a soil *catena?*
6. What is fertilizer, and why is it so highly prized by farmers the world over?

REFERENCES AND FURTHER READINGS

ASHMAN, M., and PURI, G. *Essential Soil Science* (Malden, Mass.: Blackwell, 2002).

BIRKELAND, P. W. *Soils and Geomorphology* (London/New York: Oxford Univ. Press, 3rd ed., 1999).

BRADY, N. C., and WEIL, R. R. *The Nature and Properties of Soil* (Upper Saddle River, N.J.: Prentice-Hall, 12th ed., 1999).

CHARMAN, P., and MURPHY, B., Eds. *Soils: Their Properties and Management* (New York: Oxford Univ. Press, 2nd ed., 2000).

COURTNEY, F. M., and TRUDGILL, S. A. *The Soil: An Introduction to Soil Study* (London: Edward Arnold, 2nd ed., 1984).

ELLIS, S., and MELLOR, A. *Soils and Environment* (London/New York: Routledge, 1995).

FANNING, D. S., and FANNING, M. C. B. *Soil: Morphology, Genesis, and Classification* (New York: Wiley, 1989).

FOTH, H. D. *Fundamentals of Soil Science* (New York: Wiley, 8th ed., 1990).

GERRARD, A. J. *Fundamentals of Soils* (London/New York: Routledge, 2000).

GERRARD, A. J. *Soils and Landforms: An Integration of Geomorphology and Pedology* (Winchester, Mass.: Allen & Unwin, 1981).

LOYNACHAN, T. E., et al. *Sustaining Our Soils and Society* (Alexandria, Va.: American Geological Institute, AGI Environmental Awareness Series, 2, 1999).

ROSS, S. *Soil Processes: A Systematic Approach* (London/New York: Routledge, 1989).

ROWELL, D. L. *Soil Science: Methods and Applications* (New York: Wiley/Longman, 1994).

U.S. Government Printing Office. *Soils and Men: Yearbook of Agriculture, 1938* (Washington, D.C.: U.S. Department of Agriculture, 1938).

WHITE, R. E. *Introduction to the Principles and Practice of Soil Science* (New York: Wiley, 2nd ed., 1987).

WEB RESOURCE

http://www.fertilizer.org   The International Fertilizer Industry Association's homepage, with a world fertilizer use manual, fertilizer glossary of terms, links to symposiums, and online discussion groups.

UNIT 25

Classification and Mapping of Soils

Diagnostic properties of soil form the basis of regional classification—drought-affected vertisol near Baotou, China. (Authors' photo)

OBJECTIVES

- To present a brief history of pedology and highlight problems in achieving a universal soil classification scheme

- To outline the current Canadian System of Soil Classification
- To outline the current U.S. Soil Taxonomy

- To survey the 12 soil orders in the CSSC and examine their regional patterns on the North American and world map

This unit focuses on the geographical perspective in order to discover how soils are distributed across North America and the rest of the world. Unit 16 points out the problems associated with the classification of climates and their spatial representation. It is necessary to establish criteria to distinguish climate types from one another—criteria not ordained by nature but established by scientists. Certainly there are justifications for those lines in Fig. 16.3 (pp. 210–211): climatologists found transition zones between different climate regimes that also were marked by vegetation changes and often by other modifications as well.

As noted at the beginning of Part Three, the map of world climates keeps re-emerging as soils, vegetation, and animal life are discussed. In many respects, classifying and regionalizing soils is even more difficult than classifying climates. A small area may contain a bewildering variety of soils of different profiles, thicknesses, textures, and structures. For more than a century, pedologists have been working to devise an acceptable system of classifying soils on which a map of world soil distribution could be based.

Classifying Soils

For more than a century the study of soils has been dominated by Russian and American scientists. Up to about 1850 soils were believed to be simply weathered parts of the underlying bedrock. A Russian scholar, Vasili Vasil'evich Dokuchaev (1846–1903), was the first pedologist to demonstrate what the famous scientist Mikhail Lomonosov had suggested a century before. This was that soils with the same parent material develop differently under different environmental conditions. Dokuchaev wrote a very significant book entitled *Ruskii Chernozem* ("Russian Blackearth," 1883) and began an elaborate survey and description of Russian soils based on their field characteristics (depth, profile development, colour, texture, structure, consistence, etc.). After 1870 he and his colleagues (e.g., Nikolai Sibirtsev and Konstantin Glinka) produced several successive soil classifications.

Soil mapping and classification were still very crude in North America during the early part of the twentieth century, even though pioneering work had been done by Eugene W. Hilgard (1833–1916), a German-American who had done a tremendous amount of fieldwork in the U.S. Midwest around the time of the American Civil War and for quite some time after. Hilgard had even begun considering soils in much the same way as the Russian workers had, and toward the end of his life, in 1906, he published a very important book about soils, *Soils, Their Formation, Properties, Composition and Relations to Climate and Plant Growth in Humid and Arid Regions.*

The first soil survey in Canada took place in 1914. It was undertaken by A. J. Galbraith in southwestern Ontario, south of Kingston. Galbraith used the U.S. Bureau of Soils classification, which was largely based on the type of parent materials and soil texture. He recognized nine "soil series" in this area. These were very broad areas that were similar in scale to rock formations. In the early 1920s J. H. Ellis identified field system associations of soils based on parent material and topography in parts of Manitoba.

There was limited progress in terms of classification in Canada during the 1920s and 1930s. Soil surveys were established in Ontario, the Prairie provinces, and British Columbia by 1931, but by 1936 only 1.7 percent of Canada had been surveyed. Soil classification was thus hampered by the fragmentary state of knowledge of soils in the country.

In 1914 Glinka (1867–1927) published a book, in German, on the work done on Russian soils (*Die Typen der Bilenbildung*). However, this book was unknown in the West until well after the end of the First World War. It was finally translated into English by Curtis F. Marbut, head of the U.S. Department of Agriculture's Bureau of Soils in 1927 (*The Great Soil Groups of the World and Their Development*). This book made a great impression on soil scientists in North America and elsewhere, informing them about Russian ideas concerning soil development, classification based on field properties, and the Russian soil taxonomic system. For years North American workers had been grappling with exactly the same kinds of problems faced by the Russians, and now they could adapt the Russian concepts. The Russians recognized three distinct groups of soils: *zonal, intrazonal,* and *azonal* soils. The characteristics of zonal soils reflected the influence of climate and vegetation (e.g., soils like chernozems and podzols). Intrazonal soils had characteristics that were influenced by the dominance of topography, parent material, or drainage (e.g., solonetzs and gleis). Azonal soils were poorly developed soils because of age and/or their location in geomorphologically active sites or on fairly recently deposited parent materials, as would be found on steep, unstable slopes or on floodplains.

Marbut (1863–1935) was the most important North American pedologist of the first half of the twentieth century. He laid the groundwork for the first genetic soil classification, using Russian ideas and terminology. The classification system devised by Marbut and his colleagues (the Marbut or USDA System) was published in 1938 and was frequently revised and modified during the 1940s. To arrive at this system, the American soil scientists superimposed the Russian classification onto a basic division of the soils of North America (outside of northern areas). The following soil types were recognized in this basic scheme (Fig. 25.1):

1. *Pedocal soils* occurred west of 98°W longitude. These soils retained calcium in their profiles (hence the name pedoCALs). They were unleached alkaline soils with pHs above 7. They occurred in areas where the precipitation was less than 600 mm/yr.

2. *Pedalfer soils* occurred east of 98°W longitude. These soils retained ferrous iron and aluminum in their **B** horizons (hence the name pedALFErs). They occurred in wetter areas with more than 600 mm/yr precipitation, and the bases, such as Ca, had been leached out of the soil. The soils were acidic with pHs below 7.

The Marbut classification, along with Ellis's ideas and other American developments, greatly influenced the development of soil classification in Canada. The USDA classification was used in Canada, although the concept of zonal soils was not very useful in eastern Canada, where parent material and topography domi-

nated soil development in many areas. In 1940 the National Soil Survey Committee of Canada formed the Soil Classification Subcommittee (after 1970 the Canadian Soil Survey Committee) to coordinate soil surveys across Canada, increase research into soil characteristics, and use this improved knowledge to map and classify Canadian soils. In 1945 this committee adopted a field classification system of soils similar to the one proposed earlier by Ellis. The first real Canadian soil taxonomic system was published in 1955. This came about because of an increase in knowledge concerning Canadian soils, a desire to classify soils, and the development of a new system of classification in the United States.

In the United States it had been clear for some time that the Marbut classification had fundamental flaws that no amount of modification would solve. American soil scientists had a number of problems. Many soils had been altered from their natural state by either agricultural practices or other events. Soil scientists felt that the

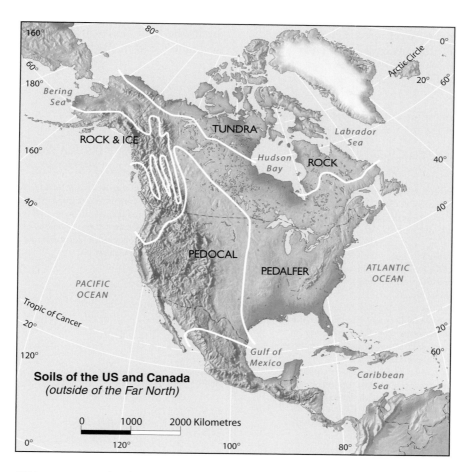

FIGURE 25.1   Soils of Canada and the United States, divided into two major classes determined by climate (after Marbut).

Marbut system laid too much emphasis on the soils' origins—that is, on soil-forming factors and soil-forming processes. They believed that the characteristics of the soils—not the formation processes—should be classified. Thus classification criteria must be stated in terms of the characteristics of the actual soils rather than in terms of the soil-forming factors, such as climate or topography. They also argued that the origin of a soil was sometimes unknown and that such a soil could not be classified genetically. The effort to build a new U.S. soil classification was begun during the 1950s by the U.S. Soil Conservation Service. The U.S. Soil Survey staff had gathered an enormous mass of data on the soils of the United States, and now an attempt was made to create the first comprehensive classification based on soil field characteristics. This initial effort was followed by a series of revisions until 1975, when the **U.S. Soil Taxonomy** was finally released.

The 1955 Canadian classification system became the basis of the current **Canadian System of Soil Classification** (CSSC). Since 1955, more precise definitions and criteria for classification have been put in place. The Canadian developments were greatly helped by the American experience, and consequently the two systems are more closely associated than any other classifications. The CSSC was published in 1970 and has been revised a number of times. The last revision was in 1998. The main differences between the Canadian and American systems can be summed up as follows: (1) the Canadian system uses the entire soil profile to classify the soils, while the U.S. taxonomy uses only the horizons below the plough level (this is because most soils in Canada will never be used for agriculture because of the climate and terrain); (2) the Canadian system is designed for use in Canada, while the U.S. system has a global scope; and (3) the Canadian system is based on soil properties but, unlike the U.S. system, has retained a genetic bias in the properties, or group of properties, and in the terminology used (e.g., the term *podzol* is used). Such terminology denotes not only the kind of properties of the soil and but also the soil-forming processes that led to the development of the soil. The number of soil orders and other taxa have been revised periodically. Table 25.1 shows the number of levels of organization in the Canadian System of Soil Classification and the U.S. Soil Taxonomy at present. Both systems are hierarchical—the *soil series* being the lowest level of classification and the *soil order* being the highest level of abstraction (see Table 25.1).

Table 25.1 Organization of the Canadian System of Soil Classification Taxonomy Compared with That of the U.S Soil Taxonomy

Level	CSSC Taxa Description	Level	U.S. Soil Taxa Description
Order (10)	Differentiated on the basis of soil characteristics that reflect the nature of the total soil environment and the effects of the dominant soil-forming factors	Order (12)	Differentiated on the basis of the degree of horizon development, degree of weathering, gross composition, and presence or absence of specific horizons
This level of organization not used in the CSSC		Suborder (96)	Differentiated on the basis of chemical and physical properties and formative and environmental factors
Great Group (31)	Differentiated on the basis of characteristics that reflect the differences in the strengths of dominant processes or a major contribution of an additional process	Great Group (230)	Same as the CSSC
Subgroup (221)	Differentiated on the basis of the kind and arrangement of horizons that reflect a conformity to the central concept of the great group, a gradation toward another soil order, or the presence of a special horizon	Subgroup (~1000)	Same as the CSSC
Family	Differentiated on the basis of the parent material characteristics (e.g., texture, mineralogy, depth, and/or reaction) and on differences in soil climatic factors	Family (~5000)	Same as the CSSC
Series	Groupings of pedons with similar arrangements of horizons, whose colour, texture, structure, consistence, thickness, reaction, and composition fall within relatively narrow, well-defined ranges	Series (~16,000)	Same as the CSSC

Source: Canadian System of Soil Classification

Source: U.S. Department of Agriculture

Some of the major soil types (orders) were encountered in Unit 23. A **soil order** is the highest level of classification in both systems, but as can be seen in Table 25.1 the definition of what constitutes a soil order differs somewhat between the two taxonomies.

Soil Distribution on a Hypothetical Continent

We can now examine the general distribution of soil orders. In our earlier discussion about the world distribution of climates, a model continent was postulated and the expected climatic distribution was mapped (see Fig. 16.2). One way to approach soil classification is to consider the spatial distribution of soil orders on a similar hypothetical continent (Fig. 25.2). The mapped contents of this model are somewhat familiar because climate is a soil-forming factor. Thus the southeastern region would be dominated by **mT** air masses, the

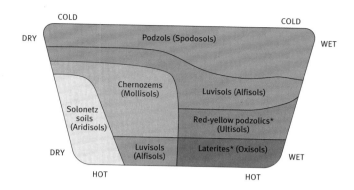

FIGURE 25.2 Distribution of Soil Order regimes on a hypothetical continent in the Northern Hemisphere. This figure uses Canadian Soil Order names, with U.S. names in parentheses. Red-yellow podzolics and laterites are not included in the Canadian classification because they occur outside of Canada.

PERSPECTIVES ON THE HUMAN ENVIRONMENT

Soil Taxonomy—What's in a Name?

Science is based in part on classification systems. Biologists organize the living world into kingdoms. Chemists classify types of changes in matter and energy. Anthropologists identify types of kinship systems and family structures. New classification systems are constantly being put forward, yet not all survive.

What defines the difference between a useful system and one that does not stand the test of time? A useful system is flexible enough to accommodate new data and phenomena, yet rigid enough so that its underlying principles can be applied again and again. Because of the increasing internationalization of science, names should have some significance in a variety of languages. Finally, a system should organize its information in ways that show useful relationships.

How do the Canadian and U.S. soil classifications surveyed in this unit, measure up according to these standards? The Canadian system uses a lot of terms

that are borrowed from Russian and that carry a genetic bias—that is, the terms imply the processes or genesis of a particular soil. An example is *podzol*. The term implies that this soil developed through the podzolization process. When the U.S. Department of Agriculture (USDA) first proposed the comprehensive soil taxonomy in the 1950s and 1960s, its major goals were to replace old terms, employ terms that suggest some properties of the soils, and use names that would have some meaning in the many world languages with words derived from Latin or Greek. The USDA employed classical scholars from the Universities of Ghent (Belgium) and Illinois to provide the Latin and Greek roots to match the soil characteristics. The etymologies of the names employed by both the Canadian and U.S. systems are shown below in Table 25.4. This chart also shows the relationship between the Canadian and U.S. soil orders.

Table 25.2 The Canadian System of Soil Classification: Soil Orders and Great Groups*

Soil Order	Great Group	Characteristics
Brunisolic	Melanic brunisol	**Ah** horizon greater then 10 cm
	Eutric brunisol	No **Ah** horizon
	Sombric brunisol	**Ah** horizon, dark coloration
	Dystic brunisol	No **Ah** horizon, has $CaCl^2$
Chernozemic	Brown chernozem	Calcium-rich soil with intermediate coloration
	Dark-brown chernozem	Calcium-rich soil with a darker colour
	Black chernozem	Calcium-rich soil with exceptionally dark coloration
	Dark-grey chernozem	Calcium-rich soil with eluviation; associated with forest vegetation
Cryosolic	Turbic cryosol	Evidence or cryoturbation; permafrost within 2 m of the surface
	Static cryosol	Formed in mineral soil; no major cryoturbation; permafrost within 1 m of the surface
	Organic cryosol	Formed primarily in organic materials; has permafrost within 1 m of the surface
Gleysolic	Humic gleysol	Has either an **Ah** horizon or an **Ap** horizon; 2% organic carbon in surface horizon
	Gleysol	Thick **O** horizon; thin blue-grey horizon below
	Luvic gleysol	Has a **Btg** horizon and usually an eluvial horizon
Luvisolic	Grey Brown luvisol	Has a forest mull **Ah** horizon and a mean soil temperature of > 8°C
	Grey luvisol	Has either an **Ah** or **Ahe** horizon
Organic	Fibrisol	Formed in relatively undecomposed organic matter
	Misisol	Formed in organic matter in an intermediate stage of decomposition
	Humisol	Formed in organic matter in an advanced state of decomposition
	Folisol	Developed in upland organic (folic) materials; seldom saturated with water
Podzolic	Humic podzol	Has a **Bh** horizon
	Ferro-humic podzol	Has a **Bhf** horizon
	Humo-ferric podzol	Has a **Bfh** horizon
Regosolic	Regosol	Has an **Ah** horizon
	Humic regosol	Has layers below the **Ah** horizon
Solonetzic	Solonetz	Saline or alkaline soil
	Solodized solonetz	Has a thick **Ae** horizon
	Solod	Has an **Ae** horizon and a distinct **AB** or **BA** horizon
	Vertic solonetz	Has a slickenside horizon within 1 m of the surface
Vertisolic	Vertisol	Surface layer cracks when dry
	Humic vertisol	Darker coloration; cracks when dry

*Canadian System of Soil Classification, Agriculture Canada 2004

northwestern area by **mP** air masses, and so forth (see Fig. 13.10). Remembering what we learned about the soil-forming processes, we can conclude that the warm moist southeast would experience the kind of leaching that produces laterites (in the U.S., **oxisols**), while the cool, moist, northwest would have soils that are leached or lessivated (podzols, luvisols; in the U.S., **spodosols, alfisols**).

Care is needed in drawing these conclusions. Whereas the regional climates might indicate such a distribution, parent materials could change the picture considerably. For the hypothetical continent, therefore, it is necessary to make some far-reaching assumptions, including the assumption of a uniform parent material (with calcareous and mixed-mineral content and a loam texture), gently rolling relief without groundwater in the soil profile, and a long period of soil formation (approximately 100,000 years). Given these idealized conditions, the generalized soil order map might look like the map in Fig. 25.2, but it does make the hypothetical continent very simplified and at some distance from the complexities of the real world.

The Soil Orders

Before looking more closely at Fig 25.2, we should become acquainted with the properties of the Canadian and U.S. soil orders in some detail (see Perspective: What's in a Name?). These are listed, along with their great groups (Canadian) and suborders (U.S.) in Tables 25.2, 25.3, and 25.4.

Table 25.3 Orders and Suborders of the U.S. Soil Taxonomy

Order	Suborder	Characteristics
1. Entisol	Aquent	Shows evidence of saturation at some season
	Arent	Lacks horizons because of ploughing or other human activity
	Fluvent	Formed in recent water-deposited sediments, as in floodplains
	Orthent	Occurs on recent erosional surfaces, such as high mountains
	Psamment	Occurs in sandy areas, such as sand dunes
2. Histosol	Fibrist	Occurs in poorly drained areas, slightly decomposed
	Folist	Occurs in poorly drained areas, mass of leaves in early stage of decomposition
	Hemist	Occurs in poorly drained areas, intermediate stage of decomposition
	Saparist	Occurs in poorly drained areas, highly decomposed
3. Vertisol	Torrert	Occurs in arid climates
	Udert	Occurs in humid climates
	Ustert	Occurs in monsoon climates
	Xerert	Occurs in Mediterranean climates
4. Inceptisol	Aquept	Wet with poor drainage
	Ochrept	Freely drained, light in colour
	Plaggept	Has a surface layer more than 50 cm thick resulting from human activity, such as manuring
	Tropept	Freely drained, brownish to reddish, found in the tropics
	Umbrept	Dark reddish or brownish, acidic, freely drained, organically rich
5. Gelisol	Histel	Previously included under entisol and inceptisol soil orders
	Turbel	Occurs at high latitudes (beyond treeline) and high altitudes
	Orthel	Underlain usually by permafrost, cryoturbation, patterned ground, and other periglacial landforms (e.g., pingos, solifluction lobes) are widespread
6. Andisol	Aquand	Occurs in wet areas
	Cryand	Occurs in cold areas, including high altitudes
	Torrand	Occurs in warm, arid climates
	Udand	Occurs in humid climates
	Ustand	Occurs in monsoon climates
	Vitrand	Formed in association with volcanic glass
	Xerand	Occurs in Mediterranean climates
7. Aridisol	Argid	Has an illuvial horizon where clays have accumulated to a significant extent
	Orthid	Has an altered horizon, a hard layer (called hardpan or duripan), or an illuvial horizon of water-soluble material
8. Mollisol	Alboll	Has a surface layer that covers a white horizon from which clay and iron oxides have been removed, and a layer of clay accumulation below
	Aquoll	Saturated with water at some time during the year
	Boroll	Cool or cold, relatively freely drained
	Rendoll	Occurs in humid climates, developed from parent materials rich in calcium
	Udoll	Not dry for as much as 60 consecutive or 90 cumulative days per year
	Ustoll	Occurs in monsoon climates
	Xeroll	Occurs in Mediterranean climates
9. Alfisol	Aqualf	Periodically saturated with water
	Boralf	Freely drained, found in cool places
	Udalf	Brownish to reddish, freely drained
	Ustalf	Partly or completely dry for periods longer than 3 months
	Xeralf	Occurs in dry climates
10. Spodosol	Aquod	Associated with wetness
	Ferrod	Has an iron-enriched sesquioxide horizon
	Hurmod	Has a humus-enriched sesquioxide horizon
	Orthod	Has significant amounts of humus and iron in the sesquioxide horizon
11. Ultisol	Aquult	Occurs in wet places
	Humult	Freely drained, rich in humus
	Udult	Freely drained, poor in humus
	Ustult	Occurs in warm regions with high rainfall but a pronounced dry season
	Xerult	Freely drained, found in Mediterranean climates
12. Oxisol	Aquox	Formed under the influence of water
	Perox	Always moist, with a high humus content
	Torrox	Occurs in arid climates, may have formed under a different climate from that now existing in that location
	Udox	Occurs in places with a short or no dry season, other than aquoxes
	Ustox	Occurs in humid climates with at least 60 consecutive dry days per year

Sources: U.S. Department of Agriculture; Birkeland, 1999.

Table 25.4 Equivalency of Canadian and U.S. Soil Orders and Derivation of Terms

The Canadian System of Soil Classification uses the whole soil profile to classify the soils. It is designed for use in Canada.			The U.S. Soil Taxonomy uses only the soil horizons below the plough level to classify soils. It is designed for global usage.		
Canadian Soil Orders	Derivation of Canadian Term	% Area of Canada	U.S. Soil Orders	Derivation of U.S. Term	% Area of U.S.
Brunisolic	French: *brun*—brown	8.8	Inceptisols, some psamments	Latin: *inceptum*—beginning	9.7
Chernozemic	Russian: *chernozem*—blackearth	5.1	Mollisols, borolls	Latin: *mollis*—soft	21.5
Cryosolic	Greek: *kryos*—icy, cold	45	Gelisols	Latin: *gelare*—to freeze	8.7
Gleysolic	Russian: *glei*—blue-grey	1.9	Aquic subgroups	Latin: *aqua*—water, wet	
Luvisolic	ELUViated	10.3	Alfisols, boralfs and udalfs	Al-Aluminum and Fe-Iron, PedAlFEr	13.9
Organic	Organisms—living things	4.2	Histosols	Greek: *histos*—tissue	1.7
Podzolic	Russian: *podzol*—under wood ash	22.6	Spodosols, some inceptisols	Greek: *spodos*—wood ash	3.5
Regosolic	Greek: *regos*—blanket	1.3	Entisols	RecENT	12.3
Solonetzic	Russian: *solon*—salt	0.6	Aridisols, natric mollisols, and alfisols	Latin: *aridus*—dry Latin: *natric*—salty	8.3
Vertisolic	Latin: *verto*—to turn	0.2	Vertisols	Latin: *verto*—to turn	2.0
Soils found outside of Canada			Andisols	ANDesite—volcanic rock	1.7
			Oxisols	French: *oxide*—Iron	0.02
			Ultisols	Latin: *ultimus*—last	9.2

1. Brunisolic Order (Inceptisols: U.S. Taxonomy)

These soils have the beginnings of a **B** horizon. **Brunisolic soils** form rather quickly but are generally older than regolsols (**entisols**). They have a weakly developed **B** horizon noted for its reddish coloration; this horizon lacks strong clay development and the accumulation of other compounds. But brunisols contain significant amounts of organic matter and/or evidence that the parent material has been weathered to some extent. Brunisols are generally found in humid climates, but they occur from the Arctic to the tropics and are often found in highland areas as well. These soils most frequently develop under forest cover, but they can also be found under tundra or grass (Fig 25.3).

2. Chernozemic Order (Mollisols: U.S. Taxonomy)

These are found in climates that normally have dry seasons, but temperatures can range from microthermal to tropical. Rainfall may be sufficient to leach these soils, but calcification is far more common. **Chernozems** are the soils of the Canadian Prairies, the grass-covered steppes of south-central Russia, and the Great Plains that lend their name to the **BS** climatic zone. The dominant attribute of a chernozem is a thick, dark, humus-

FIGURE 25.3 Profile of a brunisolic soil (inceptisol), exhibiting many physical properties described in the text.

FIGURE 25.4 Profile of a chernozemic soil (mollisol), the dominant soil beneath the grasslands of the Prairies.

rich surface layer (Fig 25.4), high in alkaline content and at least 50 percent saturated with basic cations (calcium, magnesium, potassium, sodium). This layer has a ratio of carbon to nitrogen of less than 17 percent, and the stability of its structure is moderate to strong. Chernozems occasionally are found under water-loving plants or deciduous hardwood forests, but the vast majority are found under tall- or short-grass prairie. Chernozems are often associated with large-scale commercial grain production (see Fig. 17.10) and livestock grazing. Corn is the grain of choice when precipitation is sufficient, but wheat is by far the predominant crop. Drought is the most common problem facing chernozems.

3. Cryosolic Order (Gelisols: U.S. Taxonomy) These are defined as high-latitude or high-altitude soils that have (1) permafrost within 100 cm of the soils' surface, or (2) *gelic materials* within 100 cm of the surface and permafrost within 200 cm. Gelic materials are mineral or organic soil materials that show evidence of cryoturbation (frost-churning) and/or ice segregation in the talik (seasonally thawing active layer) or the uppermost part of the permafrost just below it. In North America

cryosols are found primarily in areas poleward of 60°N (Fig. 25.5). Here they are often associated with such frozen-ground periglacial landforms as patterned ground and pingos (discussed in Unit 48).

4. Gleysolic Order (No U.S. Equivalent at Order Level—but Equivalent to Aquic Suborders) These soils can occur in any waterlogged environment in cool or cold environments and elsewhere. The characteristic thick organic layer includes decomposing and decomposed vegetation that remains because of the slow rotting process undertaken by anaerobic micro-organisms. **Gleysolic soils** occur near to and upslope of organic soils and at the base of slopes where moisture collects. Their development is influenced by temperature, topography, and drainage collection.

5. Luvisolic Order (Alfisols: U.S. Taxonomy) These soils are found in moister, less-continental climatic zones than chernozems. They are high in mineral content and usually moist. As Fig 25.6 indicates, luvisols lack the dark surface horizon of the chernozems, but they do exhibit noteworthy clay accumulation in the **B** horizon. **Luvisols** are usually found under higher-

FIGURE 25.5   A cryosolic soil, underlain by permafrost 38 cm below the surface. Such soil can be found on the foothills of the Mackenzie mountains in the Northwest Territories. The irregular horizon boundaries result from cryoturbation (frost-churning) processes.

FIGURE 25.6   Profile of luvosolic, a soil associated with some of the most productive farming areas in southern Ontario and parts of the Fraser Valley, British Columbia.

latitude mixed forests or middle-latitude deciduous forests, but occasionally can be found in areas of vegetation adapted to dryness. Areas of luvisolic soils are notable for having the most intensive forms of agriculture in North America. Luvisols are typical of highly productive agricultural areas such as Southern Ontario, parts of the Fraser Valley in British Columbia, and areas of the American Corn Belt. Market gardening, oats, soybeans, and alfalfa are the main usage of these soils. A major area of luvisols lies in tropical Africa, within two wide zones (one in the Northern and one in the Southern Hemisphere) between the moist equatorial region and the Sahara and Kalahari Deserts of the subtropical latitudes.

6. Organic Order (Histosols: U.S. Taxonomy) Organic soils are often water-saturated for most of the year. They occur in muskeg, bogs, fens, and other wetlands. Organic material tends to dominate the **O** horizon and clay in the **C** horizon (Fig 25.7). Some organics are unique among the soil orders because they can be totally destroyed over time or altered by natural or artificial drainage. It is difficult to generalize about the geographical distribution of these soils because wetland areas are so widespread. Poor drainage in low- or flat-lying topographical areas explains their occurrence bet-

ter than climate or prevailing vegetation. When they can be drained, intensive cultivation of cabbage, carrots, potatoes, and other root crops is possible (e.g., the Holland Marsh near Newmarket, Ontario).

7. Podzolic Order (Spodosols: U.S. Taxonomy) These soils result when organic soil acids associated with pine-needle decay cause the depletion of most **A** horizon minerals, like the soil in Fig 23.8. **Podzolic soils** develop mainly in more northerly latitudes of the Northern Hemisphere. They are characterized by a **Bf** (podzolic or

FIGURE 25.7 Profile of an organic soil near East Lansing, Michigan. Such soils can also be found in southwestern Ontario. In many parts of the world (e.g., Iceland and Ireland) such organic soil is dug up, cut into shoebox-sized pieces, dried, and used as fuel.

spodic) horizon with an illuvial accumulation of sesquioxides (oxides with 1.5 oxygen atoms to every metallic atom). Usually this horizon shows rounded or subangular black or very dark brown, iron-rich pellets the size of silt, or a thin indurated iron pan may develop.

FIGURE 25.8 Dunes carry regosols (entisols), developed on recently deposited, unconsolidated materials and capable of supporting some adapted vegetation. But the materials are unstable, the soil is ephemeral, and the vegetation vulnerable, which is why many dune areas are protected and people are asked to keep off.

A characteristic ash-grey or albic **Ae** horizon—the signature of silica, which, unlike other soil minerals, is resistant to dissolution by organic acids—often marks the lower part of the topsoil of podzols (see Fig 23.8) but is not itself a defining feature. Podzols are found only in humid regions, mostly with coniferous forest covers.

Because of the association of forest cover with podzols, lumbering is one of the most important human activities that takes place on these soils. Agriculture is minimal, although corn, wheat, oats, and hay are now being grown in upstate New York and other places where such soils occur.

8. Regosolic Order (Entisols: U.S. Taxonomy) This order includes all the soils that do not fit into any of the other orders. Such soils tend to be of recent origin, often developed in unconsolidated material (alluvium, for example) and on hard bedrock. **Regosols** have a thin **A** horizon overlying a **C** or **R** horizon; otherwise they show little development (Fig 25.8). Because there are numerous reasons for the absence of well-developed horizons, regosols are found in many different environments. Climate, therefore, is not a strong influence in their distribution.

9. Solonetzic Order (No U.S. Equivalent Order—Natric Suborders of Mollisols, Alfisols, and Aridisols) These soils cover a large area of the world's land surface.

FIGURE 25.9 Profile of a solonetzic soil. Such soils can be found in southwestern Saskatchewan.

FIGURE 25.10 The sequence of wetting and drying of this soil creates the cracks characteristic of vertosolic soils in some locations in the drier parts of the Prairies. The same features are created by freezing and thawing of the surface in permafrost areas in the northern part of North America and elsewhere.

FIGURE 25.11 Road cut on the island of Hawaii, revealing the profile of an andisol atop layered volcanic ash.

Solonetzic soils are usually dry unless they are artificially irrigated. They are characterized by having a thin, light-coloured horizon at the surface that is low in organic carbon. Moreover, these soils often contain horizons rich in calcium, clay, gypsum, or salt minerals, as shown in Fig. 25.9. Large expanses of solonetzic soils are found in deserts such as northern Africa's Sahara and eastern Asia's Gobi. Areas with these soils can be used for grazing or intensive crop production with the aid of irrigation. Desert shrubs and grasses are the main form of vegetation, and overgrazing of the land is often a serious problem. The soil-forming process of calcification is common in solonetzic soils.

10. Vertisolic Order (Vertisols: U.S. Taxonomy)
These are clay soils that develop large cracks in the dry season and swell with moisture when damp during the wet season (Fig. 25.10). More than 35 percent of their content is clay, especially montmorillonite. The clay particles are normally derived from the parent material, so **vertisols** are found where the clay-producing materials are available—in mesothermal or tropical climates with periodic dry and wet seasons. Their great groups are closely related to climatic divisions. They are found in the drier parts of the Prairies and Great Plains as well as

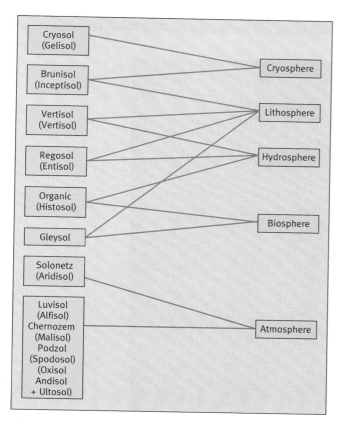

FIGURE 25.12 Primary relationships among the five spheres of the Earth System and the Soil Orders of the Canadian System of Soil Classification (the U.S. Soil Orders are in parentheses).

FIGURE 25.13 Profile of red-yellow podzolic (ultisol), exhibiting a **B** horizon rich in clay.

in Australia, India, and Sudan. Vertisols are hard to use for most human purposes, particularly construction. When they shrink and crack, fences and telephone poles may be thrown out of line. Pavements, building foundations, and pipelines can all be damaged by the movement of these "turning" soils. They also occur in permafrost areas where the surface cracks as the soil freezes and the cracks close as the talik melts in the spring and summer. These types of vertisolic soils are found in the permafrost areas of northern North America, northern Eurasia, and elsewhere.

Volcanic soils (**Andisols**: U.S. taxonomy) occur on volcanic ash and other erupted materials. These weakly developed soils lie principally in the Pacific Ring of Fire (see Unit 32), Hawaii, the Pacific Northwest, and other volcanic zones (Fig. 25.11). They occupy less than 1 percent of the world's land surface and are so locally distributed that they cannot be seen on the small-scale maps employed later in this unit. Andisols also contain much organic matter and hold water well; they are quite fertile.

As noted in Unit 23, **Laterite** soils (oxisols: U.S. taxonomy) are restricted to tropical areas with high rainfall. Organic matter is quickly destroyed, and downward-percolating water leaches the soil, leaving behind compounds of iron and aluminum. It is hard to distinguish the horizons in such soils. Laterites are therefore characterized only by a horizon with a large part of its silica, previously combined with iron and aluminum, removed or altered by weathering. This often produces a hard layer called an *oxic horizon*, which is bright red or orange in colour, caused by a high concentration of clay-sized minerals in the **B** horizon, mainly sesquioxides. The natural vegetation on most laterites is tropical rainforest or savanna, and the soils tend to be of low fertility (as explained in Unit 24), except where they develop from alluvial or volcanic deposits. These soils are found in Hawaii, Puerto Rico, other Caribbean Islands, and in other areas of the world (Fig. 25.14).

The low fertility of laterites has given rise to a pattern of *shifting*, or *slash-and-burn*, *cultivation*. The land is farmed for only a year or two and is then left for many

FIGURE 25.14 "What should have been one day in Suva, the capital of Fiji, turned into a week due to schedule complications, and we had an opportunity to study Viti Levu's interesting human as well as physical geography. Driving through the interior was challenging because maps and reality seemed to differ; but homesteads and villages were interesting and welcoming. The island has some fertile soils, but much of the centre was dominated by laterites which, when fully developed, are deep (often dozens of metres) and characteristically red-coloured due to the preponderance of iron and aluminum in the oxic horizon. The upper part of this profile of a local laterite shows the virtual absence of humus in these soils. Note also the virtual absence of colour change from very near the top of the soil all the way down."

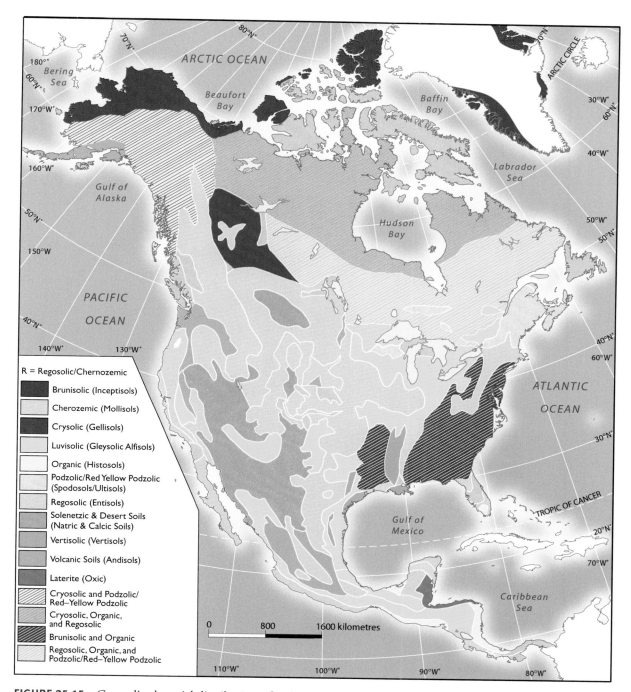

FIGURE 25.15 Generalized spatial distribution of soils in North America using the Canadian Soil Orders (U.S. Soil Orders are in parentheses).

years to renew its nutrients naturally. Population pressures in some parts of the world, such as Nigeria and Amazonia, have altered this agricultural system, and the rapid deterioration of this soil's already limited fertility is usually the result (see Unit 23's opening photo).

Warmer, wetter climatic zones host **red-yellow podzolic soils** (**ultisols**: U.S. Taxonomy), distinguished by a **B** horizon with strong clay accumulation (Fig. 25.13).

The native vegetation of these red-yellow podzolics may have been forest or savanna grassland. They contain at least a few minerals that may be subject to weathering. These soils may well be luvisols that have been subjected to greater weathering. In eastern North America, red-yellow podzolics lie to the south of the southern border of Pleistocene glaciation, and luvisols lie to the north. Therefore, red-yellow podzolics are older, some being

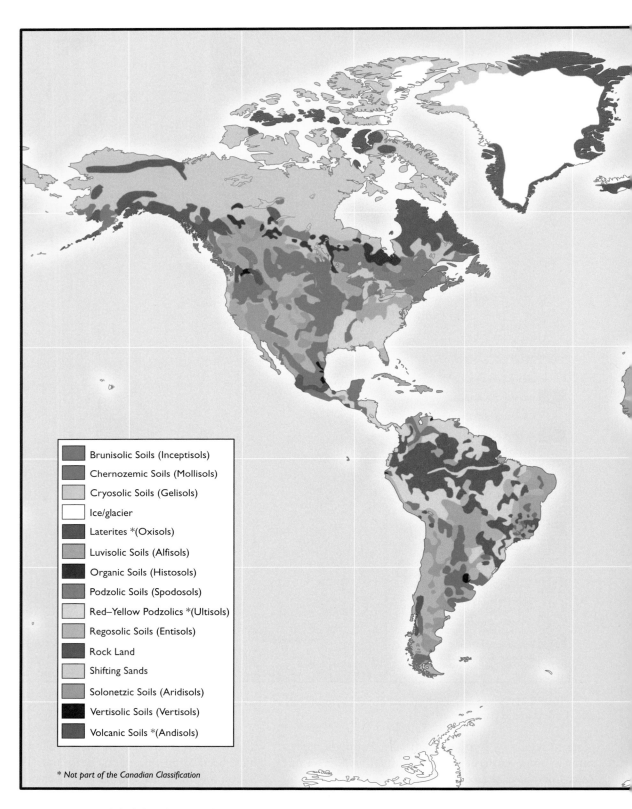

FIGURE 25.16   Global distribution of soils.

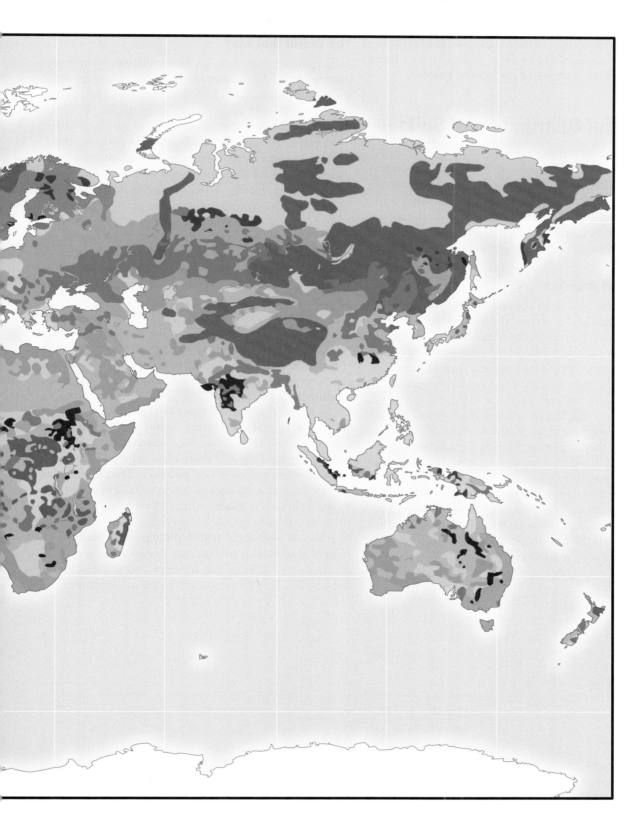

pre-Pleistocene in origin, whereas luvisols are of Pleistocene age or younger. Red-yellow podzolics are often associated with the farming of cotton and peanuts.

The Spatial Distribution of Soils

It is now possible to return to the hypothetical continent above (Fig 25.2) to model the distribution of Canadian (and U.S.) soil orders. Note that between the laterites of the southeast, the solonetzic soils of the southwest, and the podzols of the north, there lie zones of chernozems, ultisols, and luvisols (the last developing under different climatic conditions in two separate areas).

Soils of North America

The distribution of soils in the real world is more complicated. Figure 25.15 shows the spatial pattern for North America. The climatic relationships are quite clear with soils such as podzols and solonetzic soils, but complications arise because other soils, such as regosols, are caused by different factors. Thus Appalachian soils in Atlantic Canada, because of their highland environment, are poorly developed, whereas the regosols of the lower Fraser Valley are at an incipient stage of development because they occur on floodplain sediments that are sporadically flooded. This fact accounts for their relatively recent age. Terrain can complicate the actual pattern even further. The Rocky Mountain region of Canada, for instance, is a complex mosaic of podzolic, regosolic, organic, and cryosolic soils. It is therefore difficult to place all the soil orders that are not directly related to climate on a map of this scale.

The World Soil Map

At the global scale there are many distinct relationships between soils and climate, but there are also some differences in detail, as Fig. 25.16 demonstrates. The relationship between soils and climates is quite clear in central Eurasia. Soil types vary from south to north, changing from solonetzic soils to alfisols, then to podzols, and finally to cryosols. These variations parallel changes in climate from desert through steppe and microthermal to polar climates (see Fig. 16.3). A similar progression may be observed in corresponding parts of North America. Perhaps the most obvious relationship at the global scale is that between the desert climates and the solonetzs and regosols. Notice, too, that in the world-scale classification of soils, rock-dominated mountain areas (as is also the case at the continental scale of Fig. 25.15) and ice-covered terrain have been grouped into separate categories.

Despite the clear relationships between climate and soil types at this macroscale, similar climates do not always correspond to similar soil types. The humid subtropical climate (Cfa) is also a case in point. This climate type prevails in the southeastern parts of the five major continents (refer to Fig. 16.3), but another look at Fig 25.16 shows that the soil types in these areas vary. Only in the southeastern United States and southeastern China do we find ultisols. Southeastern parts of South America around the Rio de la Plata exhibit chernozems, whereas southeastern Africa possesses alfisols. And east-central Australia, an area of predominantly humid subtropical climate, is also dominated by alfisols. If you continue to compare Figs. 25.16 and 16.3, you will be able to pick out additional spatial discrepancies between climate and soils. This underscores that other factors in soil formation, such as parent material and the way people use soil, also help to determine the prevailing type of soil.

KEY TERMS

alfisol *page 322*	**gelisol** *page 325*	**podzolic soil** *page 326*
andisol *page 329*	**gleysolic soils** *page 325*	**red-yellow podzolic** *page 331*
aridisol *page 327*	**histosol** *page 326*	**regosolic soil** *page 327*
brunisolic soil *page 322*	**inceptisol** *page 322*	**soil order** *page 321*
Canadian System of Soil Classification *page 320*	**laterite** *page 329*	**U.S. Soil Taxonomy** *page 320*
chernozemic soil *page 324*	**luvisolic soil** *page 325*	**solonetzic soil** *page 328*
cryosolic soil *page 325*	**mollisol** *page 324*	**spodosol** *page 322*
entisol *page 324*	**organic soil** *page 326*	**ultisol** *page 331*
	oxisol *page 322*	**vertisolic soil** *page 328*

REVIEW QUESTIONS

1. What is the Canadian System of Soil Classification?
2. List and briefly describe the distinguishing characteristics of the 12 Canadian soil orders.
3. Which Canadian soil orders are associated with particular climatic zones?
4. Compare the Canadian and American soil classification systems.

REFERENCES AND FURTHER READINGS

ASHMAN, M., and PURI, G. *Essential Soil Science* (Malden, Mass.: Blackwell, 2002).

BIRKELAND, P. W. *Soils and Geomorphology* (New York: Oxford Univ. Press, 3rd ed., 1999).

BRIDGES, E. M., and DAVIDSON, D. A. *Principles and Applications of Soil Geography* (London/New York: Longman, 2nd ed., 1986).

BUOL, S. W., et al. *Soil Genesis and Classification* (Ames, Iowa: Iowa State Univ. Press, 3rd ed., 1989).

Canada Department of Agriculture. *The System of Soil Classification for Canada* (Ottawa: Research Branch, Agriculture Canada, 1970).

Canada Soil Survey Committee. *The Canadian System of Soil Classification* (Ottawa: Agriculture Canada, 3rd ed., 1998).

CHARMAN, P., and MURPHY, B., Eds. *Soils: Their Properties and Management* (New York: Oxford Univ. Press, 2nd ed., 2000).

CLARKE, G. R. *The Study of Soil in the Field* (London/New York: Oxford Univ. Press [Clarendon], 5th ed., 1971).

CLAYTON, J. S., et al. *Soils of Canada* (Ottawa: Research Branch, Agriculture Canada, 2 vols., 1977).

ELLIS, S., and MELLOR, A. *Soils and Environment* (London/New York: Routledge, 1995).

FANNING, D. S., and FANNING, M. C. B. *Soil: Morphology, Genesis, and Classification* (New York: Wiley, 1989).

FITZPATRICK, E. A. *Soils: Their Formation, Classification, and Distribution* (London/New York: Longman, 1983).

GERRARD, A. J. *Fundamentals of Soils* (London/New York: Routledge, 2000).

PARTON, T. R., et al. *Soils: A New Global View* (New Haven, Conn.: Yale Univ. Press, 1996).

ROWELL, D. L. *Soil Science: Methods and Applications* (New York: Wiley/Longman, 1994).

STEILA, D., and POND, T. E. *The Geography of Soils: Formation, Distribution, and Management* (Totowa, N.J.: Rowman & Littlefield, 2nd ed., 1989).

U.S. Department of Agriculture. *Soil Taxonomy: A Basic System of Soil Classification for Making and Interpreting Soil Surveys* (Washington, D.C.: USDA, Soil Conservation Service, Handbook No. 436, 1975 [reprinted by Krieger Publ., 1988]).

U.S. Department of Agriculture. *Keys to Soil Taxonomy* (Washington, D.C.: USDA, Natural Resources Conservation Service, 8th ed., 1998).

VALENTINE, K. W. G., et al. *The Soil Landscapes of British Columbia* (Vancouver: Agriculture British Columbia and Trafford, 2nd ed., 1998).

WEB RESOURCES

http://collections.lc.gc.ca/agrican/pubmeb/titles_e.asp This is the website of the Agriculture Canada Historical Series. It has many documents about the development of the Canadian System of Soil Classification, soils in general, and agriculture.

http://sis.agr.gc.ca/cansis/taxa/cssc3 This is the website of Agriculture Canada that has the online version of the most up-to-date Canadian System of Soil Classification.

http://www.itc.nl/~rossiter/research/rsrch_ss_class.html A compendium of online soil survey information, compiled by D.G. Rossiter. Materials are organized topically and by nation, and the site also includes a frequently asked question section.

http://www.statlab.iastate.edu/soils/soiltax/ The USDA-NRCS National Soil Survey has the second edition of *Soil Taxonomy, A Basic System for Soil Classification for Making and Interpreting Soil Surveys* available for download on this site.

Biogeographic Processes

Death and life in the African savanna—vultures on an elephant carcass in Tsavo West, Kenya. (Authors' photo)

OBJECTIVES

- To discuss the process of photosynthesis and relate it to climatic controls

- To introduce the concept of ecosystems and highlight the important energy flows within ecosystems

- To outline the factors influencing the geographic dispersal of plant and animal species within the biosphere

The soil is located at the base of the biosphere. Not only is the soil itself a living, maturing entity, but life exists within the soil layer in many forms. This unit and the next look at the most obvious evidence of the Earth's "life layer"—the natural vegetation. Biogeography, as noted in Unit 22, consists of two fields: *phytogeography* (the geography of plants) and *zoogeography* (the geography of animals). The plants are dealt with first.

Dynamics of the Biosphere

The story of the development of life on Earth parallels that of the formation of the atmosphere. The earliest atmosphere, about 4 billion years ago, was rich in gases such as methane, ammonia, carbon dioxide, and water vapour. A half-century ago, a scientist named Stanley Miller filled a flask with what he believed may have been a sample of this early atmosphere. He then subjected the contents to electrical discharges (to simulate lightning) and to boiling (much of the crust was volcanic and red hot). This resulted in the formation of amino acids, the building blocks of protein, which, in turn, are the constituents of all living things on Earth. Another scientist tried freezing the same components, and out of that experiment came organic material that forms one of the ingredients of deoxyribonucleic acid (DNA), a key to life. It is believed that these experiments replicated what actually happened on Earth about 4 billion years ago, events that led to the formation of the first complex molecules. The earliest forms of life—single-celled bacteria and algae—came from these molecules.

Photosynthesis

When the first bacteria colonized parts of the Earth's surface, a process could begin that would be essential to advancing life—**photosynthesis**. This process requires solar energy, carbon dioxide, and water. In those ancient bacteria, the first conversion of water (H_2O) and carbon dioxide (CO_2) under solar energy yielded *carbohydrates* (an organic compound and food substance) and oxygen (O_2). Starting about 2 billion years ago, photosynthetic organisms increased the oxygen content of the atmosphere from 1 percent to 20 percent. The atmosphere became sufficiently rich not only in oxygen but also in stratospheric ozone (O_3), and more complex life-forms could now evolve as the intensifying ozone layer increasingly afforded protection from solar ultraviolet radiation. Organisms eventually evolved in the aquatic environment and colonized the landmasses. The first land plants colonized the Earth more than 400 million years ago and were followed by "higher" forms of life (Fig. 26.1).

A fundamental requirement for photosynthesis is a green pigment, *chlorophyll,* at the surface of the part of the plant where the process is taking place. The colour of this pigment in part ensures that the wavelength of light absorbed from the Sun is correct for photosynthesis. This produces the dominant green colour of plants. If photosynthesis required a different wavelength of light, the Earth's vegetated landscapes might look blue or orange! As to the need for light or solar energy, plants constantly compete for the maximum exposure to this essential ingredient of life. Some plants have adapted to survival in low-light environments, but mostly every leaf turns toward the Sun. Where solar energy arrives on Earth in the greatest quantities, the tall trees of the equatorial and tropical forests soar skyward, spreading their

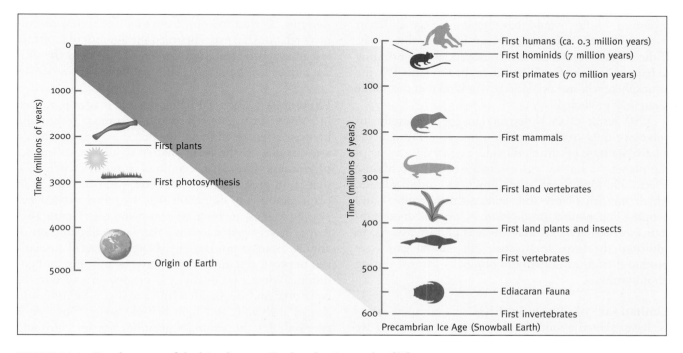

FIGURE 26.1   Development of the biosphere on Earth—the time scale of life.

FIGURE 26.2 A nearly continuous canopy of leafy vegetation marks the tropical rainforest as seen from the air (or the ground). The tall trees have spread their crowns until they interlock, competing for every ray of sunlight. This is an expanse of rainforest in eastern Bolivia.

leafy crowns in dense canopies as they vie for every ray of the Sun (Fig. 26.2).

Photosynthesis, therefore, is critical to life on Earth. It removes carbon dioxide from the atmosphere and substitutes oxygen. Humans could not live as they do in an oxygen-poor atmosphere, and had photosynthesis not altered the Earth's primitive envelope of gases, the evolution of life would have taken a very different course. Thus life depends on plants in a very direct way. If the tropical rainforests are destroyed, as is continuing to happen (see the first Perspectives box in Unit 17), the atmosphere will sustain damage of a kind that cannot be accurately predicted.

One result of such destruction could possibly involve not only oxygen depletion but also, through the relative increase of carbon dioxide, a general warming of the planet—a further enhancement of the greenhouse effect. Photosynthesis also produces carbohydrates, which nourish plants and, consequently, animals and people. The natural production of organic food substances would cease entirely without photosynthesis. In addition, the fossil fuels (coal, oil, natural gas) were produced from carbohydrates originally formed during photosynthesis.

Limitations of Photosynthesis Combining what we have learned about climatic patterns with what we know about photosynthesis, we can deduce where the process goes on most productively. Solar energy is most abundant in the tropical latitudes, and there, in general terms, photosynthesis is most active. However, some significant limitations must be recognized. In equatorial and tropical latitudes, the high solar energy also generates heat, and heat increases the plants' rates of *respiration*. Respiration runs counter to photosynthesis because it breaks down available carbohydrates, combines them with oxygen, and yields carbon dioxide, water, and biochemical energy, which sustains life. When leafy plant surfaces become hot, therefore, heightened respiration diminishes the effectiveness of photosynthesis.

Another limiting factor is the availability of water. Carbon dioxide from the atmosphere is not available for photosynthesis until it dissolves in water at the plant surface. Thus continued photosynthesis requires moisture. Small holes in the leaf surface (*stomata*), are openings for the water that arrives from the roots and stem of the plant. The more water there is at the stomata, the greater the amount of carbon dioxide that can be dissolved and the greater the production of plant food. Our knowledge of the map of moisture (see Fig. 12.11) is an important aid in understanding the distributional pattern of photosynthesis.

Several other processes occur at or near the leaf surface as photosynthesis and respiration proceed. Obviously, when heat and moisture are present, evaporation will occur. Evaporation from the leaf surfaces has a drying effect, which in turn affects photosynthesis. Plants also lose moisture in the same way that humans do, through transpiration. These two processes in combination, as learned in Unit 12, are referred to as *evapotranspiration*. As we also know from that discussion, an intimate relationship exists between the amount of moisture lost in evapotranspiration (see Fig. 12.10) and the production of living organic plant matter.

Phytomass The total living organic matter produced in a given area is referred to as its **biomass**. Technically biomass refers to all living organic things, including an area's fauna, so the plant matter should be called the **phytomass**. Biomass is expressed in terms of weight—that is, in grams per square metre—and the weight of plant matter is so dominant that the terms *biomass* and *phytomass* tend to be used synonymously. Figure 26.3 maps, in very general terms, the global distribution of annual biomass productivity. Note the overall similarities between certain climatic patterns and this configuration. Biomass productivity is greatest in well-watered equatorial and tropical lowlands; it is at a minimum in desert, highland, and high-latitude zones. But this is true only for the *natural* vegetation, not for cultivated crops. As the map suggests, forests contain the largest biomass. Replace the tropical forest with a banana plan-

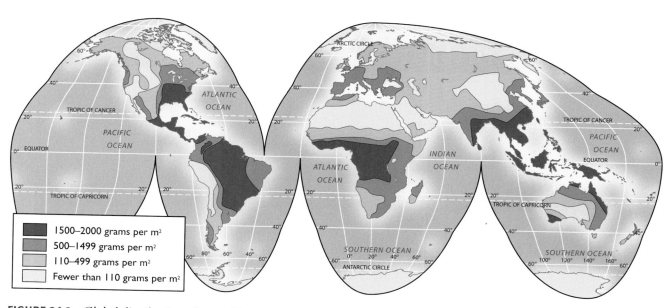

FIGURE 26.3   Global distribution of annual biomass productivity (in grams per square metre of dry biomass matter).

tation, and photosynthesis and biomass will decline precipitously.

Ecosystems and Energy Flows

An **ecosystem** is a linkage of plants and animals to their environment in an open system as far as energy is concerned: solar energy is absorbed, and chemical and heat energy are lost in several ways. You can observe part of an ecosystem in action in a sunlit freshwater pond (Fig. 26.4). Energy from sunlight is taken up in photosynthesis by microscopic green plants called *phytoplankton* (you may be able to see these in the aggregate as a greenish sheen on the water), which in turn produce carbohydrate (the food substance). Such food-producing plants are called *autotrophs,* and they provide sustenance for small larvae and other tiny life forms in the pond, collectively called *zooplankton.* Zooplankton is eaten by small fish, and these fish are later consumed by larger fish. Meanwhile plants and animals die in the pond and are broken down by decomposers, thereby releasing chemicals back into the water to be used once more by autotrophs in the production of food. Thus food energy passes from organism to organism in the ecosystem represented by our pond, generating a **food chain**. Food chains exist in all ecosystems, on land as well as in the oceans.

Ecological Efficiency

It is very difficult to measure precisely the production and consumption of energy in a food chain. Research has shown, however, that only a fraction of the food produced by autotrophs—as little as 15 percent—is actually consumed by the next participants in the food chain. For example, the zooplankton in the pond consumes only about 15 percent of the food energy yielded by the phytoplankton. A still smaller percentage of the zooplankton is eaten by the smallest fish. Each of these groups—phytoplankton, zooplankton, small fish, and larger fish—along the food chain is called a **trophic** (or feeding) **level**. On an African savanna, the autotrophs are the grasses and other plants; at the next trophic level are the animals that eat these plants, the **herbivores**. In turn, the animals that eat herbivores (as well as other animals), the **carnivores**, form a still higher trophic level.

Central to the way the biosphere operates is the loss of chemical food energy at each trophic level. We have already noted that a mere 15 percent of the food energy generated by the autotrophs in the pond is passed on to the herbivores (the zooplankton). Most of the primary production is not utilized by herbivores and is decomposed. Only 11 percent of the zooplankton reaches the carnivores (the smallest fish), and just 5 percent of these goes on to the larger fish when they eat the smaller ones. Most of the energy is used for respiration and other metabolic processes or goes to waste (is voided as faeces). These numbers indicate a very low efficiency, but they reflect efficiency at *each trophic level* in the pond. We also can estimate efficiency for entire ecosystems, averaging the efficiencies at different levels. Desert ecosystems have the lowest efficiency of all, with values of less than

FROM THE FIELDNOTES

FIGURE 26.4 "A pond like this is a crucial part of the local ecosystem. The Sun's energy reaches the surface of this lake in Britain's Lake District, where phytoplankton (microscopic green plants) convert it through photosynthesis into carbohydrate, a food substance. Tiny life forms, zooplankton, feed on this carbohydrate, and small fish eat the zooplankton. Larger fish feed on the smaller fish, and the food chain continues."

0.1 percent. Swamps in tropical areas have the highest, but even they average as little as 4 percent.

Several important consequences arise from the various efficiencies in ecosystems. First there must always be a large number of primary producers to support smaller quantities of herbivores and even fewer carnivores. The masses of living material at each trophic level therefore stack up like the graph in Fig. 26.5. Because only about 10 percent of the energy produced in the form of food is passed from one stage to another, to obtain enough food the animals at the higher trophic levels must have large territorial areas that provide enough of the species at the

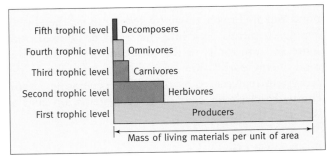

FIGURE 26.5   Mass of living materials per unit of area in different trophic levels of an ecosystem.

lower trophic level. This explains why large carnivores such as lions require a wide territorial range.

Another consequence is that because food and energy move along a chain in only one direction, the whole system collapses if earlier links of the chain are broken. Thus the removal of the autotrophs (grass) by too many rabbits in Australia caused the breakdown of an entire ecosystem. A related consequence of the chainlike structure is the fact that undesirable materials can be passed along and concentrated by the ecosystem. The insecticide DDD was applied in Clear Lake, California, to kill gnats. It was sprayed onto the water at a concentration of 0.02 parts per million (ppm). The DDD density was 5 ppm in the plankton, 15 ppm in the herbivores feeding on the plankton, 100 ppm in the fish, and 1600 ppm in the grebes (birds) that ate the fish. The grebes died. It is therefore important to understand the nature of food-energy flow through ecological systems. The next section discusses a vegetation system that changes, and we find once again that energy is crucial.

Plant Successions

The flow of energy through a food chain illustrates the interconnectivity and dynamic nature of the biosphere.

The vegetation layer, too, changes continuously and is as dynamic as the atmosphere, soil, and crust of the Earth. Some of the changes occur within a stable ecosystem, but sometimes one type of vegetation is replaced by another. This is called a **plant succession**, of which there exist three types.

A **linear autogenic succession** (primary serial succession) occurs on new terrain, e.g., created by volcanic eruptions, a fall in sea level, or continental deglaciation. Soil and plant seres develop at the same time (over 1000 years). The plants themselves initiate changes in the land surface, which consequently cause vegetational changes. "Linear" indicates that the order of succession in any one place is not normally repeated. Figure 26.6 shows how the growth of vegetation in an area that has been a lake (Stage I) is part of a linear autogenic succession. As the lake gradually fills with sediments, the water becomes chemically enriched; mosses and sedges as well as floating rafts of vegetation build up (Stage II). Plant productivity increases in the lake, and other plants encroach around its edges (Stage III). After the lake has completely filled with organic debris, dryland plants and trees may finally take over (Stage IV).

Sometimes one kind of vegetation is replaced by another, which is in turn replaced by the first. Or possibly the original vegetation follows a series of two or

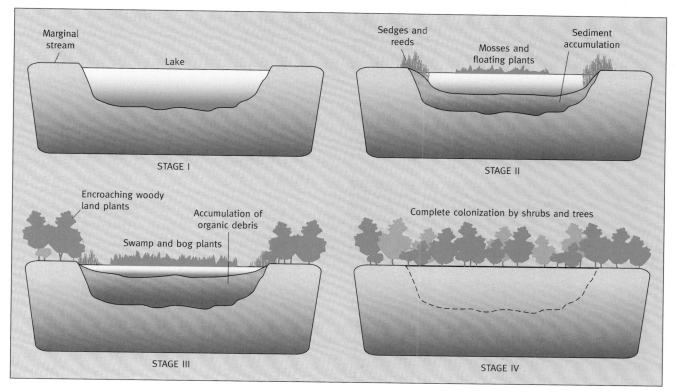

FIGURE 26.6 Idealized sequence of a linear autogenic plant succession by which a lake is eventually colonized by shrubs and trees.

three others. This is a **cyclic autogenic succession**. An example can be found at the northernmost limit of tree growth in Canada, where permafrost (perenially frozen ground) lies beneath tundra vegetation of grasses, sedges, and bare ground. The permafrost melts to a sufficient depth in summer to allow colonization by willow scrub and later by spruce trees. Gradually this forest becomes denser and forms a layer of litter. The permafrost, thus insulated, gradually rebuilds. The forest degenerates and eventually gives way to the original tundra vegetation. The cycle is then complete and ready for another sequence.

A third type of succession occurs where vegetation changes because of some outside environmental force. This kind of succession is termed an **allogenic succession** because the agent of change comes from outside the plant's immediate environment. Devastation through nuclear radiation could be one such force, but disease is more common. An epidemic of chestnut blight in eastern North America created oak and oak-hickory forests where oak-chestnut forests had once existed. Another example is the virtual elimination of the American elm tree from the landscape, caused by a lethal virus carried into tree trunks by the Dutch elm beetle during burrowing.

In all types of plant successions, the vegetation builds up through a series of stages, as indicated in Fig. 26.6. When the final stage is reached, the vegetation and its ecosystem are in complete harmony with the soil, the climate, and other parts of the environment. This balance is called a **climax community** of vegetation. If fire or disease interrupt this process and create a different type of community, they are called fire or disease disclimaxes. The major vegetation types, or *biomes* (described in Unit 27), all represent climax communities, which also are characterized by ecosystems with stable

amounts of accumulated energy. Solar energy is taken in and energy is lost through respiration and other processes, but the stored energy of the biomass is relatively constant. During a plant succession, however, the amount of energy stored in the biomass increases, as Fig. 26.7 shows. Input of energy must exceed losses for the plant succession to develop.

Geographical Dispersal

Geographers are interested in the spatial distribution of the species of the biosphere, a topic treated in Units 27 and 28. Here we investigate the factors that determine the spread and geographical limits of any particular group of organisms. The limiting factor may be either physical or biotic. Each species has an *optimum range* where it can survive and maintain a large healthy population, as shown in Fig. 26.8. Beyond this range, a species increasingly encounters *zones of physiological stress*. Although it can still survive in these zones, the population is small. When conditions become even more extreme, in the *zones of intolerance,* the species is absent altogether except possibly for short, intermittent periods.

Physical Factors

Temperature   A common limiting factor for both plants and animals is temperature. Unit 16 mentions the correspondence, suggested by Köppen, of the northern tree line and certain temperature conditions. Another example of temperature's effect on spatial distributions was discovered by the British ecologist Sir Edward Salisbury in the 1920s. One species he studied was a creeping woody plant known as the wild madder (*Rubia peregrina*). He found that the northern boundary of the wild madder in Europe coincided closely with the January 4.5°C isotherm. This temperature was critical because in January the plant formed new shoots, and lower temperatures would inhibit their development and subsequent growth. Indeed, temperatures play such a large role in determining plant distributions that plants are sometimes classified according to their propensity for withstanding heat. Plants adapted to heat are called *megatherms;* those that can withstand low temperatures are designated *microtherms;* and those with a preference for intermediate temperatures are called *mesotherms.*

Availability of Water   Another vital factor—the availability of water—limits the spread of plants and animals throughout the physical world. Water is essential in

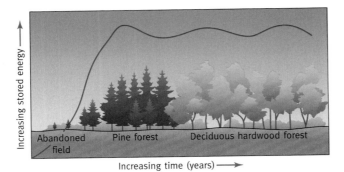

FIGURE 26.7 Increase in stored energy of the biomass in a typical secondary autogenic succession. In this case a deciduous hardwood forest takes over from an abandoned field over a period lasting about 175 years.

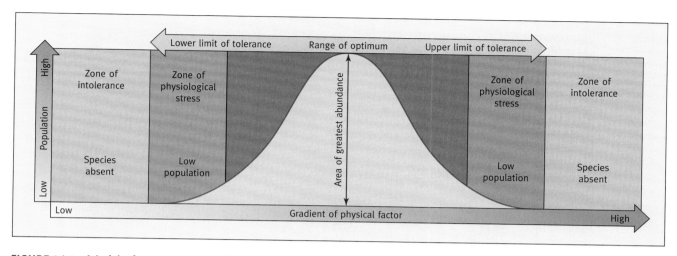

FIGURE 26.8   Model of population abundance in relation to the physical factors in the environment of a species.

photosynthesis and in other functions of plants and animals. Several plant classifications take water availability into account.

Plants that are adapted to dry areas are called *xerophytes,* and desert plants have evolved many fine adjustments. Stomata are deeply sunken into the leaf surface to reduce water loss by evapotranspiration. Roots often reach 5 m or more into the ground in search of water, or more commonly spread horizontally for great distances. Plants that live in wet environments are classified as *hygrophytes,* with rainforests, swamps, marshes, lakes, and bogs the habitats of this vegetation. The aquatic buttercup, a curious example of a hygrophyte, produces two kinds of leaves: it develops finely dissected leaves when in water and simple entire leaves when exposed to the air. Finally, plants that develop in areas of neither extreme moisture nor extreme aridity are called *mesophytes.* Most plants growing in regions of plentiful rainfall and well-drained topography fall into this category.

In tropical climates with a dry season, flowering trees and plants drop their leaves to reduce water loss during the dry season. This phenomenon spread to plants of higher latitudes, where the formation of ice in winter sometimes causes a water shortage. Trees and other plants that drop their leaves seasonally are called *deciduous,* and those that keep their leaves year-round are called *evergreen.*

Other Climatic Factors   Several other factors related to climate play a role in the dispersal of plants. These include the availability of light, the action of winds, and the duration of snow cover. The position of a species within a habitat shared by other species determines the amount of light available to it. In deciduous forests of the middle latitudes, many low shrubs grow intensely in

spring before the canopy of taller trees filters out light. The amount of available light is further determined by latitude and the associated length of daylight. Growth in the short warm season of humid microthermal (**D**) climates is enhanced by the long daylight hours of summer, and plants can mature surprisingly fast (see Fig. 19.2). Wind influences the spread of plants in several ways. It can limit growth or even destroy plants and trees in extreme situations; but it also spreads pollen and the seeds of some species.

Distribution of Soils   Another factor that affects plant dispersal is the distribution of soils. Factors concerned with the soil are known as *edaphic factors,* the most important of which are soil structure and texture, the presence of nutrients, and internal quantities of air and water. Soil structure and texture affect a plant's ability to root. Nutrients, to some extent, determine the type of vegetation. Grasses, for example, need large quantities of calcium, so they are more likely to be found in dry climates where downward percolating water is limited, which allows calcium compounds to concentrate in the upper soil. The presence of soil water depends not only on precipitation but also on the porosity and permeability of the soil. Thus, given the same amount of rainfall, a grassland might exist over permeable soils and a forest over less permeable soils.

Landforms   The final physical factor, landforms, controls vegetation distribution in many ways. On a large scale, as shown in Unit 19, vegetation changes with altitude. On the flanks of Mount Kenya in East Africa (Fig. 26.9), there is a transition from savanna grassland below 1650 m to alpine vegetation above 3650 m. Landforms have a small-scale effect as well. Steep slopes

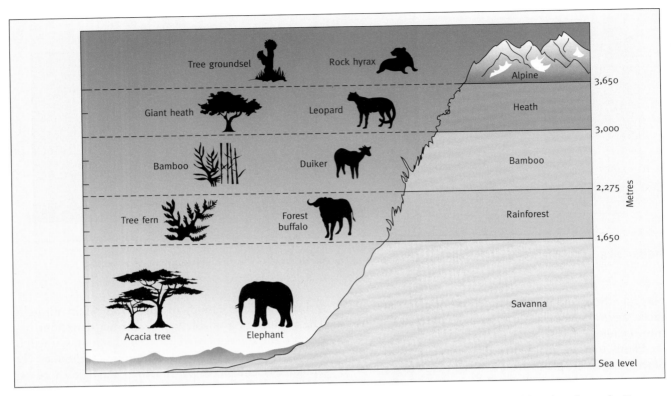

FIGURE 26.9   Zones of vegetation and animal life on the flanks of Mount Kenya in East Africa, which lies directly on the Equator.

FIGURE 26.10   Purple loosestrife (Lythrum salicaria), a European species, has taken over many wetlands in eastern North America and has choked out many native species.

foster rapid drainage and may lead to a lack of soil water. Furthermore, the aspect of a mountain slope (the direction it faces) controls the amount of incoming radiation and determines the degree of shelter from the wind, thereby influencing the local distribution of plant and animal species.

Biotic Factors

Competition   As might be expected from the interactions in any one ecosystem, many biotic as well as physical factors affect the spatial distribution of plants and animals. The biosphere is seldom static: individual species may compete with one another, be suppressed by other species, be predators or prey, or live in intimate co-operation with other species. Competition for food and space plays a strong part in plant and animal distributions. Sometimes new species compete for resources so well that they eliminate old species. For example, in large areas of eastern North America, purple loosestrife (*Lythrum salicaria*) has invaded wetlands and moist soil areas, choking out up to 60 percent of native plants (Fig. 26.10). It is estimated that approximately 200,000 hectares/year are lost to purple loosestrife in Canada.

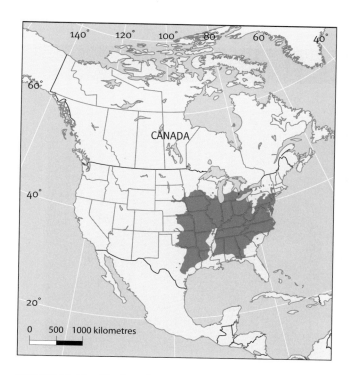

FIGURE 26.11   Black walnut (Juglans nigra) releases a toxin (juglone) from its root system which inhibits the growth of most plant species growing in its understory.

FIGURE 26.12   After their introduction and following the elimination of natural predators, the rabbit population of Australia exploded. States and individual landowners built fences to protect pastures and farmlands, but only the introduction of a rabbit-killing disease stemmed this tragic tide. Here rabbits are seen running along the rabbit-proof border fence between the states of South Australia (foreground) and New South Wales.

This plant was introduced from Europe in the early 1800s. It now dominates many wetlands from the Maritime provinces to the Great Lakes. Distribution is spotty in western Canada; the most extensive infestations are in Manitoba and British Columbia. One plant can produce over 2 million seeds. Seeds can be dispersed by air or water. Seedlings can float, so dispersal is very rapid.

Amensalism   Another form of biological interaction, the inhibition of one species by another, is called **amensalism**. The black walnut (*Juglans nigra*) is a medium-sized deciduous tree (up to 35 m tall) that grows in the deciduous forests of eastern North America (Fig. 26.11). It is a component of the Carolinian forest of southwest Ontario. This species is known for its exquisitely coloured wood and its nuts, which have been used to dye cloth. The black walnut's roots release a toxin (juglone) into the soil that inhibits most plant species from growing in its understory (under and around the tree).

Predation   Anyone who saw the ravaged landscapes of Australia before rabbit control began (Fig. 26.12) cannot doubt the efficiency of predation as a factor in the distribution of vegetation. (In 1950 the Australia's estimated rabbit population was 600 million.) But examples of one species' eating all members of another species tend to be rare. It is in the best interest of predators in balanced ecosystems to rely on a number of prey species so that their food will never be exhausted.

In this more natural situation, predation affects the plant distribution mainly by reducing the pressure of competition among prey species. In general, the presence of predators tends to increase the number of species in a given ecosystem. Charles Darwin suggested that ungrazed pasture in southern England was dominated by fast-growing tall grasses that kept out light. Consequently the ungrazed areas contained only about 11 species whereas the grazed lands possessed as many as 20.

Mutualism   Yet another biological interaction is termed **mutualism**, the coexistence of two or more species because one or more is essential to the survival of the other(s). Many examples of mutualism, or *symbiosis,* can be found in equatorial and tropical forests. When certain species in the rainforest are cut down and removed, their leaf litter and other organic remains no longer decay on the forest floor. Since equatorial laterites are so infertile, this leaf litter keeps other plants supplied with nutrients. Remove them, and the remaining plants may die. Such human intervention, of course, reminds us that another species—*Homo sapiens*—can often significantly shape the geography of plants and animals as well.

FROM THE FIELDNOTES

FIGURE 26.13 "Along the northern California coast you can see the competition between sagebrush and grass in progress, the grass losing out over time. The Mediterranean climatic regime, high relief, and thin soils give the better adapted sage a durable advantage."

Species Dispersal and Endemism Terrestrial and aquatic (freshwater and marine) plants, animals, and other biota (living organisms) are naturally present in specific geographic locations because of their adaptation to local and/or regional environments. Ancestral species from which modern species evolved arrived in a given area by movement over land, swimming, rafting, or flying (**dispersal**)—or were carried along by plate mobility over tens of millions of years (**vicariance**). A good example of vicariance is the flora, fauna, and other biota on the island of Madagascar, which split off and moved away from the African continent with the breakup of the Gondwana supercontinent that began 160 million years ago (see Fig. 32.1). As a result, Mada-

gascar, other oceanic islands, and certain isolated (or once isolated) land areas contain a significant percentage of species of plants, animals, and other life forms that exist nowhere else on Earth. Biologists call such species *endemic*. Regions of high biotic **endemism** are particularly vulnerable to the extinction of endemic species because of environmental changes caused by human modification of the landscape (e.g., deforestation) or the intended or unintended introduction of other terrestrial and marine organisms (Fig. 26.14).

Ever since humans began to travel beyond their home areas, they have brought plants, animals, and other biota with them. The process of dispersing species distant from their natural areas accelerated with long-

A Biogeographic Puzzle—The Species-Richness Gradient

For over a century it has been known that the number of species per unit area decreases with latitude. A single square kilometre of tropical rainforest contains thousands of plant and animal species; a square kilometre of tundra may contain only a few dozen. This phenomenon is known as the **species-richness gradient**, and many theories have been proposed to explain it.

Associated with the species-richness gradient is the relationship between the most abundant and important species on the one hand and lesser species on the other. This is the principle of *species dominance*. In tropical rainforest environments, where the number and the diversity of species are very large (see Perspectives box in Unit 22), it is often the case that no species is clearly dominant. But in higher-latitude environments, for example, where oak-hickory or spruce-fir forests prevail, a few species (such as an evergreen tree or a large herbivore) often predominate.

Species diversity in biotic communities increases with evolutionary time, with environmental stability, and with favourable (warm, humid, biologically productive) habitats. In general the territorial ranges of individual species are comparatively small in equatorial and tropical environments, and much larger in the higher latitudes. Biogeographers have concluded that the spatial patterns of species richness indicate that niche differentiation is the main active process in the small, favourable low-latitude microclimates, whereas adaptation to the rigours of high-latitude environments is the selective force acting on (and restricting) species there.

But there may be more to it. In their large ranges at high latitudes, species must adapt to wide fluctuations in temperature and other environmental conditions. Animals roam far and wide; plants are hardy and durable. In tropical areas, however, species tend to be closely bound to a narrow set of environmental conditions; the mosaic of microclimates reflects the limited range of many species. Such species cannot adapt to even a small change in their environment. Plants may be fragile and vulnerable. Migrating animals quickly find themselves at a disadvantage.

The species-richness gradient may thus be explained in terms of adaptation, species success and dispersal, and environmental limitations. Some ecologists argue that biological resources can be shared more finely where the environment is relatively constant; specialization is more possible under such circumstances. Considering the relationship another way, we observe that the high input of solar energy near the Equator may provide more placement scope for specialization than do weaker solar inputs at higher latitudes. An early theory, still popular among some biogeographers, is that tropical rainforests are older than temperate and high-latitude communities, and thus have had more time to accumulate complex biotic communities. But newly gained knowledge about the Pleistocene epoch seems to run counter to this idea.

Recent research by the ecologist George Stevens introduces still another factor into the debate. In any particular environment there are always very successful, abundant, well-adapted species alongside less well adapted "marginal" species. When large numbers of a successful species disperse into a less suitable environment, they should succumb to competition from established species in that environment. Often, however, they manage to survive because their numbers are constantly replenished by the continuing stream of migrants. This is known as the *rescue effect*.

Migrants in small tropical microclimates quickly move beyond their optimal environmental niches (niches are discussed on p. 364). But in high-latitude environments, where species' ranges are larger and where species are adapted to wider environmental ranges, dispersing individuals of successful species are much less likely to stray into unsuitable habitats. As Stevens points out, the rescue effect is much less influential in higher-latitude areas than in the tropics, contributing to the geographic pattern of the species-richness gradient.

Various theories combine different ideas about the species-richness gradient in various ways, but no single theory has won general acceptance. And so one of biogeography's grandest global designs continues to evoke discussion and debate.

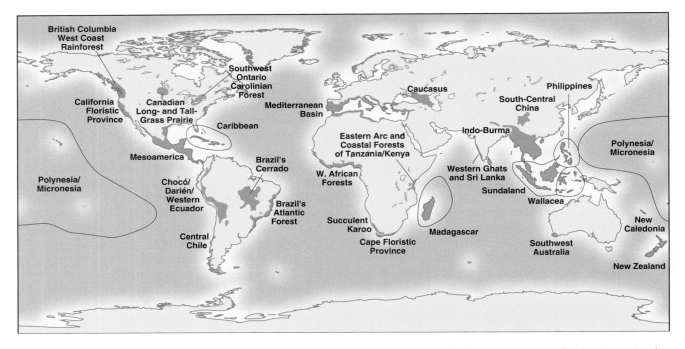

FIGURE 26.14   Global distribution of biodiversity "hot spots." These areas contain high concentrations of endemic species that are threatened by human activities.

distance sea voyaging. In more recent times, ships have been joined by aircraft and motor vehicles as agents of transfer of species from one region to another, thereby bypassing such natural barriers to the dispersal of species as oceans, inhospitable climates, and mountain ranges.

Although researchers have not been able to fully explain every major geographic variation (see Perspec-

tive: A Biogeographic Puzzle—The Species-Richness Gradient), these limiting physical and biotic factors contribute a great deal to our understanding of the distribution of plant and animal species. Unit 27 shows how the biogeographic processes discussed in this unit are expressed spatially on the world map of vegetative associations.

KEY TERMS

allogenic succession *page 342*

amensalism *page 345*

biomass *page 338*

carnivores *page 339*

climax community *page 342*

cyclic autogenic succession *page 342*

dispersal *page 346*

ecosystem *page 339*

endemism *page 346*

food chain *page 339*

herbivores *page 339*

linear autogenic succession *page 341*

mutualism *page 345*

photosynthesis *page 337*

phytomass *page 338*

plant succession *page 341*

species-richness gradient *page 347*

trophic level *page 339*

vicariance *page 346*

REVIEW QUESTIONS

1. Which subjects are encompassed by *phytogeography* and *zoogeography*?

2. Describe the process of photosynthesis, including consideration of requirements, limitations, and related processes.

3. What are food chains, and how efficient are they at transferring energy to higher trophic levels?

4. Describe how a lake might undergo linear autogenic succession.

5. Describe the physical and biotic factors that affect the geographic dispersal of plants and/or animals.

REFERENCES AND FURTHER READINGS

BAILEY, R. G. *Ecosystem Geography* (New York: Springer Verlag, 1996).

BAILEY, R. G. *Ecoregions: The Ecosystem Geography of the Oceans and Continents* (New York: Springer Verlag, 1998).

BARBOUR, M. G., et al. *Terrestrial Plant Ecology* (Menlo Park, Calif.: Benjamin/Cummings, 1980).

BRADBURY, I. K. *The Biosphere* (New York: Wiley, 2nd ed., 1998).

COX, C. B., and MOORE, P. D. *Biogeography: An Ecological and Evolutionary Approach* (Cambridge, Mass.: Blackwell, 5th ed., 1993).

HUGGETT, R. J. *Fundamentals of Biogeography* (London/New York: Routledge, 1998).

JARVIS, P. J. *Plant and Animal Introductions* (Malden, Mass.: Blackwell, 1999).

MacARTHUR, R. H. *Geographical Ecology: Patterns in the Distribution of Species* (Princeton, N.J.: Princeton Univ. Press, 1984).

MacDONALD, G. M. *Biogeography: Introduction to Space, Time and Life* (New York: Wiley, 2003).

MAURER, B. A. *Geographical Population Analysis: Tools for the Analysis of Biodiversity* (Cambridge, Mass.: Blackwell, 1994).

McGINNIS, M. V., ed. *Bioregionalism* (London/New York: Routledge, 1999).

MYERS, A. A., and GILLER, P. S., Eds. *Analytical Biogeography: An Integrated Approach to the Study of Animal and Plant Distributions* (New York: Chapman and Hall, 1988).

RAVEN, P. H., and BERG, L. R. *Environment* (Hoboken, N.J.: Wiley, 4th ed., 2004).

RICKLEFS, R. E., and SCHLUTER, D., Eds. *Species Diversity in Ecological Communities: Historical and Geographical Perspectives* (Chicago: Univ. of Chicago Press, 1993).

SMIL, V. *The Earth's Biosphere: Evolution, Dynamics, and Change* (Cambridge, Mass.: MIT Press, 2002).

TIVY, J. *Biogeography: A Study of Plants in the Ecosphere* (London/New York: Longman, 2nd ed., 1982).

WILLIAMS, R. S., Jr. "A Modern Earth Narrative: What Will Be the Fate of the Biosphere?," *Technology in Society,* 22 (2000), 303–339.

WILSON, E. O. *The Diversity of Life* (Cambridge, Mass.: Belknap/Harvard Univ. Press, 1992).

ZIMMER, C. *Evolution: Triumph of an Idea* (New York: Harper-Collins, 2001).

WEB RESOURCES

http://climcharge.cr.uses.gor/data/atlas/hltl/regmaps-faq.html
This website gives excellent distribution maps of plant species found in North America.

http://www.csiro.au/communication/rabbits/ga.1.htm Website of Australia and New Zealand Rabbit Calcivirus Disease program. Information about rabbit infestation, damage, and control. Agency wants to release rabbit calcivirus to lower rabbit numbers.

http://www.globalforestservice.org/research/trees-of-canada.html
This website has information about Canadian tree species, while associated sites have information on tree species around the world.

http://www.geocities.com/CollegePark/Union/6551/Erin.html
A brief descriptive page defining both ecological and plant succession.

http://www.nationalgeographic.com/wildworld Information and images for all 867 worldwide land-based ecoregions are available on this site, as well as data from Project Global 2000: priority areas for ecological conservation.

http://res2.agr.ca/lethbridge/medbio/plant/blostrif-e.htm This website of the Agriculture Canada Lethbridge Research Institute has lots of information about purple loosestrife and other "noxious weeds," including how to control them by biological means.

The Global Distribution of Plants

Montane forest in East Africa's Chyulu Hills, where elevation and moisture combine to sustain luxuriant flora amid steppe and savanna. (Authors' photo)

OBJECTIVES

- To briefly survey the principal terrestrial biomes

The classification and mapping of climate posed many geographical challenges. It was necessary to establish a set of measures to form the basis for Fig. 16.3, the map of world climates. That map shows the distribution of *macro*climates—climatic regions on a broad global scale. Embedded within those macroclimates, as was noted, are local microclimates, which do not always conform to the established criteria. The global map, therefore, is only a general guide to what should be found in a particular place.

Mapping vegetation is in some ways an even more difficult problem. On one of your field trips, stop near any vegetated area and note the large number of plants you can identify, probably ranging from trees and grasses to ferns or mosses. Part of the local area you examine may be tree-covered; another part of it may be open grassland; some of it may be exposed rock, carrying mosses or lichens. How can any global map represent this intricate plant mosaic? The answer is similar to that for climates and soils: plant geographers (phytogeographers) look for the key to the largest units of plant association. In the case of climate, this can be done by analyzing temperatures, moisture, and seasonality. The great Soil Orders (see Fig. 25.15) were based on a determination of the most general similarities or differences in soil horizons and formative processes. In classifying the Earth's plant cover, biogeographers use the concept of the *biome* to derive their world map.

Biomes

A **biome** is the broadest justifiable subdivision of the plant and animal world, an assemblage and association of plants and animals that forms a regional ecological unit of subcontinental dimensions. We can readily visualize the most general classes of vegetation—forest, grassland, desert, and tundra—but such a classification would not be useful to geographers. For example, there are tropical forests and high-latitude coniferous forests, and they are so different that grouping them within a single ecological unit would serve little or no purpose. However, if we subdivide forests into tropical, monsoon, temperate (midlatitude), northern (coniferous), and Mediterranean, we have identified true biomes. At this level, the classification is quite useful.

Just as geographers continue to debate the merits of the global climatic map, so biologists are not in total agreement concerning the Earth's biomes. In fact, if we were to look at maps of biomes in biology textbooks, we would find quite a range of interpretations. Moreover, biologists include both *terrestrial* and *marine* biomes in their classifications (biogeography tends to concentrate on the terrestrial biomes). Even the identity of terrestrial biomes is not uniformly accepted, and thus Fig. 27.1 should be viewed as one justifiable representation of the Earth's land biomes, but not as the only possible one.

We also must remember that biomes are not so sharply defined regionally that their limits are clearly demarcated on the surface. The lines separating biomes on the world map, therefore, represent broad transition zones. If you were to walk from one biome region to another, you would observe a gradual change as certain species thin out and vanish while others make their appearance and become established. To move from one fully developed biome to its neighbour might require several days of walking.

The distribution of biome regions results from two major factors—climate and topography. Both climate and terrain are reflected on the map of global vegetation. The key *climatic factors* are (1) the atmosphere and its

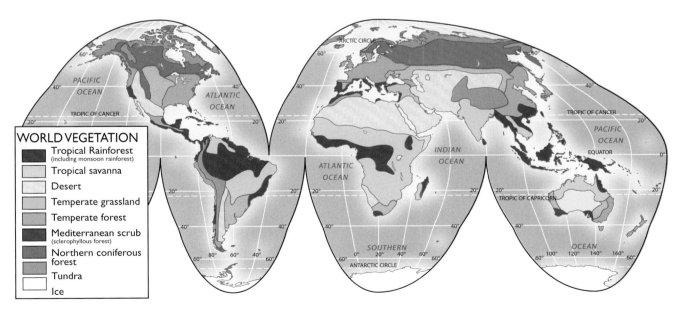

FIGURE 27.1 Global distribution of the principal terrestrial biomes.

circulation systems, which determine where moisture-carrying air masses do (and do not) go, and (2) the energy source for those circulation systems, solar radiation. (The Sun's energy not only drives atmospheric movements, but also sustains photosynthesis and propels the endless march of the seasons.) The main *terrain factors* are (1) the distribution of the landmasses and ocean basins, and (2) the topography of the continents.

Some biomes that are widely distributed in the Northern Hemisphere hardly ever occur south of the Equator because the Southern Hemisphere does not include large landmasses at comparable latitudes. The varied topography and elevation of the landmasses disrupt much of the regularity the map might have shown had the continents been flatter and lower. Accordingly, the orientations of the Earth's great mountain ranges can clearly be seen on the world map of these biomes (Fig. 27.1). Interestingly, many of these same patterns

exist at the continental scale as well (see Perspective: North America's Vegetation Regions).

It can be concluded that the latitudinal transition of biomes from the hot equatorial regions to the cold polar zones can also be observed along the slope of a high mountain. After all, mountain-slope temperatures decrease with altitude, and precipitation usually increases with altitude. Mount Kenya, in East Africa, stands with its foot on the Equator and is capped with snow. The same holds for Ecuador's Mount Chimborazo in northwestern South America. This mountain is remembered in this connection because it was there that the great naturalist Alexander von Humboldt first recognized the relationships not only between vegetation and altitude, but also between altitude and latitude. These relationships, applied to the vertical sequencing of biomes, are illustrated in Fig. 27.3. Note that it is not just mountains that have a tree line, a zone above which trees will

PERSPECTIVES ON THE HUMAN ENVIRONMENT

North America's Vegetation Regions

At the continental scale, or the level of spatial generalization below that used on the world map (Fig. 27.1), we see in more detail the results of the forces and processes that shape vegetation. The map of North America's vegetation displayed in Fig. 27.2, constructed by biogeographer Thomas Vale, parallels the world map of biome regions, most notably in its broad distinctions between forest, grassland, tundra, and desert zones. There are some differences too, but most are attributable to the downward cartographic shift from the global to the continental scale. In other words, Vale's map is a more detailed version of Fig. 27.1, the detail made possible by the larger scale of the North American map.

This comparison of spatial frameworks again suggests the possibility of multiple regionalization schemes, with the shift to the North American scale raising a host of familiar problems concerning regional boundaries. An instance is the forest–desert boundary in the Pacific Northwest, which results from the rain shadow effect east of the Cascade Mountains (see Unit 13). On the world map

(Fig. 27.1), that fairly rapid west–east change can be represented only by a line dividing two adjacent biomes. But on the North American map (Fig. 27.2), that now fuzzy "line" has become a transition zone, and Vale finds it necessary to introduce a narrow, intermediate *mountain vegetation* region to contain the phytogeographical changes that occur across the Cascade range.

The Cascades example also reminds us that the geography of vegetation on the continental scale results from the same factors that operate at the regional biome level—climate and terrain. Solar radiation and atmospheric circulation patterns are again the key climatic factors. Accordingly, much of the North American map can be related to the actions of processes that are discussed in Part Two, especially those shaping north–south temperature gradients and east–west moisture variations.

Terrain differences (which are treated in the survey of North American physiography in Unit 52) markedly influence vegetation as well, and such major topographic features as the Cascades and

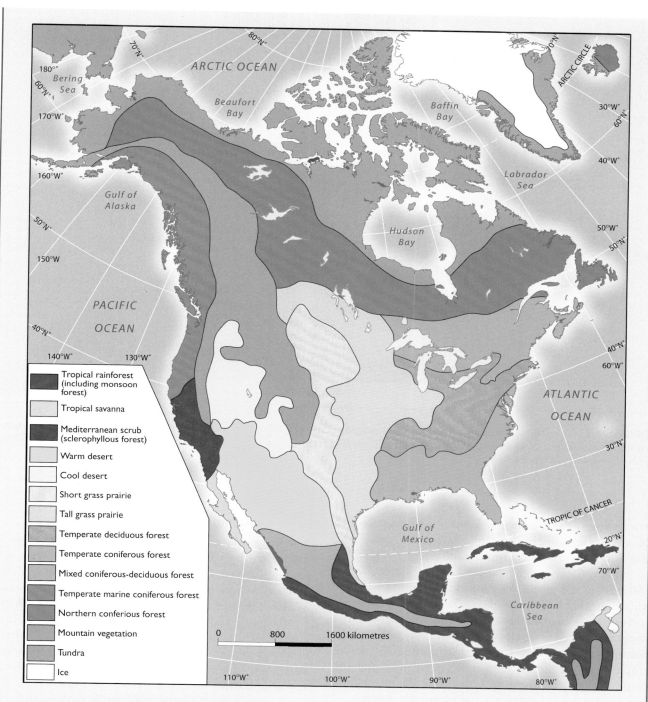

FIGURE 27.2 Distribution of natural vegetation in North America.

Legend:
- Tropical rainforest (including monsoon forest)
- Tropical savanna
- Mediterranean scrub (sclerophyllous forest)
- Warm desert
- Cool desert
- Short grass prairie
- Tall grass prairie
- Temperate deciduous forest
- Temperate coniferous forest
- Mixed coniferous-deciduous forest
- Temperate marine coniferous forest
- Northern coniferous forest
- Mountain vegetation
- Tundra
- Ice

the ranges of the Rocky Mountains in the western third of North America are prominently visible in Fig. 27.2. To the east, topography appears to play a lesser role, but the southwestward-pointing prong of the *mixed coniferous–deciduous forest* region near the central northeastern seaboard clearly reflects the presence of the Appalachian Mountains. It also suggests the existence of yet another embedded mosaic of vegetation regions at the next lower level of spatial generalization.

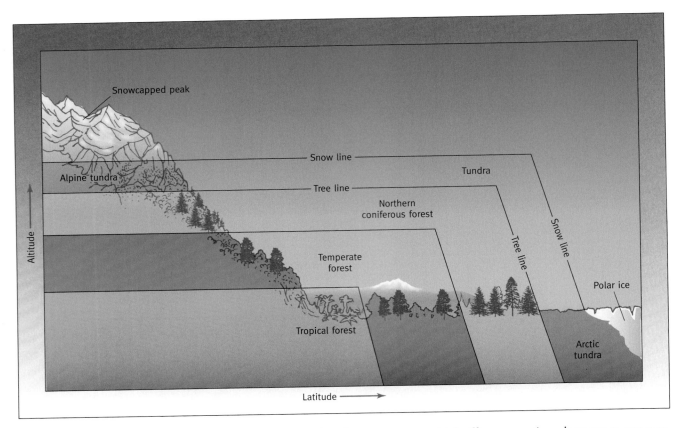

FIGURE 27.3   Vegetation changes with latitude and altitude. The temperature, which affects vegetation, decreases as one travels up a mountain or away from the Equator, so that if there is plenty of moisture, the vegetation is similar at high altitudes and at high latitudes, as shown here.

not grow—the entire Earth exhibits a tree line, poleward of which the northern coniferous forests are replaced by the stunted plants of the frigid tundra.

Another way to gain a perspective on the factors influencing the global distribution of biomes is represented in Fig. 27.4. In this scheme the latitude is increasing along the left side of the triangle and the moisture is decreasing along the base. Notice that forest biomes are generated within three latitudinal zones: tropical, temperate, and subarctic. Also note that the tropical forests develop more than one distinct biome before giving way to savanna and ultimately desert.

Principal Terrestrial Biomes

Let us now examine the Earth's major biomes, keeping in mind the tentative nature of any such regional scheme. Using Fig. 27.1 as our frame of reference, together with the photographs that accompany our discussion, we can gain an impression of the location and character of each of the eight biomes treated in this unit.

Tropical Rainforest

The **tropical rainforest biome**, whose vegetation is dominated by tall, closely spaced evergreen trees, is a teeming arena of life that is home to a great number and diversity of both plant and animal species. Alfred Russel Wallace wrote of the tropical rainforest in 1853: "What we may fairly allow of tropical vegetation is that there is a much greater number of species, and a greater variety of forms, than in temperate zones." This was an understatement. It is now known that more species of plants and animals live in tropical rainforests than in all the other world biomes combined. In fact, the rainforest often has as many as 40 species of trees per hectare, compared to 8 to 10 species per hectare in temperate forests.

True climax tropical rainforest lets in little light. The canopy of the trees is so dense (see Fig. 26.2) that sometimes only 1 percent of the light above the forest penetrates the canopy and reaches the ground. As a result, only a few shade-tolerant plants can live on the forest floor (see Fig. 17.2). The trees are large, often reaching heights of 40 to 60 m. Because their roots are usually

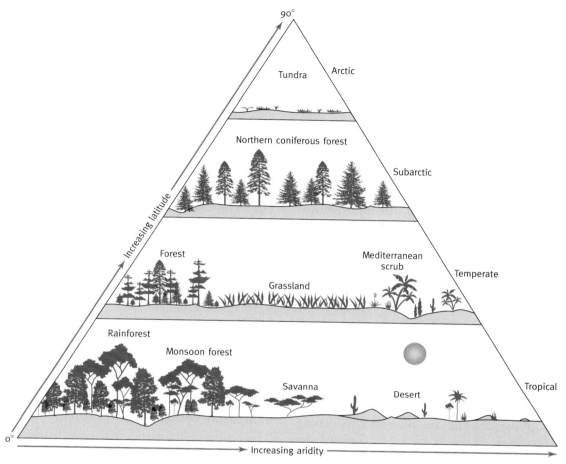

FIGURE 27.4 Simplified scheme of the major terrestrial biomes, arranged along gradients of increasing aridity at different latitudes, illustrating the dominant influence of moisture and temperature on the structure of plant communities.

shallow, the bases of the trees are supported by buttresses. Another feature is the frequent presence of epiphytes and lianas. *Epiphytes* are plants that use the trees for support, but they are not parasites; *lianas* are vines rooted in the ground with leaves and flowers in the canopy, the top parts of the trees.

What organic matter there is decomposes rapidly, so there is little accumulation of litter on the rainforest floor. Although it is easy to walk through the true climax tropical rainforest, many areas contain a thick impenetrable undergrowth (jungle). This growth springs up where river erosion or humans have destroyed the original forest. The areas where shifting agricultural practices are common are especially likely to exhibit such second growth. It has been estimated that most of the true tropical rainforest may disappear by the middle of this century. Moreover, where natural vegetation is cleared from the laterites of this biome, hardpans frequently develop through the extreme leaching of the upper soil, which produces high concentrations of iron and aluminum compounds. Agriculture is difficult and minimally productive in such untillable soil.

Monsoon rainforests are included in this biome, even though they differ slightly from tropical rainforests. Monsoon rainforests are established in areas with a dry season and therefore exhibit less variety in plant species. This vegetation is lower and less dense, and it also grows in layers or tiers composed of species adjusted to various light intensities.

Until recently, tropical rainforests covered almost half the forested area of the Earth (see Fig. 27.1). The largest expanses are in the Amazon River Basin in northern South America and the Congo River Basin in west-equatorial Africa. A third area includes parts of southeastern Asia, northeastern Australia, and Indonesia. Human destruction of rainforests (see the first Perspectives box in Unit 17) continues at an alarming rate—with devastating consequences for the tropics and possibly far beyond.

Tropical Savanna

The **savanna biome** encompasses a transitional environment between the tropical rainforest and the desert, consisting of tropical grassland with widely spaced trees (Fig. 27.5). Thorn forests, characterized by dense, spiny, low, fire-resistant trees, predominate, and bulbous plants are abundant. The most common trees of the savanna are deciduous, dropping their leaves in the dry season. These include the acacia and the curious water-storing, fat-trunked baobab tree. Grasses in the savanna are usually tall and have stiff, coarse blades.

Savanna vegetation has developed primarily because of the seasonally wet and dry climate (**Aw**) in large areas of Africa, South America, northern Australia, and India as well as in parts of Southeast Asia. However, periodic burning plays a significant role in limiting tree growth. In some places, the grasses form a highly inflammable straw mat in the dry season. This can be ignited through lightning, but humans may also set fire to it. Typical of the food chain of this biome are large herds of grazing animals (see photo on p. 363).

Desert

The **desert biome** is characterized by sparse vegetation or even its complete absence (see Fig. 17.8). Whereas the grasses of the savanna are *perennials,* persisting from year to year, many of the desert plants are *ephemerals,* completing their entire life cycle during a single growing season. These ephemerals often grow quickly after the short but intense seasonal rains, covering open sandy or rocky areas in a spectacular display (Fig. 27.6). The seeds of these ephemerals often lie dormant in the soil for many years and then germinate rapidly after a rainstorm. The perennial plants in the desert biome, such as cactuses and euphorbias (spurges), are dormant much of the year. Some, with fleshy water-storing leaves or stems, are known as *succulents.* Others have small leathery leaves or are deciduous. Woody plants have very long roots or are restricted to localized areas of water.

The sparse vegetation of desert ecosystems can support only small animals of the higher trophic levels. These animals are well adapted to the arid conditions. Rodents live in cool burrows; insects and reptiles have waterproof skins that help them retain water. There are many fossorial animals that spend the heat of the day below the surface. The desert biome, of course, coincides with areas of arid (**BW**) climates. Pedocal and regosolic soils are the most common Soil Orders associated with the desert biome.

Temperate Grassland

The **temperate grassland biome** generally occurs over large areas of continental interiors. Perennial and sod-forming grasses like those shown in Fig. 27.7 are dominant. The temperate grassland biome, like the savanna, has historically been inhabited by herds of grazing animals such as bison and saiga antelope and their predators. In North America, the short-grass prairie of the Prairies and Great Plains gradually gives way toward the east to the moister, richer, tall-grass prairie (Fig. 27.2). This transition in vegetation is accompanied by a transition in the soil layer from chernozems to luvisols (see Fig. 25.14). As in the Savanna biome, fire was important in limiting the invasion of trees.

This biome has been highly susceptible to human influence. Large areas have been turned over to crop and/or livestock farming. This is true of the interior areas of North America, the Pampas grasslands of Argentina, and the steppes of southern Russia, where the biome is most widespread (see Fig. 27.1). Temperate grasslands maintain a delicate ecological balance, and mismanagement or climatic change quickly turns them into temperate forests or deserts (desertification is discussed in Unit 17).

Temperate Forest

There are several varieties of temperate forest. The **temperate deciduous forest biomes** occur in eastern North America (Fig. 27.8), Europe, and eastern China. These forests of broadleaf trees are shared by herbaceous plants, which are most abundant in spring before the growth of new leaves on the trees. An outstanding characteristic of temperate deciduous forests is the similarity of plants found in their three locations in the Northern Hemisphere. Oak, beech, birch, walnut, maple, ash, and chestnut trees are all common. As with the temperate grasslands, large areas of this forest type—the Carolinian Forest in southern Ontario, for example—have been cleared and converted to agricultural production.

Temperate evergreen forest (temperate west coast rainforest) biomes are found on western coasts in temperate latitudes where abundant precipitation is the norm. In the Northern Hemisphere they take the form of needle-leaf forests. The coastal redwoods and Douglas firs of the northwestern coast of North America are representative (Fig. 27.9). Some of the tallest and oldest trees on Earth are located in the coastal areas of British Columbia and the U.S. Pacific Northwest (Sitka spruce, Douglas fir, western hemlock, California redwood) or in the interior just to the east (sequoias which reach over 100 m in height and 3 m in diameter over a thousand-year lifespan), although only a few relatively small areas

FROM THE FIELDNOTES

FIGURE 27.5 "The East African savanna is sometimes called a 'parkland' savanna because trees are widely spaced and give the landscape a regularity that seems cultivated, not wild. The umbrella-like acacia tree is an ally of wildlife and human traveller alike, as I can attest—its shade made many a hot day bearable. The savanna feeds grazing animals as well as browsers because it offers grasses as well as leaves to its migrants; the flat-topped acacia tends to be trimmed at around 5 m by giraffes, which are able to strip leaves from the thorniest of branches. And, as this photo shows, the acacia supports other species as well, as the large and occupied eagle's nest confirms."

FROM THE FIELDNOTES

FIGURE 27.6 "A field trip through Arizona desert country reminded us that the desert biome encompasses rich and diversified vegetation. Despite the often thin and unproductive solonetzic and other desert soils prevailing under desert climatic conditions, the infrequent and scant rainfall recorded here is enough to sustain a wide range of plant species as well as a varied fauna."

FIGURE 27.7 Canadian Prairie grasses in Alberta.

FIGURE 27.9 Lush, old-growth Douglas fir forest in British Columbia's coastal rainforest.

FIGURE 27.8 Mainly deciduous trees in the Carolinian Forest in southern Ontario.

still contain primary redwood and sequoia forests because of the high demand for such wood as a building material. The podocarps of the temperate evergreen rainforest on the western coast of New Zealand exemplify the broadleaf and small-leaf evergreen forests of the Southern Hemisphere. All these forest types, too, are subject to periodic natural fire, which cleans built-up fallen debris, opens areas for new growth, and adds nutrients to the soil. Some coniferous species need fire (heat or flame) to open their cones so that their seeds can be distributed—for example, Jack pine (*Pinus banksiana*) in eastern North America and Lodgepole

pine (*Pinus contorta var. latifolia*) in the northwestern forests of North America, both of which have very resinous cones that require flame or heat to open them and release the seeds.

Mediterranean Scrub (Sclerophilous forest)

The Mediterranean climate (see Unit 18) is characterized by hot dry summers and cool moist winters. Such climates prevail along the shores of the Mediterranean Sea, along the coast of California, in central Chile, in South Africa's Cape Province, and in southern and southwestern Australia (see Fig. 16.3). The **Mediterranean scrub biome** corresponds to these **Csa** and **Csb** climates. The vegetation of this biome consists of widely spaced evergreen or deciduous trees (pine and oak) and often dense, hard-leaf evergreen scrub. Thick waxy leaves are well adapted to the long, hot, dry summers.

Mediterranean vegetation creates a very distinctive natural landscape (Fig. 27.10). Even though this biome's regions are widely separated and isolated from each other, their appearance is quite similar. In coastal California, the Mediterranean landscape is called *chaparral;* in the Mediterranean region of southern Europe, it is referred to as *maquis* (French) or *macchia* (Italian); in Chile it is known as *mattoral;* and in South Africa it is called *fynbos.* All of these areas are adapted to sporadic burning, hence the spectacular fires seen most years in California.

Mediterranean regions are among the world's most densely populated and most intensively cultivated. Human activity has profoundly altered the Mediter-

FIGURE 27.10 "Mediterranean physical and cultural landscapes coexist in a distinctive way. Where human activity has encroached on even the steepest slopes, Mediterranean vegetation somehow survives. Italy's Amalfi coast, south of Naples, provides an example."

FIGURE 27.11   A river meanders across a taiga (snowforest) landscape on the eastern side of the Ural Mountains in Siberia. It is the Russian midsummer, and the water level is relatively low.

ranean biome through the use of fire, through grazing, and through agriculture. Today vineyards and olive groves have replaced countless hectares of natural chaparral and maquis. Great stands of trees have been removed, and many species of fauna have been driven away or made extinct. Before the rise of ancient Greece, the hills of the Greek peninsula were covered with oaks and pines that had adapted to this climatic regime. Only a few of the legendary cedars of Lebanon now survive. The cork oak, another example of adaptation, still stands in certain corners of the Mediterranean lands. From these remnants it can be deduced that the Mediterranean biome has been greatly modified, but it has not lost its regional identity.

Northern Coniferous Forest

The upper midlatitude **northern coniferous forest biome** has many different names. In North America it takes a Latin name to become the *boreal forest*. In Russia it is called the *snowforest* or *taiga*. The most common coniferous (cone-bearing) trees in this biome are spruce, hemlock, fir, and pine. These needle-leaf trees can withstand the periodic drought resulting from long periods of freezing conditions fast-draining and base-poor podzolic soils. The trees are slender and grow to heights of 12 to 18 m; they generally live less than 300 years but grow quite densely (Fig. 27.11). Depressions, bogs, and lakes hide among the trees. In such areas, low-growing

bushes with leathery leaves, mosses, and grasses rise out of the waterlogged soil. This type of growth assemblage, combined with stunted and peculiarly shaped trees, is known as *muskeg*.

All the biomes discussed here could be differentiated even more precisely. For instance, the boreal forest of Canada can be divided into three subzones: (1) the main boreal forest, which is characterized by a continuous canopy; (2) the open boreal woodland, marked by patches where the trees are broken up by open spaces of grass or muskeg; and (3) a mixture of woodland in the valleys and tundra vegetation on the ridges, called forest tundra, which is found along the polar margins of this biome (near the tree line).

Tundra

The **tundra biome** is the most continuous of all the biomes, and it occurs almost unbroken along the poleward margins of the northern continents (see Fig. 27.1). It is also found on the islands near Antarctica and in alpine environments above the tree line on mountains at every latitude. Only cold-tolerant plants can survive under harsh tundra conditions in seasonally frozen cryosolic soils. The most common are mosses, lichens, sedges, and sometimes, near the forest border, dwarf trees (see Fig. 19.8). Ephemeral plants are rare; the perennial shrubs are pruned back by the icy winter winds and seldom reach their maximum height. Nor can plant roots be extensive in this biome because the top of the permafrost is seldom more than 1 m below the surface. The permafrost also prevents good surface drainage.

During the short summer, shallow pools of water at the surface become the home of large insect populations. In the Northern Hemisphere, birds migrate from the south to feed on these insects. The fauna is surprisingly varied, considering the small biomass available. It consists of such large animals as reindeer, caribou, musk ox, and polar bear and such small herbivores as hares, lemmings, and voles. Carnivores include foxes, wolves, hawks, falcons, owls, and, of course, people.

This survey of the Earth's principal terrestrial biomes has concentrated on the vegetation that dominates their landscapes. A biome, however, consists of more than plants; the animals that form part of its biological community also must be considered. Unit 28 looks at the geography of fauna—zoogeography. Although the focus is on the larger animals, it should be kept in mind that fungi, bacteria, and other types of biota that coexist with plants and animals are also integral parts of the Earth's terrestrial and marine ecosystems.

KEY TERMS

biome *page 351*

desert biome *page 356*

Mediterranean scrub biome *page 359*

northern coniferous forest
     biome *page 361*

savanna biome *page 356*

temperate deciduous forest
     biome *page 356*

temperate evergreen forest
     biome *page 356*

temperate grassland biome *page 356*

tropical rainforest biome *page 354*

tundra biome *page 361*

REVIEW QUESTIONS

1. What is a biome?
2. What climatic and terrain features influence the distribution of terrestrial biome regions?

3. List and briefly describe each of the Earth's eight principal terrestrial biomes.

REFERENCES AND FURTHER READINGS

ARCHIBOLD, O. W.   *Ecology of World Vegetation* (New York: Chapman and Hall, 1995).

BARBOUR, M. G., and BILLINGS, W. D.   *North American Terrestrial Vegetation* (London/New York: Cambridge Univ. Press, 2nd ed., 2000).

COLLINSON, A. S.   *Introduction to World Vegetation* (Winchester, Mass.: Unwin Hyman, 2nd ed., 1988).

HENGEVELD, R.   *Dynamic Biogeography* (London/New York: Cambridge Univ. Press, 1990).

KELLMAN, M. C.   *Plant Geography* (New York: St. Martin's Press, 2nd ed., 1980).

KÜCHLER, A. W., and ZONNEVELD, I. S., Eds.   *Handbook of Vegetation Science 10: Vegetation Mapping* (Hingham, Mass.: Kluwer, 1988).

MAURER, B.   *Geographical Analysis of Biodiversity* (Cambridge, Mass.: Blackwell, 1994).

MacDONALD, G. M.   *Biogeography: Introduction to Space, Time and Life* (New York: Wiley, 2003).

MORIN, N., Chief Ed.   *Flora of North America North of Mexico* (New York: Oxford Univ. Press, 14 vols., 1992–2004).

ORME, A. R., Ed.   *The Physical Geography of North America* (New York: Oxford Univ. Press, 2002).

SAUER, J. D.   *Plant Migration: The Dynamics of Geographic Patterning in Seed Plant Species* (Berkeley, Calif.: Univ. of California Press, 1988).

VALE, T. R.   *Plants and People: Vegetation Change in North America* (Washington, D.C.: Association of American Geographers, Resource Publications in Geography, 1982).

VANKAT, J. L.   *The Natural Vegetation of North America: An Introduction* (New York: Wiley, 1979).

VAVILOV, N. I.   *Origin and Geography of Cultivated Plants* (New York: Cambridge Univ. Press, 1992).

WALTER, H.   *Vegetation of the Earth and Ecological Systems of the Geo-Biosphere* (New York: Springer Verlag, 3rd ed., 1985).

WOODWARD, F. I.   *Climate and Plant Distribution* (New York: Cambridge Univ. Press, 1987).

WEB RESOURCES

http://www.geocities.com/RainForest/2498/bsghome1.htm   The homepage for the Biogeography Specialty Group of the Association of American Geographers (AAG). This page has biogeography and ecology links, information about student paper session opportunities, the *Biogeographer* newsletter, and links to other AAG information.

http://www.worldbiomes.com   Background information about each distinct type of biome, list of reference reading, and a discussion board for the wildlife ecology unit.

Zoogeography: Spatial Aspects of Animal Populations

The vast Serengeti Plain is one of Africa's most extensive and effective wildlife refuges. Zebra, wildebeest, topi, and other herbivores still number in the millions. (Authors' photo)

OBJECTIVES

- To briefly outline the theory of evolution and related principles such as natural selection, which

- led to the present-day spatial distribution of animals
- To give a brief history of zoogeography

- To relate zoogeography to the larger context of environmental conservation

The principal terrestrial biomes discussed in Unit 27 are based primarily on the distribution of dominant vegetation. But the distribution of fauna (animals) is closely associated with plants and as noted earlier, with soils that sustain the flora. A biome, therefore, actually is an interacting set of ecosystems that extends over a large area of the Earth. Its establishment and maintenance depend not only on climate and soils but also on plants and animals—animals ranging from the tiniest bacteria to the largest mammals.

Processes of Evolution

To appreciate the work of zoogeographers (their field is pronounced "*ZOH-oh-geography*"), we should take note of some aspects of the theory of evolution. This theory has led to our understanding that both variety and order mark life on this planet. Basic to evolutionary theory is the concept of *natural selection* within a single species. Natural selection stems from reproductive processes: genetic information (*genes*) from each parent joins in such a way as to combine a small degree of randomness (chance) with a high degree of specification (stability). Thus a human child may have blue or green eyes, but very likely only two arms and legs.

The mechanism of specification (which confers continuity on the species) sometimes breaks down, and when this happens, the exact message of heredity is not passed on. The result is a **mutation** (an inheritable change in the DNA of a gene), and a new species may originate from such an occurrence. Another important part of evolutionary theory holds that a species will produce more offspring than can survive to reproduce. In all species, many immature individuals die by accident, disease, or predation. We encountered this idea in studying food chains, where we saw that autotrophs are eaten by herbivores and herbivores are consumed by carnivores. But while individuals are often killed, the entire population continues to evolve. No matter how many antelope are eaten by lions on the African plains, as long as the herds maintain a sustainable population, they will continue to survive.

An important related principle has to do with the place where a species can best sustain itself and thrive. This is referred to as its **ecological niche** (or, in the zoo-geographic context, simply *niche*), the environmental space within which an organism operates most efficiently. Some niches are very large, perhaps coinciding with entire biomes or continental parts of biomes. The ecological niche of the South American jaguar is a substantial part of the Amazonian rainforest. Other niches are very small. A specialized (or very small) niche reduces competition from other species, but it also increases the risk of total annihilation, perhaps resulting from a change in the natural environment. A large niche may overlap other niches, causing competition, but it has the advantage of permitting adjustment in the event of environmental change.

Zoogeography focuses mainly on the larger ecological niches. These are so complex that they are better termed habitats. The **habitat** of a species is the environment it normally occupies within its geographic range. A habitat usually is described in quite general terms, such as grassland, seashore or alpine. Obviously each of these habitats contains many smaller ecological niches.

Now we come to a zoogeographical-evolutionary principle of great importance. Some offspring are better adapted to their habitat or niche than others. One familiar example of this idea is the evolution of the giraffe's long neck first proposed by Darwin. We start with the assumption that neck length varied in previous giraffe populations. The animals with the longest necks could reach higher into the trees and thereby obtain more food than giraffes with shorter necks. Shorter-necked individuals had to compete for food near the ground with several other species. These shorter-necked giraffes were less successful, and over time the longer-necked giraffes came to prosper, breed successfully, and dominate the species (Fig. 28.1). Recent studies have suggested that giraffes may have developed necks greater than 2 m long and weighing up to 90 kg to win mates. In battles over the females, the male giraffes use their necks against their competitors. The giraffe with the longer and heavier neck generally wins. This implies, then, that better adapted organisms are more likely to survive and reproduce, whether they are giraffes or camouflaged insects. Through their genes, they pass on favourable aspects of their adaptation to successors.

The environment changes over time and places differing demands on species populations. There is a great deal of variation within a species (e.g., humans: tall and short people; fat and thin people; different skin, hair, and eye coloration). Some individuals are better fitted to a certain kind of environment and remain to breed and pass on their DNA, while other, less well-suited individuals die. The process is endless, and the evidence exists everywhere in the natural landscape.

A good example of complex adaptations to a shared habitat is the Serengeti Plain of East Africa, an area of savanna grassland grazed and browsed by many species. The herbivores are so finely adapted that they use different portions of the Serengeti's vegetation at different times. During part of the year, mixed herds graze on the short grass, satisfying their protein requirements without having to use too much energy in respiration while obtaining the food. Eventually the short grass becomes overgrazed. Then the largest animals, the zebras and buffalo, move into areas of mixed vegetation—tall grasses, short grasses, and herbs. Zebras and buffalo eat the stems and tops of the taller grasses, and trample and soften the lower vegetation. The wildebeests can then graze the middle level of vegetation, trampling the level

FIGURE 28.1 "Safari in Tanzania, March 1984. Spent a morning watching a small herd of giraffes as they browsed together, dispersed in the bush, reconvened, were briefly joined by a small herd of zebras, then separated again. In the competitive evolution of East Africa's herbivores, these longer-necked animals had advantages, notably their access to food beyond the reach of others, that led to larger numbers of offspring—who passed the genetic information involving the long neck to later generations."

below. Next the Thomson's gazelles move into the softened area to eat the low leaves, herbs, and fallen fruit at ground level.

The pastoral indigenous people of the Serengeti have long been part of this well-balanced ecosystem. Some scientists conclude that their regular use of fire, as well as naturally occurring fire, has helped to maintain the short grass best adapted to the native animals. In its totality, the Serengeti ecosystem perfectly illustrates the arrangement of plants and animals that has developed under the rules governing both energy flow and natural selection. An understanding of these rules can explain both the nature of species and their geographical spread throughout the biosphere.

Emergence of Zoogeography

The field of zoogeography began to develop following the publication of works by the great naturalist-explorer Alexander von Humboldt (1769–1859) and the biologist Charles Darwin (1809–1882). Von Humboldt's maps and drawings of plants in their environmental settings and of animals encountered on his adventurous explorations formed the first hard evidence for early zoogeographical theories. Darwin's momentous 1859 work on evolution, *The Origin of Species,* spurred ideas about environment and adaptation. Through his remarkable field studies, Darwin focused attention on some unique zoogeographical areas that have remained at the centre of research ever since, especially the Galapagos Islands in the Pacific off Ecuador. Here lay a diversity of habitats for a number of different species of finches, with each having different types of beaks and feeding habitats suitable for the particular environment of an individual island. During the middle part of the nineteenth century, information about the distribution of species and ideas about habitats and food chains began to crystallize quite rapidly.

As more became known about animals and plants in places distant from the centres of learning, urgent zoogeographical questions presented themselves. One of the most interesting involved the transition of fauna from Southeast Asia to Australia. Somewhere in the intervening Indonesian archipelago, the animals of Southeast Asia give way to the very different animals typical of Australia. Australia is the Earth's last major refuge of *marsupials* (animals whose young are born very early in their development and are then carried in a pouch on the abdomen—kangaroos, wallabies, wombats, and koalas [Fig. 28.2] are among Australia's many marsupials). Australia also is the home of the only two remaining egg-laying mammals (monotremes), the platypus and the echidna. Marsupials are found in New Guinea and on islands in the eastern part of Indonesia, but nonmarsupial animals (such as tigers, rhinoceroses, elephants, and primates) prevail in western Indonesia. Where, then, lies the zoogeographical boundary between these sharply contrasting faunal assemblages?

One answer to this still debated question was provided by Alfred Russel Wallace in an important work published in 1876, *The Geographical Distribution of Animals.* Wallace mapped what was then known about the animals of Indonesia. He showed how far various species had progressed eastward along the island stepping stones between mainland Southeast Asia and continental Australia; he also mapped the westward extent of marsupials. On the basis of these and other data, Wallace drew a line across the Indonesian archipelago, a zoogeographical boundary between Southeast Asia's and Australia's fauna (Fig. 28.3). **Wallace's Line** lay between Borneo and Sulawesi, and between the first and second islands (Bali and Lombok) east of Java. This line became one of the most hotly debated zoogeographical delimitations ever drawn, and to this day it remains one of the more intensely discussed boundaries in all of physical geography.

As more evidence was gathered concerning the complex fauna of the Indonesian archipelago, other zoogeographers tried to improve on Wallace's Line. In the process they proved how difficult the problems of regional zoogeography can be. The zoologist Max Weber argued that Wallace's Line lay too far to the west. His alternative line (see Fig. 28.3) was placed just west of New Guinea and north-central Australia, making virtually all of Indonesia part of the Southeast Asian faunal region. The substantial distance between the Wallace and Weber boundaries underscores that zoogeographical data can be interpreted differently.

Many biogeographers would agree that the delimitation of vegetative regions presents fewer problems than faunal regions do. It is one thing to draw maps of stands of rainforest, an expanse of desert, or the boundary between taiga and tundra, but to do the same for African lions, American jaguars, or Indian tigers is quite another matter. Animals move and migrate, their range (region of natural occurrence) varies, and they may simply be difficult to locate and enumerate.

FROM THE FIELDNOTES

FIGURE 28.2 "Moving slowly and quietly through a eucalyptus forest in New South Wales, Australia, I was rewarded with this extraordinary sight, a koala resting in a tangle of branches. The koala "bear" is part of Australia's unique fauna; it is a marsupial and carries its offspring in its pouch for as long as seven months. It eats about 1.3 kg of eucalyptus leaves daily, but only a particular kind and quality of leaf; in the wild its lifespan averages 20 years. The koala has diminished in number from an estimated several million to perhaps 150,000, and the population continues to decline as humans encroach on its natural habitat and diseases take their toll."

The Earth's Zoogeographical Realms

A global map of zoogeographical realms, therefore, is an exercise in generalization, but it does reflect evolutionary centres for animal life as well as the work of natural barriers over time (Fig. 28.4). Note that zoogeographical realm boundaries in several areas coincide with high mountains (Himalayas), broad deserts (Sahara, Arabian), deep marine channels (Indonesia), and narrow land bridges (Central America).

By many measures, the *Palaeotropical (Ethiopian) realm* contains the Earth's most varied fauna, an enormously rich assemblage of animals, many of which are unique to this realm. Some species, however, have rela-

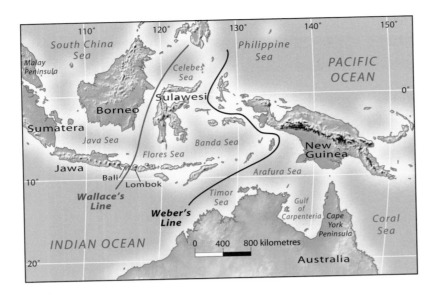

FIGURE 28.3   Wallace's Line across the Indonesian archipelago. This controversial boundary between the faunal assemblages of Southeast Asia and Australia was challenged by Max Weber, who placed his alternative Weber's Line much closer to Australia and New Guinea.

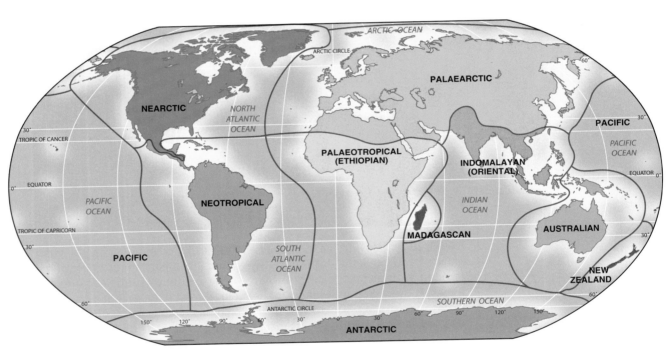

FIGURE 28.4   World zoogeographical realms.

tives in other realms. For example, the lion and the elephant also occur in the *Indomalayan (Oriental) realm.* Nevertheless, the Indomalayan realm has a less diverse fauna. The fauna of the island of *Madagascar,* shown on the map as a discrete realm, differs quite strongly from that of nearby Africa. While Madagascar is home to the lemurs, a group of small primates, the island has nothing to match East Africa's herd animals, lions, or even poisonous snakes. Just how an island so near the

Palaeotropical realm became so distinctive zoogeographically remains a problem without a satisfactory solution.

The *Australian realm's* faunal assemblage exhibits the consequences of prolonged isolation and separate evolution. This is the realm of marsupials, such as the kangaroo and the wombat, of the platypus and the thylacine or Tasmanian "tiger." While some biogeographers include New Zealand in the Australian realm, others map *New Zealand,* like Madagascar, as a discrete realm. There is ample geographical reason for doing so: New Zealand's native fauna includes no mammals, very few terrestrial vertebrates of any kind, and nothing to match the assemblage of Australia—except when it comes to birds. New Zealand has a rich variety of bird life, with a number of flightless species like the kiwi.

The *Neotropical realm* also has a rich and varied faunal assemblage, which includes such species as the tapir, the jaguar, sloths, and the boa constrictor. In both plants and animals, biogeographers can discern evidence of the theory of **convergent evolution**, which holds that organisms in widely separated biogeographical realms, though descended from diverse ancestors, develop similar adaptations to measurably similar habitats.

The two remaining realms, the *Nearctic* and the *Palaearctic,* are much less rich and much less diverse than the other major zoogeographical realms. Some biogeographers prefer to map these together as a single realm, but evidence of long-term isolation (the Beringia land bridge notwithstanding) is much stronger in the North American Nearctic than in the Eurasian Palaearctic realm. Remarkable adaptations exist, such as the polar bear (both realms), the Siberian tiger and giant panda (Palaearctic), and the bison and grizzly bear (Nearctic).

Figure 28.4 presents the global zoogeographical map at a high level of generalization, and it should be remembered that this is a map of *realms.* Embedded within each realm are numerous subdivisions, or zoogeographical *regions.* Let us use the Australian realm as an example. The fauna of mainland Australia, despite commonalities with the nearby large island of New Guinea, nonetheless differs sufficiently to make New Guinea and Australia separate zoogeographical regions within the Australian realm.

Further Studies in Zoogeography

As interest in zoogeography grew, new kinds of studies were undertaken. After 1900 zoogeography became more ecological and less cartographic. Zoogeographers became concerned with changing environments, past faunal migration routes, and present migratory habits, such as the flight paths of birds between summering and wintering grounds. This change in the field can be seen by comparing Wallace's book, published more than a century ago, with a volume by Philip J. Darlington, Jr., carrying a very similar title and published in 1957, *Zoogeography: The Geographical Distribution of Animals.* Darlington posed four questions for zoogeographers: (1) What is the main pattern of animal distribution? (2) How has this pattern been formed? (3) Why has this pattern developed as it has? (4) What does animal distri-

bution—past and present—tell us about lands and climates? Note that the first question is only the beginning, not the entire objective, as was the case in Wallace's work.

By the time Darlington did his research, much more was known about ice ages, crustal mobility, and changing sea levels than was known in Wallace's time. It was not long before **ecological zoogeography**, the study of animals as they relate to their total environment, became a leading theme. A book published in 1965, *The Geography of Evolution,* by G. G. Simpson, deals with such topics as adaptation, competition, and habitats. By the 1990s, as their titles indicate, ecological zoogeography had expanded to encompass books on *Geographical Analysis of Biodiversity* by B. Maurer and *Plant and Animal Introductions* by P. J. Jarvis.

Island Zoogeography

Biologists believe that there may be as many as 30 million species of organisms on our planet, of which only 1.7 million have been identified and classified. Obviously, many species live in the same habitat, often sharing ecological niches or parts of niches. What determines how many species can be accommodated in a specific, measured region? This is a central question in modern zoogeography. Where ranges and niches overlap, as on large landmasses, it is not practical to calculate the number of species an area can sustain because there are no controllable boundaries. But an island presents special opportunities.

A small island can be inventoried completely, so that every species living on it is accounted for. When zoogeographers did this work, their research had some expected and some unexpected results. In 1967 R. H. MacArthur and E. O. Wilson determined that the number of species living on an island is related to the size of that island. Given similar environmental conditions, the larger the island, the larger the number of species it can accommodate. This might have been anticipated, except that the larger island does not have a wider range of natural environments, so that it is the size, not the internal variability that might come with it, that affects the species total. Moreover, it was discovered that an island of a given size can accommodate only a limited number of species. New species may arrive, brought by birds from far away or entering via debris washing up onshore. If the island already has a stable population, these new species will not succeed unless another species first becomes extinct.

This conclusion, that an island's capacity to accommodate species has a numerical limit, was tested on some small islands off the coast of Florida. Zoogeographers counted the species of insects, spiders, crabs, and other arthropods living on each island. Then they took the rather radical step of spraying the islands, wiping out the entire population. After a few years, the islands were reinhabited. The same number of species had returned to them, although the number of individuals was proportionately different. That is, while there were crabs and spiders before the extinction, now there were more crabs and fewer spiders. This indicates not only that a certain number of species is characteristic of an island in a certain environment, but also that the kinds of species making up this number vary and may depend on the order in which they arrived to fill the available ecological niches.

Biogeographers can also learn about niches and habitats when new land is formed—for example, following the formation of a volcanic island. In 1883 the volcanic island of Krakatau in western Indonesia exploded, leaving small island remnants and creating a wholly new and barren landscape. Soon new soil began to form on the fertile lava base, and plant seeds arrived by air and via birds. New vegetation could be seen within a few years (Fig. 28.5), and soon animal repopulation began. The arrival of new species was monitored, adding to our knowledge about the occupation of available niches and habitats. Such knowledge permitted optimistic predictions about the revegetation and recovery of Mount St. Helens in Washington State following its destructive eruption of 1980. Just three years after this eruption, 90 percent of the plant species that originally inhabited the devastated slopes had already re-established themselves.

What has been learned about island zoogeography also applies to other isolated places, such as the tops of tepuis (in South America), buttes, and mesas (see Fig. 42.6) where steep slopes act as barriers to invasion. The stable populations atop such landforms resemble island populations in some ways, but in other ways they relate more closely to the surrounding ecosystems. By studying these hilltop faunal assemblages, zoogeographers come still closer to an understanding of the complex relationships that characterize habitats and niches in general. The next section looks at how the distribution of animal life is influenced by humans, who, even by their inadvertent actions (see Perspective: The African Stowaways), can produce widespread negative consequences.

Zoogeography and Conservation

Research in zoogeography often has important implications for the survival of species. Knowledge of the numbers, range, habits, and reproductive success of species

is crucial to their effective protection. The explosive growth of the Earth's human population and the destructive patterns of consumption by prospering peoples have combined to render many species of animals extinct, endangered, or threatened. Awareness of the many threats to the remaining fauna has increased in recent decades, and some species have been saved from the brink of extinction. But for many others hope is fading.

Animal Ranges

An important zoogeographical contribution to research in support of species conservation lies in detailed studies of the spatial properties of **animal ranges**. This concept is discussed in Unit 26, and the ranges of four North American mammals are mapped in Fig. 28.6. It is not just the size of a range, however, but also its geographical pattern that will determine whether a species can be expected to survive. The case of the spotted owl in the Pacific Northwest is a good example. What this owl needs is old forest, not secondary growth after logging. It needs soft and rotting wood so that it can establish nests in the trunks; neatly reforested slopes do not have such old decaying trees. The range of the spotted owl is therefore restricted to the dwindling stands of older forest, and the map that conservationists need will show where those patches of remaining old forest are located. The pattern of these patches—how large they are, how densely forested, how close together—will reveal more about the prospects of the spotted owl than any estimate of the total size of its range.

Human Impact on Animal Habitats

The effects of human encroachment on animal habitats is another important sphere of zoogeographical study. In many parts of the world—in the foothills of the Himalayas, on the plains of East Africa, in the forests of tropical South America—people and animals are competing for land. Not long ago, substantial parts of India teemed with herds of wild buffalo, many kinds of antelope and deer as well as their predators, lions and tigers, and large numbers of elephants and rhinoceroses. The South Asian human population explosion, together with a breakdown in the conservation programs, has destroyed one of the Earth's great wildlife legacies. The Indian lion is virtually extinct; the great tiger is endangered and survives in only small numbers in remote forest areas. In East Africa, population pressure in the areas surrounding the major wildlife reserves, along with poaching, is decimating the fauna. In the Amazon Basin, rainforest habitat destruction (see Perspectives box in Unit 17) threatens the survival of many species of animals as well as plants.

FIGURE 28.5 "We drove across an expanse of lava formed from a recent fissure eruption in Tanzania—so recent that virtually no vegetation had yet taken hold on it. Research has shown that plants manage to establish themselves quite soon (a matter of years, not generations or centuries) after new rocks are created by volcanic eruptions. This lava must therefore be quite young, but the process is clearly at work. A seed found a way to sprout in a crack in the rock, where weathered particles and some moisture supplied the essentials for growth."

PERSPECTIVES ON THE HUMAN ENVIRONMENT

The African Stowaways*

Around 1929 a few African mosquitoes arrived in Brazil. They had probably stowed away aboard a fast French destroyer in the West African city of Dakar. Once in Brazil, the immigrants established a colony in a marsh along the South Atlantic coast. Although the residents of a nearby town suffered from an unusual outbreak of malaria, nobody seemed to notice the presence of the foreign mosquitoes for a long time. Meanwhile the insects settled comfortably in their new environment, and during the next few years they spread out over about 320 km along the coast. Then, in 1938, a malaria epidemic swept across most of Northeast Brazil. A year later the disease continued to ravage the region; hundreds of thousands of people fell ill, and nearly 20,000 died.

Brazil always had malaria-carrying mosquitoes but none quite like the new African variety. Whereas the native mosquitoes tended to stay in the forest, the foreign pests could breed in sunny ponds outside the forest, and they quickly made a habit of flying into houses to find humans to bite. With the mosquito transplantation problem finally understood, the Brazilian government, aided by the Rockefeller Foundation, hired more than 3000 people and spent over $2 million to attack the invaders. After studying the ecological characteristics of the "enemy," they sprayed houses and ponds. Within three years the battle wiped out the African mosquitoes in South America. Brazil also initiated a

quarantine and inspection program for incoming aircraft and ships to keep out unwanted stowaways.

High-speed transportation developed by humans has inadvertently carried many plants and animals to other continents. In their new environment, the immigrants may react in one of three ways: they may languish and die; they may fit into the existing ecosystem structure; or they may tick away like a time bomb and eventually explode like the African mosquitoes.

Another accidental African arrival that could not be controlled in Brazil, the so-called African killer bee, threatens parts of North America today. These bees escaped from a Brazilian research facility in 1957 and have been slowly spreading out across the Americas ever since. By 1980 the bees had entered the Central American land bridge and were steadily progressing northward. By the early 1990s they had crossed all of Mexico and penetrated Texas across the Rio Grande. Today they are present in 13 southern and southwestern states. Although joint U.S.–Mexican efforts to slow the advance of the bees were moderately successful in the late 1980s, the U.S. Department of Agriculture was forced to abandon hope that the invaders could be repelled, and USDA is still testing strategies to cope with this spreading pest on American soil.

*The source for most of this box is Elton (1971).

All this is reminiscent of what happened to the wildlife of North America following the arrival of the Europeans. The North American conservation effort over the past century has concentrated on the salvageable remnants of this realm's wildlife, and there have been successes as well as setbacks. The protection of wildlife poses complex problems. Special-interest groups such as hunters sometimes demand the right to shoot particular species, endangering what may be a delicate balance in the ecosystem. Others object to closing wilderness areas to the public for any purpose, even sightseeing, when this is necessary to allow an endangered area or animal species to recuperate. And because wildlife is mobile, it may move beyond the boundaries of a wildlife refuge or national park, thus becoming endangered. The protection of birds, whose migratory habits may carry them across the length of the continent, is made especially difficult by their mobility.

Preservation Efforts

Conservationists in North America have also learned a great deal about the most effective methods of wildlife preservation. This is not simply a matter of fencing

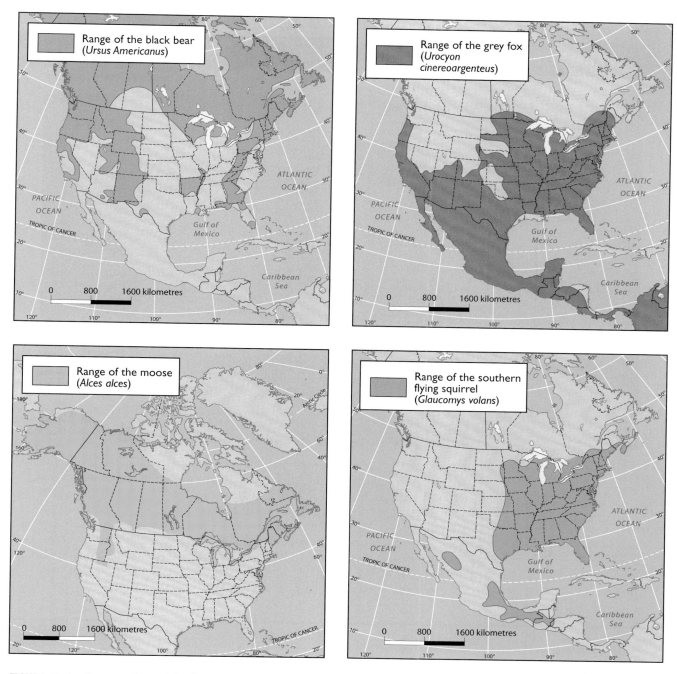

FIGURE 28.6   Ranges of some North American mammals.

off an area where particular species exist, but involves the management of the entire habitat, the maintenance of a balance among animals and plants—and, sometimes, people. A series of legislative actions and commissions during the late twentieth century served to facilitate and implement the newly developed conservation practices. There have been several successes, including the revival of the bison, the wild turkey, and the wolf as well as the survival of the grizzly bear and the bald eagle.

In European countries, as well as in the countries of the former Soviet Union to the east, the story of conservation efforts is largely one of remnant preservation. Europe's varied wildlife fell before the human expansion; it was lost even earlier than America's wildlife. Conservation is an expensive proposition, afforded most easily

FROM THE FIELDNOTES

FIGURE 28.7 "Safari, Tanzania, February 1989. A herd of buffalo stops at a small waterhole in Manyara National Park. The rift valley wall that marks the western limit of the Lake Manyara Rift is in the background; if the photographer turned around, Lake Manyara would be visible. The park constitutes a narrow strip of land, but it has a rich fauna. Such richness of animal life prevailed across much of tropical Africa before the arrival of the European colonialists, who upset the long-established balance among indigenous peoples, their livestock, and the realm's wildlife. Hunting for 'sport' was not an African custom; neither was killing for fashion."

by the wealthier developed countries. European colonial powers carried the concept to their colonies, where they could carve wildlife refuges from tribal lands with impunity. In many areas of Africa and Asia, the Europeans found the indigenous population living in harmonious balance with livestock and wildlife. The invaders disturbed this balance, introduced the concept of hunting for profit and trophies, and then closed off huge land tracts as wildlife reserves with controlled hunting zones (Fig. 28.7). That the African wildlife refuges have for so long survived the period of decolonization (some are now in danger) is testimony to a determination that was not present when orgies of slaughter eliminated much of North America's wildlife heritage. North Americans may have advanced knowledge of conservation theory and management practices but are in no position to proselytize.

Zoogeography, therefore, has many theoretical and practical dimensions. The spatial aspects of ranges, habitats, and niches require research and analysis. The results of such investigations are directly relevant to those who seek to protect wildlife and who make policy to ensure species survival.

KEY TERMS

animal ranges *page 370*

convergent evolution *page 369*

ecological niche *page 364*

ecological zoogeography *page 369*

habitat *page 364*

mutation *page 364*

Wallace's line *page 366*

REVIEW QUESTIONS

1. What is an *ecological niche* and how is it related to a habitat?

2. How were Alexander von Humboldt and Alfred Russel Wallace instrumental in developing the field of zoogeography?

3. In what ways are animal and plant conservation similar?

4. In what ways do animal and plant conservation differ?

5. What have biogeographers learned about ecological niches and habitats from their fieldwork on islands and land newly emerged from the sea?

REFERENCES AND FURTHER READINGS

ANON. "How the Giraffe Got Its Neck," *Discover Magazine*, 18, no. 3 (March 1997), 14.

BANFIELD, A. W. F. *The Mammals of Canada* (Toronto: Univ. of Toronto Press and Natural Museums of Canada, 1974).

BRIGGS, J. C. *Global Biogeography* (Amsterdam: Elsevier, 1995).

BURT, W. H., and GROSSENHEIDER, R. P. *A Field Guide to Mammals: North America North of Mexico,* Peterson Field Guide (Boston: Houghton Mifflin, 1976).

DARLINGTON, P. J., Jr. *Zoogeography: The Geographical Distribution of Animals* (New York: Wiley, 1957 [reprinted by Krieger, 1980]).

DASMANN, R. F. *Environmental Conservation* (New York: Wiley, 5th ed., 1984).

DAWS, G., and FUJITA, M. *Archipelago: The Islands of Indonesia* (Berkeley, Calif.: Univ. of California Press, 1999).

ELTON, C. S. "The Invaders," in T. R. Detwyler, Ed. *Man's Impact on Environment* (New York: McGraw-Hill, 1971), 447–458.

ILLIES, J. *Introduction to Zoogeography* (New York: Macmillan, 1974).

JARVIS, P. J. *Plant and Animal Introductions* (Malden, Mass.: Blackwell, 1999).

MacARTHUR, R. H., and WILSON, E. O. *The Theory of Island Biogeography* (Princeton, N.J.: Princeton Univ. Press, 1967).

MacDONALD, G. M. *Biogeography: Introduction to Space, Time and Life* (New York: Wiley, 2003).

MAURER, B. *Geographical Analysis of Biodiversity* (Cambridge, Mass.: Blackwell, 1994).

NEWBIGIN, M. I. *Plant and Animal Geography* (London: Methuen, 1968).

NOWAK, R. M. *Walker's Primates of the World* (Baltimore, Md.: Johns Hopkins Univ. Press, 1999).

QUAMMEN, D. *The Song of the Dodo: Island Biogeography in an Age of Extinctions* (New York: Scribner, 1996).

SIMPSON, G. G. *The Geography of Evolution: Collected Essays* (Philadelphia, Pa.: Chilton Books, 1965).

WALLACE, A. R. *The Geographical Distribution of Animals; with a Study of the Relations of Living and Extinct Faunas as Elucidating the Past Changes of the Earth's Surface* (New York: Hafner, 1962 [reprint of 1876 original]).

WHITMORE, T. C. *Wallace's Line and Plate Tectonics* (London/New York: Oxford Univ. Press [Clarendon], 1981).

WEB RESOURCES

http://animals.about.com/cs/conservation A page of wildlife conservation links, including the National Wildlife Federation and the Living Planet.

http://www.ultimateungulate.com/Artiodactyla.alces_alces.html Authoritative website about the ungulates of the world (deer, etc.).

http://www.worldwildlife.org/ecoregions/abstract.htm Background information on world ecoregions, as well as maps and information about conservation programs.

PART FOUR

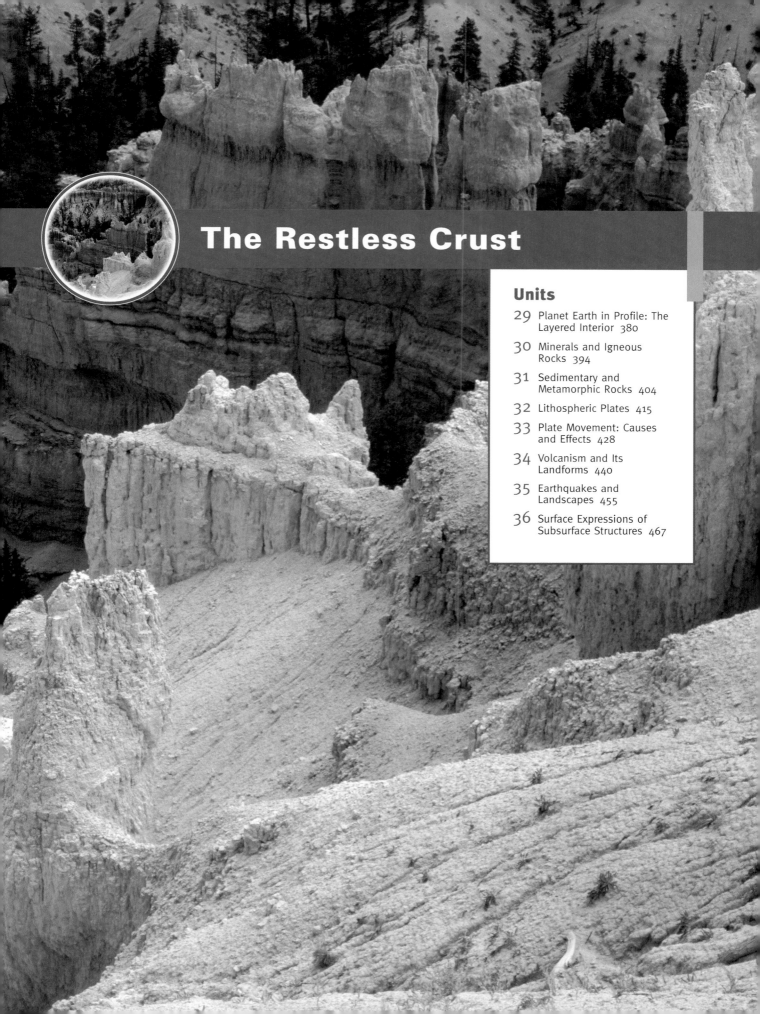

The Restless Crust

Restless Crust

The lithosphere, the oldest of the Earth's spheres, began to form as soon as superheated molten rock first solidified in patches on the planet's turbulent surface more than 4 billion years ago. Ever since, the Earth's crust has thickened and matured, but it has not stabilized. Great slabs of solid crust move, driven by heat from geochemical processes that keep subsurface rock in a molten and mobile condition. When these slabs collide, the lighter continental one overrides the heavier oceanic one, starting a process called subduction in which parts of both continental and oceanic crust are forced downward. At the surface, subduction creates spectacular scenery, causes earthquakes, and generates volcanic activity. Below, the crustal slabs are subjected to such high temperatures and pressures that their rocks remelt and become part of the molten, moving mass beneath the crust. Millions of years later, molten rock may rise along a volcanic fissure, and the cycle continues. Embedded within this giant lithospheric system, which moves continents and threatens people, is the rock cycle, a never-ending system that brings molten rock to the surface, where forces of weathering and erosion attack it. Loose material accumulates and becomes compressed into sedimentary rock, which may be heated and transformed (metamorphosed) into harder rock types; some of it gets caught up in subduction and melts in the asthenosphere. Other metamorphic rocks remain in upper layers of the crust and are exposed by uplift and erosion, and as with volcanic lava, the cycle of weathering and sedimentary accumulation begins all over again.

The Restless Crust

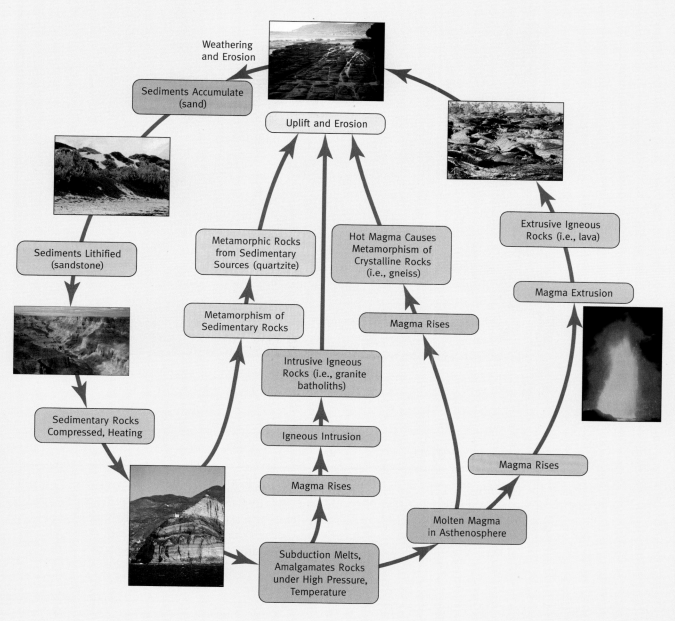

Weathering and Erosion

Sediments Accumulate (sand)

Uplift and Erosion

Sediments Lithified (sandstone)

Metamorphic Rocks from Sedimentary Sources (quartzite)

Hot Magma Causes Metamorphism of Crystalline Rocks (i.e., gneiss)

Extrusive Igneous Rocks (i.e., lava)

Metamorphism of Sedimentary Rocks

Magma Rises

Magma Extrusion

Sedimentary Rocks Compressed, Heating

Intrusive Igneous Rocks (i.e., granite batholiths)

Igneous Intrusion

Magma Rises

Magma Rises

Molten Magma in Asthenosphere

Subduction Melts, Amalgamates Rocks under High Pressure, Temperature

Planet Earth in Profile: The Layered Interior

A glimpse of the interior—gases emanate from the layered walls of a caldera (collapsed crater) on the volcanic island of Hawaii. (Authors' photo)

OBJECTIVES

- To outline the relevant properties of the Earth's five internal layers and to discuss some of the evidence leading to their discovery

- To introduce the salient properties of the Earth's lithosphere, the nature of the crust, and the underlying mantle

- To investigate the gradational processes that continually build as well as remove rock material at the Earth's surface, creating physical landscapes of great diversity

In other parts of this book various aspects of the Earth's environments are examined. Several of the *spheres* of our planet are introduced in these parts, including the atmosphere and the hydrosphere (Part Two) and certain properties of the biosphere (Part Three). The atmosphere, hydrosphere, cryosphere, biosphere, and lithosphere are the major visible layers of our planet.

Above the effective atmosphere are additional layers of thinner air and different chemical composition; their physical and chemical properties are well known because detailed data about them have been collected by balloons, high-flying aircraft, and space vehicles.

Much less is known, however, about the layers that make up the internal structure of the Earth. Even the directly observable crust of the planet, which we will examine later in this unit, is not well known. No instruments have been sent down very far into the crust. More than a third of a century after people first set foot on the Moon, the deepest boreholes have penetrated barely 12 km into the lithosphere. Since the radius of the planet is 6370 km, we have penetrated less than one five-hundredth of the distance to the centre of the Earth.

Nonetheless, scientists have established the fact that the interior of the Earth is layered like the atmosphere, and they have deduced the chemical composition and physical properties of the chief layers below the crust. This research is of importance in physical geography because the crust is affected by processes that take place in the layer below it, and this layer in turn may be influenced by conditions deeper down. So it is important to understand what is known about the Earth's internal structure and how this information has been acquired.

Evidence of the Earth's Internal Structure

Evidence that supports the concept of an internally layered Earth comes from several sources. The crust affords a glimpse of the nature of rocks normally hidden from scientists because rocks that formed very deep below the surface have occasionally been elevated to levels in the crust where they can be reached by boreholes. From these samples, as well as from analyses of more common rocks, it is possible to deduce the overall composition of the crust and its average density.

By studying the wavelengths of light emanating from the Sun, it is possible to determine the elements the Sun contains and their proportions, because certain specific wavelengths correspond to particular elements. Geophysicists have concluded that these proportions will be the same for the Earth. However, such abundant elements as iron, nickel, and magnesium are relatively depleted in the crust. This suggests that those heavy elements are concentrated in deeper layers of the planet.

This conclusion is strengthened by two pieces of evidence. First, rock samples taken from great depths do contain higher concentrations of iron and magnesium than "average" crustal rocks. Second, when the mass and size of the Earth are measured, the resulting figure is

5.5 grams per cubic centimetre (g/cm^3). This is about double the density of rocks found in the continental crust. Again, the heavier, denser part of the Earth should be in the deep interior.

Earthquakes

Further evidence for the internal structure of the Earth comes from the planet's magnetic field and from the high temperatures and pressures known to prevail at deeper levels. Not only does molten rock sometimes flow onto the surface through volcanic vents (see photo p. 431), but it is also possible to determine the temperatures at which rocks now solid were once liquefied. But the most convincing body of evidence is derived from the analysis of **earthquakes**—the shaking and trembling of the Earth's surface caused by sudden releases of stress within the crust.

Earthquakes occur in many areas of the crust, and their causes are discussed in Unit 35. For the present it should be noted that earthquakes generate pulses of energy called **seismic waves** that can pass through the entire Earth. A strong earthquake in the Northern Hemisphere will be recorded by *seismographs* in the Southern Hemisphere. Today thousands of seismographs continuously record the shocks and tremors in the crust (Fig. 29.1), and computers help interpret these earthquake data. This source has given us an important picture of the interior structure of our planet.

Seismic waves take time to travel through the Earth. In general terms, the speed of an earthquake wave is proportional to the density of the material through which it travels. The denser the material, the faster the speed.

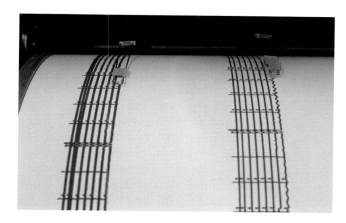

FIGURE 29.1   The Canadian National Seismograph Network (CNSN) station at the Geological Survey of Canada headquarters in Ottawa uses seismographs like the one above. The pen plotters continuously record the Earth's shocks and tremors as a series of wiggly lines on the slowly rotating paper-covered drum whose motion is precisely regulated by a clock. The printout is called a seismogram.

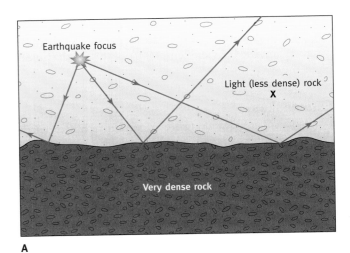

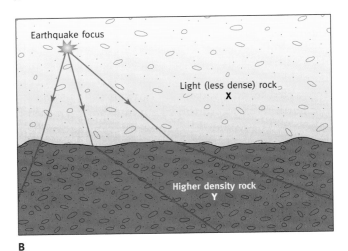

FIGURE 29.2   When seismic waves travel through the interior of the Earth, several things happen. When they reach a plane where the rock material becomes much denser, they may be *reflected* back (A). If the contrast in rock density is less, they may be *refracted* (B). Their velocities are also affected. Speeds would be less in the layers marked **X** and greater in layer **Y**.

Seismic waves, like light waves and sound waves, also change direction under certain circumstances. When a seismic wave travelling through a less dense material reaches a place where the density becomes much greater, it may be bounced back; this is known as *seismic reflection* (Fig. 29.2A). If the contrast in densities between the adjacent layers is less severe, the wave may be bent rather than reflected; here *seismic refraction* changes the course of the seismic wave (Fig. 29.2B).

Types of Seismic Waves

Seismic waves behave differently as they propagate through the Earth. Two types of waves travel along the surface of the crust and are termed a *surface* (or Long pe-

riod) *waves* (or **L** waves). There are two types: Rayleigh waves and Love waves. Rayleigh waves cause disruption of the surface causing a wave-like motion radiating out from the epicentre. Love waves move across the surface and cause ground motion zig-zagging from side to side. Two other types of waves travel through the interior of the Earth and are referred to as **body waves**. The body waves are known as **P** (primary) waves and **S** (secondary) waves. The **P** waves are compressional waves, sometimes called push waves. As they propagate, they move material in their path parallel to the direction of movement. They even travel through material in the liquid state, although their impact is then much reduced. The **S** waves (shear or shake waves) move objects at right angles to their direction of motion. They do not propagate through liquid material. This is of great importance, because if **S** waves fail to reach a seismograph in an opposite hemisphere, it may be concluded that liquid material inside the Earth halted their progress.

When an earthquake occurs, seismographs nearest its point of origin begin to record the passing of a sequence of waves. The seismogram (see Fig. 29.1) will reveal the passage of the **P, S,** and **L** waves in a nearly continuous sequence, which may reflect great destruction of structures in the area. Farther away, the different speeds of propagation begin to show on the seismogram, and reflected **P** and **S** waves from interior Earth layers make their appearance. Eventually seismographs around the world will record the earthquake. But some stations will not register any **P** or **S** waves, and others will record only **P** waves. From these data significant conclusions about the interior of the Earth can be drawn, as shown below.

The Earth's Internal Layers

The paths of seismic waves, illustrated in Fig. 29.3, reveal the existence of a layer beneath the crust that ends at a boundary where **S** waves (shown by white arrows) are not propagated. If an earthquake occurs at zero degrees, **P** as well as **S** waves are recorded by seismographs everywhere to 103 degrees from its source (a distance of 11,270 km). Then, from 103 to 142 degrees, the next 4150 km, neither **P** nor **S** waves are recorded (except for **P** waves propagated along the crust). But from 142 to 180 degrees (15,420 to 19,470 km distant from the quake), **P** waves—always shown by black arrows—reappear. From this evidence it is concluded that the Earth possesses a liquid layer that begins about 2900 km below the surface. At the contact between this liquid layer and the layer above it, **S** waves cease to be propagated and **P** waves are refracted.

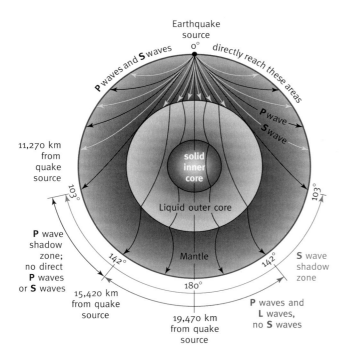

FIGURE 29.3 Imagine that a strong earthquake occurs at the North Pole (0 degrees on the drawing). This diagram shows the paths of the radiating **P**, **S**, and **L** waves as they travel through the planet. Note that no **P** waves are received over a large shadow zone in the Southern Hemisphere, between 103 and approximately 142 degrees from the quake's source at 0 degrees. This allows us to identify the depth at which the solid mantle yields to the liquid outer core. From the refraction of the **P** waves we can deduce the contrast in density between mantle and outer core materials.

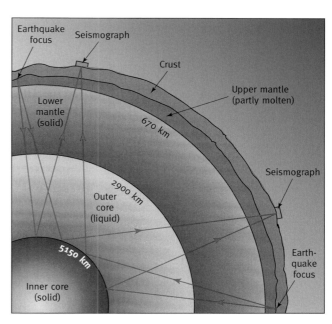

FIGURE 29.4 Certain **P** waves are reflected back toward the crust when they reach the outer edge of the solid inner core. From their travel times, the position of the contact between solid inner core and liquid outer core can be deduced. *Note:* The refraction of these waves, as they traverse the interior of the Earth, is not shown.

But some **P** waves that arrive on the far side of the Earth, between 142 and 180 degrees, have not been refracted just once or twice, but four times! Moreover, their speed has increased. This means that the **P** waves that reach the seismographs located antipodally to the earthquake source (i.e., on the exact opposite point of the spherical Earth) must have travelled through a very dense mass inside the liquid layer. Confirmation of the existence of such a dense mass at the core of the Earth comes from the fact that many **P** waves are reflected back at its outer edge (Fig. 29.4). From the travel times of these reflected **P** waves and the seismograms inside 142 degrees (Fig. 29.3), it is concluded that the Earth has a solid inner core—a ball of very heavy, dense material. This may well be where the iron and nickel, depleted from the upper layers, is concentrated.

On the basis of seismic and other evidence, therefore, the interior of the Earth is believed to have four layers: a solid inner core, a liquid outer core, a solid lower mantle, and a partially molten upper mantle (Fig. 29.5). On top of all this lies the crust, still very thin, and in places it is active and unstable.

Solid Inner Core

The solid **inner core** has a radius of just 1220 km. Its surface lies 5150 km below sea level. Iron and nickel exist here in a solid state, scientists believe, because pressures are enormous—so great that the melting-point temperature is even higher than the heat prevailing in the inner core. There is some evidence from computer models that the inner core acts like a dynamo. It rotates much faster than the Earth, creating waves or currents in the liquid outer core that "drag" the outer parts of the Earth around.

Liquid Outer Core

The liquid **outer core** forms a layer 2250 km thick. Its outer surface lies at some 2900 km below sea level, just slightly less than halfway to the centre of the planet. The liquid outer core may consist of essentially the same materials as the solid inner core, but because pressures here are less, the melting-point temperature is lower and a molten state prevails. The density of the inner and outer cores combined has been calculated as 12.5 g/cm³, which compensates for the lightness of the crust

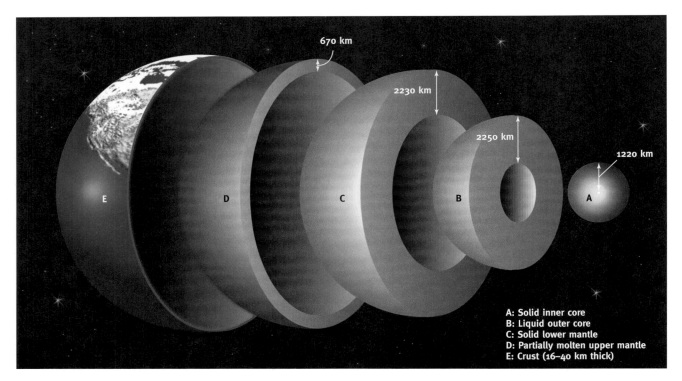

FIGURE 29.5   Principal layers of the inner Earth.

(2.8 g/cm^3) and accounts for the density of the planet as a whole (5.5 g/cm^3).

Solid Lower Mantle

Above the liquid outer core lies the solid **lower mantle** (see Fig. 29.5). Although the scale of the diagram cannot properly convey it, the contact between mantle and core is not smooth and even, but has relief—rather like the uneven upper surface of the crust. The lower mantle has a thickness of about 2230 km. Seismic data show that the lower mantle is in a solid state. Geologists believe that this layer is composed of oxides of iron, magnesium, and silicon.

Upper Mantle

The partially molten **upper mantle** is of great interest to geologists as well as to physical geographers because it interacts with the overlying crust in many ways. The upper mantle, however, still is not well understood, although it extends from the base of the crust to a depth of just 670 km. The upper mantle is differentiated from the lower mantle on the basis of mineral composition and the state of the rock material. The lower mantle is solid, but the upper mantle above it is viscous (like thick syrup, capable of flowing slowly). However, the zone of the upper mantle just beneath

the crust is solid. This portion of the upper mantle contains pockets of molten rock, some of which feed chambers from which lava pours onto the surface of the crust.

The interior of the Earth still retains many of its secrets, but our comprehension increases steadily. New knowledge about the upper mantle continues to emerge, and it may well be that this subcrustal layer can itself be subdivided into a number of additional layers. In any case, our interpretation of what we observe at the surface must begin with an understanding of what lies below. This unit continues with an examination of the lithosphere, and focuses on further aspects of this uppermost layer of the interior of the Earth.

The Earth's Outer Layer

Now that we are familiar with the Earth's interior, we can turn to the surface layer itself, the lithosphere upon which all else—air, water, soil, life—rests. The crust, as just noted, lies directly above the upper mantle (see Fig. 29.5). The uppermost parts of the crust are the only portions of the solid Earth about which scientists have direct first-hand knowledge. The rocks that make up the outer shell of our planet have been analyzed from the surface, from mine shafts, and from boreholes. Even the deepest boreholes, however, only begin to shed light on what lies below.

For many years it was believed that temperatures and pressures below the crust would be so great that the Earth material there would be in a completely molten state. Another subsequent theory, based on the study of earthquake waves, suggested that the mantle beneath the crust was solid. Quite recently more detailed, computer-assisted analyses of the paths and speeds of earthquake waves through the Earth's interior have revealed the existence of a broad viscous layer within the upper mantle (the asthenosphere). Undoubtedly there will be more revelations in the future.

Structural Properties of the Crust

One of the most significant discoveries relating to the Earth's crust occurred in 1909. In that year the Croatian scientist Andrija Mohorovičić concluded from his study of earthquake waves that the density of the Earth materials changes markedly at the contact between crust and mantle. This contact plane has been named the **Mohorovičić discontinuity**, or **Moho**, an abbreviation of his name. Despite nearly a century of far more sophisticated analyses and interpretations, Mohorovičić's conclusion has proven correct—a density discontinuity does indeed mark the base of the Earth's crust.

This information made it possible to calculate the thickness of the crust. Earthquake waves speed up at the Moho discontinuity, indicating that the crust is less dense than the mantle below. In some places this happens a mere 5 km down from the surface; elsewhere the change in earthquake-wave velocity does not come until a depth of 40 km or even more has been reached. This proved that the crust is not of even thickness. It also showed that the crust is thinner than the shell of an egg relative to the planet's diameter.

When the Moho was mapped, it was found to lie much closer to the surface under the ocean floors than under the continental landmasses (Fig. 29.6). This con-

firms a conclusion also drawn from gravity measurements: the continents have crustal "roots" that create, in a rough way, a reverse image of the topography at the surface (a matter explored in Unit 33). Under the oceans, the crust averages only 8 km in thickness; under the exposed continental surfaces, the average depth is about 40 km.

For many years it was not realized that a fundamental difference between continental and oceanic crust might account for these differences. This was so, in part, because rocks brought to the surface from the offshore continental shelves resembled those found on the continents themselves; boreholes in shallow water off the coast produced no hint of what was to come. But then technology made possible the drilling of the continental slope farther out to sea. Those rocks, it turned out, were darker and somewhat heavier than the rocks of the continental landmasses. Advances in drilling technology also raised the possibility of directly punching a borehole through the Moho into the mantle itself—a project earth scientists can still only dream about.

In any case, there are fundamental differences between continental crust and oceanic crust. The rocks that make up the continental landmasses have the lowest density of all, so that the continents are sometimes described as "rafts" that float on denser material below. These low-density rocks have come to be known as *sialic rocks,* or just **SIAL** (from the chemical symbols of their dominant mineral components—*si*lica and *al*uminum [Fig. 29.7A]). Granite is a common sialic rock, and its density is about the same as the density of the continental landmasses as a whole (2.8 g/cm³). As a result you will see continental crust referred to as "granitic" or "granitoid" crust—although the landmasses are made up of many other rocks as well, such as sandstone, limestone, shale, and marble. These are the rocks that, because of their different capacities to withstand weathering and erosion, create the diversity of landscapes we will study later.

Oceanic crust, on the other hand, consists of higher-density rocks collectively called the *simatic rocks,* or **SIMA** (for *si*lica, of which they contain much less than continental rocks, and *ma*gnesium, a heavy dark-coloured component [Fig. 29.7B]). Here the dominant rock is the heavy, dark-coloured basalt. Oceanic crust, therefore, is often referred to as basaltic crust, although many other rocks also form part of the oceanic crust. In combination, rocks of the oceanic crust have a density of about 3.0 g/cm³. Geologists define continents as having granitic crust over basaltic crust.

Despite these overall differences between low-density granitic continental crust and higher-density basaltic oceanic crust, there are places *on* the continents where

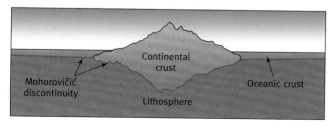

FIGURE 29.6 The Mohorovičić discontinuity (Moho) marks the base of continental as well as oceanic crust. As the sketch shows, it lies much closer to the crust's surface under the oceans than beneath the land.

A

B

FIGURE 29.7 "Baking in the African sun is some of the Earth's oldest rock: ancient granite, sialic, light-weight continental rock that has been part of the African shield for 3 billion years (A). Whenever you travel across the African landscape, you note how light-coloured these crystallines are, coloured white, beige, or pink according to their composition (dominant quartz creates the lightest colour; felspars form light shades of red). But when new rock emerges from the Earth's interior, as on Pacific islands or along midocean ridges, it is dominated by basalt, dark-coloured and heavier (B). This is young SIMA, and it constitutes the ocean floors."

oceanic-type basalt can be found. How did this supposedly oceanic rock get there? The answer is that the continental crust sometimes cracks open, allowing molten rock from deep below to penetrate to the surface. (Also in some cases, ocean-floor rocks thrust over continental rocks [e.g., the Gros Morne area of Newfoundland].) The basalt that has come to the surface through these fissures proves that heavier, denser rocks exist below the continents—so the notion of the landmasses as rafts on a simatic "sea" is not so far-fetched!

The Lithosphere

The crust terminates at the Moho, but rocks in the solid state do not. The uppermost segment of the mantle, on which the crust rests, also is rigid. Together the crust and this solid uppermost mantle are called the **lithosphere**, the sphere of rocks. Below the lithosphere, the upper mantle becomes so hot that it resembles hot plastic—it can be made to change shape, it can be moulded.

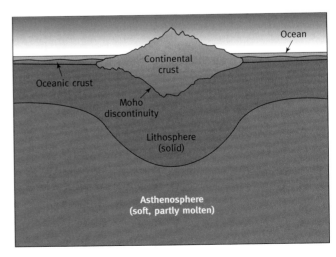

FIGURE 29.8 Position of the asthenosphere in the Earth's mantle. The boundary between the asthenosphere and the lithosphere is a transition zone rather than a sharp divide. Its depth beneath the surface is about twice as great under the continents as under the oceans.

This soft plastic layer in the upper mantle is called the **asthenosphere** (Fig. 29.8). Like the Mohorovičić discontinuity, the asthenosphere begins at a much deeper level below the continental landmasses than it does below the ocean floor. Beneath the landmasses it begins at a depth averaging 80 km below the surface. Beneath the ocean floors, it lies only about 40 km below the surface (i.e., of the seafloor, not the water).

The discovery of the existence of the asthenosphere was important to our understanding of what happens in and on the crust. Because the asthenosphere is in a hot plastic state, the lithosphere can move over it. This movement of the crust, which is related to the formation of mountains and even the movement of whole continents, takes place because heat sources deep inside the core and mantle keep the asthenosphere in motion. Unlike the Moho, the contact zone between the rigid lithosphere and the soft asthenosphere is not abrupt.

Rather, it is gradual, so that material can pass from one state to the other as it moves vertically as well as horizontally. For many years, geologists wondered what forced molten rock material into the crust, and even through it as magma. Recent research has determined that the buoyancy of such molten material is either positive, neutral, or negative with respect to surrounding rock; but only if the buoyancy remains positive will it rise through the crust via diapirism, the vertical movement of magma through the crustal rocks, and onto the surface as lava. Thus, as more became known about the asthenosphere, the mechanisms of such processes came to be better understood.

Much more remains to be learned about the lithosphere and its uppermost layer, the crust. Geophysicists today can create small Earth tremors where earthquakes normally do not originate, and they can study the behaviour of the resulting waves. For example, scientists

PERSPECTIVES ON THE HUMAN ENVIRONMENT

Lithoprobe

The idea for the Lithoprobe project originated in a meeting attended by university and government geologists in Toronto in 1981. The aim of the project was to investigate how North America had been structurally put together and to study a series of geological transects and areas of various regions of the country. When the project began in 1984, it became fully funded by the Natural Sciences and Engineering Research Council, the Geological Survey of Canada, and other sources to the sum of more than $100 million.

Lithoprobe involved many thousands of scientists divided into groups that studied the various areas of Canada (Fig. 29.9). The project addressed the following fundamental questions about the evolution of the continent of North America: (1) the origin of the North American continent; (2) how the continent was built up over time; (3) the geological history of North America; and (4) the depth of the lithosphere under various parts of North America.

The Lithoprobe project is now coming to an end. It has been the world's first national multidisciplinary investigation of the origin and growth

of a continental area and has led to the publication of many papers, as well as many workshop sessions, about the geological structure and history of North America.

FIGURE 29.9 A vibroseis crew at work in Ontario. Four vibroseis (sound source) trucks (called "dancing elephants") work in unison to send seismic signals into the ground. Nearby recording trucks record the collected signals and feed the data into computers for storage.

FROM THE FIELDNOTES

FIGURE 29.10 "Not one square metre of flat land in this dissected, high-relief area on the North Island of New Zealand. High relief prevails throughout most of New Zealand, which is positioned in the boundary zone between the Australian and Pacific Plates and is subject to volcanism and earthquakes. Glaciation, as well as stream erosion, further modify its topography, so that this is one of the most scenic locales on the planet. But this vista is not the result of nature's work alone. Before human settlers arrived less than one thousand years ago, dense forests covered this area (like much of the rest of the islands). The Maori burned significant portions of it, but it was the Europeans and their livestock who had the greater impact. They converted forest into pasture for millions of sheep, in some areas sparing not a single tree for as far as the eye can see. In this area, the pastures are seeded annually from airplanes, producing a verdant countryside—but one that is a cultural, not a natural, landscape. "

began to realize that the so-called bright spots revealed by these artificial waves were more common than they had believed since the first one was noticed in 1975. These bright spots are zones in the crust, usually 15 to 20 km below the surface, where the seismic waves are being reflected more than elsewhere in the lithosphere. One theory suggests that there is a transition zone of rock from a brittle state to a soft state within the crust, a kind of mini-Moho. The proof may not come for decades, and the discovery of the bright spots is a reminder of the limited state of our knowledge—even of the crust on which life exists.

Lithospheric Plates

The crust varies in thickness and is also a discontinuous layer. To humans, living on the landmasses, the idea that the crust is not a continuous, unbroken shell is difficult to grasp because there seems to be no evidence of cracks or fractures in it. In fact, the crust and the rest of the lithosphere are fragmented into a number of segments called **lithospheric plates** (or *tectonic plates*). These plates move in response to the plastic flow in the hot asthenosphere. Many of the Earth's mountain ranges, including the mightiest Himalayas, are zones where the

moving plates have come together in gigantic collisions. This aspect of the lithosphere is so important to our later study of landscapes and landforms that it is treated in a pair of units (32 and 33).

The Crustal Surface

The Earth's crust is subject to tectonic forces from below. The rocks that form the crust are pushed together, stretched, fractured, and bent by the movement of the lithospheric plates. These forces tend to create great contrasts at the crustal surface—jagged peaks and sharp crests, steep slopes and escarpments, huge domes and vast depressions. Before we begin an in-depth examination of those forces in the remaining units of Part Four, it is useful to take another look at the surface of the continents and their varied relief.

Topographic Relief

The term **relief** refers to the vertical difference between the highest and lowest elevations in a given area. Thus a range of tall mountains and deep valleys, such as the Rocky Mountains, is an area of *high relief* (Fig. 29.10).

FROM THE FIELDNOTES

FIGURE 29.11   "Sailing up the Seine River you can see a perfect example of low-relief topography: land lies just two metres or so above the river surface and, in the words of my British colleague, is 'as flat as a pancake.' Characteristically, the French have laid out their farms in 'long lots' that have a short window on the riverfront but extend far inland, a cultural-geographic feature they brought to Quebec when they settled the banks of the St. Lawrence."

A coastal plain is an area of *low relief* (Fig. 29.11). An area of low relief can lie at a high elevation: a nearly flat plateau with an elevation of 3000 m has lower relief than a mountainous area with peaks no higher than 2000 m and valleys at 500 m. Attempts by physical geographers to classify land surfaces notwithstanding, great liberties are often taken with such features on the map (see Perspective: Hills, Mountains, Plains, Plateaus—What's in a Name?).

When continental landmasses are viewed even at a small scale (see Fig. 2.3), it is evident that they have areas of high relief and other areas of low relief. North America, for example, has large areas of low relief, especially in central and eastern Canada, the interior United States, and the coastal plain bordering the Atlantic Ocean and the Gulf of Mexico. High relief prevails in the western third of the continent, from the Rocky Mountains westward. In the east lies an area of moderate relief in the Appalachian Mountains.

The two types of relief just identified represent three kinds of continental geology. The Earth's landmasses consist of two basic geologic components: *continental shields* and their associated platform borderlands and *orogenic belts*. In North America, the region centred on Hudson Bay is a continental shield, expressed topographically as a plain of low relief (the Canadian Shield) around this on three sides are the platform borderlands. The Rocky Mountains represent the topographic results of a period of mountain building and constitute an orogenic belt.

Continental Shields

All the continental landmasses contain shields and platform borderlands as well as orogenic belts. The **continental shields** (or *cratons*) are large, stable, relatively flat expanses of very old rocks, and they may constitute the earliest "slabs" of solidification of the molten crust into

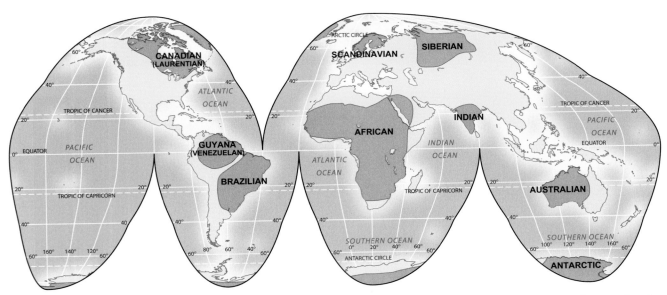

FIGURE 29.12   Continental shields of the world, representing materials that cooled from the earliest molten surface or after the impact of meteorites early in the geological history of the Earth.

PERSPECTIVES ON THE HUMAN ENVIRONMENT

Hills, Mountains, Plains, Plateaus—What's in a Name?

To distinguish regional patterns of crustal relief more sharply, these land surface features have been classified by many geographers.

Hills and mountains are defined as terrain of less than 50 percent gentle slope. In terms of local relief, *hills* exhibit variations of 0 to 300 m, *low mountains* variations of 300 to 900 m, and high mountains variations in excess of 900 m.

Plains and plateaus are land surfaces of more than 50 percent gentle slope. *Plains* are low-lying areas that exhibit less than 90 m of local relief; *flat plains* exhibit more than 80 percent gentle slope and less than 30 m of local relief. *Plateaus,* or tablelands, display more than 90 m of local relief, and more than 50 percent of their gentle slope occurs in the lower half of their elevational ranges. In addition, plateaus almost always are bounded on at least one side by a sharp rise or drop in elevation.

Despite these attempts at definitional precision, the global map is littered with *toponymy* (place names) that disregards the geographer's sense of topographic order. Plains and plateaus usually fare better than upland areas. A glaring exception would be South America's large central Andean plateau of Peru and Bolivia that lies more than 3600 m above sea level, which is called the "High Plain" (*Altiplano* in Spanish).

When studying hills and mountains on the landscape, therefore, map readers should be forewarned that place namers have taken some blatant liberties. An example from Southern Ontario is Blue Mountain, site of a popular ski area on the Niagara Escarpment near Collingwood. Its height reaches about 220 m above sea level.

hard rocks (or solidification related to a phase of meteoric impacts). This happened more than 4 billion years ago, and ever since these shields have formed the nuclei of the landmasses.

The shield in northern North America is called the *Canadian (Laurentian) Shield* (Fig. 29.12). It is larger than the area of ancient rocks presently exposed because it is covered by water in the north and by sedimentary rocks along its southern flank (the platform borderlands). In South America there are two major shield zones: the *Guyana (Venezuelan) Shield* and the *Brazilian Shield*. These shield areas, unlike the Canadian Shield, are uplands today and present the aspect of low-relief plateaus rather than plains.

Eurasia has three major shields: the *Scandinavian Shield* in the northwest, the *Siberian Shield* in the north, and the *Indian Shield* in the south. The world's largest shield presently exposed is the *African Shield,* a vast region of ancient rocks that extends into the Arabian Peninsula at its northeastern extremity. Some of the oldest known rocks deposited on top of the shield have been found in the *Australian Shield,* which occupies the western two-thirds of that continent. And under the ice in eastern Antarctica lies the *Antarctic Shield.* Wherever these shield zones form the exposed landscape, they exhibit expanses of low relief (Fig. 29.13).

Platform Borderlands occur around the margins of the Shields. They are characterized by a relatively thin cover of sedimentary rocks deposited on top of the shield that are horizontal or nearly horizontal, indicating stability.

Orogenic Belts

In contrast, the **orogenic belts**—series of linear mountain chains—are zones of high relief. The term *orogenic* derives from the ancient Greek word *oros,* meaning mountain. As we note later, the Earth during its 4.6-billion-year lifetime has experienced several periods of mountain building. These episodes are marked on the topographic map by linear mountain chains, such as the Appalachians and the Rockies in North America. The Andes Mountains in South America, the Alps and Himalayas in Eurasia, and the Great Dividing Range in Australia all represent orogenic activity, when rocks were thrust, bent, and crushed into folds like a giant accordion (Fig. 29.14). Ever since, processes in the atmosphere and the other spheres of the Earth System have been eroding those structures; but they persist to the present day, bearing witness to past orogenies.

Gradational Processes

If the Earth had no atmosphere and no moisture, those shields, platform borderlands, and orogenic belts would

FIGURE 29.13 Stream flowing slowly across the vast tundra east of Yellowknife in Canada's Northwest Territories. This is the Canadian Shield, its crystalline rocks scoured by ice but now ice-free, its depressions and valleys filled with wetlands, lakes, and rivers.

FIGURE 29.14 Inca-built structures of Machu Picchu, high in the Andes of Peru. This is high relief in the extreme, but the Inca managed to construct large stone buildings and terrace even very steep slopes. The purposes of Machu Picchu still are uncertain. It may have served as a fortress and/or as a ceremonial centre. Anthropologist Jack Weatherford has suggested that the terraces seen here were experimental farm plots to raise high-altitude-adapted crops.

stand unchallenged, destroyed only by new tectonic forces. But the Earth does have an atmosphere, and as a result the geological buildup is attacked by a set of processes that work to erode it. These are called **gradational processes** and are the focus of several units in Part Five.

The rocks of which the crust is composed are subject to various forms of *weathering*—the physical, chemical, and even biological processes that operate to distintegrate rocks, break them apart, and make them ready for removal (erosion). The force of gravity plays an important role in this removal as the motivating force for *slope movement* of soil and rock, which also takes several forms (an avalanche, for instance, is a form of mass movement). But this mass movement does not carry loosened rock material very far. That requires the longer distance removal of weathered materials. Great rivers transport rock grains thousands of kilometres from mountain slopes in the deep interiors of continents to their deltas on the coasts. There, and in their valleys upstream, the process of deposition fills the lowlands with the very material removed from the highlands. Glaciers, wind, and ocean waves participate in this erosion of the land thrust up by tectonic forces.

It is a continuous contest that affects some areas of the crust more strongly than others at different times in Earth history. This conclusion is based on the geological record: where great mountains once rose, only their roots now remain. Areas once tectonically active are today quiescent. But other zones now appear to be on the verge of great tectonic activity and will subsequently be attacked by gradational forces. It is all part of the continued recycling of Earth materials within the dynamic lithosphere.

KEY TERMS

asthenosphere *page 387*

body waves *page 382*

continental shield *page 389*

earthquake *page 381*

gradational processes *page 392*

inner core *page 383*

lithosphere *page 386*

lithospheric plate *page 388*

lower mantle *page 384*

Mohorovičić discontinuity (Moho) *page 385*

orogenic belt *page 391*

outer core *page 383*

relief *page 388*

seismic wave *page 381*

SIAL *page 385*

SIMA *page 385*

upper mantle *page 384*

REVIEW QUESTIONS

1. How do earthquakes and their seismic waves suggest a layering of the Earth's interior?

2. Give the approximate thickness of the inner core, outer core, mantle, and crust.

3. What is the Mohorovičić discontinuity, and what is its significance?

4. What are the differences between oceanic and continental crust?

5. What is the significance of the asthenosphere? How does it relate to the concept of lithospheric plates?

6. Which gradational processes contribute to the recycling of the Earth's materials?

REFERENCES AND FURTHER READINGS

ADAMS, J. J., et al. "Seismicity and Seismic Hazards," in Brooks, G. R., et al., *A Synthesis of Geological Hazards in Canada 2001* (Ottawa: Geological Survey of Canada Bulletin 548, 2001), 7–26.

BLOOM, A. L.   *The Surface of the Earth* (Englewood Cliffs, N.J.: Prentice-Hall, 1969).

BOLT, B. A.   *Inside the Earth: Evidence from Earthquakes* (New York: Freeman, 1982).

BOTT, M. H. P.   *The Interior of the Earth: Its Structure, Constitution, and Evolution* (London: Edward Arnold, 1982).

DAVIS, G. H.   *Structural Geology of Rocks and Regions* (New York: Wiley, 1976).

"The Dynamic Earth," *Scientific American* (September 1983; special issue).

ERNST, W. G.   *Earth Materials* (Englewood Cliffs, N.J.: Prentice-Hall, 1969).

GARLAND, G. D.   *Introduction to Geophysics: Mantle, Core, and Crust* (Toronto: Holt, Rinehart, & Winston, 1979).

GASS, I., et al., Eds. *Understanding the Earth* (Cambridge, Mass.: MIT Press, 1971).

HANCOCK, P. L., and SKINNER, B. J., Eds. *Oxford Companion to the Earth* (New York: Oxford Univ. Press, 2001).

KING, P. B. *The Evolution of North America* (Princeton, N.J.: Princeton Univ. Press, 1977).

PERCIVAL, J. A., et al. "PanLITHOPROBE Workshop IV: Intra-Orogen Correlations and Comparative Orogenic Anatomy" (workshop review), *Geoscience Canada,* 31, no. 1 (2004), 23–40.

POWELL, C. S. "Peering Inward," *Scientific American* (June 1991), 100–111.

PRESS, F., and SIEVER, R. *Earth* (San Francisco: Freeman, 2nd ed., 1978).

RAYMO, C. *The Crust of Our Earth: An Armchair Traveler's Guide to the New Geology* (Englewood Cliffs, N.J.: Prentice-Hall, 1983).

TREWARTHA, G. T., et al. *Elements of Geography* (New York: McGraw-Hill, 5th ed., 1967). Classification discussed on pp. 262–266.

WEINER, J. *Planet Earth* (New York: Bantam Books, 1986).

WEB RESOURCE

http://www.iodp.org This site for the International Ocean Drilling Program explains the basics of this type of research, and provides tutorial information about the internal layers of Earth. Photos are available of operations, as well as a multimedia introductory tour.

http://www.lithoprobe.ca The website of the Lithoprobe project has a lot of information, maps, images, and links to many government agencies, universities, etc., involved in the study.

http://www.seismo.nrcan.gc.ca/ The Earthquakes Canada website contains a wealth of information about all aspects of earthquakes.

http://www.seismo.nrcan.gc.ca/cnsn/stn-map@.html The Canadian National Seismograph Network website shows the location of various seismograph stations and contains data about earthquakes, links, etc.

UNIT 30

Minerals and Igneous Rocks

A quartz vein invaded this crystalline bedrock millions of years ago, filling a joint plane and cementing the stock. Now exposed and dilated, it forms a point of weakness as weathering and erosion attack. (Authors' photo)

OBJECTIVES

- To understand the relationship between rocks and their constituent minerals

- To briefly investigate the important properties of minerals and to provide an elementary scheme for their classification

- To discuss some important aspects of igneous rocks and their influence on landscape forms

The Earth's outermost solid sphere is the crust, and the crust is the upper layer of the lithosphere. The crust consists of many different types of rocks, which range from concrete-like hardness to soaplike softness. When subjected to pressure, some fracture; others bend and warp. When heated to high temperatures, some melt and flow whereas others remain solid. When exposed to the forces of weathering and erosion, some withstand these conditions better than others. To understand what we see in the physical landscape, it is essential to comprehend the properties of the underlying building materials—the rocks.

Minerals and Rocks

Matter is made up of 92 naturally occurring elements arranged in a periodic table according to their atomic numbers. Elements exist independently or in combination with other elements; each element consists of atoms (which contain protons, neutrons, and electrons) organized into a characteristic matrix. An element cannot be broken down further, either by heating or by chemical reaction. Minerals can consist of a single element, such as diamond (which is pure carbon) and gold (a metallic element), or they can be combinations of elements, such as quartz, a compound of silicon and oxygen. Minerals are **crystalline**; that is, their atoms are arranged in regular, repeating crystallographic patterns. It is often impossible to see these patterns in hand samples, but microscopes and X-ray diffraction instruments reveal them. Sometimes, however, nature displays these crystal structures in spectacular fashion (Fig. 30.1). Thus minerals have distinct properties, given to them by the strength and stability of the atomic bonds in their crystal lattices. To summarize all its characteristics, we would say that a **mineral** is a naturally occurring inorganic element or compound having a definite chemical composition, physical properties, and, usually, a crystal structure.

Many minerals can be quickly recognized by the shape of their crystals as well as by their colour and hardness. For crystals of a given mineral to form, there must be time for their atoms to arrange themselves into the proper pattern. As the formation time increases, so does the size of the mineral structure. Imagine a reservoir of molten rock contained somewhere deep inside the crust. This mass of molten rock cools slowly, and its various component crystals have time to develop their lattice structures quite fully. The atoms, therefore, have the opportunity to arrange themselves in the regular patterns of various minerals. When the mass finally hardens, its various component minerals will be large, well formed, and easily recognizable.

But what happens if that mass of molten rock does not cool slowly deep inside the crust, but is instead poured out through a fissure or vent onto the surface of the crust? Now cooling takes place very rapidly, and there is little time for the atoms to arrange themselves

FIGURE 30.1 Grossuter (garnet) from Jeffrey Quarry, Asbestos, Quebec on the Canadian Shield.

into orderly patterns. What results is a solid rock in which the atoms are arranged randomly and the mineral structure is hardly discernible. A glasslike form of lava, called obsidian, is an example of such rapid hardening (Fig. 30.2). **Rocks**, therefore, are composed of mineral assemblages. A few rocks consist of only one mineral, such as quartzite, which is mainly quartz. But most rocks contain several minerals, and these minerals have much to do with the way rocks break or bend, weather, and erode.

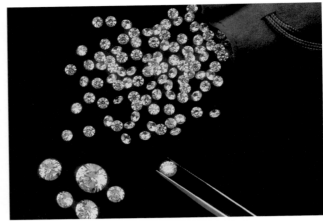

A

FIGURE 30.2 Obsidian, the shiny volcanic glass, and rhyolite form when lava cools very rapidly under certain circumstances. Dark bands of obsidian can be seen in this extrusion in Inyo National Forest, California.

B

FIGURE 30.3 Diamonds reflect this valuable mineral's hardness, clarity, and transparency (A). By contrast, the graphite form of the same carbon exhibits opposite characteristics (B) and is so inexpensive that it is commonly used as pencil "lead."

Mineral Properties

As stated above, all minerals exhibit specific properties that enable them to be identified and differentiated. These properties include chemical composition, hardness, cleavage or fracture, colour and streak, and lustre.

Chemical Composition Every chemical element is identified by a one- or two-letter symbol. Aluminum, for example, is Al; iron is Fe. This does not mean, however, that all minerals made from each element are the same. Take, for example, the element identified as C, carbon. The mineral *diamond,* one of the hardest substances known, is pure carbon. But so is *graphite,* the soft "lead" in a pencil. Chemically they are the same, but their crystalline structures differ. In a diamond, all atoms are bonded strongly to each other. In graphite, certain bonds are weaker, creating sheets that are easily

split apart. Note, too, that while diamond is clear, transparent, and very hard, graphite is opaque, grey-black, and soft—the very opposite qualities (Fig. 30.3). Other minerals are even softer than graphite, and rocks containing such soft minerals are more quickly broken down by weathering and eroded than rocks containing only harder minerals.

Hardness Hardness, therefore, is an important property of minerals. This quality can be useful in identifying minerals in the field, and it can suggest much about the overall hardness of the rock in which they occur. As long ago as 1822, Friedrich Mohs noticed that certain minerals could make a scratch mark on other min-

Table 30.1 The Mohs' Hardness Scale

Mineral	Hardness
Diamond	10
Corundum	9
Topaz	8
Quartz	7
Potassium feldspar	6
Apatite	5
Fluorite	4
Calcite	3
Gypsum	2
Talc	1

By way of comparison, here are some everyday items ranked according to their approximate hardness: pocketknife blade, 5–6; glass, 5; copper penny, 3.5; fingernail, 2.5.

Table 30.2 Composition of the Earth's Crust

Element	Percentage (by Weight)
Oxygen (O)	46.6
Silicon (Si)	27.7
Aluminum (Al)	8.1
Iron (Fe)	5.0
Calcium (Ca)	3.6
Sodium (Na)	2.8
Potassium (K)	2.6
Magnesium (Mg)	2.1
TOTAL	98.5

erals, but not vice versa. Diamond, the hardest mineral of all, will scratch all other natural mineral surfaces, but cannot be scratched by any of the others. So Mohs established a hardness scale ranging from 1 to 10, with diamond (10) the hardest. Mohs determined that talc (the base mineral of talcum powder) was the softest naturally occurring mineral, and this he numbered 1. Mohs' Hardness Scale (Table 30.1) continues to be used to this day. Notice that quartz, a commonly appearing mineral, ranks 7 and is quite hard.

Cleavage/Fracture The crystal form of minerals quickly identifies them in some cases, but not many crystals can grow unimpeded to the full form shown in Fig. 30.1. More useful is the property of *cleavage,* the tendency of minerals to break in certain directions along bright plane surfaces, revealing the zones of weakness in the crystalline structure. When you break a rock sample across a large crystal of a certain mineral, the way that crystal breaks may help to identify it. Sometimes minerals do not break as cleanly as this, however. Instead they *fracture* in a characteristic way. That glasslike obsidian mentioned earlier (Fig. 30.2) has a way of fracturing in a concoidal (shell-like) fashion when broken.

Colour/Streak A mineral's colour is its most easily observable property. Some minerals have very distinct colours, such as the yellow of sulphur and the deep blue of azurite. Other minerals have identical colours or occur in numerous colours, and therefore cannot be differentiated according to this property. However, the colour of a mineral's *streak* (the mineral in powdered form when rubbed against a porcelain plate) can sometimes help identify it. For example, although both galena and graphite are metallic grey in colour, their streaks are grey and black, respectively. Like colour,

streak is often unhelpful in that most minerals have white or colourless streaks.

Lustre A mineral also displays a surface sheen or *lustre,* which, along with colour, can be a useful identifying quality. For instance, the difference between real gold and a similar-looking but much less valuable mineral, pyrite (FeS_2), can be detected by their comparative lustres. Not surprisingly, pyrite is called fool's gold for good reason!

Mineral Types

Although nearly 100 chemical elements are known in nature, only eight make up more than 98 percent of the Earth's crust by weight (see Table 30.2). Moreover, the two most common elements in the crust, silicon and oxygen, constitute almost 75 percent of it. Geologists divide the minerals into two major groups, the *silicates* and the *nonsilicates.* Each group is in turn subdivided. This classification is a central concern of the field of mineralogy.

The silicates, as their name suggests, are the compounds containing silicon (Si) and oxygen (O) and, mostly, other elements as well. The nonsilicates include the carbonates, sulphates, sulphides, and halides. Among these, the *carbonates* are of greatest interest in physical geography. All carbonates contain carbon and oxygen (CO_3). With calcium they form calcite, the mineral of which limestone is made. Limestone is fairly widely distributed, and it creates unusual landforms under both humid and arid conditions (see Unit 44). Add magnesium (Mg) to the formula, and the mineral dolomite (or dolostone) is formed. Dolomite, too, creates distinctive landforms.

The *sulphates* (SO_4) all contain sulphur and oxygen. The calcium sulphate, gypsum, in some places lies exposed over sufficiently large areas to be of geomorphological interest. The *sulphides* (SO_3), on the other hand, occur in veins and ores, and do not build or sustain landforms themselves. Pyrite (FeS_2) is such a mineral. The *halides* consist of metals combined with such elements as chlorine, fluorine, and iodine. The most common is halite, a compound of sodium (Na) and chloride (Cl), the substance that makes ocean water salty; but halite rock salt also can create landforms.

Finally, there are the oxides and natural elements. The *oxides* are formed by a combination of metal and oxygen, nothing more. This kind of crystallization takes place in veins or ore chambers, and the result may be an economically important deposit of, for example, hematite (Fe_2O_3) or magnetite (Fe_3O_4). Oxidation also can take place as a result of the intrusion of liquid water or water vapour into concentrations of iron or aluminum. The *natural elements* are those rare and prized commodities that are among the most valuable on Earth: gold (Au), silver (Ag), platinum (Pt), and sometimes copper (Cu), tin (Sn), and antimony (Sb).

Classification of Rock Types

From what has been said about the minerals that make up the crustal rocks, it is evident that the diversity of rock types is almost unlimited. Still, when rocks

---

PERSPECTIVES ON THE HUMAN ENVIRONMENT

The World's Oldest Rocks*

Geologists have known for decades that the Earth was formed about 4.6 billion years ago, condensing from a rotating, gaseous mass along with the other terrestrial planets of the inner solar system. At first our planet consisted entirely of molten rock, but one hypothesis suggest that eventually its heavier constituent elements (iron and nickel) settled to form a solid core. Another idea is that early on in the Earth's history there was a major collision with a large asteroid. The asteroid was incorporated into the Earth, eventually reaching the Earth's core. On its way to the interior it took most of the heavier minerals in the crust with it. Above that inner core, as Fig. 29.5 indicates, three concentric layers emerged as the Earth continued to cool: the outer core, the lower mantle, and the upper mantle. Until a few years ago, scientists had little information as to when the upper mantle began to develop a crust, a process they liken to the formation of the crust atop boiling pea soup. But recent discoveries of very old rock formations in the continental shields of Canada, Australia, and Greenland have now begun to shed light on the events associated with the birth of the crust—and have produced field specimens that may rank among the first rocks ever formed.

Since 1990 the age of the oldest known rocks has been pushed back by at least 300 million years. The Acasta gneisses found about 350 km north of Yellowknife, N.W.T., have now been dated at 3.96 billion years, and neighbouring rocks may be as old as 4.27 billion years. That is also the age of individual mineral crystals (zircons) found in sedimentary rocks discovered in the Jack Hills about 690 km north of Perth, western Australia, during the 1980s. The oldest rocks dated from the mantle were found in two outcrops along the rugged coast of Labrador. They have been dated to 4 billion years ago. The older rock is a komatiite formed when some of the hot mantle erupted onto the Earth's surface (geologists are now searching for the older rocks on which this lava was deposited). Clearly, the ancient gneiss specimens prove the existence of continental crust almost 4 billion years ago, whereas the sedimentary grains strongly suggest that the cycle of transformation that affects all rocks (see discussion of the rock cycle on p. 413) was operating even earlier than that. These monumental findings have not only filled major gaps in our knowledge of the earliest stage of Earth history, they are also alerting scientists to field research opportunities that prior to the 1990s, few could even imagine existed.

---

*The source for much of this box is Hilts (1989).

are classified according to their mode of origin, they all fall into one of three families. One class of rocks forms as a result of the cooling and solidification of **magma** (molten rock), and this process produces **igneous rocks**. Because they solidified first from the Earth's primeval molten crust (see Perspective: The World's Oldest Rocks), igneous rocks are known as *primary* rocks. The deposition and compression of rock and mineral fragments produces **sedimentary rocks**, and when existing rocks are modified by heat or pressure or both, they are transformed into **metamorphic rocks**. Because they are derivatives of pre-existing rocks, sedimentary and metamorphic rocks are called *secondary* rocks. Igneous rocks are treated in the remainder of this unit; secondary rocks are the subject of Unit 31.

Igneous Rocks

The term *igneous* means "born by fire," from the Latin word *ignis,* meaning fire. The ancient Romans, upon seeing the flaming lava erupt from Italy's Mounts Vesuvius and Etna, undoubtedly concluded that fire stoked the rock-forming ovens inside the Earth. But igneous rocks actually form from cooling—the lowering of the temperature of molten magma or **lava** (magma that reaches the Earth's surface). This can happen deep inside the crust or on the surface. Magma is not only a complex melt of many minerals; it also contains gases, including water vapour. It is a surging, swelling mass that pushes outward and upward, sometimes forcing itself into and through existing layers of rocks in the crust, incorporating them as it goes (diapirism). If its upward thrust ceases before it reaches the surface, the resulting rocks formed from the cooled magma are called **intrusive igneous rocks**. If it penetrates all the way to the surface and spills out as lava or is erupted as ash or tephra, the rocks formed from these materials are called **extrusive igneous rocks**.

As noted previously, intrusive igneous rocks tend to have larger mineral crystals than faster-cooling extrusive ones. Intrusives such as granite and gabbro are coarse grained, with mineral crystals as much as 1 cm or more in diameter. For intrusive rocks with exceptionally large crystals, some ranging from 2 to 3 cm long, the cooling process obviously was unusually slow. It is concluded that this occurred at unusual depth and that the magmatic mass must have been very large. Such coarse-grained intrusive rocks are called *plutonic* igneous rocks, another term of Latin origin (Pluto was the Roman god of the underworld).

The colour of igneous rocks can tell us much about their origins. When the original magma is rich in silica (*felsic, acidic,* or *silicic*), it yields rocks rich in felspar and quartz. Such rocks are light-coloured, with pink or beige-coloured felspar and glassy quartz dominating. Magma that was poorer in silica (*basic* or *mafic*) yields darker rocks, both intrusives and extrusives. For example, a light-coloured, coarse-grained granite formed as an intrusive rock; had the same magma spilled out onto the surface, it would have yielded a light-coloured but much finer grained rhyolite. But a dark-coloured, coarse-grained gabbro came from a basic magma; had it penetrated to the surface as an extrusive rock, it would have become a fine-grained black basalt.

Intrusive Forms

In the analysis of landscapes, the form an intrusion (a mass of intrusive rock) takes becomes an important factor. Magmas vary not only in composition, but also in viscosity (fluidness). Thick, viscous masses will remain compact; if the magma is very fluid, it can penetrate narrow cracks in existing rock strata and inject itself between layers. Sometimes the pent-up gases in a magma will help force it through its chamber walls. Other magmas, containing less gas, are calmer.

In general terms, intrusions may be **concordant** if they do not disrupt or destroy existing structures or **discordant** if they cut across previously formed strata. For instance, a **batholith** is a massive *pluton* (a body of plutonic rock) that has melted and assimilated most of the existing rock structures it has invaded; a **stock** also is discordant but smaller (Fig. 30.4). Sometimes magma inserts itself as a thin layer between strata of existing rocks without disturbing these older layers to any great extent; such an intrusion is called a **sill** (Fig. 30.4). But magma can also cut vertically across existing layers, forming a kind of barrier wall called a **dyke** (Fig. 30.4). The sill is a concordant intrusion; the dyke obviously is discordant. An especially interesting concordant intrusive form is the **laccolith**. In this case a magma pipe led to a chamber that grew, dome-like, pushing the overlying strata into a gentle bulge without destroying them (Fig. 30.4).

Jointing and Exfoliation

Igneous rocks such as granite and basalt display a property that is of great importance in their breakdown under weathering and erosion. **Jointing** is the tendency of rocks to develop parallel sets of fractures without any obvious movement along the plane of separation (such as faulting). Granite often exhibits a rectangular joint

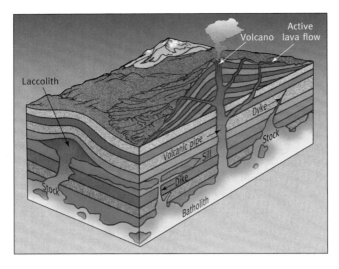

FIGURE 30.4   Diagrammatic cross-section through the uppermost crust showing the various forms assumed by plutons.

pattern so that it breaks naturally into blocks (Fig. 30.5). Basalt, on the other hand, usually possesses a columnar joint system that produces hexagonal forms. Jointing in igneous rocks appears to be related to the cooling process of the magma. The contraction of the material produces planes of weakness and separation—the *joint planes*—but jointing is not confined to igneous rocks. Sedimentary and metamorphic rocks also display forms of jointing.

A special kind of jointing, found in certain kinds of granite, produces a joint pattern resembling a series of concentric shells—not unlike the layers of an onion. The outer layers, or shells, peel away progressively, leaving the lower layers exposed (Fig. 30.6). This phenomenon, called **exfoliation** or spalling, is caused by the release of confining pressure. These granite domes were at one time buried deep inside the crust under enormous pressure. As erosion removed the overlying rocks, the pressure was re-

FROM THE FIELDNOTES

FIGURE 30.5 "With a faculty member of the University of Tasmania's Department of Geography we drove from Hobart, the capital, to Port Arthur, the former penal colony. The Tasman Peninsula presents numerous sites of physical-geographic interest, and among the most fascinating is this wave-cut platform, where marine erosion has exploited joints in igneous rock. The joint pattern now looks like a roughly tiled floor, planed down by waves rolling over it and exposed by subsequent uplift. At high tide, waves still wash over the platform, filling the joint planes and enhancing the pattern."

FROM THE FIELDNOTES

FIGURE 30.6 "The cable-car ride to the top of Sugar Loaf Mountain (Pao de Azucar) in the heart of Rio de Janeiro, Brazil, provided a dramatic vista over this massive city's unique and scenic site. Great granite stocks and batholiths, formed deep below the surface and exposed by uplift and erosion, now create towering domes among which the city's structures are nestled. As erosion removed the overburden, the release of weight on these domes resulted in exfoliation. The outer shells peeled off, leaving rounded, often smooth-surfaced landforms (**inselbergs**) rising above the countryside."

duced and these rock masses expanded. The outer shells, unable to resist this expansion force, cracked and peeled along hidden (concentric) joint planes.

Igneous Rocks in the Landscape

Igneous rocks tend to be strongly resistant to weathering and erosion. Intrusive igneous structures often form characteristic landforms when their overburdens are removed through weathering and erosion (**etchplanation**). For example, when the strata overlying a laccolith (Fig. 30.4) are eroded away, the granitic core stands as a mound above the landscape, encircled by low ridges representing remnants of the softer sedimentary cover. The intrusive sill, which long ago squeezed between sedimentary layers (Fig. 30.4), resists erosion longer than

FIGURE 30.7 Devil's Tower, a columnar basalt structure 263 m high, was the first physical feature to be declared a U.S. National Monument. Located in northeastern Wyoming, it is the remnant of a volcanic intrusion in which conditions favoured the development of basalt's hexagonal jointing.

the softer sedimentary rocks. Eventually such a sill is likely to cap a table-like landform, called a *mesa* (see Fig. 42.6), a remnant of the intrusion. A dyke (Fig. 30.4), which is also more resistant than its surroundings, will stand out above the countryside as a serpentine ridge (see photo of New Mexico's Ship Rock on p. 546). Exfoliation also can be seen in progress in many places (some spectacular examples are the domes in California's Yosemite National Park).

The most spectacular landforms associated with igneous rocks undoubtedly are shaped by extrusive structures, especially the world's great volcanoes. A famous one is Devil's Tower (it had a starring role in the movie *Close Encounters of the Third Kind*) in Wyoming (Fig. 30.7), a columnar structure of basaltic rock formed from an ancient eruption. The violent eruption of Mount St. Helens in the U.S. Pacific Northwest in 1980 provided scientists with an opportunity to witness volcanic processes and their consequences. Vesuvius, the great volcano that looms over the Italian city of Naples, is the most legendary of all such mountains. The processes and landforms of volcanism are investigated in Unit 34. But now the survey of the two remaining major rock types continues in Unit 31.

KEY TERMS

batholith *page 399*

concordant *page 399*

crystalline *page 395*

dyke *page 399*

discordant *page 399*

etchplanation *page 401*

exfoliation *page 400*

extrusive igneous rock *page 399*

igneous rock *page 399*

inselbergs *page 401*

intrusive igneous rock *page 399*

jointing *page 399*

laccolith *page 399*

lava *page 399*

magma *page 399*

metamorphic rock *page 399*

mineral *page 395*

rock *page 395*

sedimentary rock *page 399*

sill *page 399*

stock *page 399*

REVIEW QUESTIONS

1. What are minerals?

2. How are minerals related to elements and rocks?

3. How are intrusive and extrusive igneous rocks different, and how can they generally be distinguished?

4. How is a *sill* different from a *dyke?*

5. How is a *batholith* different from a *laccolith?*

REFERENCES AND FURTHER READINGS

BARKER, D. S.   *Igneous Rocks* (Englewood Cliffs, N.J.: Prentice-Hall, 1983).

COX, K. G., et al.   *The Interpretation of Igneous Rocks* (Boston: Allen & Unwin, 1979).

DEER, W. A., HOWIE, R. A., and ZUSSMAN, J.   *An Introduction to Rock Forming Minerals* (New York: Wiley, 2nd ed., 1992).

DIETRICH, R. V., and SKINNER, B. J.   *Gems, Granites, and Gravels: Knowing and Using Rocks and Minerals* (New York: Cambridge Univ. Press, 1990).

EHLERS, E. G., and BLATT, H.   *Petrology: Igneous, Sedimentary, and Metamorphic* (New York: Freeman, 1982).

HESS, P. C.   *Origins of Igneous Rocks* (Cambridge, Mass.: Harvard Univ. Press, 1989).

HILTS, P. J.   "Canadian Rock, at 4 Billion Years, Is Called Oldest," *New York Times* (October 5, 1989), 8.

HURLBUT, C. S., Jr.   *Minerals and Man* (New York: Random House, 1969).

KLEIN, C., and HURLBUT, C. S., Jr.   *Manual of Mineralogy* (New York: Wiley, 21st ed., 1993).

MacKENZIE, W. S., et al.   *Atlas of Igneous Rocks and Their Textures* (New York: Wiley/Halsted, 1982).

POUGH, F.   *A Field Guide to Rocks and Minerals* (Cambridge, Mass.: Riverside Press, 3rd ed., 1960).

PRINZ, M., et al.   *Simon and Schuster's Guide to Rocks and Minerals* (New York: Simon & Schuster, 1978).

RYAN, M. P., Ed.   *Magmatic Systems* (Orlando, Fla.: Academic Press, 1994).

WEB RESOURCES

http://csmres.jmu.edu/geollab/Fichter/IgnRx/lghome.html Lynn Fichter's site at James Madison University provides a comprehensive guide to igneous rocks and their classification. Extrusive and intrusive igneous rocks are covered, and there are many links to photos and descriptions. A self-test on classification is provided.

http://earthsci.org/rockmin/rockmin.html This Australian Earth science site presents background information on rock formation and structure. The rock cycle is explained, and both minerals and igneous rocks are covered in detail.

http://www.mineralogicalassociationofCanada Information about minerals, links to relevant sites, etc.

http://www/nature.ca/collections/earthsciencecfm#mins Web pages about Earth science, rocks, and minerals from the Canadian Museum of Nature, Ottawa.

http://www.rom.on.ca/news/releases/public/php?mediakey=m7zpp9h8yn Web page about the Royal Ontario Museum acquiring the Charles Key Mineral Collection.

Sedimentary and Metamorphic Rocks

Orphan Lake Trail, Lake Superior Provincial Park. Metamorphic processes led to the formation of banded gneiss on the Canadian Shield.

OBJECTIVES

- To discuss the circumstances under which sedimentary and metamorphic rocks form

- To identify common sedimentary and metamorphic rock types

- To discuss some observable structures within sedimentary and metamorphic rock masses

The igneous rocks have been called the Earth's primary rocks—the first solidified material derived from the molten mass that once was the primeval crust. The other two great classes of rocks could therefore be called secondary, because they are derived from pre-existing rocks. These are the sedimentary and metamorphic rocks.

Sedimentary Rocks

Sedimentary rocks result from the deposition and compaction (*lithification*) of rock fragments and mineral grains derived from other rocks. These grains are weathered and broken away from existing rocks by the action of water, wind, and ice, processes explored in Part Five. Again, the ancient Roman scholars understood what they saw: *sedimentum* is the Latin word for settling. Many sedimentary rocks begin their existence as loose deposits of sand or gravel at the bottom of a sea or lake, on a beach, or in a desert (Fig. 31.1). Later the sediment is lithified—compressed into a rock.

As successive layers of sediment accumulate, the weight of the sediments expels most of the water between the grains. Pressure caused by the weight of the overlying materials will compact and consolidate the lower strata. The rock fragments and grains are squeezed tightly together, especially in fine-grained sediments such as clays and silts. This is the process of **compaction** (Fig. 31.2A). Compaction rarely takes place alone. Most sedimentary material has some water in the pore spaces between the grains, and this fluid contains dissolved minerals. This mineral matter, such as silica or calcite, is deposited in thin films on the grain surfaces, which has the effect of gluing them together. This is the process of **cementation** (Fig. 31.2B). Together, compaction and cementation can transform a bed of loose sand into a layer of cohesive sedimentary rock called sandstone.

Clastic and Nonclastic Sedimentary Rocks

The range of agents and materials that combine to produce sedimentary rocks is wide, and as a result the structure and texture of these rocks also vary greatly. Even the finest wind-blown dust can become lithified. The same is true for a mixture of boulders, cobbles, pebbles, and sand swept down by a stream and subsequently compacted and cemented. Sedimentary rocks made from particles of other rocks are referred to as **clastic**, from the ancient Greek *klastos,* meaning broken. The vast majority of sedimentary rocks are clastic. **Nonclastic** sedimentary rocks form from chemical solution by deposition and evaporation, or from organic deposition.

Clastic sediments are most conveniently classified according to the size of their fragments, which can range from boulders to fine clay particles. The coarsest-grained sedimentary rock is the **conglomerate**, a composite rock made of gravels, pebbles, and sometimes even boulders. An important property of conglomerates is that the pebbles or boulders tend to be quite well rounded. This characteristic is evidence that they were transported by water for some distance, perhaps rolled down a stream

or washed back and forth across a beach. A large pebble may reveal the area from which it was removed, perhaps telling us something about ancient drainage courses. Sometimes pebbles are elliptical in shape, and in the conglomerate a significant number of them lie cemented with their long axes in the same direction. Such information helps reveal the orientation of the coastline where the sediment accumulated.

When pebble-sized fragments in a conglomerate are not rounded but angular and jagged, it is called a **breccia** (Fig. 31.3). The rough shape of the pebbles indicates that little transport took place prior to lithification. When compaction and cementation occur after a rock avalanche, for instance, the result is a breccia. Again, the properties of the fragments can constitute a key to the past.

Another common and important sedimentary rock is **sandstone**. In a sandstone the grains, as the name implies, are sand-sized, and they usually are quartz grains. Some sandstones are very hard and resist erosion even in humid climates. This is because the cementing material in such sandstones is silica. But other sandstones are less compacted and are cemented by calcite or even iron oxide. Such sandstones are "softer" and more susceptible to weathering and erosion. Thus sandstones are also a key to the past. They may have rounded or angular grains, depending on the distance travelled and the process of movement.

As with conglomerates, the size of sandstone grains may vary. Rounded, even-sized grains indicate long-distance travel. Variations in particle size and irregular shapes mean poor sorting and rapid deposition. Sandstones also have economic importance: because they are porous, they can contain substantial amounts of water and even oil. Under certain structural circumstances, such water or oil can form a reservoir suitable for exploitation (see Perspective: Oilfield Formation).

A sedimentary rock even softer than most sandstones is **shale**, the finest-grained clastic sedimentary rock. Shale is compacted mud. Whereas sandstone contains quartz grains that are often visible to the naked eye, shale is made from clay minerals, and the individual mineral grains cannot be seen. Shale has a tendency to split into thin layers, making this already "soft" rock even more susceptible to weathering and erosion (Fig. 31.5). In many places (such as the Appalachian Mountains in eastern North America), the low valleys are often underlain by soft shale and the higher ridges by other rocks, including hard sandstone.

One of the most interesting sedimentary rocks, because of both the way it forms and its response to weathering and erosion, is **limestone**. Limestone can form from the accumulation of marine shell fragments

FROM THE FIELDNOTES

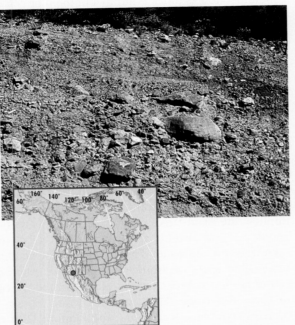

FIGURE 31.1 "You can almost feel the power of the process that transported and deposited this accumulation of poorly sorted sediment in its present location. Boulders lie closer to the surface than smaller pebbles; many fragments are angular, suggesting short-distance transportation and no time for rounding or sorting. It must have happened very suddenly, a burst of force, perhaps during a major flood in this desert environment (we are in a valley near the Gila River in eastern Arizona). This mass of material would become a conglomerate if compaction and cementation followed. More likely, future rainstorms and floods will carry most of it further downslope."

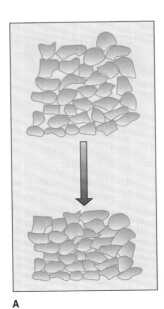

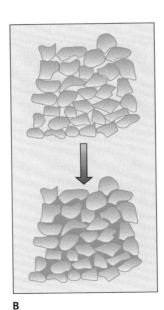

A   **B**

FIGURE 31.2 Compaction and cementation in sedimentary rocks. (A) In *compaction,* the grains are packed tightly together by weight from above. (B) In *cementation,* the spaces between the grains are filled through the deposition of a cement, such as silica or calcium carbonate.

on a beach or on the ocean floor, which qualifies it as a special kind of clastic sedimentary rock. Most limestone, however, results from the respiration and photosynthesis of marine organisms, such as foraminifer or rotifers, in which calcium carbonate is distilled from seawater. This calcium carbonate ($CaCO_3$) then settles on the ocean floor, and accumulations may reach hundreds of metres in thickness. Limestone can vary in composition and texture, but much of it is finely textured and, when exposed on the continental landscape, hard and resistant to weathering. Limestone, however, is susceptible to solution, and under certain environmental conditions it creates a unique landscape both above and below the ground (see Unit 44).

None of the nonclastic sedimentary rocks play a significant role in the formation of landscape, other than limestone in its chemical form. *Evaporites* form from the deposits left behind as water evaporates. Such evaporites as halite (salt), gypsum, and anhydrite have some economic importance, but their areal extent is small. Biological sediments include the carbonate rocks formed by coral reefs, cherts formed from silica skeletons of diatoms and radiolarians (marine micro-organisms), and, technically, the various forms of coal.

FROM THE FIELDNOTES

FIGURE 31.3 "Although it is reasonable to assume that the poorly sorted material in Fig. 31.1 will be eroded away, there are times when another process intervenes. When a fault cuts across an area underlain by such sediment, the rock material caught in the fault plane may be partially melted and welded into a highly resistant rock called breccia. We were travelling through an area of southern Spain when we saw this superb example. Note that a ridge of resistant rock stands in a natural wall between rocks dipping at different angles to the right (under the vegetation) and to the left (exposed in a scarp). The natural wall is made of breccia, formed when the fault occurred. It stands out because it is more resistant than the sediments on either side of the fault; you can judge the height by the shadow it casts."

PERSPECTIVES ON THE HUMAN ENVIRONMENT

Oilfield Formation

The first commercial oil well in North America was dug by James Miller Williams at Black Creek (soon renamed Oil Springs), Lambton County, Canada West (now Ontario), in 1858. By 1861 oil production from 400 wells in the Oil Springs area was up to 800 barrels/day. At that time, a barrel of oil sold for $10. Williams alone shipped 1.5 million litres of oil out of Lambton County in two years.

By 1862 Oil Springs had become a boom town with 1000 operating wells and a population of between 3000 to 4000. It had 12 general stores, nine hotels, and horse-drawn buses that plied the first paved main street in Canada. Oil Springs had gas lighting installed along its Main Street before any of the major cities in North America or Europe. In

fact, the first oil company in the world (International Mining and Manufacturing Company) was formed in Oil Springs in 1854 by two brothers, Charles and Henry Tripp, who discovered and utilized oil gum or tar beds as the basis for small-scale petroleum production for oil lamp fuel. Their company failed, and Williams (a major creditor) took over the property licences. Seven years after the oil rush at Oil Springs, another oil bonanza started up at Petrolea (now Petrolia), about 10 km to the south.

The Earth's proven oil reserves are now estimated to exceed 1 trillion barrels (one barrel equals approximately 140 l or 0.132 m^3). Saudi Arabia possesses the largest petroleum reserves

(261 billion barrels), while Iraq possesses 115 billion barrels, Iran 100 billion barrels, Kuwait 99 billion barrels, and the United Arab Emirates 63 billion barrels (all figures are as of 2003).

In January 2001 Canadian Oil reserves were estimated to be 4.7 billion barrels of conventional oil; if oil derived from the Alberta oil sands is included, reserves are estimated to be 174.4 billion barrels (as of January 2004), second only to Saudi Arabia (oil and gas). Canadian oil production averaged 2.7 million barrels/day during 2000. Sixty percent of this oil production came from Alberta. There are also large reserves of oil on the continental shelf around Newfoundland that have not been fully utilized and more exploration is going on.

Canada is the fifth largest energy producer, behind the United States, Russia, China, and Saudi Arabia. It is the third largest supplier of U.S. crude oil imports—1.3 million barrels/day (behind Saudi Arabia and Mexico). Canada is also responsible for 87 percent of U.S. natural gas imports (see Table 31.1). Although Canada is a major oil producer, it imports oil and refined oil products from the U.S. (16 percent), European Union (25 percent), Mexico (approximately 0.2 percent), and others (57 percent). The total amount of imports in 2002 was 15.4 billion barrels.

Petroleum occurs in the sedimentary rocks of nonshield zones (Fig. 29.12), where conditions have favoured the development of geological structures capable of containing oil reservoirs. The formation of petroleum itself involved large, shallow bodies of water where, scientists believe, microscopic plant forms (such as diatoms) contained minute amounts of an oily substance. At death, these tiny plants released this substance, so that it became part of the sediments accumulating on the seabed.

Millions of years later, a thick accumulation of sediments—now transformed into sedimentary rock layers—might contain a large quantity of oil. Then, when these rock layers were subsequently compressed and bent into arching structures called folds (see Unit 36), the accumulated oil would be squeezed into a reservoir, as shown in Fig. 31.4. Such a reservoir might be an upfold in the rock layers or a dome capped by an impermeable stratum. (Note that natural gas often forms above such an oil pool—the two energy resources frequently occur together—and that the oil also floats above any groundwater that may lie below the upfold in the porous, reservoir rock layer.) There the petroleum deposit remains under pressure until its existence is discovered by exploration. Then a well is drilled, the black liquid is pumped to the surface, and the world's oil production capacity is recorded as having increased.

Table 31.1 Destination of Canadian Oil Exports, 2002

Location	Percentage
U.S.	98.9
	(26.7 billion barrels)
European Union	0.46
Japan	0.18
Mexico	0.04
Other	0.42
Total: 27 billion barrels	

Source: Canadian Mineral Yearbook Online 2002.

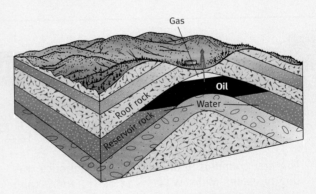

FIGURE 31.4 *Oil pool* (a body of rock in which oil occupies all the pore spaces) trapped in an upward-arching layer of reservoir rock. These curving rock structures are known as folds; they constitute the most important of all oil traps.

Sedimentary Rocks in the Landscape

A sequence of sedimentary rocks in the landscape is unmistakable because it displays variations in texture, colour, and thickness of the various layers (see unit opening photo). This layering, or **stratification**, reminds us that conditions changed as a succession of rock beds or **strata** was being deposited. Often distinct surfaces between strata, or *bedding planes,* are evident. Sometimes it is apparent that the sequence was interrupted and that a period of deposition was broken by a

FIGURE 31.5   Steeply angled limestone and shale jutting out into the water at Broom Pond, Newfoundland. This soft, thin-layered sedimentary rock is easily weathered and eroded.

period of erosion before the deposition resumed. Where such an interruption is evident in the **stratigraphy** (*order and arrangement of strata*) of sedimentary rocks, the contact between the eroded strata and the strata of resumed deposition is called an **unconformity** (Fig. 31.6).

The texture and colour of the sedimentary layers allow us to deduce the kinds of environments under which they were deposited. Sedimentary rocks, therefore, are crucial in the reconstruction of past environments. Even more importantly, sedimentary rocks contain fossils (Fig. 31.7). Much of what is known about Earth history is based on the fossil record. Interpretations from the fossil record, as well as conclusions drawn from the stratigraphy of sedimentary rock sequences far removed from one another, make correlations possible which provide further evidence for reconstructions of the past.

Sedimentary rocks can be observed as they accumulate today, providing further insight into similar conditions in the distant geological past. You may have seen ripples in the sands of a beach or in a desert area. These ripples can be created by the wash of waves or by the

FROM THE FIELDNOTES

FIGURE 31.6   "Mediterranean shores provide instructive vistas, and even a local ferry ride can constitute a lesson in physical geography. This exposed cliff on the Italian island of Ischia reveals an eventful sedimentary and tectonic history. Unconformities mark the lower strata (below the church on the cliff's flank). Note the contrasting angle of dip of the light-coloured sandstone strata (upper right). Clearly, these layers were deposited during times of much interrupted sedimentary deposition and repeated tectonic activity."

FIGURE 31.7 Fossilized fish contained in Eocene sedimentary rocks provide valuable clues to the geological past. This easily recognized school of fish was found in the Green River Formation in Wyoming and was preserved for about 40 million years. Similar samples have also been found near Cache Creek in the interior of British Columbia.

persistent blowing of wind. Most of the time they are erased again, only to reform later. But sometimes they are cemented and preserved in lithifying rock as *ripple marks*. Ripple marks formed millions of years ago have become exposed by erosion—providing evidence of wind or wave directions in the distant past.

Features of Sedimentary Strata

When originally formed, most sedimentary strata are layered horizontally. Another form of layering, **crossbedding**, consists of successive strata deposited at varying inclines. Like ripple marks, this forms on beaches and in dunes. The sand layers do not lie flat, but at angles caused by wind and water-current action over an irregular bed. We can see this happening today, and we can compare angles of repose and other aspects of the process to cross-bedded layers in old sedimentary rocks.

As noted previously, all rocks have jointing properties. Not only are sedimentary rocks layered—with their bedding planes often a factor in weathering and erosion—but they also are jointed. Joints are produced by a variety of processes, ranging from desiccation (drying) in sedimentary rocks to unloading by erosion in igneous rocks. Furthermore, over time sedimentary rocks may be folded, faulted, and otherwise deformed (see Unit 36). All these circumstances contribute to the rate of erosion in areas where sedimentary rocks dominate the landscape, and they create the sometimes spectacular, multicoloured, and varied scenery of such places (Fig. 31.8).

FIGURE 31.8 The Colorado River has cut a canyon in the Colorado Plateau that exposes hundreds of millions of years of rock accumulation. Here, at the Marble Canyon segment of the Grand Canyon, sedimentary strata display diverse colours reflecting the environmental circumstances of their deposition. Some are weakly cemented and erode quickly, forming relatively gentle inclines on the canyon wall. Others, like the uppermost layers, are more resistant and form scarps that retain their vertical configuration for a very long time. The exposure seen here is about 900 m high, the last phase of a geologic sequence that began here shortly after the planet's formation and continued intermittently for about 4 billion years.

Metamorphic Rocks

Metamorphic rocks are rocks that have been altered by varying degrees of heat and pressure. The term *metamorphic* comes from a Greek word meaning change, but the complex processes involved in rock metamorphism have only begun to be understood in modern times. All rock types may be subject to metamorphism. Igneous rocks can be remelted and recrystallized. Sedimentary rocks can be fused by heat and pressure into much harder rocks. And metamorphic rocks themselves can be transformed again.

All this happens through tectonic action in the crust (see Unit 33) or through volcanic action (see Unit 34). Zones of the Earth's crust are pushed down to deeper levels; other segments of the crust rise. The rocks making up these crustal zones are subjected to changing temperature and pressure conditions, and are modified as a result. When intrusive action by magma occurs, rocks in the zone near the batholith or dyke will be affected (Fig. 31.9A); this process is known as **contact metamorphism**. When a sheet of lava flows out over the surface, its heat changes the rocks it covers. Imagine a sedimentary sequence of limestone, sandstone, and shale being interrupted by repeated lava flows from a fissure. The heat and weight of the lava will create metamorphic rocks out of the sedimentary

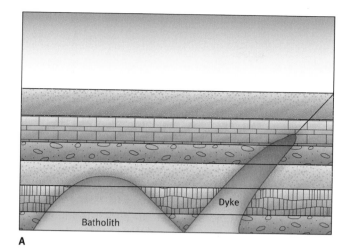

A

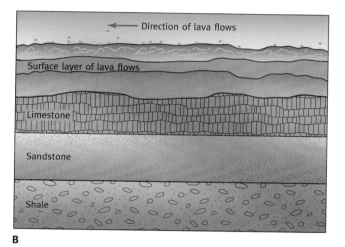

B

FIGURE 31.9 Two examples of contact metamorphism, illustrating the effects of two kinds of magmatic intrusions on the existing sedimentary rock strata. (A) Metamorphism radiates deeply into these layers from both the batholith and the dyke. (B) Effects of extrusion, in this case repeated lava flows, on underlying sedimentary layers.

rocks immediately below it (Fig. 31.9B). This also happens when a sill forms, with contact metamorphism occurring in the overlying and underlying rocks. Impact melt rocks are a form of metamorphic strata.

Metamorphic Rock Types

Some metamorphic rocks have quite familiar names. Sandstone, made of quartz grains and a silica cement, becomes **quartzite**, a very hard rock that resists weathering. Limestone is converted into much denser and harder **marble**, used by sculptors for statues that can sometimes withstand exposure to the elements for thousands of years. Shale may be metamorphosed into

slate, a popular building material; slate retains shale's quality of breaking along parallel planes.

Sometimes metamorphism alters the pre-existing rocks so totally that it is not possible to determine what the previous form of the rock may have been. A common metamorphic rock is **schist**. This rock is fine-grained, and it breaks along roughly parallel planes (but very unevenly, unlike slate). If schist was, at least in part, shale in its premetamorphic form, there is little resemblance left (see Fig. 31.5).

When schist is seen outcropping on the landscape, it displays wavy bands. These bands show that the minerals in the pre-existing rock were realigned during the metamorphic process. This realignment indicates that metamorphism did not completely melt the older rocks, but made them viscous enough for the minerals to orient themselves in parallel strips. This process gives certain metamorphic rocks their unmistakable banded appearance, or **foliation**. One of the best and most frequently seen examples is in **gneiss**, the metamorphic rock derived from granite (Fig. 31.11). Gneisses show a segregation of mafic (dark-coloured) and felsic (light-coloured) minerals, known as gneissic banding.

Metamorphic Rocks in the Landscape

Because metamorphic rocks have been subjected to heat and pressure, it might be concluded that they would be the most resistant of all rocks to weathering and erosion. But even metamorphic rocks have their weak points and planes (see Fig. 31.11). Slate, for example, is weak at the surfaces along which it breaks because water can penetrate along these planes and loosen the rock slabs. Schist often occurs in huge masses and therefore seems to resist weathering and erosion quite effectively. But schist is weak along its foliation bands and breaks down quite rapidly. Even gneiss is weakest along those foliation planes, especially where dark minerals such as biotite micas have collected. In some areas where gneiss is extensive, the dark minerals have been weathered so effectively that vegetation has taken hold in these bands. From the air one can follow the foliation bands by noting the vegetation growing in the weakest ones.

The Earth's first rocks were igneous rocks—rocks solidified from the still molten outer sphere some 4 billion years ago. Ever since, existing rocks have been modified and remodified, and there are few remains of these original, ancient-shield rocks. What we see in the landscape today are only the most recent forms in which rocks are cast by the processes acting upon them. This explains why it is so difficult to piece together the planet's history from the geological record—subsequent metamorphism has erased much of it.

FIGURE 31.10 "A meeting in Tucson, Arizona, gave us an opportunity to do a field reconnaissance in one of the most interesting geomorphological areas of North America. In the Superstition Mountains we found a variety of metamorphic rocks, including this sample of characteristically shiny schist, its appearance resulting from the alignment of small, elongated flakes of mica oriented in the same direction through the foliation process. The mountains of southeastern Arizona and New Mexico, south of the Colorado Plateau and extending southward from the Rocky Mountains, constitute a complex natural landscape in which desert conditions prevail and weathering is active, so that the relatively rare bursts of heavy rainfall cause rapid erosion and the fast removal of large amounts of loose material. Bedrock is continually being exposed, and you can find a wide variety of rock types, and even fossils, even on a short field trip."

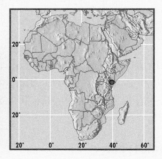

FIGURE 31.11 "We were looking for a place to cross the rain-swollen Tana River in eastern Kenya. The normally placid stream was a raging torrent in places, and this site, usually a series of rapids, showed no promise. But the physical geography here was notable because of the rocks that cause the rapids. Foliation in metamorphic rocks lines up the minerals in parallel bands so that the recrystallized rocks appear to be streaked with alternating light- and dark-coloured stripes. Metamorphic rocks tend to be quite resistant to erosion, as this gneiss outcrop, under constant attack by the river, illustrates."

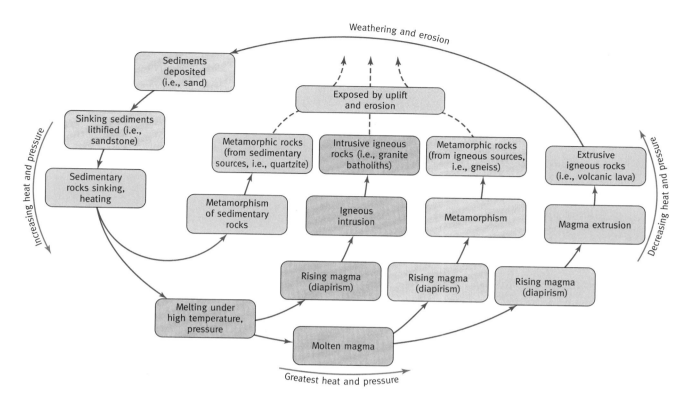

FIGURE 31.12 The rock cycle. The flow of materials within, above, and below the Earth's crust continually forms and destroys igneous, sedimentary, and metamorphic rocks.

The Rock Cycle

The Earth, therefore, is continuously changing. Plutons form deep in the crust; uplift pushes them to the surface; erosion degrades them; the sediments they produce become new mountains. This cycle of transformation, which affects all rocks and involves all parts of the crust, is conceptualized as the **rock cycle** (Fig. 31.12).

The rock cycle has neither a beginning nor an end, so it is possible to start following it anywhere on the diagram. High temperatures and pressures deep inside the crust melt the crustal (rock) material. Magma rises via diapirism, either intruding into existing rocks or extruding as lava, creating both igneous and metamorphic rocks. Weathering and erosion attack the exposed rocks; deposition creates sedimentary rocks from the frag-

ments. Crustal forces push sedimentary, igneous, and metamorphic rocks downward, and if they reach the lower levels of the crust, they will be melted and the cycle will start anew—or, rather, continue. In our lifetimes we are witnesses to just a brief instant in a cycle that affects the entire planet in space and its whole history in time.

Now that we have become familiar with the characteristics and cycling of Earth materials, we are ready to consider the forces of the restless crust. Our examination of these processes, which contribute importantly to the shaping of surface landscapes, begins in Unit 32 with an overview of the lithospheric plates that fragment the crust.

KEY TERMS

breccia *page 405*

cementation *page 405*

clastic sedimentary rocks *page 405*

compaction *page 405*

conglomerate *page 405*

contact metamorphism *page 410*

cross-bedding *page 410*

foliation *page 411*

gneiss *page 411*

limestone *page 405*

marble *page 411*

nonclastic sedimentary
  rocks *page 405*

quartzite *page 411*

rock cycle *page 413*

sandstone *page 405*

schist *page 411*

shale *page 405*

slate *page 411*

strata *page 408*

stratification *page 408*

stratigraphy *page 409*

unconformity *page 409*

REVIEW QUESTIONS

1. How are sedimentary rocks formed?
2. How do clastic sedimentary rocks differ?
3. How are metamorphic rocks formed?

4. What are the metamorphic equivalents of sandstone, limestone, and shale?
5. Briefly outline the major components of the rock cycle.

REFERENCES AND FURTHER READINGS

BLATT, H., et al.   *Origin of Sedimentary Rocks* (Englewood Cliffs, N.J.: Prentice-Hall, 2nd ed., 1980).

BOGGS, S.   *Principles of Sedimentology and Stratigraphy* (Columbus, Ohio: Merrill, 1987).

COLLINSON, J. D.   *Sedimentary Structures* (Boston: Allen & Unwin, 1982).

DEER, W. A., HOWIE, R. A., and ZUSSMAN, J.   *An Introduction to Rock Forming Minerals* (New York: Wiley, 2nd ed., 1992).

DIETRICH, R. V., and SKINNER, B. J.   *Gems, Granites, and Gravels: Knowing and Using Rocks and Minerals* (New York: Cambridge Univ. Press, 1990).

EHLERS, E. G., and BLATT, H.   *Petrology: Igneous, Sedimentary, and Metamorphic* (New York: Freeman, 1982).

HYNDMAN, D. W.   *Petrology of Igneous and Metamorphic Rocks* (New York: McGraw-Hill, 2nd ed., 1985).

MASON, R.   *Petrology of the Metamorphic Rocks* (Boston: Allen & Unwin, 1978).

NICHOLS, G.   *Dynamic Sedimentology and Stratigraphy* (Malden, Mass.: Blackwell, 1998).

PETTIJOHN, F. J.   *Sedimentary Rocks* (New York: Harper & Row, 3rd ed., 1975).

REINECK, H. E., and SINGH, I. B.   *Depositional Sedimentary Environments* (New York: Springer Verlag, 2nd ed., 1980).

STONELEY, R.   *An Introduction to Petroleum Exploration for Non-Geologists* (New York: Oxford Univ. Press, 1999).

WEB RESOURCES

http://collections.lc.gc/blackgold This website gives information about the Oil Springs–Petrolia oil industry.

http://www.geocities.com/RainForest/Canopy/1080/sedimentary.htm This webpage gives basic information about sedimentary rocks, their formation, and their classification.

http://oil.museum@county-lambton.on.ca Oil museum of Canada, 2423 Kelly Road, Oil Springs, ON N0N 1P0; ph. (519)-834-2840. This National Historic Site is concerned with the Lambton County oil rush.

http://www.petroliadiscoveries.com Petrolia Discovery, 4381 Discovery Line, Petrolia, ON N0N 1R0; ph. (519)-882-1897. This website features displays about the oil industry of Lambton County in the 1860s.

http://plaza.snu.ac.kr/~lee2602/atlas/atlas.html This atlas of sedimentary rocks provides a large number of visual images, including laboratory and textbook photographs.

Lithospheric Plates

Where plates diverge. New land arises from submarine eruptions related to the Mid-Atlantic Ridge south of Iceland. (Authors' photo)

OBJECTIVES

- To introduce the concepts of continental drift and plate tectonics

- To identify the major plates of the lithosphere
- To discuss the important boundary zones between

lithospheric plates in which rifting, subduction, and transform faulting occur

When Christopher Columbus reached America in 1492, his discovery was recorded in his ship's log—and on the first map to be based on the Atlantic Ocean's western shores. When Columbus returned on his next three voyages, and as others followed him, the Atlantic coastline of the Americas became better known. During the sixteenth century, Portuguese navigators and cartographers mapped Africa's Atlantic coasts all the way to the Cape of Good Hope at the continent's southern tip.

By the early 1600s, the general configuration of the Atlantic Ocean was fairly well known, even though the maps of the time were often inaccurate in detail. Nonetheless, the great Belgian cartographer Abraham Ortelius, in his *Theatrum Orbis Terrarum*, the first commercially successful atlas, made an observation that contained the kernel of a momentous concept. Looking at the evolving map of the Atlantic Ocean, Ortelius said that the opposite coasts of North and South America and Africa and Europe seemed to fit so well that it looked as though the continents might at one time have been joined, and he suggested that they had been torn apart by floods and earthquakes. It was a notion soon forgotten, however, and not revived until centuries later. And even then the idea that whole continents could move relative to each other was greeted with skepticism and, in some circles, derision.

Continental Drift

In 1915 the German Earth scientist Alfred Wegener (1880–1930) published a book that contained a bold new hypothesis. Not just Africa and South America, Wegener suggested, but all the landmasses on Earth once were united in a giant supercontinent. This primeval landmass, which he named **Pangaea** (meaning "All-Earth"), broke apart, forming the continents and oceans as they are known today. Wegener theorized that Pangaea consisted of two major parts,

Laurasia in the north and **Gondwana** in the south. Today Eurasia and North America are considered to be the remnants of Laurasia; South America, Africa, India, Australia, and Antarctica are considered the principal fragments of Gondwana (Fig. 32.1).

Wegener's book, *The Origin of Continents and Oceans* (1915), was not translated into English until the end of the 1920s. By then Wegener's notion of **continental drift**—the fragmentation of Pangaea and the slow movement of the continents away from this supercontinent—was already a topic of debate among geologists and physical geographers in many parts of the world. The American geologist F. B. Taylor had written a long article about the idea of continental drift in 1910. A South African geologist, L. du Toit, also supported Wegener's hypothesis and busied himself in gathering evidence from opposite sides of the South Atlantic Ocean. But most other geologists could not conceive of the possibility that whole continents might be mobile, functioning like giant rafts.

Wegener had marshalled a good deal of circumstantial evidence: fossil plants and animals from widely separated locales; climatic environments (as indicated by sedimentary rocks) unlike those now prevailing; and, of course, the remarkable jigsaw-like "fit" of the continents. Plausible as continental drift was to those who believed this evidence, there was one major problem—the process

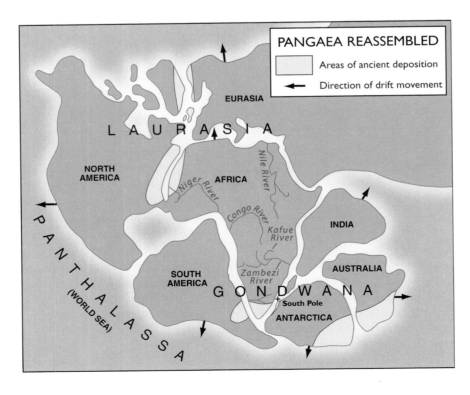

FIGURE 32.1 The breakup of the supercontinent Pangaea began more than 100 million years ago. Note the radial movement of its remnants away from Africa and how areas of ancient deposition help us understand where today's landmasses were once joined together.

that could move continents was unknown. There simply was no evidence for a propelling mechanism.

As sometimes happens when a new scientific concept emerges, the hypothesis of continental drift lost credibility among many geologists, in part because of the mechanisms proposed by Wegener himself as well as others. Wegener suggested that the Earth's gravitational force, which is slightly lower at the Equator, was over time strong enough to pull the continents apart. Taylor proposed that the Moon was torn from the Earth in what is today the Pacific Basin, and that the continents have been steadily moving into the gap thereby created. Such notions damaged the credibility of the entire continental drift hypothesis, and despite the accumulation of geological and paleontological evidence in favour of it, few geologists (especially in the United States) were willing to accept the possibility.

Some scientists, however, kept working on the problem. One British geologist, Arthur Holmes, proposed as early as 1939 that there might be heat-sustained convection cells in the interior of the Earth and that these gigantic cells could be responsible for dragging the landmasses along (see Unit 33). Others argued that the evidence for continental drift had become so overwhelming that notions of a rigid crust would have to be abandoned—there must be a mechanism, and further research would uncover it. The discussion of continental drift was reawakened in the early 1960s by J. Tuzo Wilson (1908–1993), a Canadian geophysicist. Wilson studied and named transform faults, theorized about plate movement mechanisms, worked out ways of tracing plate movement using "hot spots" or mantle plumes, and suggested the supercontinent cycle. He can truly be thought of as the father of modern **plate tectonic theory**.

Continents, Plate Tectonics, and Seafloors

Geologists and physical geographers had been searching for evidence to support the mobility of the landmasses. But a large part of the answer lay not on the exposed continents, but on the submerged ocean floor. The existence of a Mid-Atlantic Ridge—a mostly submarine mountain range extending from Iceland south to the Antarctic latitudes, approximately in the centre of the Atlantic Ocean—had been known for many years. For decades it was believed that this feature was unique to the Atlantic Ocean. But during the 1950s and 1960s, evidence from deep-sea soundings made by a growing number of transoceanic ships carrying new sonar equip-

ment began to reveal the global map of the ocean floors in unprecedented detail. The emerging map clearly revealed that midoceanic ridges are present in all the ocean basins (Fig. 32.2).

This was a momentous development, but more was to come. When oceanographers and geologists analyzed rocks brought up from the ocean floor and determined their ages, the rocks were found to be much younger than most of those on the landmasses. These basaltic rocks, moreover, were youngest near the midoceanic ridges and progressively older toward the continental margins of the ocean basins.

Further investigations revealed another startling pattern: the midoceanic ridges were not just submarine mountain ranges like those on the landmasses, but constituted a global network associated with hot upwelling magma. New basaltic rock was being formed, soon to be pushed away horizontally by still newer rock forcing its way up from below all along the midoceanic ridge. The process came to be called **seafloor spreading**, involving the creation of new crust and its continuous movement away from its source.

Obviously, if the midoceanic ridges are zones where new crust forms and diverges, the Earth's crust is divided into segments—large fragments separated along the ridges. These segments of the crust were called *plates* (**lithospheric plates** to denote their rigidity and *tectonic plates* to describe their active mobile character). Now, at last, the scientists were one giant step closer to understanding the mechanism needed to explain continental mobility. The movement of these parts of the crust is called **plate tectonics**.

If ocean floors can move and "spread," then continents can also be displaced. Moreover, if the ocean floor spreads outward from the midoceanic ridges, then the crust must be crushed together elsewhere, and parts of it must be pushed downward to make space for the newly forming crust. Thus the plates of which the crust is made are formed in one zone and destroyed in another. This process of destruction occurs where plates moving in opposite directions collide. Earthquakes, volcanism, and mountain building mark such zones of crustal collision.

Distribution of Plates

When seafloor spreading was first recognized and the map of midoceanic ridges took shape, it appeared that the Earth's crust was divided into seven major plates, all but one carrying a major landmass. But as more became known about both ocean floors and landmasses, additional plates were identified. By the 1990s,

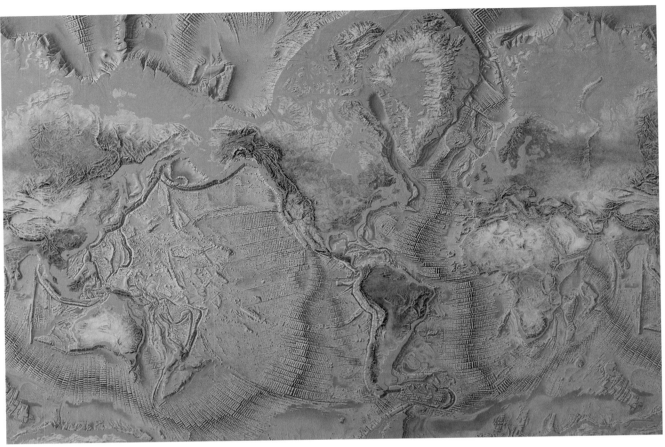

FIGURE 32.2   World ocean-floor map, underscoring the prominence of the global network of midoceanic ridges. A larger-scale version of this map is shown in Fig. 2.6.

18 lithospheric plates had been mapped (Fig. 32.3), but there is still uncertainty as to the exact margins and dimensions of several, and others may yet be discovered. The largest plates are as follows:

1. The *Pacific Plate* extends over most of the Pacific Ocean floor from south of Alaska to the Antarctic Plate.
2. The *North American Plate* meets the Pacific Plate along California's San Andreas Fault and related structures. It carries the North American landmass.
3. The *Eurasian Plate* forms the boundary with the North American Plate at the Mid-Atlantic Ridge north of 35°N. It carries the entire Eurasian landmass north of the Himalayas.
4. The *African Plate* extends eastward from the Mid-Atlantic Ridge between 35°N and 55°S. It carries Africa and the island of Madagascar, and it meets the Antarctic Plate under the Southern Ocean and the Australian and Indian Plates beneath the Indian Ocean.

5. The *South American Plate* extends westward from the Mid-Atlantic Ridge south of 15°N. It carries the South American landmass.
6. The *Australian Plate* carries Australia and meets the Pacific Plate in New Zealand.
7. The *Indian Plate* carries the Indian subcontinent and meets the Eurasian Plate at the Himalayas.
8. The *Antarctic Plate's* margins encircle the Antarctic landmass (which it carries) under the Southern Ocean.

Seven of these plates were identified early on. For some years the Australian and Indian Plates were believed to constitute a single plate, but today they appear to be undergoing separation to form two separate plates. Later a number of smaller plates were detected (Fig. 32.3). The largest among these is the *Nazca Plate,* wedged between the South American Plate to the east and the Pacific Plate to the west. Immediately to the north of the Nazca Plate, partly separating the South American Plate from the North American Plate, are two

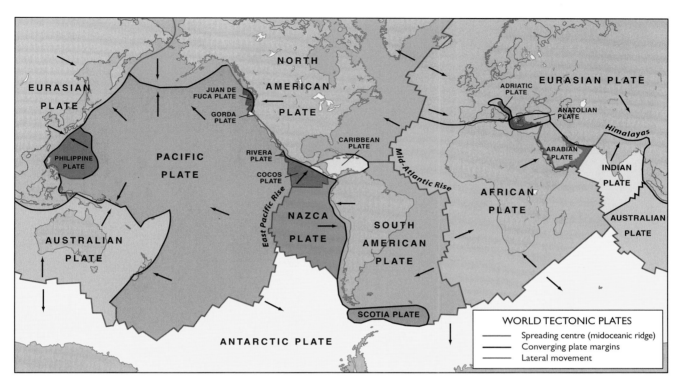

FIGURE 32.3 Lithospheric plates of the Earth. Each drifts continuously in the direction shown by the arrows. As the legend indicates, plate-margin movement falls into one of three categories: divergence (spreading), convergence, or lateral motion.

smaller plates. The larger of these, the *Caribbean Plate,* supports most of Central America and the southern Caribbean region. West of it (and thus north of the Nazca Plate) lies the *Cocos Plate,* and its northwestern extension, the *Rivera Plate,* off west-central Mexico. The Cocos and Rivera Plates are all oceanic crust and, unlike the Caribbean Plate, do not support a landmass.

At the southern end of South America lies a plate whose boundary arches eastward around an island chain much like the Caribbean Plate's eastern boundary; this is the *Scotia Plate.* Off the western coast of North America, near the point where the U.S.–Canada boundary reaches the Pacific Ocean, lies the *Juan de Fuca Plate,* and to its south, off southern Oregon and northernmost California, lies the smaller *Gorda Plate.*

Three other smaller but significant plates have also been recognized. One is the *Philippine Plate,* located between the Pacific and the Eurasian Plates, which is involved in the devastating earthquakes that have repeatedly struck the Tokyo area of eastern Japan. Another is the *Arabian Plate,* which supports the landmass known as the Arabian Peninsula. The third is the *Anatolian Plate* (located northwest of the Arabian Plate), along whose contact zone with the Eurasian Plate lie the sources of severe earthquakes that have in recent years ravaged parts of Turkey and Greece.

It is likely that the current map of lithospheric plates will be revised again, because additional smaller plates may not have been identified yet. It is noteworthy, for example, that most of the smaller plates that have been recognized lie in ocean-floor areas of the crust. We also know that the sialic landmasses lie on simatic crust that continues beneath them (see Unit 29). Therefore it is possible that the crust beneath the landmasses is more fragmented than is now known; later in this unit we examine the map of Africa to explore this possibility.

Location of Plate Margins

Once the notion of seafloor spreading gained acceptance and the segmented character of the crust became known, the search was on for the location of the margins of tectonic plates. Some earlier evidence now acquired new significance: the map showing the global distribution of earthquakes (Fig. 32.4) provided an important clue. Note that this map shows that earthquakes often originate in the midoceanic ridges, in island arcs, and in mountain belts such as South America's Andes and South Asia's Himalayas. It was concluded that these linear earthquake zones represented plate margins, and thus the early idea that there

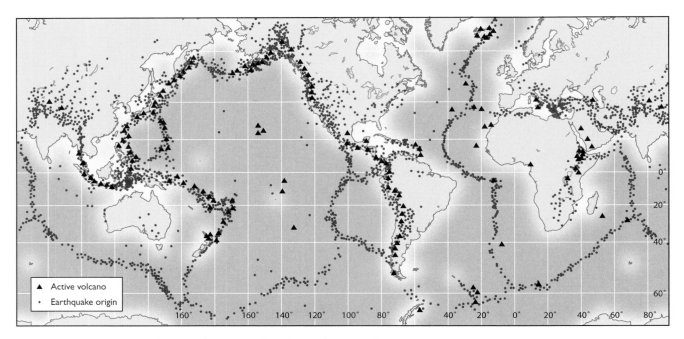

FIGURE 32.4   Global distribution of recent earthquakes and active volcanoes.

were only seven major lithospheric plates was re-examined.

The map of the world distribution of active volcanoes further supported this theory (Fig. 32.4). Of course, continental-surface patterns of volcanic activity were much better known than submarine volcanism. Volcanic activity is so common in western South and North America, in Asia's offshore *archipelagoes* (island chains), and in New Zealand that this circum-Pacific belt had long been known as the **Pacific Ring of Fire**. Thus it was at first concluded that the entire Pacific Ocean floor constituted a single, giant tectonic plate. Only later, when knowledge of the ocean-floor topography and geology improved, was the existence of smaller plates such as the Juan de Fuca and Cocos recognized.

Figure 32.5 shows the seafloor of most of the Atlantic Ocean. Note that the midoceanic ridge is not linear and unbroken, but divided into segments that are offset, giving them an overall zigzag appearance. Right-angle fractures in the crust (*transform faults*) separate the segments. This relates to the conditions that prevail where new crust is created—rock is hot, molten, and viscous. It rises and spreads, beginning to cool as it moves away from the midoceanic ridge. But the ridge itself is not rigid and stable enough to sustain continuity. Lateral forces of movement sometimes are stronger in one direction than in the other. Thus one part of the Mid-Atlantic Ridge (between 20° and

35°N) is dragged to the west; elsewhere, such as just south of the Equator, another part may lag behind or even move slightly to the east. As the rocks harden, a fault develops between the segments, and they are offset. Under the oceans, away from the landmasses, this pattern prevails.

But the map of world lithospheric plates (Fig. 32.3) also shows that the plate margins along continental edges take on another form. Along the edge of western South and North America, and off eastern Asia, the plate margins mostly appear on the map as solid black lines. The same is true for the longest plate boundary known to exist across a landmass: the contact zone between the Eurasian Plate and plates to the south of it. No new crust is being created there. Rather, crust is being crushed and may be being pushed downward. From the distribution of these plate-margin types, the movement of the lithospheric plates can be inferred.

Movement of Plates

It is now known that the lithosphere consists of eight major plates and at least ten smaller ones. These plates move relative to one another, apparently maintaining their prevailing directions of movement for millions of years. The term *plate tectonics* refers to this motion. Indeed, plates and landmasses may have been in motion ever since the Earth's crust was formed more than 4 billion years

FIGURE 32.5 Central portion of the Atlantic seafloor, between roughly latitudes 55°N and 20°S, highlighting the topography associated with the Mid-Atlantic Ridge.

ago; Pangaea existed a mere 200 million years ago. It is quite possible that Pangaea itself resulted from an earlier phase of plate movement during which landmasses coalesced to form a single supercontinent, and is only one phase of a supercontinent cycle.

The movement of lithospheric plates is directly responsible for many of the Earth's major landscapes and landforms. All studies of geomorphological processes and features must take into account the effect of crustal mobility. As plates migrate and carry landmasses along, they push, drag, tilt, bend, warp, and fracture. Lava pours out of fissures and vents. Rocks laid down as horizontal strata are deformed in every conceivable way. The weight of accumulating sediments pushes part of a plate downward. Where erosion has removed the material turned into sediment, the weight of the upper crust is reduced and the plate will rebound upward—all while movement continues.

Major directions of plate movement can be inferred from the map of the distribution of plates (Fig. 32.3). (Recent research has also provided information on the relative velocities of moving plates, the topic of the Perspectives box in Unit 33.) Clearly, the African Plate has moved eastward, and its dominant direction remains eastward today. The South American Plate moves westward. New crust for both these plates is being created along the Mid-Atlantic Ridge. For some other plates, the direction of movement is less clear. What is certain, however, is that plate margins take on three kinds of character: (1) spreading or divergence; (2) collision or convergence; and (3) transform or lateral displacement.

Plate Spreading

Plate spreading or divergence occurs along the midoceanic ridges in the process called seafloor spreading. Magma wells up from the asthenosphere, new lithosphere is created, and the lithosphere on opposing sides of the midoceanic ridges is pushed apart. Here the tectonic forces are tensional, and the crust is so thin that it **rifts** open. Some geographers have pointed out that this process can also affect continental crust. If tensional forces exist beneath a part of a plate where a landmass occurs, both the simatic crust below and the sialic crust above are pulled apart. At the surface, this results in a sometimes spectacular landform called a **rift valley** (Fig. 32.6).

At present, a major system of rift valleys occurs in eastern Africa (see Fig. 36.7), and this system may signal the future fracturing of that continent (and the African Plate) along this zone of apparent crustal thinning. The Red Sea represents a more advanced stage of this process (Fig. 36.7): the Arabian Plate has separated from the African Plate, and between them now lies a basalt-floored sea (the Red Sea). As time goes on, this sea is likely to widen and become a new ocean.

Thus the geological term *seafloor spreading* is perhaps better replaced by the geographical one, **crustal spreading**. Even today not all spreading is confined to the ocean floor. And when Pangaea was a supercontinent, the first fractures in it occurred as rift valleys. Only when the rifts widened and magma filled the now-collapsed, water-filled trenches did the spreading become "seafloor."

The map of Africa, from a physical-geographical standpoint, also cautions against taking the current map of known plates too seriously. The African Plate may well consist of three or four plates, all moving in the same general direction at this moment in geological time, but capable of separating (see Fig. 36.9)—as the

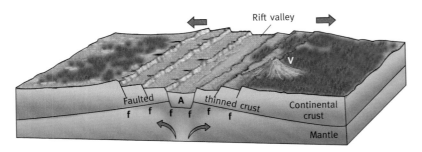

FIGURE 32.6 Development of a rift valley, which involves tensional movement related to motion in the mantle, faulting (**f**), the collapse of elongated strips of crust (**A**), and crustal thinning. Sometimes lava erupts along the tensional fault planes (**V**). Lakes fill large portions of rift valleys in East Africa (see Fig. 36.7).

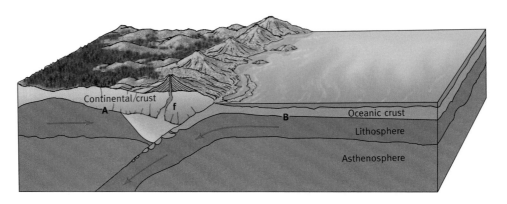

FIGURE 32.7 When continental plate **A**, moving eastward, meets oceanic plate **B**, moving westward, the process of subduction carries the heavier oceanic plate downward beneath the thicker but lighter continental plate. In this process, high relief develops along the coastline, the continental crust is heavily deformed, and magma can penetrate through vents and fissures (**f**) to erupt as lava at the surface.

great East African rifts seem to suggest. An East African Plate may exist east of the easternmost (of Africa's) rift valleys; a small Victoria Plate may exist between the eastern and western rifts (see Fig. 36.7). The surface evidence further suggests that a plate margin may exist, or be forming, along a line extending from the Gulf of Guinea toward Lake Chad in west-central Africa. Remember that Wegener made effective use of topographic information to develop his hypothesis of continental drift, thereby paving the way for plate tectonics. The landscape is still a valuable guide, even in this age of satellite remote-sensing, high-technology data analysis and geographical information systems.

Plate Collision

If plates form and spread outward in certain areas of the crust, then they must *collide* and converge in other zones. The results of such a gigantic collision depends on the type of lithosphere involved on each side. Continental crust has a relatively lower density, and in these terms, it is "light" compared to oceanic crust, which is denser, heavier, and more prone to sink or be forced downward where plates collide. When an oceanic plate

meets a plate carrying a continental landmass at its leading edge, the lighter continental plate overrides the denser oceanic plate and pushes it downward. This process is termed **subduction**, and the area where it occurs is defined as a *subduction zone* (Fig. 32.7).

A subduction zone is a place of intense tectonic activity. The plate being forced down (subducted) is heated by the asthenosphere, and its rocks melt (undergo anatexis). This magma mixes with molten lower-crust material, water seeping down from the ocean floor, and sediment dragged down on the back of the subducting plate. Some of the molten rock forces its way upward through vents and fissures to the surface, so that volcanism is common along both oceanic and continental subduction zones. The movement of the plates is comparatively slow, averaging 2 to 3 cm per year. But this motion is enough to generate enormous energy, some of which is released through earthquakes. Subduction zones are earthquake prone and rank among the world's most dangerous places to live.

Three types of collision plate margins exist, only two of which result in significant subduction. Subduction occurs where oceanic crust subducts beneath continental crust and where one oceanic plate subducts beneath another. However, where two plates with continental crust converge, a somewhat different sequence of events follows. Let us examine each of the three cases.

Oceanic–Continental Plate Collision The best example of the kind of oceanic–continental subduction zone just described (Fig. 32.7) lies along South America's western margin, where the oceanic Nazca Plate is subducting beneath the continental South American Plate. The crust in the collision zone is dragged downward to form deep oceanic trenches close to shore. A few kilometres to the east, continental rocks are crumpled up into the gigantic mountain ranges of the Andes. Andesitic volcanoes tower over the landscape; earthquakes and tremors are recorded almost continuously. Sediments are caught in the subduction zone and become part of the hot molten magma. Here we can see the rock cycle (see Fig. 31.12) in progress: basaltic crust from the ocean floor and granitic and sedimentary rocks from the landmass are melted and forced downward. They will eventually be carried back to the midoceanic ridges, where they emerge and solidify, becoming part of the lithosphere once again. The same kind of process occurs in the Cascadia collision zone of British Columbia and Washington/Oregon.

Oceanic–Oceanic Plate Collision Other convergent plate boundaries involve two oceanic plates. The contrast between lithospheric plate densities is not present, and the crust is thrown into huge contortions. One of the plates will override the other, resulting in subduction; deep trenches form and volcanoes protrude, often

above sea level (Fig. 32.8). The collision zone between the Pacific, North American, Eurasian, Philippine, and Australian Plates in the northern and western Pacific Ocean creates **island arcs**, such as the Aleutian and Japanese archipelagoes, as well as other segments of the Pacific Ring of Fire.

Continental–Continental Plate Collision Where collision involves two continental plates, the situation is different. The best example is a segment of the collision between the Eurasian Plate and the Indian Plate. The Eurasian Plate is moving southward, and the Indian subcontinent has moved to the north. (Thus a part of

FIGURE 32.9 Two continental landmasses collide at a convergent plate margin. There is much deformation of the crust, and high relief develops (South Asia's Himalayas mark such a convergent continental plate boundary). But while there is considerable thickening of the crust, less actual subduction occurs than when contrasting continental and oceanic plates converge.

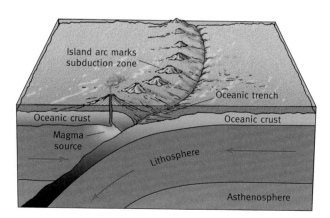

FIGURE 32.8 Convergent plate margin involving two oceanic plates. Where one oceanic plate is subducted beneath the other, a deep oceanic trench forms. Above the trench, on the margin of the upward-riding plate, a volcanic island arc is created.

FIGURE 32.10 The San Andreas Fault in action. Rows of trees in a Southern California orange grove were offset 4.5 m along a branch of the fault during the May 1940 Imperial Valley earthquake.

Gondwana was carried into collision with Laurasia.) Such continental convergence creates massive deformation and a huge buildup of sialic mass. One continental mass may override the other, but the lower mass is not forced down into the asthenosphere or mantle (Fig. 32.9). Rather, the landmass thickens along

the contact zone; earthquakes will attend the process, but not the widespread volcanism that accompanies oceanic–continental collisions.

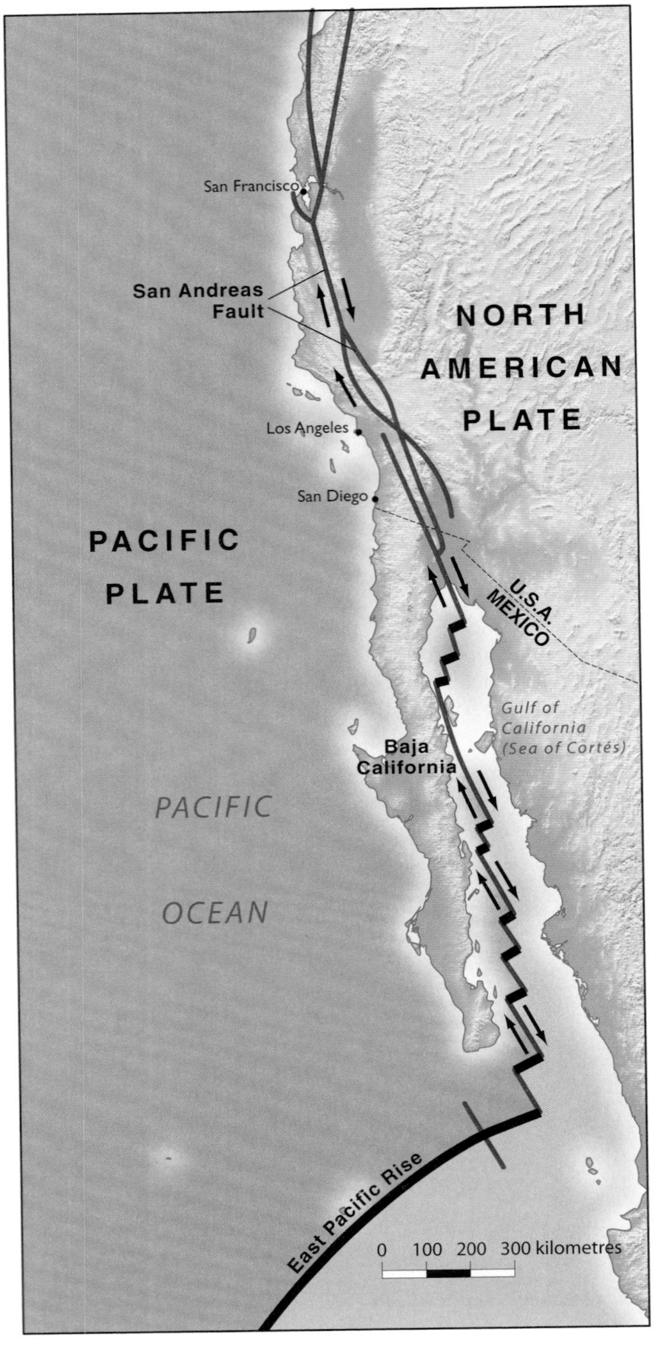

Lateral Plate Contact

For many years California's San Andreas Fault was known to be a place of crustal instability, a source of earthquakes, a line of danger on the map of the Golden State. Not until plate tectonics became understood, however, could the real significance of the San Andreas Fault be recognized. The fault marks a plate margin— not a margin of divergence or convergence, but a margin along which two plates are sliding past each other (Fig. 32.10). These margins are referred to as **transform faults**. Transform (or *lateral*) movement along such plate margins may not have the dramatic topographic consequences displayed by convergent movement, but it, too, is accompanied by earthquakes and crustal deformation.

The area to the west of the San Andreas Fault is part of the Pacific Plate, whereas the area to the east is part of the North American Plate (Fig. 32.11). The fault ex-

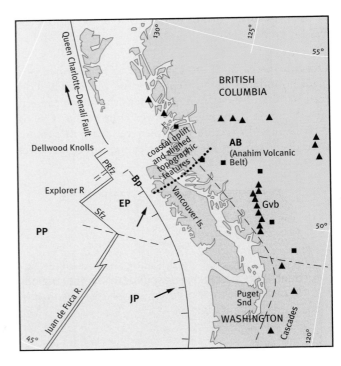

FIGURE 32.12 Triple junction tectonic setting in the Pacific northwest showing transform movement (Queen Charlotte–Denali Fault), the Cascadia Collision zone (subduction), and spreading along offshore ridges (e.g., Explorer Ridge). Note the volcanic arcs on the continent. PP–Pacific Plate; EP–Explorer Plate; JP–Juan de Fuca Plate; fz–fracture zone; Gvb–Garibaldi volcanic belt.

FIGURE 32.11 California's San Andreas Fault in its regional context. This fault separates the Pacific Plate from the North American Plate, which here are sliding past each other.

tends southward into the Gulf of California, thereby also separating Mexico's Baja California from the Mexican mainland, which is part of the North American Plate as well. At its northern end, the San Andreas Fault enters the Pacific Ocean north of San Francisco. Thus Baja California and Southern California (including metropolitan Los Angeles) are sliding north-northwestward past the North American Plate (Fig. 32.11) because of the northward motion of the Pacific Plate as a whole. This process is going on at a fairly high rate of speed, estimated to average more than 7.5 cm per year. This type of movement can also be seen along the Queen Charlotte–Denali Fault of northwest British Columbia and Alaska (Fig. 32.12).

In the case of the San Andreas Fault, earthquakes attend this movement. Moreover, the San Andreas is the major fault in a much larger and complex system of transform faults in this corridor (see Perspective: Greater Vancouver—Waiting for the Big One). But lateral movement, for obvious reasons, is comparatively quiescent. No major subduction occurs, and no great volcanoes rise to mark the zone of contact. This means that other lateral plate contact boundaries beneath continental landmasses may yet be undiscovered.

Thus the map of tectonic plates is still subject to modification. And Wegener's original vision, stimulated by the observation of geographical patterns, has been proven essentially correct. Accordingly, we continue the discussion of plate dynamics in Unit 33 by asking more questions about the breakup of Pangaea.

PERSPECTIVES ON THE HUMAN ENVIRONMENT

Greater Vancouver—Waiting for the Big One

Geologists are certain that southwestern British Columbia will be hit by an earthquake of an extremely large magnitude. The area is overdue for such a big seismic event. It has been over 55 years since the area was shaken by a large earthquake (Richter magnitude 7.3) centred just north of Courtenay on Vancouver Island (Fig. 32.13). The event killed two people (the only known deaths attributable directly to an earthquake in Canada). One of the victims, a man, fell off his boat, which was moored at a marina near Stanley Park.

Vancouver sits over the most active earthquake zone in Canada, and the over 50 years since the occurrence of a large seismic event suggest that pressures are building up along the fault lines between the tectonic plates underlying the region. There are about 300 minor quakes a year in this zone, most of them so small that they are only recorded on seismographs. Once every 20 to 50 years a major earthquake happens. These types of quakes crack walls, cause chimneys to collapse, and cause other such damage (as the Courtenay quake did in 1946). Once every 300 to 600 years the region is affected by a cataclysmic mega-thrust earthquake (Richter magnitude 8.5+) that is accompanied by 10 to 20 m movements along the

fault, slope failures, and tsunamis. If such an earthquake should occur under Greater Vancouver now, it would be catastrophic. Estimates based on an 8.5+ magnitude event suggest that 10 to 30 percent of all houses would be damaged, 60 to 100 percent of older masonry buildings, including schools and hospitals, would suffer major damage or collapse. Fifteen percent of all high-rises would be severely damaged, and many bridges and roads would be rendered unusable. Thousands of people would be killed, many more injured, and hundreds of thousands made homeless. The numbers would depend on the time of day that the quake happened and the amount of water in the sediments of the Fraser Delta. It would be the greatest natural disaster in Canada.

The tectonic situation that would cause this event would be the interaction of two major tectonic plates (the North American and Pacific Plates) and a smaller one (the Juan de Fuca Plate), which is wedged between them. Named the Cascadia subduction zone by geologists, this is an example of triple-junction tectonics. The Pacific Plate is moving northwest, and the North American Plate is moving west away from the spreading zone in the middle of the Atlantic Ocean. The North American

FIGURE 32.13   Granville Island, in the heart of Vancouver, British Columbia, was converted in 1915 from a sandbar into an industrial core. It is now an important recreational and tourist area with shops, cafes, marinas, and theatres.

Plate is also moving to the northwest at the same time. The movement of the Pacific Plate is faster than that of the North American Plate. As the North American Plate moves west, it is overriding the Juan de Fuca Plate. The Juan de Fuca Plate is being subducted; it is being thrust under the North American Plate. Research indicates that the thrust fault is stuck at the present time, but if and when it releases, it will be devastating.

The agency charged with the area's preparedness has put forward two possible quake scenarios. The most likely scenario is based on a moderately strong event, similar in magnitude to the San Francisco and Los Angeles earthquakes of the past fifteen years (Richter magnitude 6–7). This would cause significant damage, deaths, injuries, homelessness, and so on. Since the San Francisco quake in the late 1980s, a lot of engineering work has been done throughout the area to upgrade bridges, dams, and other infrastructure, such as the elevated "Skytrain" line, to minimize the damage caused by seismic events. However, little has been done to older masonry schools, hospitals, and the older parts of the downtown (e.g., Gastown and Yaletown). Large areas of Greater Vancouver are built on fill or on buried organic material (bogs). Even a moderate quake would lead to the collapse of buildings in these areas. Shaking would mix water and organic and fine-grained sediments and cause liquefaction, which would swallow up houses and other buildings. The dykes

along the Fraser Valley and Georgia Strait would break, and river and sea water would cause flooding of low-lying areas. Most of Richmond, a major suburb south of Vancouver, sits on Lulu Island in the Fraser Delta. The sediments on which the municipality has been constructed are layers of sand, clay, and bog material. If shaken, these deposits would liquefy and cause collapse and subsidence of all sorts of buildings and infrastructure. The island is surrounded by dykes that would fail and the area would be flooded.

The second, less likely scenario is based on an 8.5 mega-thrust quake with its epicentre in the Greater Vancouver area. This would produce severe destruction within a 200-km-wide zone around the epicentre. Many buildings would fail, and liquefaction would probably severely damage the airport, Richmond, and other low-lying areas. Tunnels and bridges would sink into liquefied deposits. Many people would be unable to get out of their immediate area because of damaged bridges and tunnels. The situation would be chaotic. Western parts of the Fraser Valley would flood. Up to 45 percent of Vancouver's schools would suffer moderate to total collapse. Tsunamis and submarine slumping would damage the shoreline and facilities close to the shore, such as oil refineries and chemical plants. There would be major fires (many houses are wooden). There would be mass evacuations. The dead and injured would number in the hundreds of thousands. Many more would be left homeless.

KEY TERMS

continental drift *page 416*

crustal spreading *page 421*

Gondwana *page 416*

island arc *page 423*

Laurasia *page 416*

lithospheric plates *page 417*

Pacific Ring of Fire *page 420*

Pangaea *page 416*

plate tectonics *page 417*

plate tectonic theory *page 417*

rift *page 421*

rift valley *page 421*

seafloor spreading *page 417*

subduction *page 422*

transform fault *page 424*

REVIEW QUESTIONS

1. Briefly describe some of the evidence supporting the notion of continental drift.

2. Briefly describe the global map of lithospheric plates.

3. Where are most of the present-day rifting zones located?

4. How are subduction boundaries different from transform-fault boundaries? Give an example of each.

REFERENCES AND FURTHER READINGS

ANDERSON, D. L. "The San Andreas Fault," *Scientific American* (November 1971), 52–68.

DE BLIJ, H. J., et al. *Restless Earth* (Washington, D.C.: National Geographic Society, 1997).

DU TOIT, A. L. *Our Wandering Continents* (Edinburgh: Oliver & Boyd, 1937).

Evolving Earth: Plate Tectonics (CD-ROM) (Halifax, Canada: EOA Scientific Systems, 2001).

HALLAM, A. *Great Geological Controversies* (New York: Oxford Univ. Press, 2nd ed., 1992).

HUGGETT, R. J. *Fundamentals of Geomorphology* (London/New York: Routledge, 2002).

KIOUS, W. J., and TILLING, R. I. *This Dynamic Earth: The Story of Plate Tectonics* (Reston, Va.: U.S. Geological Survey, n.d.).

NICOLAS, A. *The Mid-Oceanic Ridges: Mountains below Sea Level* (New York: Springer Verlag, 1994).

ORESKES, N. *The Rejection of Continental Drift: Theory and Method in American Earth Science* (New York: Oxford Univ. Press, 1999).

RAYMO, C. *The Crust of Our Earth: An Armchair Traveler's Guide to the New Geology* (Englewood Cliffs, N.J.: Prentice-Hall, 1983).

SCHULZ, S. S., and WALLACE, R. E. *The San Andreas Fault* (Reston, Va.: U.S. Geological Survey, 1989).

SEIBOLD, E., and BERGER, W. H. *The Sea Floor: An Introduction to Marine Geology* (New York: Springer Verlag, 1996).

TAYLOR, F. B. "Bearing of the Tertiary Mountain Belt on the Origin of the Earth's Plan," *Geological Society of America Bulletin*, 21 (1910), 179–226.

WEGENER, A. *The Origin of Continents and Oceans* (New York: Dover, 1966; translated by J. Biram from the 1929 4th ed.).

WILSON, J. T. *Continents Adrift* (San Francisco: W.H. Freeman and Co., 1973).

WILSON, J. T. *Continents Adrift and Continents Aground* (San Francisco: W.H. Freeman and Co., 1978).

WINDLEY, B. F. *The Evolving Continents* (New York: Wiley, 2nd ed., 1984).

WYLLIE, P. J. *The Way the Earth Works* (New York: Wiley, 1976).

WEB RESOURCE

http://pubs.usgs.gov/gip/earthq3/safaultgip.html This USGS informational page describes the San Andreas Fault in terms of plate tectonics, and also provides background information about earthquake mechanisms, size, and intensity.

Plate Movement: Causes and Effects

On the margin of the Caribbean Plate. Lava boils near the base of Gros Piton near La Soufrière on the eastern Caribbean island of St. Lucia. (Authors' photo)

OBJECTIVES

- To outline briefly the mechanisms and processes that move lithospheric plates

- To discuss the evolution of the Earth's continental landmasses

- To discuss the concept of isostasy and relate it to the topography of the continents

The most recent phase of crustal plate movement has broken up Pangaea, the supercontinent first envisaged fully by Alfred Wegener nearly a century ago (see Fig. 32.1). Continental drift proved to be one manifestation of plate tectonics, partial evidence for a process of planetary proportions involving immense amounts of energy. Confirmation of the breakup of Laurasia and Gondwana, however, raises new questions.

The fragmentation of Pangaea, the collision between India and Asia, the separation of Africa and South America—all this has taken place within the last 160 million years of Earth history. But that period of time is just the last *4 to 5 percent* of the Earth's total existence as a planet. What happened during previous phases of plate movement? Did earlier movements cause other supercontinents to form through a coalescence of landmasses, only to be pulled apart again? Can remnants of these former supercontinents still be found?

Certainly there are rocks older than 160 million years. As previously noted, the Earth formed more than 4.5 billion years ago. The oldest known rocks are from the geological era known as the Precambrian, and they date from as long as 3.9 billion years ago (see Perspective: Using the Geological Time Scale in Unit 37). These are all igneous and metamorphic rocks, which today form part of the core areas of the landmasses—their shields (see Fig. 29.12). Many workers consider that the shields resulted from meteoric or cometary impacts that occurred between 3.5 and 4.5 billion years ago. No rocks resembling the older shield rocks were formed before or after this period. The impacts caused crustal fracturing and melting, and could have initiated plate tectonic movement.

The ancient original shields must have been involved in every phase of crustal movement after their formation. Today the Canadian (Laurentian) Shield forms the geological core of North America (see Fig. 33.1); but during the Late Precambrian period, it probably lay at the heart of a landmass of very different shape and dimensions. This question is of interest in physical geography because the comparatively inactive continental shields carry landscapes that also are very old and have, in some areas, changed very little over many millions of years. These ancient landscapes, found in shield areas of Africa, South America, and Australia, may provide insights into the geomorphology of parts of Pangaea and other earlier supercontinents.

Mechanism of Crustal Spreading

The movement of plates forming the Earth's crust has been established beyond a reasonable doubt (Fig 33.1). Although we can accurately measure plate motion today (see Perspective: How Fast Do Drifting Plates Move?), the mechanism that propels the plates, past as well as present, is still not completely understood. The first model, proposed by Arthur Holmes, involves a set of internal convection cells in the Earth's mantle and has been refined to account for the new knowledge of seafloor spreading. A model proposed by Harry Hess

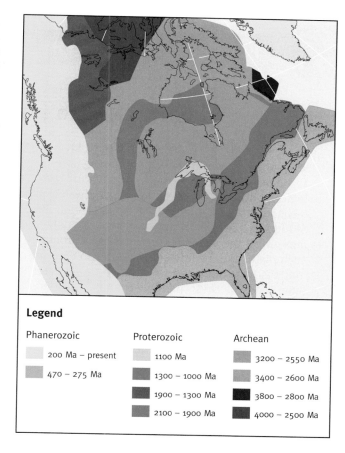

Legend

Phanerozoic

200 Ma – present

470 – 275 Ma

Proterozoic

1100 Ma

1300 – 1000 Ma

1900 – 1300 Ma

2100 – 1900 Ma

Archean

3200 – 2550 Ma

3400 – 2600 Ma

3800 – 2800 Ma

4000 – 2500 Ma

FIGURE 33.1 Simplified tectonic map of North America showing areas accreted (added) to the craton during the Pre-Cambrian (Archean and Proterozoic eras) and Phanerozoic eons.

suggests that hot mantle material rises at the spreading midoceanic ridges. Some of it emerges to form a new, thin crust; most remains in a hot plastic state, sliding slowly away from the ridges and cooling in the process.

This would explain why the temperature of the ocean-floor crust is highest near the midoceanic ridges and drops toward the continental margins. By spreading sideways and dragging the crust along, the sublithospheric magma keeps the spreading ridges open. By the time the new crust and the magma carrying it have spread as far as the continental margin of the ocean basin, they have cooled and thickened sufficiently to become so dense and heavy that they are ready to sink down again. This occurs when, at a collision plate margin, a continental (or other oceanic) plate overrides it. Now subduction takes place, and the material re-enters the asthenosphere and the mantle, where it is heated up on the return journey to the spreading midoceanic ridge. All of these relationships are shown in Fig. 33.3.

If a set of convection cells such as those shown in Fig. 33.3 exists beneath all parts of the Earth's crust,

PERSPECTIVES ON THE HUMAN ENVIRONMENT

How Fast Do Drifting Plates Move?

Today it has been ascertained that the plates of the lithosphere move at velocities ranging from 1 to 12 cm per year. We know this because recent technological advances have enabled geophysicists to measure plate motion with remarkable precision. Studies of past velocities were first calculated by measuring the magnetic orientation of rocks on each plate, and the inference was drawn that these motions have remained constant up to the present time. That hypothesis has now proven to be correct. By bouncing laser beams off specially equipped satellites, surface distances could for the first time be measured within an accuracy of 1 cm. Subsequent laser measurements quickly led to the construction of a new world map of current plate velocities (which is now being further refined through GPS technology, which brings the level of accuracy close to the nearest millimetre).

That map is shown in Fig. 33.2, and its numbers refer to plate motion in centimetres per year. Numbers along the midoceanic ridges are average velocities indicated by (now-confirmed) measurements of rock magnetism. A figure of 11.7, as indicated for the northernmost segment of the East Pacific Rise (south of Mexico), means that the distance between a point on the Cocos Plate and a point on the Pacific Plate to the west annually increases by an average 11.7 cm in the direction of the arrows that diverge from this midoceanic ridge. The thick red lines connect stations that measure plate movement by using satellite laser (**L**) technology several times each year. Note that the recorded plate velocities between these stations closely agree with the mean velocities estimated from magnetic measurements (**M**).

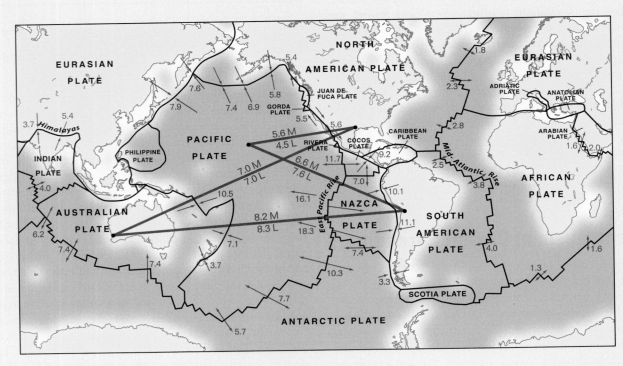

FIGURE 33.2   Current lithospheric plate velocities in centimetres per year.

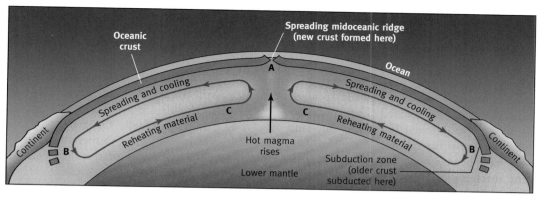

FIGURE 33.3 Convection cells in the mantle may look like this in cross-section. Hot magma rises at **A**, spreads toward **B**, and in the process drags the existing oceanic crust with it. At the spreading mid-oceanic ridge, new oceanic crust is being created from some of this upwelling magma. As the material below the crust spreads toward **B**, it cools slowly. When it reaches a convergent boundary with a continental landmass, the oceanic crust is subducted. The material in the convection cell now moves toward **C**, reheating at this depth. By the time it has passed **C**, it has enough energy to rise again into the spreading ridge. Speed of movement may be only about 2.5 cm per year.

several questions arise, some not yet fully explained. First, how many of these cells exist? Are they all the same size, or do they range in size as the plates themselves do? How deeply do they penetrate the mantle? Evidence suggests that oceanic crust can be subducted to depths of 700 km, which is far below the lower boundary of the asthenosphere. Some geologists suggest that the entire mantle may be in motion, and not just its upper layer. Does the Earth's internal heat sustain the process, or is a heat-generating process, such as radioactive decay, responsible for the energy to keep convection cells in motion?

Most of the answers to such questions remain as speculative today as Wegener's continental drift hypothesis was many years ago. For example, as the Earth has cooled, the rate of convection in the mantle and asthenosphere may have slowed down. Thus plate movement before the formation of Pangaea may have been even more rapid than it is today, and convergent margins may have been even more violently active. It follows that continental-margin landscapes had still more relief and variety than those of today's Pacific Ring of Fire.

Evolution of Continents

The evolution and areal growth of continental landmasses is also a largely unsolved riddle. It has been assumed that continental landmasses were created by the solidification of segments of the primitive crustal sphere or by impact fracturing and melting and the eruption of new lava types, perhaps as long as 4 billion years ago. This process may have given rise to the igneous and

metamorphic shields, which thus have existed ever since as the cores of the continents. When methods of dating rocks became more reliable, studies indicated that the oldest shield regions were indeed flanked by successively younger rock regions. Erosion of the original shield rocks created sedimentary strata around their margins (platform borderland areas). This would imply not only that the rocks of a continent become progressively younger away from the shield core, but also that the continents have grown, continuously or in stages, ever since their cores were first formed (see Fig. 33.1).

Crustal Formation

Other geological evidence, however, suggests that shield areas have not grown by successive consolidation of magma around the original core areas. Rather, it appears that the landmasses were formed from the solidification of the outermost cooling mantle, during a period approximately 2.5 to 3.5 billion years ago. For the last 2.5 billion years the continental landmasses appear to have retained about the same total volume (if not the familiar shapes) as today. The crust has been recycled ever since, material being lost to subduction at convergent plate boundaries and regained by reformation at the spreading ridges.

Throughout their existence, the continental shields have lost little, because subduction has affected mostly the sedimentary strata accumulated at their margins. Even when a coalesced landmass became subject to crustal spreading, as happened when Africa and South America separated and the Mid-Atlantic Ridge appeared, the shield thereby fragmented lost no part of its mass. This model of the evolution of continents is still a subject of debate, and it may be modified when more becomes known about the subcrustal convection currents.

But even the continents themselves continue to yield their secrets. Recently geologists came to realize that certain parts of landmasses do not, geologically speaking, seem to belong where they are located. Their rocks and geological histories are so different from their surroundings that the conclusion is inescapable: these chunks of continent must have been moved from faraway locales to their current, foreign positions.

The Supercontinent Cycle or Wilson Cycle

This idea of a **supercontinent** (or **Wilson**) **cycle** was suggested by J. Tuzo Wilson as far back as 1966 and was outlined in a paper in *Scientific American* in the early 1990s. The basic concept is that, over time, supercontinents are assembled, exist for up to 100 million years (Ma), and then break up as seafloor spreading occurs. It is possible that supercontinents do not fully form and that while assembly occurred in one area, breakup was occurring elsewhere. Five supercontinents have formed and broken up over the last 3 billion years. The Phanerozoic Eon was dominated by the formation and breakup of Pangaea, which existed from 300 to 200 Ma ago. The biggest mass extinctions occurred during this period of Earth history. Pangaea was huge, covering much of the world, and it was surrounded by the Panthalassa Ocean.

When assembled, a supercontinent acts as an insulator, trapping geothermal heat in the Earth. In consequence the mantle heats up and basalt magmas are formed that may reach the surface. This heralds the breakup of the supercontinent.

The steps in the supercontinent cycle are as follows:

1. Assembly of the supercontinent takes place over some 40 Ma.
2. The development of Atlantic-type ocean basins goes on for about 160 Ma.
3. The development of subduction zones in these oceans form Pacific-like ocean basins.
4. Assembly of a new supercontinent takes place over 226 to 160 Ma.
5. The supercontinent is stable for approximately 80 Ma, but heat accumulation leads ultimately to its breakup.

There is about a 500 Ma time span for completion of the cycle. The Earth is now either at the end of step 2 or just starting step 3. Six orogenic or mountain-building episodes can, so far, be related to the formation and breakup of the supercontinents. For example:

1. 2.6 Ga Archaean-Proterzoic Boundary Orogenic Episode
2. 2.1 Ga unknown [research continues regarding what happened at this point]
3. 1.7 Ga Penokean Orogenic Episode associated with the assembly of the North American craton (or shield)
4. 1.1 Ga Grenville Orogeny associated with the creation of the Supercontinent of Rodinia (Grenville rocks of this stage are found in the Canadian Shield)
5. 650 Ma Pan-African Orogeny related to Gondwanaland
6. 250–300 Ma Alleghanian-Hercynian Orogenic Episode, related to closing of an early Atlantic Ocean (Iapetus) and folding that created the Appalachian-Caledonide Mountains and the supercontinent of Pangaea

Terranes and Exotic Terranes

The movement of crustal plates creates complex lithospheric mosaics. Along the margins of a shield-anchored continent it is possible to identify bodies of rock that are unrelated to that landmass, derived from other plates and attached to it in a process called **accretion**. These fragments can be regional in extent, consistent in age, rock type, and structure, and continental or oceanic in origin. Earth scientists refer to them as **terranes**.

But there are times when observed terranes are so mismatched, and their sources so uncertain, that they are called **exotic terranes** (also *suspect terranes*). These rock masses have apparently come from distant locales. They seem to have travelled rapidly to reach their destinations in a process whose mechanics are not clear.

One of the Earth's most complex mosaics involving exotic terranes extends along western North America from Alaska to California, where long-term accretion has expanded the landmass far beyond its Pangaea-stage western margins (Fig 33.4). Many exotic terranes have been mapped here, of which the best known is the Wrangellia terrane, parts of which occur in mainland and peninsular Alaska, in British Columbia, and south of the Canada–U.S. border. Wrangellia is of volcanic, island-arc origin, its exposed fragments standing in sharp contrast to the surrounding regional geology (Fig. 33.6).

How these exotic terranes reached their present locations is still a mystery. Similar exotic terranes are known to exist in the mountain belts of other landmasses, but they have not been explained. It is also known that pieces of continental crust are lodged on the ocean floors, often visible on seafloor topographic maps as submerged plateaus. One example of such a

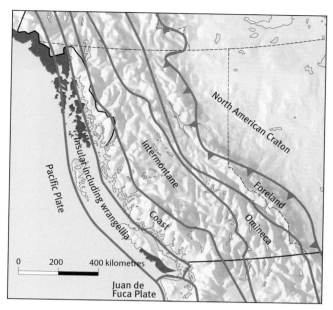

FIGURE 33.4 Megaterranes in British Columbia, Alberta, and the United States. Megaterranes are groupings of specific types of terranes. A craton is a shield/platform borderland area. The shaded areas are wrangellia.

FIGURE 33.5 The Himalayas form an awesome mountain wall when seen from the south. A view such as this undoubtedly greeted George Everest as he took his gravity measurements. This is central Nepal in the vicinity of Annapurna, the world's eleventh tallest peak.

continental rock mass rising to the ocean surface lies in the Seychelles Islands off East Africa in the western Indian Ocean. Such comparatively small rock masses of continental origins may be moved along as seafloor spreading proceeds. They may eventually reach a collision plate boundary, and parts of them may become wedged into the mountain belt being formed there. Other exotic terranes may be former island arcs, pushed into continental margins and enveloped by mountain building. Clearly, this is one way a continental landmass may grow in present times, even if the Precambrian phase of shield formation has long passed. Exotic terranes also occur in the Appalachians of eastern North America.

Isostasy

The upper surfaces of the continents display a high degree of topographic variety. Mountain ranges rise high above surrounding plains; plateaus and hills alternately dominate the landscape elsewhere. Mountain ranges have mass. Because of the law of gravity, they exert a certain attraction on other objects. If we were to hang a plumb line somewhere on the flank of a mountain range, we would expect the mountains to attract the plumb line from the vertical toward the range.

More than a century ago, the British scientist George Everest (after whom the world's highest mountain is named) took measurements along the southern flanks of the Himalayas in India (Fig. 33.5). He suspended his plumb line and did indeed find that the great Himalaya massif caused some attraction—but far less than his calculations, based on the assumed mass of the mountain range, led him to expect. Everest and his colleagues soon realized the importance of what they had discovered. If the deviation of the plumb line toward the mountains was less than calculated, there must be rocks of lesser density extending far below the Himalayas, displacing the heavier simatic material that would have caused greater attraction. In other words, the lighter sialic rocks appear to extend far down into the simatic rocks, and mountain ranges seem to have "roots" that penetrate downward farthest where the mountain ranges' surface elevations are greatest.

This possibility was realized as early as 1855 by George Airy, whose hypothesis of mountain roots is depicted in Fig. 33.7. In Fig. 33.8 the sialic part of the crust is likened to blocks of copper that, because they are less dense, float in the mercury representing the SIMA. The higher the block stands above the dashed line representing sea level, the deeper the root below pushes into the simulated SIMA. Thus the blocks, or parts of the Earth's crust, reach a kind of balance. Under the Himalayas and other major mountain ranges, the

FROM THE FIELDNOTES

FIGURE 33.6 "Traversing Glacier Bay in southeast Alaska, we were given a seminar by a National Park Service guide who enjoyed asking challenging questions. Knowing some physical geography helped, but here she had me stumped. 'Look at that outcrop,' she said. 'What can you tell me about it?' I said that the rocks looked darker than the regional grey-granite masses rising steeply from the bay, but in the absence of any knowledge of volcanic activity here, I could not do any better. 'You're looking at lava,' she explained; 'this is a fragment of one of those suspect terranes, an old basaltic island arc welded onto the local regional geology. It's called Wrangellia, and pieces of it can be identified from mainland Alaska all the way down the coast to British Columbia and the U.S. Northwest. It's out of place and we don't know how it got here, but it sure stands out in this landscape.' That is the kind of field experience you don't forget."

sialic part of the crust is comparatively thick. Under plateaus it is thinner, and under low-lying plains it is thinner still. Thus the relief of the continental landmasses has a mirror image below. Since the development of plate-tectonics theory, described in Unit 32, we have come to believe that the balance is not a question of sialic "rafts" floating on a simatic "sea." Rather, the balancing movements occur at the base of the lithosphere, far below the Mohorovičić discontinuity (see Unit 29).

The vertical changes in the crust are thought to take place for two reasons: (1) the lithosphere floats on the asthenosphere as the copper blocks float on the mercury; and (2) the lithosphere is subjected to changes of density from time to time. This situation of sustained adjust-

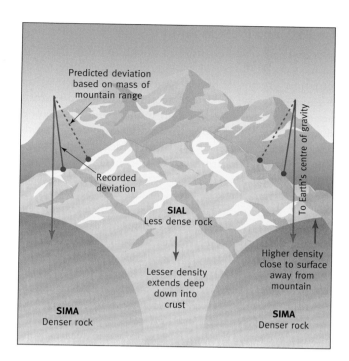

FIGURE 33.7   The Airy hypothesis: mountain ranges have roots of sialic rock that penetrate the denser simatic rock below.

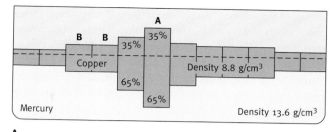

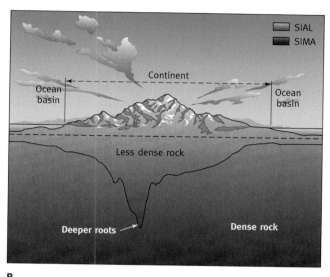

FIGURE 33.8   Isostasy. The distribution and behaviour of sial and sima is analogous to blocks of copper floating in mercury. Note that no matter how thick the block, the same percentage (35 percent/65 percent) floats above and below the surface. Each block is therefore in balance.

ment, as visualized by Airy and modified by others after him, has come to be known as the principle of isostasy. The source of this term is not difficult to determine: *iso* means equal, and *stasy* comes from the ancient Greek word meaning to stand. Thus **isostasy** is a condition of equilibrium between floating landmasses and the asthenosphere beneath them, maintained despite the tectonic and erosional forces that tend to change the landmasses all the time.

Isostasy and Erosion

We can use the model shown in Fig. 33.8A to envision what would happen if a high mountain range were subjected to a lengthy period of erosion. If we were to remove the upper 10 percent of the column marked **A**, we would expect that column to rise slightly—not quite to the height it was before but nearly so. If we were to place the removed portion of **A** on the two columns marked **B**, they would sink slightly, and their upper surface would adjust to a slightly higher elevation than before. Thus column **A** would have a lower height and a shorter root, whereas columns **B** would have a greater height and a deeper root.

This tendency explains why erosional forces in the real world have not completely flattened all mountain ranges. Scientific experiments have indicated that, at

present rates of erosion, the Earth's mountain ranges would be levelled in a single geologic period, certainly within 50 million years. But mountains hundreds of millions of years old, such as the Appalachians of eastern North America, still stand above their surroundings. What seems to happen is that as erosion removes the load from the ridges, isostatic adjustment raises the rocks to compensate. Rocks formed deep below the surface, tens of thousands of metres down, are thereby exposed to our view and to weathering and erosion.

Some puzzling questions about the deposition of enormous thicknesses of sedimentary rocks can also be answered. One sequence of sedimentary rocks found in Africa involved the accumulation of nearly 6.5 km of various sediments followed by an outpouring of great quantities of lava. Other parts of the world have even thicker deposits. It is possible to deduce the environment under which deposition took place from the character of the deposits themselves. In some areas such deposition took place in shallow water. Although thousands of metres of sediments collected over millions of years, the depth of the water somehow remained about the same. In the accumulating sediments near the Bahamas, for instance, rocks that formed in shallow or intertidal flats are now 5500 m thick.

It can therefore be concluded that some cause, or combination of causes, depresses the region of deposition continuously, keeping the surface at about the same level. Such slowly accumulating sediments might be another place to effectively dispose of waste material produced by human activity, which might slowly sink from sight within the sediments. Slow accumulation is now taking place in the Mississippi Delta. For millions of years, the great river has been pouring sediments into its delta, but these deposits have not formed a great pile, nor have they filled in the Gulf of Mexico (Fig. 33.9). The weight of the material and isostatic adjustment constantly lower the material to make room for more.

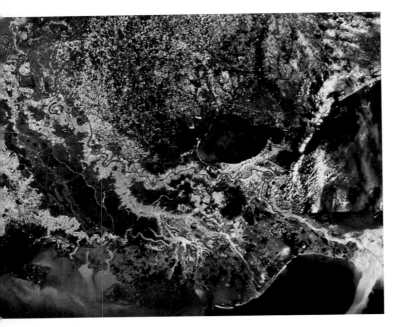

FIGURE 33.9 Ever since the glaciers melted from the Midwest 12,000 years ago, the Mississippi River and its tributaries have been carrying millions of tons of sediment from the interior of North America to its Louisiana delta on the Gulf of Mexico. The weight of this accumulating deposit is in the process of depressing the crust isostatically, but in the interior the disappearance of the ice and the removal of the sediments are causing crustal rebound. This satellite view of the Mississippi Delta shows the lower course of the river, near circular Lake Pontchartrain (in the eastern part of the image), and the "birdfoot" delta still forming.

Isostasy and Plate Mobility

If isostasy involves a condition of equilibrium, then the contact and collision of mobile plates must affect that situation greatly. When a continental plate meets an oceanic plate, the oceanic plate plunges below the continental plate, causing the deformation and dislocation shown in Fig. 32.7. Along the leading edge of the continental plate, rocks are crushed and folded, sediments are baked into metamorphic rocks, and magma penetrates and erupts along fissures and from volcanoes. In effect, the sialic mass increases in volume and, according to isostatic principles, rises upward. Right next to the high mountains so formed, the downward thrust of the oceanic plate often creates a deep trench, as deep as or deeper than the highest mountains are high. This is the situation along much of the Pacific Ring of Fire, where crustal instability and isostatic maladjustment are greatest. Earthquakes occur continuously along this zone as the plates converge and collide (see Fig. 32.4). Shallow tensional earthquakes occur as the oceanic plate bends, and compressional earthquakes increase in magnitude down the subducted plate (**Benioff zone**).

But the process does not go on forever at the same rate. It is not known just why, but the geological record shows that the Earth has gone through various rather distinct periods of mountain building and other quieter periods. Eventually even the Ring of Fire will quiet down, and plate collision and mountain building may start elsewhere. When this happens, erosion becomes dominant and begins to lower the mountains that have been created—but very slowly, because isostatic uplift will occur as mass is removed. The first phase of erosion, however, may be rather rapid.

The sialic mountains along the plate margin may have been pushed beyond the elevations justified by the depth of their roots, and isostatic readjustment will not commence until the overload has been removed. After that, the mountain masses undergo isostatic uplift as mass is eroded, a process that ensures their persistence for a long time. The Appalachians and Southern Africa's Cape Ranges have roots deep enough to ensure their topographic prominence over the past 200+ million years. Some mountain ranges have indeed been flattened by erosion all the way down to their roots, but these are much older still.

Isostasy and Regional Landscapes

In studying the effects of the theory of isostasy, we tend to be preoccupied with mountain ranges, mountain building, plate compression, and associated phenomena. But we should not lose sight of the consequences of isostasy in areas of less prominent, less dramatic relief. Erosion is active on the continents' plains too, and millions of tonnes of material are carried away by streams and other erosional agents. Even moving ice and wind denude and reduce land surfaces. Unlike the mountainous zones, however, the plains are vast in area and slopes are gentler. Rivers erode less spectacularly on the plains than in the mountains as a consequence of several factors (see Unit 41). All these circumstances mean that eroded material is removed from the plains at a slower rate.

Plains and Uplands   The sialic crust has a certain rigidity. It does not behave, as in Airy's model, as a series of discrete columns. Therefore isostasy affects plains and plateaus in phases. For a certain period, the amount of material removed does not trigger isostatic readjustment because the hardness of the crust prevents continuous uplift. But when the plain has been lowered sufficiently for the push of isostatic uplift to overcome the resistance of the crust, a change takes place. Thus at any given moment, an area may not be in isostatic equilibrium, awaiting the time when readjustment is forced by the removal of a sufficient mass of landscape.

Scientists suggest that this periodic adjustment may also occur in mountain ranges, especially older ones. In the beginning, when the sialic root is deep, isostatic uplift occurs almost continuously. But as time goes on, the root becomes shorter, erosion continues, and comparatively more eroded material must be removed for readjustment to occur. In fact, the Appalachians were probably flattened almost completely and then forced up by a recurrence of isostatic uplift. Now the old ridges are being worn down again, and the whole area may be transformed into a plain before another readjustment occurs (Fig. 33.10).

FIGURE 33.10 View from Pilot Mountain, North Carolina, overlooking the Piedmont, which yields eastward to the coastal plain. A vista like this suggests that the mountains are being eroded into lowland topography flanking them, but as the text points out, things are not that simple.

Ice Sheets and Isostatic Rebound   Some other manifestations of isostatic change also are of interest. When ice sheets spread over continental areas during glaciations, the weight of the ice (which can reach a thickness of several thousand metres) causes isostatic subsidence or sinking of the crust below, just as sediment accumulation has produced in other regions. This is what happened in northern North America and Eurasia during the most recent glaciation, where the last of the great ice sheets melted away less than 12,000 years ago. During the maximum extent of these continental glaciers, the crust below was depressed by their weight (1000 m of ice will depress the underlying crust by about 300 m). When the ice sheets retreated, isostatic readjustment caused the crust to rebound. The upward readjustment, however, could not keep pace with the relatively rapid melting of the ice. In geological terms, the melting removed the enormous load of the ice sheets almost instantaneously.

Studies show that the ensuing isostatic rebound is still going on; thus the crust is still not in equilibrium. In the centre of the Canadian Shield, the site of a huge ice sheet, the crust is rising at more than 1 m per century, a very fast rate. In some coastal areas once used by Inuit centuries ago, some parts of the northern Shield have risen 200 to 250 m since deglaciation. These areas are now much too high above sea level to be of use. Similarly, much of coastal California is flanked by ancient beaches tens of metres above the present-day sea level.

Dams and Crustal Equilibrium   Even human works on the surface of the Earth can produce isostatic reaction. When a dam is constructed, the weight of the impounded water behind it may be enough to produce isostatic accommodation in the crust. Measurable readjustment of this kind has taken place in the area of Kariba Lake, formed upstream of the great dam on the Zambezi River in Southern Africa, and around Lake Mead behind Hoover Dam on the Colorado River in Nevada. These changes cannot be seen with the naked eye, but scientific instruments detect them. In our everyday existence, the crust may seem permanent, unchanging, and solid, but even comparatively minuscule human works can disturb its equilibrium.

The dynamics of plate movement produce much of the restlessness that characterizes the Earth's crust. One of the most spectacular surface manifestations of this geological activity is volcanism, a topic that is the focus of Unit 34.

KEY TERMS

accretion *page 432*

Benioff zone *page 436*

exotic terrane *page 432*

isostasy *page 435*

supercontinent cycle *page 432*

terrane *page 432*

Wilson cycle *page 432*

REVIEW QUESTIONS

1. Describe the mechanism that is believed to drive lithospheric plate movement.

2. What are mountain "roots"?

3. How might long periods of erosion trigger uplifting of the landscape?

4. What is meant by the term *suspect terrane*?

5. Describe the process of isostatic uplift.

REFERENCES AND FURTHER READINGS

ALLEGRE, C.   *The Behavior of the Earth: Continental and Seafloor Mobility* (Cambridge, Mass.: Harvard Univ. Press, 1988).

ANDREWS, J. T. *A Geomorphological Study of Post-Glacial Uplift with Particular Reference to Arctic Canada* (London: Institute of British Geographers, 1970).

BRIDGES, E. M.   *World Geomorphology* (New York: Cambridge Univ. Press, 1990).

BURBANK, D., and ANDERSON, R.   *Tectonic Geomorphology* (Malden, Mass.: Blackwell, 2000).

Evolving Earth: Plate Tectonics (CD-ROM) (Halifax, Canada: EOA Scientific Systems, 2001).

HUGGETT, R. J.   *Fundamentals of Geomorphology* (London/New York: Routledge, 2002).

KING, L. C.   *Wandering Continents and Spreading Sea Floors on an Expanding Earth* (Chichester, U.K.: Wiley, 1983).

KIOUS, W. J., and TILLING, R. I.   *This Dynamic Earth: The Story of Plate Tectonics* (Reston, Va.: U.S. Geological Survey, n.d.).

MIYASHIRO, A., et al.   *Orogeny* (New York: Wiley, 1982).

MURPHY, J. B., and NANCE, R. D. "Mountain Belts and the Supercontinent Cycle," *Scientific American*, 226 (1992), 84–91.

NICOLAS, A.   *The Mid-Oceanic Ridges: Mountains below Sea Level* (New York: Springer Verlag, 1994).

SUMMERFIELD, M. A.   *Global Geomorphology: An Introduction to the Study of Landforms* (New York: Wiley/Longman, 1991).

TARLING, D. H., and RUNCORN, S. K.   *Implications of Continental Drift to the Earth Sciences* (New York: Academic Press, 1973).

VITA-FINZI, C.   *Recent Earth Movements* (Orlando, Fla.: Academic Press, 1986).

WILSON, J. T., Ed.   *Continents Adrift and Continents Aground* (San Francisco: Freeman, 1976).

WEB RESOURCES

http://pubs.usgs.gov/publications/text/dynamic.html The USGS presents *This Dynamic Earth: the Story of Plate Tectonics*. Plate motions, hot spots, and the historical perspective are discussed. Colour graphics guide users through this tutorial guide.

http://www.geocities.com/earthhistory/plate3.htm This web page offers a description of the evolution of the continents with coloured graphics from the USGS server. Plate tectonics are covered, as well as crustal spreading.

http://www.pgc.nrcan.gc.ca/tectonic/techome.htm Website of the Pacific Geoscience Centre contains information and research about tectonics in the British Columbia area.

http://www.pgc.nrcan.gc.ca/seismo/table.htm This website outlines seismology and seismic archives related to western Canada.

Volcanism and Its Landforms

Near Armadillo Peak, Mount Edziza, British Columbia. Over the ages, ice and fire formed this glacier-tipped volcanic mountain.

OBJECTIVES

- To relate volcanic activity to plate boundary types

- To discuss typical landforms produced by volcanic eruptions

- To cite some dramatic examples of human interaction with volcanic environments

Volcanism is the eruption of molten rock at the Earth's surface, often accompanied by rock fragments and explosive gases. The process takes various forms, one of which is the creation of new lithosphere at the midoceanic spreading margins (about 75 percent of the world's volcanoes are on the seafloor). Along some 50,000 km of ocean-floor fissures, molten rock (magma) penetrates to the surface (where it is called lava) and begins its divergent movement (see Fig. 33.3).

This is a dramatic process involving huge quantities of magma, the formation of bizarre submarine topography, the heating and boiling of seawater, and the clustering of unique forms of deep-sea oceanic life along the spreading margins. But it is all hidden by the ocean water above, and what we know of it comes from the reports of scientist-explorers who have approached the turbulent scene in specially constructed submarines capable of withstanding the pressure at great depths and the high temperatures near the emerging magma. Volcanism also occurs on the continents in the vicinity of plate margins (see Figs. 32.3 and 32.4) and leaves a characteristic signature in the form of volcanic landscapes (see photo at left).

Islands situated on midoceanic margins afford a glimpse of a process that is mostly concealed from view. Iceland and smaller neighbouring islands lie on the Mid-Atlantic Ridge between Greenland and Norway in an area where the ridge rises above the ocean surface (see Fig. 2.6). Iceland and its smaller neighbours are all of totally volcanic origin, and there is continuing volcanic activity there. In 1973 a small but populated and economically important island off Iceland's southwest coast, Heimaey, experienced a devastating episode of midoceanic-ridge volcanic activity. First Heimaey was cut by fissures, and all 5300 of its inhabitants were quickly evacuated. In the months that followed, lava poured from these new gashes in the island, and volcanic explosions rained ash (tephra) and fiery pieces of ejected magma onto homes and commercial buildings (Fig. 34.1).

Heimaey actually increased in size, but the lava flows threatened to fill and destroy its important fishing port. This threat led to an amazing confrontation between people and nature. The islanders quickly built a network of plastic pipes at the leading edge of the advancing lava. They pumped seawater over and into the lava, aware that by cooling it more quickly than nature could, the lava would form a solid dam, which might stop the advance and restrain the lava coming behind it. This daring scheme worked: part of the harbour was lost to the lava, but a critical part of it was saved and actually improved. When this volcanic episode ended, life returned to Heimaey. The heat from the lava is used to separate electricity and warm water. But Iceland and its neighbours lie on an active midoceanic ridge, and volcanism will surely attack them again. What happened above the surface at Heimaey is happening, continuously, all along those 50,000 km of submerged spreading margins.

Distribution of Volcanic Activity

Most volcanism not associated with seafloor spreading is related to subduction zones (see Fig. 32.7). As the global

FIGURE 34.1 The 1973 eruption on the Icelandic island of Heimaey generated lava flows and ashfalls that forced the evacuation of the town of 5000 and caused considerable destruction—but it also produced a heroic reaction in which local citizens fought back.

map (Fig. 32.4) shows, volcanic activity is concentrated at convergent plate margins. Not surprisingly, a majority of the world's active volcanoes lie along the Pacific Ring of Fire. But note that some volcanic activity is associated neither with midoceanic ridges nor with subduction zones. The island of Hawaii, for example, lies in an archipelago near the middle of the Pacific Plate. Lava has poured from one of its volcanic mountains, Kilauea, almost continuously since 1983. On the African Plate, where West Africa and Equatorial Africa meet, lies Mount Cameroon, another active volcano far from spreading and subductive margins. The map reveals a number of similar examples, both on ocean-floor crust and on continental crust. This distribution is difficult to explain.

Active, Dormant, and Extinct Volcanoes

Physical geographers differentiate among active, dormant, and extinct volcanoes on the basis, in some measure, of their appearance in the landscape. An *active* volcano is one that has erupted in recorded history (which, geologically speaking, is but an instant in time). A *dormant* volcano has not been seen to erupt, but it shows evidence of recent activity. This evidence lies on its surface: lava tends to erode quickly into gulleys and, on lower, flatter slopes, to weather into soils. If a volcano seems inactive but shows little sign of having been worn down, it may be concluded that its latest eruptions were quite recent, and activity may resume. When a volcano shows no sign of life and exhibits evidence of long-term weathering and erosion, it is tentatively identified as *extinct*. Such a designation is always risky because some volcanoes have come to life after long periods of dormancy.

As noted earlier, the great majority of continental volcanoes lie in or near spreading and subduction zones. Volcanic activity there is concentrated, and parts of the landscape are dominated by the unmistakable topography of eruptive volcanism. Many of the world's most famous mountains are volcanic peaks standing astride or near plate margins: Mount Fuji (Japan), Mount Vesuvius (Italy), Mount St. Helen's, Mount Rainier (U.S. Pacific Northwest), Mount Chimborazo (Ecuador), and many others. Frequently such mountains stand tall enough to be capped by snow, their craters emitting a plume of smoke. It is one of the natural landscape's most dramatic spectacles.

Lava and Landforms

The viscosity (the property of a fluid that resists flowing) of magma and lava varies with its composition. Basaltic lavas, such as those flowing from the midoceanic spreading-margin volcanoes, are relatively low in silica and high in iron and magnesium content, and are therefore quite fluid when they erupt. They flow freely and often (on land) quite rapidly—up to 50 km/h on steep slopes. Other lavas are poorer in magnesium and iron but richer in silica—and thus more acidic. These lavas tend to be more viscous, and as a result they flow more slowly. Basaltic lava can flow like motor oil; the less mafic lava moves more like a thick porridge would (e.g., andesite).

Magma also contains steam and other gases under pressure, with variations again a function of its mineral content. The acidic, silica-rich magmas tend to contain more gases, and when they erupt as lavas, these gases often escape explosively. Gobs of lava are thrown high into the air, solidifying as they fall back to the mountain's flanks. Such projectiles, not unreasonably, are called volcanic *bombs*. Smaller fragments may fall through the air as volcanic *cinders* or volcanic **ash** (or **tephra**). After the explosive 1980 eruption of Mount St. Helens in Wash-

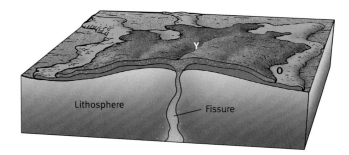

FIGURE 34.2   During a fissure eruption, lava flows onto the surface and spreads out in a sheet rather than forming a dome. When the fissure opens again, a later, younger flow (**Y**) will cover all or part of the older lava sheet (**O**).

ington State, lighter volcanic *dust* fell over a wide area downwind from the mountain. Yakima, not far from the volcano, was covered with up to 600,000 tonnes of ash. Geologists use the term **pyroclastics** for the rock material that formed part of the volcanic edifice that was fragmented and mobilized in an eruption; it usually moves down the sides of a volcano by slope processes (*pyroclastic* is ancient Greek for "broken by fire").

When lava creates landforms, still other factors come into play. The rate of cooling relates not only to the composition and viscosity of the molten material, but also to the thickness of the flow and the nature of the surface over which the lava spreads. The nature of the **vent**, the opening through the existing crust where the lava has penetrated, is an additional factor. Some eruptions do not come from pipe-shaped vents, but from lengthy cracks in the lithosphere. *Fissure eruptions* do not create mountains; rather, they release magma to form lava that extends in sheets across the countryside, creating sometimes extensive plateaus (Fig. 34.2), a very common form of eruption along spreading margins. In the United States, the best example is the Columbia Plateau, an area underlain by thick sheets of basalt that erupted in many successive layers and eventually covered 50,000 km^2 of southern Washington, eastern Oregon, and much of Idaho. In Canada, an excellent example can be found in the interior of British Columbia (Fig. 34.3). Just before Gondwana broke up, great fissure eruptions produced a vast lava plateau of which parts still exist in India, South Africa, South America, and Antarctica. These were related to "plumes" or "hot spots" in the mantle.

Volcanic Mountains

The most characteristic product of volcanic eruption is the towering mountain form or edifice, represented by such peaks as Fuji (Japan), Rainier (U.S.), Popocatépetl

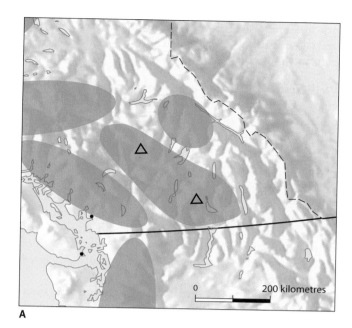

FIGURE 34.3 A. The Chilcotin Plateau basalt flows in the interior of British Columbia. B. The Chasm, British Columbia. Erosion has revealed varying tones of red, brown, yellow, and purple, formed by successive lava flows.

(Mexico), Vesuvius (Italy), and Kilimanjaro (Tanzania). But not all volcanic action, even from pipe-shaped vents, produces such impressive landforms. Some volcanoes are even larger in volume but less prominent in shape. Others are smaller and less durable. Four types of volcanic landforms exist—composite volcanoes, lava domes, cinder cones, and shield volcanoes.

Composite Volcanoes

Most of the great volcanoes that formed over subductive margins are **composite volcanoes** (or *stratovolcanoes*)—

they disgorge mainly pyroclastics including ash and gases. In cross-section such volcanoes look layered, with lavas of various thicknesses and textures interspersed with strata formed by compacted pyroclastics, such as tuff and ignimbrite and ash (Fig. 34.4). Neither the heavier pyroclastics nor the rather viscous lava travel very far from the crater. In fact lavas are fairly minor components in a lot of volcanoes of this type. Thus the evolving volcano soon takes on its fairly steep-sided, often quite symmetrical appearance. Many composite volcanoes are long-lived and rise to elevations of thousands of metres.

Composite volcanoes, with their acidic, gas-filled lavas, are also notoriously dangerous. They often erupt explosively with little or no warning, and molten lava is not the only threat to life in their surroundings. Pyroclastics can be hurled far from the crater; volcanic ash can create health hazards that choke human and animal life even farther away.

Lahars On snowcapped volcanoes the hot ash sometimes melts the snow and ice, which forms a flood of ash, mud, and water rushing downslope. Such a mudflow can be extremely destructive. In 1985 the Nevado del Ruiz volcano in the Andes of central Colombia erupted, and much of its snowcap melted. In the mudflow or lahar that swiftly followed, more than 20,000 people perished. After it was over, the scene at a town in its path at the base of the mountain range was one of utter devastation, a mass of mud containing bodies of people and animals, houses and vehicles, trees and boulders (Fig. 34.5). Such a deposit of volcanic origin is called a **lahar** (pronounced "luh-HARR") once it solidifies. Lahars are mainly triggered by eruptions (these are called *hot lahars*), but occasionally they result from intensive, warm-season orographic rainfall. Previously deposited ash can be mobilized, causing a *cold lahar*. The torrential rains

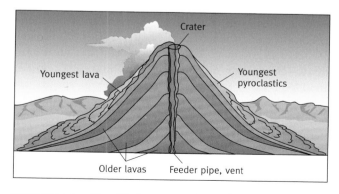

FIGURE 34.4 Simplified cross-section of a composite volcano, showing a sequence of lavas interspersed with compacted pyroclastics.

FIGURE 34.5 Aftermath of the 1985 lahar, caused by a nearby erupting volcano, which late at night buried the Colombian town of Armero without warning. This "hot" lahar killed at least 20,000 people in the immediate area, amounting to one of the worst natural disasters of the late twentieth century.

related to Hurricane Mitch caused cold lahars that devastated parts of Central America in 1998, killing approximately 20,000 people in Honduras and Nicaragua.

Nuées Ardentes   Perhaps even more dangerous is the outburst of hot gas and fine ash that may accompany or precede an eruption. Gas is pent up in magma itself, but in some composite volcanoes a large reservoir of gas may accumulate in the magma chamber below the crater. This happens when the crater becomes clogged by solidified lava, which forms a *plug* in the top of the vent. The gas cannot escape, and rising temperatures inside the mountain may well exceed 1000°C. Pressures finally become so great that the side of the volcano may be blown open, allowing the gas to escape, or the plug may be blown out of the top of the volcano's pipe, enabling the gas to rush from the crater along with heavier pyroclastics and lava. Such an event produces a **nuée ardente** (French for *glowing cloud;* pronounced "noo-AY ahr-DAHNT"), which races downslope at speeds exceeding 100 km/h. Everything in its path is incinerated because the force of the descending turbulent, heavier-than-air cloud of gas, plus its searing temperatures, ensures total destruction.

In 1902 a *nuée ardente* burst from Mount Pelée on the eastern Caribbean island of Martinique. It descended on the nearby port town of St. Pierre at its base in a matter of minutes, killing an estimated 30,000 persons (the only survivor was a prisoner in a cell in the town's thick-walled prison). The "Paris of the Caribbean," as St. Pierre had been described, never recovered and still carries the scars of its fate more than a century later.

Predicting Risk   Among the other dangers posed by volcanoes of the gas-filled, viscous-magma variety are quieter emissions of lethal gases that can reach people and animals at air temperature and kill without warning. Estimating the risk to people living near such volcanoes and predicting dangerous activity have become part of an increasingly exact science, but many volcanoes (especially in developing countries) are not yet subject to such scientific monitoring and hazard mitigation. The 1980 eruption of Mount St. Helens had been predicted by volcanologists who had measured the telltale signs of resumed activity, and their warnings probably saved thousands of lives.

Forecasting techniques have been improving since 1980, and a number of volcanoes are now being monitored by scientists in the United States, Japan, Mexico, Italy, Iceland, Papua-New Guinea, Montserrat, and elsewhere. Among their most notable successes were predictions of the eruptions of Alaska's Mount Redoubt in 1989 and of Mount Pinatubo in the Philippines in 1991 (Fig. 34.6). But the magnitude of these eruptions went well beyond what had been anticipated, reminding us that volcanic activity still defies exact prediction.

Lava Domes

When acidic lava (andesite, dacite) penetrates to the surface, it may ooze out without pyroclastic activity. This process usually produces a small volcanic mound, called a **lava dome**. A lava dome often forms inside a crater following an explosive eruption, as happened at Mount St. Helens. But lava domes can also develop as discrete landforms in a volcanic landscape. Although some grow quite large, lava domes, on average, are much smaller than composite volcanoes.

Cinder Cones

Some volcanic landforms consist not of lava, but almost entirely of pyroclastics. Normally such **cinder cones** (which may also include fragments larger as well as smaller than cinders) remain quite small, frequently forming during a brief period of explosive activity. Probably the most extensive areas of cinder-cone development lie in East Africa and Iceland associated with the rift-valley system of those regions (Fig. 34.7). In North America, a sporadic row of cinder cones, along with shield volcanoes and tuyas (volcanoes that erupted under an ice sheet), is found running from the B.C. coast inland to Wells Grey Provincial Park, these form the Anahim Volcanic Belt (Fig. 34.8). Also, the Craters of the Moon (Idaho) and the Sunset Crater (Arizona) are often cited as examples of older cinder cones. Geologists were able to observe closely the growth of a cinder cone in Mexico from 1943, when it was born in a cornfield in Michoacán State (about 320 km west of Mexico City), until 1952. This cinder cone, named Paricutín, grew to a height of 400 m in its first eight months of activity and remained intermittently active for nearly a decade.

Shield Volcanoes

Shield volcanoes are formed from more-fluid basaltic lavas. These lavas contain sufficient or "certain" gases to

create a sometimes dramatic "fountain" of molten rock (see Fig. 34.9) and some cinders, but these are tiny compared to the explosive eruptions at the craters of composite volcanoes. The basaltic lava is very hot, however, and flows in sheets over a countryside being gradually built up by successive eruptions (Fig. 34.10). Compared to their horizontal dimensions, which are very large, the tops of such volcanoes are rather unspectacular and are rounded rather than peaked. This low-profile appearance has given them the name *shield volcanoes.*

The most intensively studied shield volcanoes undoubtedly are those on the main island of Hawaii, where the U.S. Geological Survey operates an observatory. Mauna Loa is the largest active shield volcano there. It stands on the ocean floor, and from there rises 10,000 m, with the uppermost 3500 m protruding above sea level. Mauna Loa is the tallest mountain on Earth. To the north, Mauna Kea's crest is slightly higher. And to the east lies Kilauea (pronounced "kill-uh-WAY-uh"), the volcano that has experienced eruptions since the 1970s and also holds a special meaning for native Hawaiians (see Perspective: Risking the Wrath of Goddess Pele). Kilauea has a lava lake at its top that acts as its principal vent—Halemaumau (fire pit). Kilauea's lavas even flowed across a housing subdivision, obliterating homes and streets, and reached the ocean, thereby adding a small amount of land to the island. Recent studies have shown that the southern side of Kilauea is probably going to give way in a large mass movement. The Hilina Block has an area of 80 km², is 12 km deep, and moves at a rate of 5cm/yr. If this is subject to a catastrophic failure, it could generate tsunamis along the shores of The Big Island. The same kind of process is going on on Cumbre Vieja on La Palma in the Canary Islands.

A

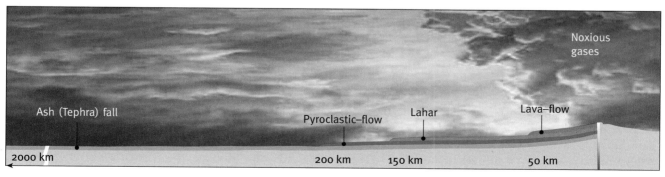

B

FIGURE 34.6   (A) A huge cloud of volcanic ash and gas rises above Mount Pinatubo in the Philippines on June 12, 1991. Three days later an explosive eruption, one of the largest in the past century, spread a layer of ash over a vast area around the mountain, with environmental as well as political consequences: a dust cloud orbited the Earth and reduced global warming, and a nearby U.S. military base on Pinatubo's island (Luzon) was damaged beyond repair. (B) Diagram showing the various types of hazards associated with a volcanic eruption and the various sizes of areas affected by the hazards.

FROM THE FIELDNOTES

FIGURE 34.7 "East Africa's volcanic landscape displays landforms ranging from great peaks such as Mounts Kilimanjaro and Kenya to small cinder cones and local fissure eruptions. Driving across this area you are reminded that volcanic activity continues; some of the cinder cones have not yet developed much vegetation. Elsewhere plants are just beginning to establish themselves on the lava. In places the landscape poses challenging questions. Many cinder cones, for example, have small crater-like depressions near their crests, but those 'craters' tend to lie to one side, as in this photo taken in Kenya. As it happens, a majority of them lie in the same compass direction from the top of the hill. What might be the cause of this pattern?"

The volcanic landscape in this area displays some interesting shapes and forms. Lava that is especially fluid when it emerges from the crater develops a smooth "skin" upon hardening. This slightly hardened surface is then wrinkled, as the lava continues to move, into a ropy pattern called **pahoehoe**. This kind of lava is associated with the formation of lava tubes where lava flows under a thin cover of hardened lava. The lava stream can be seen through windows where the surface has collapsed. Molten lavas often flow out of these tubes leaving them as a long, narrow cave system (Fig. 34.11). Less fluid lava hardens into angular, blocky forms called **aa**, so named (according to Hawaiian tradition) because of the shouts of people trying to walk barefoot on this jagged terrain! In the Hawaiian Islands, it is the big island—Hawaii—that displays the currently active volcanism. But all the islands in this archipelago originally formed as shield volcanoes. Why should Hawaii contain the only volcanic activity? And why are there volcanoes at all, here in the middle of a lithospheric plate?

These questions are answered in part by the topographic map of the northwestern Pacific Basin

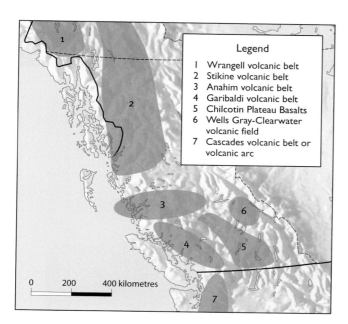

FIGURE 34.8 Canadian volcanoes.

Legend
1 Wrangell volcanic belt
2 Stikine volcanic belt
3 Anahim volcanic belt
4 Garibaldi volcanic belt
5 Chilcotin Plateau Basalts
6 Wells Gray-Clearwater volcanic field
7 Cascades volcanic belt or volcanic arc

0   200   400 kilometres

(Fig. 34.12A). Note that the Hawaiian Islands lie in an arched line from Kauai and its small neighbours in the northwest to Hawaii in the southeast. That line continues northwestward through Midway Island and then bends north-northwestward on the ocean floor as the Emperor Seamounts. It is remarkable that the only pronounced volcanic activity along this entire corridor is on Hawaii—at the very end of the chain.

Another part of the answer lies on the surface. In general, the rocks of Midway and Kauai (Fig. 34.12A) show evidence of much longer erosion than those of Oahu and, of course, Hawaii itself. Midway and Kauai seem to be much older than Oahu and Hawaii, and geological evidence confirms this. When the rocks of these Pacific islands were dated, those of Oahu were found to be around 3 million years old, those of Midway 25 million years old, and those at the northern end of the Emperor Seamounts 75 million years old.

Hot Spots Geologists theorize that the Pacific Plate has been moving over a **hot spot** in the mantle, a "plume" of extraordinarily high heat that remains in a fixed location, perhaps stoked by a high concentration of radioactivity. This idea was first suggested by a Canadian—J. Tuzo Wilson. As the Pacific Plate moved over this hot spot, shield volcanoes formed over it (Fig. 34.12B). Thus one location after another would experience volcanic activity, acquiring volcanic landforms as that plate moved.

Today Hawaii is active, but eventually that island will move to the northwest and a new island will be formed southeast of where Hawaii now lies. Already, a

large undersea volcano, named Loihi, is being built upward about 35 km southeast of Hawaii. That seamount, which lies 1000 m beneath the waves, is expected to emerge above the ocean surface in approximately 50,000 years. In the meantime the shield volcanoes of Hawaii will become extinct. Another newly forming volcanic island is forming off Sicily—Ferdinandea—because of the same process.

Hot Spots and Plate Dynamics If the hot-spot theory is correct, and subcrustal hot spots are indeed stationary, then it is possible to calculate the speed and direction of plate movement. As the map (Fig. 34.12A) shows, the Emperor Seamounts extend in a more northerly direction than the Midway–Hawaii chain. Thus the moving Pacific Plate—which today travels toward the northwest (see Fig. 32.3)—changed direction about 40 million years ago if the same hot spot is responsible for both the Emperor Seamounts and the Midway–Hawaii chain. Given the age of Midway's lavas (25 million years), we may conclude that the plate travelled some 2700 km over this period. This works out to about 11 cm per year, a rate of movement consistent with average rates for other plates (see Fig. 33.1).

The volcanic effects of hot spots under comparatively thin oceanic lithosphere can be discerned rather easily and are revealed by the ocean-floor topography (as in Fig. 34.12). But it is likely that hot spots also are active under thicker continental crust, which may account for some of the intraplate volcanism shown on the world distribution map (Fig. 32.4). The effect of hot spots under continental plates is rather more difficult to identify. Hot spots may be responsible for the geothermal activity seen at Yellowstone and for some of those giant fissure eruptions like the ones that formed the Columbia Plateau. An isolated zone of volcanic activity (e.g., Mount Cameroon in west-central Africa and the range to the northeast of it) may be associated with hot-spot activity. On the other hand, such linear activity may also represent a yet hidden crustal spreading zone beneath the continental sial. The problem is not yet totally solved.

Calderas

A volcano's lavas and pyroclastics come from a subterranean magma chamber, a reservoir of active molten rock material that forces its way upward through the volcanic vent. When that magma reservoir ceases to support the volcano, the chamber may empty out and the interior of the mountain may literally become hollow. Left unsupported by the magma, the walls of the volcano may collapse, creating a **caldera** (Fig. 34.13).

PERSPECTIVES ON THE HUMAN ENVIRONMENT

Risking the Wrath of Goddess Pele

Native Hawaiians do not regard their islands' volcanism as simply a geological phenomenon. They have lived with the Hawaiian fountains of fire far longer than the white invaders have been on their islands. The goddess Pele (pronounced "PAY-lay") rules here, and she displays her pleasure or wrath through her power over the main island's volcanoes. In accordance with tradition, Hawaiians walk barefoot on the *aa* lava to the very edges of Kilauea (Fig. 34.9) and the other steaming craters of the island of Hawaii, pray to Pele, and leave fern garlands for her.

During the 1980s plans were announced to tap geothermal energy from the interior of Kilauea. The project was expected to generate enough electricity to some day provide all the Hawaiian Islands with power. But Pele's followers argued that such a penetration of the heart of a holy mountain would destroy the goddess herself. A confrontation developed, and it reached the courts of law. Christian missionaries long ago had suppressed Pele worship, but the geothermal project proved that Pele still has many followers.

Meanwhile the goddess seemed to prove a point by sending lava into the Royal Gardens subdivision and consuming several houses. In 1988 the Pele Defense Fund even bought a full-page advertisement in *The New York Times* to state its case. The day it appeared, Kilauea put on a volcanic display described as the most spectacular in more than a year, marking the start of an eruption that is still going on.

FIGURE 34.9 Unearthly landscape of Kilauea's upper slopes on the island of Hawaii, a classic shield volcano. An eruption is in progress, one of a still continuing series that began more than 20 years ago. Lava emanating here can flow for many kilometres and reach the sea.

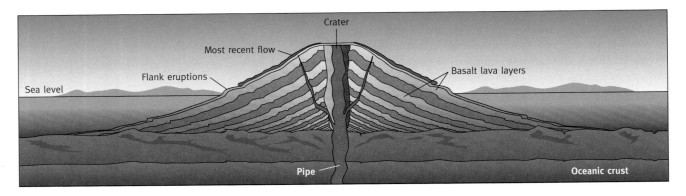

FIGURE 34.10   Simplified cross-section of a shield volcano. Vertical scale is greatly exaggerated. The base of this volcano extends over 320 km; its height above the ocean floor is around 13 km.

FROM THE FIELDNOTES

FIGURE 34.11

"Spending a semester teaching at the University of Hawaii gave me the opportunity to spend much time on the Big Island, where the great volcanoes are active today. Here on Hawaii, the product of very recent (and current) shield volcanism snow dusts the mountaintops even as palm trees grace the tropical beaches. To experience an area where the night sky reflects the glow of molten magma and the day reveals clouds of superheated gases emanating from caldera walls is memorable. Shown here is a mass of recently erupted pahoehoe lava, its smooth 'skin' wrinkled into ropy patterns by continued movement of molten rock inside."

Such an event can occur quite suddenly, perhaps when the weakened structure of the volcano is shaken by an earthquake. A caldera also can result from a particularly violent eruption, which destroys the peak and crater of the volcano. In such cases, however, the magma chamber below is at the peak of its energy and will soon begin to rebuild the mountain.

Calderas are often large and sometimes filled with water. They also are often misnamed, as, for example, Oregon's Crater Lake, which is a circular caldera 10 km across, with walls more than 1200 m high; a lake 600 m deep fills this caldera. Another misnamed caldera is the Ngorongoro Crater in Tanzania, some 18 km across and 600 m deep. Ngorongoro contains a small lake, but it is best known for the enormous concentration of wildlife that has occupied it and its fertile natural pastures for many thousands of years.

Supervolcanoes

There are volcanoes subject to extremely large catastrophic eruptions that effect a very large area and may cause changes in terms of atmospheric gases, particulates, aerosols, and temperature. Water, poured on advancing lava, can help cool and consolidate the hot crust and slow down or divert the movement of the flow. But when water penetrates into the magma chamber below a volcano, it has quite a different effect. Just as pouring water on a grease fire only intensifies the blaze, so water entering a superheated magma chamber results in an explosive reaction—so explosive, in fact, that it can blow the entire top off the volcano above. This may be the reason for the gigantic explosions known to have occurred in recorded history, explosions that involved large composite volcanoes standing in water. Such explosions are called **phreatic** or **magmatophreatic eruptions**, and their effects reach far beyond the volcano's immediate area. Some phreatic eruptions, described in the following subsections, are believed to have changed the course of human history.

Krakatau   The most recent major phreatic eruption happened in 1883, when Indonesia's Krakatau volcano blew up with a roar heard in Australia 3000 km away. The blast had a force estimated at 100 million tonnes of dynamite. It rained pyroclastics over an area of 750,000 km^2 and propelled volcanic dust through the troposphere and stratosphere to an altitude of 80 km. For years following Krakatau's eruptive explosion on the island, this dust orbited the Earth, affecting solar radiation and colouring sunsets brilliant red. Krakatau was an uninhabited, forested island located between Jawa and

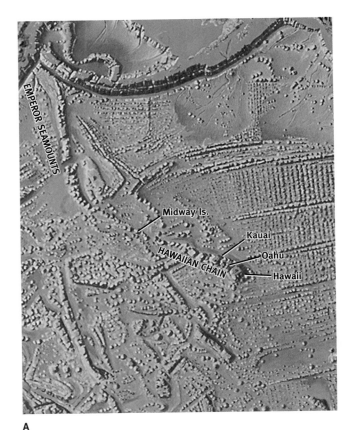

A

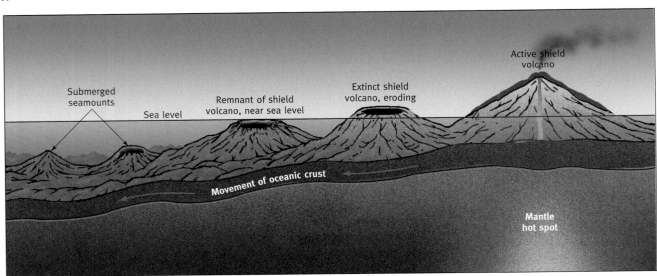

B

FIGURE 34.12   Ocean floor of the northwestern Pacific, dominated by the Emperor Seamounts and the Hawaiian Chain (A). Volcanic chain formed by the seafloor moving over a geologic hot spot (B). These volcanic landforms become progressively older toward the left.

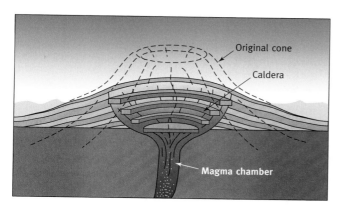

FIGURE 34.13 When the magma chamber that has long supplied an active volcano is somehow deprived of its conduit to the magma source, it empties out, leaving a hollow chamber beneath the cone. Eventually the structure of the volcano yields and the cone collapses, creating a caldera.

Sumatera. Although no one on the island was killed by its explosion, great water waves were generated that dealt death and destruction. First, the explosion itself set in motion a giant *tsunami* (a sea wave set off by crustal disturbance), which radiated to the nearby coasts of Jawa, Sumatera, and other islands. Next, water rushed into the newly opened caldera, setting off further explosions and successive tsunamis. When these waves reached the more heavily populated coasts of Indonesia, an estimated 40,000 people were killed.

Tambora   Explosive eruptions of Krakatauan dimensions occur suddenly but rarely. Nonetheless, Krakatau's actually was the second eruption of the nineteenth century in its corner of the world. In 1815 the phreatic eruption of the Indonesian volcano Tambora was even larger. The volcanic dust it generated interfered so strongly with incoming solar radiation that the weather turned bitterly cold over much of the world, and as a result 1816 was widely described as the "year without a summer." Crops failed to ripen that following year, food and fuel shortages developed, and problems lasted into the ensuing winter and beyond.

Santorini   Certainly phreatic eruptions can affect climate for a time. But possibly no such event had a greater impact on human history than the explosion of the Mediterranean volcano of Santorini (Thera), which took place in the middle of the seventeenth century B.C.E., more than 3600 years ago. The exact date of this cataclysmic event is still being debated, but its dimensions are clear.

The volcanic island of Santorini stood in the Mediterranean about 110 km north of Crete, where the Minoan civilization thrived. On a fateful day sometime around

1645 B.C.E., Santorini exploded, possibly as a result of seawater entering its magma chamber. So much volcanic ash was blasted into the air that skies were darkened for days. (It has been suggested that this was the event described in the Bible's Old Testament as the act of God in retribution against the pharaoh: "thick darkness in all the land of Egypt for three days.") The Mediterranean Sea turned into a cauldron of tsunamis that lashed the coasts of other islands and mainland Greece and Turkey.

As for Santorini itself, when daylight reappeared its core was gone, replaced by the protruding margins of a vast caldera now filled with seawater (Fig. 34.14). The loss of life cannot be estimated. Fertile, productive, well-located Santorini had towns and villages, ports and farms; fleets of boats carried trade between it, prosperous Crete, and the eastern Mediterranean. Minoan civilization was the Mediterranean's most advanced, and great palaces graced Crete as well as Santorini. Many archeologists and historical geographers have speculated that the eruption of Santorini spelled the end of the Minoan culture. Whatever the cause, the Minoan civilization went into decline at about the time of Santorini's explosion. It has also been suggested that the legend of a drowned city of Atlantis was born from accounts of Plato (427–347 B.C.E.)—in his dialogues of Timaeus and Critias—of Santorini's destruction.

Santorini's caldera did not form from collapse; rather, it resulted from explosive forces. Geologically very little time has elapsed since Santorini's explosion, but considerable volcanic activity and associated seismic (earthquake) activity have taken place. Near the middle of the caldera, probably above the original vent, a new lava dome is emerging. This forms the islands of Palea and Nea Kameni—Old and New Burnt Islands—in the middle of the caldera. The lavas forming these islands are all less than 2000 years old. The volcano remains active, and although its caldera rim is quite densely populated today, many inhabitants have fled after each volcanic and seismic event. In the meantime, archaeologists continue to excavate the ruins of a Bronze Age settlement near Akrotiri on the southern edge of the caldera, hoping to learn more about life on Santorini before its catastrophic interruption. We can only speculate on the course history might have taken if the Minoan civilization had spread throughout the archipelago in which Santorini lies, expanded onto the mainland, and given birth to what would have been a very different kind of ancient Greece.

Landscapes of Volcanism

Volcanic activity, especially the mountainous type, creates unique and distinct landscapes. As Fig. 32.4 reminds

FROM THE FIELDNOTES

A

B

FIGURE 34.14 "To realize what happened here, how a gigantic volcanic explosion changed the course of human history, is to be reminded how vulnerable humanity remains to nature's power. Thera (Santorini) bears witness to a day, more than 3600 years ago, when the Minoan civilization thrived and Thera was the Hong Kong of the eastern Mediterranean. In a cataclysmic event, the mountain that was Thera was pulverized, huge blocks of rock fell back into the Mediterranean, poisonous ash rained on countrysides hundreds of kilometres away, and dust encircled the Earth for years. Towns, villages, farms, and ports on prosperous Thera disappeared; the Minoan civilization on nearby Crete may have been dealt a fatal blow. What was left was an enormous caldera, 60 km in circumference, open to the sea, on whose inner wall homes and businesses now perch precariously (A). But Santorini's activity has not ended, and earthquakes continue to destroy lives and property. A new central cone is slowly rising in the centre of the caldera, where fresh lava signals the rise of a new mountain (B). In the background, atop the caldera wall, is the much damaged town of Oja."

us, volcanic landscapes are limited in their geographic extent, but they do dominate certain areas. Even a single composite cone, by its sheer size or threat, can dominate physical and mental landscapes over a much wider area.

Mount Vesuvius, which in C.E. 79 buried a ring of Roman towns, including Pompeii (see Fig. 1.2) and Herculaneum, under ash and lahars, still towers over the southern Italian city of Naples. Active and monitored anxiously, Vesuvius has erupted disastrously some 18 times since the first century C.E. During the twentieth century alone, it erupted in 1906, 1929, and 1944, causing destruction and death in each instance. Farther south, on Sicily, the island just off the toe of the Italian peninsula, stands Mount Etna, which has erupted in 1992, 1994–2001, 2002–2003, and 2004. The 2002 eruption was notable because of the first successful diversion of a lava flow using concrete blocks dropped from a large helicopter. Again "the mountain," as such dominat-

ing volcanic landforms seem to be called wherever they stand, pervades the physical landscape of the entire area. East Africa's Kilimanjaro, 5861 m tall, carries its snowcap within sight of the Equator (see Fig. 19.11). It has not erupted in recorded history, but its presence is predominant, its form a reminder of what could happen, its soils fertile and intensively farmed.

Volcanic landscapes are most prevalent, as noted earlier, along the Pacific rim of subduction zones, from southern Chile counterclockwise to New Zealand, and in Indonesia from Sumatra through Java and the Lesser Sunda Islands (Fig. 32.4). On the Asian side of the Pacific, these landscapes are almost exclusively associated with island arcs and collision margins between oceanic plates (Fig. 32.8). Virtually all the material here is volcanic, but not all of the topography appears to represent active volcanism. Japan's Mount Fuji, for example, towers as impressively over the area southwest of

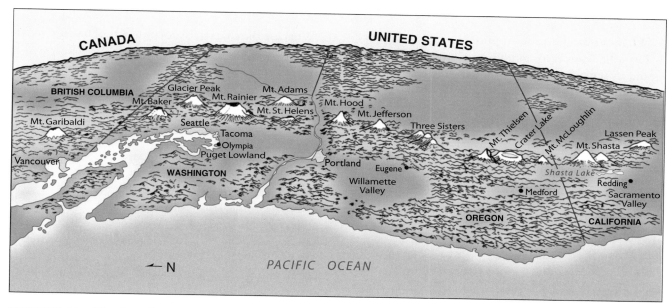

FIGURE 34.15 The Cascade volcanic arc of the Pacific Northwest.

Tokyo as Vesuvius does over Naples. Yet Fuji stands in a zone that is entirely of volcanic origin. Its morphology makes it unusual, because Japan does not consist of a row of snowcapped composite cones. In fact, Japan's eroded interior mountains do not evoke the image of a volcanic landscape.

The combination of orogenic (mountain-building) and volcanic activity is more dramatically reflected in the topography of the Americas, where oceanic and continental plates are colliding. In Chile, Peru, Ecuador, and Colombia, South America's Andes Mountains are studded with great volcanic cones. Central America and southern Mexico are similarly dominated, in their mountain backbones, by volcanic peaks, craters, and recent lava flows. In North America, the Aleutian Islands and areas of southern Alaska have volcanic landscapes. The Cascade Volcanic arc stretches from Volcano Mountain in the Yukon and Mount Edziza in northwestern British Columbia to Lassen Peak in northern California incorporates a line of volcanoes of which Mount St. Helens is only one (Fig. 34.15). Mount Hood was active as recently as 1865, Mount Baker in 1870, Mount Rainier in 1882, and Lassen Peak in 1921. The eruption of Mount St. Helens in 1980, 1986, and 2004, may signal a new round of activity in the Pacific Northwest that could change the volcanic landscape of the most vulnerable region of North America. The most recent geological event in that region occurred at Nisqually, near Seattle, in early 2001—a substantial earthquake (magnitude 6.8). Earthquakes will be examined in Unit 35.

KEY TERMS

aa *page 446*

ash *page 442*

caldera *page 447*

cinder cone *page 444*

composite volcano *page 443*

hot spot *page 447*

lahar *page 443*

lava dome *page 444*

nuée ardente *page 444*

pahoehoe *page 446*

phreatic (magmatophreatic) eruption *page 450*

pyroclastics *page 442*

shield volcano *page 445*

tephra *page 442*

vent *page 442*

REVIEW QUESTIONS

1. In what three geological settings do volcanoes occur?
2. How do shield volcanoes differ from composite volcanoes?

3. What are *hot spots,* and how do they help explain current volcanic activity in the Hawaiian Islands or the Anahim Volcanic Belt?

4. What causes a phreatic eruption?

5. Describe Santorini's monumental volcanic explosion and its impact on regional human activity.

6. What are the characteristics products of basaltic versus andesitic volcanic eruptions?

REFERENCES AND FURTHER READINGS

BEVIER, M. L. "A lead-strontium isotopic study of the Anahim volcanic belt, British Columbia: Additional evidence for widespread suboceanic mantle beneath western North America". *Geological Society of America Bulletin*, 101 1989 p. 973–981.

BEVIER, M. L., et al. "Miocene peralkaline volcanism in west central British Columbia–US temporal and plate-tectonics setting". *Geology*, 7 1979 p. 389–392.

BOAZ, N. T. *The Earth in Turmoil: Earthquakes, Volcanoes, and Their Impact on Humankind* (New York: Freeman, 1998).

BLONG, R. J. *Volcanic Hazards: A Sourcebook on the Effects of Eruptions* (Orlando, Fla.: Academic Press, 1984).

CHESTER, D. *Volcanoes and Society* (Sevenoaks, U.K.: Arnold, 1993).

DE BLIJ, H. J., Ed. *Nature on the Rampage* (Washington, D.C.: Smithsonian Institution Press, 1994).

DECKER, R. W., and DECKER, B. B. *Mountains of Fire: The Nature of Volcanoes* (New York: Cambridge Univ. Press, 1991).

DRUITT, T. H., et al. *Santorini Volcano* (London: Geological Society Memoir No. 19, 1999).

FISHER, R. V. *Out of the Crater: Chronicles of a Volcanologist* (Princeton, N.J.: Princeton Univ. Press, 1999).

FISHER, R. V., HEIKEN, G., and HULEN, J. B. *Volcanoes: Crucibles of Change* (Princeton, N.J.: Princeton Univ. Press, 1997).

FOUQUÉ, F. A. *Santorini and Its Eruptions* (Baltimore, Md.: Johns Hopkins Univ. Press, transl. A. R. McBirney, 1999).

FRANCIS, P. *Volcanoes: A Planetary Perspective* (New York: Oxford Univ. Press, 2000).

GREEN, J., and SHORT, N. M., Eds. *Volcanic Landforms and Surface Features: A Photographic Atlas and Glossary* (New York: Springer Verlag, 1971).

HARRIS, S. L. *Fire Mountains of the West: The Cascade and Mono Lake Volcanoes* (Missoula, Mont.: Mountain Press, 1991).

LEVY, M., and SALVADORI, M. *Why the Earth Quakes: The Story of Earthquakes and Volcanoes* (New York: Norton, 1995).

LIPMAN, P. W., and MULLINEAUX, D. R., Eds. *The 1980 Eruptions of Mt. St. Helens, Washington* (Washington, D.C.: U.S. Geological Survey, Professional Paper 1250, 1981).

MacDONALD, G. A., et al. *Volcanoes in the Sea: The Geology of Hawai'i* (Honolulu: Univ. of Hawai'i Press, 2nd ed., 1983).

NEWHALL, C. G. and SELF, S. "The Volcanic Explosivity Index (VEI): An Estimate for Historical Volcanism." *Journal of Geophysical Research*, 87 (C2), 1982, 1231–1238.

OLLIER, C. D. *Volcanoes* (Cambridge, Mass.: Blackwell, 1988).

RITCHIE, D., and GATES, A. E. *The Encyclopedia of Earthquakes and Volcanoes* (New York: Facts on File, 2nd ed., 2001).

ROGERS, G. C. "McNaughton Lake seismicity–more evidence for an Anahim hotspot?" *Canadian Journal of Earth Science*, 18 (4) 1981 826–828.

RYAN, M. P., Ed. *Magmatic Systems* (Orlando, Fla.: Academic Press, 1994).

SCARTH, A. *Vulcan's Fury: Man Against the Volcano* (New Haven, Conn.: Yale Univ. Press, 1999).

SIGURDSSON, H. *Melting the Earth: The History of Ideas on Volcanic Eruptions* (New York: Oxford Univ. Press, 1999).

SIMKIN, T., and SIEBERT, L. *Volcanoes of the World: A Regional Directory, Gazetteer, and Chronology of Volcanism during the Last 10,000 Years* (Tucson, Ariz.: Geoscience Press, 2nd ed., 1994).

SOUTHER, J. G., et. al. "Nazco cone: a quarternary volcano in the eastern Anahim Belt". *Canadian Journal of Earth Science*, 24 1987 (12), 2477–2485.

THORNTON, I. *Krakatau: The Destruction and Reassembly of an Island Ecosystem* (Cambridge, Mass.: Harvard Univ. Press, 1996).

WINCHESTER, S. *Krakatoa: The Day the World Exploded, August 27, 1883* (New York: HarperCollins, 2003).

WRIGHT, T. L., et al. *Hawai'i Volcano Watch: A Pictorial History, 1779–1991* (Honolulu: Univ. of Hawai'i Press, 1992).

WEB RESOURCES

http://www.nrcan.gc.ca/gsc/pacific/vancouver/volcanoes/index_e.html This Geological Survey of Canada site gives basic and in-depth information about plate tectonics and volcanism. It has a complete catalogue of Canadian volcanoes, as well as links to the U.S. Geological Survey and other websites.

http://volcanoes.usgs.gov This USGS page provides basic and historical information about volcanoes, and has links to USGS worldwide volcano monitoring programs. Video, graphics, and satellite information can be accessed.

http://www.volcano.si.edu/gvp/links The Global Volcanism Program presented by the Smithsonian, provides web links to regional volcano research centers worldwide. Links to both tutorial and research pages are available.

UNIT 35

Earthquakes and Landscapes

What sounded and felt like a violent thunderclap produced a tear in our parking lot, a reminder of the instability of the still-building crust of Hawaii's Big Island. (Authors' photo)

OBJECTIVES

- To describe and quantify the magnitude and intensity of earthquakes

- To relate the spatial pattern of earthquakes to plate tectonics

- To discuss landscapes and landforms that bear the signature of earthquake activity

Unit 29 discussed how earthquakes in the crust and upper mantle generate seismic waves that travel through the lithosphere as well as the interior of the Earth (see Fig. 29.3). These waves yield key evidence to assist our understanding of the internal structure of the planet. As the seismic database expands and methods of analysis improve, the inferred properties of the Earth's internal structure and composition become better known.

Earthquakes also have an impact at the surface of the crust of the Earth, and they affect physical as well as cultural landscapes. Following a major earthquake, physical evidence of

455

its occurrence can be seen on the ground in the form of dislocated strata, open fractures, new scarps, and lines of crushed rock. Earthquakes also trigger movements such as landslides and mudslides. Moreover, the shocks and aftershocks of an earthquake can do major damage to buildings and other infrastructural elements. Add to this the fact that certain areas of the world are much more susceptible to earthquake damage than others, and it is obvious that this environmental hazard should be studied in a geographical context.

Earthquake Terminology

Lithospheric plates collide at collision margins, producing fractures in rocks called faults. A **fault** is a fracture in crustal rock involving the displacement of rock on one side of the fracture with respect to rock on the other side. Some faults, such as the San Andreas Fault, are giant breaks that continue for hundreds of kilometres (see Fig. 32.11); others are shorter. Along the contact zone between the North American and Pacific Plates, the upper crust is riddled with faults, all resulting from the stresses imposed on hard rocks by the movement of plates. Like volcanoes, certain faults are active whereas others are no longer subject to stress. In the great continental shields that form the cores of continents lie many faults, fractures that bear witness to an earlier age of crustal instability. Today those faults appear on geological maps, but they do not pose a major earthquake hazard.

When rock strata are subjected to stress, they begin to deform or bend (Fig. 35.1). All rocks have a certain rupture strength, which means that they will continue to bend, rather than break, as long as the stress imposed on them does not exceed this rupture strength. When the stress finally becomes too great, the rocks fracture suddenly and move along a plane (the fault) that may or may not have existed before the deformation began. That sudden movement snaps the rocks on each side of the fault back into their original shape and produces an earthquake. Interplate EQs associated with plate margins account for 90 percent of earthquakes; the other 10 percent are interplate events related to fault movement and/or isostatic readjustment and/or volcanic activity (harmonic tremors).

An **earthquake**, therefore, is the release of energy that has been slowly built up during the stress of increasing deformation of rocks. This energy release takes the form of seismic waves that radiate in all directions from the place of movement (Fig. 35.2). Earthquakes can originate at or near the surface of the Earth, deep inside the crust, or even in the upper mantle. The place

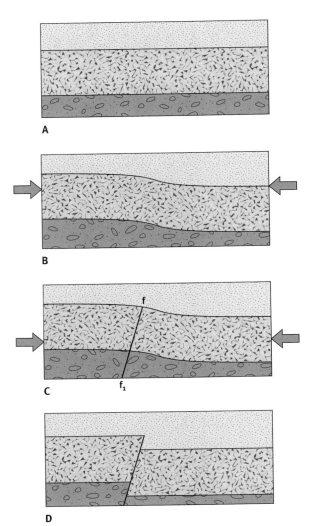

FIGURE 35.1 When stress (in this case compression) affects horizontal rock layers (A), the strata begin to bend, and they continue to do so as long as their rupture strength is not exceeded (B). When this level is exceeded, a fault plane (**f–f₁**) develops (C). Often more than one such fault plane will be formed. Sudden movement along this fault plane, accompanied by one or more earthquakes, relieves the now exceeded rupture strength, and the rock strata resume their original (horizontal) positions (D).

of origin is the **focus**, and the point directly above the focus on the Earth's surface is the **epicentre** or hypocentre (Fig. 35.2). Earthquakes range from tremors so small that they are barely detectable to great shocks that can destroy entire cities. This reflects their **magnitude**, the amount of shaking of the ground as the quake passes, as measured by a seismograph (see Fig. 29.1).

Magnitude is assessed on the *Richter Scale*, which assigns a number to an earthquake based on the measurement of the physical force of that ground motion. This open-ended scale, developed in 1935 by the geophysicist Charles Richter, ranges from 0 to 8+ (Table 35.1). It is logarithmic, so that an earthquake of magnitude 4 causes 10 times as much ground motion as one of magnitude 3 and 100 times as much as a quake of magnitude 2. It should be noted, however, that the original Richter Scale has undergone some recent changes, because more sophisticated equipment and more precise measurements of magnitude have been developed. Thus when the U.S. Geological Survey now announces a "Richter magnitude" following an earthquake, it is referring only to the magnitude of surface seismic waves. The most widely used measure today is the *Moment Magnitude Scale,* based on the size of the fault along which a quake occurs and the distance the rocks around it move. The news media still use the more familiar Richter Scale.

Another measure of an earthquake's size is its **intensity**. This measure reflects the impact of an earthquake on the cultural landscape—on people, their activities, and structures. Intensity is reported on the *Mercalli Scale,* which was first developed by the Italian geologist Giuseppe Mercalli in 1905 and updated in 1931. The *Modified Mercalli Scale* (Table 35.2) assigns a number ranging from I to XII to an earthquake (Roman numerals are always used). For instance, an earthquake of intensity IV is felt indoors, and hanging objects swing. Intensity V produces broken windows and dishes, awakens many sleepers, and cracks plaster. Intensity IX damages building foundations and breaks in-ground pipes. At intensity XII, damage is total, and even heavy objects are thrown into the air.

As Table 35.1 indicates, the severest of earthquakes occur on average perhaps once every few years. Tens of

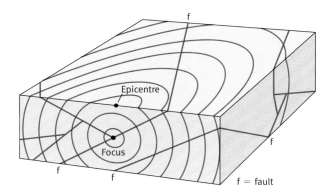

FIGURE 35.2 In an area honeycombed by faults (**f**), movement on a particular fault plane (perhaps at intersecting faults) becomes the focus for energy release. The epicentre is the point at the Earth's surface vertically above the point of focus. The energy released at the earthquake's focus radiates outward to other parts of the Earth in the form of seismic waves, represented by the rings spreading from the focus and the epicentre.

Table 35.1 Richter Scale of Earthquake Magnitudes, Compared with Mercalli Intensities

Typology	Magnitude	Approximate Maximum Intensity	Number per Year	Approximate Energy Released in Explosive Equivalents
Weak	0 1 2		} 700,000	0.45 kg TNT
	2–2.9	II	300,000	
	3			
	3–3.9		49,000	
	4	III		
	4–4.9	Minor	6,200	
Moderate	5	VI		Small atom bomb, 84 TJ (terajoule) = the bomb dropped in Nagasaki in 1945 (TNT 20 kilotons)
	5–5.9	Damaging	800	
Strong	6	VII		Hydrogen bomb, 4.2 petajoule (4.2 x 10^{15} J) (1 megaton)
	6–6.9	Destructive	120	
Major	7	X		
	7–7.9	Major	18	
Great	8	XII		60,000 4.2 petajoule (1-megaton) bombs
	8–8.6	Great	1 every few years	

Source: After Wyllie (1976), 47.

Table 35.2 Modified Mercalli Scale of Earthquake Intensities

Intensity	Qualitative Title	Description of Effects
I	Negligible	Detected by instruments only.
II	Feeble	Felt by sensitive people. Suspended objects swing.
III	Slight	Vibration like passing truck. Standing cars may rock.
IV	Moderate	Felt indoors. Some sleepers awakened. Hanging objects swing. Sensation like a heavy truck striking building. Windows and dishes rattle. Standing cars rock.
V	Rather strong	Felt by most people; many awakened. Some plaster falls. Dishes and windows broken. Pendulum clocks may stop.
VI	Strong	Felt by all; many are frightened. Chimneys topple. Furniture moves.
VII	Very strong	Alarm; most people run outdoors. Weak structures damaged moderately. Felt in moving cars.
VIII	Destructive	General alarm; everyone runs outdoors. Weak structures severely damaged; slight damage to strong structures. Monuments toppled. Heavy furniture overturned.
IX	Ruinous	Panic. Total destruction of weak structures; considerable damage to specially designed structures. Foundations damaged. Underground pipes broken. Ground fissured.
X	Disastrous	Panic. Only the best buildings survive. Foundations ruined. Rails bent. Ground badly cracked. Large landslides.
XI	Very disastrous	Panic. Few masonry structures remain standing. Broad fissures in ground.
XII	Catastrophic	Superpanic. Total destruction. Waves are seen on the ground. Objects are thrown into the air.

Source: After Wyllie (1976), 45.

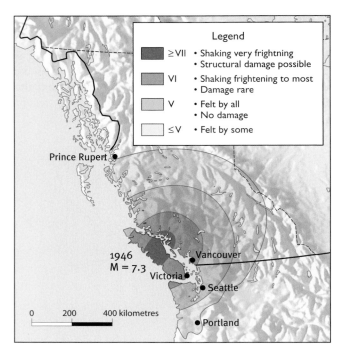

FIGURE 35.3   In June 1946 an earthquake with a magnitude of 7.3 struck central Vancouver Island just west of Courtenay and Campbell River. It caused considerable damage on the island and was felt as far away as Portland, Oregon, and Prince Rupert, B.C.

FIGURE 35.4   Earthquakes affecting major urban areas often start fires from broken gas mains, kitchen stoves, and other sources. The damage from the 1906 earthquake that struck San Francisco was worsened enormously by such fires, which raged out of control for days afterward.

thousands of smaller quakes occur annually, many felt only by sensitive seismographs. Great earthquakes that cause death and destruction are long remembered; several of the more recent ones are listed in Table 35.3. Probably the most infamous earthquake in North America during the twentieth century was the 1906 San Francisco quake, which is estimated to have had a magnitude of 8.3 and an intensity of XII. A dangerous associated effect of such a severe shock is fire, which rages out of control from many points of origin (especially when gas lines rupture) and cannot be fought because water supply systems are disrupted or destroyed (Fig. 35.4).

The world's most recent serious earthquake, as of press time, occurred on December 27, 2003, and devastated the area in and around the Ancient Silk Road city of Bam in Iran's southeastern Kerman Province (Fig. 35.5). The 6.5-magnitude quake struck at 5:28 a.m.

FIGURE 35.5   This aerial photograph of Bam, Iran, was taken on Tuesday December 30, 2003, three days after the initial quake struck. The earthquake damaged or destroyed 85 percent of the ancient city and killed 26,000 people.

Table 35.3 Noteworthy Earthquakes of the Twentieth Century

Year	Place	Richter Magnitude	Estimated Death Toll
1906	San Francisco, California	8.3	700
1908	Messina, Italy	7.5	120,000
1920	Kansu, China	8.5	180,000
1923	Tokyo-Yokohama, Japan	8.2	143,000
1935	Quetta, Pakistan (then India)	7.5	60,000
1939	Chillan, Chile	7.8	30,000
1962	Northwestern Iran	7.3	14,000
1964	Southern Alaska	8.6	131
1970	Chimbote, Peru	7.8	66,800
1976	Tangshan, China	7.6	242,000*
1985	West-central Mexico	7.9, 7.5	9,500
1988	Armenia, (then) U.S.S.R.	7.0	55,000+
1989	Loma Prieta, California	7.0	63
1990	Northwestern Iran	7.7	40,000+
1992	Landers, California	7.5	1
1994	Northridge (L.A.), California	6.8	61
1995	Kobe, Japan	7.2	6,400
1999	Western Turkey	7.4	17,900

*Reliable reports persist that as many as 750,000 died in this deadliest natural disaster of the twentieth century.

when most of the people were still asleep. The quake's epicentre was 10 km southwest of the city. The intensity of the earthquake was worsened by its shallowness (less than 56 km below the surface). The earthquake damaged or destroyed about 85 percent of the city, including its historical citadel and buildings dating from the fifth to eighteenth century—some were as old as 2000 years. The quake's maximum Modified Mercalli intensities were IX. Most of the buildings were constructed out of mud-brick, which is prone to collapse in quakes greater than magnitude 5. Over 26,000 people were killed, more than 9,000 injured, and 60,000 left homeless. Compare this with an earthquake of the same magnitude that hit central coastal California in the same week, killing only two people. The buildings in California were constructed to survive earthquakes. In October and November of 2004 a sequence of earthquakes hit the central part of Niigasta Prefecture on the west coast of the Japanese island of Honshu. The most powerful was a magnitude of 6.8 event on October 4, 2004 that killed 39 people. It was followed by a series of large aftershocks ~M 5.8 to M 6 in October and November.

Earthquake Distribution

The global distribution of earthquake epicentres, whatever the period of record, indicates that a large number of earthquakes fortunately originate in locations less vulnerable than most of the heavily populated places listed in Table 35.6. The greatest concentration is along the *Circum-Pacific belt* of subduction zones associated with the Pacific and Nazca Plates and their neighbouring plates (Fig. 35.6). About 80 percent of all shallow-focus earthquakes (depths of less than 100 km) originate in this belt. As the map indicates, earthquakes with deeper foci in the lower lithosphere are even more heavily concentrated in this zone.

A comparison of Fig. 35.6 with a map of the world distribution of population (Fig. 2.5), immediately shows that large numbers of people are at risk from earthquakes. All of Japan's 127 million people live in an area of high earthquake incidence and, therefore, high risk. The Philippines and Indonesia also are earthquake-prone and now home to more than 300 million people. But the earthquake-affected zone then extends into a less populated area of the Pacific Ocean and turns south, lessening in intensity just to the north of New Zealand.

In the north, the Circum-Pacific earthquake zone affects the sparsely populated Aleutian Islands, but also penetrates populated areas of southern Alaska. A particularly severe earthquake struck Anchorage on Good Friday, 1964, causing death and destruction. That earthquake's magnitude was 8.6 (the strongest ever recorded in the United States), and its epicentre was only about 120 km from the coastal city. The damage was caused not only by the shaking ground, but also by the massive ocean waves generated by the shock. As the

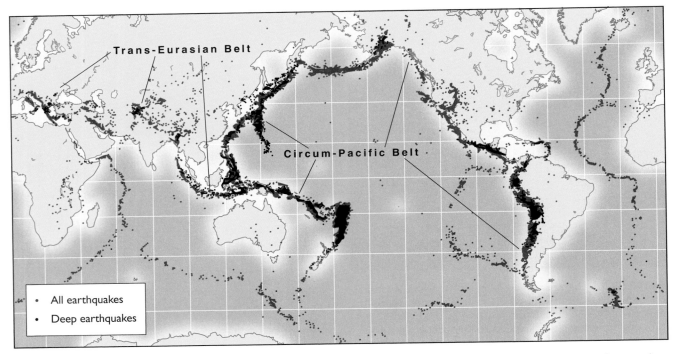

FIGURE 35.6 Global distribution of recent earthquakes. The deep earthquakes, shown by black dots, originated more than 100 km below the surface.

map shows (Fig. 35.6), between the main body of Alaska and Vancouver Island in southwesternmost Canada there is comparatively little earthquake risk—but the population is also rather sparse. In the Vancouver–Seattle area, earthquake frequency rises again, endangering the large population centres of the Georgia Strait–Puget Sound areas. This area awaits a high-magnitude event in the near future.

Earthquakes pose a constant threat to populous areas in Mexico and Central America. Virtually all of western South America is an active earthquake zone, including major population centres in Colombia, Ecuador, Peru, and Chile.

Another zone of high earthquake incidence is the *Trans-Eurasian belt,* which extends generally eastward from the Mediterranean Sea through Southwest Asia and the Himalayas into Southeast Asia, where it meets the Circum-Pacific belt. The incidence of major earthquakes in this corridor is not as high as it is in parts of the Circum-Pacific belt, but some important population centres are at risk. These include the countries of former Yugoslavia, Greece, Turkey, Iraq, Iran, and the highlands of Afghanistan, northern Pakistan, northernmost India, and Nepal.

A third zone of earthquakes is associated with the global system of *midoceanic ridges* (compare Figs. 35.6

and 32.2). The earthquakes there are generally less frequent and less severe than in the Circum-Pacific belt, and except for population clusters on islands formed by these ridges, this earthquake zone does not endanger large numbers of people.

From Fig. 32.3 it is evident that known contact zones between tectonic plates form the Earth's most active earthquake belts. But earthquakes, some of them severe, can and do occur in other areas of the world. Note (in Fig. 35.6) the scattered pattern of epicentres in interior Asia, in eastern Africa from Ethiopia to South Africa, and in North America east of the west coast transform/subduction zone. The causes of these **intraplate earthquakes** are still not well understood, but they can produce severe damage because people in the affected areas are less well prepared for earthquakes (India's Bhuj earthquake of 2001 is a classic example). For instance, municipal ordinances governing high-rise construction in the cities of British Columbia, Washington, Oregon, and California take seismic hazards into consideration; in eastern North America, local building codes do not. Yet the most severe earthquake ever experienced in the conterminous United States did not occur in California but in the central Mississippi Valley.

In 1811 and 1812 three great earthquakes, all with epicentres near New Madrid (pronounced "Mad-Rid") in the "boot heel" of extreme southeastern Missouri, changed the course of the Mississippi River and created a 7300-hectare lake in the valley. The severity of these quakes has been estimated to have been as high as magnitude 8.5. Had nearby St. Louis and Memphis been major cities at that time, the death toll would have been enormous. In 1886 an earthquake of magnitude 7.0 devastated Charleston, South Carolina, and the ground shook as far away as New York City and Chicago. Thus eastern North America, too, must be considered a potentially hazardous seismic zone (see Perspective: Earthquake Risk in North America). Shocks are felt over larger areas of eastern North America because the rock beds are not "cut up" by many large faults.

In East Asia the earthquake that cost the largest number of lives in the past century did not originate in the offshore subduction zone but in eastern China. In 1976 the city of Tangshan was destroyed by an earthquake of magnitude 7.6 whose focus lay directly beneath the urban area. The exact loss of life will never be known, but estimates persistently range as high as 750,000 (the Chinese government insists the toll was 242,000). Damage occurred over more than an 80-km-long corridor that reached as far as the major port city of Tianjin and the capital, Beijing.

The global map of earthquake distribution should not lead us to the conclusion that areas outside the plate-contact zones are free from seismic hazard. Even apparently stable shields, such as Australia's and Africa's, can be shaken by significant earthquakes. Beyond the subduction zones, other areas of plate contact, and midoceanic ridges, the understanding of the pattern of epicentres is far from complete.

Earthquakes and Landscapes

Earthquakes, as noted earlier, are not comparable to volcanic action as builders of a distinct landscape. But earthquakes do *modify* physical and cultural landscapes, and some landforms actually are created by earthquake movements. When movement along a fault generates an earthquake, or when a fault is newly created following the long-term deformation of rock strata, the result may be visible at the surface in the form of a **fault scarp**. As Fig. 35.7 shows, a fault scarp is the exposed clifflike face of the **fault plane**, the surface of contact along which blocks on either side of a fault move.

Not every earthquake produces a scarp, and in some cases the movement is lateral (sideways) rather than vertical. But if one block is raised with respect to another, a fault scarp is produced. Such a scarp may have a vertical

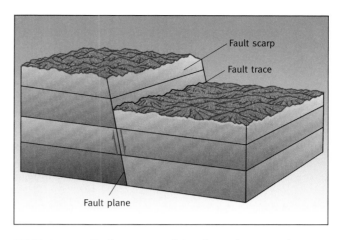

FIGURE 35.7 Fault scarp resulting from the vertical movement of one block with respect to another. The blocks are in contact along the fault plane, whose exposed face is the fault scarp. If the upper block were eroded down to the level of the lower block, the only surface evidence of the fault plane would be the fault trace.

extent (or *face*) of less than 1 m; others may exceed 100 m. Repeated vertical movement along the fault scarp can raise the height of the exposed face in stages. As Fig. 35.7 shows, the lower edge of the fault scarp is called the **fault trace**. Imagine that erosion wears down the raised block to the left so that the scarp is no longer visible. The existence of the fault is then only revealed at the surface by the trace. Along the trace may lie a band of crushed, jagged rock fragments called *fault breccia,* evidence of the powerful forces that created the fault.

Earthquakes affect different types of rocks in different ways. When a major earthquake struck Mexico City in 1985, parts of the city were devastated while other areas of it showed little damage. The reason lay in the underlying geology: where the rocks were solid, there was little impact. But where the buildings stood on the "soft" ground of an old lake bed on which part of Mexico City is built, the damage was great because the earthquake waves were significantly amplified. Many high-rise structures collapsed or simply fell over as the ground liquified and wobbled like a bowl of gelatin. In Anchorage the 1964 earthquake had a similar effect: houses and other buildings that stood on solid rock sustained minor damage, but areas of the city that were underlain by clays or soft and uncemented sedimentary strata sank into liquified areas or slid downslope. Hundreds of houses were carried away and destroyed, and in places the whole topography of Alaska's leading urban area was changed (Fig. 35.9).

The effect of a major earthquake, therefore, is to produce movements of different kinds. In the same affected

PERSPECTIVES ON THE HUMAN ENVIRONMENT

Earthquake Risk in North America

A map of earthquake risk in North America suggests that the West is not the only portion of the continent to face this hazard. Major risk exists in four areas of the East: the middle Mississippi Valley, the coastal Southeast, the St. Lawrence Valley and Lake Ontario area, and the Atlantic provinces and northern New England (Fig. 35.8). There is also a major high-risk area stretching north from northern Quebec (Nunavik) into the very north of the Arctic Archipelago of Canada. Moderate risk exists not only in the surroundings of these areas, but also in a zone extending from eastern Nebraska south to Oklahoma. Only, the Prairie provinces and the Canadian Shield, southern Texas as well as southern and northwestern Florida are believed to be free of earthquake hazard.

This assessment (and the accompanying map) is based on more than 300 years of records of earthquakes. In the East a great many significant earthquakes have been recorded since 1663, all with an estimated magnitude of 5.0 or more. A many tens have taken place since 1925. Geologists report that an eastern earthquake could devastate an area 100 times as large as would be affected by an equivalent quake in the West because the shock waves are cushioned much more in the fault-infested crust of the West.

But the map is based on a past that gives little clue to the future. There was no evidence of major earthquake activity in the middle Mississippi Valley or in coastal South Carolina before great earthquakes struck there in 1811–1812 and 1886, respectively. Recently it has been suggested that major faults underlie Lake Ontario and may even go close to nuclear power stations. This evidence suggests that inclusion of provisions for seismic hazards in Ontario building codes should be done immediately. The next large quake could strike an area deemed to have only moderate or minor earthquake risk. The science of earthquake prediction is still in its infancy; the available record is short-term and unreliable. In facing earthquake threats, however, western North America is not alone.

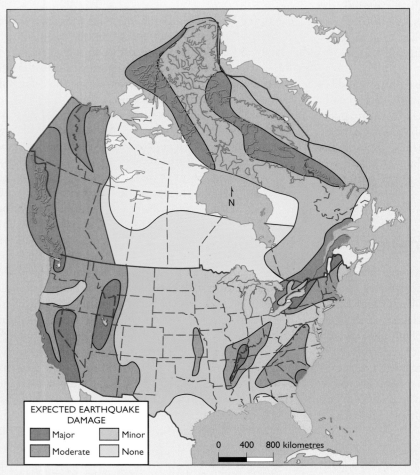

EXPECTED EARTHQUAKE DAMAGE

Major Minor
Moderate None

0   400   800 kilometres

FIGURE 35.8   Earthquake risk in North America.

FIGURE 35.9 A ferocious earthquake (magnitude 8.6) devastated parts of Anchorage, Alaska, on March 27, 1964. This is Fourth Avenue the day after—only part of the destruction that extended from the harbour to the interior.

area, blocks of solid rock will shake but remain stable; loosely compacted sediments, especially on slopes, will slide downhill. When there has been prolonged rain in an area of thick clay, the saturated clay may stay in place—until an earthquake or even a tremor provides the impetus to dislodge or liquefy it (Fig. 35.11). In snowy mountain terrain, an avalanche may be started by a slight Earth tremor when otherwise the snowpack would have stayed in place. Avalanches, flows, and other forms of slope movement (discussed in Unit 39) often result from a combination of circumstances among which a quake can be crucial.

Undoubtedly, as the photos in this unit demonstrate, the impact of a major earthquake on the cultural landscape is its most dramatic manifestation (Figure 35.12). Such effects range from the offsetting of linear features such as fences and hedges, roads and pipelines, to the devastation of major structures such as skyscrapers, highways, and bridges. An earthquake's capacity to reduce to rubble a structure built of steel and concrete inspires awe and terror. And the risks involved are not confined to known earthquake zones. A nuclear power plant

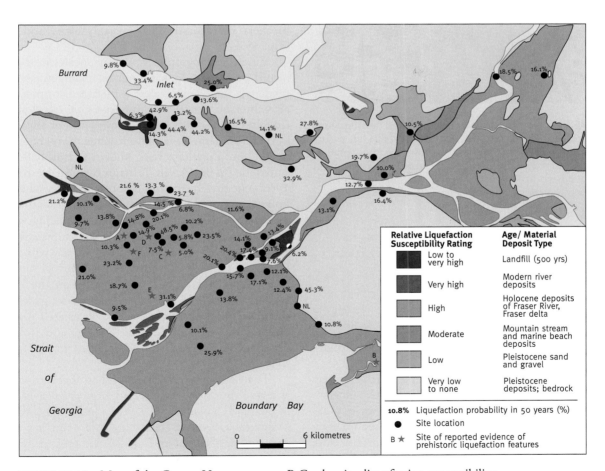

FIGURE 35.10 Map of the Greater Vancouver area, B.C., showing liquefaction susceptibility.

FIGURE 35.11 Landslides are a major hazard arising from earthquakes in high-relief areas. In January 2001 an earthquake (magnitude 7.6) struck near San Salvador, the capital of El Salvador in Central America. The town of Santa Tecla would have been little affected except for this massive landslide, which brought death and destruction.

could be demolished by a quake, resulting in a release of lethal radiation over a wide area.

Tsunamis

The Japanese word for a great sea wave, **tsunami** (harbour wave), has come into general use to identify a seismic sea wave. When an earthquake's epicentre is located on the ocean floor or near a coastline, its shock will generate one or more waves on the water. These waves radiate outward from the point of origin. In the open ocean, they look like broad swells on the water surface, and ships and boats can ride them out quite easily. But a tsunami's vertical magnitude, when it reaches the water

FIGURE 35.12 One of the most catastrophic tsunamis of the twentieth century had its origin in an earthquake in Alaska in 1946, when a wall of water struck the town of Hilo on the island of Hawaii, killing 156 people and devastating the waterfront. Unlike hurricanes, tsunamis strike without warning, although monitoring systems today reduce the risk to coastal dwellers.

near shore, may be many times that of an ordinary wind-caused swell. Near the shore it can create huge breakers that smash into coastal towns and villages (Fig. 35.12).

When seismographs in various locales in the Pacific record a severe underwater quake, a tsunami alert is immediately issued. This alert is intended for places along all vulnerable coastlines. But tsunamis travel very fast, reaching 1000 km/h, and warnings do not always arrive in time. Tsunami waves have reached more than 65 m in height, and they have been known to travel all the way across the Pacific Ocean. A major earthquake in Chile in 1960 generated a tsunami that reached Hawaii about 15 hours later, smashing into coastal lowlands with breakers 7 m high. Ten hours later, the still-advancing wave was strong enough to cause damage in Japan. Situated in the Pacific, the Hawaiian Islands are especially vulnerable to tsunamis. In 1946 a tsunami caused by an earthquake near Alaska struck the town of Hilo on the island of Hawaii, killing 156 persons. The tsunami generated by the 1964 Alaska earthquake that devastated Anchorage flooded the port of Kodiak, Alaska, and drowned a dozen people in a California coastal town far to the south.

The December 26, 2004 Indian Ocean earthquake and resulting tsunamis ravaged large areas of Indonesia, Malaysia, Thailand, Sri Lanka, India, Myanmar, the Maldives, and other coastal areas of countries in south Asia and east Africa and caused the greatest impact of any tsunami in the last millennium. The earthquake occurred at 6:58 a.m. local time and had a Moment magnitude of 9 (the quake was felt as far away as Somalia). It was caused by subductive movement along a 1200–1300 km long, 100 km-wide section of the seafloor at the margin of the Indian and Burma plates (Sumatera was moved about 30 metres southwest of its former position by the plate activity. The focus of the quake was 10 km below the seafloor, and the fault moved vertically. A massive column of water over the area became unstable (billions of tonnes of water) and led to the tsunamis that devastated large coastal areas around the Indian Ocean (Fig. 35.13). There were many aftershocks of magnitude 6 and above (the largest was 7.1). The resulting tsunamis killed well over 200,000 people and injured over 500,000 people in the six nations most badly affected. The Sumateran province of Aceh and its capital Banda Aceh were the worst-hit areas, with 66 percent of all the fatalities and over 400,000 homeless. In Sri Lanka 10,000 people were killed and 150,000 left homeless and in need of food, clothing, and other aid. The tsunamis left over 1 million homeless in the entire affected area and 5 million needing some form of aid. The search for survivors and the clean-up of vast areas were made difficult by monsoon rains. Aid was rushed in from all over the world to help the survivors.

Kofi Annan, the Secretary-General of the United Nations, called the effects of the earthquake and tsunamis "an unprecedented global tragedy." A one-day crisis meeting of world leaders took place in Djakarta on January 6, 2005 to discuss the need for aid and determine what kinds of help would be needed to aid survivors, deal with the dead and injured, and rebuild the communities and economies of the devastated regions. On the same day, the World Health Organization stated that the death-toll from the tsunamis could reach 300,000 from disease and infection. The impact of these devastating tsunamis was truly global and will dominate peoples' thoughts for an extremely long time.

FIGURE 35.13 A devastated village near the coast of Sumatera after the December 26, 2004 Indian Ocean earthquake and resulting tsunamis. These were the most catastrophic tsunamis of the past millenium.

Seismic waves are not tidal waves, as they are sometimes misnamed. Waves with tsunami-like properties are sometimes created by explosive volcanic eruptions, such as that of Santorini and Krakatau (see pp. 450–452). When these giant waves break onto an exposed shore, they can modify the coastal landscape significantly. Occasionally they can do more to change a coastline in a few moments than normal processes do in centuries of erosion and deposition.

This unit has focused on the sudden, dramatic movements of rocks that produce earthquakes and the accompanying impacts on overlying landscapes. But the surfaces of the Earth's landmasses are also affected by the consequences of less spectacular stresses on their underlying rocks. Unit 36 examines those types of stresses and the rock structures they shape.

KEY TERMS

earthquake *page 456*
epicentre *page 456*
fault *page 456*
fault plane *page 461*

REVIEW QUESTIONS

1. Compare the Richter and Mercalli scales for measuring earthquakes.
2. Where on the Earth are earthquakes most frequent? Why?
3. How are fault scarps produced?
4. What is the Circum-Pacific belt of seismic activity?
5. Why are parts of eastern North America considered to constitute a hazardous earthquake region?

REFERENCES AND FURTHER READINGS

ADAMS, J. J., et al. "Seismicity and Seismic Hazards in Canada," in Brooks, G.R., et al., *A Synthesis of Geological Hazards in Canada* (Ottawa: Geological Survey of Canada Bulletin 548, 2001), 7–26.

BAGNALL, N. H., and SCHROEDER, R. B., Eds. *On Shaky Ground: The New Madrid Earthquakes of 1811–1812* (Columbia, Mo.: Univ. of Missouri Press, 1996).

BOAZ, N. T. *The Earth in Turmoil: Earthquakes, Volcanoes, and Their Impact on Humankind* (New York: Freeman, 1998).

BOLT, B. A. *Earthquakes* (New York: Freeman, 4th ed., 1999).

BRUMBAUGH, D. S. *Earthquakes: Science and Society* (Upper Saddle River, N.J.: Prentice-Hall, 1998).

CLAGUE, J. J. "Tsunamis," in Brooks, G.R., et al., *A Synthesis of Geological Hazards in Canada* (Ottawa: Geological Survey of Canada Bulletin 548, 2001), 27–42.

COLLIER, M. *A Land in Motion: California's San Andreas Fault* (Berkeley, Calif.: Univ. of California Press, 1999).

DE BLIJ, H. J., Ed. *Nature on the Rampage* (Washington, D.C.: Smithsonian Institution Press, 1994).

DOYLE, H. A. *Seismology* (New York: Wiley, 1996).

DUDLEY, W. C., and LEE, M. *Tsunami!* (Honolulu: Univ. of Hawai'i Press, 2nd ed., 1998).

FRADKIN, P. L. *Magnitude 8: Earthquakes and Life along the San Andreas Fault* (Berkeley, Calif.: Univ. of California Press, 1999).

GERE, J. M., and SHAH, H. C. *Terra Non Firma: Understanding and Preparing for Earthquakes* (New York: Freeman, 1984).

GONZALEZ, F. I. "Tsunami!," *Scientific American* (May 1999), 56–65.

HOUGH, S. E. *Earthshaking Science: What We Know (and Don't Know) about Earthquakes* (Princeton, N.J.: Princeton Univ. Press, 2002).

LEVY, M., and SALVADORI, M. *Why the Earth Quakes: The Story of Earthquakes and Volcanoes* (New York: Norton, 1995).

LOMNITZ, C. *Fundamentals of Earthquake Prediction* (New York: Wiley, 1994).

MUSTARD, P. S., et al. "Geology and Geological Hazards of the Greater Vancouver Area," in Karrow, P. F., and White, O. L., *Urban Geology of Canadian Cities* (Geological Association of Canada Special Paper 42, 1998), 39–70.

RICHTER, C. F. *Elementary Seismology* (New York: Freeman, 1958).

RITCHIE, D., and GATES, A. E. *The Encyclopedia of Earthquakes and Volcanoes* (New York: Facts on File, 2nd ed., 2001).

SCHENK, V., Ed. *Earthquake Hazard and Risk* (Amsterdam: Kluwer, 1996).

WYLLIE, P. J. *The Way the Earth Works* (New York: Wiley, 1976).

YEATS, R. S., SIEH, K. E., and ALLEN, C. R. *Geology of Earthquakes* (New York: Oxford Univ. Press, 1997).

WEB RESOURCES

http://gsc.nrcan.gc.ca/index.html This Geological Survey of Canada site has a wide range of geological information of all types.

http://quake.wr.usgs.gov The USGS earthquake hazards page contains general information and links to research material. A real-time earthquake map is available, as well as strike probability data. Earthquake preparedness information is included and links to an "ask a geologist" question-and-answer site.

http://seismo.nrcan.gc.ca/hazards/of4459/index-e.php This Geological Survey of Canada site has information on earthquake risk in Canada.

http://www.pgc.nrcan.gc.ca/sidney.index_e.html The homepage of the GSC's Pacific Geosciences Centre has information about the geology of British Columbia, earthquakes, volcanoes, and many other topics.

http://www.pmel.noaa.gov/tsunami NOAA presents data from its Tsunami Research Program on this website. Information includes tsunami-event data, real-time tsunami information, tsunami modelling graphics, and hazard mitigation program information.

http://www.seismo.nrcan.gc.ca/cqinfo.cameomap-e.php Maps of earthquakes in Canada

http://www.seismo.nrcan.gc.ca/historic Maps of earthquake zones in western and southeast Canada.

http://www.seismo.nrcan.gc.ca/index_e.php Homepage of Earthquakes Canada. This website includes information about earthquakes, earthquake research, and historical earthquakes. It also has maps and links.

Surface Expressions of Subsurface Structures

Agents of erosion have exposed a volcanic plug (Black Tusk) in the Garibaldi Provincial Park, Southwestern British Columbia.

OBJECTIVES

- To introduce basic terminology used in describing rock structure

- To distinguish between types of fault movements and the landforms they produce

- To discuss the folding of rocks and relate it to the landforms produced

T he physical landscapes of the continental landmasses are sculpted from rocks with diverse properties. Some of these properties are discussed in other units: the hard, resistant, crystalline batholiths formed deep in the crust and exposed by erosion (Unit 30); the flows of lava (Units 30 and 34); the foliated schists (Unit 31); and the layers of sedimentary strata (Unit 31). Rocks may also be changed after their formation, metamorphosed from one state to another (Unit 31). The geological structure of the rocks reveals the nature of the stress that changed them and reflects the way the rocks reacted to this stress. Brittle rocks fracture under pressure. Rocks exhibiting plastic behaviour can bend or even fold, and when the stress is removed, these structures remain permanent.

Stresses of many kinds are imposed on rocks. In plate collision margins, rock strata are crushed into tight folds. In continental shield areas and at midoceanic ridges, spreading movement driven by processes in the mantle below can pull segments of rock apart, creating parallel faults. Where sediments accumulate, their growing weight pushes the underlying rocks downward. Where erosion removes rock, the crust has a tendency to "rebound." Rocks are deformed in so many ways that the resulting forms seem endlessly complicated. But, in fact, certain geological structures occur many times over and can be recognized even on topographic maps that do not contain any stratigraphic information. Our understanding of the surface must begin with what lies below, and in this unit we study the relationships between geological structure and visible landscape.

Terminology of Structure

If we are to describe the nature and orientation of structures below the surface accurately, we must use consistent terminology. Imagine a ridge of quartzite rising above the surface and extending from northeast to southwest (Fig. 36.1). This is the **strike** of that ridge—the compass direction of the line of intersection between a rock layer and a horizontal plane. Thus the strike of the ridge is recorded in fieldnotes as N45°E. The strike of any linear feature is always recorded to range from 0° to 90°E or W.

The ridge of quartzite may consist of a layer of this metamorphic rock that angles downward between less resistant strata (Fig. 36.1). This is referred to as the **dip** of that layer, which is the angle at which it tilts from the horizontal. If the quartzite layer tilts 30° from the hori-

zontal, its dip is recorded as 30°. In addition, the direction of the dip must be established. If the quartzite layer tilts downward toward the southeast, its dip is recorded as 30°SE. As the diagram indicates, the direction of dip is always at a right angle to the strike.

A prominent feature such as the quartzite ridge is called an *outcrop,* a locality where exposed rock occurs. Here the hardness of the rock and its resistance to erosion have combined to create a prominent topographic feature whose length and straightness indicate tilting, but little or no other deformation. Where rock strata are bent or folded, the determination of strike and dip can become difficult, and the field map may have to record many variations in strike and dip along segments of the outcrop.

Fault Structures

The rocks of the Earth's crust are honeycombed by fractures. Some areas, such as the zones near the subductive margins of tectonic plates, are more strongly affected by faulting than other locales. But detailed geological maps of even the "stable" shields of the continental cores reveal numerous fractures, legacies of earlier periods of stress. There are several types of faults related to collision and spreading that are expressed at the surface of the crust in the landscape.

A **fault** is a fracture in crustal rock involving the displacement of rock on one side of the fracture with respect to the rock on the other side. A fracture without displacement is called a *joint,* so slippage along the fault plane is key evidence for faulting. Faulting results when brittle rocks come under stress, cannot bend or fold, and therefore break. But even rocks that exhibit plastic behaviour can be subjected to such severe stress that they, too, can fracture (see Fig. 35.1).

As explained in Unit 35, sudden slippage along a fault plane generates an earthquake or a tremor, depending on the amount of energy released. Slippage may involve a few millimetres or 100 m or more. At the surface a fault may be barely visible—or it may be marked by a tall scarp. Sometimes, when a sequence of sedimentary layers is faulted, it is possible to locate the same bed on opposite sides of the fault plane, and the amount of vertical displacement (the *throw*) can be determined. But if the blocks on either side of the fault consist of the same rock (say, a mass of granite), it may not be possible to measure displacement.

Our increased understanding of plate tectonics has contributed to better comprehension of faulting, its causes, and its effects. Where plates converge and collide, *compressional* stresses are strong and rocks are crushed tightly together. The lithosphere is forced to

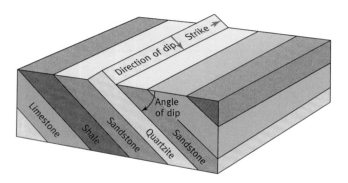

FIGURE 36.1   Strike, direction of dip, and angle of dip.

occupy less horizontal space, and rocks respond by breaking, bending, folding, sliding, and squeezing upward and downward. Where plates diverge, and where the crust is subjected to spreading processes elsewhere, the stress is *tensional* and rocks are being pulled apart. Some plastic rocks respond by thinning, but others break and faults result. Where a series of parallel faults develop, blocks of crust between the faults may actually sink down, having been left with less support from below than existed previously. And where plates slide past each other, or where forces below the crust are lateral, the stress is *transverse*. Rock masses that slide past each other also are subject to faulting and associated earthquakes.

Compressional Faults

Where crustal rock is compressed into a smaller horizontal space, shortening of the crust is achieved by one block riding over the other along a steep fault plane between them (Fig. 36.2). Such a structure is called a **reverse fault**. When vertical movement occurs during faulting, blocks that move upward (with respect to adjacent blocks) are referred to as *upthrown*, whereas blocks

that move downward are termed *downthrown*. In the case of reverse faults, note that the upthrown block creates an initial scarp that overhangs the downthrown block (Fig. 36.2A). Such an overhanging scarp soon collapses under the effects of weathering, erosion, and gravity. Rock avalanches and other slope processes (see Unit 39) are associated with such scarps, and these processes soon produce a slope at an angle to the original fault plane (Fig. 36.2B). Therefore when we see a fault scarp in the field, we cannot conclude without further investigation that it represents the dip of the fault plane from which it has resulted.

Compressional forces sometimes produce series of nearly parallel (or *en echelon*) faults. A strip of crustal rock positioned between reverse faults may assume the dimensions of a blocklike plateau (Fig. 36.3). When the angle of a fault plane in a compressional fault is very low, the structure is referred to as a **thrust fault** (sometimes *overthrust fault*) (Fig. 36.4). Note that the overriding block slides almost horizontally over the downthrown block, covering much more of it than is the case in a reverse fault. Following erosion, the resulting scarp would be lower and less prominent.

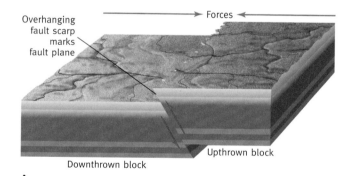

A

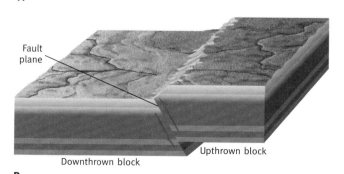

B

FIGURE 36.2 In a reverse fault, the overhanging scarp of the upthrown block (A) soon collapses, and a new slope, which lies at an angle to the original, is produced by erosional forces (B).

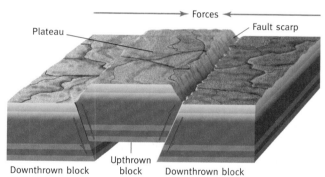

FIGURE 36.3 Plateau formed by an upthrown block that lies between two reverse faults that run parallel to each other where they intersect the surface.

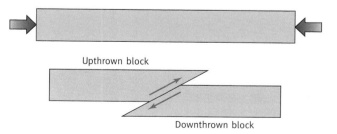

FIGURE 36.4 Side view of a thrust fault resulting from compression. The low angle of the fault plane produces substantial overriding by the upthrown block.

Tensional Faults

Tensional stresses pull crustal rock apart, so that now the situation is the opposite—there is more horizontal space for crustal material, not less as in compressional faults. The result is one or more **normal faults** (Fig. 36.5). The typical normal fault has a moderately inclined fault plane separating a block that has remained stationary, or nearly so, from one that has been significantly downthrown. As Fig. 36.5 shows, the resulting fault scarp initially reflects the dip angle of the fault plane, although erosion may modify it over time. Sometimes the fault scarp has been eroded for so long that it has retreated from its original position. In such instances, the fault trace (see Fig. 35.7) reveals the original location of the scarp. The eastern and western sides of the Rocky Mountain Trench in British Columbia, are excellent examples of large fault blocks produced by tensional stresses on the crust.

As tensional forces continue to stress the affected area, slippage may continue along a major normal fault. The lower (downthrown) block will continue to sink, and the upper (upthrown) block may rise. But the tensional forces are likely to generate additional normal faults, generally parallel to the original one. This creates conditions favourable to the development of rift-valley topography (Fig. 36.6). The midoceanic ridge system, as noted elsewhere, is essentially a vast rift system, where tensional forces are pulling the crust apart.

On the continental landmasses, the best example of rift-valley topography lies in eastern Africa (Fig. 36.7). You do not need a geological map to see this magnificent example of crustal rifting, because East Africa's Great Lakes fill the rift valley over much of its length. The system actually extends northward, through the Red Sea, into the Gulf of Aqaba and the Jordan River Valley beyond. In eastern Africa it crosses Ethiopia and reaches Lake Turkana, the northernmost large lake in the rifts. South of the latitude of Lake Turkana the system splits

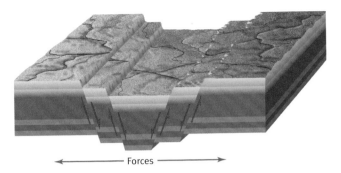

FIGURE 36.6 Formation of a rift valley as tensional forces generate parallel normal faults between which crustal blocks slide downward.

into two gigantic arcs, one lying to the east of Lake Victoria and the other to the west. These arcs come together just to the north of Lake Malawi. The system then continues southward through the valley in which that lake lies, and it does not end until it has crossed Swaziland.

As long ago as 1921, the British geomorphologist J. W. Gregory offered an interpretation of the rift valleys of East Africa. He concluded that the floors of the valleys, in places thousands of metres below the adjacent uplands, were **grabens** (sunken blocks) between usually parallel normal faults (Fig. 36.8). This theory of a tensional origin of East Africa's rift valleys was later upheld for the arc that lies east of Lake Victoria. But the western arc, in which Lake Tanganyika lies, proved to have compressional origins. The fault scarps looked similar to those of the eastern arc, but they had begun as overhanging scarps (Fig. 36.2A). One of Africa's greatest mountain massifs, Ruwenzori, proved to be a **horst**, a block raised between reverse faults (see Fig. 36.3).

If the East African rift valleys originated, at least in part, from tensional forces, we should expect volcanism to be associated with them, just as volcanism affects the spreading midoceanic ridges. These expectations are confirmed in that composite cones, lava domes, cinder cones, and fissure eruptions all mark the region. Volcanic activity still continues along segments of the East African rifts: as recently as January 2002, a major eruption of Mount Nyiragongo sent lava flows travelling at 65 km/hr into the heart of the Congolese city of Goma—north of Lake Tanganyika and 50 km south of the volcano—destroying half of the abandoned city and killing at least 45 people. Seismic activity, too, is stronger there than in other areas of the great African shield (Fig. 35.5). Some geologists now believe that the African Plate may not be a single tectonic unit, and that an East African Plate (or Somali Plate, as it is also

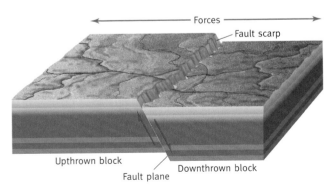

FIGURE 36.5 Unlike compressional stresses, tensional stresses pull the crust apart. Normal faults result, and the fault scarp often reflects the dip angle of the fault plane.

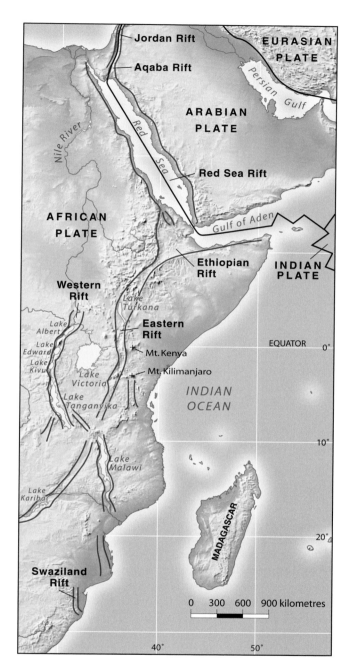

FIGURE 36.7 African rift-valley system, which extends from beyond Africa in the north (the Jordan–Aqaba segment) to Swaziland in the south.

FIGURE 36.8 Aerial view of the East African rift valley in southern Ethiopia. The tensional stresses pulling the crust apart here are evident in the fault scarps and the downthrown crustal strips at their base. This scene provides a striking example of the landscape illustrated in Fig. 36.6.

Transverse Faults

Where blocks of crustal rock move laterally, motion along the fault plane is horizontal, not vertical. Thus there are no upthrown or downthrown blocks. The fault is **transcurrent**, that is, movement is in the direction of the fault (Fig. 36.10). Lateral plate contact is exemplified by the San Andreas Fault, the contact plane between the Pacific and North American Plates (see Fig. 32.11). The San Andreas Fault is a special case of transcurrent faulting, being a **transform fault**, which marks the boundary between plates. Because movement at a transcurrent fault takes place along the strike of the fault, transcurrent faults are also known as **strike-slip faults**. To describe the fault completely, we also give the direction of movement. This is determined by looking *across* the fault and stating the direction in which the opposite block is moving. Accordingly, the San Andreas Fault is a right-lateral strike-slip fault. A similar fault is the Queen Charlotte–Denali transform fault off British Columbia and in Yukon and Alaska.

Field Evidence of Faulting

These three types of faults—reverse, normal, and transcurrent—exhibit many variations, and regional fault patterns and structures can become very complicated. Even in the field it is not always easy to distinguish a scarp formed by a fault from one formed by erosion. If the upthrown block contains water-bearing rock, water may pour from the scarp face in springs, probable evidence of faulting. The movement of the rocks along the fault plane may also produce smooth, mirrorlike surfaces on

known) is separating from Africa just as the Arabian Plate did earlier. In that case, millions of years from now a Red Sea-like body of water may invade Africa from near the mouth of the Zambezi River and penetrate northward into Lake Malawi, and a Madagascar-like chunk of the continent will move off the new East African coastline (Fig. 36.9).

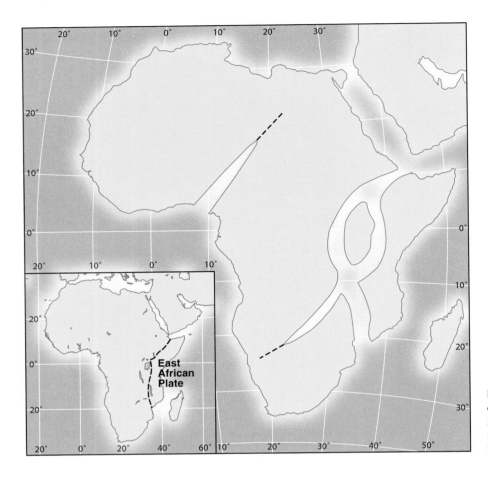

FIGURE 36.9 Possible configuration of Africa, about 10 million years from now, if the East African Plate (inset map) completes its separation from the rest of the continent.

the scarp face, and these *slickensides* are further evidence that faulting created the scarp. If the fault trace is marked by a breccia (a shattered rock layer), faulting is indicated as well. Most often a combination of evidence provides the surest basis for interpretation.

FIGURE 36.10 Horizontal or transcurrent fault, also known as a strike-slip fault.

Fold Structures

When rocks are compressed, they respond to the stress by **folding** as well as by faulting. All rocks—even a sill of granite—have some capacity to bend before fracturing. But the fold structures discussed here are most characteristic of layered sedimentary rocks. Folds, again like faults, come in all dimensions. Some are too small to see; others are road-cut size; still others are the size of entire mountain ridges (Fig. 36.11).

Unlike faults, however, folds are primarily compressional features. In areas where crustal rocks are under stress, the crust may bend into basins hundreds of kilometres across in association with normal faulting. But the accordion-like folds in western North America's Rocky Mountains and coastal mountains, the Andes, the Appalachians, and parts of Eurasia's Alpine Mountain system (such as the Zagros Mountains of Iran) are the result of intense compression. Not surprisingly, folding and faulting generally occur together: just as even brittle rocks can bend slightly, so the most plastic rocks have a limited capacity to fold.

FROM THE FIELDNOTES

FIGURE 36.11 "The Mescal Mountains in south-central Arizona display some complex structures. The sedimentary strata shown here were laid down horizontally, but were later folded into the anticline of which both limbs are visible in the lower half of the photo and one in the upper part."

Anticlines and Synclines

Folds are rarely simple, symmetrical structures. Often they form a jumble of upfolds and downfolds that make it difficult to discern even a general design in the field. But when we map the distribution of the rock layers and analyze the topography, we discover that recognizable and recurrent structures do exist. The most obvious of these are upfolds, or **anticlines**, and downfolds, or **synclines**. An anticline is an archlike fold, with the limbs dipping away from the axis (Fig. 36.12, left). A syncline, on the other hand, is troughlike, and its limbs dip toward its axial plane (Fig. 36.12, right).

When flat-lying sedimentary strata are folded into anticlines and synclines, the cores of the synclines are

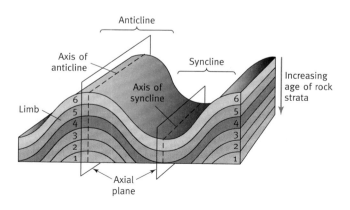

FIGURE 36.12 Anticlines are arching upfolds while synclines are troughlike downfolds. Note the relative age of rock layers within each type of fold.

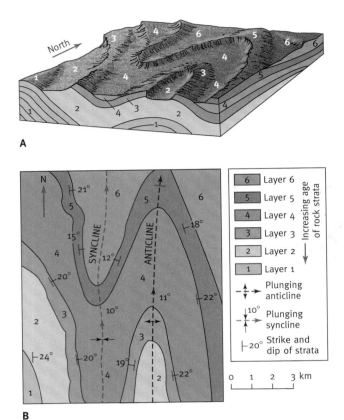

A

B

FIGURE 36.13 Eroded anticline–syncline landscape of surface outcrops with parallel strikes (A). The age sequence of these rock formations can be interpreted by referring to the geological map (B).

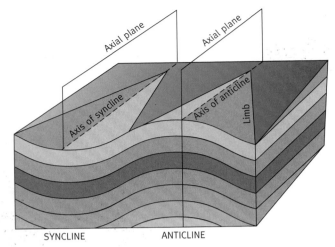

FIGURE 36.14 Anticline–syncline structure plunging in opposite directions.

constituted by younger rocks. Imagine that erosion removes the upper parts of both anticlines and synclines. What is left are a series of surface outcrops with parallel strikes and a sequence of rocks showing a succession of ages. From these data it is possible to interpret the geological structures here—based on our understanding of anticlines and synclines (Fig. 36.13).

Plunging Folds and Associated Landscapes

Folds are rarely as symmetrical as shown in Fig. 36.12, however; nor are their axes usually horizontal. Anticlines and synclines often *plunge,* which means that their axes dip. You can easily demonstrate the effect of this by taking a cardboard tube and cutting it lengthwise. Hold it horizontally and you have a symmetrical anticline (and a syncline, if you place the other half adjacent). Now tilt the tube, say, about 30 degrees from the horizontal, by the edge of a table or other flat surface. Draw the horizontal line, and cut the tube along it. The second cut represents the outcrop of the youngest rocks of

the anticline. Note how they form a "nose" at one end and open progressively toward the other end. In the field, such an outcrop signals an eroded, plunging anticline; the adjacent syncline would plunge in the other direction (Fig. 36.14).

In the intensely folded central Appalachian Mountains, plunging anticlines and synclines adjoin each other in wide belts, eroded into attractive scenery by streams over many millions of years. But as the Appalachians' topography suggests, there is considerable regularity and even symmetry to the pattern (Fig. 36.15). That is not always the case in areas of intense compression and folding. Europe's Alps, for instance, are much more severely distorted. Not only are the folds there anticlinal and synclinal, but many of the anticlines have become **recumbent** and even **overturned** (Fig. 36.16). Add to this the presence of intense faulting and erosion by streams and glaciers, and complex spectacular alpine landscapes are produced.

At this point an important distinction must be made between what some geomorphologists call **primary landforms**, the structures created by tectonic activity, and **secondary landforms**, the products of weathering and erosion. Sometimes geologic and topographic maps reveal amazing contradictions. An anticline of less resistant sedimentary rocks may be eroded into a low valley, whereas a nearby synclinal structure, composed of more resistant rocks, stands out as a ridge or upland. Thus the geologic upfold forms a geographical lowland, and vice versa. The relationship between structure, rock resistance, and erosional processes forms a major theme that runs through many units in Part Five.

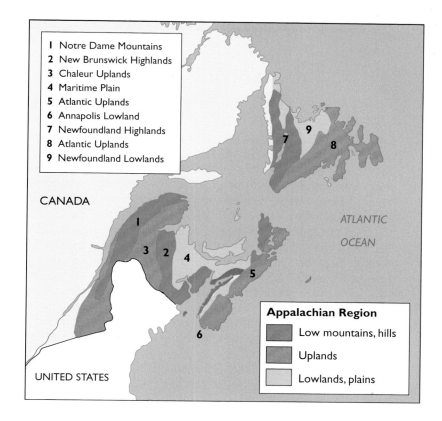

FIGURE 36.15 The Canadian Appalachians.

Map legend:

1 Notre Dame Mountains
2 New Brunswick Highlands
3 Chaleur Uplands
4 Maritime Plain
5 Atlantic Uplands
6 Annapolis Lowland
7 Newfoundland Highlands
8 Atlantic Uplands
9 Newfoundland Lowlands

CANADA

ATLANTIC OCEAN

UNITED STATES

Appalachian Region
Low mountains, hills
Uplands
Lowlands, plains

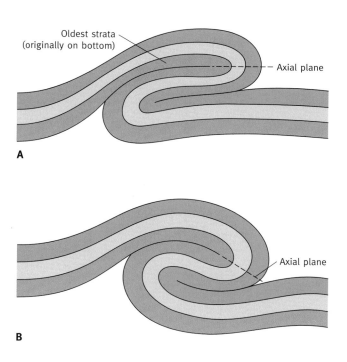

FIGURE 36.16 Extreme compression can produce folds that double back upon themselves with axial planes that approach the horizontal. The anticline in (A) is termed recumbent; the anticline in (B) is classified as overturned.

Regional Deformation

Not all types of crustal deformation are encompassed by the various types of faulting and folding discussed in this unit. Over large areas of stable lithosphere, especially in the major continental shields, the crust undergoes slight deformation *without* being faulted or folded. Geologists in the past gave various terms to these and other crustal movements. *Diastrophism* was one, and *crustal warping* was another. Yet another term, still in occasional use, is *epeirogeny;* it refers to the vertical movement of the crust over very large areas, involving little or no bending or breaking of the rocks.

Such rising or sinking of the upper crust undoubtedly is related to the movement of lithospheric plates over the mantle's convection cells, and in that sense it is subsumed under plate motion. But in physical geography these very slight regional movements are extremely important. Even the slightest change in the slope of a large region can have an enormous impact on an entire drainage basin, rates of erosion and deposition, and other aspects of the regional geomorphology (see Perspective: Subsidence in the Windsor Area of Southern Ontario). It should be remembered, therefore, that while this unit focuses on the tectonically active zones of the world (present and past), more subtle but still highly significant deformation also affects the more stable sectors of the landmasses.

Subsidence in the Windsor Area of Southern Ontario

The Salina Formation (upper Silurian age) includes two or three thick beds of halite or salt (NaCl) in the Windsor–Sarnia area of southern Ontario. These beds taken together are approximately 190 m deep and are worked for table and road salt. The Windsor salt mines are some of the most productive on Earth, and the product is shipped all over the world. The salt layers were formed in a shallow tropical sea that invaded the centre of North America in late Silurian times. In some areas the salt was deposited around coral reefs, indicating a shallow tropical environment. Some salt may also have been deposited in shallow seaside lagoons. It is known that salt deposits form close to sea level.

Today the top of the Salina Formation occurs at a depth of about 490 m below the surface, indicating that subsidence has occurred in what is called the Michigan Basin. The downwarping of the Michigan Basin and upwarping of the Canadian Shield has also meant that Palaeozoic rocks of southern Ontario that were deposited close to the horizontal, now dip slightly toward the Michigan Basin at approximately 3 degrees.

A different form of subsidence has also been caused by salt mining. In 1954 a large crater developed at the site of the Windsor Salt Mine. The subsidence was very rapid. It swallowed a locomotive and a service building. Experts hypothesized that the subsidence had been caused by the undetected dissolution of the salt (solution mining was used in this area) at 430 m below the surface. Some experts suggested that this accidental dissolution was aided by the regional dip toward the middle of the Michigan Basin.

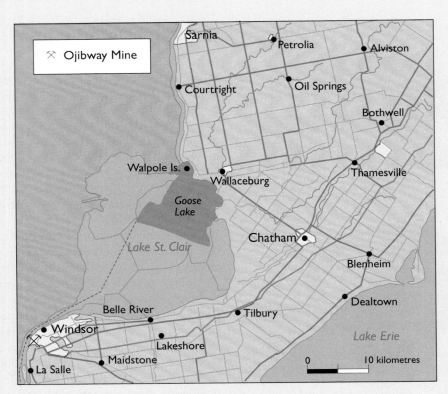

FIGURE 36.17 Location of the Ojibway Mine of the Canadian Salt Company, Windsor, Ontario.

KEY TERMS

anticline *page 473*	normal fault *page 470*	strike *page 468*
dip *page 468*	overturned fold *page 474*	strike-slip fault *page 471*
fault *page 468*	primary landform *page 474*	syncline *page 473*
folding *page 472*	recumbent fold *page 474*	thrust fault *page 469*
graben *page 470*	reverse fault *page 469*	transcurrent fault *page 471*
horst *page 470*	secondary landform *page 474*	transform fault *page 471*

REVIEW QUESTIONS

1. What is the basic difference between normal and reverse faulting?

2. What evidence of faulting might one encounter when looking at an isolated rock outcrop?

3. Differentiate between *anticlines* and *synclines,* and describe how plunging affects their orientation.

4. What is the difference between *primary* and *secondary* landforms?

5. Differentiate between the concepts of strike and dip in describing a ridge on the Earth's surface.

6. What is a rift valley? Why are these formations so widespread in eastern and northeastern Africa?

REFERENCES AND FURTHER READINGS

BENNISON, G. M., and MOSELEY, K. A. *An Introduction to Geological Structures and Maps* (London/New York: Arnold, 6th ed., 1997).

BILLINGS, M. P. *Structural Geology* (Englewood Cliffs, N.J.: Prentice-Hall, 3rd ed., 1972).

BIRD J. B. *The Natural Landscapes of Canada: A Study in Regional Earth Science* (Toronto: Wiley, 2nd ed., 1980).

DAVIS, G. H. *Structural Geology of Rocks and Regions* (New York: Wiley, 1984).

HOBBS, B. E., et al. *An Outline of Structural Geology* (New York: Wiley, 1976).

HILLS, E. S. *Elements of Structural Geology* (New York: Wiley/Longman, 1991).

HUDER, P. P. "Geology and Geotechnical Properties of Glacial Soils in Windsor," in Karrow, P. F., and White, O.L., Eds., *Urban Geology of Canadian Cities* (Geological Association of Canada Special Publication 42, 1998), 225–236.

MIYASHIRO, A., et al. *Orogeny* (New York: Wiley, 1982).

OLLIER, C. D. *Tectonics and Landforms* (London/New York: Longman, 1981).

POWELL, D. *Interpretation of Geological Structure through Maps: An Introductory Practice Manual* (New York: Wiley/Longman, 1992).

RAGAN, D. M. *Structural Geology: An Introduction to Geometrical Techniques* (New York: Wiley, 3rd ed., 1984).

SANFORD, B. V., and BRADY, W. B. *Palaeozoic Geology of the Windsor–Sarnia Area, Ontario* (Ottawa: Department of Mines and Technical Surveys, Geological Survey of Canada Memoir 278, 1955).

TRENHAILE, A. S. *Geomorphology: A Canadian Perspective* (Toronto: Oxford Univ. Press, 1998).

WEYMAN, D. *Tectonic Processes* (Boston: Allen & Unwin, 1981).

WINDLEY, B. *The Evolving Continents* (New York: Wiley, 2nd ed., 1984).

WEB RESOURCE

http://www.platetectonics.com/index.asp This site has information regarding many facets of plate tectonics. Searching the site will reveal articles describing rift valleys, seafloor spreading, and many other subjects. Press releases concerning plate tectonics are also available by hyperlink.

PART FIVE

Sculpting the Surface

Degradational and Aggradational Systems

The natural landscapes we observe and study are the products of a set of seven systems of breakdown (degradation) and accumulation (aggradation), whose combined effect is to create the infinite variety that marks the terrestrial surface of our planet. These are open systems, and while it is possible to identify the dominant system at work in a certain region, it is almost never the sole system functioning there. For example, glacial forces have sculpted the general topography of the European Alps and the Rocky Mountains, but stream gradation under milder conditions has modified the landscapes the glaciers forged. Again, wave action fashions coastlines, but the effect of wave power is enhanced where subduction creates deep water immediately offshore. The systems and processes at work range from weathering (decomposition and disintegration) and mass movement (collapse) to stream gradation (valley formation in the degradational form, delta formation in the aggradational form) and from karst processes (the dissolving of rock by slightly acidic water) to wind action, which can erode as well as deposit. All these systems involved in the sculpting of the surface have "signature" landforms, some of which are shown here. Because they operate over large areas, they tend to produce characteristic landscapes we know by such names as the Rocky Mountains, the Canadian Shield, the Prairies, and the St. Lawrence Lowlands.

Sculpting the Surface

Weathering Processes

Stream Processes

Slope Processes

Glacial Processes

Karst Processes

Coastal Processes

Wind Action

The Formation of Landscapes and Landforms

The Pinnacles, columnar remnants of a limestone formation, on the west coast of Australia. (Authors' photo)

OBJECTIVES

- To introduce three primary degradational processes: weathering, mass movements, and erosion

- To focus attention on the aggradational processes that produce secondary landforms

- To recognize the roles of degradation and aggradation in the formation and evolution of landscapes

The Earth's landscapes are the temporary result of many processes. As the units in Part Four detail, the continents are affected by the horizontal and vertical movements of tectonic plates. These movements result in the folding, faulting, tilting, and warping of the crust, and are often accompanied by earthquakes and volcanic eruptions. These movements and processes create **primary landforms**. A volcano, for example, can be worn down over a long period of time by various agents of erosion, such as water, wind, and even ice in certain places. But the original mountain is a primary landform created by volcanic activity.

When erosion sculpted it into the form seen today, a **secondary landform** was produced. The same is true, over a larger area, in a subduction zone. Crustal plates move several centimetres per year, and the enormous energy involved is expressed in part by the crushed, folded, and faulted rocks that mark the scenery of these subduction zones (see Fig. 29.10). Here it may be more difficult to differentiate between primary and secondary processes because both happen at the same time. Even as the crust buckles and breaks, erosion attacks; in combination, these processes produce characteristic terrain.

All parts of the landmasses, even relatively stable areas unaffected by subduction or other severe deformation, are subject to vertical and horizontal movements that affect the evolution of their landscapes. As the plates carrying the continents move over the mantle, the landmasses are pushed, dragged, pressed, and stretched. Geologists still are not certain about the exact nature of the tectonic activity beneath the landmasses. Hot spots such as those noted for the Pacific Plate (Unit 34) also exist beneath continent-bearing plates; the Anahim Wells Gray area of British Columbia and the Yellowstone National Park region are good examples (see Fig. 40.11).

As noted in Part Four, at least some of the extensive continental plates may, like the oceanic plates, consist of segments. These segments may exhibit convergent, divergent, and lateral contact. The effect of these movements on the landmasses is not yet completely understood. However, there can be no doubt that they continuously deform the continental crust—and thus its surface, the landscape. Part Five concentrates on the secondary processes that mould the scenery of the continents, but we should keep in mind that the processes sculpting the surface that we observe are the result of forces from below as well as from above.

Landscapes and Landforms

As the title of this unit indicates, the concern here is with the surface configuration of the exposed land, not the submerged seafloor. Thus reference is made frequently to particular types of *landscapes* and *landforms*. A **landform** is a single and typical unit that forms part of the general topography of the Earth's surface. A solitary mountain (such as a composite volcano), a hill, a single valley, a dune, and a sinkhole are all landforms. A **landscape** is an aggregation of landforms, often the same types of landforms. A volcanic landscape, for example, may consist of a region of composite cones, lava domes, lava flows, and other features resulting from volcanic activity, all modified, to a greater or lesser extent, by erosion. A dune may be part of a desert landscape or a coastal landscape. So the term *landform* often refers to the discrete product of a set of processes; a *landscape* is the areal (or regional) expression of those processes.

Gradation

When a dirt road is "graded," it is levelled off to a smooth horizontal or sloping surface, usually by a machine designed to perform this task. The forces of erosion, too, work to sculpt the surface of landmasses. Landscapes and landforms represent the progress made by the agents of weathering and erosion as they transform the surface of the landmasses rising above sea level. Landscapes reveal the nature of these erosional agents, the hardness and resistance of the rocks, the geological structures below, and the tectonic activity affecting the crust.

The key force is that of the Earth's *gravity*. When soil and loose rock on a hillside become waterlogged, the force of gravity pulls them downslope where stream water (also responding to gravity) removes them (Fig. 37.1). When a mineral grain on a rock face is loosened, gravity causes it to fall to the ground below and the wind may carry it away. Streams flow and glaciers move down their valleys under the laws of gravity—steeper slopes mean faster movement. Even winds and waves are subject to the Earth's gravitational pull. Rock avalanches, waterfalls—all reveal the ever-present force of gravity in the wearing down of the Earth's landmasses.

The result is a reduction in the relief of the landmasses—a lowering of the mountains, a filling of the valleys, a lowering of the continents down to close to sea level. Millions of tonnes of sediment are annually carried downstream by the great rivers of the world (Fig. 37.2). This material comes from the interior uplands, and it may be deposited in river deltas or on the ocean floor. Some of it is laid down in the valleys of the streams themselves, so that many streams in their lower courses no longer flow in rock-floored channels but over their own sediments.

The wearing down of the landmasses goes on through a combination of processes collectively referred to as **degradation**. This term implies that a landmass is being lowered and reduced. When a stream cuts an ever-deeper channel, or a glacier scours its valley, or waves erode a beach, degradation prevails. But the opposite also occurs: a combination of processes removes material from one area and deposits it elsewhere. When a

FROM THE FIELDNOTES

FIGURE 37.1 "Driving westward from Christchurch, New Zealand, across the Canterbury Plain and into the mountains via Arthur's Pass, you encounter diverse landscapes. On the way up, the evidence of recent glaciation is all around, but now subaerial processes (that is, those proceeding under atmospheric conditions) prevail, and the topography is being modified by weathering, mass movement, and stream erosion. Here, in the Craigeburn area, a talus cone or scree slope has formed from rock originally loosened under glacial conditions, augmented now by mechanical weathering and moved downslope under the force of gravity. The talus has not moved far from its source; stream erosion is not yet playing a major role here."

stream builds a delta at its mouth, or when a valley fills with sediment, or when a glacier melts and deposits the material it is carrying along, **aggradation** takes place. Aggradation also contributes to landscape development by reducing the height differences between the high points and the low places in an area.

Degradational Processes and Landscapes

The processes and agents that work to lower the uplands of the continents range from the quiet disintegration of regolith (loose rock material) to the violent cascade of boulder-filled mountain streams. In Part Five we study the multiple processes that combine to destroy and remove the rocks of the continents and the landscapes they create. Degradational processes can be divided into

FIGURE 37.2 The Yangzi (Chang) River in China originates deep in the Asian interior and flows across the heart of the country to the Pacific Ocean. In the process it sculpts numerous dramatic landforms, but perhaps none as scenic as the famous Three Gorges. Now the Chinese government is building a massive dam and flood-control system that will drown the gorges seen here, forever changing the local (and regional) hydrography and altering human–environment relationships that have prevailed here for millennia.

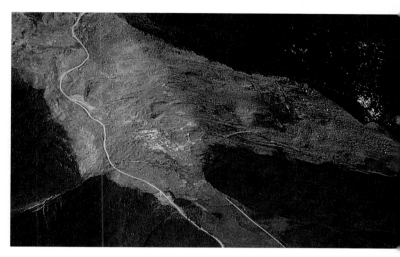

FIGURE 37.3 On January 9, 1965, the southwestern slope of Johnson Peak, 18 km east of Hope, BC, collapsed, spreading rock, mud, and debris 85 km thick and 3 km wide across the Hope–Princeton Highway. The Hope Slide was one of the largest landslides in Canadian history.

two general categories: (1) *weathering,* and (2) *slope processes.* We devote entire units to weathering and slope processes, and several to the agents and processes of erosion.

A good way to understand how these degradational processes differ is to consider the *distances* travelled by loosened rock particles. In weathering a rock disintegrates, but the loose grains do no more than fall to the ground below under the force of gravity (Fig. 37.1). Slope processes (such as rock avalanches) move rock material farther downslope over distances that can reach 20 km or more. Erosional processes can carry material hundreds, even thousands of kilometres.

As the term implies, **weathering** is the breakdown of rocks in situ, that is, their disintegration or decomposition without distant removal of the products. As discussed in Unit 38, rocks can be weakened in many ways: by exposure to temperature extremes, by chemical action, and even by the growing roots of plants. The processes of weathering prepare the rock for later removal by slope processes and other mechanisms.

A **slope process** is the spontaneous downslope movement of Earth materials under the force of gravity. Anyone who has witnessed or seen a picture of a rock avalanche or mudflow knows what such slope failure involves. Houses, roads, even entire hillsides tumble downslope, often after the weathered surface material has become waterlogged (Fig. 37.3). Unit 34 makes note

of the great volcanic mudflow (or *lahar*) that occurred on Colombia's volcano, Nevado del Ruiz, when it erupted in 1985. Saturated by abruptly melted snow from the volcano's peak, this lahar travelled over 50 km down valleys from the base of the mountain and buried at least 20,000 people living in its path (see Fig. 34.5). Thus slope processes (treated in Unit 39) can involve large volumes of material, sometimes with disastrous consequences. But other forms of slope processes are slow and almost imperceptible.

Most of our attention, however, is devoted to the fascinating processes of **erosion**. Here the particles resulting from weathering and mass movement are carried away over long distances. During this process of transportation, additional breakdown occurs, both of the transported particles *and* of the rocks of the valleys through which they travel. For example, a boulder first loosened in a mass movement is removed by a stream and bounces along the stream channel as the water transports it. It breaks into smaller pieces, which become rounded into pebbles, and the parts that are broken off during this process form smaller particles. As these and other boulders, pebbles, gravel, and sand move along, they can erode pieces of material off the channel bed and banks. In this way, stream erosion involves both transportation and breakdown.

Running Water Running water is by far the most effective and significant agent of erosion, as noted in Units 40 to 43. Streams are complex gradational systems whose effectiveness relates to many factors, including the gradient (slope) of the valley, the volume of water, and

FIGURE 37.4 Stream system in its drainage basin. The trunk stream is built up by the smaller tributary streams that empty into it.

the form of the valley. Few places on Earth are unaffected by the erosional power of water. Even in deserts, water plays a major role in shaping the landscape. Many stream systems consist of a major artery, the *trunk stream,* that is joined by *tributaries,* smaller streams that feed into the main stream (Fig. 37.4). The spatial pattern of these systems can reveal much about the rock structures below. Certain patterns are associated with particular structures and landscapes. Often the configuration of a regional stream system can yield insights about the underlying geology and geomorphological history of an area, as explained in Unit 42.

Glaciers   Streams are not the only agents of erosion; ice, in the form of glaciers, is also an important agent of degradation. During the Late Cenozoic Ice Age, great glaciers covered much of northern North America and Eurasia. These ice sheets modified the landscape by scouring the surface in some areas and depositing their "loads" elsewhere. At the same time, valleys in high mountain areas (such as the Alps and the Rockies) were filled by glaciers that snaked slowly downslope. These mountain glaciers widened and deepened their containing valleys, carrying away huge loads of rock in the process. When the global climate warmed up and the glaciers melted back, the landscape below had taken on an unmistakable and distinctive character. This is examined in Units 45 to 48.

Wind   Wind, too, is a degradational agent. Globally, compared to running water and moving ice, wind is an insignificant factor in landscape genesis. In certain areas of the world, however, wind *is* an effective modifier of the surface. Wind can propel sand and dust at high velocities, wearing down exposed rock surfaces in its path. Wind is also capable of moving large volumes of sand from one place to another, creating characteristic dune landscapes (Fig. 37.5). The processes and landscapes of wind action are treated in Unit 49.

FIGURE 37.5   Wind is a frequent (but not the sole) landform sculptor in desert environments. These massive dunes form part of the coastal Namib Desert between Namibia's mountains (seen in the background) and the South Atlantic Ocean behind the photographer.

Coastal Waves   Coastal landscapes are of special interest in physical geography. Where land and sea make contact, waves attack and rocks resist, and the resulting scenery often is spectacular as well as scientifically intriguing. As in the case of wind action, it is not the waves alone that erode so effectively. When waves contain pieces of loosened rock, they are hurled against the shore, sometimes with enormous impact. The erosional results are represented by wave-cut platforms, cliffs and other high-relief landforms (Fig. 37.6). Coastal landscapes and landforms are the focus of Units 50 and 51.

Chemical Dissolution   A special case of degradational action involves the removal of rock not by physical breakdown but by chemical dissolution. As seen in Unit 44, this process produces a landscape of highly distinctive surface and near-surface features. When soluble rocks, principally limestone, are layered in a suitable way and subjected to humid climatic conditions, the limestone dissolves. Partially carried away in solution, the limestone strata are honeycombed by caves and underground channels. As the ground above collapses into these subsurface cavities, the landscape is pocked by sinkholes, evidence of the efficacy of chemical dissolution in sculpting the Earth's surface.

FROM THE FIELDNOTES

FIGURE 37.6 "Oregon's coastal Route 101 provides some magnificent scenery and many superb field examples of coastal landforms. Drive it southward, so you are on the ocean side! Ample rainfall in this **Csb** environment sustains luxuriant vegetation. Below, the waves do their work even as tectonic forces modify the geology. Here two natural bridges have formed following wave penetration of a fault-weakened section of the coastline, the waters rushing in through one and out through the other."

Aggradational Processes and Landforms

Streams, glaciers, wind, and waves are erosional, degradational agents—but they also have the capacity to build, to deposit, and thus to create aggradational landscapes and landforms. As we study the degradational power of streams, we note that what is removed as boulders and pebbles from interior highlands may be laid down as mud or silt in a coastal delta. The Late Cenozoic ice sheets that scoured the surface of much of the Canadian Shield deposited their ground-up load of sediments to the south, much of it in the Prairies and U.S. Midwest. Mountain glaciers excavated the upper valleys, but they filled their lower valleys with deposits. Wind action wears rocks down in some places but builds dunes in others. Waves that cut cliffs create beaches in other locales and under different circumstances. So the degradational agents, the agents of erosion, also are aggradational agents, or agents of deposition. The key is transportation: the removal of rocks, their long-distance conveyance, and their pulverization or grinding in the process. All of this is part of the rock cycle (see Fig. 31.12), which is driven by gravity and sustained by the hydrological cycle (see Fig. 12.2), and serves to reduce the relief of the landmasses.

Erosion and Tectonics

If the continental landmasses were static (that is, if they were not subject to tectonic forces as parts of lithospheric plates), they would indeed eventually be worn down to near sea level. Moreover, in the context of the Earth's lifetime, it would not take very long. To prove this, geomor-

phologists first calculated the total mass of the continents presently existing above sea level. Next they estimated the quantity of sediment that all the world's streams carried to the oceans in an average year. By dividing the total mass by the amount annually removed, and by factoring in the reduced efficiency of streams as the continents are (theoretically) lowered, it was possible to estimate the number of years it would take for the continental landmasses to be worn down to near sea level. The surprising result: 270 million years, just a small fraction (about 6 percent) of the Earth's total history!

Obviously this calculation is not consistent with observed reality. Continental landmasses probably have existed for at least 4 billion years, and in approximately their present form (if not shape) for at least 650 mil-

PERSPECTIVES ON THE HUMAN ENVIRONMENT

Using the Geological Time Scale

The **geological time scale**, shown in Fig. 37.7, has evolved over many years of research and extrapolation, and it continues to be subject to revision. Its broad outlines, however, are stable and useful in many areas of physical geography. As Fig. 37.7 shows, the broadest division of Earth history is into *eons*, of which the most recent, the Phanerozoic, began about 570 million years ago, when explosive growth of marine life heralded a new stage of planetary history. Because of the momentous nature of this "Cambrian Explosion," all that preceded it is often referred to simply as the Precambrian.

The Phanerozoic Eon, as the chart shows, comprises only the most recent 12 percent or so of Earth history. Rocks and fossils from this eon permit a more detailed timetable than is possible for earlier eons such as the Proterozoic and the Archean, although recent research is producing exciting information about these Precambrian times. The Phanerozoic Eon is divided into three *eras*, of which the Palaeozoic, beginning with that Cambrian *Period* of mushrooming marine life, is the longest with more than 300 million years. Next comes the Mesozoic Era, when reptilian life as depicted in the movie *Jurassic Park* flourished. The

final period of the Mesozoic was the Cretaceous, which came to a cataclysmic end possibly when a comet struck the Earth 65 million years ago, ending the dominance of reptiles and opening the Cenozoic Era, the age of mammals. (The violent transition from the Cretaceous to the following Tertiary Period is referred to as the "K/T boundary.")

The Cenozoic Era, for obvious reasons (abundant fossils, younger rocks, more environmental evidence), is the best known and therefore further divided into *epochs*. Around the middle of this era, the Earth's surface temperatures began to cool as the Late Cenozoic Ice Age came to dominate global environments. Ice accumulated on high mountains, glaciers filled valleys previously occupied by streams, and permanent ice developed on Antarctic land and on Arctic waters. As global temperatures seesawed, alternating between long stretches of cold and shorter intervals of warmth, the overall trend was ever colder, making the Pleistocene Epoch the most frigid yet. Meanwhile adaptable hominids had made their appearance and, more than 50,000 years ago, *Homo sapiens sapiens* (anatomically modern humans), the human species that rose to dominate the planet.

Note that the "geological" time scale displays

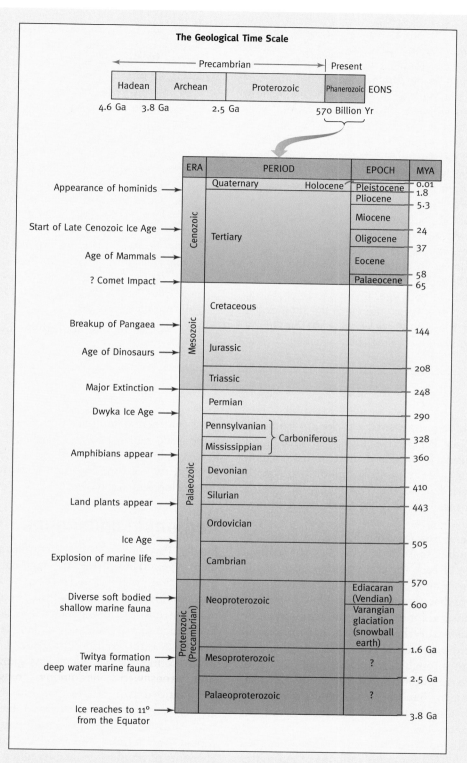

FIGURE 37.7 Geological time scale, calibrated according to dates established since the late 1990s.

some anthropocentrism as well. The current epoch, beginning about 10,000 years ago, is designated the Holocene—but there is no evidence that this so-called epoch is anything other than another warm phase (interglacial) during the Pleistocene's successive glaciations. What is new about the Holocene is that it marks the rise of human civilization and the explosive growth of humanity's numbers; but to conclude that it also opens a new geological epoch is premature.

It is important to be familiar with the geological calendar in Fig. 37.7, because the past in physical as well as human geography often is the key to the present. We will have occasion to refer to this time scale much as we refer to the years and months of our own lifetimes. To better understand the magnitudes of the time periods involved, let us relate the Earth's life span to your age. If you are 20 years old and we take as the age of the Earth the time of the formation of the oldest rocks we can find (more than 4 billion years), consider the following:

1. One *year* of your life equals 230 million years of the Earth's. That puts you in the early Mesozoic just one year ago.
2. One *month* of your life equals just over 19 million years of the Earth's. The Rocky Mountains started forming just 3½ months ago.
3. One *week* of your life equals nearly 5 million years of the Earth's. The Pleistocene glaciations began three days ago.
4. One *day* of your life equals about 630,000 years of the Earth's. Human evolution was still in its early stages just yesterday at this time.
5. One *hour* of your life equals over 26,000 years of the Earth's. In that single hour, the human population grew from less than 100,000 to over 6 billion, and the major civilizations developed.

Where will we be one hour from now?

lion years. The oldest sedimentary rocks are from the Proterozoic Era (see Perspective: Using the Geological Time Scale). Thus we know that degradation and aggradation were taking place at least 570 million years ago. It must be concluded that the continents are being rejuvenated tectonically as they are worn down by erosion.

The principle of isostasy (Unit 33) relates to this rejuvenation. According to isostatic principles, the removal of a large volume of rock (or other burden, such as the melting of ice) from an area of the crust leads to an upward "rebound" of that part of the crust. Thus downward erosion is compensated for by the upward rebound of the lithosphere. If this is true, then it follows that erosion will go on indefinitely, because the crust will always replace what has been lost through degradation.

This also has implications for the study of landscapes. It may mean that landscapes retain their relief properties much longer than had previously been believed. For instance, a topography such as that of the Appalachian highlands may retain its ridge-and-valley scenery (see Fig. 52.10) for many millions of years after erosion *should* have worn the steep-sided ranges down. Compensating isostatic uplift may do more than preserve continental landmasses; it also may preserve landscapes. We return to this theme several times later in Part Five, but as noted elsewhere, it is important to keep in mind the tectonic forces from below when assessing the erosional forces above.

Regional Landscapes

Finally, Part Five includes the application of a fundamental geographical theme—regional analysis—to the distribution of physical landscapes. Unit 52 concentrates on North America. Landscapes often display a certain sameness or homogeneity over large areas. We acknowledge this in our everyday language by referring to such areas as the Prairies or the Rocky Mountains. But if we are to map such regional landscapes with any precision, we must establish criteria on which to base the boundaries drawn. This leads us into the field of *regional physiography*, where everything we have learned in this book thus far comes together: climate, soil, vegetation, topography, terrain, and relief. In combination, these elements of physical geography allow us to view North America regionally and to better understand its many faces, from sea to sea to sea.

KEY TERMS

aggradation *page 484*

degradation *page 483*

erosion *page 485*

geological time scale *page 488*

landform *page 483*

landscape *page 483*

primary landform *page 482*

secondary landform *page 483*

slope process *page 485*

weathering *page 485*

REVIEW QUESTIONS

1. How does a secondary landform differ from a primary landform?

2. Briefly describe the processes of gradation.

3. What is meant by the term *weathering*?

4. Describe the major time divisions of the geological time scale.

REFERENCES AND FURTHER READINGS

BUTZER, K. W. *Geomorphology from the Earth* (New York: Harper & Row, 1976).

CURRAN, H. A., et al. *Atlas of Landforms* (New York: Wiley, 1984).

GOUDIE, A. *The Changing Earth: Rates of Geomorphological Processes* (Malden, Mass.: Blackwell, 1995).

HANCOCK, P. L., and SKINNER, B. J., Eds. *Oxford Companion to the Earth* (New York: Oxford Univ. Press, 2001).

HARLAND, W. B., et al. *A Geologic Time Scale 1989* (London/New York: Cambridge Univ. Press, 1990); *A Geologic Time Scale 1989—Wallchart* (New York: Cambridge Univ. Press, 1990).

HUGGETT, R. J. *Fundamentals of Geomorphology* (London/New York: Routledge, 2002).

KING, L. C. *The Morphology of the Earth: The Study and Synthesis of World Scenery* (New York: Hafner, 1967).

OLLIER, C. D. *Tectonics and Landforms* (London/New York: Longman, 1981).

PHILLIPS, J. D. *Earth Surface Systems: Order, Complexity and Scale* (Malden, Mass.: Blackwell, 1998).

PITTY, A. F. *Landforms and Time* (New York: Blackwell, 1989).

RITTER, D. F. *Process Geomorphology* (Dubuque, Iowa: Wm. C. Brown, 2nd ed., 1986).

SNEAD, R. E. *World Atlas of Geomorphic Features* (Huntington, N.Y.: Krieger, 1980).

STODDART, D. *Process and Form in Geomorphology* (London/New York: Routledge, 1996).

THORNBURY, W. D. *Principles of Geomorphology* (New York: Wiley, 2nd ed., 1969).

WEB RESOURCES

http://mercator.upc.es/nicktutorial/TofC/toc1.html A discussion of remote-sensing image interpretation and analysis, which includes a section covering geomorphology. Specific types of landforms and their formation are described, and full colour remote-sensing images are included for each type of landform.

http://vulcan.wr.usgs.gov/Glossary/time_scale_.html A graphical representation of the geological time scale from the USGS, with links to the Cascades Volcano Observatory.

Weathering Processes

Mechanical and biological weathering on a rock face in the Blue Mountains of eastern Australia. (Authors' photo)

OBJECTIVES

- To differentiate the major categories of weathering—mechanical, chemical, and biological

- To introduce and briefly discuss common weathering processes

- To note the general environmental controls over weathering processes

On the northeast coast of Brazil, about 1300 km north of Rio de Janeiro, lies the city of Salvador, capital of the state of Bahía. Two centuries ago, Salvador was a wealthy, thriving place. Agricultural products from nearby plantations and whales from offshore waters yielded huge profits. The Salvadorans, under the tropical Sun, built themselves one of the world's most beautiful cities. Ornate churches, magnificent mansions, cobble-stoned streets, and manicured plazas graced the townscape. Sidewalks were laid in small tiles in intricate patterns, so that they became works of art. And speaking of art, the townspeople commissioned the creation of many statues to honour their heroes.

FROM THE FIELDNOTES

FIGURE 38.1 "A first visit to the coastal city of Salvador, Bahía (Brazil), in the early 1980s was a depressing experience. In the old part of the city, the historic Pelourinho District, hundreds of centuries-old buildings ranging from ornate villas to elaborate churches lay in dreadful disrepair. Weathering—mechanical, chemical, and biological—was destroying one of civilization's great legacies. The top floor of this mansion revealed evidence of all three, and it, like many others, appeared beyond salvation. But the story has a happy ending. United Nations World Heritage designation and international assistance brought on a massive restoration program, and during the 1990s much of the Pelourinho's heritage was saved."

But times eventually changed. Competition on world markets lowered incomes from farm products, and overexploitation eliminated the whale population. There was no money to maintain the old city; people moved away, and homes stood abandoned. Salvador had to await a new era of prosperity. But when things improved, the better-off residents preferred to live in high-rise luxury buildings on the coast or in modern houses away from the old town. Old Salvador lay unattended, exposed to the elements (Fig. 38.1). The equatorial Sun beat down on roofs and walls; moisture seeped behind plaster; mould and mildew formed as bright pastel colours changed to ugly grey and black. Bricks were loosened and fell to the ground, and statues began to lose their features. Noses, ears, and fingers wore away. People who knew the old city in its heyday were amazed at the rapid rate of decay that was evident everywhere.

The fate of old Salvador reminds us of nature's capacity to attack and destroy—not just with swirling streams, howling winds, or thundering waves, but quietly, persistently, and intensively. Nature's own structures are affected just as much as buildings and statues are. As detailed in Unit 23, the first steps in soil formation involve the breaking down of rocks into smaller particles. The same processes that destroy abandoned buildings also contribute to the degradation of landforms. This quiet destruction proceeds in many ways. When the Sun heats an exposed wall, iron particles in that wall expand. The bricks may expand more than the mortar that binds them. Day after day, this repeated, differential expansion will destroy the bond between brick and mortar. On vulnerable corners, bricks will fall.

The same process affects rocks, and when various minerals expand at different rates, they will be loosened. Moisture also plays a critical role. Just as water seeps behind plaster, it can invade rocks, for example, along cracks and joints. Once there, water exploits the rocks' weaknesses, opens cracks wider, and allows moist air to penetrate. Soon the rocks are broken into pieces, and the next rainstorm carries the smaller fragments away.

Other forces also come into play in the silent, unspectacular breakdown of rocks. In combination, these processes are called *weathering*—a good term, because it signifies the impact of the elements of weather examined in Part Two of this book. Weathering goes on continuously, not only at exposed surfaces but also beneath the ground and within rock strata. It is the first stage in that series of processes called degradation. Several kinds of weathering processes can be recognized. The three principal types are (1) *chemical weathering*, (2) *physical weathering*, and (3) *biological weathering*. The terms are self-explanatory, and each will be examined in turn. But it must not be assumed that these processes are mutually exclusive or that if one occurs the others do not. In fact, weathering processes usually operate in some combination, and it is often difficult to separate the effects of each process.

Chemical Weathering

The minerals that rocks are made of are subject to alteration by **chemical weathering**, as shown by Egypt's Great Sphinx in Fig. 38.2. Some minerals, such as quartz, resist this alteration quite successfully, but others, such as the calcium carbonate, dissolve easily. In any rock made up of a combination of minerals, the chemical decomposition of one set of mineral grains leads to the disintegration of the whole mass. In granite, for instance, the quartz resists chemical decay much more effectively than the felspar,

FROM THE FIELDNOTES

FIGURE 38.2 "Our field trip from Cairo was focused on Egypt's pyramids, but in many ways the Great Sphinx at Giza was the highlight. Created about 4500 years ago, it has suffered from weathering but still stands against the elements. I took this photograph in 1982, before a major restoration project got under way. Known to be a portrait of the Fourth King of the Fourth Dynasty, the sphinx became a format for royal images that lasted through most of Egyptian history—a lion's body with a human head. 'We Arabs have a different name for it,' said my Egyptian colleague. 'Did you know that it is called Abu al-Hawl, Father of Terror?' As the backdrop to concerts and operas that attract the upper crust of Egyptian society, that hardly seemed appropriate, but history has a way of perpetuating itself."

which is chemically more reactive and weathers to become clay. Often you can see a heavily pitted granite surface. In such cases, the felspar grains are likely to have been weathered to clay and blown or washed away. The quartz grains still stand up, but they may soon be loosened too. So even a rock as hard as granite cannot withstand the weathering process forever. Three kinds of mineral alteration dominate in chemical weathering: hydrolysis, oxidation, and carbonation.

Hydrolysis

When minerals are moistened, **hydrolysis** occurs, producing not only a chemical alteration but expansion (hydration) in volume as well. This expansion can contribute to the breakdown of rocks. Hydrolysis, it should be noted, is not simply a matter of moistening, it is a true chemical alteration, and minerals are transformed into other mineral compounds in the process. For example, felspar hydrolysis yields clay minerals, and a carbonate or bicarbonate of potassium, sodium, or calcium in solution. The new minerals tend to be less resistant and weaker than their predecessors. In granite boulders, hydrolysis combines with other processes to cause the outer shells to flake off in what looks like a miniature version of exfoliation. This is **spheroidal weathering**

(Fig. 38.3), and it affects other igneous rocks besides granite.

Oxidation

When minerals in rocks react with oxygen in the air, the chemical process is known as **oxidation**. There is plenty of evidence of this process in the reddish colour of soils in many parts of the world and in the reddish-brown hue of layers exposed in such places as the Grand Canyon (see Fig. 31.8). The products of oxidation are compounds of iron and aluminum (see Fig. 25.13). In tropical areas, oxidation is a very dominant chemical weathering process.

Carbonation and Solution

Various circumstances may convert water into a mild acid solution, thereby increasing its effectiveness as a weathering agent. With a small amount of carbon dioxide, for instance, water forms carbonic acid (a process called **carbonation**), which in turn reacts with carbonate minerals such as limestone and dolomite (a harder relative of limestone, composed of carbonate of calcium and magnesium). **Solution weathering** is especially vigorous in humid areas, where limestone and dolomite formations

FROM THE FIELDNOTES

FIGURE 38.3 "Walking along the east-facing slope of the Swaziland Lowveld, checking the geological map against rock exposures. Light-colored granite, rich in silica, suddenly changes to what the map suggests is dolerite (but another map shows it as 'dark, large-grained granite'). Whatever the analysis, the exposure of this darker rock is marked by an expanse of boulders, most of them rounded and many undergoing spheroidal weathering. Peeled the shells off the boulder on the right until I reached the yet unaffected core; the one at left is for contrast."

are often deeply pitted and grooved, and where the evidence of dissolution and decay are prominent. This process even attacks limestone underground, contributing to the formation of caves and subterranean corridors (Unit 44). In arid areas, however, limestone and dolomite stand up much better, and although they may show some evidence of solution weathering at the surface, they appear in general to be much more resistant strata.

Chemical weathering is the more effective agent of rock destruction in humid areas because moisture promotes chemical processes and is very important in all environments. Physical or mechanical weathering is important in dry and cold zones. But water plays an important role in the dry as well as the moist environments. The growth of destructive salt crystals in porous rocks of arid areas, for instance, takes place only after some moisture has entered the pores and then evaporated, thereby triggering the crystals' growth. The role of water in all rock-destroying processes is paramount.

Physical Weathering

Physical weathering, also called *mechanical weathering*, involves the destruction of rocks through the imposition of certain stresses. A prominent example is **frost action**. We are all aware of the power of ice to damage roads and sidewalks and to split open water pipes (water increases in volume by about 9 percent as it freezes). Similarly, the water contained by rocks—in cracks, joints, even pores—can freeze into crystals that shatter even the strongest igneous rock masses. This ice can produce about 1890 metric tonnes of pressure for every 0.1 m^2.

Of course, frost action operates only where winter brings subfreezing temperatures. In high-altitude zones, where extreme cooling and warming alternate, the water that penetrates into the rocks' joint planes freezes and thaws repeatedly during a single season, wedging apart large blocks and boulders and separating the fragments completely (Fig. 38.4). Then, depending on the local relief, these pieces of rock may either remain more or less where they are, awaiting dislodgement by wind or precipitation, or they may roll or fall downslope and collect at the base of the mountains.

When the fragments of rock accumulate near their original location, they form a **rock sea** (Fig. 38.5) (also known as *blockfield* or *felsenmeer*). When the rock fragments roll downslope, they create a *scree slope* or **talus cone**. If you have been in the Rocky Mountains or other mountainous areas in western North America, you have probably seen such piles of loose boulders. They often lie at steep angles and seem ready to collapse (Fig. 38.6).

FIGURE 38.4   This massive granite boulder in Joshua Tree National Park, California, has been split in two along a joint plane by temperature fluctuations and the wedging effect of moisture. So far neither part of the boulder has been dislodged from the place where it was wedged apart, but gravity may act differently on the two masses as time goes on.

Rocky soils can also reflect the action of frost. For a long time physical geographers wondered what produced the remarkable geometrical structures of stone that mark the soils in Arctic regions (see Fig. 48.6). These *stone nets* are created when ice forms on the underside of rocks in the soil, a process that tends to wedge the rock upward and sideways. Eventually, the rocks meet and form lines and patterns that look as though they were laid out by ancient civilizations for some ceremonial purpose.

In arid regions, too, mechanical weathering occurs. There the development and growth of salt crystals has an effect similar to that of ice. When water in the pores of such rocks as sandstone evaporates, small residual salt crystals form. The growth of those tiny crystals pries the rocks apart (in a process called salt burst hydration or *salt wedging*) and weakens their internal

CANADIAN GEOGRAPHERS IN THE FIELD

"Once in a while geomorphological processes produce intriguing and 'grotesque-like' forms within the landscape. This example from Switzerland called 'Les Pyramides' is found in the Val d'Herens in Valais. Here due to differential weathering a large Late Glacial lateral moraine that contains occasional large boulders has been disaggregated by slope processes due to rainwash resulting in these capped pyramidal cones of glacial debris (till) being left upstanding in the manner of 'hoodoos' as can be observed in parts of southern Alberta and Saskatchewan."

John Menzies, B.Sc., Ph.D., P.Geo. is Professor of Geography and Earth Sciences, at Brock University.

FROM THE FIELDNOTES

FIGURE 38.5 "Looking up this steep slope formed by loose, angular boulders, I wondered whether there was a risk of sudden collapse. But this *felsenmeer* (rock sea), developed from mechanical weathering of quartzite, was stable. After having been pried apart, the angular fragments of various sizes have moved very little, creating a distinct element in this Montana landscape."

structure. As a result, caves and hollows form on the face of scarps, and the water and wind may remove the loosened grains and reinforce the process (see Perspective: The Dust Bowl).

The mineral grains that rocks are made of have different rates of expansion and contraction in response to temperature changes. Therefore the bonds between them may be loosened by continual temperature fluctuations. Although difficult to replicate in the laboratory, this kind of weathering may play a role in the mechanical disintegration of rocks. Over many thousands of years, daily temperature fluctuations could well have a weakening effect on exposed rocks. But other weathering processes also enter the picture—as the contacts between the grains are loosened, moisture enters and promotes decay of the minerals.

Biological Weathering

Weathering is very important to soil formation (see Unit 23). It is through the breakdown of rocks and the accumulation of a layer of minerals that plants can grow—plants whose roots and other parts, in turn, contribute to the weathering processes. But it is likely that the role of plant roots in forcing open bedding planes and joints is somewhat overestimated. The roots follow paths of least resistance and adapt to every small irregularity in the rock (see unit-opening photo). Roots certainly keep cracks open once they have been formed. More importantly, however, areas of roots tend to collect decaying organic material, which is involved in the chemical weathering processes.

One of the most important aspects of **biological**

FIGURE 38.6 Talus slope in the southern interior of British Columbia.

the air with various substances, we greatly accelerate some chemical weathering, especially in and around large urban centres (see Unit 21). (2) By quarrying and mining, we accelerate mechanical, chemical, and biological weathering through the exposure of deep strata to these processes (Fig. 38.7). (3) By farming and fertilizing, we influence soil-formation processes, sometimes destructively. Through dam construction, excavation of canals, surface mining, deforestation, urban development, road building, and myriad other activities, humans have altered and continue to make significant modifications of the Earth's surface—and may have become one of the planet's most important geomorphological agents.

Geography of Weathering

As noted, particular weathering processes are more prevalent and effective in certain areas than in others. In very general terms, soils are much thicker in equatorial and tropical areas than in the polar and subpolar latitudes, a contrast that reflects the comparative intensities of weathering in those locales. The heat, high humidity, and often copious rainfall of low-latitude zones are conducive to particularly active weathering. But certain processes occur only under specific conditions. For example, the wedging effect of frost action occurs only in higher latitudes (the **D** climates with their strong seasonal and diurnal temperature contrasts are a good indicator) and at high, frost-affected altitudes. Again, stone nets of various kinds are formed only where a special set of conditions prevails. This happens in Arctic latitudes, yet not all Arctic areas have stone nets.

It would be impractical to devise a small-scale global map of weathering incidence because the various processes are not confined to specific regions and different processes are at work in the same areas. But the maps of world temperature (Fig. 8.12), world precipitation (Fig. 12.12), world climate (Fig. 16.3), and world soils (Fig. 25.16) provide some indication of what might be expected to happen in particular places. Where moisture (as indicated by the rainfall map) and temperature are high, weathering is intense. Where temperature ranges are high and moisture is low (as in **BW** and **BS** climate regions), mechanical weathering may take a more prominent role, and chemical weathering and biological weathering somewhat less effective ones. In the higher latitudes, the dominant form of mechanical weathering is frost action.

The regional geological map also must be consulted. In regions where precipitation is low, limestone and dolomite are quite resistant to weathering. But where temperatures are moderate to high and where moisture

weathering is the mixing of soil by burrowing animals and worms (*bioturbation*). Another interesting aspect is the action of lichens, a combination of algae and fungi, that live on bare rock. Lichens draw minerals from the rock by ion exchange (*chelation,* a mechanism discussed on p. 303). The swelling and contraction of lichens as they alternately get wet and dry may also cause small particles of rock to fall off.

Technically, humans are also agents of biological weathering. Human activity contributes to various forms of weathering in a number of ways. (1) By polluting

PERSPECTIVES ON THE HUMAN ENVIRONMENT

The Dust Bowl

In the 1930s the Canadian Prairie provinces and the American Plains states suffered through the Dust Bowl, but today they are very productive grain-growing areas. Kathleen Laird, an ecologist at Queen's University, Kingston, Ontario, has reconstructed the past climatic conditions of these areas using diatoms (water-dwelling algae), which indicate salinity and therefore aridity. Her research suggests that the region has had repeated droughts for thousands of years. It has also shown that the last 700 years have been wetter than the average. This work indicates that dust-bowl conditions are not unusual.

Laird took diatoms and water samples from lakes throughout the region and then homed in on Moon Lake, North Dakota. This lake had no streams draining into or out of it, and was therefore reliant on rainfall and evaporation. She took diatom samples from sediments on the lake bottom that had accumulated since the end of the Wisconsinan glaciation (which ended approximately 10,000 years ago). The sediments were radiocarbon dated, and diatom numbers and species were correlated with the salinity levels of the lake sediments.

Laird's findings indicate that extreme dryness persisted for very long periods and occurred more frequently in the past. The worst periods of drought occurred between 200 and 370 C.E., 700 and 850 C.E., and 1000 and 1200 C.E. The cause of those ancient droughts is unknown, but it is known that poor farming techniques and inadequate land-management practices were definite contributors to the 1930s Dust Bowl.

_____

* Much of the information in this section is from a short article in *Discover* (April 1997).

is ample, chemical weathering of limestone and dolomite can be so effective that the whole landscape may be transformed. This special case of chemical weathering forms the basis of Unit 44. In Unit 41's discussion of the mass removal of loose Earth material, focus is placed on the great rivers that sweep vast amounts of rock fragments and particles downstream. It should not be forgotten that much of that material was first loosened by the quiet, relentless processes of weathering. Gravity acts on weathered materials prior to their removal by streams, and its important influence on slope stability is explored in Unit 39.

FIGURE 38.7 Human impact on the natural environment. Open-pit mining leaves huge scars on natural landscapes. This was one of the largest pits in Canada, the Iron Ore Corporation of Canada's Schefferville Mine in the Canadian Shield near the Quebec–Labrador border.

KEY TERMS

biological weathering *page 498*
carbonation *page 495*
chemical weathering *page 494*
frost action *page 496*

hydrolysis *page 495*
physical weathering *page 496*
oxidation *page 495*
rock sea *page 496*

solution weathering *page 495*
spheroidal weathering *page 495*
talus cone *page 496*

REVIEW QUESTIONS

1. Why is frost action such an aggressive mechanical weathering agent?
2. How does spheroidal weathering occur?
3. Under what environmental conditions could chemical weathering be most aggressive?

4. What is meant by the term *dust bowl?*
5. What is biological weathering?

REFERENCES AND FURTHER READINGS

BIRKELAND, P. W. *Pedology, Weathering, and Geomorphological Research* (London/New York: Oxford Univ. Press, 2nd ed., 1984).

BLAND, W., and ROLLS, D. *Weathering: An Introduction to the Scientific Principles* (New York: Oxford Univ. Press, 1998).

CARROLL, D. *Rock Weathering* (New York: Plenum, 1970).

COLMAN, S. M., and DETHIERS, D. P., Eds. *Rates of Chemical Weathering of Rocks and Minerals* (Orlando, Fla.: Academic Press, 1986).

KELLER, W. D. *The Principles of Chemical Weathering* (Columbia, Mo.: Lucas Brothers, 2nd ed., 1962).

OLLIER, C. D. *Weathering* (London/New York: Longman, 2nd ed., 1984).

REICHE, P. *A Survey of Weathering Processes and Products* (Albuquerque, N. M.: Univ. of New Mexico Publications in Geology, No. 3, 1962).

RITTER, D. F. *Process Geomorphology* (Dubuque, Iowa: Wm. C. Brown, 2nd ed., 1986).

ROBINSON, D. A., and WILLIAMS, R. B. G., Eds. *Rock Weathering and Landform Evolution* (New York: Wiley, 1994).

SELBY, M. J. *Hillslope Materials and Processes* (London/New York: Oxford Univ. Press, 1982).

STATHAM, I. *Earth Surface Sediment Transport* (London/New York: Oxford Univ. Press, 1977).

STEINBECK, J. *The Grapes of Wrath* (New York: Viking, 1939).

WHALLEY, B., and McCREEVY, P. J. *Weathering* (Malden, Mass.: Blackwell, 1998).

YATSU, E. *The Nature of Weathering* (Osaka, Japan: Sozosha, 1988).

YOUNG, A. *Slopes* (London/New York: Longman, 2nd ed., 1975).

WEB RESOURCES

http://ltpwww.gsfc.nasa.gov/globe/soilform/weather.htm This NASA site gives background information on all types of weathering processes, with links to other pages covering soil formation and types, creation of landforms, and mineral classification.

http://www.drought.unl.edu The University of Nebraska's National Drought Mitigation Center presents background information on the causes and effects of drought, with historical descriptions of the dust bowl, and El Niño data.

Slope Processes

Talus slope in the Rocky Mountains. (Authors' photo)

OBJECTIVES

* To demonstrate the role of gravity in promoting slope processes in weathered materials

* To discuss the various types of slope processes and the circumstances

under which they usually occur

I n 1998, when thousands of Hondurans were buried by mudslides (actually cold lahars) as Hurricane Mitch devastated the hills and mountains of this Central American country, the world was again reminded of the dangers posed by unstable slopes. As this ferocious storm slowly made its way across the heart of Honduras for two days, it unleashed almost 2000 mm of wind-driven rain, which mobilized previously deposited blankets of volcanic ash (lahars) and triggered massive flooding. As the Perspectives box in Unit 14 reveals, almost 10,000 people died, 1.5 million were left homeless, more than 70 percent of the country's infrastructure was washed away, and agricultural losses alone resulted in an economic crisis that will continue for the foreseeable future. This disaster was, admittedly, a rather spectacular example of the hazards posed by slope processes. But in all mountain zones, rocks, soil, and other unconsolidated materials can move in quantities ranging from individual boulders to entire hillsides. It happens at different rates of speed. Some rocks actually fall downslope, bounding along and occasionally even landing on highways or railway lines, while other material moves slowly, almost imperceptibly.

There are times when the signs of coming collapse are unmistakable and people at risk can be warned. At other times a collapse occurs in an instant. In 1970 a minor earthquake loosened a small mass of rock material high up on Mount Huascaran in the Peruvian Andes. This material fell about 650 m down the upper part of the slopes. Normally it would have done little damage, but at an elevation of about 6000 m it happened to land on a steep slope of snow and loose rock material on the mountainside. The falling mass, the snow, and the loose material combined and roared down the slope in a lahar. According to later calculations, the combined debris took only two minutes to move 14.5 km, in the process reaching a speed of 435 km/hr. By the time it stopped, it had travelled 16 km. The loss of life is estimated to have exceeded 25,000 persons. No trace was ever found of entire communities, in particular Yungay (Fig. 39.1), which alone accounted for the loss of 17,000 lives. As can be seen from this story, slope processes can be devastating.

Slopes are very important elements of the physical landscape. In fact, there are few naturally occurring flat areas other than old lake beds. Slopes have a great influence on the character of an area. Good examples are the steep, debris-mantled slopes of the Rocky and Coast Mountains or the gently undulating till plains of the Prairies and Southern Ontario.

Differences in slope form are obviously related to variations of bedrock, climate, glacial history, fluvial erosion, and human-induced changes. In many parts of the Earth—for example, in the mountains of western Canada—slopes have adjusted to ice-age conditions, that is, to the presence of glacial ice that has filled the valleys and eroded and held up the very steep valley sides. However, the ice has melted and many of these slopes, in an attempt to bring their form into equilibrium with the current conditions (i.e., no ice), are undergoing an adjustment (**relaxation**) by failing.

Slope processes are common all over Canada. They occur in the Rocky and Coast Mountains as noted above. They also occur along the sides of the St. Lawrence Valley and the valley sides in the Prairies. Unstable slopes occur around the James Bay lowlands, along the shores of the Great Lakes, and on all sea coasts.

FIGURE 39.1 The 1970 debris avalanche that destroyed the Peruvian town of Yungay (left of centre).

The permafrost areas of the Canadian north are also affected by slope processes. Slope deposits associated with volcanic centres indicate past activity similar to that seen during the eruption of Mount St. Helens in 1980. Some very large mass movements (e.g., the Frank Slide in Alberta and the Hope Slide in British Columbia) have been associated with earthquake shocks.

The force of gravity plays a major role in the modification of landscape. Gravity pulls downward on all materials. Solid bedrock can withstand this force because it is strong and tightly bonded. But as weathering or the shock of an earthquake loosens a fragment of bedrock, that particle's first motion is likely to be caused by gravity. Slopes consist of many different kinds of material. Some are made of solid bedrock; others consist of bedrock as well as loose rock fragments; still others are composed of regolith and soil. A key factor is how well these materials are held together. Another factor is the steepness of the existing slope.

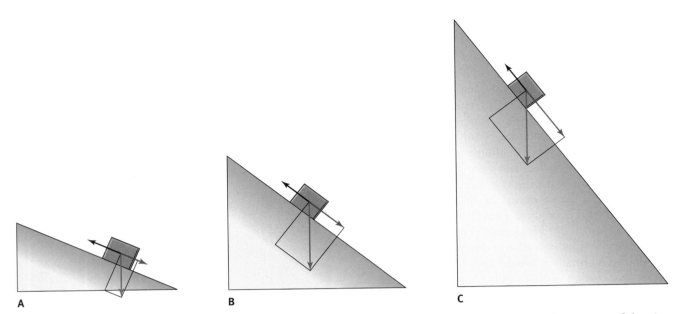

A   B   C

FIGURE 39.2 Slope angle and slide potential. In this drawing the length of the green arrow represents the amount of shearing stress on a block of rock placed against a slope. On the low-angle slope (A), the shearing stress is low, and is not enough to dislodge the rock. On the medium-angle slope (B), the shearing stress is greater, and the downslope pull is nearly enough to move the rock. Note how long the green arrow has become on the high-angle slope (C)—it exceeds the friction that held the rock against the other slopes, and the rock will tumble down. Thus the greater the slope angle, the stronger the shearing stress or downward pull on particles large and small. (In these diagrams the black arrows indicate friction, the red arrows gravity.)

Here is an easy experiment that shows the importance of the slope angle. Take a cafeteria tray and cover it with a layer of sand about 2.5 cm thick. Tilt the tray slightly; say at an angle of 5 percent (note: a 100 percent slope equals 45°). The material is unlikely to move. Tilt the tray slowly to a steeper angle, and notice that movement will begin at a specific angle. You might see some small particles moving individually at first, but soon the whole mass will move downslope because the **threshold angle** (or angle of repose in granular material) has been exceeded. The threshold angle is the maximum angle at which granular material remains at rest. All slopes have a threshold angle. For solid bedrock the angle may be very steep; for loose sand it is less than 10 percent. For a slope consisting of regolith (weathered material or transported sediment) and soil, it may be between 15 and 30 percent, depending on the composition.

In our experiment the slope was oversteepened because the tray was tilted to a higher angle. Slopes become oversteepened in nature too, as, for example, when a stream undercuts its valley sides, exceeding their threshold angle. Then debris from the valley sides falls into the stream and is carried downstream. Oversteepening can also occur because of glacial or coastal erosion. In general, it may be said that the steeper the slope, the stronger the downslope pull or **shear stress**. Counteracting this is the **shear strength** of the slope, which includes the friction and cohesional resistance along the contact between the loose material and the bedrock on the slope (Fig. 39.2). This is easy to imagine. When there is little friction or cohesion between particles, they cannot remain stable on a high-angle slope; for example, had ball bearings or marbles been used in the experiment instead of sand, they would have rolled off the tray at the slightest angle of slope, because there would be no friction or cohesional resistance between the spherical hard balls. Another factor in the downslope movement of material is water, or, more technically, fluid. Material that is below its threshold angle may become unstable when saturated by water from heavy or long-duration rainfall, snowmelt, or groundwater sources. The water has the effect of adding significant weight and of reducing friction because it acts as a lubricant.

The threshold angle of a specific slope can be determined by using the formula for the **factor of safety**:

$$f = \frac{\text{Shear strength (forces resisting movement—e.g., friction and cohesion)}}{\text{Shear stress (forces driving instability—e.g., weight, gravity, slope angle)}}$$

When **f** equals 1, the shear stress is the same as the shear strength. This is the **critical threshold** (Table 39.1). If **f** is greater than 1.0, the slope is stable, but when **f** is less than 1, the slope is unstable and liable to fail. Most natural slopes subject to mass movements have a factor of safety ranging between 1.0 and 1.3. Something like an earthquake, stream undercutting, or increased moisture content can therefore easily trigger movement.

FROM THE FIELDNOTES

FIGURE 39.3 "From Carmel along G-16 toward the Soledad loop. Vineyards along the river, deeply incised. Mediterranean vegetation on the steeper hillslopes. Noted a small tributary that had oversteepened a slope and caused a landslide not even the dense natural vegetation could prevent."

The threshold angle varies with:

a) The type of material(s) involved (e.g., bedrock versus regolith, sand versus clay)
b) Climate
c) Vegetation cover (type and density)
d) Soil moisture and drainage
e) Land use
f) Slope foot processes (e.g., undercutting by a stream or coastal wave action or various types of construction, such as road or rail cuts)

A change in any of the variables can upset the balance and lead to slope processes changing the slope.

Table 39.1 Examples of Threshold Angles in the Greater Toronto Area

Material	Threshold Angle
Consolidated undrained clay	14–20°
Consolidated drained clay	20–24°
Sandy gravel	35–50°
Medium gravel	40–55°
Unconsolidated silt or silty sand	20–22°
Saturated sensitive (quick) clay	flows on slopes of 0°
Bedrock subject to mass movement	>42°

Slope Processes

It is possible to distinguish two distinct groups of slope processes on the basis of how the debris is transported.

1. Mass movements (mass wasting, slope failures) are caused by gravity overcoming the strength of the slope materials. The debris is not carried by water, snow, ice, or wind, but merely tumbles, rolls, or generally moves downslope. Processes in this group include:

   a) Snow, rock, and debris avalanches (landslides)
   b) Rock or debris fall or topple
   c) Rainsplash erosion
   d) Apparent "flows"/slides
   e) Creep and solifluction

2. Hillslope processes involve running water or another agent transporting debris downslope. They include:

   a) Wash (**slopewash**, sheetwash)
   b) Rilling and gullying
   c) True flows, including debris torrents and lahars
   d) Subsurface processes such as solution, leaching, and lessivation

In reality, two or more mass movement or hillslope processes can act on the same slope at the same time or in sequence.

The characteristics of regolith or sediments associated with stability are important. The more significant aspects to consider are (1) the texture of the material, especially the amount and type of clay minerals; (2) the packing or loading of the material (whether weighted down by ice, etc.); and (3) its moisture content

The effect of these factors is shown by the **Atterberg limits** of the material. All Atterberg limit tests are carried out on remoulded (i.e., disturbed, mixed up) soil in which all the fabric has been deliberately destroyed. The two most commonly used limits are the *plastic limit* and the *liquid limit.* Together these define the range of moisture contents through which the material behaves as a solid, a plastic, or a liquid. At moisture levels below the plastic limit the material behaves like a brittle solid; at moisture levels above the liquid limit it acts like a liquid if disturbed. The difference between the plastic limit and the liquid limit of any material is called the **plasticity index.** For any material there is a close linear relationship between its plasticity index and moisture content. Quick clays with a high moisture content, for example, can lead to a loss of strength; the soil will behave like a suspension of fine spherical grains because of the post-depositional removal of salt. In this case the two limits are extremely close together.

It is possible to distinguish between two types of slopes—*weathering-limited slopes* and *transport-limited slopes*—and their processes:

   1. **Weathering-limited slopes** are characterized by very little regolith, and the effects of erosional processes are restricted because of the lack of debris. The slope form will be strongly influenced by the threshold angle(s) of the rock(s). These slopes are characteristic of arid and semi-arid areas where the dominant slope form is a cliff-pediment assemblage.
   2. **Transport-limited slopes** have a deep regolith cover. The slope form and processes are limited by the type and intensity of the processes. All surface processes would be transport-limited, but some subsurface processes may be weathering-limited. The slope form will be strongly influenced by the threshold angle (angle of repose) of the regolith. The deep regolith mantles the cliff-pediment form in these areas.

The Threshold Angle Model of Slope Development

Mass movement processes appear to be important in establishing the initial form of slopes after stream downcutting. Thus they can be considered *slope-creating processes.* If there was a change in any one of the fundamental controlling factors—climate, geology, or base level—fluvial action would have generated new slopes. The mass movement processes reduce these newly formed slopes from their initial instability to their threshold angle, where sliding stops. After this angle is reached, the hillslope processes take over to maintain the slope at that angle or modify it if conditions change. These are considered *slope-modifying processes.*

Mass Movement Processes

Debris or *rock avalanches* form part of a continuum with snow avalanches at one end. Snow avalanches occur in alpine areas, in snow on slopes usually of 30–45° (Fig. 39.4). They are generally triggered by the wind (85–90 percent), by melting, or by overloading of snow. They may occur as a slab failure, affecting a large area of the slope, or they may be channellized. The same kind of process can take place in pure snow or mixtures of snow and other materials. The result of the failure is a turbulent density flow of snow, rock material, and other debris that moves downslope at very high speeds on a cushion of compressed air, dust, and vaporized water.

FIGURE 39.4 Start of a snow avalanche on Mount Dickey, Alaska. As the snow thunders downslope, its volume increases and the area it affects widens.

The flow is preceded by an air blast or shock wave that can knock down trees, houses, and so forth.

Debris and rock avalanches are very important in high mountainous terrain with glacially steepened slopes, especially where the rock beds or structures dip at 35–40° toward the valley floor. The failure usually occurs parallel to the slope face along joints or bedding planes. Movement can be initiated by a rockslide or rockfall, or it can be triggered by earthquakes or a buildup of water pressure along joints, bedding planes, and so on. Many avalanches change their character as they move downslope and mix with water (from surface and subsurface sources) and debris from lower down on the slope and/or in the valley bottom (rock debris, soil, organic material, trees). The debris consists of large angular blocks, rounded blocks (up to 500 tonnes), slabs, boulders, smaller material, tree trunks, and so on. The diagnostic landforms left by this process include a scar on the slope where the material came from and a drape of debris on the valley floor that contains very large cal-

ibre material. In the marginal areas, one sees boulders, flattened trees, defoliated trees, buried features, and detours (e.g., streams and roads). We can calculate the velocity of the event if we know the height of the top of the failure and the distance of travel of the transported debris. A good example of a rock avalanche is the Frank Slide in the mountains of Alberta (see Perspective: The Frank Slide).

Another large rock avalanche, the Hope Slide, occurred in the Nicolum Creek valley in the Cascade Mountains, on the southwest slope of Johnson Peak, about 18 km east of Hope, B.C., early on a Saturday morning in January 1965 (Fig. 39.6). Forty-seven million m^3 of rock material was involved in the failure. The failure covered the valley bottom in 85 m of rubble and buried a 3-km stretch of highway and four people travelling in cars along it.

Rock or Debris Falls or Topples

Falls involve the rapidly falling, leaping, bouncing, and rolling descent of material (Fig. 39.7). Topples result from the tilting or rotating of well-jointed rocks. Small falls are common on north-facing slopes in the Rockies between November and March and are related to fluctuations of temperature, freeze–thaw activity, and saturation. This kind of failure can also be triggered by earthquakes. Rock or debris falls or topples can initiate avalanches. The diagnostic landforms and deposits include a scar where the material originated, unsorted angular rock debris (scree, talus), and tree debris—scarred and broken trees. A good example of this kind of activity was the Hell's Gate Rock Fall in the Fraser River Canyon (February 1914). This occurred when Canadian National Railways work crews were blasting rock to construct a rail line through the canyon. It is estimated that 100,000 tonnes of rock fell into the Fraser River at its narrowest point, constricting its width to 25 m. Some blocks were over 100 m^3. During the spring flood the rock debris caused the river to rise 25 m above its normal level. This caused back-ponding of the Fraser River for about 100 km, to near Ashcroft, B.C. Long bolts were installed in the rock walls above the rail line to stop further large falls. The blockage of the Fraser decreased the cross-sectional area of the river and caused stream velocity to increase to a point where migrating salmon (sockeye and chum or pink) could not get up the river to spawn; the fish were massed in the 16-km stretch downstream of the blockage and died without mating. Finally some of the debris in the river was dynamited and the flooding went down. Fish ladders were later installed to get the salmon over the blocked area, but the salmon run on the Fraser never recovered from this event. The

PERSPECTIVES ON THE HUMAN ENVIRONMENT

The Frank Slide

The Frank Slide near Braemore, Alberta, is the most famous rock avalanche in Canada (Fig. 39.5). At 4.10 a.m. on April 29, 1903, about 33 million m³ of rock and debris (3.6 million tonnes) slid down the eastern slope of Turtle Mountain on the south side of the Crowsnest Pass. In less than 100 seconds the leading edge of the debris had crossed the Crowsnest River and valley and climbed up the slopes on the other side of the valley to about the 120-m mark. Above this the trees were defoliated. The material travelled at speeds of between 350 and 400 km/hr and was preceded by a very strong air blast. The debris buried between one-third and one-half of the coal mining town of Frank, covered 2.5 km of the Canadian Pacific Railway track, and killed at least 76 people (only 12 bodies were found). Most of the killed were women, children, and older folk. The men were at work in the mine under Turtle Mountain.

The Frank Slide was the worst disaster in Canada up to that point. The federal government launched a royal commission to look into what had happened. But the state of scientific knowledge about any slope processes was poor at that time. It is now known that the avalanche took place down the bedding planes of the limestone rocks. The failure was probably triggered by a heavy frost that followed rather warm weather. There were other triggers, too. Coal mining, especially blasting, may have been an added stress. The slope was being undercut by the Crowsnest River, and there may have been a number of small-magnitude earthquakes (there were no seismographs in the area at the time). All of these events added up to disaster. It has been estimated that 100 dump trucks carrying 3-tonne loads and making 10 trips a day would take 66 years to remove all of the debris from the rock avalanche.

FIGURE 39.5   The Frank Slide.

number of salmon migrating upriver after the rockfall was 66 percent less than the pre-fall number.

Apparent "Flows" (Mantle Slides)

Apparent "flows" occur as shallow failures where the regolith slides over the bedrock, or as blocks of bedrock break away and shear over subjacent bedrock, or as deep-seated failures occur in deeper uniform materials.

The shallow movements are caused by the weight of the regolith or rock concerned and the pull of gravity. This process is typical of slopes in temperate environments. The slide is sometimes masked by a cover of material that gives the impression of a flow, but a lack of deformation in stakes placed in the material involved in the slide shows that movement is taking place *en masse*. This is indicative of a slide rather than a flow.

Deep-seated failures are called **slumps**, rotational slides, or slips (Figs. 39.8 and 39.9). They occur in uniform incoherent materials like lake or glacial deposits. A shear plane develops in these types of deposits in the form of a segment of a circle, and failure occurs. This is because of the initial angle and the form of the slope. The major stress that results is curved toward the lower ground. The angle between this direction and the failure plane remains the same as in an ordinary block/angled surface situation. This type of mass movement is very common in deep Pleistocene deposits in the temperate zone or in deeply weathered regoliths in the tropics. The diagnostic landforms include a deep-walled scar where the material originated, a staircase of slumped blocks, and a tongue-shaped lobe of debris on the valley floor.

A

B

FIGURE 39.6 Rockslide. Note the steep slope and the parallel planes of weakness in the rockface (A). Such breakaway mass movements are a constant danger in high-relief terrain. The photo (B) shows a rockslide that closed the Karakoram Highway in northern Pakistan's Hunza Valley—except to intrepid truck drivers who risk their and their passengers' lives by negotiating the rocky obstruction.

FIGURE 39.7   Rockfall—free falling of detached bodies of bedrock from a cliff or steep slope. The loosened boulders usually come to rest at the base of the slope from which they fell.

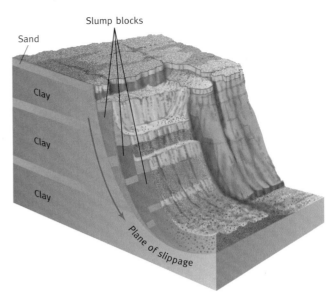

FIGURE 39.9   Example of slumping in which three slump blocks have moved downslope. Note the backward rotation of each slump block, the scarp at the head of the slump cavity, and the forward flow at the toe of the mass.

FIGURE 39.8   One of the most dramatic photographs ever taken of a slumping event. This hillside flow halted traffic on a major road in the San Francisco Bay Area in 1952 and received wide attention in the press.

Creep

Creep can affect the regolith or the entire slope (slope sagging, mass creep), the soil (soil or seasonal creep), or talus (talus creep). An invigorated form of creep occurs in periglacial areas (solifluction-gelifluction and frost creep). Creep involves the downslope movement of material. It is driven by the weight of the regolith, or soil material, and gravity. It is important in areas where there may be a loss of coherence of slope material because of an increase in moisture content or because of weathering. Slope sagging is effective to a depth of over 100 m in deeply weathered materials. Movement is in the order of 1 mm/yr. The Downie Slide near Revelstoke, BC, is a very large example of this process. It has an estimated volume of between 1 and 2 billion m^3 and a surface area of approximately 9 km^2. Movement began at least 6600 years ago and continues at a rate of a few centimetres a year.

The evidence for creep includes the pulling out of rock beds downslope (outcrop curvature), stone lines, tree deformation (trunk curvature), the tilting of structures (walls, telegraph poles, gravestones—Fig. 39.10), and the accumulation of soil on the upslope sides of walls. Talus creep involves the same type of movement of the surface layers of stones or boulder material downslope over talus cones. This may be caused by frost heave.

The same kind of creep process, though much intensified, can be seen in periglacial environments where the *talik*, or active layer, on slopes is subject to shearing over permafrost or lenses of ice during the melt season. This is especially true on south-facing slopes. This process is called *solifluction* or *gelifluction*. **Solifluction** is the flow of supersaturated soil that has reached its liquid limit

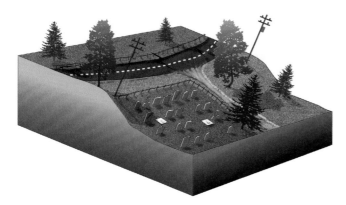

FIGURE 39.10   Effects of soil creep in the cultural and physical landscape—objects tilting downslope.

downslope. **Gelifluction** is solifluction associated with frozen ground.

Frost creep is associated with gelifluction. It involves the expansion of slope material during freezing and its settling on thawing. Stones can be heaved through the talik in this way as it freezes and then settle when thawing takes place. The landforms associated with this process are sheets, lobate (tongue-shaped) features, terraces, benches, or streams of soil material on slopes. The features have crude bedding and tend to thicken downslope. Downslope from these features there is often evidence of wash, as water escaped out of the supersaturated soliflual material and flowed downslope. In areas with bare surfaces, such as the High Arctic, solifluction sheets form smooth terrain with 1–3° gradients. This occurs because the lack of vegetation allows uniform movement to take place. Farther south in the tundra–boreal forest transition zone, lobes and streams of material are more common because of the effect of the presence of patches of vegetation. The lobes may be turf- or stone-banked (turf or stone garlands). This type of process is common in the southern Canadian Rockies. Solifluction lobes have average rates of surface movement of approximately 60 cm/yr on steep slopes and between 0.5 and 4 cm/yr on less-angled slopes. There is very little movement below 50 cm depth and zero movement at 1 m.

The material moved by this kind of movement may become oriented with its long axes parallel to the direction of movement. Delicate weathered minerals, such as felspars, may be crushed by movement. The solifucted material thickens in a downslope direction, and there may be evidence of wash on the lower slopes. The solifucted material may be found with cryoturbation features, such as **involutions**, **ice wedges** or **ice-wedge casts**, and **drag structures**.

Rock glaciers or *block streams* are linear forms of soli-fluction-gelifluction form. These are composed of slowly moving masses of rock particles, some of which are ice-cored.

Rainsplash Erosion

This process is intimately linked to the wash process (see below). It is not as immediately impressive as the catastrophic mass movements discussed so far, although it can be very significant in areas with bare sandy soils—for example, in abandoned crop fields in the Amazon Basin. **Rainsplash erosion** is caused by the impact of raindrops on bare soil surfaces. The disruptive nature of the raindrops' impact is like a greatly scaled-down version of a meteorite impact. Much of the energy of the impact of raindrops is dissipated by vegetation, stones, coarse soil material, plant residues, and water covering the surface. Nevertheless, the impact can break down large *peds*, or clumps of soil, and small soil particles can be thrown up to 2 m horizontally and as much as 70 cm vertically. The process causes finer material to move downslope in a ballistic trajectory, while leaving coarser material in place. The larger material is transported downslope by gravity as it is undermined (*pipkrake effect*). No rounding or wearing of the transported material occurs. The effectiveness of the process depends on a number of factors, which including slope angle, the intensity of the rainfall, the extent of vegetation, and the soil texture (fine particles).

As well as causing disruption of small particles, the impact of raindrops can cause compaction of the soil surface (puddling or sealing) to occur. This leads to a decrease in infiltration rates and an increase in runoff and consequently an increase in erosion by wash.

Hillslope Processes

When water falls onto, or snow and ice melt on, a slope, the water can do one of three things: (1) it can sit on the slope surface in puddles and evaporate over time (hence it is not important to slope processes); (2) it can infiltrate into the soil, regolith, or rock and thereby add weight and thus stress to the slope, which may lead to mass movements or some kinds of hillslope processes (e.g., true flows); or (3) it can become overland flow when (*a*) all the voids or pores in the material are full and then runoff (*saturation overland flow*) occurs, or (*b*) the rainfall intensity is greater than the infiltration rate (**Ri>Ir**) and the water thus builds up in puddles, resulting in runoff (*Hortonian overland flow*). Both types of overland flow are rare.

PERSPECTIVES ON THE HUMAN ENVIRONMENT

The Human Factor

Slope processes most frequently are caused by natural forces and conditions, but human activities also contribute. Sometimes people fail to heed nature's warnings, as in the case of the disastrous Langarone landslide in northern Italy in 1963. The materials on the slopes of the Langarone Valley were known to have low shear strengths. Nevertheless, a dam was constructed across the valley, and a large artificial reservoir (Lake Vaiont) was impounded behind it. The water rose and lubricated the inundated valley sides, adding to the risk of failures. When heavy rains pounded the upper slopes in the summer and early autumn of 1963, major instability seemed to be inevitable.

In early October, the severity of the hazard was finally realized, and it was decided to drain the reservoir. But it was too late, and on October 9 a mass of rock debris with a surface area of 3 km² slid into Lake Vaiont, causing a huge splash wave in the reservoir. The wave spilled over the top of the dam and swept without warning down the lower Langarone Valley, killing more than 2600 persons.

Yet despite this tragic lesson, the building of houses and even larger structures on failure-prone slopes continues in many areas. This includes North America, which contains numerous areas that are susceptible to slope instability risks (Fig. 39.11).

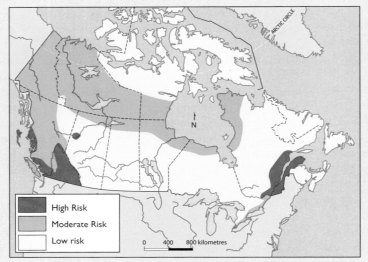

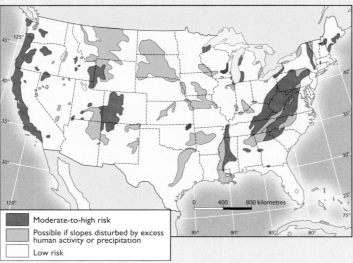

FIGURE 39.11   Susceptibility to future slope failures in North America.

True Flows

The movement of material in a true flow is similar to that of a viscous fluid. The velocity decreases with depth because of friction with the underlying material. The flows usually terminate in gently sloping areas like valley floors or at obstructions such as valley walls or stream channels.

True flows can be subdivided on the basis of a number of characteristics: (1) the material involved in the flows (whether they are **earth** or **mudflows** [earth/mud-flows have less than 50 percent sand; see Fig. 39.12] or debris flows [debris flows have coarser material]); (2) their rate of flow (rapid flows—more than 1 km/hr; slow flows—less than 1km/yr); and (3) the extent of the flow into slope flows or channel flows.

Slope Flows

These are flat or slab failures affecting large areas of a slope. This type of failure is typically confined to sensitive or quick clays that are subject to liquefaction and structural collapse when moist and shaken by earthquakes or undercut by streams. There are instances in Quebec where heavy vehicles are said to have started this kind of movement. These flows are very rapid, the velocity ranging from 26 km/hr to about 330 km/hr. There are many examples of this type of failure in the Champlain Sea sediments along the St. Lawrence Valley in Quebec and eastern Ontario (over 750 flows are known in an area of more than 4000 km²). These deposits are covered by fluvial or deltaic sands. The infiltration of rainwater into the overlying sands causes saturation of the underlying Leda clay. If shaken or undercut

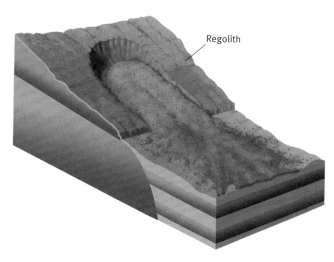

FIGURE 39.12   Earth flow. This lobe-shaped mass leaves a small scarp at its upper end and pushes a tongue of debris onto the valley floor in the foreground.

by a stream, the clays liquefy and flow, carrying blocks of the overlying sands along. The flows leave semicircular scars (depletion zones) with steep head scarps in the source areas and tongues of debris leading onto flatter terrain. A good example of this process is the Nicolet Earthflow, which occurred in 1955. It left a crater 215 m long and 122 m wide (22,000 m²). This earthflow killed three people, destroyed several buildings, including a bishop's palace, and damaged part of a large church. The flow also blocked about half of the Nicolet River. Another flow occurred at St. Jean Vianney near Chicoutimi, Quebec, in May 1971. It left a crater about 1 km across and 25 m deep. It moved at about 26 km/hr along the valley, causing 31 deaths and carrying 34 houses (a total of 40 were destroyed), a bus, and an unknown number of cars. It also took out a bridge. This failure, which occurred within a much larger relic flow dating from the seventeenth century, was set off by an earthquake.

Channel Flows

Channel flows are essentially superconcentrated or excessively loaded stream flows. These flows include debris torrents and lahars. Slow flows are less rapid because they lack moisture and move only a few centimetres to a metre a year. An example is the Drynoch Flow, an approximately 5-km-long (17 million m³ of material) rock glacier that flows into the Thompson Valley in the central interior of British Columbia.

Debris torrents (debris flows) are composed of coarser material flowing in water in a channel. These events deposit sediments on large alluvial fans at the foot of a mountain slope. They have killed approximately 160 people and have caused more than $100 million damage to houses and infrastructure in British Columbia, especially along the "Sea to Sky Highway," which connects Vancouver with Whistler. Many of the deaths were caused by bridge washouts in the early 1980s. The number of fatalities increased with the development of the ski areas and an increase in urbanization and the construction of houses on the alluvial fans. Debris torrents usually result from heavy rainfall or snowmelt, which mobilizes debris that has built up in mountain drainage basins (rock and tree debris from avalanches and rockfalls). Logging and construction can cause a greater buildup of material. The velocity of the torrents is between 3 and 12 m/s (10.8–43 km/hr), and they usually carry up to 50,000 m³ of debris. Deposition on the fans is mainly coarse, poorly sorted, unstratified material with large boulders, rock fragments, gravel and clays, trees and tree mulch. Some fans have well-defined levees and terminal lobes. The deposits wrap around trees and structures at the margins of the flows.

Another special type of channel flow is the *lahar*. These are channelled volcanic mud- or debris flows composed of mixtures of avalanche debris, pyroclastics, ash, snow, ice, and water from surface and groundwater sources (Fig. 39.13). They can be triggered by volcanic eruptions or by intense rainfall on previously deposited fine volcanic ash blankets. The lahars triggered by eruptions are often hot and are very large ($>10^7 m^3$). The Toutle Valley Lahar caused by the eruption of Mount St. Helens in 1980 travelled 43.2 km in 100 minutes (430 m/min or 26 km/hr). This was comparatively slow compared to the Huascaran Lahar (see above), which travelled at between 270 and 360 km/hr. Lahars caused by rainfall on previously deposited ash mantles are cold and generally smaller (10^5–$10^7 m^3$) and travel at much lower velocities.

Wash

Wash (slopewash, sheetwash) involves the flow of water across the soil surface in a sheet (overland flow). It is closely linked to rainsplash erosion (a mass movement—see above) and usually occurs *pari passu* (at the same time). The sheet of water is usually shallow and lacks any

morphological boundaries. The process is variable in form, especially in terms of width. There are great differences in the scale of this process depending on whether it occurs in temperate or tropical areas or with or without a vegetation cover. The water moves in a pulsing motion, as it is dammed by undulations, vegetation debris, and so on, and then breaches these obstacles. In temperate areas the depth of wash tends to be less than 1 mm over bare rock surfaces, but in semi-arid environments it can be several centimetres deep and therefore much wider. In such environments it is associated with the erosion of flat-bottomed valleys called gulches, washes, canyons, or wadis. The volume of water influences the size of material transported, but generally clays, silts, and fine sands are moved. The process sorts debris, and the material it carries is abraded and reduced in size in transport. The rates of wash vary depending on the intensity of the rainfall and the amount of vegetation cover, ranging from less than 60 cm/s to more than 1 m/s. Bare surfaces are essential for this process to be significant, so it is important in semi-arid areas, on glacial debris near the snout of glaciers, and on spoil heaps.

The amount of soil loss by wash and rilling can be calculated using the Universal Soil Loss Equation (USLE) and its refinements (Revised USLE 1 and 2):

$$A = R \times K \times LS \times C \times P$$

Where

A is the average annual soil loss (tonnes/ha);
R is the rainfall erosivity index (based on rainfall and runoff; **R** is the meteorological or active factor; all other elements are passive local factors—i.e., erosion cannot occur without rainfall and runoff);
K is the soil erodability factor (cohesiveness, resistance to dislodging and transport);
LS is the topographical index (based on slope length [**L**] and slope angle [**S**]);
C is the cropping and management index (based on plant canopy, surface mulch cover, and root density); and
P is the conservation practice factor (contouring, strip cropping, terracing, etc.)

LS, **C**, and **P** are dimensionless ratios.

In Southern Ontario the median loss of material eroded on 5–30° slopes is 0.09 cm³/cm²/yr, but in areas with torrential rainfalls and mainly bare surfaces (e.g., the Black Hills of South Dakota), the loss on pediment surfaces is between 200 and 500 cm³/cm²/yr. In more temperate areas the increased vegetation cover intercepts the raindrops and the roots bind the soil together and cut down the efficacy of the process.

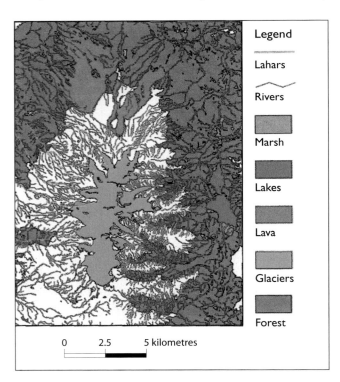

FIGURE 39.13 A theoretical illustration of potential lahars around Mt. Edziza, Northwestern B.C.

Legend

Lahars

Rivers

Marsh

Lakes

Lava

Glaciers

Forest

0   2.5   5 kilometres

Rilling and Gullying

An arbitrary division is used to distinguish rilling and gullying. These processes arise because of the concentration of wash resulting from the undulations on a slope. They form part of a continuum, with wash at one end and fluvial processes at the other.

Rilling (sapping) refers to the formation of microchannels on usually bare surfaces such as badlands, unsodded roadsides, and spoil heaps. The micro-channels are limited by self-generated boundaries. The rills are re-occupied several to many times a year or over a period of years. The rill dimensions are usually up to 1 m deep and 2 m across and can be up to 10 m in length. The United States Department of Agriculture defines rills on the basis of their elimination by ploughing or bulldozing. Gullies cannot be eliminated by these means. The processes associated with rilling are small-scale fluvial and slope processes. The same type of features can be seen in micro-scale (e.g., meandering slope failures that can be seen in a stream channel and its valley). A fan or delta develops at the rill mouth.

Rilling rates are lacking in the literature, but there is a rate for soil erosion by wash and rilling for a site in Ottawa during a flash rainstorm (74 mm). The slope angle was 9° on clay, and the erosion amounted to 27.3 tonnes/hectare.

Gullying is distinguished from rilling by the greater size and permanence of the features. Gullies can be taken as the uppermost branches of the fluvial system. They are occupied during periods of peak runoff (during and just after rainfall or snowmelt). The processes occurring in gullies are identical to fluvial and slope processes seen in full-sized streams and valleys.

Rills and gullies are generated by a differential increase in the velocity of wash (overland flow) at various points on a slope. The differential increase is in turn initiated by pre-existing irregularities on the slope that concentrate the flow of water and increase the discharge and therefore the sediment transport. Good examples of rilling and gullying can be seen in the Alberta Badlands, along the sides of valleys in the Prairies, in the central interior of British Columbia, and in areas of lower relief that have been subjected to severe soil erosion, such as the shale badlands in various locations near the Niagara Escarpment in Southern Ontario (northwest of Milton, at Inglewood, and in the Aldershot area of Burlington).

The rill pattern is subject to changes in position, so that the whole slope is affected over time. Lateral movement occurs on coarse material as debris is deposited in the rill, very much like in a braided stream. Channels persist through flows until another higher-magnitude event. Weathering tends to obliterate channels cut into finer materials between flow events. The cross-section of a rill or gully can be either V-shaped or trough-shaped. The V-shaped rills and gullies tend to develop in more competent materials, while trough-shaped cross-sections occur in more easily eroded material. The shape is related to the ease at which the sides and bed of the channels are excavated. The prerequisites for rilling and gullying are similar to those for wash but differ in intensity. The concentration of overland flow is especially important. Once a channel has been established by a large discharge, a smaller discharge will occupy the feature because less energy is needed for the transportation of debris than for the erosion of the channel.

Subsurface Processes

Subsurface processes include eluviation, solution, and lessivation. *Eluviation* (subsurface wash) and *solution* involve the mobilization and movement of material in solution or as exceedingly small individual minerals through the structure and fabric of the regolith or the weathering zone. Tunnels and pipes develop because of these processes. The rates of the processes are not well known, except for in limestone terrains. There is increasing evidence that a significant amount of material is removed from the landscape in all environments through these processes, much more than by any other processes. Eluviation, solution, and lessivation act primarily near to or at the surface. The main component of change occurs backwards into the slope, and thus slope angles stay the same. Studies in the Sudan have shown that about 60 percent of material removed from granite areas was removed by solution. Similar figures have also been reported from northern Sweden.

The morphological evidence for eluviation and solution include the fairly infrequent development of pipes and tunnels (with diameters of a few millimetres to a metre) in the affected areas, showing the removal of soluble material. The occurrence of these features may be a function of the structure and texture of the reglith or weathering zone. Eluvial-illuvial horizons are another form of evidence. These show the leaching of minerals from close to the surface of the soil (eluviation) and their subsequent redeposition lower down the soil profile (illuviation). In extremely arid areas, evaporation from the surface can cause the capillary rise of groundwater through the regolith and soil, and the removal of a mineral from the subsoil and its deposition close to, or at, the surface (e.g., epsomite, salt, calcium carbonate).

Lessivation is the removal of clay in suspension and its subsequent accumulation downprofile (as in luvisolic soils) or downslope. In the study of the Sudanese granite areas, it was not known whether the material lost from the weathered areas was transported in particulate or colloidal form, but some evidence suggests that the colloidal form was significant.

Two conditions must be met for subsurface processes to occur. First, there has to be sufficient rainfall (continuity being more important than intensity), and second, there must be permeability of the regolith or weathering zone. The minerals in the bedrock, regolith, and soils are important here because the type and amount of minerals influence the permeability of the material through the type and amount of weathering occurring and the development of the regolith.

The Importance of Slope Processes

It is easy to underestimate the importance of slope processes among the processes of erosion. Some of these

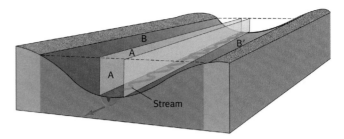

FIGURE 39.14 Comparison of the amount of rock eroded directly by a stream (**A**) and that first moved to the stream by various types of mass movement (**B, B′**).

processes occur almost imperceptibly. But they take place along the sides of many valleys and along shorelines, and a large portion of the materials swept out to sea by the world's streams is brought to these water channels through slope processes. Figure 39.14 compares the volume of rock eroded directly by a stream and the volume first moved by mass movement. Even slow, sluggish, meandering streams undercut their banks,

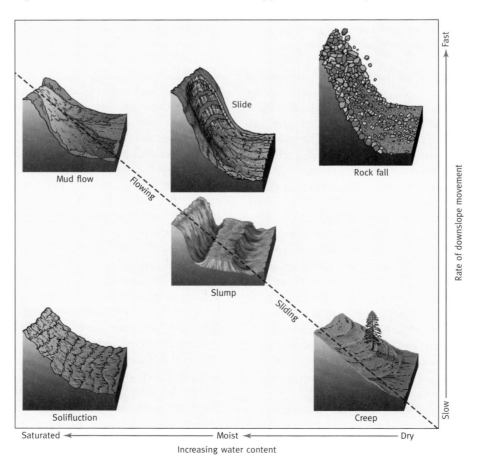

FIGURE 39.15 Common types of slope processes classified according to rate of movement and water content.

FIGURE 39.16   Eroding cliffs along the shores of Lake Ontario leave this house hanging precariously over the Scarborough Bluffs. The owners left nearly a year before this photograph was taken.

causing the collapse of materials into their waters. Rapidly eroding streams in highland areas and streams in deep canyonlike valleys cause much oversteepening and constant collapse along their valley walls. Within these categories there is sometimes more than one type of movement. These movements can be summarized in terms of the rate of downslope movement and the amount of water involved. Figure 39.15 shows how the different types of slope processes relate to one another with respect to these two parameters.

Why should so much time be spent examining the sliding and flowing earth? A knowledge of slope processes can help in planning and policymaking. It is quite costly to use public money to build public high-ways in unstable areas (see Fig 39.11). Moreover, many people have little or no regard for the stability of the land and choose to build their houses where the view is spectacular. Some of these residents have had rude awakenings, as Fig 39.16 shows.

Physical geographers are interested in slope processes for other reasons. In sculpting the land surface, slope processes perform the important job of exposing new bedrock to the forces of weathering. By the time the material sags and collapses in a flow or slide, weathering has become much less effective in attacking deeper rock layers. But the slide removes the weathered material. Thus slope processes are vitally important in the total complex of erosional processes.

KEY TERMS

Atterberg Limits *page 506*

creep *page 510*

critical threshold *page 504*

drag structure *page 511*

earth flow *page 513*

factor of safety *page 504*

gelifluction *page 511*

hillslope process *page 506*

ice wedge *page 511*

ice-wedge cast *page 511*

involution *page 511*

mass movement *page 506*

mudflow *page 513*

plasticity index *page 506*

rainsplash erosion *page 511*

relaxation *page 503*

shear strength *page 504*

shear stress *page 504*

slopewash *page 506*

slump *page 509*

solifluction *page 510*

threshold angle *page 504*

REVIEW QUESTIONS

1. What is the threshold angle and why is it significant?

2. What fundamental force acts to restrain mass-movement processes?

3. How does creep differ from a flow type of movement?

4. Where (in a tectonic setting) would one expect the highest frequency of large debris and rock avalanches?

5. What is solifluction? How does it differ from gelifluction? In what environment is gelifluction most common?

REFERENCES AND FURTHER READINGS

ALLISON, R. *Rock Slopes* (Cambridge, Mass.: Blackwell, 1999).

BRABB, E. E., and HARROD, B. L., Eds. *Landslides: Extent and Economic Significance* (Rotterdam, Netherlands: Balkema, 1989).

CARSON, M., and KIRBY, M. *Hillslope Form and Process* (London/New York: Cambridge Univ. Press, 1972).

COUTURE, R. *Workshop on Landslide Hazards and Risk Management in Canada* (Ottawa: Geological Survey of Canada Open File Report 4316, 2003).

CROZIER, M. J. *Landslides: Causes, Consequences and Environment* (London/New York: Methuen, 1986).

CRUDEN, D. M. "Major Rockslides in the Rockies," *Canadian Geotechnical Journal* 13 (1976), 8–20.

EISBACHER, G. H. "First Order Regionalization of Landslide Characteristics in the Canadian Cordillera," *Geoscience Canada* 6 (1979), 69–79.

EISBACHER, G. H., and Clague, J. J. *Destructive Mass Movements in High Mountains: Hazards and Management* (Ottawa: Geological Survey of Canada Paper 84-16, 1984).

ERISMANN, T. H., and ABELE, G. *Dynamics of Rockslides and Rockfalls* (New York: Springer-Verlag, 2001).

EVANS, S. G. "Landslides," in Brooks, G. R., *A Synthesis of Geological Hazards in Canada* (Ottawa: Geological Survey of Canada Bulletin 548, 2001), 43–79.

EVANS, S. G., and SAVIGNY, K. W. "Landslides in the Vancouver–Fraser Valley–Whistler Region," in Monger, J. W. H., Ed., *Geology and Geological Hazards in the Vancouver Region, Southwestern British Columbia* (Ottawa: Geological Survey of Canada Bulletin 481, 1984), 251–286.

HAYS, W. W., Ed. *Facing Geologic and Hydrologic Hazards* (Washington, D.C.: U.S. Geologic Survey, Professional Paper 1240-B, 1981).

JAMIESON, B. "Snow Avalanches," in Brooks, G. R., *A Synthesis of Geological Hazards in Canada* (Ottawa: Geological Survey of Canada Bulletin 548, 2001), 81–100.

SCHUMM, S. A., and MOSLEY, M. P., Eds. *Slope Morphology* (Stroudsburg, Pa.: Dowden, Hutchinson and Ross, 1973).

SCHUSTER, R. L., and KRIZEK, R. J., Eds. *Landslides: Analysis and Control* (Washington, D.C.: National Academy of Sciences, 1978).

SELBY, M. J. *Hillslope Materials and Processes* (London/New York: Oxford Univ. Press, 1982).

SHARPE, C. F. S. *Landslides and Related Phenomena: A Study of Mass Movements of Soil and Rock* (Paterson, N.J.; Pageant Books, 2nd ed., 1960).

VOIGHT, B., Ed. *Rockslides and Avalanches* (Amsterdam, Netherlands: Elsevier, 2 vols., 1978).

YOUNG, A. *Slopes* (London/New York: Longman, 2nd ed., 1975).

ZARUBA, Q., and MENCL, V. *Landslides and Their Control* (Amsterdam, Netherlands: Elsevier, 1969).

WEB RESOURCES

http://earthsci.org/geopro/massmov/massmov.html This website provides descriptions, diagrams, and many photographs of landslides, soil creep, debris flow, mudflows and lahars, solifluction, and rockfalls and slides.

http://vulcan.wr.usgs.gov/Projects/MassMovement This USGS page provides links to a variety of topics relating to the dynamics of mass movements, including the USGS National Landslide Hazards Program website.

Water in the Lithosphere

Boiling water emanates from joints and fissures in the rocks in the Upper Hot Springs, Banff, Alberta.

OBJECTIVES

- To discuss the various paths water may take on and within the surface of the lithosphere

- To introduce fundamental aspects of river flow

- To outline basic concepts related to groundwater hydrology

W ater is the essence of life on Earth. Humanity's earliest civilizations arose in the valleys of great rivers. Our ancestors learned to control the seasonal floods of these streams, and irrigation made planned farming possible. Today we refer to those cultures as *hydraulic civilizations* in recognition of their ability to control and exploit water. Our current dependence on water is no less fundamental. Society's technological progress notwithstanding, water remains the Earth's most critical resource. Human beings can do without oil, coal, or iron, but they cannot survive without water. Thus the historical geography of human settlement on this planet is in no small part the history of the search for, and use of, water.

The operations of the hydrological cycle are introduced in Fig. 12.2, in the unit that treats the part of the hydrosphere found in the atmosphere (water vapour). In the present unit the focus is on the part of the hydrosphere contained in the lithosphere. In Units 41 to 43 streams are discussed, the primary agents of landscape formation. But before water collects in streams, it must travel over or through the surficial layer. Arriving as precipitation (snowfall and rainfall), some of it evaporates. Some of it falls on plants; some of it moistens the upper soil layers; some of it seeps deeper down and collects in underground reservoirs. And part of it runs downslope and collects, first in small channels, then in larger creeks, to become part of the volume of streams.

Water at the Surface

Our inquiry starts with a raindrop that arrives at the Earth's surface. What happens to it depends on the nature and state of the surface. In some cases, raindrops never actually reach the ground; they fall on vegetation and evaporate before they can penetrate the soil. Figure 40.1 shows where this **interception** occurs.

The amount of water intercepted by vegetation depends on the structure of the plants involved. In Australia, for example, eucalyptus trees intercept only 2 to 3 percent of the rain. Hemlock and Douglas fir forests in British Columbia possess a different structure and intercept as much as 40 percent of the rain. If the rainwater reaches the ground, it can be absorbed by the surface. Such surfaces as concrete roads or granite outcrops that

FIGURE 40.1   Vegetation intercepts a percentage of rainfall. These drops on a few blades of grass do not seem to amount to much, but over a large area such interception can amount to a substantial volume of water that does not reach or saturate the soil.

do not permit water to pass through them are said to be *impermeable*. Most natural surfaces absorb a portion of the water that falls on them and are considered *permeable*, although the degree of permeability depends on many factors.

The flow of water into the Earth's surface through the pores (spaces between particles) and openings in the soil mass is called **infiltration**. The infiltration rate depends on several factors: (1) the physical characteristics of the soil, (2) how much moisture is already in the soil, (3) the type and extent of the vegetation cover, (4) the slope of the surface, and (5) the nature of the rainfall.

The most evident characteristics of soil that affect infiltration are its structure and the closeness of the soil particles. For the most part, water can infiltrate more rapidly into coarse, sandy soils than into clay soils. In a much studied valley in Switzerland, forest soil absorbs 100 mm of water in two minutes, but a pasture where cattle graze requires three hours to take in the same amount of water.

A soil that is already wet will allow less infiltration than a dry soil because the soil surface becomes compacted by the rain. The clays in the soil also may swell, closing small openings. Small particles wash into the surface openings, decreasing the porosity, and the existing pores become filled with water and cannot accept any more. Infiltration rates are usually highest in vegetated areas because the vegetation prevents raindrops from compacting the soil, and the roots act to increase the permeability of the surface layer. Moreover, organic litter provides a home for burrowing animals, whose activities further loosen the soil.

The type of vegetation also affects infiltration. The infiltration rate of a bluegrass meadow is decidedly greater than that of a tilled cornfield. Figure 40.2 shows the typical shape of an infiltration curve for two kinds of vegetation. Infiltration rates for both kinds are high at the start of a rainfall event and then decrease over time.

Steep slopes may encourage runoff before water can be absorbed, so the infiltration rate is likely to be somewhat higher on gentler slopes and flat surfaces. The characteristics of local rainfall are also critical to the infiltration rate. Rainfall can vary in intensity, duration, and amount. The *intensity* is the amount of water that falls in a given time. A rainfall intensity of 5 mm per hour is quite heavy; if it kept up for a *duration* of 10 hours, it would produce a total amount of 50 mm of rain.

If the rainstorm has a great enough intensity and duration, it will exceed the infiltration rate. Water begins to accumulate in small puddles and pools. It collects in any hollow on a rough ground surface, detained behind millions of little natural dams. This situation is called

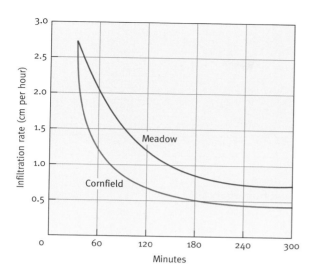

FIGURE 40.2   Infiltration rates for two different vegetated areas. Both show higher rates at the beginning than at the end of the rainfall, but the meadow has higher rates throughout.

surface retention. When there is more rainwater than the small detention hollows can hold, the water flows over the land as surface **runoff** (or *overland flow*). After a short period of detention, any rainfall that does not infiltrate the soil runs off. Thus, as precipitation continues and infiltration rates decrease, runoff rates increase.

Once surface runoff has started, the water continues to flow until it reaches a stream or an area of permeable soil or rock. An area of land on a slope receives all the water that runs off the higher elevations above it. The longer the total flow path, assuming that the runoff flows across uniform material, the greater the amount of runoff flowing across the area. Therefore the largest runoff rates occur at the base of a slope, just before the runoff enters a stream. This emphasizes the need for sound land management practices. If water is needed for raising crops, then the less that runs off the better. Because infiltration and runoff rates are inversely related, runoff depends on all the factors that affect infiltration. By employing appropriate farming techniques, high infiltration rates can be maintained and runoff rates reduced (see Fig. 23.1).

Water Flow in Streams

A study of stream flow helps us to make predictions about such matters as pollution and floods. From the smallest flow in a tiny rivulet to the largest flow in a major river, certain general rules apply.

Stream Channels

One fundamental property of a stream channel is its **gradient**, or **slope**, the difference in elevation between two points along the stream course. Gradients can be measured for the entire course of a stream or over a reach (a short stretch of it). When a gradient is high, the flow of water is very turbulent, as in a mountain stream that has rapids and falls along its channel (Fig. 40.3). By contrast, the lower portions of rivers such as the Mackenzie and the Amazon have very low gradients. The Amazon River, for instance, falls only about 6 m over its final 800 km.

FIGURE 40.3   Lower Falls, Gold Creek, Alberta.

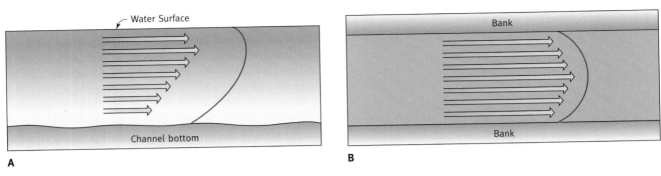

FIGURE 40.4   Velocity variation in a stream, viewed from the side (A) and from above (B).

Not all water in a stream channel moves at the same speed, or **velocity**. Water tends to move fastest in the centre of the channel, just below the surface, and slowest close to the bed and banks of the channel, where it encounters roughness and resistance (Fig. 40.4). The **discharge** (Q) of a stream is the volume of water passing a given point of the channel per unit of time. It is measured using the average water velocity (m/s) multiplied by the cross-sectional area (m²). Thus, **Q** (discharge) is measured in m³/s.

In Canada the Water Survey maintains gauging stations on numerous streams of all sizes. Two types of observations are made: (1) water depth and (2) velocity. These data can be used to construct a **rating curve** from which the discharge can be ascertained for a certain flow depth (Fig 40.5).

Long-term records of stream discharge are very important in flood-control strategies or dam construction. Discharge and sediment records indicate how much ma-

terial the stream can carry downstream in suspension (i.e., kept in the flow by its turbulence and movement). This reflects the stream's effectiveness as an erosional agent.

Stream Flow

Measurements of stream flows and sediment loads produce some surprises. For example, some sparkling mountain "torrents" have lower velocities than the placid lower segments of the Mackenzie River. This happens because water in mountain streams often flows in circular *eddies*, whose backward movement is almost as great as their forward movement. Only careful measurement can prove the eye wrong. Hydrologists have devised various instruments to obtain some measure of the properties of streams. Some of these instruments are designed to be hung from bridges or other structures, and other stations use weirs or culverts. Once installed they begin to record the behaviour of the stream.

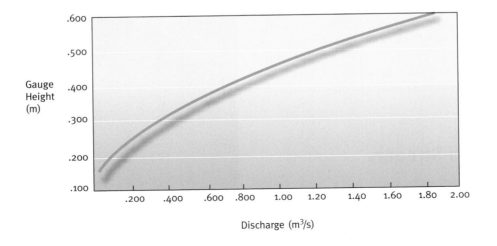

FIGURE 40.5   A rating curve (Stage-Discharge) for Sheridan Creek, Interior British Columbia.

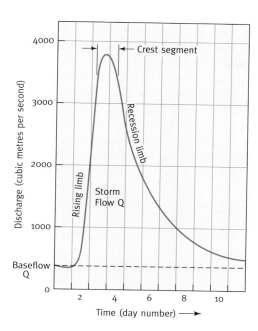

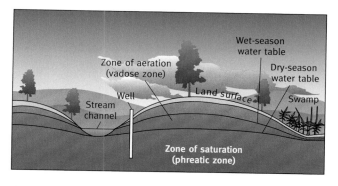

FIGURE 40.7 Two subsurface water-holding zones. The term *groundwater* applies to water lying below the water table—in the zone of saturation.

FIGURE 40.6 Hydrograph for the St. Mary River, Nova Scotia, Canada, showing the discharge associated with an individual storm.

The most important aspect of a stream to be measured is its discharge, from which other properties can be deduced. But discharge varies—by season, by year, and over longer periods. A graph of a stream's discharge over time is called a **hydrograph** (Fig. 40.6), and the one shown here records a 10-day period during which the discharge was affected by a storm in Nova Scotia's St. Mary River drainage basin. This is only one event in that river's life. The longer the hydrographic record, the more accurate our knowledge of a stream basin's hydrology.

Water Beneath the Surface

Despite the beauty and importance of streams, they contain only 0.03 percent of all the freshwater in the world. Twice as much is stored as soil moisture, and 10 times as much is held in lakes. By far the greatest proportion of the world's freshwater (75 percent) is locked in glaciers and ice sheets. But about a quarter of the total freshwater supply is available only under certain conditions. This water is hidden beneath the ground, within the lithosphere, and is called **groundwater**. A raindrop that falls to the Earth may remain above ground or it may infiltrate into the soil and rock. Two zones within the ground may hold this water. The upper zone, usually unsaturated except at times of heavy rain, is called the **zone of aeration** or the *vadose zone;* below this is the

zone of saturation, sometimes called the *phreatic zone* (Fig. 40.7). Water infiltrates into the vadose zone first.

Soil Moisture in the Zone of Aeration

Once rainwater has infiltrated into the soil, it is called *soil moisture,* and any further movement is by processes other than infiltration. The downward movement of water through the pores and spaces in the soil under the influence of gravity, called *percolation,* is the most common method of water movement in a soil. In a contrary motion, described in Unit 23, water may also move upward, like liquid in a straw, through *capillary action.* Moisture can also move around within the soil through evaporation, movement of water vapour, and recondensation onto new surfaces.

The texture and structure of the soil determine the amount of water it can hold. **Field capacity** is the maximum amount of water that a soil can hold by capillary tension against the force of gravity. Theoretically, soil moisture can fall to zero. But it takes a lot of drying to reach this limit because a thin film of water clings tenaciously to most soil particles. This *hygroscopic* water is unavailable to plant roots. A more practical lower limit to soil moisture is termed the *wilting point,* and it varies for different soils and crops. Below this point a plant dries out, suffering permanent injury. The total *soil storage capacity* for agricultural purposes is the product of the average depth in centimetres to which roots grow and the water storage per centimetre for that soil type.

Groundwater in the Zone of Saturation

Below the zone of aeration is a zone that is permanently saturated with water. The top of the phreatic zone is a surface called the **water table** (see Fig. 40.7). Instead of lying horizontally, the water table tends to follow the

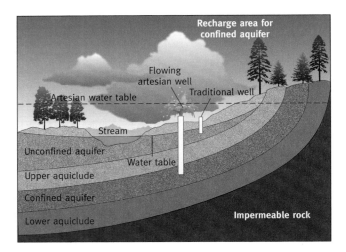

FIGURE 40.8 Aquifers, aquicludes, and their relationship to the water table and wells.

outline of the land surface, as Fig. 40.8 indicates. Where it intersects the surface, a spring, stream, lake, or wetland occurs (Fig. 40.8 shows the location of a stream in relation to the water table).

The materials of the lithosphere below the water table can be classified according to their water-holding properties, and these are also exhibited in the diagram. Porous and permeable layers that can be at least partially saturated are called **aquifers**. Sandstone and limestone often are good aquifers. Other rock layers, such as mudstone and shale, consist of tightly packed or interlocking particles and, therefore, are usually quite impermeable and resist groundwater infiltration. These are known as **aquicludes** (sometimes called *aquitards*).

An *unconfined aquifer* obtains its water from local infiltration, but a *confined aquifer* exists between aquicludes and often obtains its water from a distant area where the rock layer of the aquifer is exposed at the surface (as shown in the upper right-hand portion of Fig. 40.8).

Wells and Springs

In many parts of the world, settlements are located near wells and springs. In such cases, geology directly influences human locational decision-making. Wells can be dug wherever an aquifer lies below the surface, and in most cases springs are formed when an aquifer intersects the surface. In recent years the effect of agricultural runoff on well-water quality has been in the news because of the pollution of groundwater (trapped by artesian wells) and the resulting illness of many hundreds of people in the Walkerton area of Southern Ontario.

There are two kinds of wells—the traditional and the artesian. The *traditional well* is simply a circular opening or drill hole in the ground that penetrates the water table. Water is then drawn or pumped to the surface. Traditional wells usually are sunk below the average level of the water table. The actual level of the water table may vary seasonally and because of droughts or long periods of rainfall. So the deeper the well is sunk below the water table, the less chance there is of the well's becoming dry when the water table falls. Most modern wells are drilled, cased in metal or plastic from the surface into the water table to prevent contamination from surface runoff (e.g., road salt) and infiltration by other chemicals. A submersible pump is then installed to raise water to the surface.

The French region of Artois has a confined aquifer whose water supply is recharged from a remote location. Wells sunk into this aquifer produce water that flows to the surface under its own natural pressure (see Fig. 40.8). Artois has lent its name to this type of well, and now **artesian wells** are common in many parts of the world. The pressure in artesian wells can sometimes be quite strong. One dug in the Prairies spouted water over 30 m into the air and had to be plugged with 15 wagon loads of rock before it could be brought under control.

Wells sometimes suffer from side effects that limit their use. In some cases the water is withdrawn faster than it can be replaced by water flowing through the aquifer. When this happens, the local water table directly surrounding the well drops, forming a *cone of depression* like that in Fig. 40.9A. The amount of the drop in the local water table is called the *drawdown*. When it drops, energy must be used to bring the water to the surface. In addition, saltwater can intrude into a well near a coastline. Excessive pumping gradually moves denser, saline seawater (a saline wedge) into the well, as diagrammed in Fig. 40.9B. Wells, therefore, must be used with care.

Flowing water that emerges from the ground is called a **spring**. Springs can be formed in a number of ways. Most commonly, an aquiclude stops the downward percolation of water, which is then forced to flow from a hillside, as indicated in Fig. 40.10A. Occasionally, as this diagram also shows, the aquiclude leads to the formation of a separate water table, called a **perched water table**, at a higher elevation than the main water table. Sometimes water finds its way through joints in otherwise impermeable rocks, such as granite, and springs form where it reaches the surface. Often, faulting rearranges aquifers and aquicludes so that springs form, as shown in Fig. 40.10B. And exceptionally high water tables after long periods of heavy rainfall can occasionally raise the water

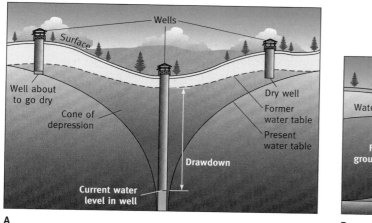

A

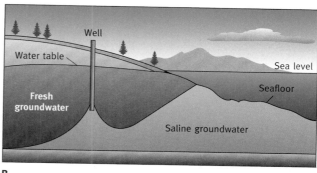

B

FIGURE 40.9 Potential disadvantages of wells. When water is pumped out faster than it can be replaced, the local water table drops in the form of a cone of depression (A). Near a coastline, excessive pumping can lead to the intrusion of seawater into the well (B).

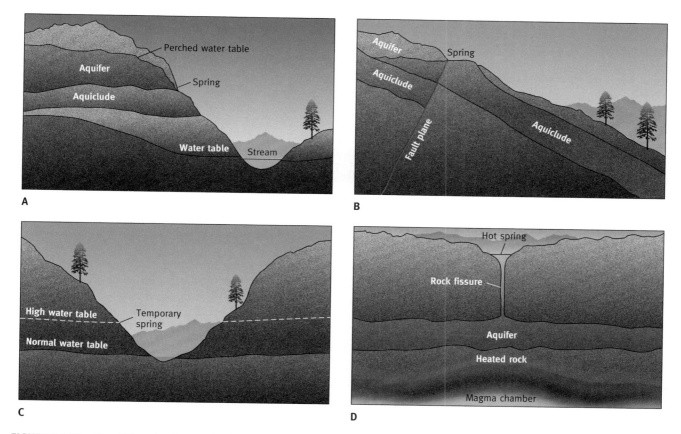

A

B

C

D

FIGURE 40.10 Conditions leading to the formation of springs.

level high enough to cause temporary springs, as shown in Fig. 40.10C.

An interesting variation is the formation of *hot springs*. The water flowing from these has a temperature averaging more than 10°C. It often comes from springs

overlying portions of the Earth's crust that contain magma chambers close to the surface (as in Fig. 40.10D). Hot springs are common in the western mountain region of Canada—in the Rockies (Cave and Basin Springs at Banff, Alberta; Fairmont Hot Springs,

FIGURE 40.11 Old Faithful geyser in Yellowstone National Park, which erupts approximately once an hour. A *geyser* is a hot spring that periodically expels jets of heated water and steam.

B.C.; and Takhini Hot Springs, Yukon), in the Coast Mountains (Harrison Hot Springs, B.C.), and in Nahanni National Park, N.W.T. (Rabbit Kettle Hot Springs). Yellowstone National Park in the United States has many geothermal springs and geysers (Fig. 40.11).

Geothermal steam can be used to produce electricity. Heated water from hot springs is used to run the Svartsengi geothermal power station, which supplies most of Reykjavik, the capital of Iceland, with electricity. Submarine, mineral-rich hot water springs also occur in spreading zones. These are called **black and white smokers** (depending on the colour of the water and minerals involved). They are associated with mineral chimneys and **chemotrophic** communities of the worms, crabs, and fish.

Hot springs containing large quantities of minerals dissolved from the surrounding rocks are sometimes called *mineral springs,* and the mineral water may be used for medicinal purposes. Although it is very pleasant to sit in the warm-water bath of a tapped mineral spring, this is one of the less important uses of water. A far more significant human impact is the growing pollution of subsurface water supplies (see Perspective: Groundwater Contamination).

PERSPECTIVES ON THE HUMAN ENVIRONMENT

Groundwater Contamination

Residents of highly developed, industrialized countries have long taken it for granted that when they turn on a faucet, safe, potable water will flow from the tap. Throughout most of the rest of the world, however, the available water—particularly groundwater—is usually unfit for human consumption. Although natural dissolved substances make some of this water undrinkable, the more common situation is that these groundwater supplies have become contaminated through the introduction of human, industrial, or agricultural wastes at the surface (e.g., Walkerton, Ontario).

The most common source of water pollution in wells and springs is sewage. Drainage from septic tanks, malfunctioning sewers, privies, and barnyards widely contaminates groundwater. If water contaminated with sewage (coliform) bacteria passes through soil and/or rock with sizeable openings, such as coarse gravel or cavity-pocked limestone, it can travel considerable distances while remaining polluted.

Vast quantities of human refuse and industrial waste products are also deposited in shallow basins at the land surface. When such a landfill site reaches its capacity nowadays, it is usually sealed within an impermeable membrane, topped by a layer of soil, and then revegetated. (Older landfills, and there are thousands of them, large and small, have simply been abandoned.) Many of the waste products, now buried below ground, are activated by rainwater that percolates downward through the site, carrying away soluble substances. In this manner, harmful chemicals slowly seep into aquifers and contaminate them. The pollutants mi-

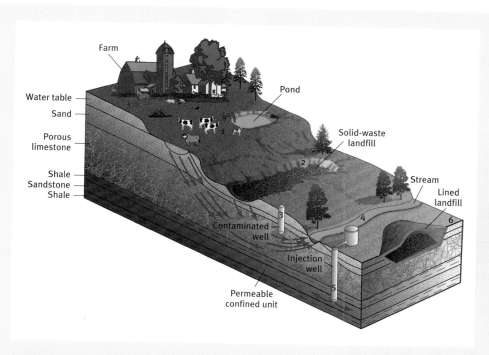

FIGURE 40.12 Groundwater system contaminated by toxic agricultural and other wastes. Toxins in animal waste (**1**) and an unlined landfill (**2**) percolate downward and contaminate an underlying aquifer. Also contaminated are a well downslope (**3**) and a stream (**4**) at the base of the hill. Safer alternative approaches to waste management include injection into a deep, confined rock layer (**5**) that lies well below aquifers used for water supplies, and a carefully constructed surface landfill (**6**) that is fully lined to prevent downward seepage of wastes. Since neither of the latter approaches is completely reliable, constant monitoring at both sites would be necessary.

grate from landfill sites as plumes of contaminated water, following the regional groundwater flow regime, and they are dispersed at the same rates as the natural flow of subsurface water (Fig. 40.12). Moreover, these effluents are frequently toxic not only to humans but also to plants and animals in the larger biotic environment.

Yet another hazard is posed by toxic chemicals. Each year pesticides and herbicides are sprayed in massive quantities over countless farm fields to improve crop quality and productivity. As is well known, some of these chemicals have been linked to cancers and birth defects in humans; other toxic substances of this type have led to disastrous declines in animal populations. Because of the way in which they are spread, toxic agricultural chemicals can invade the groundwater system beneath huge areas as precipitation flushes them into the soil.

The movement of water on and through the surface of the Earth has important consequences for the erosion, transportation, and deposition of surficial materials. In the following units we highlight the various pathways this water takes, the environmental controls determining their relative magnitudes, and the resultant geomorphic work that is being done. We begin our survey in Unit 41, which explores the processes of stream erosion.

KEY TERMS

aquiclude *page 524*

aquifer *page 524*

artesian well *page 524*

black and white smokers *page 526*

chemotrophic *page 526*

discharge *page 522*

field capacity *page 523*

gradient (slope) *page 521*

groundwater *page 523*

hydrograph *page 523*

infiltration *page 520*

interception *page 520*

perched water table *page 524*

rating curve *page 522*

runoff *page 521*

slope *page 521*

spring *page 524*

velocity *page 522*

water table *page 523*

zone of aeration *page 523*

zone of saturation *page 523*

REVIEW QUESTIONS

1. What general factors influence infiltration characteristics within a soil mass?

2. What is a hydrograph?

3. How does the water table relate to the zones of aeration and saturation?

4. Describe an aquifer and an aquiclude.

5. What is an artesian well?

REFERENCES AND FURTHER READINGS

BALDWIN, H. L., and McGUINNESS, C. I.   *A Primer on Groundwater* (Washington, D.C.: U.S. Geological Survey, 1963).

CECH, T. V.   *Water Resources* (New York: Wiley, 2003).

CHAPELLE, F. H.   *The Hidden Sea: Ground Water, Science, and Environmental Realism* (Tucson, Ariz.: Geoscience Press, 1997).

FREEZE, R. A., and CHERRY, J. A.   *Groundwater* (Englewood Cliffs, N.J.: Prentice-Hall, 1979).

GLEICK, P. H.   *The World's Water 2000–2001: The Biennial Report on Freshwater Resources* (Washington, D.C.: Island Press, 2000).

GREGORY, K. J., and WALLING, D. E.   *Drainage Basins: Form, Process and Management* (Malden, Mass.: Blackwell, 1998).

GURNELL, A., and PETTS, G., Eds.   *River Channels* (New York: Wiley, 1996).

HICKIN, E. J., Ed.   *River Geomorphology* (New York: Wiley, 1995).

LEOPOLD, L. B.   *Water: A Primer* (San Francisco: Freeman, 1974).

LEOPOLD, L. B.   *A View of the River* (Cambridge, Mass.: Harvard Univ. Press, 1994).

MATHER, J. R.   *Water Resources: Distribution, Use, and Management* (New York: Wiley/Winston, 1984).

MAURITS LA RIVIÈRE, J. W.   "Threats to the World's Water," *Scientific American* (September 1989), 80–94.

MILLER, D. H.   *Water at the Surface of the Earth: An Introduction to Ecosystem Hydrodynamics* (New York: Academic Press, 1977).

MOORE, J. E., and WILSON, W. E., Eds.   *Glossary of Hydrology* (Alexandria, Va.: American Geological Institute, 1998).

OUTWATER, A.   *Water: A Natural History* (New York: Basic Books, 1996).

PIELOU, E. C.   *Fresh Water* (Chicago: Univ. of Chicago Press, 1998).

PRICE, M.   *Introducing Ground Water* (London/New York: Chapman and Hall, 1985).

WEB RESOURCES

http://www.dnr.state.mn.us/groundwater/aquifers.html This web page provides basic information about aquifer formation and classification. Each type of aquifer is described in detail, and links are provided to other water resource pages.

http://www.nps.gov/yell/nature/geothermal This site, created by the National Park Service at Yellowstone, is a tutorial covering the mechanisms of many geothermal features, including hot springs, mud pots, fumaroles, mammoth terraces, and geysers. Photographs are included.

http://www.nwri.ca This website has links to many useful sites that concentrate on all aspects of water in Canada.

Slopes and Streams

Small drainage basin in British Columbia's Rocky Mountains.

OBJECTIVES

- To discuss the processes associated with the erosion of hillslopes
- To outline the factors influencing the erosional activity of streams and to discuss the mechanisms of stream erosion and sediment transport
- To characterize the stream as a system and to identify the processes associated with this system

Streams are the most important sculptors of terrestrial landscapes. Elsewhere in Part Five landscapes carved by glaciers, moulded by the wind, and shaped by waves are discussed. However, none of these erosional agents come close to flowing water as the principal creator of landforms and landscapes on our planet. Even where ice sheets advanced and receded, and where deserts exist today, channellized flowing water plays a major role in modifying the surface.

The Latin word for river is *fluvius*, from which the term *fluvial* is derived, denoting running water. Thus **fluvial processes** are the geomorphological processes associated with flowing water, and fluvial landforms and landscapes are produced by streams. Unit 37 notes that streams degrade (erode) and aggrade (deposit). Hence the landscape contains *degradational* or *erosional* landforms, created when rock is removed, and *aggradational* or *depositional* landforms, resulting from the accumulation of sediment. The Grand Canyon of the Nahanni River in the N.W.T. is essentially an erosional landscape; the delta of the Mackenzie River is an assemblage of depositional landforms. After we have studied fluvial processes, we will examine the landscapes they create.

Erosion and the Hydrological Cycle

Unit 12 examines the hydrological cycle, the global system that carries water from sea to land and back again (see Fig. 12.2). This unceasing circulation of water ensures the continuation of fluvial erosion because the water that falls on the elevated landmasses will always flow back toward sea level. As it does so, it carries the products of weathering with it.

Rainfall comes in many different forms, from the steady, gentle rain of a cloudy autumn day to the violent heavy downpour associated with a midsummer afternoon thunderstorm. During a misty drizzle, the soil generally is able to absorb all or most of the water because its **infiltration rate** (the rate at which it is able to absorb water from the surface) is not exceeded. This means that no water collects at the surface. But when rain falls at higher intensities, it may quickly saturate the soil and exceed the infiltration rate, resulting in *runoff* (Ri > Ir). Many small, temporary streamlets form, and with such runoff comes erosion.

Large, heavy raindrops dislodge soil particles in a process called *rainsplash erosion,* a form of mass movement (Fig. 41.1). Once loosened, these grains are quickly carried away by sheetwash in the streamlets that form during an intense rainstorm. If the surface is flat, much of the loosened soil may be deposited nearby, and the area suffers little net loss of soil. But if the exposed soil lies on a slope, rainsplash erosion results in a downslope transfer of soil. The steeper the slope, the faster this degradation proceeds. If the rate of erosion, over the long term, exceeds the rate of soil formation, the slope will lose its soil cover and suffer **denudation** (the reduction in the relief of a landscape resulting from the combined processes of weathering, mass movement, and erosion).

Vegetation plays an important role in restraining erosional forces. Leaves and branches break the fall of raindrops and lessen their erosive impact, and the roots

FIGURE 41.1 Rainsplash erosion. The impact of a drop of water is shown here on a lake surface, but if the drop hits the ground, soil particles are thrown into the air ballistically. If this occurs on a slope, the particles will fall back below their original positions. Cumulatively this process contributes to downslope movement of the uppermost soil surface.

of plants bind the soil and help resist its removal. Leaf litter and grass cover form a cushion between raindrop impact and the soil. Wherever vegetation cover is dense and unbroken, erosion is generally slight. But where natural vegetation is removed to make way for agriculture or construction, or is perhaps decimated by overgrazing, accelerated erosion often results (see Fig. 22.3).

Streams and Basins

Rain that is not absorbed by the soil runs off as *sheet wash* (*sheet flow*). Sheet wash is a thin layer of water that moves downslope without being confined to channels. This thin film of water can cause considerable erosion as it removes fine-grained surface materials. Such **sheet erosion** is an important degradational process in certain areas, especially in deserts where the ground is bare and unable to absorb water rapidly. Continued runoff causes undulations in a surface or the initiation and growth of small channels called *rills,* which may merge into larger *gullies,*

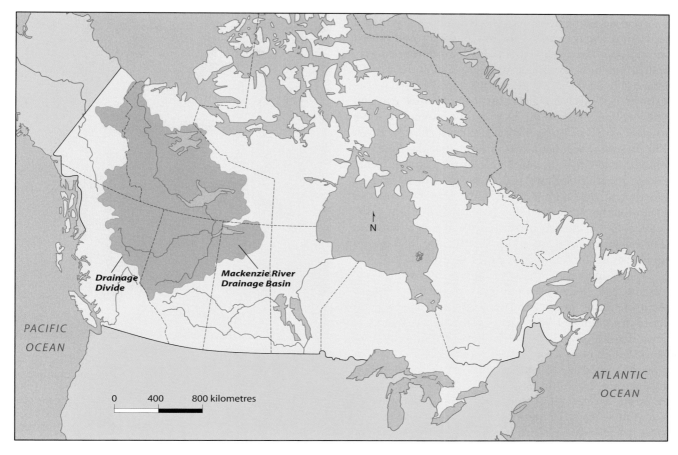

FIGURE 41.2   Drainage basin of the Mackenzie River. It includes all the areas drained by the Mackenzie (trunk stream) and its chief tributaries, the Liard, Arctic Red, and Hare Indian rivers.

and these in turn coalesce into more permanent streams. This water carries sediment with it, and both water and sediment become part of the stream system that is in the process of shaping the regional landscape.

A stream system consists of a *trunk* stream joined by a number of *tributary* streams, which are themselves fed by smaller tributaries. These branch streams diminish in size the farther they are from the trunk stream. The complete system of the trunk and its tributaries forms a drainage network that occupies a region known as a **drainage basin**. One of the best-defined drainage basins in the world is the Mississippi Basin in North America. The Mackenzie River is the trunk stream in the basin; the chief tributaries are the Liard, the Arctic Red, and Hare Indian rivers. In Canada the Mackenzie Basin is a good example of a drainage basin (Fig. 41.2).

A drainage basin is defined by the organization and orientation of water flow. Within it, all streams flow into other streams that ultimately join the trunk stream. The drainage basin supplies runoff and sediment to sustain the stream. A drainage basin is also sometimes referred to as a *watershed*. Adjacent drainage basins are separated from each other by topographical rises called drainage *divides*. One of the most prominent divides in the world is the Continental Divide in western North America, where it follows the spine of the Rocky Mountains (see Fig. 45.1B). Water from the eastern slope of the Rocky Mountains in Canada flows across the Prairies and into Hudson Bay (Fig. 41.2). Water falling on the western slope drains into streams that flow into the Pacific Ocean.

To assess the erosional activity of a stream system in a defined basin, physical geographers take a number of measurements. An obvious one is the quantity of sediment that passes a point on a stream at or near its mouth. The measurement of the total volume of sediment leaving a stream basin in a year is the *sediment yield* (tonnes/yr). But this may not reveal all the erosional work that goes on inside the drainage basin, because some sediment is deposited as **alluvium** at the lower ends of slopes and in the floodplains of streams and thus does not reach the lowest part of the trunk stream.

Another set of measurements identifies every stream segment of the network and the sedimentary load carried by each one. This research has yielded some interesting results. It might be expected, for example, that the larger a drainage basin the larger the sediment load carried by the streams. But this is not always the case. The vast Amazon Basin of equatorial South America, for instance, is more than six times as large as the basin of India's Ganges River. But its annual sediment load, measured at the Amazon's mouth, is less than one-fifth that of the Ganges. Other comparisons also indicate that basin size and the amount of sediment yield are not reliable indicators of the amount of erosion that occurs within a drainage basin. Most of the erosion in the Amazon basin occurs through solution. The Amazon's solution load (dissolved solid) is far greater and far more important than its sediment load.

What influences the rate of erosion? Obviously the amount and type of weathering is a major factor (in the Amazon Basin, because of the high temperatures and humidity, chemical weathering is intense and occurs to great depths [>30–50m plus in places]). The amount of *precipitation* is a factor—more water means more erosion. But the cover of *vegetation* also plays an important role because it inhibits erosion. The dense forests in the Amazon Basin undoubtedly help slow down erosion; but as these tropical rainforests are removed—at a prodigious pace, as is explained in Unit 17—the rate of erosion also increases. The *relief* in the drainage basin is important as well. In a basin where the relief is generally low, slopes are less steep, water moves more slowly, and erosion is less active than in a basin where the relief is high. Another factor is the underlying *lithology*, or rock type. "Soft" sedimentary and "weak" metamorphic rocks are degraded much more rapidly than are hard crystalline rocks. In fact, any factors influencing the permeability of the drainage basin surface also influence erosion rates. More-permeable surfaces such as sandy or gravelly soils allow more infiltration. This means that there is less surface erosion, but as the water moves below the surface, it interacts with minerals in the soil, sediments, and rocks, and weathers some of this material, putting it into solution (dissolved solids). This groundwater is released at a fairly slow and constant rate to the stream. The residence time for groundwater can be 10,000 years plus. (This is called a *baseflow stream regime.*) If the surface is less permeable (as would be the case with clayey or silty soils), more water is routed across the surface and can pick up soil particles and carry them to the stream. The runoff occurs during and after rainfall or snowmelt. Thus there are sporadic pulses of water and fine sediment arriving at the stream over the course of the year. Streams that rely on the sporadic or seasonal input of rain- or snowmelt-generated runoff are

FIGURE 41.3   The Aswan High Dam, built during the 1960s in the Nile Valley of southern Egypt, is a classic example of human interference in the river erosion process. In this 1988 photo, taken by an astronaut aboard the space shuttle, the area is dominated by a huge reservoir (Lake Nasser) that has filled behind the dam (top centre, where the lake ends). Besides enhancing erosion all around the new lake, the dam has caused increased deposition within the reservoir, as well as an entirely new flow regime in the river below the dam (to the north), all the way from Aswan to the densely populated Nile Delta (see Fig. 41.5).

called *ephemeral streams.* These are characterized by a *flashing* (as in flash flood) *stream regime. Human impact* must also be a factor influencing stream-basin erosion rates. Although human activity can affect the fluvial system in many ways, the usual result is an increased rate of regional degradation (Fig. 41.3).

The Stream as a System

The stream is one of the simplest and most easily understood examples of a system that occurs on the Earth's surface (systems are discussed in Unit 1). It is an open system, with both matter and energy flowing through it, as shown in Fig. 41.4. The most obvious material flowing through the system is water, entering as precipitation on any part of the drainage basin and leaving by either evapotranspiration or stream discharge.

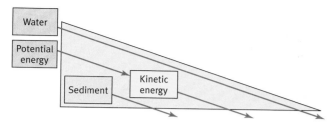

FIGURE 41.4 A stream as an open system.

Energy and Work in a River System

The water generates kinetic energy as it flows downstream. Through the action of the hydrological cycle (see Fig. 12.2)—powered by energy from the Sun—water vapour and, after condensation, liquid water are given potential energy. Any object possesses potential energy by virtue of being raised above the Earth's surface and of work having been done against gravity. The motion of water in a stream represents the transformation of potential energy into kinetic energy, the energy of movement. The water uses kinetic energy to carry its load and move itself. By the time the water has reached its base level, there is no more potential energy available. Thus no kinetic energy can be generated, and the stream is unable to do further work.

Another kind of material, sediment, enters and leaves the fluvial system. Sediment is produced by weathering processes, mass movement, erosion, and scouring of the stream bed and banks. Its movement through the fluvial system is facilitated by the kinetic energy of the flowing water. The two "flows," water and sediment, are used to define the behaviour of the river system.

A stream is often characterized as a *steady-state* system—one in which inputs and outputs are constant and equal—at least with regard to water and energy. The environment is always changing (e.g., one year there is more rainfall, the next less than average rainfall) and therefore streams (and other natural systems) are in a state of **dynamic equilibrium** rather than in a steady state (Fig. 41.5). Physical laws suggest that energy and matter in such a system must move in a particular way. First, there is a tendency for the least work to be done. In a stream where all the water starts at the top of one tributary, the least-work profile would be a waterfall straight down to sea level. More practically, the least-work profile would be steep near the head and close to horizontal near the mouth of the stream, as demonstrated in Fig. 41.6. It is possible that the sediment carried and deposited by the stream could interfere with or complicate these states.

Another tendency in a system is for work to be uniformly distributed. A stream in which this occurred

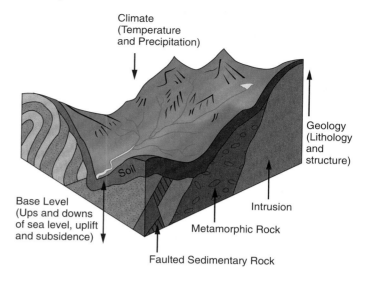

FIGURE 41.5 The controlling factors of dynamic equilibrium.

would get wider downstream but have a nearly constant slope, as in the uppermost curve in Fig. 41.6. A *graded* stream profile is a compromise between the principles of least work and uniform distribution of work, but the graded profile is possible only when the channels are in a material that can be degraded and aggraded. The fact that this profile is indeed typical of many streams suggests that the graded stream represents some sort of steady-state system, and it also requires us to look more closely at the concept of grade.

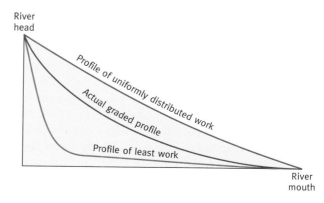

FIGURE 41.6 Formation of a stream profile as a compromise between the principles of uniformly distributed work and least work. This profile is reached if the material of the river channel is adjustable (i.e., capable of being degraded and aggraded).

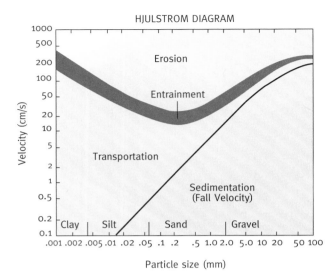

FIGURE 41.7 The Hjulstrom Diagram shows the relationship between flow velocity and particle size.

Stream Functions and Valley Characteristics

As streams modify the landscape, they perform numerous functions. These functions can be grouped under three headings: *erosion* (degradation), *transportation* (transfer), and *deposition* (aggradation). Before we examine these processes, let us consider what happens to the river valley itself. A stream is not static—it changes continuously. In fact, one conceptual model used by geographers in the early twentieth century describes the life cycle of a river in organic terms, suggesting that it evolved through stages of youth, maturity, and old age.

As the stream develops, the characteristics of its valley change. In the area where the river has its origin, streamlets merge to form the main valley. Over time the "head" or source of the valley is extended upslope in a process called **headward erosion**. This has the effect of lengthening the stream valley, but it is not the only way a river's course grows longer. At the other end of the valley, the stream reaches the coast of a sea or lake and may deposit its sedimentary load in a **delta** (Fig. 41.7). Now the river must flow across its own deltaic deposits, which lengthens the distance to its mouth. And between source and mouth, a river will develop bends and turns that make its course longer still. Valley *lengthening*, therefore, affects river valleys as the streams within them perform their erosional and depositional functions.

Streams tend to flow more rapidly, even wildly, in mountainous areas (see Fig. 40.3). Many streams arise in the mountains and rush downslope in deep valleys. The

FIGURE 41.8 An astronaut's view of the Nile Delta, looking southward from a position over the Mediterranean Sea (bottom). The city of Cairo, Egypt's capital, lies near the junction of the apex of the delta's triangle and the Nile River channel. A small part of the El Faiyum Depression is visible just west (to the right) of the Nile River at the top of the photograph. A portion of the Gulf of Suez, Great Bitter Lake, and the Suez Canal can be seen to the east (left); some cirrus clouds hover near the ancient city of Alexandria near the western point of the delta (far right). The dark colour of the delta itself reflects intensive agriculture, in contrast to the nearly empty desert flanking it. A huge population is concentrated here and, as the image shows, in the lower valley of the Nile beyond.

high velocity of the water, its growing volume, and the sediments being swept along all contribute to valley *deepening*.

Erosion by Streams

Stream erosion takes place in three ways: *hydraulic action, abrasion,* and *solution.*

Hydraulic Action The work of the water itself, as it dislodges and drags away rock material from the stream-channel bed and banks, is referred to as its **hydraulic action**. You can feel the force of the water by wading across a shallow mountain stream. Even in water little more than 30 cm deep, you may have trouble keeping your balance. Large volumes of fast-moving water can break loose sizeable material and move it downstream. In its rough-sided channel, the stream develops numerous eddies and swirls that can gouge out potholes and other depressions with the aid of its load.

Abrasion   **Abrasion** refers to the mechanical erosive action of boulders, pebbles, and smaller grains of sediment as they are carried along the stream channel. These fragments dislodge other particles along the stream bed and banks, thereby contributing to the deepening and widening process. Gravel- and sand-sized particles tend to scour the channel bed, wearing it down while eroding the banks. Abrasion and hydraulic action most often function in combination; without abrasive action, hydraulic action would take much longer to erode the stream perimeter.

Solution   In terms of the volume of rock removed, **solution** may be the most important form of erosion by streams in some areas (e.g., in the humid tropics). It is the process by which certain rocks and minerals are dissolved by water. Limestone, for instance, is eroded not only by hydraulic action and abrasion, but also through solution. A sandstone held together by a calcite matrix will be weakened and removed because the water dissolves the cement. In Unit 44 there is a discussion of the special landscapes formed when solution is the dominant form of erosion in limestone terrain but they are unusual and develop only under certain environmental conditions.

Transportation by Streams

Erosion and transportation go hand in hand. The materials loosened by hydraulic action and abrasion, as well as dissolved minerals, are carried downstream. The Hjulstrom Diagram shows the relationship between flow velocity and particle size. It indicates at what velocities certain sizes of material are mobilized or entrained, transported, and deposited (Fig. 41.7). Note that more velocity is needed to mobilize clay and sand particles than medium sand particles when electrochemically bound. Also note that the distance between the entrainment and fall velocity lines decreases with increasing particle size, indicating that a slight change in velocity can cause erosion or deposition. Smaller particles need a high entrainment velocity but fall out of transport (are deposited) at very low flow velocities. Along the way, different transportation processes are dominant. In the mountains, streams carry coarser material (sand and gravel) along in a high-velocity rush of water; near the coast, slow-moving water is brown- or grey-coloured

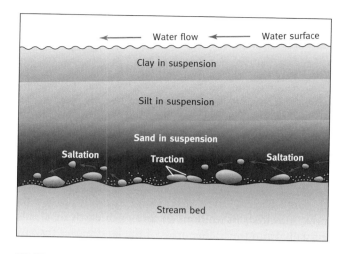

FIGURE 41.9   Heavier sand and gravel fragments are dragged along the stream bed by traction, while lighter fragments in the bed load advance downstream by saltation. Finer silt and clay particles are carried above in the suspended load, maintained there by the stream's turbulence until the water flow nears a standstill. The finest suspended material is flushed out of the stream system and deposited in a lake or the sea.

with concentration of fine sediment. Let us now identify the four ways a stream transports its load: *traction, saltation, suspension,* and *solution.*

Traction   **Traction** refers to the sliding or rolling of heavier particles along the stream bed. This is accomplished by hydraulic action, as large pieces of rock are literally rolled or dragged along the stream bed channel (lag) (Fig. 41.9). Traction breaks down larger material into gravel- and sand-sized fragments, which may begin to bounce along the stream bed.

Saltation   The speed of the water lifts these fragments off the river bed, and they bounce along in a process called **saltation** (from Latin, meaning jump). Saltation, therefore, is a combination of traction and suspension: the particles make contact with the stream bed, but they also are briefly suspended as they move downstream (Fig. 41.9). They travel in a ballistic trajectory downstream and hit other particles, putting them into the same kind of motion.

Suspension   Very fine sediment, in the silt- and clay-sized grades, is carried within the stream by a process known as **suspension** (Fig. 41.9). When suspension dominates, stream water becomes muddy, and even when it moves very slowly, it can carry huge amounts of fine sediment. Material in suspension does not make contact with the river bottom except when the water is slowed to a near standstill. The finest suspended material (wash load) is usually completely flushed out of the stream system is deposited in a lake or the sea.

Solution　As noted earlier, some rock material dissolves in stream water and is carried downstream in *solution*. It is not confined to calcium-rich rocks. Numerous other minerals can be partially dissolved, and even a clear mountain stream contains ions of sodium, potassium, and other materials.

Stream Deposition

In combination, these four transportation processes move hundreds of millions of tonnes of earth materials annually from the higher areas of the landmasses toward lower areas, where deposition takes place (as, for example, at the bottom of valleys and in deltas). In the upper reaches of drainage basins, sediment particles in streams are generally large. These are left behind because they are too large to move. With increasing distance downstream, the particle size decreases. Aggradational processes dominate in some areas. This depositional work of streams is discussed in Unit 43; but first we need to explore the factors that govern the effectiveness of streams as they erode and transport their loads.

Factors in Stream Erosion

Stream Power

Stream capacity is used to denote the maximum load of sediment that a stream can carry at a given *discharge* (volume of water). It is rather obvious that a stream with a large discharge has a larger capacity than a smaller stream. Another way to measure the erosional effectiveness of a stream is by determining its *competence*, which depends on the velocity (speed) of water movement. The faster a stream flows, the greater is its ability to move large material in its channel. A combination of large volume *and* high velocity gives a stream substantial capacity and competence.

The *velocity* of a stream (usually measured in m/s), therefore, is a critical factor in its ability to erode and transport. As a rule, the greatest water velocity meanders across the stream channel and is usually associated with the thalweg or low-flow channel (deepest part of the stream). At meander bends the fastest velocities are generally found toward the outer banks. As the water flows from one bend to the next (through the straightaway), the fastest velocity will actually be found close to the midpoint of the stream. Because of friction, the velocity is slowed as the banks and bed are approached. In Fig. 41.10 the red line represents the line of maximum

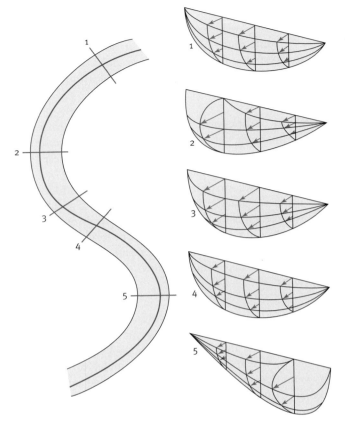

FIGURE　41.10　Velocity distribution in cross-sections through a meandering or curving channel (lengths of arrows indicate relative flow velocities). The zones of highest velocity (red arrows), associated with the thalweg, lie near the surface and toward the middle of the stream where the channel is relatively straight (cross-sections 1 and 4). At meander bends the maximum velocity swings toward the outer bank and lies below the surface (cross-sections 2 and 5).

velocity (and the thalweg); note that it lies toward the outside of the bends in the channel meander bends. Stream erosion is most active on the outside of those bends, (creating a cut bank or meander or river *cliff*) enlarging them over time.

The *gradient*, or slope, is the key factor in a stream's velocity. Again, this is obvious: a stream plunging down a steep mountain slope has a much higher velocity than a stream of equal volume crossing a coastal plain. What is less obvious, however, is the effect of even a slight change in gradient on the velocity (and thus the erosional power) of a stream. Sometimes the region across which a stream flows is tilted slightly upward by tectonic forces. This may not be very obvious in the landscape, but a stream whose gradient is increased immediately begins to erode its bed with new vigour.

The shape and size of the stream channel also affects velocity and erosional capacity. An open, bowl-shaped, fairly smooth channel cross-section promotes rapid water flow and efficient action. A wide, shallow channel generates too much friction and reduces both velocity and erosional capacity. And a stream channel that has irregular sides and a rock-strewn floor also slows water movement.

Stream Floods

Streamflow volume varies through time as a result of changing water inputs from various areas of the drainage basin and the stream's tributaries. Abnormally high rainfall or abrupt seasonal snowmelt can produce a **flood** in the stream system. A flood occurs when stream discharge overflows its channel banks onto the **floodplain**. These floods often result in aggressive scouring of stream beds and banks, the reshaping of the channel, the undercutting of valley sides, and many other consequences. The erosional power of large catastrophic floods is visually striking and temporarily devastating. Such floods are important in terms of erosion, transportation, and the reworking of the floodplain. Overbank flows (floods) occur about every 1.5 to 1.6 years on all types of rivers. Extremely large events, though high in magnitude, are infrequent (50, 100, 150 years). As the flood abates, sediment is put into storage on the lower parts of slopes, in the floodplain, and in in-channel bars.

The below bankfull discharge is the other important type of flow. Below bankfull discharge occurs 98 to 99 percent of the time. This type of discharge plays a significant role in shaping the stream channel. Most erosion occurs early in the spring before bank vegetation grows and defends the bank. At this point the banks are wet (because of rainfall and snowmelt) and therefore heavier and prone to collapse if undercut by the sediment and water flow. Then bank material collapses into the stream and is carried downstream.

Not all floods are exclusively erosional, of course. Streams, particularly in their lower courses, often rise above their average levels and sometimes overflow their normal channels. During such episodes the rivers inundate their floodplains, the low-lying ground adjacent to the stream channel. Fine-grained and mineral-rich overbank deposits give rise to highly productive soils, often attracting dense human settlement. Although floodplain dwellers know the risks involved in living on the low ground near flood-prone streams (see Perspective: The Hazards of Floodplain Settlement), the fertility of the soils has made that gamble worth taking (Fig. 41.11).

FIGURE 41.11 Floodplains are frequently endowed with highly fertile soils, which encourages many people to undertake the risk of farming them. This is the Red River floodplain in Manitoba.

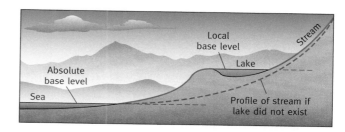

FIGURE 41.12 Profile of a stream showing its relationship to local and absolute base levels.

Base Levels

We can learn much about the behaviour of streams by studying their longitudinal *profiles,* their downward curve from the source to their mouths. As a stream erodes and modifies its valley by deepening, widening, and lengthening its channel, it also tends to create a smooth, downstream profile. This does not occur in areas affected by the Late Cenozoic Ice Age. The profile in these areas is stepped. A critical factor in this process is the stream's **base level**—the level below which a stream cannot erode its bed. When a stream reaches the ocean, its capacity to erode ends (although muddy currents offshore are known to be capable of some degradation). For our purposes, a stream's **absolute base level** lies no more than a few metres below sea level. There the stream slows down, deposits its sedimentary load, and its erosional work is terminated.

Some streams, however, do not reach the ocean. A stream that flows into a lake does not relate to the global sea level. The effective base level is the lake level, at

CANADIAN GEOGRAPHERS IN THE FIELD

"As an undergraduate research project at Simon Fraser University, I studied the geomorphic impacts of reservoir construction on the sand-bed braided South Saskatchewan River. This photography was taken during a flight with a local pilot from the town of Outlook. As part of my fieldwork for this research, I conducted cross-sectional channel surveys using historic benchmarks installed during the 1960s. Within these cross-sections, which were 500 to 1000 metres wide, sediment was also sampled to characterize downstream changes."

Roger T.J. Phillips is a graduate student at York University studying meander migration and the Holocene evolution of rivers in Southern Ontario.

PERSPECTIVES ON THE HUMAN ENVIRONMENT

The Hazards of Floodplain Settlement

Episodes of abnormally high stream discharge—known more commonly as *floods*—can have a major impact on the cultural as well as the physical landscape in a river basin. About one-eighth of the population of the United States now resides in areas of potential flooding. To these people the advantages of living in a flood-prone area outweigh the risks (just as people continue to live on the slopes of active volcanoes and near the San Andreas Fault).

The advantages include the fertility of the soils in these floodplain zones and the flatness of the land. Crops grow bountifully, and the land is easy to farm and develop. The risks, however, are great, and they are not only financial. Recent flood losses in North America have exceeded $1 billion per year, and dozens of human lives are lost annually.

The decision to live on or to avoid a floodplain is not strictly rational. The geographers Gilbert White, Robert Kates, and Ian Burton have shown that human adjustments to the known dangers of flooding do not increase consistently as the risk becomes greater, because people tend to make an optimistic rationalization for continuing to live in a potential flood zone.

There are other decisions and tradeoffs associated with floodplain settlement and development.

Floods are natural events, but we sometimes try unnatural methods to prevent their worst effects. Dams and high artificial banks or *levees* like those in Fig. 41.13 can be built, but such structures sometimes have some unwanted side effects. Dams, although they help control flooding, can prevent the natural replacement of fertile alluvial soil because the sediment collects behind the dam instead. The Aswan High Dam in Egypt (see Fig. 41.3), in the middle Nile Valley, holds back sediment that would otherwise be deposited on the highly productive agricultural land in the lower Nile floodplain and delta. Furthermore, artificial levees in floodplains can create a false sense of security.

These levees are seldom designed to cope with the worst possible flood because of the great expense that would entail. But often the higher the levee, the more people will live in the area and the greater the disaster will be when a major flood (such as a "100-year flood" event) does occur. Therefore it is essential for us to have an understanding of floodplains as well as other natural phenomena of the Earth. Otherwise we cannot make rational decisions about where to live or make the necessary adjustments if we do choose to live in a floodplain. One day you may have to vote on issues such as these.

FIGURE 41.13 Close-up aerial view of the artificial levee system that lines the banks of the lower Mississippi Valley, here in northeastern Louisiana about 50 km downstream from the riverfront city of Vicksburg in the neighbouring state of Mississippi. Note the service roadway that runs on top of the protective levee, which separates the village of St. Joseph and its surrounding farmscape from the often inundated trees that grow along the river's natural banks. This is part of the regional water-control system built by the U.S. Army Corps of Engineers that extends all the way to New Orleans and the delta beyond.

Table 41.1 Factors Involved in the Tendency of a Stream to Achieve Equilibrium

Independent	Semidependent	Dependent
Climate (Q & sediment load)	Channel width	Slope
Geology (sediment & Q)	Channel depth	
Base level (energy)	Bed roughness	
	Grain size of sediment load	
	Velocity	
	Meander/braid tendency	

Source: Information from Bloom, A. L. *The Surface of the Earth* (Englewood Cliffs, N.J.: Prentice-Hall, 1969).

whatever altitude it may lie; the lake therefore becomes the stream's **local base level** (Fig. 41.12). On occasion, a stream that erodes downward reaches an especially hard, resistant rock barrier, perhaps in the form of a dyke (see Unit 30). That barrier may keep the stream from developing a smooth profile until the stream has penetrated it. This creates a **temporary base level**, which temporarily limits further upstream channel incision.

The Concept of the Graded River System

This concept states that streams ultimately establish a longitudinal profile, which allows the stream's load to be transported with neither degradation nor aggradation at any part of the profile. If this happens, the river is said to be **graded**. A graded stream represents a balance among long profile, water volume, water velocity, and transported load. Many factors are involved in the tendency for a stream to attain a graded state, and these factors may be classed as either independent, semidependent, or dependent (Table 41.1).

Independent factors are those over which the stream has little or no control and to which it must simply adjust. Climate and ultimate base level are good examples. The stream must adjust to its ultimate base level because at this point it no longer has any potential or kinetic energy. The *semidependent* factors are partly determined by the three independent factors in Table 41.1, but also, partly, they interact among themselves. The roughness of the stream channel bed and the grain size of the sediment load, for example, interact. The bed roughness is partly determined by the size of the sediment grains and, in turn, partially determines the degree of mixing, or *turbulence,* in the stream. The sediment size generally decreases downstream. Only finer particles remain in suspension in the lower part of the river, where turbulence decreases. Thus sediment grain size and bed roughness interact via the turbulence factor.

There is only one variable in the table that appears to be *dependent* on all others, and this is the gradient or slope of the stream. The stream has virtually complete control of this by either depositing or eroding away material as necessary. It was the propensity of a stream to change its slope that first set investigators thinking about the concept of grade. Not until later was it completely realized that many other factors could be involved.

The consensus is that a graded stream is one in which, over a period of time, stream slope, channel characteristics, and flow volumes are delicately adjusted to provide just the velocity required for the transportation of the load supplied from the drainage basin. A graded stream is a system in dynamic equilibrium. Its diagnostic characteristic is that any change in any of its controlling factors causes a displacement of the equilibrium in a direction that tends to absorb the effect of the change (negative feedback loops). So if a stream was dammed, erosion might occur downstream but ultimately would stop once coarser material was exposed that could not be eroded by the reduced water flow. In some cases deposition might occur.

Not all streams are graded, and not all graded streams assume a smooth longitudinal profile. A newly uplifted tectonic landscape or a recently deglaciated area (e.g., Canada) would present a chaotic drainage system, with profiles far from graded. The semidependent variables are usually the first to adjust themselves to the process of moving material downstream. It has been argued that a stream usually establishes grade in its lower reaches first, and then the graded condition is slowly extended upstream toward its source. But, because of differences in rock resistance and other factors, it is quite possible for grade to exist in isolated segments of the

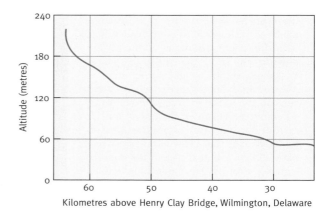

FIGURE 41.14 Longitudinal profile of Brandywine Creek in Pennsylvania and Delaware, a graded river without a smooth profile.

complete river profile. Brandywine Creek (in Pennsylvania and Delaware) manifests an irregular profile; yet it has been shown to have achieved grade, as Fig. 41.14 demonstrates.

Streams degrade, transport, and aggrade. Here we have studied the processes of stream erosion, and in Units 42 and 43 we examine the products of the work of streams in the landscape. These products range from spectacular canyons and deep gorges to extensive deltaic plains. As we study these landforms, we will learn still more about stream processes.

KEY TERMS

abrasion *page 534*

absolute base level *page 537*

alluvium *page 531*

base level *page 537*

delta *page 533*

denudation *page 530*

drainage basin *page 531*

dynamic equilibrium *page 533*

flood *page 536*

floodplain *page 536*

fluvial processes *page 529*

graded river *page 537*

headward erosion *page 533*

hydraulic action *page 534*

infiltration rate *page 530*

local base level *page 537*

saltation *page 535*

sheet erosion *page 530*

solution *page 534*

stream capacity *page 536*

suspension *page 535*

temporary base level *page 537*

traction *page 535*

REVIEW QUESTIONS

1. How does overflowing water accomplish erosion? What processes are involved?
2. Describe the arrangement of streams within a drainage basin.
3. What factors determine the erosional activity of streams within a drainage basin?
4. Describe the three stream functions.
5. What is the base level, and how is it related to the development of the longitudinal profile?
6. What are the primary independent controls on the development of a graded river system?

REFERENCES AND FURTHER READINGS

ALLEN, P. A. *Earth Surface Processes* (Malden, Mass.: Blackwell, 1997).

BROOKS, G. R., et al. "Floods," in Brooks, G. R., *A Synthesis of Geological Hazards in Canada* (Ottawa: Geological Survey of Canada Bulletin 548, 2001), 101–143.

BAKER, V. R., et al., Eds. *Flood Geomorphology* (New York: Wiley, 1988).

BLOOM, A. L. *Geomorphology: A Systematic Analysis of Late Cenozoic Landforms* (Englewood Cliffs, N.J.: Prentice-Hall, 2nd ed., 1990).

BRIDGE, J. *Rivers and Floodplains* (Malden, Mass.: Blackwell, 2002).

CALOW, P., and PETTS, G. E. *Rivers Handbook, Vol. 2* (Malden, Mass.: Blackwell, 1994).

CLIFFORD, N. J., et al., Eds. *Turbulence: Perspectives on Flow and Sediment Transport* (New York: Wiley, 1993).

GORDON, N. D., McMAHON, T. A., and FINLAYSON, B. L. *Stream Hydrology: An Introduction for Ecologists* (New York: Wiley, 1992).

GREGORY, K. J., and WALLING, D. E. *Drainage Basins: Form, Process and Management* (Cambridge, Mass.: Blackwell, 1995).

HACK, J. T. "The Interpretation of Erosional Topography in Humid Temperate Regions," *American Journal of Science* 258-A (1960), 80–97.

HERSCHY, R. W.   *Streamflow Measurement* (New York: Elsevier, 1985).

KIRKBY, M. J., Ed.   *Hillslope Hydrology* (New York: Wiley, 1978).

KNIGHTON, D.   *Fluvial Forms and Processes: A New Perspective* (New York: Oxford Univ. Press, 1998).

LAENEN, A., and DUNNETTE, D. A., Eds.   *River Quality: Dynamics and Restoration* (Boca Raton, Fla.: Lewis, 1996).

LEOPOLD, L. B., et al.   *Fluvial Processes in Geomorphology* (San Francisco: Freeman, 1964).

MALANSON, G. P.   *Riparian Landscapes* (New York: Cambridge Univ. Press, 1993).

MOORE, J. E., and WILSON, W. E., Eds.   *Glossary of Hydrology* (Alexandria, Va.: American Geological Institute, 1998).

MORISAWA, M.   *Streams: Their Dynamics and Morphology* (New York: McGraw-Hill, 1968).

PETTS, G., and FOSTER, I.   *Rivers and Landscapes* (London: Edward Arnold, 1985).

SCHUMM, S. A.   *River Morphology* (Stroudsburg, Pa.: Dowden, Hutchinson & Ross, 1972).

SMITH, D. I., and STOPP, P.   *The River Basin* (New York: Cambridge Univ. Press, 1978).

STATHAM, I.   *Earth Surface Sediment Transport* (London/New York: Oxford Univ. Press, 1977).

WARD, R.   *Floods: A Geographical Perspective* (New York: Macmillan, 1978).

WEB RESOURCES

http://sts.gsc.nrcan.gc.ca/clf/geoserv.floods.asp This website of the terrain science division of the Geological Survey of Canada website has information, data, and research about floods in Canada.

http://www.cwra.org/publications/cura This website of the Canadian Water Resources Association has information about the character of floods in different regions of Canada and offers general considerations about floods. Planning and design.

http://www.ec.gc.ca/water/er/manage/gloodgen/e-floods.htm Freshwater website. Floods table of contents. Flood links.

http://www.riverwebmuseums.org/river_facts/river_dynamics This site gives a brief overview of river basin formation and erosional processes, and includes a linked glossary of terms. Photographs and satellite images of river basins are included.

Stream Erosion

The Canadian Horseshoe Falls, Niagara Falls, drops roughly 57 metres into the Lower Niagara River. The crestline of the falls is about 670 metres and at peak times more than 168,000 cubic metres of water go over the falls every minute.

OBJECTIVES

- To outline the roles of geological structure, lithology, tectonics, and climate in influencing fluvial erosion

- To introduce terminology to characterize drainage networks and controls on fluvial erosion

- To briefly consider how landscapes might change or evolve through time in response to stream erosion

When streams erode the landscape, many processes occur simultaneously. Rock material is being removed, transported, processed, and deposited. Stream valleys are widened and deepened. Mass movements are activated. Slopes are being flattened in some places, steepened in others. Long-buried rocks are exhumed, exposed, and eroded. Endlessly, the work of streams modifies the topography.

The regional landscape—and the individual landforms comprising parts of it—reveal the erosional process or processes that dominate in particular areas. Certain fluvial landforms of desert areas, for example, do not occur in humid environments. Wide, flat floodplains, occupied by meandering stream channels, are not found in mountainous areas. Concave slopes and sharp, jagged ridges are more likely to be found in arid areas; round, convex slopes and rounded hilltops reflect moister conditions. It is possible to draw many conclusions about the processes shaping the landscape from simple observational evidence.

Factors Affecting Stream Degradation

Among the many factors influencing fluvial erosion, four have special importance: geological structure, bedrock type (or lithology), tectonic activity, and climate.

Geological Structure

Geological structure refers to features such as synclines, anticlines, domes, and faults that were formed originally by geological processes (see Unit 36). These geological structures are sculpted by streams into characteristic landforms. One of the simplest examples is a landform that results from a high-angle intrusion, a dyke.

Hogbacks and Cuestas   The crystalline rock layer of the dyke dips at a high angle and penetrates softer surrounding rocks (Fig. 42.1A). Originally this dyke might not have reached the uppermost of the sedimentary rock layers through which it penetrated, but stream erosion has degraded the countryside and exposed the much harder rock of the dyke. *Geologically* this tilted structure remains a dyke; *geographically* it stands out as a prominent, steep-sided ridge called a **hogback**. Stream erosion exposes the differences in resistance between the crystalline rock of the dyke and the sedimentary rocks surrounding it.

Other less prominent ridges may form when a sequence of sedimentary strata of varying hardness lies at a low-angle dip. This is seen in Fig. 42.1B, where erosion by streams etches out the "softest" rock strata first, leaving a low ridge with one fairly steep slope (scarp) and another very gentle one (dip). This landform, known as a **cuesta**, or an escarpment, is not usually as pronounced in the landscape as a hogback, but cuestas can be hundreds of kilometres long—for example, the Niagara Escarpment of Ontario or the Missouri Coteau of the Prairies.

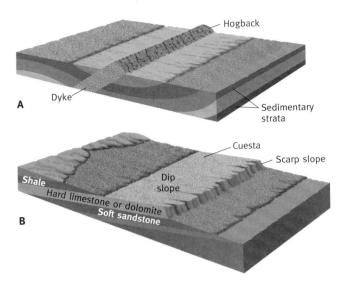

FIGURE 42.1   Hogback (A) and cuesta (B) landforms. Note that hogbacks dip at a high angle whereas cuestas dip at a low angle. (The cuesta in this drawing is associated with a dry climate.)

Ridges and Valleys   When structures become more complicated, so do the resulting landforms. The erosion of synclines and adjacent anticlines produces a series of parallel ridges and valleys that reveal the structures below. If the axes of the folds plunge, as is frequently the case, the result is a terrain of zigzag ridges (see Fig. 36.13A). Note that the steep face of the resistant layer (numbered 3 on that diagram) faces *inward* on the anticline and *outward* on the syncline, providing us with preliminary evidence of the properties of the folds below the surface. The Appalachian Mountains of eastern North America provide many examples of this topography (see Figs. 36.15 and 52.14).

Domes   In areas where sedimentary strata have been pushed upward to form a dome, stream erosion may produce a characteristic landscape in which the affected layers form a circular pattern, as shown in Fig. 42.2. An example of this type of landscape is Isachsen Dome on Ellef Ringnes Island, Nunavut. There the gypsum diapir core of the dome has already been exposed by erosion, but the overlying sedimentary layers (sandstone and shale) still cover its flanks in all directions. As a result, the regional topography consists of a series of concentric cuestas of considerable prominence, separated by persistent valleys. In some areas not only physical geographic configurations but also the human geographic features reveal the dominance of this concentric pattern: ridges, rivers, roads, and towns all exhibit circular patterns (e.g., in the Black Hills area of South Dakota and Wyoming).

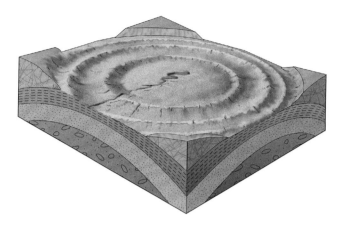

FIGURE 42.2   Circular cuestas produced by stream erosion of sedimentary rock layers pushed upward to form a structural dome.

Faults   Faults, too, are exposed and sometimes given relief by stream erosion. Of course, normal and reverse faults create topography by themselves because one block moves upward or downward with respect to the other. But after the faulting episode, stream erosion begins and the fault becomes a geographical as well as a geological feature. In fact, physical geographers distinguish between a *fault scarp* (Fig. 42.3A), a scarp (cliff) created by geological action without significant erosional change, and a *fault-line scarp,* a scarp that originated as a fault scarp but that has been modified, even displaced, by erosion (Fig. 42.3B). And where the geological structures are formed by numerous parallel (*en echelon*) faults, as happens in regions where lithospheric plates are affected by collision movements, the fault-generated terrain is also modified by stream erosion. Even prominent upthrust blocks may be worn down to a reduced relief, and valleys fill with sediment derived from these up-

lands. The overall effect is to lower the regional relief, as shown in Fig. 42.4.

Extrusive Igneous Structures   Unit 34 looked at volcanoes as geological phenomena and as landforms. Created by volcanic action, volcanic landforms are quickly modified by stream erosion. Extinct and long-dormant volcanic cones reveal their inactivity through numerous, often deep stream-cut valleys carved into their slopes. Eventually the entire mountain may be worn down to its plug and radiating dykes (Fig. 42.5). Fissure eruptions create hard sills, which may become the caprocks of plateaus or smaller landforms known as **mesas** and **buttes** (Fig. 42.6), although these two landforms may develop in sedimentary rocks with duricrusts (e.g., caliche or laterite cuirasses) as well.

Intrusive Igneous Structures   The sedimentary, fault-dominated, and volcanic structures discussed so far have quite characteristic erosional forms. From topographic and drainage patterns, we can often deduce what lies beneath the surface. But vast areas of the landmasses are underlain by granitic and metamorphic rocks that do not display such regularity. In Part Four we learned that large batholiths formed within the crust have been uplifted and exposed by erosion and that large regions of metamorphic crystalline rocks form the landscapes of the ancient shields. Some batholiths now stand above the surface as dome-shaped mountains (Fig. 42.7), smoothed by weathering and erosion. The great domes, such as Sugarloaf Mountain (Pao de Azucar), that rise above the urban landscape of Brazil's Rio de Janeiro are such products of deep-seated intrusion and subsequent erosion (see Fig. 30.6), as is the Stawamus Chief near Squamish, B.C., a granite dome rising nearly 705 m above the Howe Sound/Squamish valley bottom, north of Vancouver.

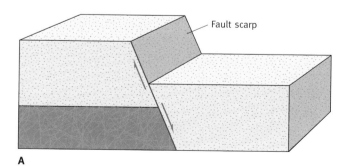

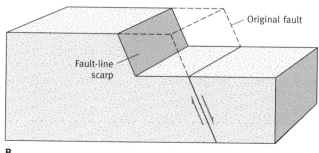

FIGURE 42.3   A fault scarp (A) originates as a result of geological activity without much erosional modification. A fault-line scarp (B) originates as a fault scarp but then undergoes significant erosional change.

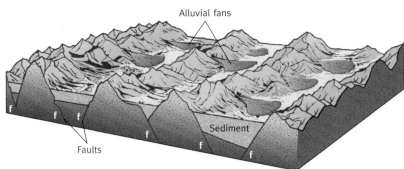

Alluvial fans

Sediment

Faults

FIGURE 42.4 The erosion of upthrown blocks leads to the filling of their intervening valleys with sediment. In the interior of British Columbia (e.g., around Ashcroft and Kamloops), parallel faults create a so-called basin-and-range topography in which the fault-formed valleys are filling up with sediment from the ranges. Short streams flowing off the uplands produce alluvial fans—fan-shaped sedimentary landforms where stream velocity is sharply reduced when the streams enter the flat valleys (see Fig. 43.1).

FROM THE FIELDNOTES

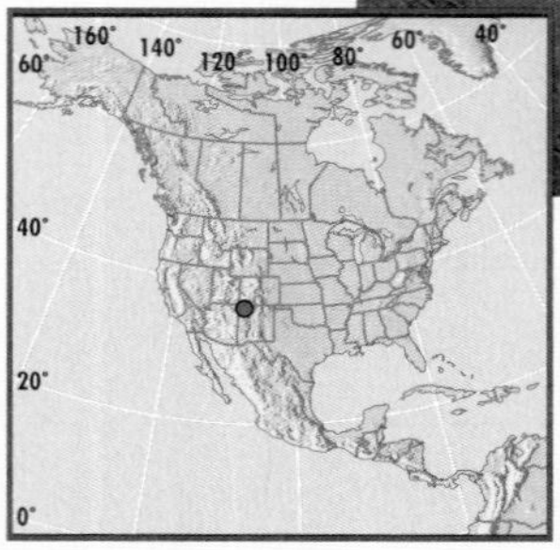

FIGURE 42.5 "Flying to the U.S. west coast from Miami I had a superb view of Ship Rock in New Mexico, a famous geological as well as cultural landmark. It is the 420-m-high remnant of a large volcano that was once active in this now stable area. Dykes radiate outward from the eroding core, marking the dimensions of this extinct giant."

Metamorphic Structures Metamorphic rocks often display regional foliation (see Unit 31), and sometimes this tendency to form belts of aligned minerals is re-flected in the drainage lines that develop upon them. Some metamorphic rocks, furthermore, are much more resistant than others, so that zones of quartzite, for in-

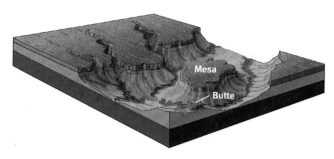

FIGURE 42.6 Mesa and butte landforms.

stance, are likely to stand above softer rocks such as weak slates and schists. Gneiss, on the other hand, is quite hard and often supports uplands reminiscent of those formed on granite batholiths.

Geological structure, therefore, is an important factor in stream erosion, a relationship that cannot be overlooked when human technology attempts to influence river courses (see Perspective: Controlling Rome's River). It also affects the development of drainage systems. Later we will discover that the actual pattern of drainage lines can reveal the nature of the underlying structural geology.

Bedrock Type (Lithology)

Rock type, for obvious reasons, strongly influences landscape evolution. This is true not only because different rock types have different properties of hardness and

FIGURE 42.7 Stawamus Chief Provincial Park protects the 700 metre massive granite cliffs, the second largest granite monolith in the world, that stand at the southern entrance to Squamish, British Columbia.

resistance against erosion, but also because they exhibit varying capacities to form slopes. A resistant crystalline rock mass, for example, can form and maintain nearly vertical scarps, but weak shales may, under certain circumstances, support a slope angle of not more than 35 degrees. In Fig. 42.9 weak shales lie between more resistant sandstone layers, creating a segmented slope in which the sandstone forms small cliffs while the shale

PERSPECTIVES ON THE HUMAN ENVIRONMENT

Controlling Rome's River*

Rivers flow through most of the world's large cities, and trying to make these water courses behave has been a priority since people first clustered alongside them. Europe's great cities, in particular, have had long experience in attempting to control local river channels, and the famous stone walls and embankments that line the Seine in Paris and the Thames in London are testimony to the fair degree of success that has been achieved.

No European city, however, has been engaged in this battle longer than Rome, and the latest Roman skirmish with its Tiber River is a reminder of the limitations that constrain the efforts of hydrologists and engineers.

Taming the Tiber is a struggle that dates back more than 2000 years, to the time of Julius Caesar, when stone bridges (still in use today) were built across the river and "improvements" made to

FIGURE 42.8   The Castel Sant'Angelo (Hadrian's Tomb) overlooks the walled embankments of the Tiber River as it flows through the heart of Rome.

its banks. Nonetheless, because the Tiber is a relatively short stream that emanates from the nearby rugged Appennine Mountains, serious floods continued to bedevil its valley regularly. By the late nineteenth century, following modern Italy's unification and the restoration of Rome as the country's capital, the new government decided to act and ordered that the Tiber be corseted by stone walls to protect the city's treasured riverside monuments (Fig. 42.8). Unfortunately, to save money, the construction program avoided erecting heavy structures that could have significantly enhanced the walls' stability. Not surprisingly, parts of the stonework collapsed a few years later during an especially bad flood. It was quickly (and cheaply) rebuilt—but this patchwork mentality prevailed until just a few years ago.

Finally realizing that their "quick fixes" would invariably be negated by natural fluvial processes, Rome's engineers are now marshalling the resources to try to achieve a long-term solution. But first they must overcome an additional problem. Upstream from Rome, the Tiber has recently been

dammed to the extent that not enough silt and sand are available to replenish the riverbed. With the removal of most of these deposits, the Tiber's erosive power has concentrated on cutting into bedrock, which threatens to undermine bridges, stone walls, and buildings adjacent to them. To meet the challenge, the most vulnerable bridges are being re-anchored to the solid bedrock, huge concrete slabs are being inserted below the water to trap silt and gravel to reinforce bridge foundations, and the heavy structures to stabilize the walls, dismissed by the builders of a century ago, have at last reached the planning stage.

Whatever happens, human ingenuity and technology will not succeed in controlling the Tiber or any other major river. That realization has been a long time in coming to the so-called Eternal City, which only after two millennia has begun to work more harmoniously with nature to do what is possible to mitigate the Tiber's hazards.

---

*The source for most of this box is Tagliabue (1993).

forms low-angle slopes. If the bedrock shown in this diagram had been uniform, no such alternation would have developed, and the valley would exhibit an unbroken **V**-shape, the angle of the sides depending on the nature of the rock.

The bedrock type also influences the sculpting of landforms, such as the zigzag pattern on plunging anticlines and synclines described earlier. If the strata folded into those structures were uniform, then the resulting landscape would not display the variation shown in Fig. 36.13. Again, when a fault has the effect of thrusting soft sedimentary rocks upward adjacent to hard crystallines, the weak sedimentaries will soon yield to erosion and the resulting landscape may *reverse* the geological imprint.

Tectonic Activity

Fluvial erosion is affected significantly by tectonic activity, especially in areas affected by collision plate movement. The landmasses are continuously influenced by the movement of lithospheric plates. Not only are peripheral areas of collision plate contact deformed, but also larger regions of the continents are subject to slight but important warping and tilting. All this has a significant effect on drainage systems and erosional effectiveness. Even a very slight increase in regional "tilt" can greatly increase a stream's effectiveness. Sometimes the profile of a stream valley indicates that the river has been *reinvigorated,* that is, its energy increased. This may be the result of several factors, among which tectonic activity is the most obvious. Uplift results in increased velocity of streamflow and enhanced erosional capacity.

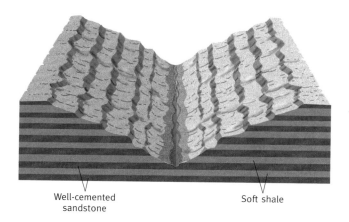

FIGURE 42.9 Alternating cliffs and gentle slopes produced by the differential erosion of resistant sandstone and weak shale.

Well-cemented sandstone

Soft shale

Climate

Climate plays a role in the evolution of landscape, but this role remains open to debate. The answer would seem to be obvious: landscapes of humid areas tend to be rounded and dominated by convex slopes, whereas landscapes of arid environments are stark, angular, and dominated by concave slopes. But detailed geomorphological research has not confirmed this contrast—or at least it has not confirmed that climate is the key factor.

Part of our impression, geomorphologists say, has to do with the cloak of vegetation in humid areas, as opposed to the barrenness of arid zones. Strip away this vegetation, they suggest, and the contrast between humid and arid landscapes may be less pronounced than we expect. Moreover, we should take climate change into account. Areas that are humid today were dry just a few thousand years ago, and vice versa. Elsewhere glaciers dominated the topography of mountains now being eroded by rivers. There are solution caves in arid areas, indicating the presence of much more water than may currently be the case. And there are valleys in high mountains that were gouged out by glacial ice, not streams. Over the long term, therefore, climate certainly plays a role in forging the landscape. But just how climate and hillslopes are related remains a contentious issue.

Drainage Patterns

The structures and rock types that are sculpted by streams into characteristic landforms strongly influence the drainage patterns that develop on them. The drainage pattern often reveals much about the geology that lies below (Fig. 42.10). By examining the way a river system has evolved in a certain area, we can begin to unravel the origins of the regional landscape. Before we study actual drainage patterns, we should acquaint ourselves with the concepts of drainage density and the constant of channel maintenance.

The effectiveness of a drainage system as an erosional force is directly related to the **drainage density**—the total length of the stream channels that exist in a unit area of a drainage basin (km/km^2). The higher the drainage density, other things being equal, the greater is the erosional efficiency of the system. More stream channels in an area means that more water is routed across the surface of the drainage basin, more erosion can take place, and more slopes are directly affected by degradation. You might expect the drainage density to be higher in humid areas than in arid locales, so that upland surfaces, virtually unaffected by stream erosion, are

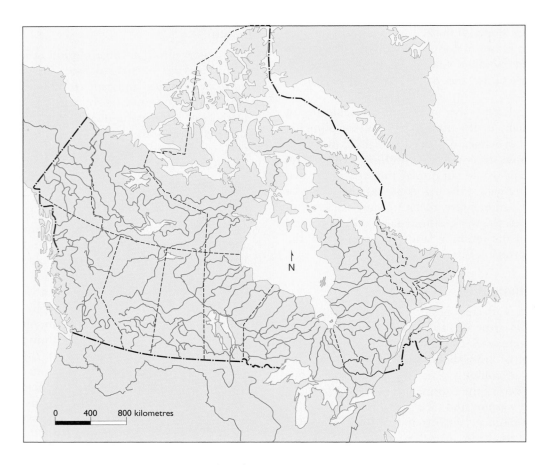

FIGURE 42.10   Dranage patterns in Canada.

more likely to exist in dry than in humid regions. If drainage density is low, more water is being infiltrated into the groundwater system, so fewer streams are necessary. In reality, drainage density is influenced by other factors besides climate, so this simple generalization is not always accurate.

Drainage density can be stated quantitatively, (see above) but it can be described as low, medium, or high. On the windward side of the Coast Mountains in British Columbia, in the path of moist winds, the drainage density is likely to be high; on a mountain range in the arid interior of the province, it will be low. When the drainage density is medium to high, drainage patterns become clear. The **constant of channel maintenance** (Ccm) is the reciprocal of drainage density. It is the area of drainage basin necessary to sustain part or all of a stream (km²/km). In humid temperate areas, such as British Columbia or Southern Ontario, Ccm is in the order of 1.5–2 km²/km. In more arid areas, such as Arizona or New Mexico, it is approximately 350 km²/km because of less precipitation, greater evapotranspiration,

and so on. To see a drainage pattern most clearly, it is best to study a map that shows *only* streams, nothing else. The pattern alone will be useful in later interpretations of structures and rocks.

A **radial drainage** pattern, for instance, shows the drainage of a conical mountain flowing in all directions (Fig. 42.11A). It is possible to tell that the drainage in this example flows outward in all directions from the way tributaries join. Except under the most unusual circumstances, tributaries join larger streams at angles of less than 90 degrees, and often at much smaller angles. Radial patterns of the kind shown in Fig. 42.11A develop most often on volcanic cones, such as Mount Edziza in northern British Columbia.

Another highly distinctive drainage type is the **annular drainage** pattern, the kind that develops on domes like South Dakota's Black Hills structure. Here the concentric pattern of valleys is reflected by the positioning of the stream segments, which drain the interior of the excavated dome (Fig. 42.11B).

One of the most characteristic patterns is the **trellis**

drainage pattern, in which streams seem to flow in only two orientations (Fig. 42.11C). This pattern appears very regular and orderly, and often develops on parallel-folded or dipping sedimentary rocks of alternating degrees of competence. The main courses are persistent, but tributaries are short and join the larger streams at right angles.

The **rectangular drainage** pattern also reveals right-angle contacts between main streams and tributaries, but the pattern is less well developed than in the case of trellis drainage (Fig. 42.11D). What the diagram cannot show is that rectangular patterns tend to be confined to smaller areas, where a joint or a fault system dominates the structural geology. Trellis patterns, on the other hand, usually extend over wider areas. This type of pattern is well defined in Carboniferous sandstones and salt deposits of northern Nova Scotia around Cobequid Bay.

The tree-limb-like pattern shown in Fig. 42.11E is appropriately termed the **dendritic drainage** pattern because it resembles the branches of a tree. It is the most commonly developed drainage pattern in North America and elsewhere mainly outside of the parts involved in the late Cenozoic Ice Age, and it is typical on extensive batholiths of generally uniform hardness or on flat-lying sedimentary rocks. The entire drainage basin is likely to slope gently in the direction of the flow of the trunk stream. Good examples of this are the streams of the North Shore of Lake Ontario—Bronte Cree, Oakville Creek, the Credit River, Don River, and Rouge River.

A **deranged drainage** pattern (Fig. 42.11F) of small stream segments, wetlands, and lakes seemingly arranged independently of bedrock structure occurs on recently deposited glacial debris and is characteristic of many areas of Canada.

The six drainage patterns shown in Fig. 42.11 are not the only patterns that may be recognized. Other, less common patterns also develop, and some representative names are *convergent* (or *centripetal* streams flowing into a central basin), *contorted* (disorderly drainage in an area of varied metamorphic rocks), and *parallel* (streams flowing down a steep slope or between elongated landforms). Physical geographers employ this nomenclature to convey the prevalent character of regional drainage systems, often as a first guide to the interpretation of landforms.

Overcoming Geological Structure

The drainage patterns just discussed would suggest that structure exercises powerful control over stream systems in some areas. Certainly the underlying geology influences the development of the patterns seen in Fig. 42.11, but there are places where streams seem to ignore structural trends. In some areas, streams actually cut across mountain ranges when they could easily have flowed around them. What lies behind these discordant relationships?

Antecedent Streams

Why do some streams flow through mountain ranges? The ridge through which the river now flows may not have been buried but may have been gradually pushed up by tectonic processes. A stream flowing across an area so affected (Fig. 42.12A) may have been able to keep pace, eroding downward as rapidly as the ridge was being formed (Figs. 42.12B and C). This stream, therefore, predates the ridge and is referred to as an **antecedent stream**.

Stream Capture

One of the most intriguing stream processes involves the "capture" of a segment of one stream by another. Also called **stream piracy**, this process diverts water from one channel into another, weakening or even eliminating some stream courses while strengthening others. This is not just a theoretical notion, nor does it affect only small streams.

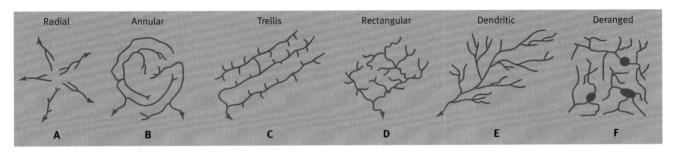

FIGURE 42.11 Six distinctive drainage patterns. Each provides clues about their underlying geological structures.

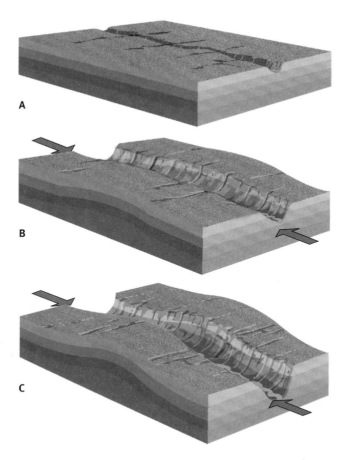

FIGURE 42.12 Evolution of an antecedent stream, which kept flowing (and eroding downward) as the mountain ridge was being tectonically uplifted across its path. Tectonic forces are shown by the purple arrows.

A map of south-central Africa, shows the great Zambezi River. Flowing toward the Zambezi from the north is the Upper Kafue River. But at Lake Iteshi the Kafue River makes an elbow turn eastward, joining the Zambezi, as shown in Fig. 42.13. What happened here is a classic case of stream capture. The Upper Kafue River once flowed south-southwestward, reaching the Zambezi as shown by the dashed line (Fig. 42.13). But another stream, the Lower Kafue, was lengthening its valley by headward erosion toward the west. When the upper part of the Lower Kafue intersected the Upper Kafue and its continuation in the area of Lake Iteshi, the flow of water from the Upper Kafue was diverted into the Lower Kafue, and its original connecting channel to the Zambezi was abandoned. Today a small stream (appropriately termed *underfit*) occupies the large valley once cut by the Kafue below Lake Iteshi. Its waters have been pirated.

This is a large-dimension case of capture, and many smaller instances can be found on maps of drainage systems. It is important, however, to realize the effect of capture. The capturing stream, by diverting into its channel the waters of another river, increases its capacity to erode and transport, and is, in that sense, reinvigorated. From the valley profile of the Lower Kafue River it is possible to see how this river's competence was increased after its piracy was successful.

Regional Geomorphology

Physical geographers perform research on landforms and drainage systems, erosional processes, and stream histories. Like other scientists, however, they also want

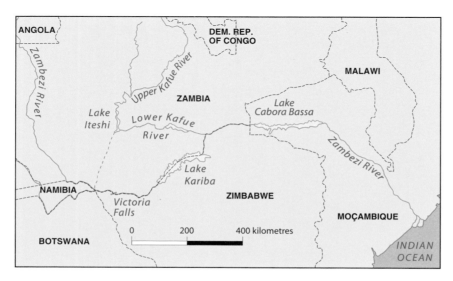

FIGURE 42.13 Stream piracy enabled the headward-eroding Lower Kafue River to capture the Upper Kafue in the vicinity of Lake Iteshi. Previously the Upper Kafue River drained into the Zambezi via the (now abandoned) connecting channel, shown by the dashed line.

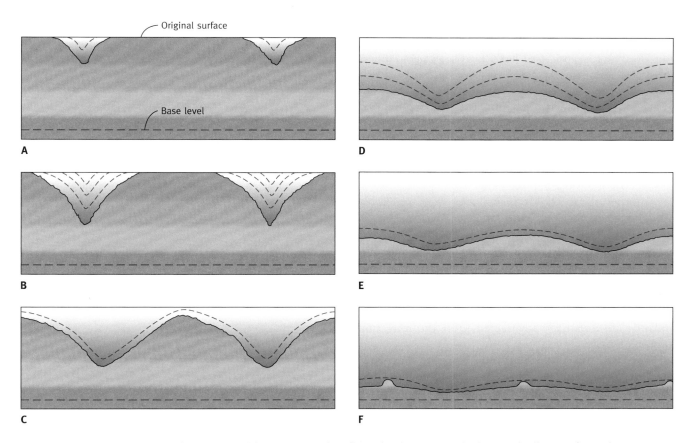

FIGURE 42.14   Davisian peneplanation model. Streams erode a flat upland area (A), which is gradually transformed into mountainous terrain (B, C). These highlands are subsequently lowered until only the hilly interfluves remain (D, E). Finally these hills are eroded away, leaving the peneplain with a few monadnocks (F).

to understand the "grand design"—the overall shaping of the landscape, the sculpting of regional geomorphology, and the processes that achieve this. At first it would seem that this is merely a matter of the sum of the parts. If the factors affecting erosional efficiency are known (such as those discussed in Units 40 and 41), then shouldn't the evolution of landscape surely be understood? The answer is, not yet. Physical geographers today still debate some very basic issues concerning regional geomorphology.

Ideas about Slopes and Landscapes Evolution

One particular debate has been going on for more than a century. It was started by William Morris Davis (1850–1934), pioneer physical geographer and professor at Harvard University from 1878 to 1912. Davis proposed that a **cycle of erosion** would affect all landscapes. This cycle had three elements: geological *structure,* geographical *process,* and time or *stage.* Every landscape, Davis argued, has an underlying geological structure; it is being acted upon by streams or other erosional processes, and it is at a certain stage of degradation. A high mountain range was thought to be in an early stage. It would eventually be worn down to a very nearly flat surface, a "near plain" or **peneplain.** This sequence of events is illustrated in Fig. 42.14. In Figs. 42.14A and B an upland is being attacked by a network of streams. The upland slopes gradually attain lower angles until the upland is transformed into mountainous terrain (Fig. 42.14C). Now the mountains are lowered until they are little more than convex hilly **interfluves** (Figs. 42.14D and E). Finally even these hills are eroded away, leaving a nearly flat plain (peneplain) with a few remnants on it (Fig. 42.14F). Davis called the most prominent, not-yet-eroded remnants **monadnocks,** after Mount Monadnock in southern New Hampshire.

In Davis's view, slopes are worn *down,* that is, they become increasingly convex in appearance, then are flattened. For many years this idea was fairly widely accepted, although many slopes were seen *not* to have a convex form. Nevin Fenneman and Grove Karl Gilbert, in the opening decades of the twentieth century, were among the first to suggest that the Davisian model did not fit all landscapes, and later, European geographers were doubtful of its simplistic view of landscape development. One of these was a friend of Davis's, Walther Penck, who published his doubts (his book, published posthumously in the 1920s, was not translated into English until the 1950s) and proposed an alternative theory concerning slopes. Penck suggested that slopes retreated backwards and in doing so were replaced by a less-steep slope (slope replacement).

Another theory holds that slopes wear *backward* while maintaining the same angles. According to a group of scholars, including Alan Wood and Lester C. King, slope retreat is the process whereby highlands are reduced to plains—not peneplains but **pediplains**, plains at the foot of mountains. This sequence of events is illustrated in Fig. 42.15. Note that the interfluves in this model retain their near vertical slopes and that the uplands are essentially unaffected until the retreating slopes intersect.

The dynamic equilibrium model is time independent and suggests that slopes are adjusted to a set of environmental conditions, including climate, base level, geology (solid or superficial), and what processes are occurring at the base of the slope or slope foot (e.g., undercutting by stream erosion or the sea) (J. T. Hack). The environment is ever changing, so it improbable that long-term erosion to a plain-like *entropy* surface would occur. **Entropy**, which is the complete lack of energy in a system, is a factor in this case because the landscape is too close to sea level.

Landscapes in different areas seem to support all four interpretations, and it was not long before some physical geographers began to link theories of slope change to climate. In humid climates, it was suggested, slopes tend to become convex. It is therefore not surprising that Davis reached such conclusions, because most of his fieldwork was done in humid areas. In arid climates, they held, slopes would develop concave properties because the drainage density was much lower, and weathering and

mass movement played more important roles. But when these ideas about *climogenetic* or *morphogenetic* landscapes (purportedly sculpted by geomorphological processes resulting from certain climatic conditions) were put to the test, they failed to account for so many exceptions that they were abandoned. And so the debate about the evolution of landscapes continues.

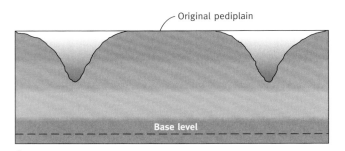

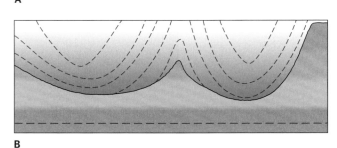

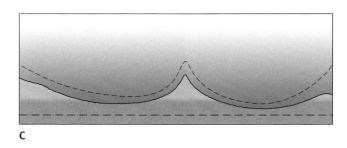

FIGURE 42.15 The pediplaination model, whereby slope retreat reduces highlands to plains. Note that the steep slope angles of the interfluvial uplands are retained throughout the entire erosional sequence.

KEY TERMS

annular drainage *page 550*

antecedent stream *page 551*

butte *page 545*

cuesta *page 544*

cycle of erosion *page 553*

dendritic drainage *page 551*

deranged drainage *page 551*

drainage density *page 549*

entropy *page 554*

geological structure *page 544*

hogback *page 544*

interfluve *page 553*

mesa *page 545*

monadnock *page 553*

pediplain *page 554*

peneplain *page 553*

radial drainage *page 550*

rectangular drainage *page 551*

stream piracy *page 551*

trellis drainage *page 551*

REVIEW QUESTIONS

1. How can lithology influence stream erosion?

2. What kinds of landforms are most likely to exhibit a radial drainage pattern?

3. Contrast a dendritic drainage pattern with a trellis pattern.

4. How might stream piracy result in the reinvigoration of a stream?

5. Briefly describe the cycle of erosion as envisioned by William Morris Davis.

6. Compare and contrast the Davisian model of slope evolution tot he idea of dynamic equilibrium.

REFERENCES AND FURTHER READINGS

ALLEN, P. A. *Earth Surface Processes* (Malden, Mass.: Blackwell, 1997).

BRIDGE, J. *Rivers and Floodplains* (Malden, Mass.: Blackwell, 2002).

CALOW, P., and PETTS, G. E. *Rivers Handbook,* Vol. 2 (Malden, Mass.: Blackwell, 1994).

CHORLEY, R. J., Ed. *Introduction to Fluvial Processes* (London: Methuen, 1971).

CHORLEY, R. J., et al. *Geomorphology* (London/New York: Methuen, 1984).

DAVIS, W. M. *Geographical Essays* (New York: Dover, 1954, reprint of 1909 original).

GORDON, N. D., McMAHON, T. A., and FINLAYSON, B. L. *Stream Hydrology: An Introduction for Ecologists* (New York: Wiley, 1992).

GREGORY, K. J., and WALLING, D. E. *Drainage Basins: Form, Process and Management* (Malden, Mass.: Blackwell, 1998).

GURNELL, A., and PETTS, G., Eds. *River Channels* (New York: Wiley, 1996).

HACK, J. T. "The Interpretation of Erosional Topography in Humid Temperate Regions," *American Journal of Science* 258-A (1960), 80–97.

HICKIN, E. J., Ed. *River Geomorphology* (New York: Wiley, 1995).

KING, P. B., and SCHUMM, S. A. *The Physical Geography of William Morris Davis* (Norwich, UK: GeoBooks, 1980).

KNIGHTON, D. *Fluvial Forms and Processes: A New Perspective* (New York: Oxford Univ. Press, 1998).

LEOPOLD, L. B., et al. *Fluvial Processes in Geomorphology* (San Francisco: Freeman, 1964).

MALANSON, G. P. *Riparian Landscapes* (New York: Cambridge Univ. Press, 1993).

MORISAWA, M. *Streams: Their Dynamics and Morphology* (New York: McGraw-Hill, 1968).

PETTS, G., and FOSTER, I. *Rivers and Landscapes* (London: Edward Arnold, 1985).

RICHARDS, K. S. *Rivers: Form and Process in Alluvial Channels* (London/New York: Methuen, 1982).

ROBERT, A. *River Processes: An Introduction to Fluvial Dynamics* (London: Arnold, 2003).

ROLAND A. E. *Geological Background and Physiography of Nova Scotia* (Halifax: Nova Scotia Institute of Science, 1982).

SCHUMM, S. A. *The Fluvial System* (New York: Wiley, 1977).

SMITH, D. I., and STOPP, P. *The River Basin* (New York: Cambridge Univ. Press, 1978).

TAGLIABUE, J. "Still Trying to Make the Tiber Behave," *New York Times* (September 16, 1993), A6.

WEB RESOURCE

http://vulcan.wr.usgs.gov/Monitoring/Descriptions/description_river_survey.html This USGS webpage describes river channel erosion in several areas of the Pacfic Northwest. Specific monitoring techniques are described, and links to other hydrologic monitoring pages are provided.

Aggradational Landforms of Streams

Sandbars have formed in the Hector Gorge of the Vermillion River, Kooteney National Park, British Columbia.

OBJECTIVES

- To identify the types of landforms built by streams

- To examine the formation and development of the stream floodplain

- To investigate the evolution of river deltas

Unit 42 examined streams as sculptors, carvers, and cutters, and explained how streams degrade and how running water can denude countrysides. This unit focuses on streams as builders. Although the world's streams disgorge hundreds of millions of tonnes of sediment annually into the oceans, part of the transported load does not reach the sea but is laid down in floodplains, in deltas, and elsewhere on land. Whereas the landforms of stream aggradation are not as spectacular as those in high mountains and incised plateaus, they are nevertheless very important. Often the deposits along a stream's lower course reveal the history of the stream's upper course, and can help us unravel the complexities in understanding the development of a regional drainage basin.

Alluvial Fans

In certain areas, especially in arid zones of the world, precipitation is infrequent and streamflow is discontinuous. Rainstorms in the mountains produce a subsequent rush of water in the valleys, and turbulent, sediment-laden streams flow toward adjacent plains. Emerging from the highlands, the water slows down and deposits its sedimentary load. Much of this water infiltrates the ground, and evaporation in the heat removes the remainder. Meanwhile it has stopped raining in the mountains, and soon the stream runs dry. A stream that flows intermittently like this is called an **ephemeral stream**.

Ephemeral streams often construct alluvial fans where they emerge from highland areas. As the term suggests, an **alluvial fan** is a fan-shaped deposit consisting of stream-carried material, located where a mountain stream emerges onto a plain (Fig. 43.1). In this situation the stream is not part of the regional drainage basin that ultimately leads to the ocean. Streams that form alluvial fans are unlikely to flow far beyond the edge of the fan. And when the mountain rains are below average, the stream may not even reach the outer margin of its own deposits.

Fan-shaped deposits are not unique to arid areas, although they are best developed there. They can also be found in areas where glaciation has taken place and where streams now carry heavy loads of debris to the edges of glacier-steepened mountains. Others are located on the flanks of steep-sided volcanoes. But the typical alluvial fan is primarily an arid landform, a product of stream aggradation.

The alluvial fan attains its conical or semicircular shape because the stream that emanates from the often gorge-like mountain valley tends to have an impermanent course on the fan surface. The sediment-clogged water, when it surges from the edge of the upland, quickly slows down, so that it must drop part of its load. Figure 43.2A shows what happens.

As the discharge drops, it exposes **midstream bars**, and water flows around these obstructions. Soon more deposition takes place, and many bars, some submerged, develop. At lower flows the stream divides into many smaller channels that intertwine with one another to form a **braided stream** (a process that in certain cases can reach several kilometres in width [Fig. 43.2B]). Under such conditions, the stream obviously cannot

FIGURE 43.1   Alluvial fan and basin Keremeos, British Columbia.

erode a deep valley. In fact, it is flowing on deposits that may build to an elevation above the rest of the fan surface. The next time rains generate a stream surge, the water may seek a different direction.

An alluvial fan, therefore, consists of a series of poorly stratified layers, thickest near the mountain front and progressively thinning outward. The coarsest sediments are normally located nearest the apex of the fan and finer-grained material toward the outer edges. Since the fan lies on bedrock and has layers of greater and lesser permeability, infiltrating water can be contained within it. Many alluvial fans in the southwestern United States and throughout the world are sources of groundwater for permanent settlements.

When environmental conditions exist for alluvial fan development, a mountain front may have not just one or two but dozens of larger and smaller alluvial fans, coalescing across the *pediment* (the smooth, gently sloping bedrock surface that underlies the alluvial cover and extends outward from the foot of the highlands). When this happens, the cone shapes of individual adjacent fans may be difficult to distinguish, and the landform is called an *alluvial apron* or a **bajada** (Spanish for slope). Such an assemblage of alluvial fans can exhibit many features. Where streamflow has increased, **arroyos** (gullies) have been cut into the fans, and thus the older

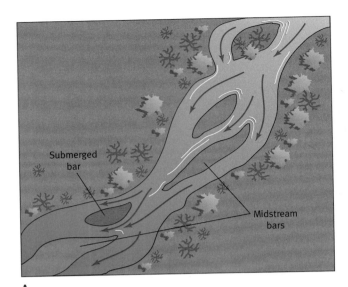

A

FIGURE 43.3   An extensive area of desert pavement covers the surface of a section of Signal Park in Arizona's Kofa National Wildlife Refuge.

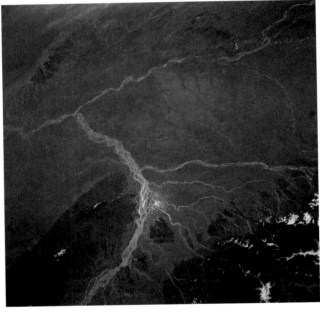

B

FIGURE 43.2   Braided streams begin with the deposition of midstream bars as discharge decreases after a flood (A). These obstacles split the stream into many channels as the discharge decreases, widening the stream greatly. Some braided streams can reach widths of 8 km, as is the case with the Brahmaputra River as it flows through northeastern India into neighbouring Bangladesh (B). In this photo, taken from the space shuttle, the Brahmaputra Valley's width is enhanced by flooding associated with the wet monsoon. The river it joins in central Bangladesh at the lower end of its braided segment is the mighty Ganges. Their combined channels flow southward for another 200 km into the Bay of Bengal (upper left corner), crossing the massive compound delta they have built.

upper parts of the fan surface are no longer subject to the shifting stream process described above. These older

areas become stable, may support vegetation, and often develop a varnished appearance on the weathered lag gravel surface, which has earned the name *desert pavement* (Fig. 43.3).

Streams to the Sea

All of the world's major streams, are parts of drainage systems that ultimately flow into the oceans rather than into a closed basin. As stream capacity increases in its lower course, a stream ceases degrading and begins aggrading and building alluvial landforms. This is manifested in the development and widening of its floodplain and ultimately in the formation of the coastal equivalent of the alluvial fan—the delta.

The course of the stream exhibits several changes as its depositional function gains strength. While the stream fully occupied its valley upstream (see Fig. 41.4A), the channel now begins to erode laterally, and for the first time the valley becomes slightly wider than the stream channel. Bends in the stream channel, called **meanders**, are increasingly evident (Fig. 43.4). Erosion occurs on the outside of the bends of these meanders, and deposition on the inside of the bends; in this way the stream migrates across and down its floodplain.

Meandering and the Floodplain

Meandering probably develops because of imbalanced energy loss along a stream channel caused by water flow over pools and riffles. All streams have undulating beds (pool and riffle sequences). The shallower parts that may break the surface are the *riffles*; these are characterized by their shallowness, their symmetrical shape, their coarser bed material (gravel, boulders, etc.), and their being slightly wider than the pools. Pools are deeper sections of the bed; they are associated with an asymmetrical section and finer bed materials (fine sand, salt, and clay), and are slightly narrower than the riffles. This means

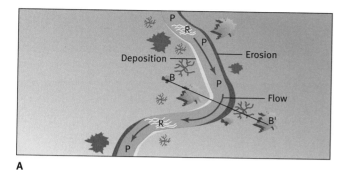

A

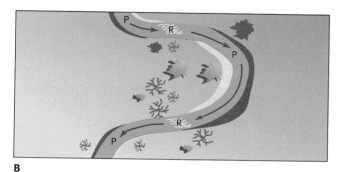

B

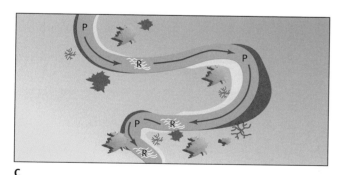

C

FIGURE 43.4 The development of meanders in a stream caused by differential energy loss over pools and rivers. Pools must lengthen an attempt to balance the energy loss. (A) A stream bend displays pools and riffles evidence of deposition on the inside of the bend and erosion on the outside curve. (B) The stream's bends are close to developing meander properties. Erosion on the outside of the now sharper bend (cut bank) is increasing, whereas deposition is occurring on the point bar on the inside. (C) The process has advanced to the meander stage. The stream is building its floodplain; the inside of the meander is a growing point bar. On the outside curve of the meander, erosion is strongest toward the lower part (the southeast in this sketch), resulting in the cross-floodplain down-valley migration of the meander.

that the same volume of water (discharge) has to get through the areas with larger (pools) and smaller (riffles) cross-sectional areas. For this to be done, the velocity has to increase as water moves from a pool to a riffle (because of the venture effect) and slow as it goes from a riffle to a pool. The differences in velocity, bed roughness, and turbulence between the two areas mean that more energy is lost over the riffles. To bring the energy loss over the pools up to balance that over the riffles, the pools lengthen, adding more bed and banks, and therefore increasing roughness and causing more energy loss. To lengthen, they have to bend (see Fig. 43.4).

When meanders develop in a stream channel, they move in two directions. First, as Fig. 43.4 shows, they erode laterally and increase in size; second, they migrate downstream. These two motions, the lateral swing and the downstream shift, have the effect of widening the stream's valley and creating an extensive **floodplain**—the flat, low-lying ground on either side of the stream channel that is inundated during periods of larger discharges (Fig. 43.5). Note that the channel of the stream still fills almost the entire valley at first (Fig. 43.6A), but becomes an ever smaller part of the valley floor as deposition occurs (Figs. 43.6B and C). Also, observe that the bottom of the stream channel, swinging back and forth across the valley, may create the base of the floodplain in the underlying bedrock unless it is on a pile of alluvial sediments. But by now the channel is flanked by deposits laid down by the stream itself. The floodplain is also defined by a very characteristic sequence of sediments (a fining-upward sequence). This looks like:

Figure 43.6C shows the development of two small, crescent-shaped lakes. These are **oxbow lakes**, which form when a meander is cut off, as shown in Fig. 43.7. Such *cutoffs* can occur, as seen in the diagram, when the downstream movement of one meander "catches up" with the lagging movement of the bend immediately below it (Figs. 43.7B and C). Another way this can happen is during a flood, when a *meander neck,* such as that shown in Fig. 43.7A, can be swept away and the channel is deepened along the course of the dashed lines. When

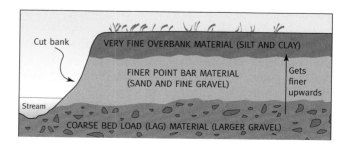

FIGURE 43.5 Section of cut bank showing the characteristic fining-upwards sequence.

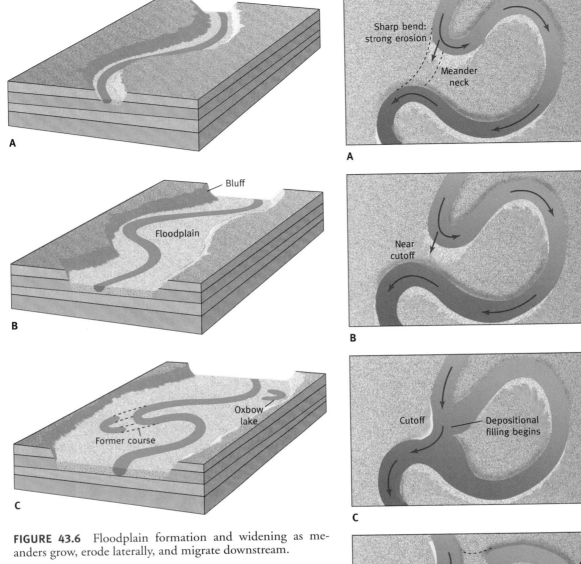

FIGURE 43.6 Floodplain formation and widening as meanders grow, erode laterally, and migrate downstream.

the flood subsides, the new cutoff may be deep enough to have the same effect as in Fig. 43.7D, and an oxbow lake, or a slough, will ultimately form.

The alluvium-filled floodplain is bounded by *bluffs,* cut by the meandering stream (Fig. 43.6). Over time the floodplain may become many kilometres wide, and *meander belts* themselves may form giant meanders, as shown in Fig. 43.8. If you draw a line through the approximate centre of the meanders shown, you will see that the pattern is repeated. And, as in the case of individual meanders, the entire meander belt tends to move down stream. As a result, a floodplain is full of evidence of previous meanders, meander-belt, oxbow-lake, and other positions. These are referred to as scars, so that a dried-up oxbow lake becomes a *meander scar,* a place where a meander once existed.

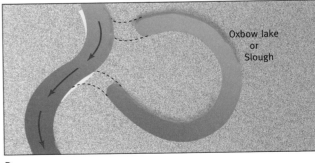

FIGURE 43.7 Formation of an oxbow lake as a result of meander neck cutoff.

As noted earlier, a floodplain is so named because this plain, between the bluffs, is subject to frequent flooding. Annual floods, during which the river overflows its banks, are a normal part of the floodplain's development.

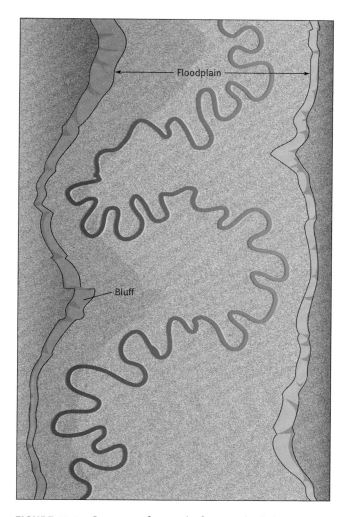

FIGURE 43.8 Segment of an underfit meander belt.

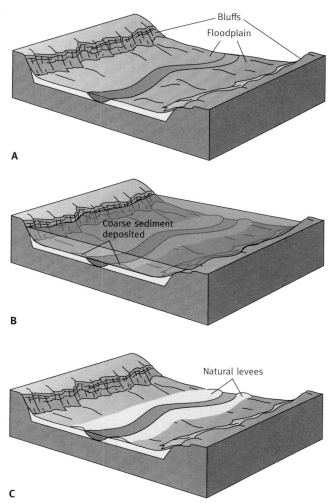

FIGURE 43.9 Relationship between floods and natural levee development. The river's coarsest deposits are laid down closest to the overflow (B). After repeated flooding, these deposits are built up as levees that contain the stream channel (C).

These floods deposit sediments that may build the stream's **natural levees** (it remains controversial whether these really occur), broad ridges that run along both sides of the channel (Fig. 43.9). As the river spills out of its channel, the coarsest material it is carrying is deposited along the levees. When the river contracts after the flood, it stays within its self-generated levees (Fig. 43.9C).

But not all floods are so regular and productive. Infrequently—perhaps once in a century—a stream may experience a flood of such magnitude (50-year, 100-year flood) that its floodplain is greatly modified. Water up to several metres deep may inundate the entire floodplain, destroying submerged levees, eroding bluffs, and disrupting the entire system. These floods have cost millions of lives in the densely populated floodplains of Asia's major streams. They also occur in the Red River basin of Manitoba, where the damage, too, can be enormous (see Perspective: The Red River Flood of 1997).

No reinforcement of natural levees or construction of **artificial levees** (see Fig. 41.8) can withstand the impact of such a powerful "100-year" flood.

Terraces

After a flood, a stream returns to preflood volume and functions. But what happens in a floodplain if a stream is reinvigorated? Increased volume (through stream capture or longer-term climatic change in the drainage basin) or tectonic events may increase a meandering stream's capacity to erode.

A stream may cut into its own alluvial deposits (Fig. 43.11). For simplicity, levees and other features have been left off the diagram. The stream cuts downwards a newly-imposed baselevel from its original level on the

The Red River Flood of 1997

The Red River is 877 km long. Its source is near Detroit Station, close to the western border of Minnesota, and it flows north through North Dakota and into Canada at Emerson, Manitoba. Spring melt occurs earlier in the southern part of the basin while the northern reaches of the river are still frozen. This leads to flooding. People living in this area of Manitoba have had to deal with floods since settlement began. The largest flood on the historical record occurred in 1826. Another large flood occurred in 1950, and this led to the construction of the Red River Floodway, familiarly called "Duff's Ditch" after Dufferin Roblin, the Manitoba premier at the time the floodway was planned and built (it was constructed between 1962 and 1969).

During the spring of 1997, near-record winter snowfalls (up to 250 cm snowpack) occurred in the Red River basin. This amount of snow, together with frozen soils and a rapid spring melt, resulted in extremely extensive flooding in North Dakota and Manitoba. The Red River crested in Winnipeg on May 3, with a discharge of 3904 m³/s (enough to fill an Olympic-sized swimming pool once every second). Half the flow was diverted past the city by the 47-km-long floodway, which lessened the potential damage. By the next day, floodwaters had covered 1950 km². The floodwaters eventually covered 202,500 ha (or 5 percent) of Manitoba's farmland.

The rising water forced 28,000 Manitobans (including 6000 Winnipeggers) from their homes. Without the floodway it has been estimated that 80 percent of Winnipeg would have been underwater and about 550,000 city residents would have to have been evacuated. Many hundreds of workers, armed forces, and volunteers worked at sandbagging and helped evacuate people and livestock. Large earth dykes were erected on the southern margin of Winnipeg to stop possible flooding of low-lying neighbourhoods and divert water toward the floodway.

Losses to dairy farmers alone were estimated to be $1.31 to $2 million; some 2000 cattle and 45,000 laying hens had to be moved out of the floodwaters' path. Whole towns and farms were sandbagged and left as isolated islands in the "Red Sea" (Fig. 43.10).

Eight thousand six hundred and twelve Canadian Armed Forces personnel were involved in "Operation Assistance." Their equipment included over 2500 vehicles, 58 watercraft, and 33 aircraft (the aircraft logged over 1500 flight hours).

Damages have been estimated at over $815 million. This can be compared with data on the 1950 flood. That disaster had damages of $606 million, large sections of the downtown were underwater, and 100,000 people were evacuated.

FIGURE 43.10 These remotely sensed Radarsat images of the area around Winnipeg show: (a) the normal course of the Red River and (b) the same region after the river spilled over its banks in May 1997.

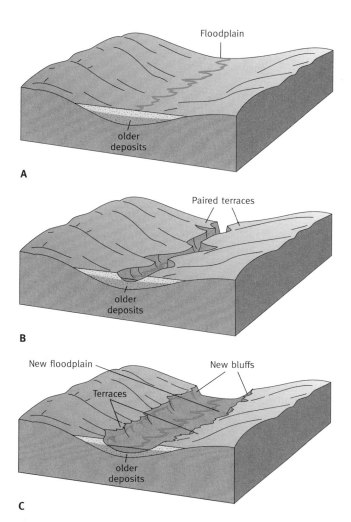

FIGURE 43.11 Paired terraces emerge as the reinvegorated stream cuts downward into its own floodplain in an area unaffected by glaciation (B). Eventually a new floodplain embedded within the older one develops, bordered by newer bluffs formed by the inner slopes of the paired terraces (C).

FIGURE 43.12 Entrenched meanders mark the sharply incised Colorado River, here at the confluence with the Green River, as it winds its way through southeastern Utah.

floodplain (A) to a new level (B), where it stabilizes and meanders develop. Soon a new floodplain within the older floodplain develops (C), complete with a new set of bounding bluffs.

Remnants of the older floodplain stand above these newer bluffs as **terraces**. These terraces reveal the two-stage evolution of the valley, and may be correlated with other information about the climate, base level, or tectonic uplift in the region involved. The terraces shown in Fig. 43.11 are *paired terraces;* that is, they lie at the same elevation on each side of the incised stream. Sometimes terraces are not paired as a result of a combination of valley deepening and lateral (sideways) erosion. This can destroy one side of a set of paired terraces, sometimes making studies of valley history quite difficult.

Terrace deposits in formerly glaciated areas show a sequence of deposits distinct from those of floodplains. These terraces are characterized by much coarser material, such as large gravels, and they may contain huge ice-rafted blocks. The whole sequence appears to be chaotically deposited by a torrentially flowing braided stream supplied with discharge from deglaciation and lots of sediment (glacial material).

Conceivably the stream could remove all of its alluvial base in the floodplain, leaving a *rock terrace* rather than creating an alluvial terrace. Technically such a rock terrace is a degradational landform, but its genesis relates to an earlier phase of floodplain aggradation. Under certain circumstances, such as the uplifting of the land surface above base level, whole meander belts can be incised into hard bedrock from overlying floodplain topography. These incised or **entrenched meanders** can produce some spectacular scenery, as in the San Juan and Colorado River valleys of southern Utah (Fig. 43.12).

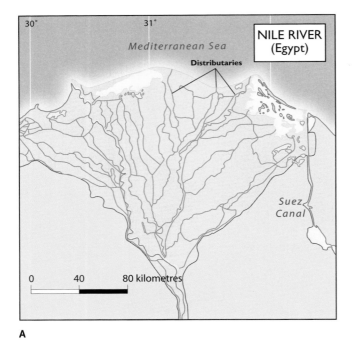

A

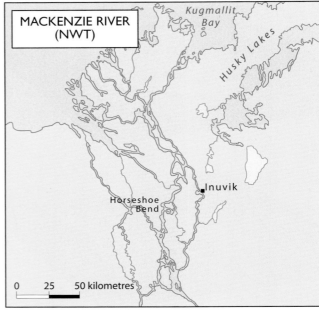

B

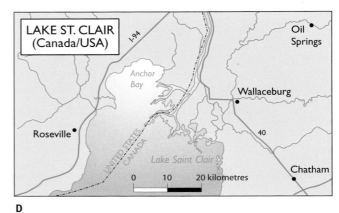

C

D

FIGURE 43.13 The spatial form of a delta depends on the quantity of sediment carried by the stream, the configuration of the continental shelf or lake bed beyond the stream mouth, and the power of waves and currents in the sea or lake. The Nile Delta (A) exhibits the classic triangular shape. The Mackenzie (B), exhibiting a birdfoot shape, results from large quantities of sediment carried into quiet water as does the Lake St. Clair delta (D). The Niger Delta (C) is shaped by strong waves and currents that sweep sediment along the coast.

Deltas

About 2500 years ago, the ancient Greek scholar Herodotus, studying the mouth of the Nile River, found that this great stream of northeastern Africa forms a giant fan-shaped deposit where it reaches the Mediterranean Sea. Noting the triangular shape of this area of sedimentation, he called it a **delta** (after the fourth letter of the Greek alphabet, Δ). Ever since, river-mouth deposits have been called deltas, even when they have a different shape.

Near its mouth a stream comes close to its base level and slows down markedly. Even the finest sediment being carried in suspension is deposited, so that the stream mouth may become clogged. As a result, the stream channel breaks down into smaller

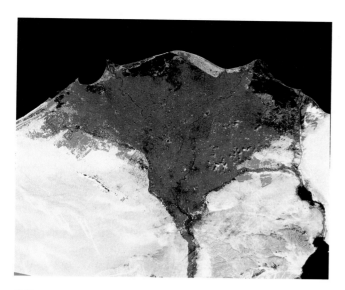

FIGURE 43.14 Remotely sensed image of the Nile Delta, whose intensively cultivated croplands show up in brilliant red. This image should be compared to Fig. 41.5, which shows the same region (rotated 180 degrees) in its true colours.

channels, which flow over the accumulated sediment. These channels, which begin at the apex of the delta and carry the stream's water in several directions over the surface, are called **distributaries**. Thus a trunk stream receives *tributaries* in its drainage basin and develops *distributaries* where it forms a delta.

As the map of the Nile Delta (Fig. 43.13A) shows, the Nile forms a few prominent distributaries and many smaller ones. When Herodotus did his fieldwork, the Nile Delta was an uninhabited swampy area. Today it is an area of dense rural settlement and intensive cul-

tivation (Fig. 43.14). Control of the Nile's distributaries and land reclamation have made this transformation possible.

The exact form of a delta is determined by (1) the volume of the stream and the amount of sediment it carries, (2) the configuration of the offshore continental shelf or lake bed near the river mouth, and (3) the strength of marine or lake currents and waves. Notice, on a world map, that the Nile and Mackenzie Rivers have large deltas, but that the Niger River of West Africa does not. The Nile and the Mackenzie flow into relatively quiet waters, and offshore depths increase gradually. The Niger River, however, flows into deeper water immediately offshore, coastal currents are strong, and its sediment supply is less than the Nile's. As the map of the Nile Delta (Fig. 43.13A) shows, the Mediterranean Sea is not without coastal currents, but these have the effect of creating sandbars and lagoons rather than of destroying the advancing delta.

As the delta grows seaward, the *deltaic plain* (the flat landward portion of the delta) stabilizes. The distributaries of many deltas are dredged and controlled today, affecting the process of formation. In the case of the Mississippi Delta, for example, many distributaries that would have become blocked by sediment are kept open, creating a deltaic form known as a *birdfoot delta*. The Mackenzie delta and the delta entering Lake St. Clair are good examples of this formation in Canada (Fig. 43.13D). This shape differs considerably from that shown in Fig. 43.13C, where the seaward edge of the delta displays none of the fingerlike extensions of the birdfoot delta. Here currents and waves cannot prevent the formation of the Niger Delta on the coast of West Africa, but they do sweep sediment along the

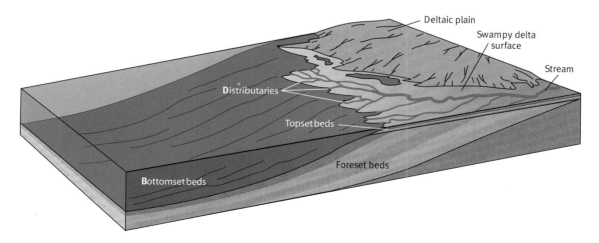

FIGURE 43.15 Internal structure of a small delta. Large deltas, such as those mapped in Fig. 43.13, are far more complex in their composition.

shoreline rather than allowing the evolution of birdfoot characteristics.

The Delta Profile

No two deltas form in exactly the same way, and the process is extremely complicated. A simplified version of delta formation is illustrated in Fig. 43.15. The finest deposits to be laid down are the *bottomset beds*. The stream in our diagram is depositing its finest-grained material ahead of the delta, where (it may be assumed in this instance) the water is quiet and such deposition can occur. In the meantime, the stream is adding to the *topset beds* of the delta, the horizontal layers that underlie the deltaic plain. As the delta grows outward, the *foreset beds* are built from the leading edge of the topset beds. Later the newly accumulated foreset beds will be covered by extended topset beds.

The thickness and the resulting weight of deltaic sediments can depress the coastal crust isostatically, complicating the process of delta development still further. Areas of surrounding coastland, but not part of the delta structure itself, may be affected by such subsidence, with serious consequences. The Mississippi Delta (see Fig. 33.7), where it enters the Gulf of Mexico in southeastern Louisiana, is a classic example of this phenomenon, and much land has been lost over the past few decades (at a rate of approximately 80 km² per year).

Deltas are among the largest aggradational features related to streams. Some of the boulders and pebbles that were dragged down mountain valleys now lie as fine grains on the coast—pulverized, transported, and deposited by streams, those great sculptors and builders of the landscape.

We have now completed our survey of the geomorphological processes associated with running water and the fluvial landscapes and landforms they shape. But we are not yet ready to turn our attention away from water as a geomorphogical agent. A special case of degradational action involves the removal of rock not by physical breakdown but by chemical dissolution. This process produces landscapes of highly distinctive surface and near-surface features, which are examined in Unit 44.

KEY TERMS

alluvial fan *page 557*

arroyo *page 557*

artificial levee *page 561*

bajada *page 557*

braided stream *page 557*

delta *page 564*

distributaries *page 565*

entrenched meander *page 563*

ephemeral stream *page 557*

floodplain *page 559*

meander *page 558*

midstream bar *page 557*

natural levee *page 561*

oxbow lake *page 559*

terrace *page 563*

REVIEW QUESTIONS

1. Describe the circumstances under which alluvial fans form.
2. How is the process of meandering related to the formation of floodplains?
3. Describe the stages of formation of an oxbow lake.
4. What are stream terraces, and how are they formed?
5. Describe the similarities between alluvial fans and river deltas.
6. Compare and contrast river terraces found in areas that were glaciated in the Lake Cenozoic ice age to terraces in unglaciated areas.

REFERENCES AND FURTHER READINGS

BRIDGE, J. *Rivers and Floodplains* (Malden, Mass.: Blackwell, 2002).

BROOKS, G. R., et al. *Geoscientific Insights into Red River Flood Hazards in Manitoba* (Ottawa: Geological Society of Canada Open File Report 4473, 2003).

BROOKS, G. R., et al. "Floods," in Brooks, G. R., *A Synthesis of Geological Hazards in Canada* (Ottawa: Geological Survey of Canada Bulletin 548, 2001), 101–143.

CALOW, P., and PETTS, G. E. *Rivers Handbook,* Vol. 2 (Malden, Mass.: Blackwell, 1994).

CARLING, P. A., and PETTS, G. E., Eds. *Lowland Floodplain Rivers: Geomorphological Perspectives* (New York: Wiley, 1992).

CHORLEY, R. J., Ed. *Introduction to Fluvial Processes* (London: Methuen, 1971).

DE BLIJ, H. J., Ed. *Nature on the Rampage* (Washington, D.C.: Smithsonian Institution Press, 1994).

DURY, G. H., Ed. *Rivers and River Terraces* (London/New York: Macmillan, 1970).

GORDON, N. D., McMAHON, T. A., and FINLAYSON, B. L. *Stream Hydrology: An Introduction for Ecologists* (New York: Wiley, 1992).

GRAF, W. L. *Fluvial Processes in Dryland Rivers* (New York/Berlin: Springer-Verlag, 1988).

GURNELL, A., and PETTS, G., Eds. *River Channels* (New York: Wiley, 1996).

HICKIN, E. J., Ed. *River Geomorphology* (New York: Wiley, 1995).

HOYT, W. G., and LANGBEIN, W. B. *Floods* (Princeton, N.J.: Princeton Univ. Press, 1955).

KNIGHTON, D. *Fluvial Forms and Processes: A New Perspective* (New York: Oxford Univ. Press, 1998).

LEOPOLD, L. B., et al. *Fluvial Processes in Geomorphology* (San Francisco: Freeman, 1964).

MALANSON, G. P. *Riparian Landscapes* (New York: Cambridge Univ. Press, 1993).

MORISAWA, M. *Streams: Their Dynamics and Morphology* (New York: McGraw-Hill, 1968).

PETTS, G., and FOSTER, I. *Rivers and Landscapes* (London: Edward Arnold, 1985).

RACHOCKI, A. H., and CHURCH, M., Eds. *Alluvial Fans: A Field Approach* (New York: Wiley, 1990).

RICHARDS, K. S. *Rivers: Form and Process in Alluvial Channels* (London/New York: Methuen, 1982).

ROBERT, A. *River Processes: An Introduction of Fluvial Dynamics* (London: Arnold, 2003).

SCHUMM, S. A. *The Fluvial System* (New York: Wiley, 1977).

WARD, R. *Floods: A Geographical Perspective* (New York: Macmillan, 1978).

WEB RESOURCES

http://www.canadiangeographic.ca/specialfeatures/flood/rrfed.asp This website has information, maps, photos, and links relating to floods in Canada.

http://www.usgs.gov/themes/flood.html This USGS hazards page has links to water resources management by location, El Niño related flood information, Mississippi and Missouri River data, and other hazard preparedness pages.

http://wrgis.wr.usgs.gov/docs/usgsnps/deva/galfan.html This USGS page focuses on the alluvial fans present in Death Valley National Park, with many color photographs and links to more information about the region and its accompanying geology. A virtual field trip guides viewers through the park.

UNIT 44

Karst Processes and Landforms

Karst topography in Halong Bay, near the port of Haiphong, northern Vietnam. (Authors' photo)

OBJECTIVES

- To discuss the general environmental conditions that favour the formation of karst landscapes

- To analyze the landforms that characterize karst landscapes

- To relate karst processes to the development of extensive underground cave systems

Water erodes rocks of all kinds, sculpting the surface into many distinctive landscapes. Under certain special conditions, however, water dissolves soluble rocks and minerals, transporting them away in solution. Water performs this function both at and *below* the surface. When it dissolves rocks beneath the surface, it may remove soluble layers while leaving overlying as well as underlying strata in place. This dissolution process leads to the formation of caves and associated subterranean features.

Caves occur in many areas of the world, and some are so large and spectacular that they have become quite famous. Mammoth Cave, located in west-central Kentucky, is a network of underground chambers and passages totalling over 500 km in length. Carlsbad Caverns in New Mexico has more than 37 km of explored chambers and tunnels. Other major cave systems lie in the Appalachians, the Canadian Rockies, Northwest Territories, United States; they also can be found in many parts of Europe, in China, Australia, Africa, and South America. In short, caves have developed wherever the conditions for their formation were favourable, and such conditions exist, or have existed, in thousands of places beneath the Earth's surface.

Although this unit focuses on caves and other features formed by dissolution, we should note that not all caves are sculpted this way. Caves are also carved by waves along shorelines; they can be created by tectonic movements; and they can even result from large-scale eluviation processes. Here, however, as this unit's title indicates, the focus is on *karst* topography, which is associated with *limestone*. Other caves and caverns, including those formed in other materials, are not karst features.

Archaeologists have discovered that caves were purposely occupied hundreds of thousands of years ago, and some caves contain valuable evidence about their occupants. In the Lascaux Cave in southwestern France, the cave walls were decorated by artists, from whose drawings we can deduce what kinds of animals were hunted and how the inhabitants may have lived. Other caves, such as the Sterkstroom Caves in South Africa, have yielded skeletons whose dimensions helped anthropologists unlock the secrets of the chain of human evolution. Caves, therefore, are more than mere curiosities to Earth scientists and archaeologists. They are expressions of a particular set of geomorphic processes that also produce many additional related landforms.

Karst

Except for its entrance, a cave cannot be seen from the surface. But the processes that form caves also produce visible landforms and, indeed, entire landscapes. If rock removal by dissolution can go on beneath the ground, it obviously can also take place at the surface. When this happens, the landscape takes on a distinctive, sometimes unique appearance (Fig. 44.1). Such scenery is called **karst** landscape, a term that has its origin in the area of east-central Europe where Slovenia and Croatia (now independent countries that were components of former Yugoslavia) and Italy meet. There, in a zone bordering the Adriatic Sea (an arm of the Mediterranean), lie some of the most spectacular and characteristic of all karst landscapes. Surface streams disappear into subsurface

FIGURE 44.1 A karst window near Willow Creek in the Bruce Peninsula, Ontario.

channels, steep-sided and closed depressions dot the countryside, and stark limestone hills crown a seemingly chaotic topography. This terrain extends to the Adriatic coast itself, and where sea and limestone meet, the shore becomes a monument of natural sculpture.

Karst landscapes are not always as spectacular as this, but some karst areas are world famous for their angular beauty. Perhaps the most remarkable of all lies in southeastern China, centred on the city of Guilin (see Fig. 18.4B). Here the Li River winds its way through a landscape of limestone hills (fenglin) that has for millennia inspired artists and writers. And to the west, in the province of Yunnan, lies another unique manifestation of karst processes, the fantasy-like Stone Forest (Fig. 44.2).

Karst terrain is widely distributed across the Earth, occurring on all the continents in hundreds of localities. More than a century ago, in 1893, a Serbian scholar named Jovan Cvijic (pronounced "yoh-VAHN SVEE-itch") produced the first comprehensive study of karst processes and landscapes, under the title that translates as *The Karst Phenomenon*. Ever since, the term *karst* has been in use. Cvijic also described and gave names to many landforms resulting from karst processes. However, he was not aware of the numerous places where karst topography also existed, and later additional karst phenomena were identified and named. As these studies progressed, karst geomorphology became an important part of physical geography.

There are widespread areas of karst in Canada (Fig. 44.3). They occur in Arctic, alpine, and temperate environments, although they are often buried by glacial sediments. The best examples of alpine karst are found in West Glacier National Park, around Mount Robson, in

FROM THE FIELDNOTES

FIGURE 44.2 "It was a long road trip from Kunming in China's Yunnan Province to the so-called Stone Forest, through heavily eroded minority lands and on some badly neglected roads. But the destination was worth it: an aptly named expanse of limestone columns, interspersed with small lakes whose rise and fall are marked on the rock walls. Here a once continuous, thick layer of jointed limestone is attacked by solution from above (rainwater) as well as below (groundwater). The cumulative result is a jagged landscape as far as the eye can see."

the Bocock Peak region of the headwaters of the Peace River, and in Waterton, Banff, and Jasper National Parks. Arctic karst occurs in the Nahanni area of the southern Mackenzie Mountains. Karst features are also developed along the Niagara Escarpment (*karren* developed on limestone pavements).

Karst Processes

Karst landforms and landscapes are the products of a complex set of geomorphological processes, conditions, and lithology. These include the stratigraphy, local relief, surface drainage, and groundwater. Karst landscape develops only where certain particularly soluble limestones, rich in calcite ($CaCO_3$), form all or part of

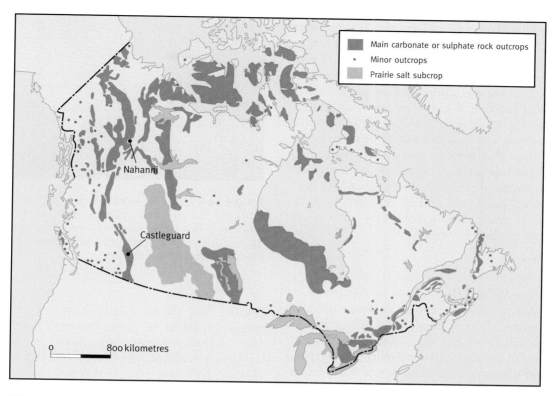

FIGURE 44.3 Map showing the main carbonate and sulphate rocks in Canada and the location of the Castleguard and Nahanni karst areas.

the stratigraphy. *Dolomite* or *dolostone* (CaMg[CO₃]₂) is another soluble rock that can also form karst topography.

But as was noted earlier, not all limestones dissolve easily. Calcite-poor limestones are much less soluble. Also, where metamorphism has created marble from limestone, dissolution proceeds more slowly. In arid areas, limestone may resist weathering, dissolution, and erosion more than other rocks do, and thus may form ridges and plateaus rather than depressions and caves.

The texture and structure of the limestone also influence the dissolution process. The greater the permeability and porosity (water-holding capacity) of the rock, the more susceptible it is to dissolution and removal. When there are many joints, faults, and cracks in the limestone or dolomite strata, subsurface water can flow more easily. This, in turn, increases the rate of erosion.

The Role of Water

Even when the lithology and stratigraphy are suitable, karst topography may not fully develop unless other conditions also prevail. The most important of these other conditions are water and drainage. In karst areas,

three kinds of water movement contribute to erosion: (1) surface streams, (2) underground drainage flows, and (3) groundwater. Surface streams may be poorly developed in karst terrain, but they supply the underground system. The underground network of interconnected channels is the most important agent of dissolution. The fluctuations of groundwater and the water table also influence karst processes.

Together these waters, moving across and through the limestone-layered rocks, create karst landforms. But the dissolution process is not uniform. Rainwater absorbs atmospheric gases as it passes through the atmosphere. Thus water (H₂O) plus a small quantity of carbon dioxide (CO₂) combine to become a weak acid (carbonic acid [H₂CO₃]). In this form, and depending on its acidity, rainwater becomes an effective solvent for limestone. Recent studies have shown that some cave formation occurs because of the presence of sulphidic bacteria; these bacteria produce sulphuric acid, which dissolves the limestone (resulting in **sulphidic caves**). The bacteria occur as floating rafts on the water surface or as **biofilms** on the rock surface. Many caves are now being studied to see if they were developed by sulphidic bacteria.

Another factor has to do with the soil and vegetation present in a karst area. They contribute to the presence of carbon dioxide, which is critical to the karstification process. More carbon dioxide dissolves into water in the soil because it is released during the decomposition of dead plants. Therefore, if soil water seeps into underground channels, it will increase the acidity of the water in those channels and thus the water's capacity to dissolve limestone. This helps to explain why more fully developed karst topography is found in warmer as well as moister climatic regions. Higher temperatures promote biogenic action, and this in turn enhances the effectiveness of the available water (in the form of carbonic acid) as an agent of erosion.

Relief

The formation of karst landscape is further promoted when the area of limestone and/or dolomite strata affected lies under at least moderate relief. Where the surface is flat or nearly so, and where surface streams have not succeeded in creating some local relief, underground drainage and dissolution are slowed, and karst formation is inhibited. Research has shown that in this respect, at least, surface rivers and subsurface streams have something in common.

Increasing water velocity at the surface increases a river's capacity to carry loads and perform erosion. Below the surface, water in tunnels also retains its erosional capacity longer if it moves rapidly, and loses it if it is slowed down. Sluggishly moving water soon becomes saturated with dissolved limestone and thereby loses its capacity to dissolve more of it. Dipping strata plus moderate relief combine to favour speedy subsurface water movement. Another condition favouring dissolution is the substantial uplift of the affected area. This allows underground streams to descend from one level to the next. Many cave networks lie on several levels, indicating that uplift and/or dropping water tables played a role in the evolution of the system (Fig. 44.4).

Groundwater

Below the water table, porous rock is saturated, its pores and other open spaces occupied by water. The water table fluctuates seasonally, and rises and falls locally after rainstorms and during prolonged dry periods. But karst conditions are different because the rocks in limestone areas are soluble. Thus the groundwater does more than simply occupy openings: in the form of weak carbonic acid, it contributes to underground erosion by changing the calcium carbonate in limestone into calcium bicarbonate, which is removed in solution.

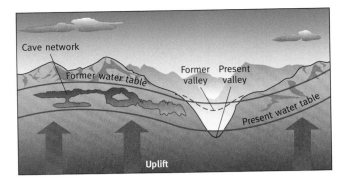

FIGURE 44.4 Cave network formed by water that entered limestone fractures and enlarged them below the (former) water table. When that water table dropped—due partly to uplift and partly to the nearby stream's deepening of its valley—the cave system filled with air.

Studies have shown that karst areas contain *perched aquifers,* pockets of groundwater situated above the level of the local water table. Water in these perched aquifers is confined, just like water under artesian conditions, and sometimes it emerges in natural springs (see Fig. 40.10A).

By tracing the movement of water in underground drainage networks, scientists have made significant discoveries about cave systems. One way to accomplish this is by putting dyes in surface water where it disappears below the ground, and then to check for the appearance of the coloured water in certain accessible cave locations and at springs. This research has indicated that a cave-riddled karst area may have several underground drainage systems that are separate, not interconnected.

In a single karst area, therefore, there may be as many as half a dozen subsurface drainage systems, functioning at different levels but not linked to one another. This means that an extensive cave system in a honeycombed mountain may have many tunnels leading inward from the entrance, but there are other tunnels that are not directly accessible above as well as below. Thus water entering the subsurface from one location on the surface becomes part of one underground system, whereas water from another ground-level location joins a different and separate network below.

Karst Landforms and Landscapes

A topographic map of a karst area quickly reveals the unusual character of relief and drainage (Fig. 44.5). It seems that all the rules learned so far from other areas are broken. Surface streams are interrupted and stop (or

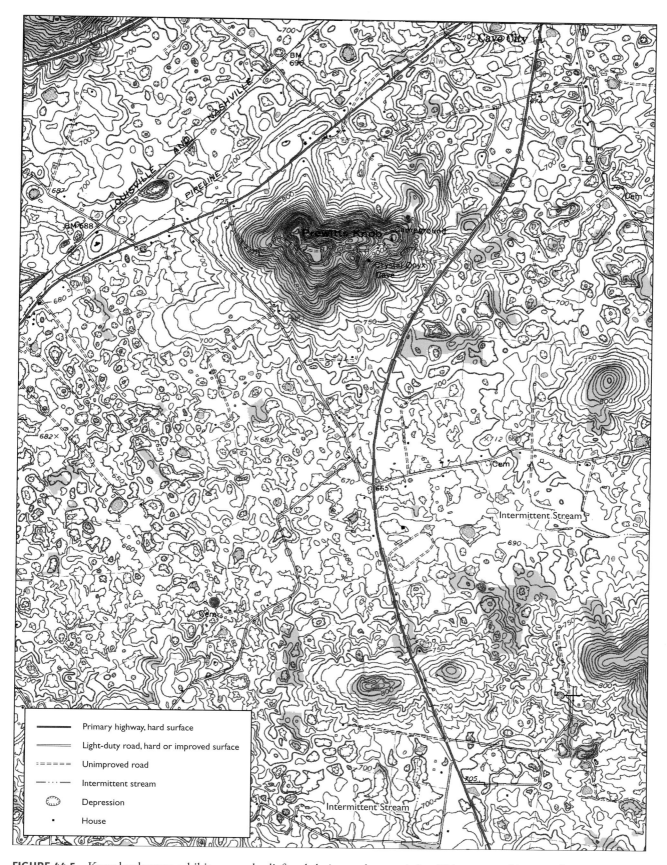

FIGURE 44.5 Karst landscapes exhibit unusual relief and drainage characteristics. This topographic map shows the surface near Mammoth Cave in west-central Kentucky, one of the most prominent areas of temperate karst in North America. Note (1) the myriad small depressions lacking outlets; (2) the pair of intermittent, disappearing streams; and (3) the steep slopes of Prewitts Knob rising from the nearly flat surrounding plain.

shrink) in midvalley. Contour lines reveal basins without outlets and without streams entering or leaving them. Steep-sided hills rise from flat plains without displaying familiar slope characteristics.

Close examination of maps reveals the clear signature of karst topography, but it is not the same everywhere. Geomorphologists identify three types of karst landscape: temperate, tropical, and Caribbean.

1. **Temperate karst**, of which the "type" area in Slovenia and Croatia is an outstanding example, forms more slowly than tropical karst. Disappearing streams, jagged rock masses, solution depressions, and extensive cave networks mark temperate karst (Fig. 44.6).

2. **Tropical karst** develops rapidly as a result of the higher amounts of rainfall and humidity, biogenic action, and organic acids in the soil and thus the subsurface water. Steep-sided hills tend to be vegetation-covered, and solution features are larger than in temperate karst landscapes.

3. **Caribbean karst** is a special case found only in a few locations. In the type area of central Florida (Fig. 44.7), nearly flat-lying limestones are eroded underground, although they lie barely above sea level. Water comes from the hill country to the north, seeps through the limestones, and leaves the system through offshore submarine springs. This situation exists in Mexico's Yucatán Peninsula. There, as in Florida, the roofs of the subsurface conduits have in many places collapsed, creating those characteristic depressions ("sinks") in the ground (see Fig. 44.1).

Disappearing Streams and Sinkholes

Where a surface stream "disappears," flowing into an underground channel, the place of descent is called a *swallow hole* (Fig. 44.6, top left). This may occur at a fault or an enlarged joint that has been widened by dissolution and leads to a subsurface system. Interrupted drainage of this sort is a general indicator of karst conditions. Another common karst landform is the surface depression, ranging in size from small hollows to large basins (called *dolines* in Europe). The dominant process of formation, as noted, is dissolution. Depressions also can form from the collapse of part of the roof of an underground stream conduit. Logically the former are referred to as solution sinkholes and the latter as collapse sinkholes (see Fig. 44.6).

Solution sinkholes (Fig. 44.6, top right) range in size from a bathtub to a football stadium. A single area of karst topography may contain tens of thousands of them, some old and established, others just starting to form. Their relative location probably has to do with the configuration of the terrain when karstification began; low-lying places became solution hollows first. These subsequently expanded, and others formed as the surface was lowered overall. In cross-section (see sinkhole at front edge centre of Fig. 44.6), solution hollows resemble funnels, water seeping down the sides to the approximate centre of the basin. There a *shaft* leads downward, and the water joins the regional groundwater (or subsurface conduit) through this outlet.

Collapse sinkholes (Fig. 44.6, left front corner) are created by the collapse or failure of the roof or overlying material of a cave, cavern, or underground channel. The

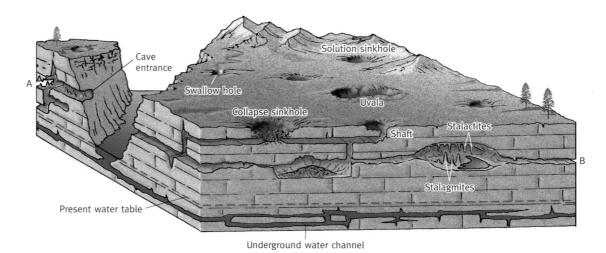

FIGURE 44.6 Surface and underground features of temperate karst. When the groundwater table was higher, the solution features at levels **A** and **B** formed. Now the water table is lower and solution proceeds. A new cave network will form when the next drop in the water table occurs.

dissolution process also created these subsurface tunnels, so even a collapse sinkhole ultimately owes its origin to the dissolution process. Physical geographers distinguish between a *collapse sink,* in which the rock ceiling of the sinkhole collapses into the underground solution hole, and a *suffosion sink,* created when an overlying layer of unconsolidated material is left unsupported. Where such loose material lies on top of limestone strata affected by the karst process, lower parts of this material are drawn downward into the enlarging karst joints. This creates a void in the lower stratum of this unconsolidated layer, and when the void becomes large, it will collapse. That can happen quite suddenly (see Perspective: Florida's Winter Park Sinkhole), unlike the slow development of solution sinkholes. Obviously, building in a zone of collapse or suffosion sinkholes can be a hazardous proposition.

Occasionally two or more neighbouring sinkholes join to become an even larger depression, called an **uvala** (Fig. 44.6, centre). Uvalas can reach a diameter of more than 1.5 km. Some have rough, uneven floors that are dry and vegetated; others are filled with water and form scenic lakes. Studies of sinkhole terrain indicate that this kind of karst landscape develops best where the environment is humid, so that there is plenty of water to sustain the underground drainage system. It also appears that the rise and fall of the water table may have something to do with the distribution of collapse sinkholes. Where groundwater levels rise and fall rapidly and substantially, this process seems to trigger more frequent collapses.

FIGURE 44.7 Satellite image of east-central Florida, a classic Caribbean karst region, centred on the Orlando metropolitan area (NASA's rocket-launch complex at Cape Canaveral juts out into the Atlantic at the far right). The large number of round lakes, formed in sinkholes, is characteristic of this landscape. Lake Apopka is the largest in the Orlando area, whose sprawling urban development is revealed by the pale whitish colour; it lies just to the west of the city's western suburbs at the latitude of Cape Canaveral. This image also shows that lakes have coalesced in a number of places (for example, in the extreme south), and the topography continues to evolve.

Karst Towers

If sinkholes are the signature landforms of temperate karst areas, then the dominant feature in tropical karst regions is the *tower.* Sinkholes and towers have various other names, but there is no need to complicate our terminology. A **tower** is a cone-shaped, steep-sided hill that rises above a surface that may or may not be pocked with solution depressions. Even when many such sinkholes are also present, the towers, sometimes hundreds of metres tall, dominate the landscape. In tropical karst zones, the contrast between towers and depressions is so sharp that the whole scene is referred to as **cockpit karst**, the term *cockpit* referring to the irregular, often steep-sided depressions between the towers.

Tropical karst, studded with such towers, is found in such locales as Puerto Rico, Jamaica, Cuba, and Vietnam (Fig. 44.9). Exactly what determines the location and distribution of the towers is still uncertain.

The towers are remnants of a thick bedrock sequence consisting of limestone and/or dolomite layers. Before the karst topography developed, and following regional uplift (or the lowering of the sea level), the original surface presumably developed a soil cover and plants took hold. This initial pattern of soil and vegetation (thick and well developed in some places, thin and sparse in others) probably was determined by the original terrain.

Where the surface was low, moisture collected and soil soon formed, but higher places stayed barren. Eventually these higher places became the tops of karst towers as the intervening hollows grew ever deeper. China's Guilin area (Fig. 18.4B) and Yunnan Stone Forest (Fig. 44.2) may have originated in this way, although fluctuating groundwater also was a factor in the process. In fact, some of the limestone towers (fenglin) in the Stone Forest still rise from lakes whose levels vary seasonally.

PERSPECTIVES ON THE HUMAN ENVIRONMENT

Florida's Winter Park Sinkhole

Cultural landscapes often experience sudden change in areas of collapse and/or suffosion sinkholes. A well-publicized disruption of this kind occurred in 1981 when, without warning, a large sinkhole materialized near the centre of Winter Park, an elegant suburb of Orlando in central Florida's karst region. Within moments of its appearance, the yawning abyss swallowed a three-bedroom house, half a municipal swimming pool, several motor vehicles (including five new Porsches standing at the rear of a dealership), and part of a nearby street. In all, the damage amounted to more than $2 million (US) in property losses—as well as the disappearance of some prime real estate.

This scene is documented in the photo in Fig. 44.8, which was taken on the day of the collapse. The dimensions of the new sinkhole were a diameter longer than a football field (107 m) and a depth of at least 40 m. The sinkhole soon stabilized and remains essentially unchanged today. The only difference is that it has mostly filled with water to become one of the thousands of small round lakes that pockmark this part of peninsular Florida (see Fig. 44.7).

Thanks to high-profile television news coverage at the time, the Winter Park sinkhole remained an object of curiosity for years after its formation. Within a week, local authorities had surrounded the collapse with a chain-link fence, and the public just kept coming to see it. It became a landmark complete with souvenir shops, a popular stop for many of the tourists who yearly stream into the Orlando area to visit its theme parks and related attractions. Perhaps it was even on your itinerary during a trip to Walt Disney World.

FIGURE 44.8   One of North America's most famous sinkholes lies in the middle of Winter Park, Florida. Appearing quite suddenly in the spring of 1981, it swallowed parts of an automobile dealership and a city pool in the process (this photo was taken only a few hours after the collapse).

Karst and Caves

In this section, we examine caves in more detail. Technically, a **cave** is any substantial opening in bedrock that leads to an interior open space. The word "substantial" here has a human connotation: it is generally agreed that a cave, in order to be called a cave, must be large enough for an average-sized adult person to enter. Thus even a vacated swallow hole, where a stream once flowed into an underground channel, is a cave. This is one way a *cave shaft* forms, and many unsuspecting animals and people have fallen into such vertical cave entrances.

Cave Features

A fully developed cave consists of an entrance (portal) and one or more chambers, passages, and terminations. A *termination,* in accordance with this definition, marks the place beyond which a person cannot crawl any farther along an underground passage or conduit. Passages in a fully developed cave system form a network of interconnected conduits. The pattern of this network depends on the stratigraphy, faulting, and jointing of the bedrock sequence. It may consist of one major subsurface artery (the *linear form*); it may look like the branches of a tree (*dendritic*); or, if block jointing is well developed, it may have an *angulate* (right-angle, stepped) form. Given the complexity of karst features, various other, more detailed models have been developed, accounting also for the overall structure of the maze of caves, caverns, and conduits.

Where passages grow exceptionally large, chambers or "rooms" develop. These chambers, some with the dimensions of a large hall, contain many fascinating forms. Lakes stand in some of them, and drops of water falling from the ceiling create eerie musical echoes in the dark void. Streams may even flow through them, with the magnified sound of a waterfall.

Dripping water that is saturated with calcium carbonate ($CaCO_3$) precipitates its calcite in the form of the mineral *travertine.* This water, entering the cave, contains calcium bicarbonate. If the air in the cave contains less carbon dioxide than it could, then there will be excess carbon dioxide in the water solution dripping from the cave ceiling or wall. This results in the degassing of some carbon dioxide from the water solution to the air, which means, of course, that some of the calcium bicarbonate that contains the carbon dioxide will have to chemically revert to calcium carbonate. When this happens, the form of $CaCO_3$ that is deposited is *not* calcite but travertine dripstone, a less soluble form of limestone.

FIGURE 44.9 A low aerial view of central Jamaica's "Cockpit Country," a classic, tower-studded tropical karst landscape.

This process leaves icicle-like **stalactites** hanging from the ceiling and **stalagmites** standing, sentinel-like, on the floor (Fig. 44.10). These white opposing pinnacles can become several metres tall and often coalesce to form **columns** (Fig. 44.10). They have been compared to the pipes of a huge organ and have also been perceived as the teeth of a lurking giant. Small wonder that caves attract so many visitors.

Cave Networks

To physical geographers, however, caves present other mysteries. In 1988 divers for the first time penetrated the water-filled tunnels of a cave system beneath northern Florida's Woodville Karst Plain near Tallahassee. They entered a sinkhole lake and followed a flooded passage, using battery-powered motors and floodlights. The passage went 75 m below the surface, and they followed it for more than 2.5 km until they saw daylight above and returned to the surface through another sinkhole. The cave passages, they reported, were as much as 30 m wide, but also narrowed considerably. They saw side passages joining the main conduit, and realized that they were seeing only a fraction of a very large and unmapped network. These Florida cave systems, now below sea level and filled with water, were formed more than 35 million years ago during a period of lower sea level.

Much remains to be learned about caves. Their formation is generally understood, but many details remain unclear. How important is abrasion by underground streams? What role does groundwater play? How do the

FIGURE 44.10   Close-up view of some of the wonders of New Mexico's Carlsbad Caverns, showing myriad columns, stalagmites, and stalactites.

underground processes combine to produce such extensive cave systems? What happens when those systems are submerged? As yet there is no general agreement on such issues, which proves that physical geography still holds some dark secrets.

Karst terrain and associated caves are widely distributed across the Earth. Some of the world's most impressive karst regions are only now becoming known and understood (such as the karst structures of Australia's Kimberley region in the northern part of Western Australia). Karst topography has been submerged by coastal subsidence, and it also has been uplifted into high mountains. There is karst terrain under Canadian glaciers (e.g., Upper Castleguard Cave System under the Columbia Icefields in the Rockies) and on frigid Andean slopes in South America. Sometimes karst landforms occur where solution is not an important contemporary process—for example, in semiarid New Mexico. Thus the map of karst and cave distribution contains valuable evidence for climatic as well as geologic change. The geomorphological signature of karst is indeed one of the most distinctive elements in the global environmental mosaic.

The recent studies indicating possible bacterial action linked to karst processes has reawakened interest in the subject.

KEY TERMS

biofilm *page 571*

Caribbean karst *page 574*

cave *page 577*

cockpit karst *page 575*

collapse sinkhole *page 574*

column *page 577*

doline *page 574*

karst *page 569*

solution sinkhole *page 574*

stalactite *page 577*

stalagmite *page 577*

sulphidic caves *page 571*

temperate karst *page 574*

tower *page 575*

tropical karst *page 574*

uvala *page 575*

REVIEW QUESTIONS

1. Which rock types are prone to karst development?

2. Describe the general climatic conditions that favour karst development.

3. What chemical weathering process is instrumental in the development of karst landscapes?

4. What is the difference between temperate and tropical karst?

5. How do towers form in karst regions?

6. Discuss the difference between limestone dissolution by solution and the action of sulphidic bacteria.

REFERENCES AND FURTHER READINGS

BECK, B. F., Ed. *Engineering and Environmental Impacts of Sinkholes* (Rotterdam, Netherlands: Balkema, 1989).

BECK, B. F., and WILSON, W. L., Eds. *Karst Hydrogeology: Engineering and Environmental Applications* (Rotterdam, Netherlands: Balkema, 1987).

FORD, D. C. "Effects of Glaciations upon Karst Aquifers in Canada," *Journal of Hydrology*, 61 (1983) 177–180.

FORD, D. C., and WILLIAMS, P. W. *Karst Geomorphology and Hydrology* (Winchester, Mass.: Unwin Hyman, 1989).

GILLIESON, D. *Caves: Processes, Development and Management* (Malden, Mass.: Blackwell, 1996).

GUNN, J., Ed., *Encyclodpedia of Caves and Karst Science* (London/New York: Routledge, 2003).

HERAK, M., and SPRINGFIELD, V. T. *Karst Regions of the Northern Hemisphere* (Amsterdam, Netherlands: Elsevier, 1977).

JAKUCS, L. *Morphogenetics of Karst Regions* (New York: Wiley/Halsted, 1977).

JENNINGS, J. N. *Karst Geomorphology* (New York: Blackwell, 1985).

LAFLEUR, R. G. *Groundwater as a Geomorphic Agent* (Winchester, Mass.: Allen & Unwin, 1984).

"Living With and Teaching About Karst: Special Theme Section," *Focus* (Summer/Fall 1998), 13–27.

SWEETING, M. M. *Karst Landforms* (New York: Columbia Univ. Press, 1972).

SWEETING, M. M. *Karst Geomorphology* (Stroudsburg, Pa.: Dowden, Hutchinson & Ross, 1981).

TRENHAILE, A. S. *Geomorphology: A Canadian Perspective* (Toronto, Oxford Univ. Press, 1998).

TRUDGILL, S. A. *Limestone Geomorphology* (London/New York: Longman, 1986).

VENI, G., et al. *Living with Karst: A Fragile Foundation* (Alexandria, Va.: American Geological Institute, 2001).

WHITE, W. B. *Geomorphology and Hydrology of Karst Terrains* (New York: Oxford Univ. Press, 1988).

WHITE, W. B., et al. "Karst Lands," *American Scientist*, 83 (1995), 448–459.

WEB RESOURCES

http://hum.amu.edu.pl/~sgp/spec/linkk.html The karst link page provides a comprehensive listing of all websites related to karst topography. Varying levels of technicality are available, and the page is subdivided by world regional areas.

http://www.cancaver.ca The website of the Canadian Cave and Karst Information Server has lots of information about caves, cave research, and so on; it includes a bibliography of Canadian publications.

http://www.goodearthgraphics.com/virtcave.html This page is called the virtual cave and provides a stunning photographic tour of solution caves, lava tube caves, sea caves, and erosional caves. Cave maps are provided as well as links to the National Speleological Society and U.S. show caves directory.

Glacial Degradation and Aggradation

The Saskatchewan Glacier in the Columbia Ice Fields, Alberta.

OBJECTIVES

- To discuss the different categories of glaciers

- To give a brief history of how glaciation has influenced the Earth's surface

- To outline how glaciers form, move, and erode the landscape

In this unit and in Units 46 to 48 we address various aspects of the cryosphere, one of the five major components of the Earth System (see Fig. 2.1 on page 19). The **cryosphere** consists of all the forms of frozen water that exist above, on, and just below the Earth's surface. It includes all types of glaciers, snow cover, ice floating atop water bodies, and permanently frozen ground (permafrost). The focus here will be on glaciers as powerful agents of landscape modification in high-latitude and high-altitude regions, where they create an array of distinctive degradational and aggradational landforms. Beyond their geomorphological role, as seen in Unit 20, glaciers are also of interest to physical geographers because they provide valuable

FROM THE FIELDNOTES

A

FIGURE 45.1 "Flying over glaciated terrain suggests how the planet changes as climatic cycles run their course. When mountain glaciers develop over an area originally sculpted by rivers, they bury most of the terrain and fill the valleys with ice, leaving only the crests and peaks of ranges and mountains protruding above, as you can imagine from a view over a section of the Alaska Range (A). When the glaciers have melted away (and they may even melt from the Alaska Range), the exposed topography reveals their work in a variety of landforms, including their steep-sided valleys, jagged mountain peaks, and sharp-edged ridges (B). This photo was taken over a part of Colorado's southern Rocky Mountains, where most of the once prevailing ice has melted away in the warmth of the current interval."

evidence in the study of environmental dynamics. This includes information about past and present climate change, the evolving composition and temperature patterns of the atmosphere, and the rise and fall of the global sea level.

A **glacier** is a body of ice, formed on land, that is in motion. This motion is not readily apparent over short time periods, however, and to an observer glaciers appear to be mere accumulations of ice, snow, and rock debris. Yet glaciers do move, and they steadily erode their valleys. Scientists realized this centuries ago, and in the Swiss Alps they calculated glacial movement by putting stakes in the ice and in the rock on the sides of the valley and measuring the annual downslope advance of the ice. But just how mountain glaciers move and how they modify the landscape below (Fig. 45.1) continues to be a subject of debate and ongoing research. In many ways glaciers and glacial activity are more difficult to understand than rivers because of the difficulty in observing processes within and beneath the flowing ice.

The glaciers of Canada's Rockies and Coast Mountains and of Switzerland's Alps are **mountain (alpine)**

glaciers. These glaciers are confined in valleys that usu-ally have steep slopes (they are sometimes called *valley glaciers* as well). However, not all glaciers occur in val-leys. Some glaciers consist of huge masses of ice that are not confined to valleys but that bury whole countrysides beneath them. These glaciers are called **continental glac-iers**, **ice sheets**, or icecaps. Today Antarctica, a conti-nent almost twice as large as Australia, is almost com-pletely covered by a vast icecap, and so too is Greenland, the world's largest island. Continental glaciers move, but generally even more slowly than mountain glaciers. Accordingly, they conform to our definition: they are bodies of ice and they exhibit motion.

Glaciers of the Past

As noted in Unit 20, the Earth has periodically experi-enced ice ages. An **ice age** is an interval of geological time during which the Earth's average atmospheric tempera-ture was lowered, resulting in the expansion of glacial ice in high latitudes and the growth of glaciers at high alti-tudes in lower latitudes. During an ice age, which may endure for millions of years, stages of global cooling alternate with stages of warming. As a result, glacial ice respectively expands (advances) and contracts (recedes) over periods measured in tens or hundreds of thousands of years.

A cooling period, during which the ice expands, is known as a **glaciation**. During such a time, ice sheets become continental in size and gain many hundreds or even thousands of metres in thickness. At the same time, mountain valleys fill with glacial ice, often replacing streams that formerly flowed there. After the cooling period has reached its peak and the glaciers have expand-ed as far as they can, the climate begins to warm up. Now the glaciers start melting and receding in a phase known as **deglaciation**. After deglaciation, the global climate may stabilize for some tens of thousands of years as the Earth awaits a new cooling episode. This interval between the most recent deglaciation and the onset of the next glaciation is referred to as an **interglacial** (~10–15,000 years).

The Earth today is comparatively warm, glaciers have withdrawn to the coldest of the polar (and moun-tainous) regions, and areas once covered by continental ice sheets are dominated by other geomorphological processes. In other words, we are presently experiencing an interglacial. Just 12,000 to 15,000 years ago, how-ever, Canada was almost entirely covered by continental glaciers, (about 97 percent) and these ice sheets reached as far south as the Great Lakes. Over the past 10 millen-nia, the Earth has warmed up and the glaciers have re-

ceded—but the present interglacial is unlike any other this planet has witnessed. During the interglacial now in progress, the world's human population has grown ex-plosively. Geologically, these last 10,000 years constitute the Holocene Epoch (see Fig. 37.7). Geographically, the Holocene has witnessed the transformation of the planet—not only by climatic change but also by human activity.

The present interglacial is unprecedented because, for the first time in the Earth's history, humans have be-come an agent of environmental change. On the basis of what is known about the patterns of previous glacia-tions and interglacials, it may be assumed that another cooling episode lies ahead and that the glaciers will once again expand and advance. But human interfer-ence in the composition of the atmosphere may affect the course of events. Many scientists now warn of the human contribution to the intensification of the atmos-phere's greenhouse effect. This might lead to further warming of the Earth, thereby causing additional melt-ing of ice in polar and high-mountain regions, a rise in the global sea level, and widespread flooding of low-lying areas. It also may contribute to a sudden "trigger effect" when the next glaciation occurs, again with an unpredictable impact.

The ice age of the present is often called the *Pleisto-cene Ice Age* because it has seemed to coincide almost exactly with the Pleistocene Epoch of the Cenozoic Era (see the geologic time scale, p. 471). But geologists now know that the current ice age began during the Pliocene Epoch, the epoch preceding the Pleistocene, probably between 2.5 and 3 million years ago. In fact, there is evidence of even earlier cooling, so their preferred name for this ice age is the **Late Cenozoic Ice Age**. (However, the Pleistocene Epoch remains closely identified with this whole episode.)

The Late Cenozoic Ice Age is only the latest in a se-ries of such events in the Earth's environmental history. For example, there is no longer any doubt that the great supercontinent of Gondwana (see Unit 32) experienced an ice age before it broke apart. During the Permian Period of the Palaeozoic Era, the Dwyka Ice Age spread great ice sheets over the polar regions of Gondwana. More than 250 million years ago, these continental glaciers left ample evidence of their activity. When Gondwana split apart, its several fragments (Africa, South America, India, Australia, Antarctica) all carried this evidence in their landscapes and underlying rock strata. When geologists discovered it, they had a major clue to the former existence of Gondwana—as well as its polar orientation during Permian times. Moreover, much older rocks from West Africa indicate an even earlier ice age dating probably to the Silurian Period about

PERSPECTIVES ON THE HUMAN ENVIRONMENT

What Causes Ice Ages?

It is known that the Earth has experienced repeated glaciations. The Late Cenozoic Ice Age is only the most recent. When Gondwana was still a supercontinent, it experienced a prolonged glacial age (the Dwyka Glaciation), and there is evidence of still earlier ice ages (e.g., the Precambrian "Snowball Earth"). Much is known, too, about ice sheets and mountain glaciers, and their erosional and depositional work. But scientists remain unsure about the causes behind nature's grand design. Why are the glacial ages periodic? Do they come at regular intervals? Are they caused by terrestrial conditions, or are they the result of conditions in the solar system and planetary orbits? Several theories have been formulated to account for what we know about ice ages, but none has yet gained general acceptance.

One theory attributes ice ages to *plate tectonics*. This theory holds that when landmasses are moved into the polar latitudes through plate tectonics, their elevation, combined with polar coldness, generates ice sheets—like Antarctica's today. But what is known about past movements of landmasses does not completely support this idea. Nor does it explain why ice ages are marked by alternating periods of cooling (glaciations) and warming (interglacials).

A second theory links ice ages to *crustal bulging* resulting from plate collisions. The Late Cenozoic Ice Age, for example, is thought to have its origins in the vertical uplift of Asia's Himalayas and the adjacent Tibetan Plateau over the past 20 million years, and the contemporaneous uplift of North America's Sierra Nevada and southern Rocky Mountain ranges. These raised crustal segments, it is argued, would interfere with jet streams and other atmospheric windflows, combining the coldness from the elevation with a latitudinal shift of air circulation, thereby creating hemispheric cooling. A problem here is the absence of such a landmass-generated cooling in the Southern Hemisphere, except in the case of Antarctica—which can be explained by other means.

Yet another theory relates glaciations to episodes of *volcanic activity*. Certain periods in Earth history have been marked by intense volcanism. The dust spewed into the atmosphere might, according to this hypothesis, interfere with solar radiation to such an extent that the volcanically derived dust aerosols cool the surface sufficiently to trigger a glaciation.

Still another set of theories attributes glacial cooling to changes in the Earth's *atmosphere* and *hydrosphere*. Fluctuations in carbon dioxide in the atmosphere could cause alternating warming (intensified greenhouse conditions) and cooling. When global vegetation is abundant, more carbon dioxide is consumed and its presence in the atmosphere is reduced. This would lead to cooling and glacial conditions; but when the vegetation dies, more carbon dioxide is released into the atmosphere, and greenhouse warming resumes. One problem with this idea, however, is that evidence for the short-term vegetation changes required for the model is lacking.

Theory building also focuses on changes in *oceanic circulation,* which are postulated to be controlled by the tectonic movement of continents. Some scientists believe that the inflow of warm Atlantic water into the basin of the Arctic Ocean would melt part of that ocean's ice cover, thereby releasing moisture for snow-bearing air masses. Huge amounts of snow would then accumulate in high-latitude North America and Eurasia—just where the great continental glaciers of the Pleistocene formed. At present, with Greenland and North America located as they are, warm Atlantic water cannot enter the Arctic Basin in large quantity. Thus the Arctic Ocean remains frozen most of the time, and the supply of snow is much reduced. The obvious problem with this theory is that it fails to explain the rapid alternations between glaciations and interglacials.

Additional theories look beyond the Earth and suggest that *Earth–Sun relationships* and *planetary orbits* (**Milankovitch forcing**) are ultimately responsible for ice ages (as noted in Unit 20). Over many millions of years, the distance from the Earth to the Sun during orbits changes slightly. More-over, the angle of the Earth's axis to the plane of the ecliptic also undergoes some variation. In combination, these changes affect the amount of solar radiation received by all areas on the Earth's surface. Data from various sources now suggest that this may be the fundamental cause of ice ages, in-cluding the short-term advances and withdrawals of the ice of the Pleistocene. Therefore the intensity and the duration of each global ice age probably are determined by orbital variation, plus some of the conditions on which other theories are based.

420 million years ago. Ice ages, therefore, have affected our planet repeatedly. Even though its causes are uncertain (see Perspective: What Causes Ice Ages?), the present ice age is unusual—but hardly a unique event in Earth history.

When we study glaciers, present or past, it is important to remember their significant connections to global environments. Even today, when the ice is of comparatively limited areal extent, the glaciers of Greenland and Antarctica influence the radiation and heat balances of the planet. Continental ice sheets contain huge volumes of freshwater and thereby affect the global water balance as well. When a glaciation begins, precipitation in the form of snow is compacted into glacial ice. Therefore it is not returned to the oceans (remember the hydrologic cycle diagrammed in Fig. 12.2), so that the sea level drops by as much as 100 m and continental shelves are exposed as the glaciation proceeds.

Later, when deglaciation begins, the melting glaciers yield their large volumes of water and the sea level rises again. Thus glaciation and deglaciation are accompanied, in turn, by falling and rising sea levels. During an interglacial such as the present one, continental shelves (see Fig. 2.6) are inundated. When the glaciers expand again, the flooded continental shelves will be exposed once more. Taking the long view of the future occupation of the Earth by humankind, it is therefore true that land lost in the high latitudes to glacial advance will be partly compensated for by land exposed by the drop in global sea level at lower, unglaciated latitudes.

The Formation of Glaciers

Glaciers consist of ice, and this ice is formed from compacted, recrystallized snow. But not all snow, not even in mountainous areas, becomes part of a glacier. In a high mountain area such as the Rocky Mountains, there is a *snow line,* a line above which snow remains on the ground throughout the year. Below this snow line the winter's accumulation of snow melts during the next summer, and none of it is transformed into ice. But above the snow line—also known as the *firn line*—the snowpack thickens over time. There some permanent snow survives the summer and contributes to the growing thickness of the snowpack. Where summer snow loss is less than winter gain, conditions favourable to the formation of glacial ice exist.

Snow is converted into ice in stages. Newly fallen snowflakes are light and delicately structured crystals. A layer of freshly fallen snow generally has a low density. Some melting of the outer "points" of the crystals may take place, changing them into irregular but more spherical grains (Fig. 45.2A). Or a later snowfall might compress the layer below it, packing the crystals more tightly together and destroying their original structure. All this has the effect of increasing the density of the lower layer and reducing its open spaces, or porosity. In areas where periodic melting occurs, fluffy snow can be converted into dense granular snow in a matter of days.

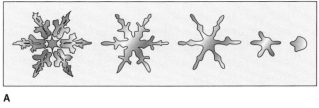

A

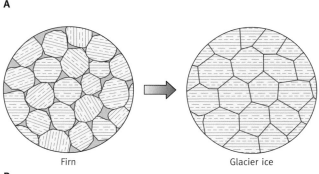

Firn   Glacier ice

B

FIGURE 45.2 The transformation of a snowflake into a granule of old snow (firn) can take several weeks as the outer "points" of the crystal melt (A). The conversion of firn into glacier ice takes decades, even centuries, in the coldest climates as recrystallization and further compression slowly squeeze out the open spaces between individual granules (B).

But this first stage does not yet yield glacial ice. The granular, compacted snow—called **firn**—undergoes further compression and recrystallization (Fig. 45.2B). That takes time, more time in cold polar areas than in moister temperate zones. This is so because in the temperate areas, where melting occurs, percolating meltwater fills the remaining pore spaces, refreezes there, and adds to the weight of the snowpack. Glaciologists calculate that the transformation from firn to ice in temperate areas may require less than 50 years. In polar areas, it may take 10 times as long. This means that a snowpack in temperate areas needs to be less thick to be converted into glacial ice.

A glacier in coastal northwestern British Columbia may need a firn less than 15 m deep for ice to form. On the other hand, in the colder and drier Antarctic, 100 m of firn would be required to produce glacier ice of the same density. Such data are useful in determining the age of the great ice sheets. Snow accumulation on the Antarctic ice sheet is very slow, but the firn is of enormous depth. Obviously this continental glacier required a long time (probably several million years) to achieve its present dimensions.

The Glacier as a System

A glacier is an open system, as shown in Fig. 45.3. If the glacier is in equilibrium, it will gain as much matter in the form of precipitation in its **accumulation zone** (or **névé**) as it loses through various processes in its **ablation zone**. These are separated by the equilibrium line. The term *ablation* denotes all forms of loss at a glacier's lower end, including melting and evaporation. Material is moved continuously downslope from the accumulation zone to the ablation zone.

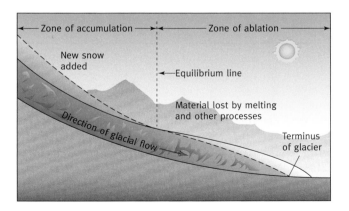

FIGURE 45.3 A glacier is an open system, with new snow added in its upper zone of accumulation and material lost in its lower ablation zone.

In this system, therefore, matter enters in the solid state as snow, undergoes two changes (to granular and then to crystalline form), and leaves the system in a liquid or vaporized state. Under conditions of equilibrium, a glacier neither grows nor shrinks. But equilibrium conditions rarely exist, and never occur over a long period of time. Glaciers therefore tend to exhibit evidence of fluctuation, especially in the ablation zone. When the *mass balance*—the gains and losses of matter in the system—is positive, the glacier thickens and advances, and its leading edge is steep and icy. When the balance is negative, the glacier thins and recedes, and its front end becomes less pronounced and is marked by grey melting ice covered by melted-out rock debris.

Glacial Movement and Erosion

It is certainly true that glacier movement, even in high-relief mountain zones, is not as rapid as streamflow. But the erosional power of glaciers is enormous. When mountain glaciers have melted away and vacated their valleys, they leave exposed some of the world's most spectacular scenery (Fig. 45.4). Valley sides are sheer and scarplike; waterfalls plunge hundreds of metres onto flat, wide valley floors. Whole mountainside spurs, once rounded by a meandering stream before the glacier occupied its valley, are sheared off as if by a giant knife, as the ice straightened and smoothed the valley's course. Lakes are formed behind natural dams made from glacial debris. Angular peaks and ridges rise above the landscape. The glaciers may be gone, but the landscape bears the dramatic imprint of their work.

Temperature and Glacial Erosion

Observations of the contact plane between ice and bedrock—where erosion takes place—are difficult to make, and movement within various parts of the glacier cannot be easily measured. Temperature, is a critical factor in glacial erosion. Indeed, the temperature of the ice at the base of a mountain glacier, together with the melting point of the ice, may be the most important factor of all in that glacier's capacity to erode its valley.

The temperature of glacial ice does not decrease steadily with depth. Various factors, including the pressure exerted by the weight of the ice and the temperature in the bedrock below, affect the temperature of the lowest ice layer, the **basal ice**. When the basal ice is at the melting temperature (as is the case with **wet-based** or **temperate ice**, which can reach pressure melting point), the glacier moves faster, erodes more effectively, and transports a larger sedimentary load than when the basal

FIGURE 45.4 "The magnificent scenery of Yosemite National Park in California's Sierra Nevada was sculpted by streams and glaciers. Half Dome (right) seems to have been halved by a powerful glacier coming down the **U**-shaped valley it overlooks, but scientists are not unanimous on this point."

ice is cold (cold or polar ice). **Cold ice** is frozen to its bed and cannot move. Mountain glaciers in temperate zones, therefore, erode more strongly than similar glaciers in very cold polar areas, where the temperature of the basal ice is much lower, but many glaciers are **polythermal**, having both wet-based areas where the ice is thicker and cold areas where there is thinner ice. Continental glaciers such as those covering Greenland and Antarctica are of massive dimensions, but their movement is very slow. Their erosional work, compared to their size, is much less effective than that of lower-latitude mountain glaciers. The interplay of cold ice and wet-based ice in a glacier is very important. Where wet-based ice pulls away from cold-based ice crevasses form (extension flow). These allow material and water on the surface to enter the glacier and become englacial or subglacial. Wet-based ice moves faster than cold-based sections. The wet-based ice shears over the slower cold-based section (compression). The shear zones formed in this way bring basal debris into the glacier.

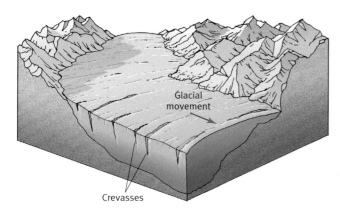

FIGURE 45.5 A glacier's brittle upper layers are studded with large crevasses. Down below, plastic flow predominates.

The Movement of Ice

Glaciers move slowly. The great continental ice sheets move as little as 2 to 3 cm per day, and even some cold-area mountain glaciers move just a few centimetres daily. In a rapidly moving alpine glacier, the daily advance may amount to as much as 4 or 5 m or even more. Occasionally a mountain glacier develops a **surge**, a rapid movement of as much as one metre per hour or more, sustained over a period of months, producing an advance of several kilometres in one season. Surges are caused by the damming up of the glaciers internal plumbing system. Water builds up under the ice and lubricates movement. Surges end when the dam breaks and the water gushes out in a **glacial burst flood** (or **jökulhlaup**).

A profile through the centre of a mountain glacier reveals that its upper layer consists of rigid, brittle ice that is often cut by large cracks called **crevasses**; below this rigid layer, the ice takes on the properties of a plastic material (Fig. 45.5); and the masses of ice between the crevasses are *seracs*. When the glacier moves downslope, its centre advances most rapidly and the sides most slowly (Fig. 45.6). In vertical cross-section, the upper surface moves fastest while the basal ice moves more slowly.

Glaciers move in two different ways. The first, called **glacial creep**, involves the internal deformation of the ice, with crystals slipping over one another as a result of the downslope movement just described. This occurs in both wet-based and cold ice, and is a consequence of weight, slope, and gravity. The second flow mechanism, called basal or peripheral **sliding**, is the movement of the entire glacier over the rocks below it. This process only occurs in wet-based ice, and it directly involves the glacier's erosional work. It is generally conceded that glacial sliding is enhanced by the existence of a thin film

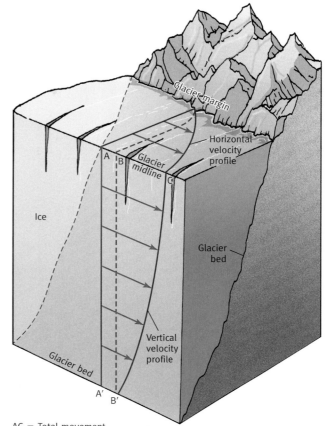

AC = Total movement
AB = A'B' = Sliding on the bed
BC = Internal flow (creep)

FIGURE 45.6 Differential movement rates within an advancing glacier. Vertically the upper surface moves fastest and the basal ice slowest. Horizontally the centre moves fastest and the sides move slowest.

of water between the basal ice and the bedrock floor. This film of pressurized water is just millimetres thick and is probably discontinuous. But it is enough to lubricate the contact plane between glacier and bedrock, and speeds the glacier's movement downslope.

Glacial Erosion

Erosion by glaciers can take place through **plucking** (also called *quarrying*), a complicated process in which the properties of the bedrock (rather than the transported rock debris) are most significant. In plucking, blocks or fragments of bedrock beneath the glacier are pulled from the bed as the ice moves forward. Glacial erosion also can occur by **abrasion**, the scraping process produced by the impact of rock debris carried in the ice upon the bedrock below. Despite its appearance, ice is not a hard substance; on the Mohs hardness scale

FROM THE FIELDNOTES

FIGURE 45.7 "Our Northwestern University field camp was based in Platteville, Wisconsin, during the summer, and one of our tasks was to find evidence in the landscape of the action of Wisconsinan glaciers. It was not difficult (except in the Driftless Area, which the glaciers missed!), because these most recent glaciers left numerous manifestations of their former presence. This is hard bedrock planed by a glacier and carved with striations, scratches made when the ice dragged embedded rocks across the surface. From this evidence we can reconstruct the direction of movement, indicated by the compass."

(see Table 30.1) it would rate only about 1.5. Thus ice by itself cannot be an effective erosional agent. Abrasion, therefore, must be performed by the rock fragments being dragged along the bedrock floor (and the submerged valley sides) by the moving ice.

Abrasion   Some of these rock fragments are, of course, quite "soft" themselves and do not have much effect on glacial erosion. Such soft material is soon pulverized and becomes part of the dark zones within the ice visible on the glacier's surface (**ogives** or **dirt bands**). Harder fragments, however, do have a powerful impact on the bedrock floor beneath the glacier. The enormous weight of the glacier pushes a boulder downward while dragging it along, and this combination can create rapid degradation. Other factors also come into play: the rate of movement of the glacier, the temperature of the basal ice, and the character of the underlying bedrock.

How fast do glaciers degrade? Various studies have been undertaken, but it is not possible to generalize from these. In one area of temperate-zone glaciers, average erosional rates ranged up to 5 mm per year, but in another area a rate nearly seven times as high was recorded. The effectiveness of the abrasion process is quite variable. Abrasion can produce several telltale features in the landscape. When the abrading debris consists of fine but "hard" particles (quartz grains, for instance) and the underlying bedrock also is quite hard, abrasion produces a polished surface that looks as though the bedrock surface has been sandpapered. But when the rock fragments are larger, the underlying surface may be scratched quite deeply. These scratches, made as the boulder or pebble was dragged along the floor, are called glacial **striations** (Fig. 45.7). They often are me-tres long and centimetres (but more often millimetres) deep. They can be useful indicators of the direction of

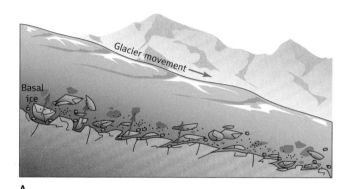

A

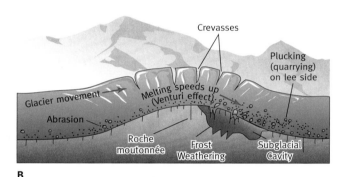

B

FIGURE 45.8 Plucking occurs when glacial-bed rock frag-ments are torn loose (by ice freezing into cracks that are sub-sequently enlarged by wedging), rotated upward, and carried away downslope embedded in the basal ice flow (A). Larger moundlike landforms, called *roches moutonnées,* are also cre-ated by this process, with the plucking found on the leeward side (B).

ice movement where the topography provides few clues, because striations tend to lie parallel to the direction of ice movement.

Plucking Plucking, a process diagrammed in Fig. 45.8A, also leaves evidence in the landscape. The most common landform associated with glacial plucking is the ***roche moutonnée*** (Fig. 45.8B). This characteristic, asymmetrical bedrock mound appears to result from abrasion on the upglacier side and plucking on the lee-ward side. A complicated process allows the glacier to quarry this leeward side, lifting out and carrying away loosened parts of the feature. Studies suggest that joint-ing in the bedrock and, probably, frost-caused fracturing contribute to the glacier's ability to "pluck" the mound over which it passes. Other evidence suggests that the lee-side is affected by frost wedging in a **subglacial cavity**. Whatever the nature of the process, *roches moutonnées,* like striations, help us reconstruct the path of the glacier.

As in the case of streams, glaciers deposit (aggrade) as they erode (degrade). The degradation of their source areas is matched by aggradation at their terminal edges. Like rivers, glaciers grind up the sedimentary loads they carry; but unlike rivers, fragments of hard rock that have taken the long trip encased in glacial ice appear at the glacier's end as angular boulders. The debris carried downslope by alpine glaciers tends to concentrate in cer-tain zones of the glacier, and appears on the surface as a series of parallel bands (active lateral and medial moraines). Once deposited, this material leaves no doubt as to its origin: rounded fragments are a sign of fluvial action, whereas angular fragments signify the work of ice. Continental glaciers, too, degrade their source areas and aggrade where their advance is slowed or stopped. Much of the topography of the area of the Great Lakes and the surrounding areas is underlain by glacial debris scoured by continental ice sheets from the Canadian Shield and deposited to the south. The next unit deals with the landforms and landscapes created by the great ice sheets of the past.

KEY TERMS

ablation zone *page 585*

abrasion *page 587*

accumulation zone *page 585*

basal ice *page 585*

basal or peripheral sliding *page 587*

cold ice *page 586*

continental glacier *page 582*

crevasse *page 587*

cryosphere *page 580*

deglaciation *page 582*

equilibrium line *page 585*

firn *page 585*

glacial burst flood (jökulhlaup)
  page 587

glacial creep *page 587*

glacial sliding *page 587*

glacial surge *page 587*

glaciation *page 582*

REVIEW QUESTIONS

1. Where do continental glaciers presently exist?

2. What is meant by the term *Late Cenozoic Ice Age?*

3. How does snow become transformed into glacial ice?

4. Describe how the mass balance of a glacier controls the glacier's movement.

5. How is a *roche moutonnée* formed?

REFERENCES AND FURTHER READINGS

ANDREWS, J. T.   *Glacial Systems: An Approach to Glaciers and Their Environments* (North Scituate, Mass.: Duxbury Press, 1975).

BENN, D. I., and EVANS, D. J. A.   *Glaciers and Glaciation* (New York: Oxford Univ. Press, 1998).

BROECKER, W. S., and DENTON, G. H.   "What Drives Glacial Cycles?," *Scientific American* (January 1990), 39–45.

EVANS, R.   *The Geography of Glaciers* (New York: Wiley, 1996).

EYLES, N., Ed.   *Glacial Geology: An Introduction to Engineers and Earth Scientists* (New York: Oxford, Pergamon, 1983).

HAEBERLI, W., and WALLÉN, C. C.   *Glaciers and the Environment* (Nairobi, Kenya: United Nations Environmental Program, 1996).

HAMBREY, M., and ALEAN, J.   *Glaciers* (New York: Cambridge Univ. Press, 1994).

HUGHES, T. J.   *Ice Sheets* (New York: Oxford Univ. Press, 1998).

IMBRIE, J., and IMBRIE, K. P.   *Ice Ages: Solving the Mystery* (Short Hills, N.J.: Enslow, 1979).

JOHN, B. S.   *The Ice Age: Past and Present* (London: Collins, 1977).

MATSCH, C. L.   *North America and the Great Ice Age* (New York: McGraw-Hill, 1976).

POST, A., and LACHAPELLE, E. R.   *Glacier Ice* (Seattle, Wash.: The Mountaineers, 1971).

SHARP, R. P.   *Living Ice: Understanding Glaciers and Glaciation* (London/New York: Cambridge Univ. Press, 1988).

SUGDEN, D. E., and JOHN, B. S.   *Glaciers and Landscape: A Geomorphological Approach* (New York: Wiley, 1976).

WILLIAMS, R. S., Jr.   "Glaciers and Glacial Landforms," in N. M. Short and R. W. Blair, Jr., Eds., *Geomorphology from Space: A Global Overview of Regional Landforms* (Washington, D.C.: NASA, Special Publication SP-486, 1986), 54–77.

WILLIAMS, R. S., Jr., and HALL, D. K.   "Glaciers," in R. J. Gurney, J. L. Foster, and C. L. Parkinson, Eds., *Atlas of Earth Observations Related to Global Change* (New York: Cambridge Univ. Press, 1993), 114–123.

WEB RESOURCES

http://members.aol.com/scipioiv/glmain.html This page discusses glacier formation, facts, and locations. There are links to glacier photographs produced by NASA and USGS.

http://nrmsc.usgs.gov/research/glaciers.htm This page describes glacier monitoring techniques and data for Glacier National Park.

Landforms and Landscapes of Continental Glaciers

Mountains submerged by ice sheets on Ellesmere Island, Nunavut.

OBJECTIVES

- To delineate contemporary continental glaciers and define their former
- extent during the Late Cenozoic Ice Age
- To identify typical landforms produced by continental glaciers

During an ice age the Earth's surface is transformed. Great ice sheets form over landmasses situated at high latitudes. Whole regions are submerged under ice—mountains, plateaus, plains, and all. The weight of the ice, which may reach a thickness of more than 3000 m, pushes the underlying crustal bedrock downward isostatically (see Unit 33). So much water is converted into snow (and subsequently into glacial ice) that the sea level can drop more than 100 m. Large areas of continental shelf are exposed, coastlines are relocated accordingly, and continental outlines change shape. As the ice sheets expand, thereby expanding the region of polar-type temperatures, global climatic zones are compressed toward the lower latitudes. Midlatitude lands that were previously temperate become cold, barren, and subpolar in character; vegetation shifts equatorward.

This unit focuses on the great continental glaciers, present and past, and on the landforms they create. Like mountain glaciers, the continental ice sheets migrate, erode, and create characteristic landforms through degradation as well as aggradation. But whereas mountain glaciers tend to increase the relief, continental glaciers have the opposite effect. Mountain glaciers gouge and excavate; continental glaciers scour and fill. In terms of total area affected, continental glaciers have the larger impact by far. It is estimated that glacial deposits laid down by ice sheets cover nearly 59 percent of the North American continent. Add to this the vast areas scoured bare by the ice sheets, and the significant role of continental glaciers is even more evident.

The Antarctic Icecap

The present climate is relatively warm compared to the atmospheric conditions of the past few million years, and glaciers have receded from many areas. But two representative ice sheets, or **icecaps**, persist to this day—in Antarctica and Greenland (Kalaalit nunaat). An icecap is a dome-shaped mass of ice that covers a large area of land.

The *Antarctic Icecap,* which began forming about 40 million years ago, has existed throughout the entire Late Cenozoic Ice Age and is unlikely to melt in Holocene times. This massive ice sheet allows us to measure and observe the properties of continental glaciers and to better understand how they affected the now deglaciated areas of the Northern Hemisphere. The Antarctic Icecap (Fig. 46.1) is of a size comparable to that of the Laurentide Ice Sheet that covered Canada and the northern United States repeatedly during the Late Cenozoic Ice Age. The Antarctic Icecap covers an area of more than 13 million km², constituting almost 9 percent of the "land" area of the globe.

Beneath this great glacier lies an entire continental landmass, including an Andes-sized mountain range and a vast plateau. In places on top of this plateau—particularly the region to the right of the South Pole in Fig. 46.1—the ice is more than 4000 m thick. A few of the highest mountain peaks protrude through the ice and snow; such exposed tips are called **nunataks**. Except for the outer parts of the Antarctic Peninsula, the Antarctic Icecap prevails from coast to coast. In schematic profile it looks like a giant dome, resting on the landmass below (Fig. 46.2). Because of this great ice accumulation, Antarctica has the highest average altitude of all the continents.

FIGURE 46.1 Infrared satellite image of Antarctica in its standard orientation, with the Antarctic Peninsula extending northwest toward South America. Snow is represented in white, ice in blue, and nunataks in black (the girdling Southern Ocean also appears in black). The mostly buried Transantarctic Mountains can be observed extending across the continent from the landward end of the Antarctic Peninsula. The huge bay to the east of the peninsula is the Weddell Sea, and the blue area at the apex of that sea is the Filchner-Ronne Ice Shelf. The Ross Ice Shelf directly across from the Filchner-Ronne, flanking the Transantarctic Mountains, is even larger.

Volume and Weight of the Icecap

The volume and the weight of the Antarctic Icecap are perhaps best illustrated by the following data. About 65 percent of all the freshwater on Earth is presently locked up in the Antarctic ice. If this ice sheet were to melt, the

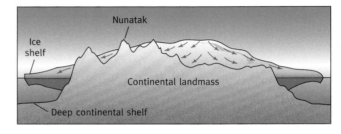

FIGURE 46.2 The Antarctic Icecap forms a gigantic dome that depresses the landmass below. In a few places mountain peaks (nunataks) rise above the icecap. Outlet glaciers flow off the icecap into the sea. Vertical scale is markedly exaggerated.

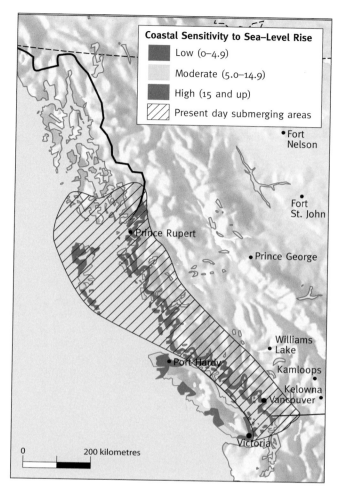

Coastal Sensitivity to Sea–Level Rise
- Low (0–4.9)
- Moderate (5.0–14.9)
- High (15 and up)
- Present day submerging areas

Fort Nelson

Fort St. John

Prince Rupert

Prince George

Williams Lake

Port Hardy

Kamloops

Kelowna

Vancouver

Victoria

0   200 kilometres

FIGURE 46.3 Effects of a 0.09–0.88-m rise in sea level on British Columbia, showing coastal zones and some of the major cities that would be affected.

global sea level would rise by some 0.09–0.88 m and possibly more, thereby drowning many low lying areas (the effects of such a rise on British Columbia are shown in Fig. 46.3). The weight of the Antarctic Icecap is so great that the landmass below it has sunk isostatically by an estimated 600 m. Thus if the ice were to melt, the Antarctic landmass would rebound upward exceptionally slowly by about 600 m as a result of the removal of this load, further contributing to global sea-level rise.

At present the Antarctic icecap system experiences very little mass input in the interior zone of accumulation. Average annual snowfall in the interior amounts to less than 10 cm of water equivalent, which qualifies this region as a desert. But over this vast area, even that meager amount of snow is sufficient to keep the great icecap flowing outward at rates varying from 1 to 30 m per year.

Features of the Antarctic Ice Sheet

The Antarctic Icecap exhibits several features that are useful in the study of other, extinct continental glaciers. One of these is the division of the ice dome into **flow regimes** (Fig. 46.4). The ice does not move outward in a simple radial manner. Rather, it flows seaward in several discrete regions, each of which has its own basin or catchment area (supply of ice) and its own rates of snow accumulation, ice formation, and velocity.

Another interesting feature of the ice sheet is its behaviour in Antarctica's marginal areas. Here the ice thins out, and the underlying topography plays a much more important role than it does under the thicker ice of the continental interior. In places the ice sheet fans out into valley glaciers and *ice tongues* (outlet glaciers that extend into the sea). These marginal glaciers are fed in part by the icecap and in larger part by heavy snows falling on their local basin areas. As a result, they move faster than the main body of the icecap. Moreover, recent research suggests volcanism is a factor here as well, which produces ground warmth that melts sufficient basal ice to keep the marginal glaciers flowing seaward atop a slippery layer of mud and meltwater.

Still another feature of the Antarctic Icecap is the formation of **ice shelves**. These are floating extensions of the main glacier, which remain attached to the continental ice sheet as they protrude from land into the frigid seawater (see far left edge of Fig. 46.2). Antarctica presently has two prominent ice shelves—the Ross Ice Shelf in the Ross Sea and the Filchner-Ronne Ice Shelf in the Weddell Sea (shown in Fig. 46.1)—plus many smaller ice shelves. The Ross Ice Shelf has an area of 535,000 km^2 and is under half the size of Ontario; the Filchner-Ronne Ice Shelf is nearly 400,000 km^2, just under the size of Newfoundland and Labrador.

The thickness of the ice in these shelves declines with distance from the mainland. At the coast, the Ross Ice Shelf is 300 m thick; at its seaward edge, about 600 km from shore, thickness is reduced to about 180 m. At this outer edge the ice shelves break up into huge tabular icebergs (Fig. 46.5) in a process called **calving** (which is a form of ablation). These flat-topped icebergs generally range in size from a few hundred metres to about 35 km across, although some are several times larger. For example, in 1956 one was sighted that was about 333 km in length and 90 km wide (20,092.8 km^2). Very large icebergs have broken off Antactica recently, too.

The tabular iceberg is characteristic of Antarctic waters. Icebergs, whatever their appearance or origin, have a slightly lower density than the cold water in which they float. Only about one-sixth of the mass of an iceberg appears above the water. A peaked iceberg in

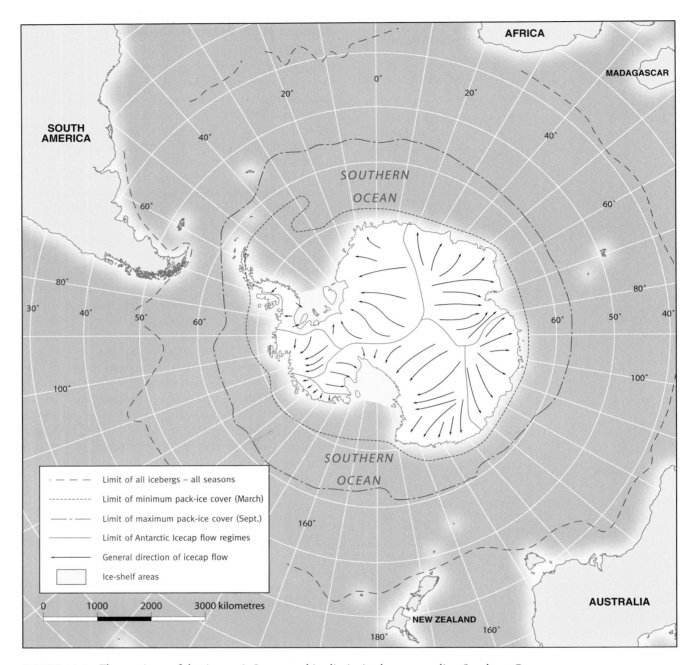

FIGURE 46.4   Flow regimes of the Antarctic Icecap and ice limits in the surrounding Southern Ocean.

northern waters may have an underwater base extending far beyond its exposed form, and many ships have collided with icebergs that still appeared to be a safe distance away.

Surrounding the great Antarctic Icecap and its zone of tabular icebergs lies a zone of floating sea ice that mostly covers the water's surface. This **pack ice** (see Fig. 46.4) does not derive from the ice sheet: it forms from the freezing of water in the adjacent Southern

Ocean. During the winter the belt of pack ice thickens and spreads. Thus from March to November Antarctica lies encircled by a nearly solid zone of floating ice, so wide that it nearly doubles the "size" of the continent. There are permanently open areas of water in the pack ice in the Antarctic and Arctic-Polynas. These are associated with rich mineral Faunas. After November the pack ice rapidly breaks up, and *leads,* or channels of open water, form through it, allowing ships carrying

A

B

C

FIGURE 46.5 "To watch (and hear) the calving of a tidewater glacier is one of the most memorable field experiences ever. We had sailed slowly north toward the head of Alaska's Glacier Bay, where the Grand Pacific Glacier marks the end of navigation. But it was a smaller nearby glacier entering from the left (west), the Margerie Glacier, that provided the action. Even before we reached it, we began to hear what sounded alternately like thunder, gunshots, loud groans, and gusts of wind. As its thick ice disgorged into Glacier Bay accompanied by booming and crashing noises that echoed up the valley, huge columns of it collapsed into the water, making large waves and leaving car-sized chunks of ice floating in widening semicircles. And not just ice, but also boulders (A), pebble-sized rocks (B), and surges of pent-up meltwater (C) crashed into the bay, roiling and muddying its waters and contributing to the glacial sediments accumulating below."

supplies and equipment to reach the continent's coastal research stations.

The Greenland Icecap

In total area, the *Greenland Icecap* is about one-eighth as large as Antarctica's continental glacier, covering about 1.7 million km² of surface (Fig. 46.6). Indeed, this icecap creates most of the surface of Greenland, the largest of all the world's islands. But in terms of volume, the Greenland Icecap is far less important, and it contains only about 11 percent of the world's freshwater supply. Like the Antarctic Icecap, Greenland's glacier exhibits the shape of a dome (see Fig. 46.2), reaching its highest elevation (over 3000 m) in the east-central part of the island. From there the surface drops quite rapidly toward the coasts, where the thickness of the ice is reduced to 150 m and even less.

The icecap also leaves about 19 percent of Greenland uncovered, which is nearly 10 times proportionally more than in Antarctica. It appears to be quite stable, ablation in the coastal zone approximating the accumulation in the interior. But there are no ice shelves here comparable to those of the Antarctic Ice Sheet. Indeed, the only ice-shelf feature in the Arctic lies not in Greenland but along the northern coast of adjacent Ellesmere Island, Nunavut, to the northwest. Where the Greenland Icecap reaches the edge of the ocean, it extends seaward in valley outlet glaciers. From these, large masses of ice calve and float as icebergs into the Arctic and North Atlantic Oceans.

Unlike the Southern Hemisphere, the Northern Hemisphere does not have a polar continent. Thus, while the South Pole lies almost in the geometric centre of Antarctica (see Fig. 46.1), the North Pole lies encircled by, but not on, land (see Fig. 46.8). It can therefore concluded that true ice sheets do not form over water, they form only on high-latitude landmasses. In the Northern Hemisphere there is no major landmass at a latitude higher than that of Greenland, and the polar region is an ocean—the Arctic Ocean. This ocean surface

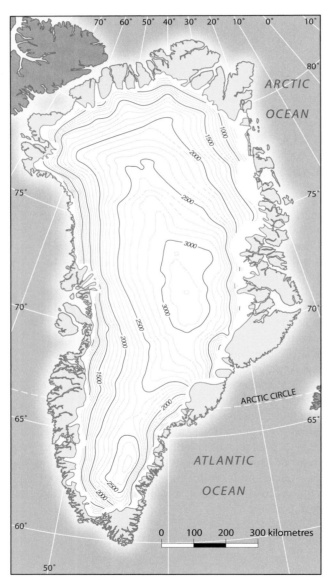

FIGURE 46.6 The Greenland Icecap, which is one-eighth the size of the Antarctic Icecap (Fig. 46.1). Ice thickness contours are given in metres.

FIGURE 46.7 Floating pack ice fills most of the Arctic Ocean. The cracks and pressure ridges reflect the crushing and breaking that take place in this constantly churning surface, which at present is being monitored carefully in the search for evidence of global warming.

is filled with pack ice, thick enough to be traversed, but subject to crushing, buckling, and breaking (Fig. 46.7). In the summer, when the open leads of water form, ships venture into the Arctic as many wooden boats did in the centuries when the (futile) search was on for a "northwest passage" (around North America) from the Atlantic to the Pacific. Many a ship has been doomed by the rapid closing of the pack ice at the onset of the long Arctic winter. Two famous examples are the HMS *Terror* and the HMS *Erebus*, the ships of Sir John Franklin's Northwest Passage expedition (1847–1848), lost in pack ice west of King William Island.

Age of the Present Ice Sheets

The Antarctic and Greenland Icecaps have survived the warm interglacial of the Holocene. But were they permanent throughout the present ice age? How old are they? These questions can now be answered because new research methods have been developed to solve the problems of ice-age chronology. As in the case of plate tectonics and crustal spreading, the oceans provided crucial evidence.

Episodes of cooling and warming occur during an ice age, and these stages are recorded by the microorganisms that become part of the deep-sea sediments. These tiny organisms lived at the surface of the sea, like plankton, then died and sank to the ocean floor. Cores of such sediments, obtained by deep-sea drilling, now allow geologists and marine scientists to study the sequence and length of ice-age glaciations, analyze palaeomagnetic data, and search for the presence of certain isotopes of oxygen in proportions that reveal the times of arrival of meltwater and the removal of seawater during the successive deglaciations and glaciations.

In combination, these data sources have produced evidence that the present ice age began well before the onset of the Pleistocene Epoch 1.8 million years ago. According to the scientists engaged in this research, there have been more than 30 glaciations since the ice age began. Glaciations appear to occur an average of 90,000 to 100,000 years apart. Within individual glaciations, there are fluctuations when the advancing ice stalls or temporarily recedes before resuming its forward progress.

As for the Antarctic Icecap, the evidence indicates that cooling and ice formation in Antarctica began about 40 million years ago, long before the Late Cenozoic Ice Age commenced. This great continental ice mass grew slowly at first and probably reached its full extent (somewhat larger than its present size) about 3.5 million years ago. It has survived all of the interglacials of the Late Cenozoic Ice Age, as it is now surviving the warm Holocene.

Other Late Cenozoic Ice Sheets

The Antarctic and Greenland Icecaps are the two Holocene survivors of a larger group of Pleistocene ice sheets. During Late Cenozoic glaciations, larger and smaller continental glaciers formed in the middle latitudes of both hemispheres, but to a greater extent in the Northern Hemisphere, where there is far more land.

Former Northern Hemisphere Ice Sheets

The biggest of all was the *Laurentide Ice Sheet,* the vast continental glacier that occupied Canada east of the Rocky Mountains and expanded repeatedly to cover the North American continent as far south as the Ohio and Missouri River Valleys (Fig. 46.8). To the west of the Laurentide Ice Sheet, the Rocky and Coastal Mountains were covered by a separate, smaller body of ice called the *Cordilleran Icecap.* There was also ice over the Canadian Arctic (High Arctic glacial complex).

In Eurasia the largest continental glacier was the *Scandinavian (Fennoscandian) Ice Sheet.* This glacier, centred on the eastern segment of the Scandinavian Peninsula, extended southward into central Europe (Fig. 46.8). Southwestward it coalesced with a smaller regional icecap situated atop the British Isles. The Scandinavian Ice Sheet was only slightly less extensive than the Laurentide Ice Sheet. Elsewhere in Europe a separate icecap also developed over the Alps, and a smaller one over the Pyrenees. The island of Iceland, too, was buried under ice.

A third major continental glacier in the Northern Hemisphere is believed to have developed with its centre approximately over Novaya Zemlya, the elongated island north of central Russia (Fig. 46.8). This ice sheet is variously known as the *Siberian* or *Barents Ice Sheet* (some glaciologists believe it was largely an ice shelf); it may have coalesced with the Scandinavian Ice Sheet to the west. So far it is less well known than the Laurentide or Fennoscandian Ice Sheets, but its mass has been calculated to match that of the Scandinavian Ice Sheet. As for the rest of Eurasia, major icecaps also developed over the Himalayas and the adjacent highlands of central Asia (Fig. 46.8).

Former Southern Hemisphere Icecaps

In the Southern Hemisphere only the Antarctic Icecap reached continental proportions. The smaller extent of high-latitude landmasses in the Southern Hemisphere led to the formation of smaller icecaps. The largest of these lay in southern South America, covering the southern Andes Mountains and much of Patagonia to

CANADIAN GEOGRAPHERS IN THE FIELD

"The shorelines of the Great Lakes are superb outdoor laboratory sites for field work investigations. This site near Port Burwell, southern Ontario on the north shore of Lake Erie reveals a complex stratigraphy of upper glaciolacustrine laminated muds, below that glaciofluvial sands and gravels and subglacial lodgement and waterlain tills in the lower half of the photograph. In a single exposure, therefore, one can find all the needed evidence of the late Wisconsinan Laurentide Ice Sheet glaciation and associated retreat sediments related to ice marginal proglacial sedimentation, first within a shallow near ice marginal proglacial zone then at the top of the section within an increasingly deeper glacial lake environment."

John Menzies, B.Sc., Ph.D., P.Geo. is Professor of Geography and Earth Sciences at Brock University.

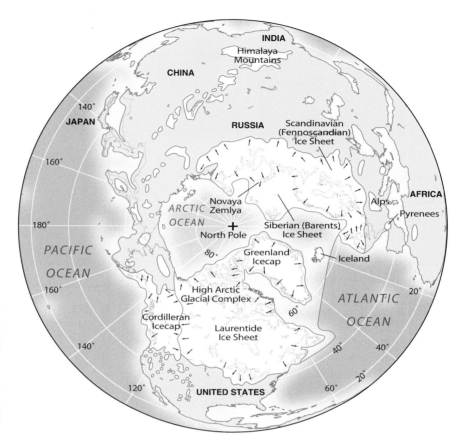

FIGURE 46.8 Late Cenozoic continental glaciers of the Northern Hemisphere. Arrows indicate the general direction of ice flow. Today's coastlines are shown as dashed lines. The Pleistocene coastlines on the map developed when the global sea level was about 100 m lower than at present. The pack ice covering the Arctic Ocean at that time extended much farther south, reaching the North Atlantic.

the east. Another icecap developed on the South Island of New Zealand, where substantial mountain glaciers still exist (see Unit 47).

North America's Glaciation: The Final Four

Before the days of deep-sea drilling and oxygen-isotope analysis, researchers had to rely on stratigraphic evidence to unravel the complicated glacial past. By mapping the surface geology and constructing cross-sections they tried to determine the succession of glaciations and interglacials. Dating these in absolute terms was not yet possible, so chronologies were based on what was known about the rates of accumulation of glacial deposits, on the depth of soils that developed between glacial episodes, and on related data. In part, certain assumptions were made that the alpine chronology could be used in North America.

Under these circumstances, this field research achieved some remarkably good results. In North America it was assumed that there were four major advances of the Laurentide Ice Sheet, of which the

Wisconsinan glaciation was the most recent (Table 46.1). In the meantime, Alpine glaciologists (Albrecht Penck and Edouard Bruckner) had also identified four major, corresponding glaciations (more recent studies have shown that Penck and Bruckner's study was flawed). Thus it was assumed that the Pleistocene glaciation was a four-stage sequence, involving a total period variously estimated to have lasted from 0.5 to 1.5 million years.

The current state of knowledge is that these four glaciations actually represent the last of the more than 30 glacial episodes of the Late Cenozoic Ice Age. The Wisconsinan, it is now clear, consists of two major advances, not just one—the Early and the Late Wisconsinan stadials. In Europe the Mindel glaciation is now called the Mindel Complex because there is evidence of repeated glacial advances. The pre-Günz (pre-Nebraskan) glaciation also is now recognized. Nonetheless the four-stage sequence (Table 46.1) was a remarkable approximation, given that it was based on evidence that exists only in the landscapes of Europe and North America. The last phases of glaciation form the record of perhaps the last 400,000 to 450,000 years of the Late Cenozoic's 3 million years of rhythmic global cooling.

Table 46.1 Four North American Late Cenozoic Glaciations and Their Alpine Equivalents

North America	Interglacial	Alpine
	Holocene	
Late		
Wisconsinan		Würm
Early		
	Sangamonian	
Illinoisan		Riss
	Yarmouthian	
Kansan Complex		Mindel Complex
	Aftonian	
Nebraskan		Günz
(pre-Nebraskan)		(pre-Günz)

When the technique of radiocarbon dating of carbon-bearing substances in the most recent (Wisconsinan) glacial deposits became possible, the story of this last pre-Holocene deglaciation emerged. The final advance of the Wisconsinan ice was so rapid in some areas that the leading edge of the ice sheet toppled trees and encased them. When deglaciation began, these tree trunks were deposited along with the glacier's rock debris. Radiocarbon dating revealed the age of the trees when they were engulfed by the ice. This was about 12,000 years ago, so the final deglaciation that led directly to the present Holocene interglacial has lasted barely 10 millennia.

Landscapes of Continental Glaciers

Unit 45 dealt with the ways glaciers erode and described two kinds of degradational features—polished and striated surfaces, and *roches moutonnées*. These landforms are neither prominent nor very common. But ice sheets do create extensive landscapes of degradation. They acquire their enormous sedimentary load by scouring huge parts of their source areas clear of soil, regolith, and loosened rock. Where the underlying topography has valleys roughly parallel to the direction of ice movement, a continental glacier can even behave like a mountain glacier, deepening and widening such valleys. This is what happened in the southern Ontario and Finger Lakes region of upstate New York (Fig. 46.9).

More often, when a continental glacier melts away, what is left is a vast ice-scoured plain marked by depressions, which are filled with water where the ice sheet did its gouging and scouring. Much of the surface of the Canadian or Laurentian Shield and northern Europe's Scandinavian Shield (see Fig. 29.12) displays such landforms. Erosion has created extensive continental-glacier landscapes.

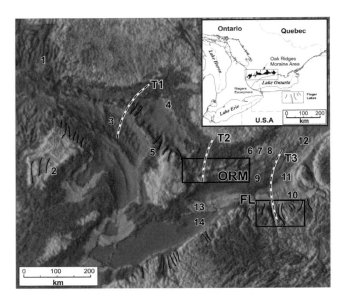

FIGURE 46.9 Satellite view of the Oak Ridges Moraine in southern Ontario. The moraine was created by glaciation and acts as a ground and surface water reserve. It extends for 160 km between the Niagara Escarpment and the eastern end of Rice Lake.

Glacial Lakes

Glacial lakes, including those just described, are of great importance and interest in the study of glaciated landscapes. In addition to the lakes formed in depressions sculpted at the bottom of continental glaciers, lakes also formed when glacial deposits blocked the path of outflowing meltwater at the leading edge of ice sheets. Such dammed-up lakes formed during the recession of valley glaciers as well as of continental glaciers. These lakes, born on the margins of melting glaciers (proglacial lakes), contain sediments that are layered in a characteristic pattern.

A cross-section of such lake-bottom sediments reveals pairs of layers: each pair consists of a light-coloured band of silt and a dark-coloured, finer-textured band of clay. Together these two bands represent one year's deposition. The coarser silt was washed into the lake during the summer, when the ice was melting and sediment entered the lake in quantity; this material settled quickly on the lake floor. During the ensuing winter the lake surface froze and no meltwater or new sediment arrived. But finer material, still in suspension, now settled slowly on top of the silt. This finer material consisted of clay particles and organic matter, which created the dark band.

The paired layers, one light and one dark, each constitute a *varve*. By counting varves, glaciologists can calculate the lifespan of a glacial lake, much as tree rings can be used to date the age of a tree. Elaborate systems of correlations were developed to extend the varve counts from lake to lake. Such research made an important contribution to early estimations of the timing of glacial movements.

Glacial Lake Agassiz Glacial Lake Agassiz formed 11,500 years ago from the meltwaters of the Laurentide Ice Sheet that covered Northern Ontario, Manitoba, and Saskatchewan. At its maximum size it covered 500,000 km² of these areas and parts of North Dakota and Minnesota. It was the largest lake in North America during the deglaciation. The lake lasted for 4500 years, its level rising and falling a number of times. These changes were related to advances and retreats of the ice front and the opening and closing of various spillway channels. At some points, water from the lake was discharged to the south, through the Mississippi River system to the Gulf of Mexico. At other times, the lake discharged water through the Great Lakes–St Lawrence system to the Atlantic Ocean and at still others to the north (Arctic Ocean and Hudson Bay).

During this period the three largest cooling events in the Northern Hemisphere occurred, each following closely after four of the largest outbursts of water from Lake Agassiz. The cooling events can be summed up as follows:

1. **The Younger Dryas** (a readvance of ice sheets in Europe during deglaciation) This cooling event was preceded by a discharge of 9500 km³ of water to the North Atlantic.
2. **The Pre-Boreal Oscillation** This was preceded by two outbursts of lake water to the Atlantic (9300km³ and 5900 km³).
3. **The "8.2 k cold event"** This cooling event was preceded by the largest outburst (163,000 km³) through the Great Lakes–St. Lawrence system.

These massive discharges of cold water inhibited the thermohaline circulation system in the North Atlantic and provided triggers that brought about changes in ocean circulation; these changes, in turn, caused a widespread drop in temperature in Western Europe.

Glacial Lake Bonneville As the map of the maximum extent of the Laurentide Ice Sheet and its adjoining Rocky Mountain Icecap indicates, the continental glacier never reached as far as Utah, Nevada, Oregon, or California (see Fig. 46.8). Still, the glaciations had far-reaching effects there. Today the basins in this area of the Far West are arid. During the glaciations, however, precipitation in this region was substantially higher than at present, and more than 100 lakes, known as **pluvial lakes**, developed as a result (Fig. 46.10).

FIGURE 46.10 Pluvial lakes of the U.S. Far West during the glaciation stage. Blue dashed lines represent overflow channels.

The largest of them, Lake Bonneville, was the forerunner of Utah's Great Salt Lake. Glacial Lake Bonneville at one stage was about as large as Lake Michigan is now. It reached a maximum depth of 300 m and overflowed northward through Idaho into the Snake River and the Columbia River. Although Glacial Lake Bonneville has now shrunk into the Great Salt Lake, its former shorelines still can be seen on the slopes of the mountains that encircled it. Today only a few of the pluvial lakes still contain water, and this water is saline; the Great Salt Lake is the largest of them. As for the other pluvial lakes, they have evaporated away, leaving only geomorphological and sedimentological evidence of their former existence.

The Great Lakes and Their Evolution The Great Lakes owe their origin to the Late Cenozoic ice sheets. The area occupied by the present six (with Lake St. Clair) Great Lakes (the largest cluster of freshwater lakes in the world) was probably an area at a low elevation and of low relief when the glaciers advanced over it. The ice excavated a set of shallow but very extensive basins early on in the ice age. When the ice receded, deposits left along its leading edge blocked the outflow of meltwater southward except through a few channels, and the first stage in the evolution of the Great Lakes began.

The major outlet to the south led from near the southern end of present-day Lake Michigan across

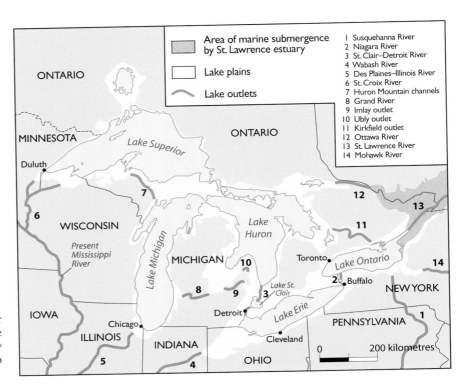

FIGURE 46.11 Lake plains (former lake bottoms) of the late Pleistocene Great Lakes and major outlets used by these lakes during their evolution into the present-day Great Lakes.

Illinois into the Mississippi River (Fig. 46.11, route 5). What began as a set of separate, marginal lakes that linked up sporadically with Glacial Lake Agassiz grew into an interconnected group of major water bodies. Not only was their overflow channelled southward into the Mississippi Basin, but they also drained eastward into the Hudson via Rome, N.Y., (route 14) and the St. Lawrence Valleys (routes 12 and 13).

The Great Lakes reached their maximum extent in the early Holocene interglacial, when Lake Huron far exceeded its present size and flowed through the Ottawa River into the St. Lawrence Valley (Fig. 46.11, route 12). Then, with the meltwater sources gone, the lakes began to shrink. Lowered water level closed the Lake Michigan outflow; crustal rebound closed the Ottawa River exit. But the lakes continued to flow into each other, and the St. Lawrence River and its estuary eventually became the only outlet for Great Lakes water (Fig. 46.11, route 13). At certain points there were large quantities of meltwater from the deglaciation of the Prairies funnelled through the Lake Agassiz–Great Lakes system into the North Atlantic—related to the onset of the Younger Dryas glaciation in Europe.

The future of the Great Lakes is uncertain. The lowering of the lake levels exposed large areas of fertile soils, and these lakeshore zones now constitute one of the continent's most densely populated areas. Major cities have evolved on the shores of the Great Lakes, including Chicago, Cleveland, and Toronto. Urban and agricul-

tural pollution have had a severe impact on the lakes, and Lake Erie in particular has been gravely threatened in recent decades. In the meantime the lake levels are kept up by the considerable precipitation received in the lakes region. Over the longer term, however, continued crustal rebound at the outlet of Lake Ontario is rising more than the western end of the lake following the recession of the Wisconsinan ice, plus a changing water budget, will continue to modify the map of the Great Lakes and their tributary region.

Aggradational Landforms of Ice Sheets

A continental glacier transports huge amounts of rock debris as it thickens and expands, scouring and sculpting the surface beneath it. When the Laurentide Ice Sheet moved from the hard crystalline rocks of the Canadian Shield to the softer rocks of adjacent areas, its sedimentary load increased even more. If we were able to take a view in profile of such a sediment-charged glacier, we would note that virtually all of the sediment **subglacially** load is carried near the bed of the glacier. Other material would be carried on the top of the ice (**supraglacially**). Some of the rock material would be fine-grained, but much of the load would be pebble and boulder-sized or even larger. Laden with all this debris, the ice sheet edged forward, depositing some of its load in places along the way and eroding material elsewhere.

Glacial Drift

When deglaciation begins, deposition increases in several ways. Solid material carried at the base of the glacier is dropped as an unsorted mass called **basal** or **lodgement till**, which consists of fragments ranging in size from fine clay particles to extremely large rocks the size of buses and large masses of frozen sediments. (Compacted and lithified into *tillite,* till provides evidence for the existence of glaciers hundreds of millions of years ago.) The rock debris carried supraglacially is deposited as the ice melts as **ablation till**. Other rock material carried by the ice is moved some distance by the meltwater coming from the ablating glacier. This material is to some degree sorted during the transportation by water, and shows some layering by size (as clay, silt, gravel, or pebbles). This is known as **fluvioglacial** or **stratified drift**. Together, unsorted till and stratified drift are referred to as **glacial drift**.

Over a long period of repeated ice advances and recessions, glacial drift can become very thick, completely burying the underlying bedrock topography. Much of the Canadian Prairies, southern Ontario, and the U.S. Midwest is covered by glacial drift of varying thickness. Some 30 m below the present surface in such areas lies a very different buried landscape, covered now by glacial drift accumulated during repeated glaciations and deglaciations. Some areas of glacial drift deposits are even thicker, reaching a depth of 60 m; but southwestern Wisconsin was bypassed by the ice sheets and exhibits a rather different landscape (see Perspective: The Driftless Area). The dominant aggradational landscape of continental glaciation, therefore, is a flat to undulating plain underlain by heterogeneous material, often studded with boulders, called *erratics,* that were transported far from their source area by the ice sheet.

Moraines

Ice-sheet topography, however, is not always of low relief. Continental ice sheets carry large loads of rock debris in their leading fronts and even push mounds of such debris ahead of them as they advance (Fig. 46.12A). When progress stops, this material is left as a curving irregular ridge, marking the outline of the farthest extent

PERSPECTIVES ON THE HUMAN ENVIRONMENT

The Driftless Area

Time and again the ice sheets of the Late Cenozoic moved southward in North America, covering older landscapes with glacial drift across the continent from coast to coast. But one small area never was buried (see Fig. 46.13). In southwestern Wisconsin lies a 400-km stretch of scenic landscape of moderate relief, supported by exposed bedrock and exhibiting landforms that could not have survived the overriding of ice sheets.

Surrounded on all sides by the characteristic scenery of glacial drift, Wisconsin's *Driftless Area* provides a unique glimpse of the landscape now concealed from view throughout most of glaciated North America. Economically this region's poorer soils have deflected the Corn Belt to the south (even though the climate is hospitable), and local agriculture is dominated by less crop-intensive dairying.

There are, in fact, two interpretations of the history of this unique region. One theory holds that the Driftless Area was never glaciated, escaping the advances of the ice sheets because of its location midway between the valleys that became Lakes Superior and Michigan. Thus the main mass of the advancing ice went down these valleys and was repeatedly diverted around the area. But other glaciologists believe that the Driftless Area escaped only the most recent glaciation. Earlier advances may have covered the area, but the evidence in the form of glacial drift was removed by subsequent stream erosion.

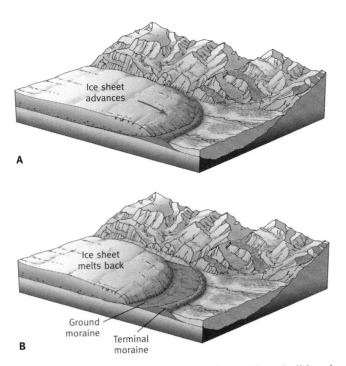

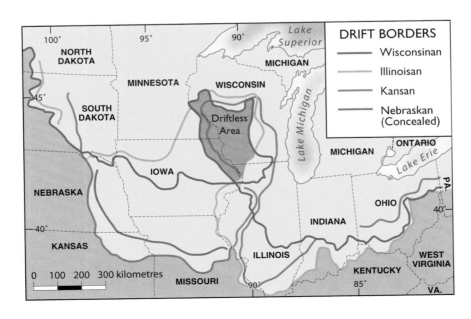

FIGURE 46.12 A terminal moraine is formed from bulldozed debris at an advancing ice sheet's front edge and from meltout material falling down the front of the ice (A). When forward glacial movement ends, this debris remains as a ridge after the ice melts back (B).

of the ice lobe (Fig. 46.12B). Such a ridge is called a **terminal moraine**, and many such moraines can be mapped in Canada and the north-central United States. From the properties of the glacial drift and the positions and relationships of the terminal moraines, geomorphologists have been able to reconstruct and map the glacia-

tions shown by the drift margins in Fig. 46.13. Many moraines contain mixtures of glacial, fluvioglacial, and lake deposits (e.g., Oak Ridges Moraine of southern Ontario).

The term **moraine** is applied to many kinds of glacial features. As noted in Unit 47, even material still being carried on a mountain glacier is referred to as a moraine. In all glaciers, a *terminal moraine* is distinguished from a **recessional moraine**. A terminal moraine marks the farthest advance of the ice, but a recessional moraine develops when an already receding glacier becomes temporarily stationary. Thus a receding glacier can form several recessional moraines, but it will leave only one terminal moraine. The term *moraine* also is applied to that extensive blanket of unsorted till that is laid down at the base of a melting ice sheet (Fig. 46.12B). In this case it is called a **ground moraine** (also known as basal till).

Fluvioglacial or Glacial Meltwater Deposits

Terminal, recessional, and ground moraines are ice-deposited. But when meltwater becomes part of the depositional process, the landform picture becomes more complicated. Meltwater flows in channels from beneath in, on top of, and in front of the ice. In the process it carries rock debris away from the ice and sorts it to varying degrees (depending on such factors as the distance of transportation, the volume and velocity of the water, and the sedimentary load carried). In the field, unsorted till is easily distinguished from meltwater-deposited layers of sand and gravel, which are called **glacial outwash**.

One of the most interesting outwash landforms is the **esker**. Under certain circumstances, water flowing

FIGURE 46.13 Drift margins of the north-central United States. The positions of these terminal moraines indicate that in each of the final four glaciations the continental ice sheet reached a different line of maximum advance.

CANADIAN GEOGRAPHERS IN THE FIELD

"While mapping the bedrock geology north of Yellowknife, Northwest Territories for the Geological Survey of Canada, my field crew and I set up camp on this small beach derived from the esker immediately behind it. This area has become famous since the discovery of diamonds in the Lac de Gras area just to the east. The eskers were deposited from rivers flowing below glaciers covering the area during the Late Wisconsinan glaciation that receded in this area about 8–10 thousand years ago. Geologists found minerals associated with diamonds in the eskers and followed the eskers back to find the diamond deposits, currently estimated to be worth approximately CAN$21 billion."

Blair Hrabi has a B.Sc. (McMaster University) and M.Sc. (Queen's University) in geology and studies the geochemical composition of volcanic rocks and the structural evolution of Precambrian rocks in the Canadian Shield.

FIGURE 46.14 The unmistakable topography of drumlins studs this portion of the agricultural landscape of upstate New York's Finger Lakes district (shown in a satellite image in Fig. 46.9). These cigar-shaped landforms, created by meltwater under an ice sheet flowing toward the viewer, are often called whalebacks by those who live among them.

in, on, or at the base of melting continental ice as englacial and subglacial streams form long tunnels that begin well (even kilometres) inside the ice and lead to the ice margin. Rock debris collects in these tunnels, sorted considerably by the water even as the tube is

being clogged. Eventually, when the entire glacier has melted away, the tunnel's outline is marked by a long, sinuous ridge, the esker, that may look like a terminal or recessional moraine—until its sorted and stratified profile is examined (Fig. 46.15, lower centre). Many eskers have lake sediments in them, which suggest that they flowed into proglacial lakes (e.g., Codrington Esker in Kingston, Ontario).

Most outwash landforms, however, form ahead of, not beneath, the stalled or receding glacier. A **sandur** or **outwash plain** is the product of meltwater carrying (and to some extent sorting) rock debris from the wasting ice front. In some places large blocks of unmelted ice are initially buried in the sandur. When these blocks melt, they create steep-sided depressions known as **kettles** in some cases these become water-filled (**kettle lakes**) (Fig. 46.15, upper right). Occasionally there are so many of these kettles that the affected portion of the outwash plain is described as *pitted*.

We noted earlier that lakes form when meltwater is dammed up by terminal or recessional moraines. Often these marginal lakes do not survive for very long, but they do leave evidence of their brief existence in the landscape. The deposits that constitute this evidence are called *glacio-lacustrine* (glacial-lake) deposits. **Kames** are deposited from material sliding or rolling down the

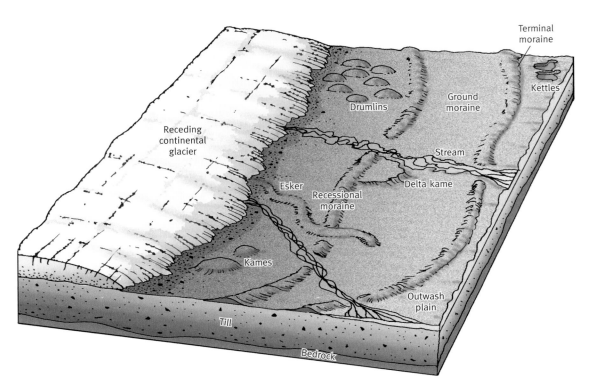

FIGURE 46.15 Some aggradational landforms associated with a receding ice sheet.

CANADIAN GEOGRAPHERS IN THE FIELD

"My passion for physical geography began with an interest in glacial landforms. This is an aerial photograph of one of the many drumlins in the Lunenburg drumlin field, on the south eastern shore of Nova Scotia. I ended up writing my undergraduate thesis on the morphological properties of the drumlins in the 'field'. I think I was really interested in these features because, at the time, there was a lot of debate surrounding the specific processes of their formation. These features are sometimes difficult to distinguish from the ground, but from the bird's eye view, you can see the moulding effect of the glacial ice. Many important cultural features reside atop drumlins, like Citadel Hill in Halifax, for example."

Cathy Conrad is currently an Associate Professor in the Department of Geography at Saint Mary's University and is a former student of the same program.

snout of a glacier. They form flat-topped masses of sands and gravels. Some have lacustrine deposits indicating formation around and the edges of a proglacial lake and various landforms associated with it, such as beaches, bluffs, etc. As in any location where sediment-laden water flows into standing water, the glacial streams form deltas when they pour into marginal glacial lakes. These glacial deltas are made of characteristically coarse-textured material. They may represent embryonic eskers. When the lake drains away or dries up, the deltaic material is left standing in the morainal landscape (Fig. 46.15, right of centre). It is typically flat-topped, as the delta surface was. Such a flat-topped hill, sometimes flanked by terraces marking the lowering of the lake level, is a kame. Kames and kettles are found together in many locations (creating thermokarst).

Drumlins (Whalebacks, Hogbacks)

Drumlins are small, aerodynamic, elliptically shaped hills rising from the till plain. The size, shape, and spac-ing is very consistent within an area. The long axis of a drumlin lies parallel to the direction of meltwater move-ment under the ice sheet. It is believed that drumlins are formed when megafloods of meltwater under the ice (under hydrostatic pressure) curve and reshape pre-exist-ing till, fluvioglacial, or preglacial surfaces. Characteris-tically covered with a veneer of ablation till, they occur in groups called fields or fleets.

These landforms and landscapes associated with continental glaciers represent the main features created by ice-sheet aggradation. As you can imagine, many other features could be identified and their origins analyzed. By understanding the processes that formed these features, we are able to interpret the sequence of events that prevailed during the several glaciations of the Late Cenozoic Ice Age. The landforms of conti-nental glaciers may not be as scenic as those associated with mountain glaciers (which we examine in Unit 47), but they are valuable indicators of past processes and environments.

KEY TERMS

ablation till *page 603*

basal or lodgement till *page 603*

calving *page 593*

drumlin *page 608*

esker *page 604*

flow regime *page 593*

fluvioglacial or stratified drift
   page 603

glacial drift *page 603*

glacial outwash *page 604*

ground moraine *page 604*

icecap *page 592*

ice shelf *page 593*

kame *page 606*

kettle *page 606*

kettle lake *page 606*

moraine *page 604*

nunatak *page 592*

pack ice *page 594*

pluvial lake *page 601*

recessional moraine *page 604*

sandur or outwash plain *page 606*

subglacial *page 602*

supraglacial *page 602*

terminal moraine *page 604*

REVIEW QUESTIONS

1. What is the approximate size (area and thickness) of the Antarctic Ice Sheet?
2. Name the three Northern Hemisphere Late Cenozoic ice sheets and their major geographic dimensions.
3. How might continental glaciation produce lakes on the landscape?
4. How do pluvial lakes relate to glaciation?
5. What is the difference between tills, moraines, and erratics?

REFERENCES AND FURTHER READINGS

BENN, D. I., and EVANS, D. J. A. *Glaciers and Glaciation* (New York: Oxford Univ. Press, 1998).

BOULTON, G. S. "Modern Arctic Glaciers as Depositional Models for Former Ice Sheets," *Journal of the Geological Society* (London), 128 (1972), 361–393.

CHAPMAN, L. J., and PUTNAM, D. F. *The Physiogeography of Southern Ontario* (Toronto: Government of Ontario, Ontario Geological Survey Special Vol. 2, 1984).

CROSSLEY, L. *Explore Antarctica* (New York: Cambridge Univ. Press, 1995).

DREWRY, D. *Glacial Geological Processes* (London: Edward Arnold, 1986).

EMBLETON, C., and KING, C. A. M. *Glacial Geomorphology* (New York: Wiley/Halsted, 2nd ed., 1975).

EVANS, R. *The Geography of Glaciers* (New York: Wiley, 1996).

HAMBREY, M., and ALEAN, J. *Glaciers* (New York: Cambridge Univ. Press, 1992).

HUGHES, T. J. *Ice Sheets* (New York: Oxford Univ. Press, 1998).

MATSCH, C. L. *North America and the Great Ice Age* (New York: McGraw-Hill, 1976).

PATERSON, W. S. B. *The Physics of Glaciers* (Elmsford, N.Y.: Pergamon, 2nd ed., 1981).

PENCK, A., and BRUCKNER, E. *Die Alpen in Eiszeitalter* (The Alps in the Ice Age) (Liepzig, 1909).

PIELOU, E. C. *After the Ice Age: The Return of Life to Glaciated North America* (Chicago: Univ. of Chicago Press, 1991).

ROBERTS, N. *The Holocene* (Malden, Mass.: Blackwell, 2nd ed., 1998).

SHARP, R. P. *Living Ice: Understanding Glaciers and Glaciation* (London/New York: Cambridge Univ. Press, 1988).

SUGDEN, D. E. *Arctic and Antarctic: A Modern Geographical Synthesis* (Totowa, N.J.: Rowman & Littlefield, 1982).

SUGDEN, D. E., and JOHN, B. S. *Glaciers and Landscape: A Geomorphological Approach* (New York: Wiley, 1976).

TELLER J. T., et al. "Freshwater Outbursts from Glacial Lake Agassiz and Their Role in Climate Change during the Last Deglaciation," *Quaternary Science Reviews,* 21, nos. 8–9 (2002), 879–887.

THEAKSTONE, W. H., et al. *Glaciers and Environmental Change* (Sevenoaks, U.K.: Edward Arnold, 1994).

TITUS, J. G. and RICHMAN, C. "Maps of lands vulnerable to sea level rise in the U.S.," *Climate Research,* vol. 18, No. 3 (2001), 205–228.

WILLIAMS, R. S., Jr., and FERRIGNO, J. G., Eds. *Satellite Image Atlas of Glaciers of the World* (Reston, Va.: U.S. Geological Survey, Professional Paper 1386 A-K, 1988).

WILSON, R. C. L., DRURY, S. A., and CHAPMAN, J. A., Eds. *The Great Ice Age: Climate Change and Life* (London/New York: Routledge, 2000).

WEB RESOURCES

http://atlas.gc.ca/site/english/maps/climatechange/potentialimpacts/coastalsensitivitysealevelrise Maps of coastal sensitivity to sea-level rise for all coasts of Canada.

http://oceans.nasa.gov/csp/index2.html This introductory page describes the study of ice sheets, and has links to NASA research data pages. Information about both the Greenland and Antarctic ice sheets is available.

http://tapestry.usgs.gov/features/39moraines.html This USGS page is devoted to recessional moraines and places subsequent landform formation on a geologic timeline. There are links to the Pleistocene ice sheet and various geological epochs.

Landforms and Landscapes of Mountain Glaciers

The Athabasca Glacier, in Jasper National Park, Alberta, flows northeasterly from the Columbia Icefields.

OBJECTIVES

- To examine the current distribution of mountain glaciers and to comment
- on the Late Cenozoic extent of these glaciers
- To discuss the landforms produced by mountain glacier erosion and deposition

The global climate during the Cenozoic Era was generally mild until the onset of the Late Cenozoic Ice Age. Before the ice age began, even Antarctica was mostly ice-free; on high mountains, streams—not glaciers—sculpted the landscape. The landforms associated with river erosion and deposition also characterized such major mountain ranges as the Rockies, Alps, Andes, and even the Himalayas. Hilltops displayed rounded forms, valleys were eroded by meandering streams, and most tributary junctions were concordant (structurally concurrent). The mountain regions of the world looked much like today's Great Smoky Mountains (southeastern United States), Atlas Mountains (northwestern Africa), or Great Dividing Range (eastern Australia), except that higher relief generally prevailed.

When the first cooling episode occurred and the altitude of the snow line dropped, the formation of glaciers began. The Antarctic Ice Sheet probably was the first continental ice mass to develop because of Antarctica's polar location and its high overall elevation. Gradually, on the other continents, permanent ice formed on higher mountain slopes. Snow accumulated above the firn line, and *alpine glaciers* flowed down the high valleys.

These glaciers occupied valleys first carved by rivers, and glacial erosion now replaced stream erosion. Permanent ice appeared on high mountains even in equatorial areas, and the Earth was indeed transformed. This unit focuses on glaciers that form on mountains and erode and deposit material in these alpine settings. These glaciers differ from the ice sheets of continental glaciation in that they are generally confined to valleys, and their behaviour is influenced by the topography they inhabit (see Perspective: Mountain Glaciers—The View from Space). In other respects, they are quite similar to continental icecaps and ice sheets.

Mountain Glaciers Today

Unit 46 noted that two large icecaps or ice sheets survive to the present (the Antarctic and Greenland Icecaps) and that several other major continental glaciers and icecaps wasted away with the onset of the Holocene interglacial. Mountain glaciers, too, were larger and much more prevalent before the current interglacial began. Many mountain glaciers melted away and vacated their valleys as the firn line rose and ice formation in their source areas diminished or ceased. But despite the warmth of the present global climate, numerous mountain glaciers endure. Some have not disappeared, but have receded up their formerly occupied valleys, leaving abundant evidence of their earlier advances.

Global Distribution

Every major landmass on Earth except Australia contains alpine glaciers. It has been estimated that there are as many as 150,000 individual mountain glaciers in the world today, ranging in size from huge bodies to small narrow ribbons of ice. One of the largest mountain glaciers lies in Antarctica's Queen Maud Mountains, where it feeds the continental icecap. This is the Beardmore Glacier, and it remains a mountain glacier for more than 200 km before it merges into the Antarctic Icecap. The

Beardmore Glacier is as much as 40 km wide, vastly larger than anything seen in the Rockies, Alaska, or the Alps.

The remote Beardmore Glacier has been observed by comparatively few people, but other glaciers lie in more accessible areas. Cruise ships visit the Alaskan glaciers where they enter the Gulf of Alaska, and tourists can see active mountain glaciers from the Icefields Parkway in the Canadian Rockies and from their cable-car gondolas in the French and Swiss Alps. Landscapes produced by alpine glaciation are among our most dramatic and underscore the significance of ice in shaping the surface of the Earth.

North America Many alpine glaciers lie on the islands that encircle the Arctic Ocean, such as Spitsbergen, Ellesmere Island, and Novaya Zemlya (see Fig. 47.1). In North America major clusters of mountain glaciers lie in southeastern Alaska, the Yukon Territory and the Coast Mountains of British Columbia, and in the Canadian Rocky Mountains along the Alberta–British Columbia border (Fig. 47.2 and Fig. 47. 3).

Equatorward of 50°N latitude, glacier formation becomes less common. The South Cascade Glacier near Mount Rainier in western Washington State is an example of a temperate glacier in a moist maritime environment, where abundant orographic snowfall sustains a glacier despite relatively high summer temperatures. In Colorado, where there is much less snowfall in the Rockies, strong winds create high-elevation snowdrifts deep enough to produce ice formation and maintain small remnant glaciers.

South America In South America there are large mountain glaciers in the southern Andes of Chile. These begin just south of latitude 45°S (about the latitude of Montreal in the Northern Hemisphere) and become progressively larger at higher latitudes. At the Strait of Magellan, where the South American mainland ends, glacial ice reaches the sea. As the world map shows, the Antarctic Peninsula reaches toward South America, but much of this peninsula is not covered by the Antarctic Icecap. However, large mountain glaciers descend from the highland backbone of the peninsula (an extension of the Andes Mountains) toward the coasts.

Africa Africa has high mountains in the far northwest (the Atlas massif) and south (the Drakensberg), but neither of these ranges carries glaciers, although they do receive winter snows. Almost all of Africa's glaciers lie on two soaring volcanoes near the Equator, Mount Kilimanjaro (5861 m) and Mount Kenya (5199 m). Glaciers descend from near the summits of both mountains, and on Mount Kilimanjaro they reach as far down

PERSPECTIVES ON THE HUMAN ENVIRONMENT

Mountain Glaciers—The View from Space

The relationship between alpine glaciers and their surrounding landscapes is strikingly visible in satellite imagery. The Landsat photographic image in Fig. 47.1 is a particularly fine example and should be contrasted against the space view of the continental-scale Antarctic Icecap shown in Fig. 46.1.

The subject of Fig. 47.1, Bylot Island, is located off the northern coast of Canada's Baffin Island (inset map). More than two dozen active mountain glaciers can readily be seen, and there are several excellent examples of individual valley glaciers coalescing to form a single main (trunk) glacier. All of them emanate from the island's interior uplands (whose elevation exceeds 600 m) and flow outward and downslope toward the sea. Because of Bylot's high latitude (73°N), the snow line lies at a relatively low elevation and many glaciers come close to reaching the coast (two in the northwest actually do). Overall, the island's area is 10,880 km², its longest east–west dimension measures approximately 145 km, and its widest north–south extent is about 115 km. Surprisingly, given Bylot's remote location and inhospitable setting, humans have long made inroads here: several thousand Inuit people each spring and summer occupy the wide, low-lying, ice-free southern peninsula to take advantage of local marine resources.

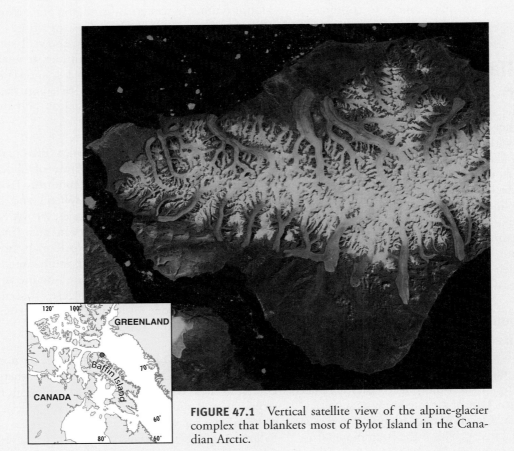

FIGURE 47.1 Vertical satellite view of the alpine-glacier complex that blankets most of Bylot Island in the Canadian Arctic.

FROM THE FIELDNOTES

FIGURE 47.2 "My flight from Seattle to Tokyo afforded spectacular views of the glacial landscape of Alaska. Cirques are filled with snow and ice, **U**-shaped valleys are steep-sided, and moraine-streaked glaciers coalesce and flow downvalley. The narrow medial moraine near the bottom of the photo widens quickly as rock debris is added. Tributary glaciers thicken the lateral moraines, and by the time the glacier makes its turn in the distance, it is choked with rocky debris. When I took this photo, we were near Gulkana, Alaska."

as 4400 m on the south side (see Fig. 19.11). There are a dozen small glaciers on Mount Kenya, two of which are still quite substantial, although, like the others, they are receding.

Australia and New Zealand Australia's mountains are too low to support glaciers, but higher latitude, higher elevation, and greater precipitation combine to sustain large valley glaciers on the South Island of New Zealand. The Southern Alps, the mountain backbone

of this island, reach their highest point in Mount Cook (3764 m). In the vicinity of Mount Cook lie another 15 mountains over 3000 m high. The entire mountain range was covered by an icecap in glacial times, and several major glaciers survive in the area of Mount Cook. Among the best known are the Franz Josef Glacier and the Fox Glacier. The Fox Glacier is receding quite rapidly, and its withdrawal is marked by signposts in its lower valley along the road leading to the present glacial margin (Fig. 47.4).

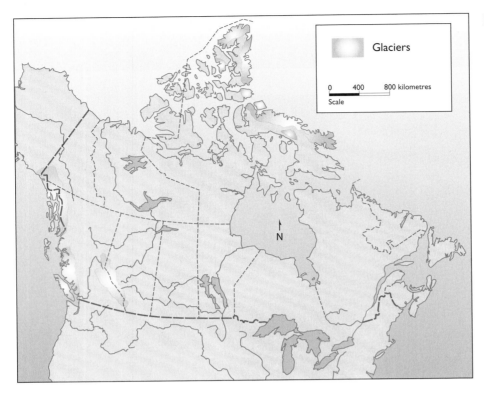

FIGURE 47.3   Canadian glaciers.

FROM THE FIELDNOTES

FIGURE 47.4 "The Fox Glacier flows westward off New Zealand's Southern Alps. There was a time when this glacier surged into the forested lowlands near the coast, cutting down trees like matchsticks; but today you can walk up a vacated valley to its receding face. The glacier's recession has been monitored for decades, and signposts in the valley mark where it stood years ago. Global warming, reduced snowfall in its catchment area, and possibly other factors as well combine to stagnate this once aggressive glacier. Today morainal deposits in a wide, **U**-shaped valley evince the Fox Glacier's former power, but the glacier itself is covered by rock rubble, and meltwater streams emanate from its base, feeding small lakes downvalley."

Europe Most of the world's mountain glaciers lie in two major clusters on the Eurasian landmass. Of these two, the European Alps are undoubtedly the most famous, and the south-central Asian zone is by far the largest (see Fig. 46.8). Much of what is known about the degradational and aggradational work of glaciers was learned through research performed in the European Alps. Europe's Alps extend in a broad arc from southeastern France through the area of the Swiss–Italian border into central Austria (Fig. 47.5). Mont Blanc, 4807 m high, is the tallest peak, but several other mountains exceed 4000 m. Active glaciers abound in the Alps, and virtually every erosional and depositional landform associated with glaciation is found there. From the deposits left by the repeatedly advancing glaciers, European scientists deduced the glacial sequence presented in Table 46.1.

Asia The glacial topography of the European Alps is dwarfed, however, by the vast expanse of glacial landscape that extends across the soaring highlands of south-central Asia from Afghanistan to southwestern China (Fig. 47.6). This region was the site of one of the Late Cenozoic's largest icecaps, and tens of thousands of residual glaciers now provide testimony of that phenomenon. The glacial landscape extends from northeastern Afghanistan along the length and breadth of the highlands, marking the boundary between the Eurasian and Indian Plates (see Fig. 32.3).

Many of the world's highest mountains—including the tallest of all, Nepal's Mount Everest (Saganatha to Nepalis; Chomuolungma to Tibetans), 8850 m high—lie in this zone. Much of the region still remains buried under ice and snow, and many of the mountain glaciers here are hundreds of metres thick and many kilometres

FIGURE 47.5 Central Europe's Alps form a gigantic crescent of spectacular mountain ranges. The large lowland they frame just to their south is northern Italy's Po Plain. The Italian peninsula, with its Apennine Mountains backbone, extends seaward from the southern margin of the Po Valley.

FIGURE 47.6 A space-shuttle view of the Himalayas, looking westward from a point above the easternmost part of India's Ganges Plain. With the Tibetan Plateau to the north (right), they constitute the Earth's most prominent highland zone.

wide. Maximum development occurs in the Himalayan–Tibetan area (Fig. 47.6). Vast as the ice and snow cover is, however, there is abundant evidence that here, too, the glaciers have receded during the Holocene: glacial topography and glacial deposits extend far beyond the margins of the present ice.

Isolated Remnant Glaciers   In addition to the Earth's notable clusters of alpine glaciers, there are isolated glaciers in some places, such as the high-elevation glaciers of equatorial East Africa; similar glacier development also occurs on the highest slopes of the Andes Mountains in tropical-latitude Ecuador and Peru. Remnant glaciers also exist in northern Norway, where it is latitude, not altitude, that supports them. Mount Elbrus, the highest peak in the Caucasus Mountains (between the Black and Caspian Seas along Russia's southern flank), reaches 5642 m and carries several small glaciers. All of these glaciers are surrounded by evidence that they, too, are remnants of larger ones that existed in the past.

The Mass Balance

The **mass balance** or **budget** of a glacier defines the relationship between the gain and loss of glacial ice mass.

The *gains* may occur over the entire glacier during the winter season, but generally the new snow cover on the lower part of the glacier is removed (by various processes listed below) during the summer melt season. The gains are usually preserved on the upper part of the

glacier in the *accumulation zone* or *neve*. The accumulation of mass occurs through the following processes:

1. Refreezing of meltwater either on, in, or under the ice
2. Snowfall and/or rainfall onto the glacier surface
3. Windblown snow brought in from other glaciers or surrounding slopes
4. Snow avalanches from surrounding slopes

The *losses* occur in the lower part of the glacier (the ablation zone) where summer temperatures are usually higher than in the accumulation zone. The ablation of mass occurs through the following processes:

1. Melting on, or under the ice (the change from solid ice to liquid water)
2. Evaporation (the change from water to gas)
3. Sublimation (the change from solid to gas)
4. Wind erosion
5. Chunks of ice breaking off the snout of the glacier

In tidewater glaciers that end in the sea, or in glaciers that end in lakes, essentially the same process occurs as iceberg break off from the terminus of the glacier. This process, called calving can be a very important loss of glacier mass for some tidewater glaciers. The Rink Glacier on the West coast of Greenland, for example, loses an estimated 500 million tonnes of ice by this process. The calving takes only a few minutes and occurs on an average once every two weeks. It is suggested that as many as 10,000 to 15,000 icebergs of various sizes break off the Greenland Icecap every year. One tabular iceberg that broke off Antarctica Ice in November 1987 was about 1000 km² larger than Prince Edward Island. An iceberg that broke away in 1956 was estimated to be approximately 31,000 km²—twice as big as Belgium.

The gains and losses of ice from a glacier are closely related to local energy balances (temperature, evaporation, etc.). The Victoria Glacier at Lake Louise in the Canadian Rockies provides a good example of glacier mass balance.

The Victoria Glacier

Bn (net balance) is measured in m/yr water equivalent (the depth of water produced by the melting of the icesnow; 25–30 cm of snow produces about 2.5 cm of water).

Net accumulation	1.52 m/yr
Net ablation	1.43 m/yr
Bn	+ 0.09 m/yr

This glacier had a weakly positive mass balance for the above year. It has experienced a loss of mass averaging

0.21 m/yr for over 12 years (1966–1978). It usually has small-scale variations around the zero mark, but there have been three periods with bigger negative balances—1960–70, 1977–78, and 2003–2004.

If **Bn** is zero for many years, the glacier would be considered to be in balance or equilibrium (steady state).

There is a lag time between a change in the mass balance and a response seen at the snout of the glacier (e.g., advance or recession). The average lag time for fairly small valley glaciers is between three and 30 years. The Athabasca Glacier, which flows off the Columbia Icefields in the Canadian Rockies, has a lag time of about 100 years, while the immense glaciers flowing off Greenland and Antarctica have lag times of about 5000 years.

Ice and debris continue to move through a glacier at all times whether there is a positive or negative balance or not the glacier is in equilibrium.

Degradational Landforms of Mountain Glaciers

There is no mistaking a landscape sculpted by mountain glaciers, even long after the glaciers have melted away. Mountains, ridges, valleys, and deposits all bear the stamp of the glaciers' degradational or aggradational work. Before examining the major landforms created by glacial action, we should review the nature of alpine glaciers' mass balance as well as their appearance and general morphology. The zones of mass accumulation of these glaciers lie on high mountain slopes. There, snow is compacted into ice, and the ice moves downhill under the force of gravity, assisted by basal lubrication in wet-based ice, to occupy valleys formed earlier by stream erosion. Unlike the surface of an ice sheet, which tends to be snow-white or ice-blue, the surface of a mountain glacier normally is streaked by bands of rock debris.

Glacial Valleys

A mountain glacier, when it occupies a river valley, immediately begins to change the cross-section and profile of that valley. Glaciers work to widen as well as deepen their valleys, and the typical cross-section of a glacial valley is U-shaped (Fig. 47.7). The U-shaped glacial valley, or **glacial trough**, is one of the most characteristic of the glacial landforms.

Maps and aerial photographs of glacial troughs also reveal other properties of these valleys: they are characterized by straight steep sides. Glaciers are powerful erosional agents that can destroy obstacles in their paths. As a result, many mountainside slopes *around* which rivers once flowed are sheared off by glaciers, thereby straightening the

A

B

C

FIGURE 47.7 Evolution of a glacial trough. Diagram (A) shows the stage of peak glaciation, with the U-shaped trough gouged out by the trunk glacier that is advancing toward the viewer. When the valley glacier has melted away, truncated spurs and hanging valleys are readily apparent (B). If the glacial trough is near the coast and has been deepened below (rising) sea level, it will become inundated and a fjord will form (C). After Arthur N. Strahler, copyright Arthur N. Strahler.

valley course. Such straightened steep slopes (**truncated spurs**) are further evidence of glacial action in the landscape after the glaciers have melted away (Fig. 47.7B).

When a stream is joined by a tributary, the water surface of both streams is at the same level and the floors of the two valleys tend to be concordant as well. In other words, there is no sharp break between the floor of the main stream valley and that of the tributary valley. But when a smaller glacier joins a larger one, the base of the tributary glacier is not nearly as low, nor the valley as deep, as that of the larger trunk glacier. Their ice surfaces will be at about the same level (as shown in Fig. 47.10), but their bedrock floors are discordant, sometimes by hundreds of metres. When both glaciers melt away, the valley of the tributary glacier, as viewed from the floor of the main glacier, seems to "hang" high above. Such a discordant junction is appropriately called a **hanging valley** or hanging trough (Fig. 47.7B), still another sure sign of the landscape's glacial history. A hanging valley is often graced by a scenic waterfall where the stream now occupying the tributary glacier's valley cascades down the steep valley sides of the main trough.

High-Mountain Landforms

Above the "trim line" of the glaciated valleys (the highest points affected by general erosion), the landscape is generally more rounded and is much like it must have been in preglacial times. This area is called an **alp**. In some mountains the source areas of the glaciers occur above the glacial valleys. There the landscape is also transformed. The series of three block diagrams in Fig. 47.8 suggests a possible sequence of events. Initially the landscape consists of rounded ridges and peaks (Fig. 47.8A). With the onset of glaciation, deep snow accumulations form on the higher slopes, and the ice subsequently thickens. The ice moves downslope under gravity, and glacial erosion begins (Fig. 47.8B).

In the upper area of continuous snow accumulation, the ice hollows out shallow basins, which become the glacier's source area. Not only does the ice excavate such basins, but frost wedging on the walls above them, plus undercutting by headward erosion, also creates distinctive, amphitheatre-like landforms, which are referred to as **cirques** (Fig. 47.8C). A cirque is a bowl-shaped, steep-sided depression in the bedrock with a gently sloping floor; many are overdeepened and have a bedrock lip. Two, three, or even more cirques may develop near the top of a mountain. In time these cirques, growing by headward erosion, intersect. Now nothing remains of the original rounded mountaintop in the centre of the diagram except a steep-sided, sharp-edged peak known as a **horn** (Fig. 47.9). The Matterhorn in the Swiss Alps is the quintessential example. Thus, when the ice melts or the ice thins out, these horns tower impressively above the landscape (see Fig. 47.8C).

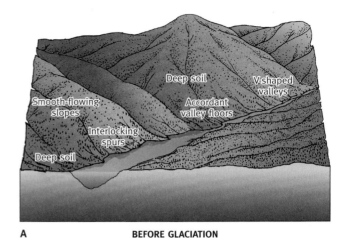

FIGURE 47.8   A possible sequence showing the transformation of a mountain landscape by alpine glaciation. Note how the initial rounded ridges and peaks are sculpted into a much sharper-edged topography by frost wedging and glacial erosion.

FROM THE FIELDNOTES

FIGURE 47.9 "Boarded a two-seater airplane to fly from the airstrip at Whataroa (on New Zealand's South Island) up the Franz Josef Glacier toward the Mount Cook area in the Southern Alps. This scenery seems even more spectacular than the 'real' Alps. How I wish that I could have my whole physical geography class with me here—what a matchless laboratory! This view of a basin-shaped, snow-accumulating, ice-generating *cirque* also reveals a developing *horn* (right background) and a sharp-edged *arête* (left foreground)."

Other dramatic elements of mountain glacier topography are shown in Fig. 47.8C. One is the large number of razor-sharp, often jagged ridges that rise above the ice-containing troughs. These ridges often separate adjacent glaciers or glacial valleys and are known as **arêtes**. They can develop when two or more large cirques intersect, but they more frequently form from erosion and frost wedging in two parallel glacial valleys or cirques.

Another major feature occurs as the glaciers move downslope. They not only straighten their courses, but they also create steplike profiles (valleys emanating forward below the horn in the centre of Fig. 47.8C). Such landforms result from a combination of factors. One relates to the differential resistance of various rocks over which the glacier passes. The jointing of the bedrock (and therefore its susceptibility to frost wedging, etc.)

also affects this process. In the postglacial landscape, **rock steps** reveal the local effects of such glacial erosion.

Lakes

As in the case of continental glaciers, depressions gouged by alpine glaciers are filled by water during interglacials such as the present period. Where the climate is warm enough so that even high-altitude cirques are no longer filled with snow, small circular lakes are found on the floors of the cirque basins. These lakes, dammed up behind the "lip" of the cirque, are known as **tarns** (one is labelled in the upper far right of Fig. 47.8C). Lakes also may form on the rock steps previously described, as again shown in those three valleys below the horn in the central portion of Fig. 47.8C. There may be a sequence of lakes separated by streams with rapids and waterfalls (as the stream tumbles down a step). From above the drainage looks like a section of a bead necklace. The largest lakes fill substantial parts of glacial troughs, as the lower left of the diagram shows. Such lakes may be several kilometres wide and 50 km or more long and are called **finger lakes**. (Those in upstate New York are shown in Fig. 46.9.) Some of the world's most scenic lakes, from the Alps of Switzerland to the Southern Alps of New Zealand, owe their origins to glacial erosion.

Fjords

Among the most spectacular landforms associated with glacial erosion are fjords. A **fjord** is a narrow, steep-sided, elongated estuary (drowned river mouth) formed from a glacial trough inundated by seawater (see Fig. 47.7C). During glaciations many glaciers reach the ocean. Ice, as noted elsewhere, has a density about five-sixths that of seawater, so a glacier reaching the ocean can continue to erode a valley many metres below sea level. Thus vigorously eroding glaciers created seaward troughs. When the ice melted, ocean water inundated the glacial valley, creating a unique coastal landscape. Fjords developed mainly in places where glaciated mountains lie near a coastline, such as in British Columbia, southern Alaska, and western Norway. Other famous and scenic fjords lie along the southwestern coast of Chile and along the southwestern coast of New Zealand's South Island.

FIGURE 47.10   This freshwater fjord at Western Brook Pond, Gros Morne National Park, Newfoundland, was cut off from the sea after the last ice age.

Aggradational Landforms of Mountain Glaciers

As components of scenery, the depositional landforms of alpine glaciers are no match for the erosional features just discussed and illustrated. Some of the debris carried downslope is ground into particles so fine that this is called **rock flour**, and when the glacier melts and deposits this rock flour, much of it is blown away by the wind. Larger fragments, as in the case of continental glaciers, are deposited at the (stalled) edge of the advancing glacier as *terminal moraines*. Again, as with continental glaciers, stationary periods during a glacier's retreat are marked by *recessional moraines* (see Fig. 46.15). Terminal and recessional moraines lie in low ridges across the valley floor. These mounds can form dams that impound meltwater, creating temporary glacial lakes and associated glaciofluvial features (see Unit 46).

Moraines

Debris carried by an alpine glacier comes not only from the valley floor it erodes but also from slope processes on the valley sides above the glacial ice. Frost wedging, the repeated freezing and thawing of water in rock cracks and joints, loosens pieces of bedrock (see Fig. 38.2). These fall onto the glacier's surface along the margins of the ice, where they become part of bands of debris called **moraines** (the same term used in relation to ice sheets on pp. 572–575, but with a somewhat different meaning here). The vigorously eroding glacier also tends to undercut its valley sides so that mass movement contributes additional material to the glacial surface.

Material that falls from the valley wall first becomes part of the glacier's **lateral moraines**, the moraines situated along the edges of the ice (Fig. 47.10). When a trunk glacier is joined by a substantial tributary glacier or dams another glacier, their lateral moraines join to become a **medial moraine**, which is situated away from the glacier's edges (Fig. 47.11). This pattern may be repeated several times as additional tributary glaciers enter the main glacier's channel.

Furthermore, as shown in Fig. 47.11, erosion at the base of the valley glacier creates till or **ground moraine** (in this case the term has the same connotation as for ice sheets). The ground moraine is exposed on the floor of the glacial trough as the ice recedes, and is thickened by the deposition of the contents of the melting, debris-laden glacier. Recession of the valley glacier will also result in the deposition of the lateral and medial moraines, which form irregular ridges and mounds of unsorted material.

CANADIAN GEOGRAPHERS IN THE FIELD

"This photo shows a large igneous glacial erratic, near Rio Grande, northern Tierra del Fuego, Argentina. This erratic was transported eastward from the Darwin Mountains in Chile. Although there are no other glacial landform features on the landscape, the presence of this erratic indicates that the area was glaciated. By dating the buildup of cosmogenic radioisotopes on the surface, resulting from bombardment by solar insolation, the time of glacial deposition can be determined. This technique is essentially analogous to looking at a suntan; we are determining how long the erratic has been exposed to solar insolation. Weathering is extremely slow in the dry climate of northern Tierra del Fuego."

Norm Catto is Professor of Geography, Memorial University.

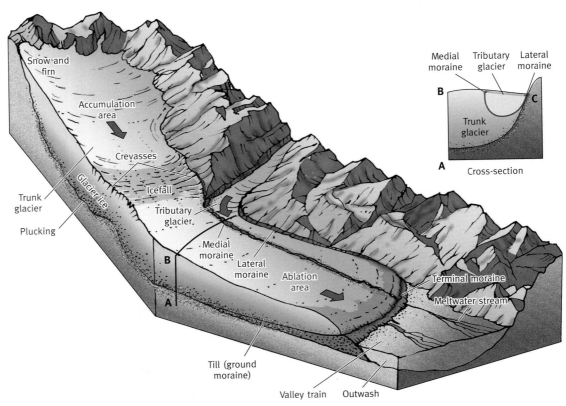

FIGURE 47.11   Cutaway view of a valley glacier and one of its tributaries, showing depositional features. Note the positions of the lateral, medial, and terminal moraines. When the glacier recedes, the till on the valley floor behind the terminal moraine is left behind as a ground moraine.

Postglacial Landscape Change

Stream action begins to modify the aggradational landforms in glacial troughs as soon as the glaciers vacate them. When meltwater starts to fill the valley floor with alluvium derived from the morainal material left behind, the new deposit is known as a *sandur* (plural sandar) or **valley train** (Fig. 47.11). Modification of the glacial deposits (not the bedrock topography) usually is quite rapid. Glacial lakes are drained, material is sorted and redistributed fluvioglacial, and vegetation recovers.

Glacial topography is scenic, and it attracts countless tourists to ski lodges and other highland resorts.

But as the foregoing has made clear, glaciated areas are not stable. The glaciers retreated from valleys with over-steepened walls. Frost wedging loosened huge quantities of rock, much of it perched precariously on steep slopes. Snow accumulations can lead to avalanches that would be harmless in remote terrain, but are often fatal when humans populate these landscapes. Mass movements of various kinds form a significant natural hazard in alpine-glaciated regions, as the large landslide and its dammed lake suggest in the lower central portion of Fig. 47.8C.

KEY TERMS

REVIEW QUESTIONS

1. What are the two regions that contain the greatest concentration of mountain glaciers?
2. In what way does a glacial trough differ in shape from a stream valley?
3. What is a hanging valley and how does it form?
4. How would mountain glaciation produce abundant lakes?
5. What is a fjord and how is it formed?

REFERENCES AND FURTHER READINGS

BENN, D. I., and EVANS, D. J. A. *Glaciers and Glaciation* (New York: Oxford Univ. Press, 1998).

BIRD J. B. *The Natural Landscapes of Canada: A Study of Regional Earth Science* (Toronto: Wiley, 2nd ed., 1980).

DREWRY, D. *Glacial Geologic Processes* (London: Edward Arnold, 1986).

EMBLETON, C., and KING, C. A. M. *Glacial Geomorphology* (New York: Wiley/Halsted, 2nd ed., 1975).

EVANS, R. *The Geography of Glaciers* (New York: Wiley, 1996).

FITZGERALD, D. M., and ROSEN, P. S., Eds. *Glaciated Coasts* (Orlando, Fla.: Academic Press, 1987).

HAMBREY, M., and ALEAN, J. *Glaciers* (New York: Cambridge Univ. Press, 1992).

IVES, J. D., Ed. *Mountains* (Emmaus, Penna.: Rodale Press, 1994).

OWEN, L. A., et al. *Polar and Alpine Geomorphology* (Malden, Mass.: Blackwell, 1998).

PATERSON, W. S. B. *The Physics of Glaciers* (Elmsford, N.Y.: Pergamon, 2nd ed., 1981).

POST, A., and LACHAPELLE, E. R. *Glacier Ice* (Seattle, Wash.: The Mountaineers, 1971).

PRICE, L. W. *Mountains and Man: A Study of Process and Environment* (Berkeley, Calif.: Univ. of California Press, 1981).

RYDER J. M. "Geomorphology of the Southern part of the Coast Mountains of British Columbia," *Zeitschrift für Geomorphologie,* Supplementband 37 (1981), 120–147.

RYDER, J. M. *Geomorphological Processes in the Alpine Areas of Canada* (Ottawa: Geological Survey of Canada Bulletin 524, 1998).

SHARP, R. P. *Living Ice: Understanding Glaciers and Glaciation* (London/New York: Cambridge Univ. Press, 1988).

SLAYMAKER, O. "Climate-Related Landscapes in the Canadian Cordillera," *Zeitschrift für Geomorphologie,* Supplementband 9 (1993), 95–109

SLAYMAKER, O., and McPherson H. J. "An Overview of the Geomorphic Processes in the Canadian Cordillera," *Zeitschrift für Geomorphologie* (1977), 169–186.

SUGDEN, D. E., and JOHN, B. S. *Glaciers and Landscape: A Geomorphological Approach* (New York: Wiley, 1976).

SYVITSKI, J. P. M., et al. *Fjords: Processes and Products* (New York/Berlin: Springer-Verlag, 1987).

TRENHAILE, A. S. *Geomorphology: A Canadian Perspective* (Toronto: Oxford Univ. Press, 1998).

WILLIAMS, R. S., Jr., and FERRIGNO, J. G. "Cold Beauty: Rivers of Ice," *Earth Magazine* (January 1991), 42–49.

WILLIAMS, R. S., Jr., and HALL, D. K. "Glaciers," in R. J. Gurney, J. L. Foster, and C. L. Parkinson, Eds., *Atlas of Earth Observations Related to Global Change* (New York: Cambridge Univ. Press, 1993), 114–123.

WEB RESOURCES

http://www.geocities.com/goodlordtom/prehistory.html This page focuses on aggradational landform building, including the prehistory of Switzerland and the formation of the Alps. Colour graphics and photographs illustrate the process.

http://www.virtualmuseum.ca/Exhibitions/Fjord/english/f_formation_e.html This page describes formation of the Saguenay fjord in Canada, and has detailed graphics of the formation process.

Periglacial Environments and Landscapes

Tundra environment—Bathurst Inlet, Northwest Territories.

OBJECTIVES

- To discuss the unique landscapes that develop under near-glacial conditions at high latitudes and high altitudes
- To highlight the important weathering and mass-movement processes that shape periglacial landscapes

The Earth is undergoing an interglacial at present; yet large regions of the world are anything but warm, even during the summer. Figure 16.3 shows the large expanses of existing **Dfc, Dfd,** and **E** climates. Conditions in these high-latitude regions are nearly, but not quite, glacial. The technical term for such environments is **periglacial**—on the perimeter of glaciation. In this unit we study the processes and landforms that characterize periglacial areas.

Periglacial zones today occupy high polar and subpolar latitudes, almost exclusively in the Northern Hemisphere. No periglacial environments exist in southern Africa or in Australia, although the highlands of Tasmania (off the southeastern coast of Australia) show evidence of recent periglacial conditions. Only small areas of southernmost South America (most notably the island of Tierra del Fuego) and the Antarctic Peninsula exhibit periglacial conditions. Accordingly, this unit deals almost exclusively with the Northern Hemisphere. Nonetheless it is estimated that as much as one-quarter of the entire land surface of the Earth is dominated by periglacial conditions, and this alone should persuade us to learn more about these cold environments.

In the past, periglacial conditions migrated into the middle latitudes when Pleistocene ice sheets expanded. When the Wisconsinan ice sheets covered much of northern North America, periglacial conditions extended far to the south, where the landscape still bears the imprints. This reminds us that the Earth's comfortable living space during the next glaciation will be much smaller than the land area not actually covered by ice. Periglacial conditions, extending in a wide belt from the margin of the ice, will restrict the ecumene even more (see Perspective: Humans and the Periglacial Environment).

Permafrost

It is difficult to define the environmental limits of periglacial regions exactly. Perhaps the most practical way to delimit periglacial conditions is based on a phenomenon unique to these regions—**permafrost**, or perenially frozen ground (frozen for more than two years). Much of the permafrost is a remnant of the Pleistocene glaciations. In periglacial zones, the ground (soil as well as rock) below the surface layer is permanently frozen. What this means, of course, is that all the water in this subsurface layer is frozen. The permafrost layer (Fig. 48.2) normally begins between 15 cm and 5 m below the surface.

The upper surface of the permafrost is called the *permafrost table*. The soil above the permafrost table is subject to annual freezing and thawing. This is the **active layer** or **talik**; it is thickest in the subarctic region and becomes thinner both poleward and southward. Below the permafrost table the frozen ground can be very deep. In North America it averages around 300 m, but in the heart of high-latitude Eurasia permafrost

PERSPECTIVES ON THE HUMAN ENVIRONMENT

Humans and the Periglacial Environment

Cold and inhospitable as periglacial environments are, people have lived in and migrated through these regions for many thousands of years. Those who stayed there adapted to the difficult conditions. The Inuit, best known of the Arctic peoples, skillfully exploited the environment's opportunities on both land and sea. Their numbers remained small, their social organization was comparatively simple, and their impact on the fragile periglacial domain was very slight.

But the recent invasion of technologically advanced societies, driven by the search for resources, generated new and major problems and threatened local environments as never before. Examples are the Yukon Gold Rush of the latter part of the 1890s, the Alcan (Alaska–Canada) Highway, the building of airfields to supply material to the Russian allies during the Second World War, the Distant Early Warning Line (DEW Line) of the Cold War years, the creation of permanent settlements for the Inuit, and the MacKenzie Valley Pipeline. The catastrophic 1989 oil spill in Prince William

Sound, Alaska, underscores this kind of intervention (Fig. 48.1). The periglacial environment poses engineering, construction, and maintenance problems unknown in warmer regions. Despite the arrival of modern technology in the subarctic, however, population numbers remain low. Nevertheless, the impact of the new era is felt throughout the region in the form of frontier towns and highways, oil facilities, and military installations.

The periglacial world is a landscape of recent glaciation, of scoured bedrock, of basins and lakes, of thin and rocky soil, and of scattered glaciofluvial deposits such as kames, eskers, and drumlins. Winter is protracted and bitter; nights are frigid and long. Summer is short and cool, depending on latitude and exposure. The surface is frozen half the year or more, but when the accumulated snow melts, the ground is saturated. Plants, animals, and indigenous peoples have adapted to a combination of environmental conditions that are delicately balanced and so easily disturbed.

FIGURE 48.1   North America's most serious high-latitude environmental disaster to date: the fully loaded *Exxon Valdez* disgorging some 42,000,000 l of crude oil into Prince William Sound, Alaska, shortly after the supertanker ran aground on March 24, 1989. A major study in 2001 revealed that oil contamination still plagued the Sound's shoreline, and the aftereffects of this ecological tragedy are likely to linger for decades to come.

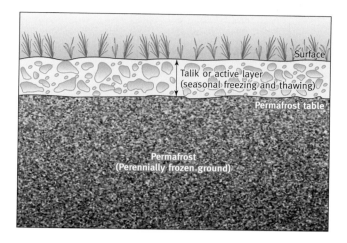

FIGURE 48.2 The talik or subsurface active and permafrost layers characteristic of periglacial zones. Note how the upper active layer contains ice-fractured rock fragments of varying size that have been deposited in the soil as frost wedging in the harsh environment above constantly breaks down boulders and pebbles.

depths of more than 1200 m have been measured. Like a growing glacier, the permafrost would keep thickening season after season, except that heat from the Earth's interior eventually limits this process.

The distribution of permafrost in the Northern Hemisphere is mapped in Fig. 48.3. Note that the map first differentiates between *continuous permafrost,* located in northernmost Canada, and *discontinuous permafrost,* found as far south as the latitude of James Bay. Continuous permafrost, as the term implies, is thick and unbroken, thinning somewhat only under lakes or wide rivers. Discontinuous permafrost is generally thinner and contains unfrozen gaps. Also shown on the map are lower-latitude patches of permafrost. These patches, known as *sporadic* or *alpine permafrost* zone(s), mostly occur at high elevations in mountains such as the Rockies, and are remnants of the permafrost of glacial times (see dashed-line boundary in Fig. 48.3).

The map of world vegetation (see Fig. 27.1) indicates that a certain correspondence exists between the boundary separating continuous and discontinuous permafrost and the treeline that delimits tundra from forest vegetation. While it is not clear whether the vegetation influences the properties of the permafrost or vice versa, it is clear that many factors, including not only vegetation but also precipitation and temperature regimes, affect permafrost development and persistence.

Geomorphological Processes in Periglacial Environments

The modification of the landscape in periglacial zones takes place in ways that differ from other regions, because freezing and thawing and mass movements play such dominant roles. Water, when changing phases from the liquid to the frozen state, is an important force. When a permanently frozen layer exists below the surface, water cannot drain downward; therefore it often saturates the active layer. In this upper stratum, boulders are shattered by frost, and fragments are constantly moved by freezing and thawing and the force of gravity. This results in landforms that are unique to periglacial areas.

Frost Action

The key disintegrative combination in periglacial environments is the amount of water in soil and rock and the freezing and thawing of that water. **Frost wedging** or *shattering* occurs when the stress created by the freezing of water into ice becomes greater than the cohesive strength of the rock containing it. Research has proven that the more water a rock contains, the greater the power of frost wedging. For instance, porous sedimentary rocks containing water will shatter more rapidly than less porous rocks. Joints and cracks in nonporous crystalline rocks are zones of weakness that are exploited by frost shattering (see Fig. 38.4). Frost wedging is capable of dislodging boulders from cliffs, of splintering boulders into angular pebbles, of cracking pebbles into gravel-sized fragments, and of reducing gravel to sand and even finer particles. Thus the active layer consists of a mixture of ice-fractured fragments of all sizes (Fig. 48.2).

The surface layer of terrain is often characterized by the sorting of fragments by size. This sorting is done by repeated freezing and thawing of the talik and produces a phenomenon called *patterned ground* (see Fig. 48.8). Once rock fragments have been loosened by frost wedging, they are moved by frost heaving. **Frost heaving** causes vertical (upward) displacement when the formation of ice in the ground expands the total mass. Large fragments are moved upward a greater distance than smaller ones, so that the surface sometimes seems studded with small boulders rising above the ground (Fig. 48.4). The same frost heaving that moves boulders upward also pushes concrete blocks, road segments, posts, poles, and other artificial fixtures out of the ground (see Fig. 19.3).

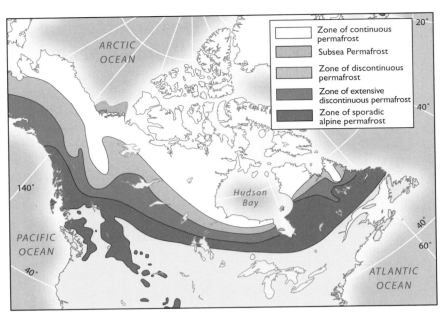

FIGURE 48.3 Permafrost zones in North America.

In addition to frost heaving, there are processes that move material horizontally. One of these processes is **frost thrusting**. The mechanics of this process are not well understood, but there can be no question that it moves rock fragments horizontally within the active layer. Another process is **frost creep**, the movement of particles in the talik under the influence of gravity (Fig. 48.5). A piece of rock brought to the surface by frost heaving will move downslope during the thawing phase. Frost wedging, frost heaving, and frost creep combine to produce some remarkable landforms.

FIGURE 48.4 The effects of frost heaving—as boulders under the ground are thrust upward—can be seen on the tundra in Kootenay, British Columbia.

Solifluction

Another process closely associated with periglacial conditions is solifluction (also known as gelifluction). **Solifluction** is a form of soil creep, the slow flowage of saturated soil. The upper horizons of cryosolic soils in permafrost areas are often saturated because water cannot drain below the permafrost table. In the warm season such saturated soil begins to move as a mass, even when the slope angle is low (Fig. 48.6). The texture of the soil is important, because highly permeable materials such as gravel and sand are not likely to move by solifluction whereas silt-laden soils move quite freely.

Periglacial areas are cold, but they are not without vegetation, which plays a significant role in stabilizing the talik and in impeding solifluction. Again, human intervention can have devastating effects. When the protective vegetative cover (whether tundra or forest) is removed, binding roots are destroyed, summer thawing reaches a greater depth, and more of the active layer is destabilized. Recovery, in fact, may not occur at all, even after the damaged area is vacated. Periglacial ecologies are particularly fragile.

Landforms of Periglacial Regions

Landforms in periglacial regions are not as dramatic or spectacular as those of mountain-glaciated areas. They are nonetheless quite distinctive, resulting from a combination of frost action and slope process. The geomorphological features thus produced often take the

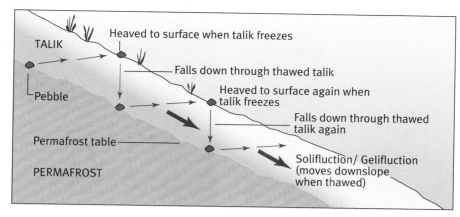

FIGURE 48.5 Frost creep and solifluction/gelifluction processes.

form of special patterns that look as though they were designed artificially.

Ice Wedges

One of these remarkable shapes is created by *ice wedges*. During the frigid Arctic winter, the ground in the active layer (and even the upper permafrost) becomes so cold that it cracks, much as mud cracks form (see Unit 38). During the following summer, snow, meltwater, and sediment will fill this crack, creating a wedge of foreign material. The next winter the mix freezes, and the crack, now filled with the ice wedge, opens and widens a little more, and additional water, snow, and sediment enter it. This process is repeated over many seasons.

Some ice wedges reach a width of 3 m and a depth of 30 m. They align in patterns that from the air look like an interlocking network, referred to as **ice-wedge polygons** (Fig. 48.7). In some instances so much fine-grained sediment is available that the wedges become filled with soil. Ice- and soil-wedge patterns are typical of permafrost zones, and when climatic conditions change, they remain imprinted on the landscape.

Patterned Ground

Another characteristic feature of periglacial regions, is patterned ground. **Patterned ground** consists of rock and soil debris shaped or sorted in such a manner that designs are formed on the surface resembling rings, polygons, lines, and other repeatedly regular arrangements (Fig. 48.8). Such forms are characteristic of periglacial regions, but unlike ice-wedge features, permafrost is not essential for their formation. Patterned ground results from the frost shattering of bedrock, the lifting and sorting of fragments by frost heaving, and the

FIGURE 48.6 The talik or active layer above the permafrost, frozen in winter but thawed and very wet in summer. Even where slope angles are low, the whole active layer may move slowly downslope. While younger vegetation may not yet reflect this, older trees may lean as a result of this solifluction process.

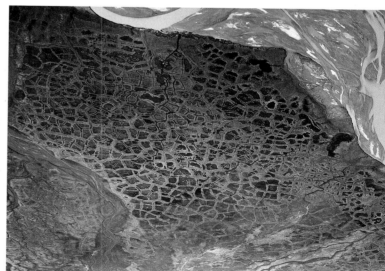

FIGURE 48.7 View from an airplane over a landscape of ice-wedge polygons in the Canadian Arctic.

FIGURE 48.8 Ground-level view of a plain filled with rock debris sorted into myriad stone circles 3 to 5 m in diameter. This striking example of patterned ground was photographed in western Spitsbergen, part of the Arctic Ocean's Svalbard island chain, which belongs to Norway.

FIGURE 48.9 This prominent pingo, located in the Mackenzie River Delta in northwesternmost Canada, certainly ranks in the largest size category exhibited by these periglacial landforms.

force of gravity. Stones of various sizes can be moved into circular (or other) arrangements, the smaller fragments accumulating toward the centre of the circle or polygon. When it occurs, patterned ground is not just a local feature of limited spatial extent—the phenomenon can persist for kilometres, dominating the landscape and giving it an unmistakable appearance.

Pingos

Yet another characteristic periglacial landform is a mound called a pingo. **Pingo** is the Inuit word for hill. Permafrost conditions are a prerequisite for the formation of these mounds, which are round or elliptical at the base and can grow quite large. While many are comparatively small and occur in clusters of hundreds, some isolated pingos are as large as 600 m in diameter and 60 m high (Fig. 48.9). The core of a pingo is made of ice, not rock or soil. The greatest number of pingos are found in the Mackenzie Delta, N.W.T. Pingos are found to be as-

sociated with shallow oriented lakes. Many pingos have broken tops that expose the Icy Core. Some have small lakes in their "centres."

Pingos are believed to form from drained lakes where the permafrost table rises to the surface and bulges upward. As it does so, the saturated overlying lake sediments also are frozen and remain atop the bulging ice. Eventually only this uppermost active zone remains free of permanent ice and may sustain vegetation, even trees. Pingos are unique to periglacial environments, and thus they are indisputable evidence of former periglacial conditions if they are found as "fossil pingos" in now temperate zones.

When such fossil pingos are found, they of course represent collapsed features because their icy cores have long since melted. What remains in the landscape is a low circular mound, the remains of the soils of the active layer. Fossil pingos have been found in northern Illinois, proof that periglacial conditions prevailed there when the Late Cenozoic ice sheets lay farther north.

Boulder Fields

Although streams do flow through periglacial areas (the northward-flowing streams in the Northwest Territories and Siberia, for example), they do not create distinctive landforms.

The main mover of loosened material in periglacial zones is *gravity*. Gravity does more than move material in the active layer. In areas of substantial relief, where there are bare bedrock surfaces, large boulders pried off the rock faces by frost wedging are moved into boulder fields. **Boulder fields** (rock sea, felsenmeer) are what the name implies: slopes covered by blocky pieces of rock covering a large area (see Fig. 38.3).

CANADIAN GEOGRAPHERS IN THE FIELD

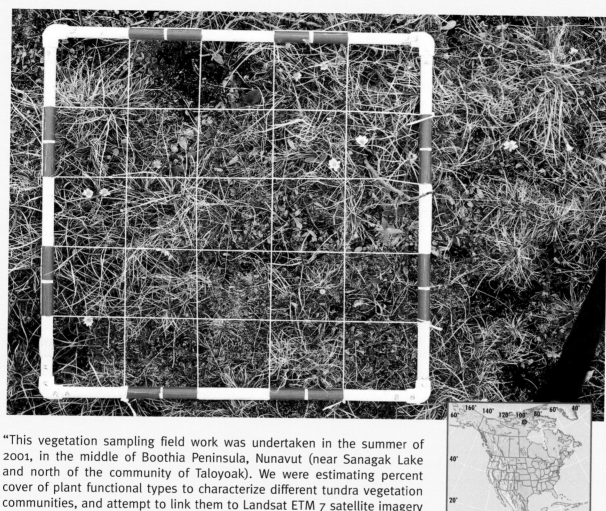

"This vegetation sampling field work was undertaken in the summer of 2001, in the middle of Boothia Peninsula, Nunavut (near Sanagak Lake and north of the community of Taloyoak). We were estimating percent cover of plant functional types to characterize different tundra vegetation communities, and attempt to link them to Landsat ETM 7 satellite imagery and IKONOS imagery. The percentage of tundra vegetation cover was estimated visually, within a 50cm x 50cm quadrat. The 10cm red and white divisions were augmented by a grid of string to aid in estimating the relative abundance of each plant functional type (i.e., graminoids, forbs, shrubs, and mosses). Along with percent cover estimates, we collected biomass samples and spectral samples to help characterize tundra vegetation productivity and spectral characteristics (also to help link to satellite imagery)."

Gita J. Laidler is a Ph.D. candidate in the Department of Geography at the University of Toronto. She is studying environmental/cultural geography, exploring the importance and uses of arctic sea ice from Inuit and scientific perspectives.

The boulders or blocks (angular stones) that make up boulder fields are large, as much as 1 to 3 m in diameter. They are loosened from bedrock slopes, cliffs, or other exposed surfaces by frost action, but then gravity takes over. When they are moved downslope, they accumulate in fields as large as 100 m wide and over 1 km long. Exactly how movement takes place is still being investigated. Apparently it does not occur in a single rock avalanche; there is evidence that slow downslope progress continues, the speed being related to the angle of the slope against which the boulder field lies.

Boulder fields can also be quite deep, and some have been measured to be 20 m in thickness. Another interesting aspect is that the long axes of the boulders tend to be lined up approximately parallel to each other, indicating that some sorting does take place. Certain geomorphologists believe that movement may have been aided by a matrix of finer material between the boulders, so that the whole mass was capable of being saturated, thereby facilitating movement. Later the finer material was eroded away. Others suggest that ice may have filled the openings between the boulders, so that the blocks originally moved as a *rock glacier*.

Whatever the answer, boulder fields are known to occur in periglacial areas and in cold mountainous zones above the timber line. They clearly result from the combination of frost action and slope process, and although the mechanisms may not be clearly understood, they do provide evidence that near-glacial conditions once prevailed where they exist. We might therefore expect that the Driftless Area of Wisconsin (see Perspectives box in Unit 46), the place the continental glaciers missed but surrounded, ought to be a likely locale in which to find a boulder field. Not surprisingly, this type of landform does indeed occur there.

Resource Development in Periglacial Environments

Periglacial environments and landscapes are experienced by a very small minority of the Earth's population. Our general understanding of these landforms and landscapes is based mainly on what we have learned in the temperate and tropical areas of the world. But now, in our search for resources to satisfy the requirements of the developed countries (especially in fossil-fuel energy), we are invading a realm well known to its indigenous peoples but little understood by outsiders. It is the realm of migrating caribou and reindeer, of muskoxen and wolves, of huge flocks of birds and dense swarms of insects. The landscape is one of unfamiliar forms and plants, of mosses and lichens, of needle-leaf evergreen trees, and of large patches of barren ground.

So far the modern invasion is limited. The realm is vast, and the invaders are few. But radioactive fallout from the 1986 Chernobyl disaster in the former Soviet Union poisoned the reindeer of Scandinavia's Sámi (Lapps), and caribou migration has been adversely affected by Alaska's development since 1970. New economic realities have changed Inuit ways of life. And for all their engineering prowess, developers can never be certain that their impact on subarctic environments will be as they predict. Like Antarctica, the periglacial realm lies open, vulnerable, and fragile in a world of burgeoning demand for what it may contain.

The remote location of most periglacial environments has also severely limited their scientific study. We have repeatedly pointed out knowledge gaps concerning the exact nature of the geomorphic processes operating in these regions. As interest in them continues to grow, there will likely be an expansion of research efforts to better understand this vast, but still superficially explained, landscape.

KEY TERMS

active layer *page 625*

boulder field *page 630*

frost creep *page 628*

frost heaving *page 627*

frost thrusting *page 628*

frost wedging *page 627*

ice-wedge polygon *page 629*

patterned ground *page 629*

periglacial *page 624*

permafrost *page 625*

pingo *page 630*

solifluction *page 628*

talik *page 625*

REVIEW QUESTIONS

1. Define the term *periglacial* and describe the general spatial distribution of these environments.
2. Which Köppen climatic zones favour the development of periglacial landscapes?
3. Describe permafrost. How is it instrumental in the process of solifluction?
4. How do patterned ground and ice-wedge polygons form?
5. How does the existence of "fossil pingos" help in the reconstruction of climatic conditions?

REFERENCES AND FURTHER READINGS

BENN, D. I., and EVANS, D. J. A. *Glaciers and Glaciation* (New York: Oxford Univ. Press, 1998).

BONE, R. M. *The Geography of the Canadian North* (Toronto: Oxford Univ. Press, 1992).

BROWN, R. J. E. *Permafrost in Canada* (Toronto: University of Toronto Press, 1970).

CLARK, M. J., Ed. *Recent Advances in Periglacial Geomorphology* (New York: Wiley, 1988).

DIXON, J. C., and ABRAHAMS, A. D., Eds. *Periglacial Geomorphology* (New York: Wiley, 1992).

DREWRY, D. *Glacial Geologic Processes* (London: Edward Arnold, 1986).

EMBLETON, C., and KING, C. A. M. *Periglacial Geomorphology* (New York: Wiley/Halsted, 2nd ed., 1975).

EVANS, D. J. A., Ed. *Cold Climate Landforms* (New York: Wiley, 1996).

FOUNTAIN, H. "For Patterned Stone and Soil, the Earth Moved," *New York Times,* January 21, 2003, D3.

FRENCH, H. M. *The Periglacial Environment* (London/New York: Longman, 2nd ed., 1996).

HARRIS, S. A. *The Permafrost Environment* (Totowa, N.J.: Rowman & Littlefield, 1986).

HEWITT, K. et al., Eds. *Landscapes of Transition: Landform Assemblages and Transformations in Cold Regions* (Dordrecht, Netherlands: Kluwer, 2002).

KING, C. A. M., Ed. *Periglacial Processes* (Stroudsburg, Pa.: Dowden, Hutchinson & Ross, 1976).

KRANTZ, W. B., et al. "Patterned Ground," *Scientific American* (December 1988), 68–76.

MATHEWS, J. A. *The Ecology of Recently-Deglaciated Terrain: A Geoecological Approach to Glacier Forelands* (London/New York: Cambridge Univ. Press, 1992).

OWEN, L. A., et al. *Polar and Alpine Geomorphology* (Malden, Mass.: Blackwell, 1998).

PIELOU, E. C. *A Naturalist's Guide to the Arctic* (Chicago: Univ. of Chicago Press, 1994).

PRICE, L. W. *The Periglacial Environment, Permafrost, and Man* (Washington, D.C.: Association of American Geographers, Commission on College Geography, Resource Paper 14, 1972).

PRICE, R. J. *Glacial and Fluvioglacial Landforms* (Edinburgh, U.K.: Oliver & Boyd, 1972).

RADFORTH, N. W., and BRAWNER, C. O. *Muskeg and the Northern Environment in Canada* (Toronto: Univ. of Toronto Press, 1977).

SCHNEIDER, K. "In Aftermath of Oil Spill, Alaskan Sound Is Altered," *New York Times,* July 7, 1994, A1, A9.

SMITH, S. L., et al. "Permafrost in Canada, a Challenge to Northern Development," in Brook, G. R., *A Synthesis of Geological Hazards in Canada* (Ottawa: Geological Survey of Canada Bulletin 548, 2001), 241–264.

SUGDEN, D. E., and JOHN, B. S. *Glaciers and Landscape: A Geomorphological Approach* (New York: Wiley, 1976).

WASHBURN, A. L. *Periglacial Processes and Environments* (London: Arnold, 1973).

WILLIAMS, P. J., and SMITH, M. W. *The Frozen Earth: Fundamentals of Geocryology* (London/New York: Cambridge Univ. Press, 1989).

WEB RESOURCES

http://atlas.gc.ca/site/english/maps/environment/land/permafrost Map of permafrost zones in Canada.

http://sts.gsc.nrcan.gc.ca/permafrost/index_html This Geological Survey of Canada permafrost website has lots of information, data, research, and links.

http://sts.gsc.nrcan.gc.ca/permafrost The Geological Survey of Canada provides background information and current research data for regions of permafrost. Graphics and links to other geological sites are available.

http://www.fakr.noaa.gov/oil/default.htm NOAA's National Marine Fisheries Service provides impact and restoration data for the region affected by the *Exxon Valdez* oil spill of 1989. The Gulf Ecosystem Monitoring (GEM) Program continues to provide information about resource development in this periglacial environment.

UNIT **49**

Wind as a Geomorphological Agent

Sand dunes are formed as the wind pushes sand on shore on a beach in Prince Edward Island.

OBJECTIVES

- To examine the mechanisms of wind erosion and the landforms produced by this process

- To relate various types of sand dunes to environmental controls

- To note the importance and environmental significance of loess

The role of **aeolian** (wind-related) processes in shaping the Earth's surface has been the subject of ongoing debate among geomorphologists and physical geographers. Whereas the effects of running water, flowing ice, and coastal wave action are generally obvious, the role of wind as a geomorphic agent is usually more subtle and difficult to measure. In hot and cold arid landscapes with little vegetation, wind redistribution of material weathered at the surface takes the form of sand dunes, the morphology of which is controlled by aspects of the local windflow pattern and its strength.

634

In general, as conditions become more humid, the stabilization of the surface by vegetation diminishes the role of the wind, and other processes become more important in shaping the physical landscape. Complicating this simple assessment is the realization that much of the Earth's surface bears the signature of processes that are no longer operating. There is no question that aeolian processes have had an important influence on the landscapes of various regions during previous climatic regimes. Furthermore, human activities often destabilize the surface vegetation, and in some areas aeolian processes are even becoming more significant (see Perspective: The Winds of Interstate 10). Thus we need to examine wind as a geomorphological agent and see how it influences the form and dynamics of the landscape.

Wind Erosion

In order for wind to be an aggradational agent, it must also be able to erode—to degrade the surface. As in the case of water erosion, the speed of the wind is of primary importance. The higher the velocity of the moving air, the greater is the wind's degradational power. Wind direction also influences the cumulative effect of wind erosion: when the wind blows fairly constantly in the same direction, it erodes more rapidly than it would otherwise.

Moving air alone, however, is not an effective agent of erosion. Only when the wind picks up sand particles does its power to erode become important. These moving particles strike and wear away exposed rock surfaces in a process called **wind abrasion** (sandblasting). Wind abrasion is strongest near the surface and diminishes with height. The largest grains carried by the wind move along in the lower 20 cm or so. Almost all wind abrasion takes place within 2 m of the ground surface.

Degradational Landforms

When the wind sweeps along a surface and carries away the finest particles, the process is called **deflation**. The results of the deflation process can be seen in desert areas today, because the arid landscape often includes shallow basins without outlets (Fig. 49.2). These basins lie in rows parallel to the prevailing wind direction. They begin as small local hollows that are continuously enlarged as the wind removes freshly weathered particles. Eventually these basins grow quite large (to hundreds of square kilometres in area), and other processes may reinforce their growth.

Not many landforms can be attributed exclusively to wind erosion. The **deflation hollows** just described as desert basins created by wind erosion undoubtedly result from degradation by moving air (e.g., Qattara Depression in northwest Egypt). Where wind has removed finely textured material, a surface concentration of closely packed pebbles (lag deposit) is left behind as **desert pavement** or *gibber plain* (see Fig. 43.3). Although desert pavement is a residual landform, it may be interpreted to be a feature of wind erosion. The most common product of wind abrasion is the **yardang** (Fig. 49.3). Yardangs are low ridges that form parallel to the prevailing wind direction. They tend to develop in dry sandy areas affected by strong winds, especially where the bedrock is fairly soft and unprotected by vegetation. The yardangs are separated by troughs that are scooped out and smoothed to a polished-looking surface by wind abrasion. Large-scale yardangs (megayardangs) can be tens of kilometres long; many tens-of-metres-high yardangs have been found in the Sahara and on Mars.

PERSPECTIVES ON THE HUMAN ENVIRONMENT

The Winds of Interstate 10

The arid southwestern corner of the United States is unlike any other desert environment on Earth because, since the mid-twentieth century, it has been invaded by high-technology civilization and several million new urban settlers. Much of this de- velopment has occurred along the Interstate 10 corridor, the region's main east–west artery, which crosses the Sonora and Mojave Deserts (in southern Arizona and southern California, respectively) as it threads its lonely way westward for 800 km from Tucson in the east to Los Angeles on the Pacific coast.

To accommodate all this growth, humans have transformed desert landscapes all along I-10. They have forged huge sprawling cities such as Phoenix, which today is the U.S.'s sixth largest; they have built hundreds of resort and retirement communities, of which Palm Springs is the most famous; they have converted millions of hectares of desert into productive, irrigated farm fields; and they have created massive water- and power-supply networks to make the whole system work. Harmoniously adapting this still expanding settlement complex to its harsh habitat is a constant challenge, and the ever-present winds that have sculpted these drylands are a particular concern.

When human–environmental interaction is well conceived, the desert winds can be a boon to regional development. Such is the case around Palm Springs, California, where the local power supply is generated mainly by harnessing the hot, dry winds that blow off the Mojave. A few kilometres northwest of Palm Springs, the narrowing Coachella Valley reaches its apex at the San Gorgonio Pass, which I-10 crosses into the neighbouring Los Angeles Basin. Here the local topography funnels the wind through the low-lying (450 m) pass and provides the opportunity for windmills to convert the moving air into a weak electrical current. By concentrating thousands of windmills in the pass (see Fig. 49.1), all designed to rotate with the shifting airstream, energy producers are able to generate a nonpolluting power supply sufficient to meet the demands of thousands of local customers.

Unfortunately, throughout the I-10 corridor one is far more likely to encounter examples of misuse of the environment, and where land users have been careless and ignored the effects of desert winds, problems have quickly arisen. Summer duststorms are endemic to this part of the world, and residents must protect their homes, engines, crops, and even their breathing against periodic bombardment by blowing dust. Driving can be especially hazardous because fast-moving duststorms can reduce highway visibility significantly in a matter of moments. Multiple-vehicle pileups are not uncommon on the interstate highways, and the heavily travelled stretch of I-10 between Phoenix and Tucson contains the scars of dozens of serious chain-reaction collisions.

FIGURE 49.1   Converting wind to electric energy—one of the many windmill farms that line Southern California's San Gorgonio Pass, east of Los Angeles.

Geographers Melvin Marcus and Anthony Brazel have studied these accidents and have determined that duststorms here are exacerbated by human modification of the desert surface. The leading problem is the abandonment of farmland adjacent to the I-10 right-of-way, caused initially by groundwater depletion and the disruption of local irrigation networks when the expressway was built in the 1960s. Today these interstate-paralleling land parcels have largely lost their soil-binding vegetation and have attracted all sorts of surface-disturbing activities, from off-road vehicle usage to livestock raising, that make them—and I-10—particularly vulnerable to the wind-borne movement of large quantities of dust. Belatedly, public agencies are implementing protective land-use practices, but it is still important to be especially alert at the wheel while driving in this part of southern Arizona.

FIGURE 49.2 Wind action is the second most powerful degradational force in desert areas, shaping the landscape in some places. Here the floor of Golden Canyon in California's Death Valley is being shaped by deflation.

FIGURE 49.3 The striking topography of a zone of yardangs dominates the foreground and centre of this photo. This locale is near Minab, a coastal town on the Persian Gulf's Strait of Hormuz in southeastern Iran.

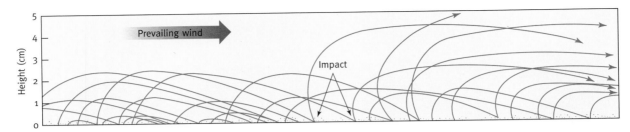

FIGURE 49.4   Wind causes movement of coarse sand grains by saltation. Impacted grains bounce into the air and are carried ballistically by the wind as gravity pulls them back to the loose sand surface where they impact other particles, repeating the process (repartation).

Wind Transportation

The movement of rock particles by wind takes place in three ways. The finest material, such as silt and clay, is carried higher in the air in *suspension*. Sometimes this material is carried so high that it enters the upper atmospheric circulation. For example, following the explosive eruption of the Indonesian volcano Krakatau in 1883, an enormous dust cloud encircled the Earth for years afterward. Saharan dust is often found in Europe and South America.

Coarser particles are too large to be picked up and carried very far above the ground. The wind still moves them, but during transportation these grains bounce along the ground, sometimes at a high rate of speed. This process is known as *saltation* (Fig. 49.4). Accordingly, sand-sized particles are swept along in the lowest layer of moving air, mostly below about 20 cm but virtually always below 2 m above the ground. Sandstorms are the most extreme form of saltation (Fig. 49.5). In contrast to high-altitude-reaching duststorms, in which suspension is the major process (see Fig. 22.9), sandstorms are confined to the lower layers of moving air, and saltation is the dominant mode of movement.

Wind also moves larger rock fragments by actually rolling or pushing them along the surface in a process called **surface creep**. Pebbles and even small boulders of considerable weight can be moved by strong windstorms.

Aggradational Landforms

It is important to remember that wind action is not confined to deserts or semi-arid steppelands. Wind also has erosional functions in glacial and periglacial zones, in savannas and humid midlatitude grasslands, and in other areas as well. During a severe windstorm in England in 1987, for example, an estimated 1 million trees were toppled.

Nevertheless, wind does its most effective work in dry environments. Some deserts and semideserts are dominated by aeolian processes, and the landforms and landscapes of wind action are best developed in North Africa's Sahara, Southwest Asia's Arabian Desert, the Great Sandy Desert of Australia, and the Earth's other extensive drylands. But even in these desert areas, the landforms typically associated with aeolian deposition are confined to relatively small sections of the desert. Where sand accumulations are large and extensive, there may still not be any prominent aeolian landforms. Over large expanses of sandy desert landscape, the dominant feature is the **erg** or *sand sea*. Wind directions may vary seasonally to such an extent that there is no dominantly prevailing airflow, so the sand is continuously moved about. The landscape in such places takes on an undulating (gently rolling) appearance. The surface of the sand may be formed into *ripples* by saltation and surface creep, but otherwise the topography is unremarkable.

FIGURE 49.5   A sandstorm bears down on a settlement in Arizona. Overgrazing and general overuse of land in fragile ecosystems generate conditions like this. Much of West Africa's Sahel suffers from recurrent sandstorms, as does East Asia.

Sand Dunes

The landform most commonly associated with wind deposition is the dune. A **dune** is an accumulation of sand that is shaped by wind action. This definition is clear and concise, but when you look at an aerial image of a dune landscape, it is clear why the many dune formations are difficult to interpret. Dunes come in many shapes and sizes: as straight or curving ridges, as quarter-moon-shaped crescents, as irregular mounds, and more. Physical geographers are interested in three aspects of dunes: (1) whether or not they are stable, (2) what their shape or form is, and (3) how they are arranged in the landscape.

Dunes in sandy desert areas normally support no vegetation. The wind modifies them continually, removing sand from the windward side and depositing it on the leeward side (Fig. 49.6). This has the effect of moving the dune across the landscape, so that the dune is unstable, or *active*. Over time, however, dunes may migrate into moister areas on the desert margin, or a climate change may affect a dune area. Then plants will take hold, and the vegetation will slow or even halt the dune's movement; in such instances a dune is described as stable, or *fixed*. Dunes close to the coast may be fixed by the growth of grass.

Dune Features

Every dune has a profile, a cross-section that reveals much about its history. This profile consists of three elements: the windward slope, or **backslope**; the top, or *crest;* and the leeward slope, or **slip face** (Fig. 49.6). As this diagram shows, the windward slope has a lower angle than the leeward slope. The wind drives the sand grains up the length of the backslope, pushes them over the crest, and lets them drop on the slip face, on which they may fail or slip down. Thus a dune has a degradational and an aggradational side, and the prevailing wind can be determined from the dune profile.

Dune Forms

Given these conditions, it might be assumed that loose sand influenced by prevailing wind will be arranged into one dominant landform. That is not the case. Dunes develop various forms, and the exact origin of some of them is not completely understood.

Barchans The most common dune form in the deserts and former periglacial areas of North America is probably the **barchan**, a crescent-shaped dune. The best way to understand its form is to look at Fig. 49.7A. The convex side of this dune is the windward side, so that its points lie *downwind*. Thus the low-angle backslope faces the wind on the outside, whereas the steeper slip face lies inside. A cluster of barchans, therefore, immediately indicates the prevailing wind direction in its locality. The "horns" tend to move faster than the main part of the barchan because of the relative volumes of sand.

Parabolic Dunes Not all dunes with a crescent shape are barchans, however. A **parabolic dune** also has a crescent shape, but in this type of dune the concave side is the windward side, so that the points of the crescent lie *upwind* (Fig. 49.7B). Parabolic dunes often develop longer sides than barchans do, and they begin to look like giant horseshoes rather than crescents. In deserts they sometimes develop in association with deflation hollows; they also occur frequently along coastlines.

Transverse Dunes A similar-looking dune is a low sand ridge, called a **transverse dune**, which is usually straight or slightly curved and positioned at a right angle to the prevailing wind (Fig. 49.7C). In fact, barchans and parabolic dunes also are transverse dunes, but their sides

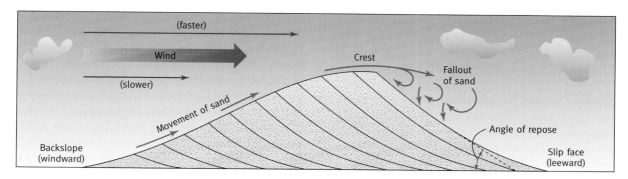

FIGURE 49.6 Cross-section of an active sand dune that is migrating from left to right. The lower-angle, windward backslope is the degradational side of the dune, with surface sand grains pushed upward toward the crest. The steeper, leeward slip face is the aggradational component of the dune, where wind-driven sand is deposited. The accumulation of sand grains on the advancing slip face produces strata inside the dune, much like the foreset beds in a delta (see Fig. 43.14).

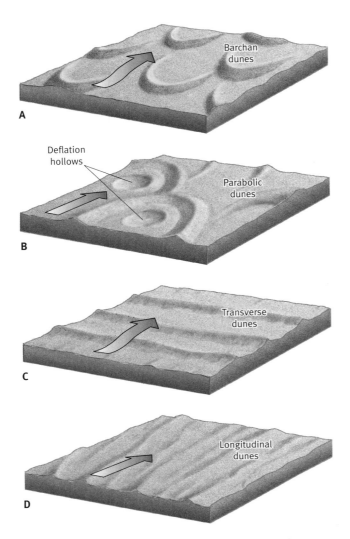

FIGURE 49.7   The four most common types of sand dunes. In each diagram the prevailing wind direction is indicated by the arrow. Note that longitudinal dunes lie parallel to the prevailing wind, whereas the others form at right angles to it.

begin to adjust to the wind and they become rounded. This is not the case with true transverse dunes, however, which look like ripples on the landscape. Indeed, transverse dunes often mark ergs, giving the topography the look of a sandy sea complete with wave crests.

Longitudinal Dunes   Longitudinal dunes (also known as linear or seif dunes), like transverse dunes, form lengthy sand ridges, but they lie *parallel* to the prevailing wind direction (Fig. 49.7D), not perpendicular to it. It has been suggested that when the sand supply is plentiful, as in an erg, transverse dunes will develop, but that when the sand availability is limited, longitudinal dunes will develop. Certainly, longitudinal dunes are prominent. Between Adelaide on the coast of South Australia and Alice Springs

in the heart of the continent, an entire landscape looks like corrugated cardboard. Thousands of longitudinal dunes over 3 m high, with many as tall as 20 m, extend continuously for as far as 100 km.

Dune Landscape Research

These are just some of the many dune shapes and forms that have been classified and whose origins are understood. Many others remain to be studied. Research on present-day dune landscapes, both in deserts and along coasts, also contributes to the interpretation of the past because dunes offer clues about climate change. Certain areas where dunes now lie are no longer arid, and the dune landscape has become fixed (Fig. 49.8)—for example, Hillsburgh Sandhills in the Orangeville area of southern Ontario and the approximately 120 dunefields in the Prairie provinces (Brandon and Oak Lake Sandhills of Manitoba) and Quebec. From the morphology of the dunes, however, conclusions may be drawn about earlier climates not only in general terms but, more specifically, about wind directions and velocities as well.

Another reason to know as much as we can about wind erosion and dune formation is immediate and practical. As explained in Unit 17, *desertification* has become a global problem. There even are places along desert margins where advancing dunes are overtaking inhabited land. By understanding how dunes migrate and how wind action drives them, we are in a better position to develop ways to stabilize them and to halt their progress (see Fig. 17.12).

Loess

Perhaps the most impressive evidence of the capacity of wind to modify the landscape comes from ice-age times. As described in Unit 47, glacial processes are associated with tremendous quantities of finely textured sediment, and such fine material became part of the extensive sandur deposits formed during glacial recession. Strong winds, which were common in periglacial environments during the Late Cenozoic, carried away huge quantities of these fine particles to the south of the margin. At times the sandur must have looked like the duststorm depicted in Fig. 22.9, as vast clouds of dust darkened the skies and obscured the Sun. Because prevailing winds were fairly steady, much of the dust moved in certain specific directions. When the air motion eventually subsided, the fine-grained dust was deposited on the ground, sometimes hundreds of kilometres from its source. In this way sedimentary deposits called **loess** (pronounced "lerss") accumulated (in this case, periglacial or cold loess).

FROM THE FIELDNOTES

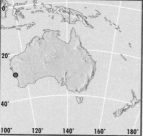

FIGURE 49.8 "A model dune, in my experience, is a landform fashioned from sand accumulations by wind action; vegetation does not form a part of this construct. But this notion applies more accurately to desert dunes than to coastal dunes. The latter can reach considerable size and permanence, and when the coastal location brings some moisture to the setting, vegetation can spread even on the sandy surface and anchor the dune, as is happening here along the west coast of Australia, about 160 km north of Perth."

Distribution of Loess Deposits

Loess was laid down in many areas south of the ice sheets in the Northern Hemisphere, and it also occurs in the Southern Hemisphere (Fig. 49.9). In North America the most prominent loess deposits extend from the Great Plains to the lowlands of the Mississippi, Ohio, and Missouri River Basins (Fig. 49.10). As this map shows, some of the thickest deposits lie in Nebraska and Iowa, where as much as 60 m of loess has buried the underlying topography. Most of these loess deposits, however, are between 1 m and 30 m thick. Streams eroded the area after the loess was deposited, and the loess deposits can be seen in the walls of many river valleys. Another major deposition of loess occurred on the Columbia Plateau in the Pacific Northwest, near where the states of Washington, Oregon, and Idaho meet (Fig. 49.10). Thin and discontinuous loess is found in many places around these areas, and around all this there is a region where a loess component is found in the soils.

As the world map (Fig. 49.9) shows, loess deposits are even more extensive in Eurasia than in North America. Loess was first identified in the Rhine Valley as long ago as 1821, which is how it got its name (German for "loose"). It also exists in France's Paris Basin, in the Danube Valley of Eastern Europe, and in large areas of southern and central Russia. Many different kinds of loess are recognized in central Europe: slope loess, fluvial loess, etc. But the thickest loess accumulations are in Asia, especially in east-central China. These were first described by Ferdinand, Baron von Richthofen in the 1880s who suggested that they were carried and laid down by aeolian action.

Almost the entire surface of the North China Plain consists of loess, and to the west, in the hilly middle basin of the Huang He (Yellow River), lies an even

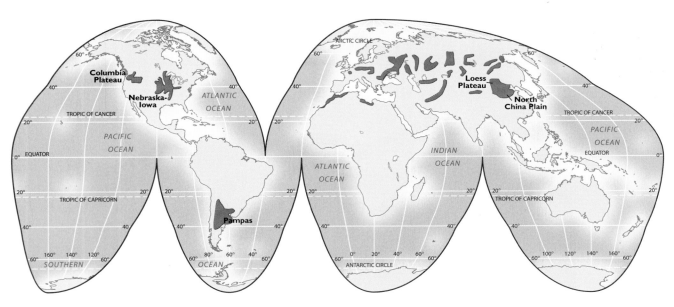

FIGURE 49.9   Major loess deposits of the world.

thicker loess deposit. In fact, the Chinese call this region the Loess Plateau, and here the loess averages 75 m in thickness and in places reaches as much as 180 m (Fig. 49.11).

Loess also occurs over a sizeable area of southern South America, including Argentina's productive Pampas. Other smaller deposits of loess (as well as loess-like sediments) have been found elsewhere in the Southern Hemisphere. But as with periglacial phenomena in general, the bulk of the world's loess deposits lie well north of the Equator.

Properties of Loess

Ever since loess was first identified, the origins of its various deposits have been debated. Is loess really a wind-

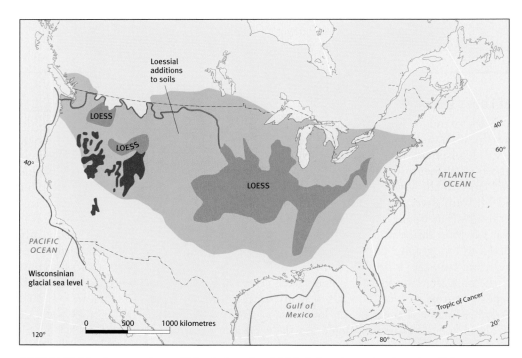

FIGURE 49.10   Loess regions of North America, highlighting the major deposits of the east-central Great Plains, the Mississippi Valley, and the Pacific Northwest.

FROM THE FIELDNOTES

 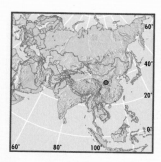

FIGURE 49.11 "Riding the train from Anyang to Xian, China, you cross part of the Loess Plateau and observe physical and cultural landscapes that are in many ways unique. Here the loess is as much as 180 m thick in places; the average is 75 m, and its capacity to stand in unsupported vertical cliffs, even in areas of considerable rainfall, has produced a terraced landscape that seems to defy the rules of erosion. Since loess is fertile, this part of China has attracted a large population—but the risks of life on the Loess Plateau are serious."

borne sediment, or did water also play an aggradational role? The answer seems to be that loess is indeed a product of wind transportation and deposition. The deposits do not form landforms but blanket the terrain below, filling valleys and covering hilltops in ways that fluvial deposits do not.

Certainly there is no argument about the interest in and importance of loess. If you compare the maps of loess deposits, agricultural productivity, and population distribution, you will see that some of the world's most fertile areas—and some great human agglomerations—lie in loess regions. In the United States the loess of Iowa and Illinois yields massive harvests of corn, soybeans, and other crops. In the drier Great Plains farther west, the wheat of Kansas and Nebraska also comes from loess-derived soils. In terms of population size and density, however, nothing on Earth matches the great human cluster centred on the North China Plain, supported by vast wheatfields on fertile loess-based soils. The most productive farmlands of Russia and Ukraine, too, depend on loess.

Just what makes loess such an unusual sediment? It consists of silt-sized quartz particles along with felspars, carbonates, clays, and other minerals. Loess contains the whole range of minerals derived from ground-up bedrock, which is about as ready for plant absorption as in alluvium is. Moreover, its fertility is not confined to an upper layer; loess is fertile all the way

down its profile. Scrape off the top horizon, and lower layers of it will support plants just as well. But there is more to it.

Technically loess is described as a fine-grained, unstratified, homogeneous, highly porous deposit. After deposition, compaction causes slight shrinkage in the mass, so that vertical passages develop. These vertical passages may take the form of capillaries or may resemble the joints found in harder sedimentary rocks (see Unit 31). Water, seeping downward through the loess, dissolves some of its mineral matter and redeposits it, thereby strengthening the walls of capillaries and cleavages. These processes combine to give loess a capacity to stand in upright walls and columns, and to resist collapse when it is excavated.

These qualities (fertility, vertical strength) are on display in what must be the world's most interesting loess region, China's Loess Plateau (Fig. 49.11). This region is neither as large nor as populous as the great North China Plain, having more relief and less water. But here loess is more than fertile soil—loess also serves as living quarters.

In stream valleys, against hillsides, and in the walls of deep road cuts, the local inhabitants have excavated the loess to create dwellings that are sometimes large and elaborate (Fig. 49.12). The entrances to these underground living quarters are sometimes ornately decorated, but in fact they are caves. As long as the region remains geologically stable, the millions of people dwelling un-

FROM THE FIELDNOTES

FIGURE 49.12 "My train ride from Anyang to Xian was interrupted by several unscheduled stops because of equipment problems, and I had a chance to walk some distance from the tracks into the Loess Plateau countryside. Can't remember being thirstier anywhere, even in Africa—temperature in the high 90s, a stiff breeze, dust in the air. Water is a problem here, but where a pipeline brings a supply, patches of green prevail. It also concentrates population, which in large part lives below the ground in excavated dwellings, some of which are quite elaborate and connected by underground tunnels. Most, however, are very basic, and all are susceptible to collapse from earthquakes, which have cost tens of thousands of people their lives here."

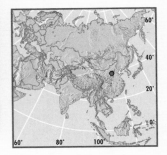

derground are safe. But whereas loess withstands erosion and has vertical strength, it collapses when shaken. In 1920 a severe earthquake struck the Loess Plateau, and an estimated 180,000 people lost their lives, most of them buried inside their caved-in homes.

Periglacial loess deposits leave no doubt that wind erosion has played a major role in shaping the post-glacial landscape. But loess and loess-like deposits also are found in areas far from glaciers, for example, near midlatitude deserts (hot or desert loess). There winds have laid down accumulations of fine-grained material derived from the dry, dusty desert surface. Some other loess-like deposits may in fact be the work of water, not wind. The great loess deposits of Eurasia and North America, however, confirm the role of wind as a major aggradational agent.

KEY TERMS

aeolian *page 634*	**dune** *page 639*	**surface creep** *page 638*
backslope *page 639*	**erg** *page 638*	**transverse dune** *page 639*
barchan *page 639*	**loess** *page 640*	**wind abrasion** *page 635*
deflation *page 635*	**longitudinal dune** *page 640*	**yardang** *page 635*
deflation hollow *page 635*	**parabolic dune** *page 639*	
desert pavement *page 635*	**slip face** *page 639*	

REVIEW QUESTIONS

1. Describe the vertical limits of wind erosion.
2. Describe the typical sand-dune profile and how the prevailing wind direction might be deduced from it.
3. Describe and differentiate among barchan, parabolic, longitudinal, and transverse dunes.

4. What is loess? Describe its major physical properties.
5. How have the thick loess deposits in North America accumulated?

REFERENCES AND FURTHER READINGS

ABRAHAMS, A. D., and PARSONS, A. J., Eds. *Geomorphology of Desert Environments* (New York: Chapman & Hall, 1995).

BROOKFIELD, M. E., and AHLBRANDT, T. S., Eds. *Eolian Sediments and Processes* (Amsterdam, Netherlands: Elsevier, 1983).

COOKE, R. U., WARREN, A., and GOUDIE, A. S. *Desert Geomorphology* (Bristol, Pa.: Taylor & Francis, 1992).

CÔTE D., DUBOIS, J-M. M., and NADEAU L. "Les dunes du Quebec meridional: contribution à l'etude de vents doumants duvant l'Holocene" *Canadian Geographer* 34 p. 49–62.

DAVID P. P. *Sound dune occurrences of Canada.* Indian and Northern Plains. National Parks Branch. Contract no 79-230 Report (Ottawa 1977).

DE BLIEU, J. *Wind: How the Flow of Air Has Shaped Life, Myth, and the Land* (Boston: Mariner Books/Houghton Mifflin, 1998).

EDEN, D. N., and FURKERT, R. J., Eds. *Loess: Its Distribution, Geology and Soils* (Rotterdam, Netherlands: Balkema, 1988).

GLENNIE, K. W. *Desert Sedimentary Environments* (Amsterdam, Netherlands: Elsevier, 1970).

GOUDIE, A. S., and WATSON, A. *Desert Geomorphology* (London: Macmillan, 1990).

LANCASTER, N. *The Geomorphology of Desert Dunes* (London/New York: Routledge, 1995).

LEIGHTON, M. M., and WILLMAN, H. B. "Loess Formations of the Mississippi Valley," *Journal of Geology,* 58 (1950), 599–623.

LIVINGSTONE, I., and WARREN, A. *Aeolian Geomorphology: An Introduction* (London/New York: Longman, 2nd ed., 1996).

MABBUTT, J. A. *Desert Landforms* (Cambridge, Mass.: MIT Press, 1977).

MARCUS, M. G., and BRAZEL, A. J. "Summer Dust Storms in the Arizona Desert," in D. G. Janelle, Ed., *Geographical Snapshots of North America* (New York: Guilford Press, 1992), 411–415.

MARES, M. A. *A Desert Calling: Life in a Forbidding Landscape* (Cambridge, Mass.: Harvard Univ. Press, 2002).

ODYNSKY, W. U-shaped dunes and effective wind directions in Alberta. *Canadian Journal of Soil Science* 38, 1958, 56–62.

PYE, K. *Aeolian Dust and Dust Deposits* (London, Academic Press 1987).

PYE, K. "The nature, origin, and accumulation of loess." *Quarternary Science Review* 14(7-8), 653–667.

PYE, K., and TSOAR, H. *Aeolian Sand and Sand Dunes* (Winchester, Mass.: Unwin Hyman Academic, 1990).

SIEVER, R. *Sand* (New York: Scientific American Library, 1988).

TCHAKERIAN, V. P., Ed. *Desert Aeolian Processes* (New York: Chapman & Hall, 1994).

THOMAS, D. S. G. *Arid Zone Geomorphology* (London: Belhaven Press, 1989).

Various "Holocene Dune Activity and Drought & Aridity" (2 special sections) in *Géographie physique et quarternaire,* vol 56 (no 2-3) (5 papers) 2002, 191–259.

WALKER, A. S. *Deserts: Geology and Resources* (Reston, Va.: U.S. Geological Survey, 2000).

WOLFE, S. A. and Brooks G. R. et al *A Synthesis of geological hazards in Canada.* 2001 Geological Survey of Canada, Bulletin 548 pp. 231–240 (Ottawa).

WEB RESOURCES

http://pubs.usgs.gov/gip/deserts/dunes The five types of sand dunes are discussed on this USGS page, including crescentic, linear, star, dome, and parabolic dunes. Colour photographs accompany each description.

http://www.eru.ksu.edu The USDA, in cooperation with Kansas State University, presents the wind erosion research unit website. Wind erosion consequences and simulations are discussed, and a multimedia archive is available. Links to other wind erosion sites are listed.

Coastal Processes

Long Beach is located in Pacific Rim National Park, on the west coast of Vancouver Island, between the towns of Tofino and Ucluelet. The 13,715 hectares of coastland include numerous rocky points and headlands, offshore islets and mudflats.

OBJECTIVES

- To establish the importance of coastal zones as areas of interaction between physical processes and human settlement

- To examine the physical properties of waves and their significance in the operation of coastal processes

- To discuss other sources of energy in the coastal zone and their erosional and depositional significance

S ome of the world's most spectacular scenery lies along the coasts of the continents. Sheer cliffs tower over surging waves. Curving beaches are fringed by steep-sided headlands. Magnificent bays lie flanked by lofty mountains. Great rivers disgorge into the open ocean. Glaciers slide and calve into the water. Coastlines are shaped by many forces: by waves from the sea, by rivers emptying from land, by ice, even by wind. Rising and falling sea levels, tides and currents, and tectonic forces all contribute to the development of coastal topography. The complexity and variety of coastal landforms and landscapes are the result, and these are the topics of Units 50 and 51.

Our interest in coastal processes stems from two considerations. On the one hand we seek to understand how coastal landscapes are created and what processes are presently operating in these zones of interface between land and sea. The other motivation is more practical, stemming from the fact that coastlines are probably the most intensively used landscapes for a variety of human activities. In such heavily developed areas, coastal processes can have very significant consequences. Our ability to manage these landscapes successfully rests on our knowledge of the environmental processes operating within them.

Coasts and Shores

In this unit and in Unit 51 we study the **littoral zone**, where land meets sea. In physical geography the term **coast** refers in a general sense to the strip of land and sea or lake where the various coastal processes combine to create characteristic landscapes, ranging from dunes and beaches to islands and lagoons. The term **shore** has a more specific meaning and denotes the narrower belt of land bordering a body of water (the most seaward or lakeward portion of a coast). A *shoreline* is the actual contact border between water and land. Thus we often refer to a coastal landscape, of which the shoreline is but one part.

Coastal areas have special problems. Sometimes beaches must be closed because harmful waste materials that have been dumped into the sea or lake are washed onto them. Some popular beaches become ever narrower and must be protected by jetties or groynes, or they will wash away. Parts of shores are threatened by urban pollution, and their wildlife is endangered. Overcrowding and expansion of waterfront towns and cities imperil local ecologies.

Most of the time, however, people seem to be unaware of these happenings because the changes tend to be slow, not dramatic. The beaches visited year after year look pretty much the same. The strip of beachfront hotels and motels is lengthening, but gradually. Less obvious are the connections among the many processes at work in coastal zones. When coastal authorities dredge the outlet of a port, build a series of jetties, construct a breakwater, or flatten a dune, the consequences may be far-reaching. Beach erosion may slow down in one place but speed up in another. The offshore turbidity (muddiness) of the water may change, affecting reef life. Coastal zones, therefore, are not only scenic and attractive; their landforms and landscapes result from the complex interaction of many processes.

Waves and Their Properties

Many forces help shape coastal landforms, but the key erosional agents are ocean *waves*. Most waves (not only in oceans, but also in seas and lakes) are generated by wind. Waves form when energy is transferred from moving air to water. Large waves form in water when the wind *velocity* is high, the wind *direction* is persistent, the wind *duration* is protracted, and the *fetch* (the distance over which the wind blows) is long. When conditions are favourable, the ocean's upper layer is stirred into long rolling waves or *swells*, which can travel thousands of kilometres before they break against a shore. When conditions are less favourable (changing wind directions, for example), waves are generally smaller but may have a more complex result.

Once a series of swells are well developed and moving across open water, their properties can be observed. The **wave height** is the vertical distance between the *crest*, or top, of a wave, and its *trough*, or bottom (Fig. 50.1). Wave height is important when it reaches the coast, because a high wave will do more erosional work than a low wave. The **wave length** (Fig. 50.1) is the horizontal distance from one crest to the next (or from trough to trough). A wave's *period* is the time interval between the passage of two successive crests past a fixed point.

In the open ocean, swells may not look large or high because they cannot be observed against a fixed point. But they often reach heights of up to 5 m and lengths ranging from 30 m to several hundred metres. Storm waves tend to be much higher, often exceeding 15 m; the highest wave ever measured reached 34 m during a Pacific storm in 1933.

When swells travel across the open ocean, they seem to move the water itself in the direction of their movement. But this is not the case. In reality, the passing wave throws the water into an orbital motion. As shown in Fig. 50.2, a water parcel (or particle) affected by the

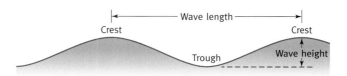

FIGURE 50.1 Wave height is the vertical distance between the wave crest and the wave trough. Wave length is the horizontal distance between two crests (or two troughs).

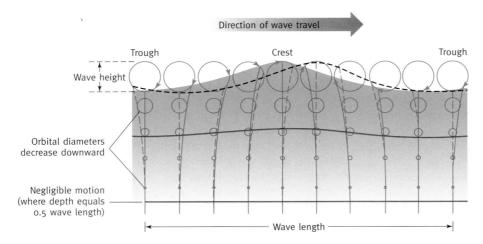

FIGURE 50.2 Orbital motion of water parcels within a wave of oscillation in deep water. To follow the successive positions of a water parcel at the surface, follow the arrows in the largest loops from right to left. This is the same as watching the wave crest travel from left to right. Parcels in smaller loops below have corresponding positions, marked by continuous, nearly vertical lines. Dashed lines represent wave forms and water parcel positions one-eighth of a period later.

passing wave takes a circular, vertical path. When the wave approaches, the parcel rises and reaches the height of the crest. Then it drops to the level of the trough, coming back to where it started when the wave arrived. Waves that move water particles in this circular up-and-down motion are called **waves of oscillation**. As Fig. 50.2 shows, the depth of a wave of oscillation is half its length—if a swell has a length of 100 m, it will have a depth of 50 m.

Waves against the Shore

Once they have been formed by steady strong winds, swells (a series of long-period waves) may move across vast reaches of open ocean without losing their strength or energy. They retain their length, height, and period even far from their sources, and they can travel across entire ocean basins. As they approach the coastline, they usually enter shallower water. Obviously the free orbital motion of the water will be disrupted when the wave begins to "feel" (be affected by) the ocean bottom. At this point, the swell becomes a *wave of translation*. No longer do water particles in orbital motion return to their original positions. The wave has begun its erosional work.

Because we know that the depth of a wave is half its length, we can determine where it will "feel" bottom first. The wave in our example, with a length of 100 m, will begin to interact with the ocean bottom when the water depth becomes less than 50 m. There the circular orbit of a water particle is compressed into an oval one (Fig. 50.3A, bottom). Contact with the bottom also slows the wave down, so that the wave length is forcibly decreased. As the water becomes still shallower, the coastward-moving wave pushes water upward, increasing the wave height. Soon the wave becomes so steep

that its crest collapses forward, creating a *breaker*. This happens along the breadth of the advancing wave, which is now capped by a foaming, turbulent mass of water.

From the beach one sees a series of approaching waves developing breakers as they advance toward the shore (Fig. 50.3B); such a sequence of breaking waves is referred to as the **surf**. When a wave reaches the shore, it finally loses its form and the water slides up the beach in a thinning sheet called **swash**. The dying wave still has some power, and the uprushing water carries sand and gravel landward. Then the last bit of wave energy is expended, and the water flows back toward the sea as **backwash**, again carrying sand with it. Along the shore, therefore, sand is continuously moved landward and seaward by wave energy.

Wave Refraction

When we look out across the surf from the top of a dune, it seems as though the surf consists of waves arriving parallel, or very nearly parallel, to the coastline. In actuality the parallel approach is quite rare, but the impression is produced during the **shoaling** process, the impact of shallow water on an advancing wave.

When a wave approaches a beach at an oblique angle, only part of it is slowed down at first—the part that first reaches shallow water. The rest of the wave continues to move at a higher velocity (Fig. 50.4). This process obviously bends the wave as the faster end overtakes the end already slowed by shoaling. This bending is known as **wave refraction**. By the time the whole wave is in shallower water, its angle to the shoreline is much smaller than it was during its approach through deep water. The angled approach of the waves vis-à-vis the beach sets up a littoral **longshore current** flowing parallel to the shoreline (Fig. 50.4).

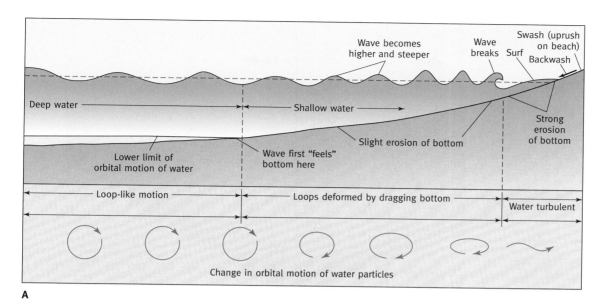

A

B

FIGURE 50.3 In the diagram (A), circles, ovals, and wave lengths are not drawn to scale with the waves on the surface. Waves are transformed as they travel from deep water through shallow water to shore along the coast of PEI, producing evenly spaced breakers as they approach the beach (B).

When a coastline has prominent headlands (promontories) and deep bays, wave refraction takes place as shown in Fig. 50.5. The waves approach the indented coastline roughly parallel to its general orientation. They reach shallower water first in front of the headlands, so that they are slowed and their length is reduced. The segment of the wave headed for the bay has yet to reach shallow water, so it continues at open-water velocity.

This has the effect of refracting the wave as shown in Fig. 50.5, concentrating its erosional energy on the point of the headland. Rock material loosened from the promontory is transported toward the concave bends of the bays, where it forms a beach. Wave action, therefore, has the effect of straightening a coastline, wearing back

the promontories and filling in the bays. Wave refraction is a crucial part of this process.

Longshore Drift

When a wave's swash rushes up the beach carrying sand and shingle (gravel), it does so at the angle of the arriving wave. But when the backwash (undertow) carries sand back seaward, it flows straight downward at right angles to the shoreline. The combined effect of this is to move sand along the beach, as shown in Fig. 50.6.

This process, called **longshore** (or littoral) **drift**, can easily be observed on a beach. The movement seen in one area of swash and backwash is continuously

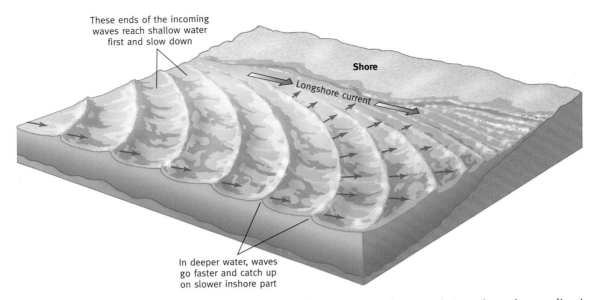

FIGURE 50.4 Refraction of incoming waves at the shoreline. Waves are bent, so their angle to the coastline is much smaller than in the deep water at the beginning of their approach. However, the inshore angle of the waves is still sufficient to produce a longshore current that flows parallel to the shoreline.

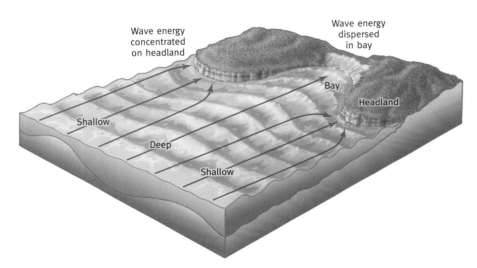

FIGURE 50.5 As the arrows indicate, the refraction of waves concentrates wave energy on headlands and dissipates it along bay shores. Note how, on the sea surface, the incoming waves are increasingly distorted as they approach the irregular coastline above a bottom that is deepest in front of the bay.

repeated along the entire length of beach. The larger process of **beach drift** moves huge amounts of sand or shingle along the shore and sometimes becomes so powerful that it threatens to move the whole beach downshore. The amount of longshore drift on sandy beaches in the upper Great Lakes amounts to between 50,000 and 100,000 m³/yr. When that happens, engineers build groynes and other structures at an angle to the beach and out into the surf, hoping to slow the drift of beach sand (Fig. 50.7). The building of groyne fields may conserve the beach, but erosion usually occurs where the groyne field ends. This is because the waves beyond the groyne field have expended little energy in sediment

transport and thus have energy to erode the coast; that is, they have the energy to gain sediment to transport. This process is called *terminal groyne scour*. When this occurs, engineers either extend the groyne field or use rip-rap (revetments)—large rocks or concrete blocks—to stop further erosion.

While we can see beach drift occurring, longshore drift also affects materials in the surf zone where the waves of translation operate. We may not be able to observe it directly, but longshore drift in the breaker zone can create ridges of sand and shingle parallel to the shore. Those elongated ridges may interfere with the advance of the very waves that build them as they grow longer and

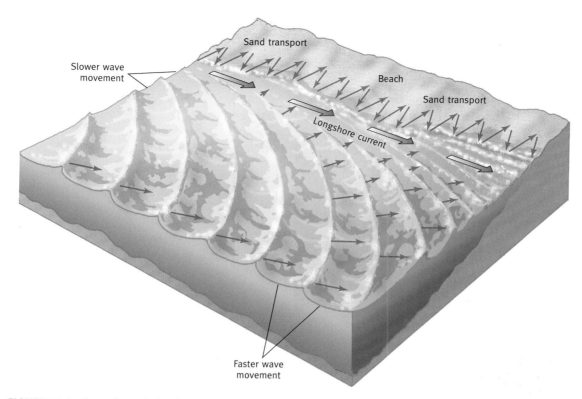

FIGURE 50.6   Longshore drift of sand at the water's edge. The larger process of beach drift is heightened by the longshore current in the surf zone. The net effect is to move the entire beach slowly downshore.

wider, eventually rising above the water surface as **barrier islands**. As explained in Unit 51, such landforms may even grow across the mouths of rivers and bays, often creating ecological as well as economic problems.

Degradation and Aggradation by Waves

Waves are powerful erosional agents, but they also are capable of deposition. The above examples describe waves that, after developing in the open ocean, reach shallow water and lose their energy as they approach the shore. But the water does not always become so shallow near a coast. There are many places where the land descends steeply into the water, and where the water is hundreds of metres deep just a few metres offshore. In such places the waves advancing toward the land do not

FIGURE 50.7   Groynes, extending into the surf at a 90-degree angle, mark the beaches of the resort hotels that line the Atlantic shore of Miami Beach. These structures prevent the excessive loss of sand by beach drift, which piles up on the upcurrent side of each groyne. The narrowness of the beach, however, indicates that this method is not very effective.

FROM THE FIELDNOTES

FIGURE 50.8 "On the advice of a Chilean colleague I took the coastal road north from Viña del Mar, and high relief evinces the submergence of this coastline as waves pound the promontories. The rocks themselves show ample evidence of the stresses imposed by tectonic-plate motion in the form of numerous fractures and faults, planes of weakness attacked by the waves. Much of South America's western coastline, from the cliffs of western Colombia to the fjords of southern Chile, reflects the forces of subduction; turn westward, and beneath those onrushing waves lies no gently sloping continental shelf. This is fast-changing scenery."

"feel" bottom, are not slowed down, and do not form breakers and surf. Where this happens, of course, the full force of the onrushing wave strikes the coast.

The speed and weight of the water smashing against the vertical bedrock contribute to erosion by *hydraulic action*. Hydraulic action is especially effective where rocks are strongly jointed or otherwise cracked (for instance, along bedding planes). Air enters the joints and cracks; when the water pounds the rock face, this trapped air is compressed. Next the wave recedes, and the air expands almost explosively. This process, repeated over thousands of years, can fracture and erode coastal rocks quite rapidly.

Like streams and glaciers, waves break pieces of rock from the surface being attacked, and these fragments enhance the waves' erosional effectiveness. This mechanical erosion process is known as **corrasion**. A wave loaded with rock fragments, large and small, erodes much more rapidly than water alone. Some coastal bedrock is also susceptible to chemical action by seawater. The breakdown of coastal bedrock by solution or other chemical means is referred to as *corrosion*. Limestones and dolostones are not attacked by solution as much as other rocks. This is because the seawater is saturated with $CaCO_3$ or $MgCO_3$.

Where offshore water is deep and coastal topography steep, the onslaught of waves produces a set of degradational landforms that tell us immediately what processes are going on. No gently sloping beaches or sandy offshore islands grace these high-relief coastlines (Fig. 50.8). All the evidence points toward the hardness and resistance of the rocks, the erosional force of the waves, and the exposure of the coastline to storms.

Alternatively, where offshore water is shallow and waves break into surf, the coastal landforms also are characteristic. Aggradational landforms dominate, and coastal relief is usually low: beaches, dunes, and sandy islands reveal the dominant processes at work here.

CANADIAN GEOGRAPHERS IN THE FIELD

"During a period of field work studying coastal sand dunes on Iles de la Madeleine (Magdalen Islands), Quebec, in the Gulf of St. Lawrence, I came across this excellent display of beach cusps on the coastline of Ile du Havre aux Maisons. The shore faces west and is on the leeward side of the island, protected from prevailing westerly winds. It is known that beach cusps develop best on gravel beaches with waves of consistent height and period approaching directly onshore. Those factors are all present here, and the regularity of the cusps is enhanced by the straightness of the beach."

Philip Giles is an Associate Professor in the Department of Geography at Saint Mary's University.

Wherever they erode or deposit, waves continually move loose material about. Gradually, larger fragments are reduced to smaller ones in a process called *attrition*. We associate a beach with sand, but much of the material along a shallow-water shoreline is even more finely textured.

Tides and Shore Zone Currents

Waves do the bulk of the degradational and aggradational work along shorelines, but other kinds of water movements also contribute to the shaping of the coastal landscape.

Effects of Tides

The sea level rises and falls twice each day (see Perspective: Tides and Their Behaviour). Again, the beach tells the story: what has been washed ashore during the *high tide* lies along the upper limit of the most recent swash, ready for beachcombing during *low tide*. Thus the whole process of wave motion onto the beach, discussed previously, operates while the tides rise and fall. This has the effect of widening the sloping beach. During high tide, the uprushing swash reaches farther landward than during low tide; during low tide, the backwash reaches farther seaward than during high tide.

Along a straight or nearly straight shoreline, the *tidal range* (the average vertical distance between sea level at high tide and at low tide) may not be large, usually between about 1 and 4 m. But in partially enclosed waters, such as estuaries, bays, and lagoons, the tidal range is much larger. The morphology (shape) of the inlet and its entrance affect the range of the tide. Probably the world's most famous tides occur in the Bay of Fundy on

PERSPECTIVES ON THE HUMAN ENVIRONMENT

Tides and Their Behaviour

The Earth's envelope of water—the hydrosphere—covers more than 70 percent of the planet. The surface of this layer of water unceasingly rises and falls in response to forces that affect its global distribution. This cyclical rise and fall of the sea level is known as the **tide** recorded at any given place in the world ocean. The *tidal range* is the vertical difference between sea levels at high tide and low tide.

Three principal forces control the Earth's tides: (1) the rotation of the planet, (2) the gravitational pull of the Moon, and (3) the gravitational pull of the Sun. The Earth's daily rotation has the effect of countering the gravitational pull of its own mass. The rotational velocity is greatest near the Equator and lowest at the poles, so that the layer of water bulges slightly outward toward the Equator. This is a permanent condition. But the Earth orbits around the Sun and is, in turn, orbited by the Moon. This means that the gravitational pulls of Moon or Sun come from different directions at different times.

Tidal levels at a coastal location rise and fall rhythmically based on the Earth's rotation and the 28-day lunar revolution, which produce two high tides and two low tides within a period slightly longer than 24 hours. When the Earth, Moon, and Sun are aligned, as shown in Fig. 50.9A, the effects of terrestrial rotation, lunar attraction, and the Sun's attraction are combined, and the result is an unusually high tide, or *spring tide*. But when the Moon's pull works at right angles against the Sun's attraction and the rotational bulge, the result is a *neap tide*, the least extreme tide (Fig. 50.9B).

Tides play a major role in coastal erosion. They can generate strong tidal currents that rush into and out of river mouths. They carry waves to higher coastal elevations during spring-tide extremes. And when a severe storm attacks a coastline in conjunction with a spring tide, substantial erosion

may occur. The contribution of tides to shoreline erosion also is influenced by the coastal topography, both below the water (shallow and sloping or deep and steep) and above (long narrow estuaries or wide curving bays). Compared to the constantly pounding waves, tides are not prominent as coastal modifiers—but their impact is still significant.

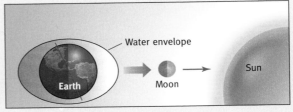

A

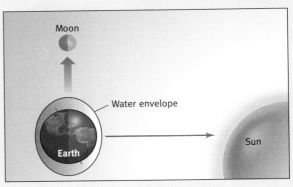

B

FIGURE 50.9   Schematic diagram of tides. (A) *Spring tide:* the Earth's rotational bulge and the gravitational pulls of both the Sun and the Moon combine to produce an unusually high tide. (B) *Neap tide:* the Moon's gravitational pull is at a right angle to the Sun's pull and the terrestrial rotation bulge, resulting in the least extreme tide. The Earth's water envelope and astronomical distances are strongly exaggerated.

Canada's Atlantic coast; there the tidal range is as much as 11 m, creating unusual problems for people living on the waterfront. A similar situation occurs in the bays that surround Moray Firth on Scotland's northeastern coast (Fig. 50.10).

Tides have erosional and depositional functions. In rocky narrow bays, where the tidal range is great and tides enter and depart with much energy and power, tidal waters erode the bedrock by hydraulic action and corrasion. The changing water level associated with tides sets in motion *tidal currents,* which rush through the sandy entrances of bays and lagoons, keeping those narrow thresholds clear of blockage. Where the tidal current slows down, the sediment it carries is deposited in a fan-shaped, delta-like formation (we examine such tidal features in Unit 51).

Tides occasionally take on the form of waves. A *tidal bore,* or eagre, is created when a rapidly rising high tide creates a wave front that runs up a river or bay. A dramatic example is sometimes seen in the lower course of Brazil's Amazon River, where the tide is known to rush in like a foamy breaker that never collapses forward. It is reported to start as a wall of water as much as 8 m high, moving upstream at a rate of 20 km/hr. It loses its height as it advances upriver, but has been observed more than 400 km inland from the Atlantic coast.

Shore Zone Currents

We have now learned that tides generate currents, and earlier in this unit we were shown how sand is moved by longshore drift arising from the refracted, oblique-angled arrival of waves onshore. However, not just the sand along the beach but also the water itself moves along the shore in the direction governed by the angle of the waves' approach. This water movement, parallel to the shore, is called a **longshore** (or littoral) **current**, and its generation and operation are shown in both Figs. 50.4 and 50.6. Longshore currents can also develop from tidal action and from storms along the coast. They are important agents because in total they move huge amounts of material. They are capable of erosion as well as deposition, creating lengthwise hollows and ridges in the surf zone. Moreover, they can erode beaches as well as build sand ridges across the mouths of rivers and bays.

Another type of current is the **rip current**. Even as the surf is surging landward, narrow streamlike currents cut across it, flowing from the shore seaward (Fig. 50.11A). These rip currents travel primarily in the surface layer of the water and can attain a high velocity, although they die out quickly beyond the surf zone. Rip currents have complex origins. They begin as small feeder

FROM THE FIELDNOTES

A

B

FIGURE 50.10 "Sailing along the eastern coast of Scotland I noticed numerous signs of large tidal ranges in funnel-shaped bays, reminiscent of what I had seen in Canada's maritime provinces. We sailed toward Invergordon on the Moray Firth at high tide, when the causeway was barely above the water level (A). A field trip to Loch Ness and Fort William took about six hours, and when I walked back across the same causeway afterward, the tide was still going out, exposing a beach at the foot of the seawall (B) and the tall pillars on which the causeway rested. On that day in 1992, the tidal range here was 5.5 m (18 ft), about average for the site."

currents in the shore zone, flowing parallel to the beach, sometimes behind low, surf-built sand ridges. At certain places along the beach, usually at fairly regular intervals, enough water gathers from these feeder currents to rush seaward, carrying a cloud of muddy sediment.

Because the rip current advances against the incoming surf, the breakers are interrupted where the rip current encounters them. Patches of mud carried by the rip current are visible against the less muddy surf (Fig. 50.11B). Rip currents vary in strength. When the tide is high and waves are strong, rip currents are especially powerful. When the waves are lower, the rip current is weaker.

The erosional work of rip currents is limited but is still of geographical interest. One spatial peculiarity just mentioned is that they tend to develop at rather regular intervals along the beach. This seems to be related to the feeder channels that supply the water from two directions (Fig. 50.11A). These longshore feeder currents hollow out their courses, so that the shore zone is marked by lengthwise depressions. Where the rip currents turn seaward, the beach surface is slightly lowered because the current carries much of its muddy sediment away from the beach. Thus rip currents do have an erosional function, moving fine beach particles outward beyond the surf zone.

The Role of Storms

Most of the year the world's coasts are slowly modified by the erosional and depositional processes described in this unit. Except under special circumstances, these changes are slow to occur. Beaches are susceptible to seasonal cut and fill. During the winter, when there is a higher frequency of storms that affect wave action, beaches are eroded. During the summer, when there are fewer storms and less wave action, beaches are aggraded. This can be seen along the shores of the lower Great Lakes. But virtually all coastlines are vulnerable to unusual and even rare events that can greatly transform them in a very short period of time. These events are storms. Unit 14 discussed the various kinds of storms that can develop over water. In the lower latitudes, tropical cyclones or hurricanes can generate enormous energy in ocean waves. At higher latitudes, storms are most often associated with weather fronts and contrasting air masses.

Whatever the source, the powerful winds whipped up in these storm systems, in turn, spawn large waves. Propelled against the coastline, such waves produce a **storm surge**, a combination of rising water and forceful wave action. During a storm surge, waves attack coastal-zone areas normally untouched by this kind of erosion.

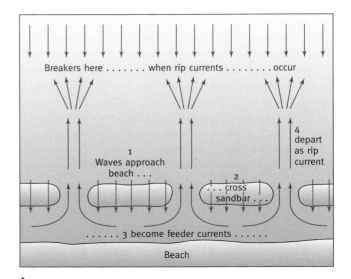

A

B

FIGURE 50.11 Rip currents are generated by small feeder currents in the shore zone that at regular intervals rush seaward directly into the oncoming waves (A). Rip currents die out beyond the surf zone, and swimmers caught in them can easily exit to the side. Rip currents have an erosional function, moving the beach particles outward beyond the surf zone. This can be seen in their usually muddy composition (B).

One severe storm surge can break through stable, vegetation-covered barrier islands, erode dunes lying well above the normal swash zone, and penetrate kilometres of coastal plain. When such a storm strikes the coast at the time of high tide, or during a spring tide, its impact is all the more devastating (see Fig. 51.8). These dramatic events notwithstanding, physical geographers disagree as to the long-term geomorphological effects of severe storms. It is certainly true that much of the coast and shore will return to prestorm conditions after the surge. But some effects of the storm may be long lasting, if not permanent.

Crustal Movement

When we study coastal processes, we must be mindful not only of the many and complex marine processes discussed in this unit, but also of the vertical mobility of the Earth's crust. When we first observe a section of coastline, we classify it as a coast of erosion (degradation) or deposition (aggradation), depending on the dominant landforms we identify. That observation is based on the present appearance of the coast and the prevailing processes now at work.

Over the longer term, however, the coastal bedrock may be rising (relative to the sea level) or sinking. For instance, the Scandinavian Peninsula is undergoing isostatic rebound following the melting of the heavy ice sheet that covered it until recently (see Fig. 46.8). This means that its coasts are rising as well. Along the coastlines of Norway and Sweden, therefore, we should expect to find evidence of marine erosion is now elevated above the zone where wave processes are taking place. In other areas the coast is sinking. The coastal zone of Louisiana and Texas (see Perspectives box in Unit 36) shows evidence of subsidence, in part because of the increasing weight of the sediments of the Mississippi Delta, but probably for other reasons as well.

Add to this the rising and falling of the sea level associated with the Late Cenozoic Ice Age, and we can see that it is impossible to generalize about coasts—even over short stretches. Ancient Greek port cities built on the waterfront just 2500 years ago are now submerged deep below Mediterranean waters as a result of local coastal subsidence. But in the same area there are places built on the waterfront that are now situated high above the highest waves. Unravelling the marine processes and Earth movements that combine to create the landscapes of coastlines is one of the most interesting challenges of physical geography.

KEY TERMS

backwash *page 648*

barrier island *page 651*

beach drift *page 650*

coast *page 647*

corrasion *page 652*

littoral zone *page 647*

longshore current *page 648*

longshore drift *page 649*

rip current *page 655*

shoaling *page 648*

shore *page 647*

storm surge *page 656*

surf *page 648*

swash *page 648*

tide *page 654*

wave height *page 647*

wave length *page 647*

wave refraction *page 648*

waves of oscillation *page 648*

REVIEW QUESTIONS

1. Why is an understanding of coastal processes an important part of physical geography?
2. Under what environmental conditions do large waves develop?
3. Describe what happens as incoming waves enter shallow water.
4. What is longshore drift, and how is it generated?
5. What are tides? What are their controlling forces?

REFERENCES AND FURTHER READINGS

BASCOM, W. *Waves and Beaches: The Dynamics of the Ocean Surface* (Garden City, N.Y.: Anchor/Doubleday, 2nd ed., 1980).

BIRD, E. C. F. *Coasts: An Introduction to Coastal Geomorphology* (New York: Blackwell, 3rd ed., 1984).

CARTER, R. W. G., Ed. *Coastal Environments: An Introduction to the Physical, Ecological and Cultural Systems of Coastlines* (Orlando, Fla.: Academic Press, 1989).

CHARLIER, R. H., and DE MEYER, C. *Coastal Erosion: Response and Management* (New York: Springer-Verlag, 1997).

DAVIES, J. L. *Geographical Variation in Coastal Development* (London/New York: Longman, 2nd ed., 1980).

DAVIS, R. A., Jr., and FITZGERALD, D. *Beaches and Coasts* (Malden, Mass.: Blackwell, 2002).

DEAN, C. *Against the Tide: The Battle for America's Beaches* (New York: Columbia Univ. Press, 1999).

HANSOM, J. D. *Coasts* (London/New York: Cambridge Univ. Press, 1988).

HARDISTY, J. *Beaches: Form and Process* (Winchester, Mass.: Unwin Hyman Academic, 1990).

HASLETT, S. *Coastal Systems* (London/New York: Routledge, 2001).

KETCHUM, B. H., Ed. *The Water's Edge: Critical Problems of the Coastal Zone* (Cambridge, Mass.: MIT Press, 1972).

LEATHERMAN, S. P. *America's Best Beaches* (Miami, Fla.: www.topbeaches.com, annual).

LENCEK, L., and BOSKER, G. *The Beach: The History of Paradise on Earth* (New York: Penguin Putnam, 1999).

PETHICK, J. S. *An Introduction to Coastal Geomorphology* (London: Edward Arnold, 1984).

SCHWARTZ, M. L., Ed. *The Encyclopedia of Beaches and Coastal Environments* (Stroudsburg, Pa.: Dowden, Hutchinson & Ross, 1982).

SIEVER, R. *Sand* (New York: Scientific American Library, 1988).

TRENHAILE, A. S. *Coastal Dynamics and Landforms* (New York: Oxford Univ. Press, 1997).

VILES, H., and SPENCER, T. *Coastal Problems: Geomorphology, Ecology and Society at the Coast* (New York: Oxford Univ. Press, 1995).

WEB RESOURCES

http://co-ops.nos.noaa.gov NOAA's Center for Operational Oceanographic Products and Services maintains a web page that includes online tide information, predictions and observations, water-level data, and maritime navigation safety information.

http://www.nearctica.com/ecology/habitats/beaches.htm This site is a comprehensive list of links to beach erosion and formation. Both technical data and nontechnical descriptive articles are available.

UNIT 51

Coastal Landforms and Landscapes

Percé Rock, located off the Gaspé Peninsula on the eastern coast of Quebec, is a spectacular sight as it rises from the sea. This limestone block, carved by wind and water, is 438 m long and 88 m high and is connected to the mainland by a tombolo.

OBJECTIVES

- To examine the characteristics of a beach
- To relate beaches to the coastline's topographic and tectonic setting

- To recognize related coastal landforms of aggradation, such as sand dunes, offshore bars, and barrier islands

- To identify landforms typical of erosional coastlines
- To relate erosional and depositional processes to a general classification of coastlines

U nit 50 reviewed the numerous marine processes that contribute to the formation of coastal landforms and landscapes. This unit examines those features themselves. The landforms of shorelines and the landscapes of coasts reveal the dominant processes at work. Cliffs and caves suggest that erosional activity is paramount. On the other hand, beaches and barrier islands indicate deposition. Coastal landforms can therefore be divided into two groups—aggradational and degradational. However, most coastal landscapes display evidence of both deposition and erosion.

Aggradational Landforms

Undoubtedly the most characteristic depositional landform along the coastline is a **beach**, defined as a coastal zone of sediment that is shaped by the action of waves and longshore currents. This means that a beach is much wider than the part of it we can see. On the landward side it begins at the foot of a line of dunes or some other feature, but on the seaward side it continues beneath the surf. Beaches are constructed from sand and other material, derived from both local and distant sources. Beach material in the coastal environment comes from a number of sources. When streams enter the ocean, the sediments they carry are deposited and transported along the shore by waves and currents. In addition, beach material may be produced locally: by the erosion of nearby sea cliffs and the physical breakdown of those particles as they are moved along the shore. Material can be blown in from the land by wind. It can also be brought in from along shore and offshore. Some material has glacial provinace.

Beach Dynamics

The character of a beach reflects the nature of the material of which it is composed. Most beaches along the North American Atlantic coast are made of sand, their light colour a result of the quartz fragments that make up the sand grains. In areas where dark-coloured igneous rocks serve as the source for beach material, as they do in parts of Hawaii, beaches are dark-coloured.

Along the coasts of British Columbia, northern California, Oregon, and Washington, high-energy conditions prohibit sand from being deposited on the beach, and larger particles make up the beach fabric. The resulting gravel and pebble beaches are often called *shingle* beaches.

A beach profile has several parts (Fig. 51.1). The **foreshore** is the zone that is alternately water covered during high tide and exposed during low tide. This is the zone of beach drift and related processes. Seaward of the foreshore lies the **nearshore** (sometimes called *offshore*), which is submerged even during an average low tide. One or more **longshore bars** (a ridge of sand parallel to the beach) and associated troughs often develop in this zone, where longshore drift, currents, and wave action combine to create a complex and ever-changing topography. Landward of the foreshore lies the **backshore**, which extends from the high-water line to the dune line. As Fig. 51.1 shows, the backshore consists of one or more sandy beaches called **berms**. These flat berms were laid down during storms and are beyond the reach of normal wave action.

Beach profiles show a considerable amount of seasonal variation. Where seasonal contrasts in wave energy are strong, a beach will have one profile during the winter and another during the summer (Fig. 51.2). The summer's long, steady, low waves carry sand from the nearshore zone onto the beach and create a wide summer berm that may develop a crest and slope gently landward. During the following winter, higher and more powerful storm waves erode much of the summer berm away, carrying the sand back to the nearshore zone and leaving a narrower winter berm. Thus a beach displays evidence of erosion as well as deposition.

Material is transported to and along a beach by various processes. Some material is carried dissolved in the water (solution load). Sediment is carried in a number of

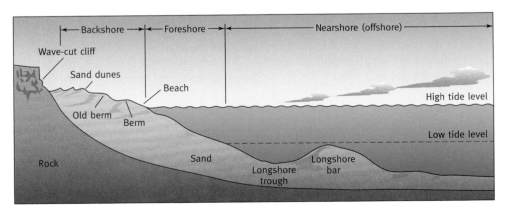

FIGURE 51.1 Parts of a beach shown in cross-sectional profile. The length of the profile is between 100 and 200 m. Vertical exaggeration is about twice.

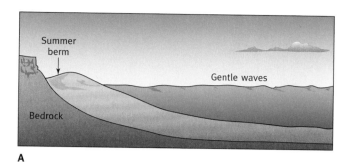

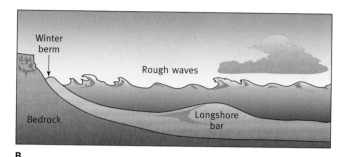

FIGURE 51.2 Seasonal variation in beach cut and fill. Gentle summer waves produce a wide berm that slopes gently landward (A). The rougher waves associated with winter storms produce a cold-season beach profile, which shows the summer berm eroded to a narrower, steeper-sloped remnant (B).

ways, much as material is moved in a stream. The finest muds are carried as the wash load, which is kept aloft by wave turbulence. The wash load will only be deposited in very tranquil water. Other fine material (clay to sand size) forms the suspended load, which again is kept in the water by turbulence. Heavier material is rolled or dragged along the seabed or beach by the current (traction load) or saltates along the bottom in a series of ballistic jumps. Another way material is moved is by kelp rafting. Kelp is a form of seaweed. Large forms of kelp (*Macrosystis sp.*) attach themselves to the seabed using holdfasts, which hold on to pebbles (shingle) and other material. When the wave action or current increases, as in a storm, some of the kelp is detached from the seabed and carries some sediment with it.

The entrainment, transport, and deposition of material is governed by the velocity and turbulence of the water and by the size and shape of the material; for example, shingle that is disc- or rod-shaped is transported the greatest distances.

Beaches are best viewed as open systems, characterized by inputs, outputs, and changes in storage. The size of the beach reflects the material in storage, and is therefore a measure of the balance between the availability of sediment and wave energy. The input of sediment is derived from local erosion, from offshore, and from upshore sections of the beach. Outputs of sediments can occur onshore (i.e., to the land), offshore, or downshore, and the width of the beach reflects the magnitude of the inputs and outputs.

Beach Mass Balance Figure 51.3 illustrates **beach mass balance**—that is, the balance between inputs and outputs. *Inputs* of material to a beach include longshore transport from upcoast, stream-supplied sediment, erosion of adjacent cliffs, and transport of material from offshore. *Outputs* from a beach take place by longshore drift to downshore, offshore transport, estuary filling, and finer material being blown off the beach into dune areas.

The mass balance varies seasonally, yearly, and over longer periods depending on the amount of inputs and outputs. If inputs equal outputs, there is a state of equilibrium. If inputs are greater than outputs, there is a positive mass balance and beach progradation will occur (the beach will grow). If outputs are greater than inputs, there is a negative balance and the beach will undergo

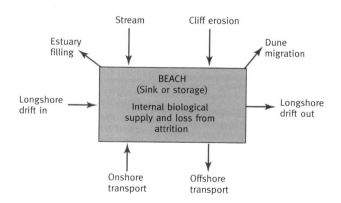

FIGURE 51.3 Beach mass balance.

Beach Mass Balance Equation:

$$L_I - L_O + O_I - O_O + S_I - E_O + C_I - D_O = O$$

Longshore − Longshore + Onshore − Offshore + Stream − Estuary + Cliff − Dune = 0
drift   drift   transport transport input   filling   erosion migration
[in]   [out]   [in]   [out]   [in]   [out]   [in]   [out]

retrogradation (the beach will be eroding). As an example, see Table 51.1 and Figure 51.4.

Two scenarios illustrate the behaviour of a beach. Temporary increases in wave energy, say, associated with a storm, promote temporary erosion (increased output to offshore zones). When wave energy conditions return to normal, offshore material is redeposited on the beach and it rebuilds to its former configuration. Long-term changes in sediment supply, however, can disrupt this general balance and produce substantial, and rather permanent, changes in the beach. Most often coastlines experience a decline in sediment supply from streams because of upstream dams and reservoirs, groynes on shorelines upcoast, etc. Since the wave energy is not affected, the decreased sediment supply results in heightened beach erosion (Fig. 51.5). Accordingly, the beach gets smaller as the storage of sediment decreases to reflect the lower inputs from streams or along shore it may even cause cliff erosion. In such cases rip rap, or revetments, are placed to stop cliff erosion and artificial beach nourishment of coarser material may be used.

The location and distribution of beaches is therefore related to both sediment availability and wave energy. Where the coastal topography is being shaped by convergent lithospheric plate movement, coasts are steep, the wave energy is generally high, and beaches are comparatively few. On the mainland of North America, for example, beaches on the coast of the Pacific Northwest and to the Maritime provinces generally are discontinuous, short, and narrow; but the Gulf and Atlantic Coasts, from the Mexican border to New York's Long Island, are almost continuously beach-fringed, and beaches tend to be wide. Long, wide beaches (strands) are also found in southern Labrador. The global map of continental shelves (see Fig. 2.6) generally provides a good indication of the likelihood of beach development. Where shelves are wide, beaches usually are well developed. Along high-relief coastlines, where shelves are frequently narrow, beach forms are generally restricted to more sheltered locations, and the material composing the beach tends to be larger.

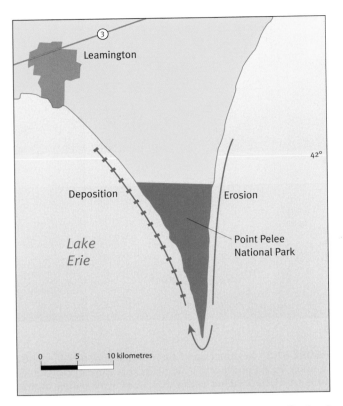

FIGURE 51.4 Point Pelee, Lake Erie. A cuspate foreland that is gradually moving westward because of erosion and deposition.

There is a general latitudinal zonation in terms of different types of beach sediments:

1. **Polar and subpolar regions** Shingle beaches are characteristic and pure sand is present in long exposed beaches. Quartz and rock fragments dominate sand material.

2. **Temperate regions** Quartz sand dominates. Rock fragments and felspar are abundant in sand near stream moarhs and along eroding bedrock coasts.

Table 51.1 Annual Mass Balance, Point Pelee (Cuspate Foreland), Ontario (All values m³ × 10³)

| | West Side | | | East Side | | |
	Offshore	Nearshore	Beach	Beach	Nearshore	Offshore
Year 1	134.1	130.0	28.7	−13.0	−338.7	−69.4
Year 2	−422.5	−173.7	13.5	55.3	89.1	−60.0
Avg. 5 yr.	240.7	−126.7	102.9	−432.9	−625.3	−246.6

Net movement of sediment over this period

Source: Coakley, "Nearshore sediment studies in western Lake Erie," 1972.

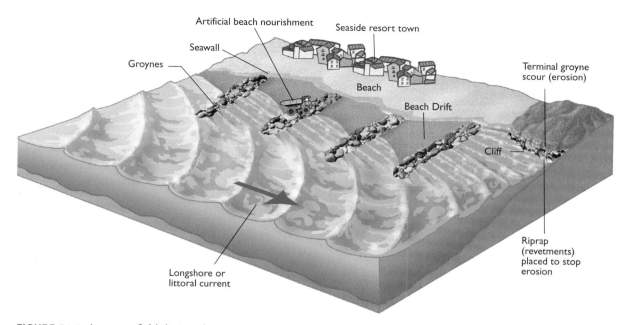

FIGURE 51.5 A groyne field designed to preserve a beach infront of a seaside resort. Erosion of the coast occurs down coast of the last groyne (Terminal groyne scour). Rip rap, or revetments, are put in along the shore or more groynes are built to stop further erosion. Artificial beach nourishment can also be used to enhance the beaches (dumping of coarser beach material).

3. **Tropical regions** Tropical beaches consist of carbonate sand composed of coral and algal fragments, shell, and carbonate precipitates. Quartz and rock fragments are common in sand, especially in areas of eroding bedrock and close to stream mouths.

4. **Oceanic islands** Beaches here have volcanic sands (normally black coloured). In other places carbonate sands dominate.

Coastal Dunes

Wind is an important geomorphological agent in coastal landscapes, and many beaches are fringed by sand dunes that are primarily the product of aeolian deposition (Fig. 51.6). Lines of dunes are sometimes breached by a storm surge, but wind remains their prime aggradational agent. Coastal zones are subject to strong sea breezes; sand on the winter berm is constantly moved landward by these winds and, less frequently, by storms. Even when an offshore storm does not generate waves high enough to affect the winter berm, its winds can move large amounts of berm sediment landward.

In this way, coastal dunes are nourished from the beach. Usually they appear simply as irregular mounds, rarely exhibiting the characteristic formations of desert dunes. Some, however, display a variation of the parabolic form (see Fig. 49.7B), reflecting the persistent wind direction during their development. An important point of difference between desert and coastal dunes is that coastal dunes, as a result of moist conditions, often are covered with vegetation and are relatively stable (Fig. 51.6).

FIGURE 51.6 Photo of dunes at Sandbanks Provincial Park, Ontario.

Sandspits and Sandbars

In this section the depositional landforms of the surf zone and beyond are discussed. One of the most characteristic of the aggradational coastal landforms is the **sandspit**. When longshore drift occurs and the shifting sediment reaches a bay or a bend in the shoreline, it may form an extension into open water as shown (twice) in the central portion of Fig. 51.7. In effect, the spit is an extension of the beach. It begins as a small tongue of sand, and grows larger over time. It may reach many kilometres in length and grow hundreds of metres wide, although most spits have more modest dimensions. Two well-known sandspits are the Toronto Islands and Long Point in Lake Erie (Fig. 51.8). The Toronto Islands are a recurved spit. Another example is the Naikoon or Rose Point Spit near Masset at the northern end of Haida Gwaii, the Queen Charlotte Islands, B.C.

Some sandpits are affected by two currents from different directions. This forms a cuspate foreland (e.g., Point Pelee near Leamington, Ontario [Point Pelee National Park]).

Some sandspits continue to grow all the way across the mouth of a bay, and become **baymouth bars** (Fig. 51.7 centre). The bay may simply be an indentation in the coastline, or it may be a stream estuary. At first, tidal currents may breach the growing bar and keep the bay open (where the tidal inlet is located to the right in Fig. 51.7). But if the longshore drift is strong and sediment plentiful, the bay will soon be closed off.

This has important consequences, because if the tidal action ceases, the bay is no longer supplied with cleansing ocean water. If the mouth of an estuary is closed off, the river that enters it will drop its sediments in the bay instead of the ocean. Thus the bay becomes a lagoon, and its former saltwater environment changes as river water and sediment fill it. Behind the baymouth bar, the ecology of the new lagoon changes to that of a swamp or marshland (Fig. 51.7). Examples of a baymouth bar can be found at Hamilton, Ontario, and in Prince Edward County, Ontario. A growing sand spit also may form a link between an offshore island and the mainland, creating a landform called a **tombolo** (Fig. 51.7, right front). Examples of tombolos are in Pres'quile Provincial Park near Brighton, Ontario, or on Panmure Island, Cardigan Bay, on the east coast of Prince Edward County or at Percé Rock in Gaspé—for example, the Sandbanks at West Lake (Sandbanks Provincial Park) and the bar at East Lake. Spits, bars, and tombolos can take on many different shapes as they bend, curve, and shift during their evolution (Figs 51.8, 51.9 and 51.10).

Offshore Bars and Barrier Islands

A sure sign of offshore aggradation is the *sandbar,* or **offshore bar**, which lies some distance from the beach and is not connected to land. We referred to longshore bars in connection with the beach profile (Fig. 51.1), and such offshore bars can be observed to expand and contract depending on wave action and sediment supply. Once formed, offshore bars interfere with the very waves that built them. Waves will break against the seaward side of a bar, then regenerate and break a second time against the shore itself (see Fig. 51.2B). Some offshore bars become stable enough to attain permanence, rising above the water surface during low tide and being submerged only during high tide.

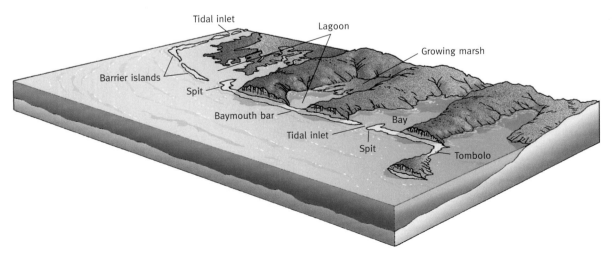

FIGURE 51.7 Common depositional landforms along a stretch of coastline.

FIGURE 51.8 Long Point, a 40-km long sand spit that juts out into Lake Erie, Ontario, offers refuge and a stopover for migrating birds in fall and spring. It is recognized by the United Nations as a biosphere reserve.

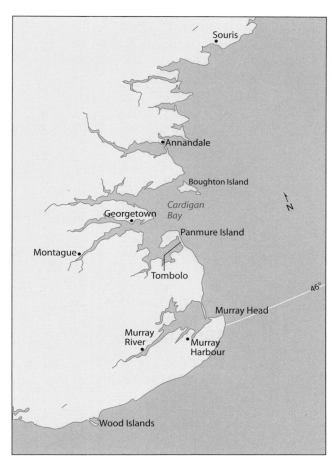

FIGURE 51.9 Map showing Panmure Island (Cardigan Bay, Prince Edward Island) attached to the mainland by a tombolo.

Along certain stretches of the earth's coasts lie large and permanent offshore bars, appropriately called **barrier islands**. These islands are made of sand, but they reach heights of 6 m above sea level and average from 2 to 5 km in width. They can lie up to 20 km from the coast, but more commonly are half that distance from shore, and they often stretch for dozens of kilometres, unbroken except by tidal inlets. The offshore barrier island strip (known locally as the Outer Banks) that forms North Carolina's Cape Hatteras is a classic example, as are the barrier beaches along the north coast of Prince Edward Island (Fig. 51.11).

Barrier islands may have had their origins as offshore bars during the last glaciation, when the sea level was much lower than it is today. As the sea level rose, these offshore bars migrated coastward, growing as they shifted. Since about 7000 years ago, when the sea level stopped rising rapidly, the barrier islands have moved landward slowly. In the meantime they have developed a distinctive profile. There is a gently sloping beach on the seaward side, a wind-built ridge of dunes in the middle, and a zone of natural vegetation (shrubs, grasses, mangroves) on the landward side (Fig. 51.12). Finally, a lagoon almost always separates the barrier island from the mainland. Because barrier islands are breached by tidal inlets, however, tidal action keeps these lagoons from becoming swamps (Fig. 51.7, left top).

Because of their recreational and other opportunities, which often attract intensive development (see

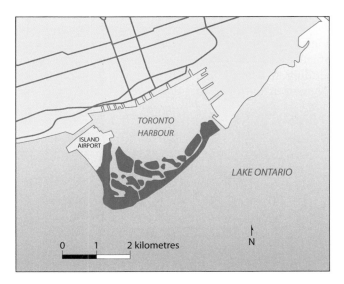

FIGURE 51.10 Map showing the Toronto Islands. Originally a recurved spit built from eroded material from the Scarborough Bluffs, Lake Ontario now formed into islands by dredging and infilling.

South Texas to New York along the Gulf of Mexico and lower Atlantic coast of the United States. Between these islands and the mainland lies the Intracoastal Waterway, an important artery for coastwise shipping. Being low and exposed, the barrier islands are vulnerable to hurricanes, and severe storm waves can temporarily erase parts of them. In heavily developed areas the hazard is particularly obvious (see Perspective: Hazards of Barrier Island Development).

Degradational Landforms

Where wave erosion (rather than deposition) is the dominant coastal process, a very different set of landforms develops. Exposed bedrock, high relief, steep slopes, and deep water are key features of this terrain. If there are islands, they are likely to be rocky remnants of the retreating coast, not sandy embankments being built in shallow water. Unit 50 discusses the processes of degradation by waves: hydraulic action, corrasion, corrosion, and the attrition of rock fragments. Just as a stream seeks to produce a graded profile, so wave erosion works to straighten an indented, embayed coastline. Wave refraction concentrates erosional energy on the headlands that stick out into the water, while sedimentary material collects in the concave bends of bays, a process whose beginning was observed in Fig. 50.5.

A possible sequence of events that follows is depicted in Fig. 51.14. When headlands (A) are eroded by waves, steep **sea cliffs** develop (B). Waves vigorously erode the bottom part of the cliff, seeking out joints, layers of softer strata, and other weaknesses, excavating a wave-cut notch. In so doing, the waves often create **sea caves** near the base of the cliff, undercutting it. Soon the overhanging part of the cliff collapses, so that wave action combines with mass movement to erode the coastal bedrock.

FIGURE 51.11 Aerial view of the white sandy beaches along the North Coast of Prince Edward Island.

Fig. 50.7), barrier islands are of more than geomorphological interest. In fact, several large cities and many smaller towns have developed on these strips of sand, including Miami Beach, Galveston, and Atlantic City. Numerous long stretches of barrier island extend from

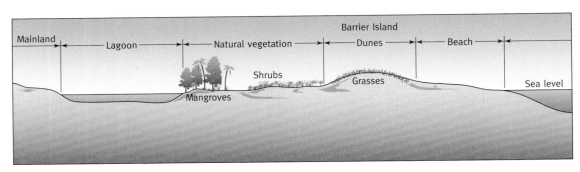

FIGURE 51.12 Cross-sectional profile of a barrier island and adjoining lagoon. Vertical exaggeration is about twice.

PERSPECTIVES ON THE HUMAN ENVIRONMENT

Hazards of Barrier Island Development

From Bar Harbor, Maine, to the mouth of the Rio Grande at Brownsville, Texas, more than 4000 km away, 295 barrier islands lie along much of the U.S. Atlantic and Gulf of Mexico coastlines. Given Americans' love of the seashore—and the fact that more than half of them reside within an hour's drive of a coast—it should come as no surprise that most of these islands have witnessed the development of lengthy oceanside strips of summer homes, resorts, high-rise condominiums, commercial and tourist facilities, fishing piers, and public beaches.

Barrier islands, as we know, are in constant motion, migrating slowly landward in response to increases in sea level (which have totalled about 30 cm over the past century along the eastern coast of the United States). The myriad structures built on loose sand atop these islands, therefore, are always threatened by erosional processes, which are strongest on the seaward side, directly facing the most desirable beachfront development sites.

To protect themselves, barrier island communities construct seawalls parallel to the beach and groynes or rock jetties perpendicularly outward into the surf (see Fig. 50.7). They also spend lavishly to replenish beaches by pumping in massive amounts of new sand from offshore, deeper water sources (artificial beach nourishment). These measures, unfortunately, buy only a few years' time and may actually worsen erosion in the longrun. Seawalls block the onrushing surf, but the deflected swash returns to the ocean so quickly that it carries with it most of the new sand that would otherwise have been deposited—and soon the beach has disappeared. Groynes are more successful at trapping incoming sand, but studies have shown that saving one beach usually occurs at the expense of destroying another one nearby. As for replenishing shrinking beaches by pumping in sand, all the evidence shows that this, too, is only a stopgap measure. For the past quarter-century the U.S. Army Corps of Engineers has shifted massive amounts of beach sand along 800 km of the eastern seaboard, with little more than a $10-billion expenditure to show for its herculean efforts.

The greatest hazard to these low-lying offshore islands are the 30 or so cyclonic storms that annually move over the East Coast. Even a moderate-strength cyclone can accentuate coastal erosion processes to the point where major property losses occur. The gravest of such threats to these vulnerable sand strips, of course, are the occasional bigger storms—which are long remembered by local residents.

A particularly severe late-winter cyclone in 1962 smashed its way northward from Cape Hatteras to New England, leaving in its wake a reconfigured coastline (as the flooding ocean created new inlets across barrier islands) and nearly $1-billion worth of storm damage in today's U.S. dollars (Fig. 51.13).

FIGURE 51.13 The March 1962 storm is still remembered as one of the most destructive in the recorded history of the U.S. Atlantic coast. This is the aftermath of that storm on Fire Island, the barrier island off the south-central shore of Long Island, about 80 km east of New York City.

The worst devastation, however, is associated with tropical cyclones. After Hurricane Camille (one of the most powerful of the past century) attacked the Louisiana and Mississippi Gulf Coast in 1969, the United States was spared this kind of awesome damage for 20 years—until Hurricane Hugo roared across the South Carolina shoreline in 1989. Most importantly, this uncharacteristic lull of the 1970s and 1980s was accompanied by the largest coastal construction boom in history.

Only belatedly are the federal and state governments taking a hard look at all this development, and in many seaside locales a new consensus is emerging that it was a mistake to build in such unstable environments. Thus the realization is dawning that nature is certain to win the battle of the barrier islands in the end—despite the best efforts of policymakers, planners, and coastal engineers to manage the precarious human presence that has cost so many billions of dollars to put into (temporary) place.

The cliff continues to retreat (Fig. 51.14B and C). A **wave-cut platform** (also called an *abrasion platform*) develops at the foot of the cliff (B), marking its recession. These platforms are nearly flat bedrock surfaces that slope seaward. At low tide we can see boulders and cobbles, broken from the cliff laying on this platform. Soon the waves of a high tide (or a storm) will hurl these fragments back against the cliff face. As the headlands retreat, certain parts invariably prove to be more resistant than others (B and C).

Sections of the headlands survive as small islands, and as wave erosion continues, these islands are sometimes penetrated at their base and become **sea arches** (C). Other remnants of the headlands stand alone as columns called **stacks** (B and C). Arches (see unit opening photo) and stacks are typical of coastlines being actively eroded, but they are temporary features, and soon they, too, will be eroded down to the level of the wave-cut platform. Eventually the headlands may be completely removed, as are the beaches that lay at the heads of the bays. A nearly straight, retreating cliff now marks the entire coastal segment (Fig. 51.14C), with a portion of the wave-cut platform, covered by sediment, at its base.

Cliffs can form in any coastal strata, ranging from hard crystalline rocks to soft and loose glacial deposits. England's famous White Cliffs of Dover are cut from chalk (a very pure limestone). Tall cliffs in the Hawaiian Islands are carved from volcanic rocks. Cliffs along coastlines of the Mediterranean Sea are cut from layers of sedimentary rocks (see Fig. 31.6). The speed of cliff retreat depends on a number of conditions, including the power of the waves and, importantly, the resistance of the coastal rocks. In the Point Grey area of Vancouver the coast is formed by glacial deposits, and this loose material retreats as much as 1 m per year. Along parts of

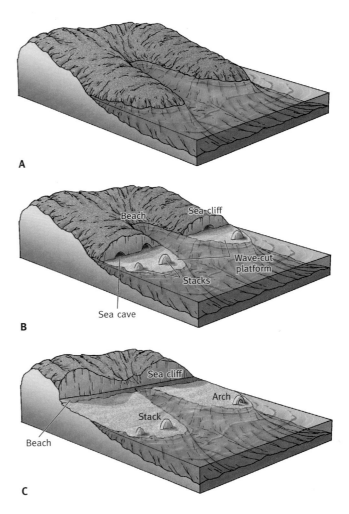

FIGURE 51.14 Hypothetical model of straightening of an embayed, indented coastline by wave erosion. When degradation is the dominant coastal process, a very different set of landforms develops (compare to the aggradational landforms in Fig. 51.7).

FROM THE FIELDNOTES

FIGURE 51.15 "A short climb to an overlook near the Oregon–California border provides an instructive perspective over an active segment of the Pacific coastline here. Deep water, unobstructed fetch, and pounding waves drive back the shore along steep cliffs. Note the virtual absence of stacks, suggesting that the rocks being attacked here are not as resistant to erosion as the harder crystallines seen farther north. The owners of those apartments must have dramatic ocean views, but future generations will face the reality of nature's onslaught."

the B.C. Coast, deeper water and soft bedrock combine to produce an even faster rate of retreat, but in other segments of the same coast the hard crystalline rocks wear away at a much slower rate (Fig. 51.15).

Coastal Landscapes

The events just described constitute a possible model for the evolution of a shoreline from an initially irregular shape to a straight, uniform beach. The reason so few beaches resemble this model is that many coastlines have experienced marked fluctuations in the conditions that shape shoreline evolution. Simply put, most beaches are too recent to have achieved their equilibrium form. Recent sea-level fluctuations, as well as tectonic movements along plate margins, continually disrupt the operation of coastal processes. With this in mind, it is convenient to distinguish between two general types of coastlines— *emergent* and *submergent* coasts.

Emergent Coasts

The landscapes of *uplifted* or **emergent coasts** carry the imprints of elevation by tectonic forces. Some coastal zones have been uplifted faster than postglacial sea levels rose. The net effect of this is that such features as cliffs and wave-cut platforms are raised above (sometimes tens of metres above) the present sea level (Fig. 51.16). When raised this way, a wave-cut platform is termed an **uplifted marine terrace**. Occasionally such landforms as stacks and arches still stand on the uplifted marine terrace.

Coasts where aggradational processes dominate also may be uplifted, but such depositional coastlines tend to lie in more stable lithospheric zones. There the evidence is more rapidly erased by erosional processes, because uplifted landforms—dunes, berms, bars, spits—are far less resistant than bedrock cliffs and wave-cut platforms. Sometimes cultural features reveal recent uplift. Stone structures of coastal settlements (including docks) may survive longer than soft sedimentary landforms. When such settlements lie well above the water, we can conclude that uplift has occurred. Some Maya buildings, constructed on the waterfront more than 1000 years ago, now lie elevated on uplifted segments of the Mexican and Central American coasts.

Submergent Coasts

More coastlines are **submergent coasts**, that is, *drowned* rather than uplifted. This submergence was caused in large part by the rise of the sea level over the past 10,000 years. At the beginning of the Holocene the sea level stood perhaps 120 m below its present average mark. This exposed large parts of the continental shelves (see Fig. 2.6) that are now under water. Streams flowed across these areas of land as they do today across the coastal plain, eroding their valleys to the edge of the lowered ocean.

The courses of many such streams, in fact, can be traced from their present mouths across the continental shelf to their former outlets. When Holocene glacial melting raised global sea levels by many metres, these marginal areas were submerged and the stream valleys became submarine canyons. The water rose quite rapidly until about 7000 years ago. This was the time when the world's barrier islands formed and began to migrate landward. Over the past seven millennia the sea level has continued to rise, but so slowly that many coastlines have stabilized.

In the drowned stream mouths, it is possible to witness the effects of submergence. Streams often flow into these estuaries and leave no doubt regarding their origins. Sometimes the tops of nearly submerged hills rise as small islands above the water within the estuary. If sea levels were still rising rapidly, this invasion of stream valleys by advancing ocean water would continue today. However, the rise of the sea level has slowed sufficiently to permit longshore drift to form spits and bars across many estuaries.

Evidence of submergence also can be seen on tectonically active, high-relief coasts and in areas affected by glacial erosion that were adjacent to coastlines. A combination of crustal subsidence and rising sea levels produces very deep water immediately offshore (for instance, along the western coasts of North and South America). This exposes the coastal bedrock to the onslaught of powerful, deep-water waves not slowed by shoaling. Where fjords were carved by glaciers reaching the ocean, rising water has filled the U-shaped troughs above the level of the ice. Fjords, of course, are drowned glacial valleys, their waters deep, their valley sides sheer and often spectacular (see Fig. 47.6C). Submergent coastlines, therefore, display varied landscapes, all resulting from rising water or subsiding crust, or both.

Living Shorelines

Living organisms, such as corals, algae, and mangroves, can shape or affect the development of shores and coasts. A **coral reef** is built by tiny marine organisms that discharge calcium carbonate. New colonies build on the marine limestone deposits left by their predecessors, and this process can create an extensive network of coast-fringing ridges. To grow, corals need clear water, warm

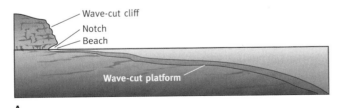

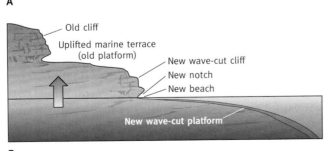

FIGURE 51.16 A wave-cut platform (A) is transformed into an uplifted marine terrace (B) when tectonic uplift elevates the coastal zone above the existing sea level.

temperatures, and vigorous cleansing wave action. This wave action does erode the reef, but it also washes the growing coral. Ideally, the coral is covered with water during high tide and exposed to the air during low tide.

Where conditions are favourable, wide, flat-topped coral reefs develop. Sometimes they are attached to the shore; others lie offshore and create lagoons between shore and reef. Still other corals create atolls. **Atolls** are roughly circular reefs that surround a lagoon, but without any land in the centre. The round shape of atolls, many of which are found in the lower latitudes of the Pacific Ocean, was studied more than 150 years ago by Charles Darwin. He concluded that the corals probably grew on the rims of eroded volcanic cones. As the flattened volcano subsided (or the sea level rose), the corals continued to build upward (Fig. 51.17).

Vegetation also influences the evolution of shorelines. In parts of West Africa, Southeast Asia, and the southeastern United States, mangroves and their elaborate root systems have become builders of shorelines. Once these unique plants have taken hold, the erosional power of waves and currents is harnessed by those root systems. As a result, a zone of densely vegetated mud flats develops, creating a unique ecological niche.

The landforms and landscapes of coastlines are formed and modified by many processes and conditions. No two stretches of shoreline are exactly alike because the history of a coastal landscape involves a unique combination of waves, tides, currents, wind, sea-level change, and crustal movement.

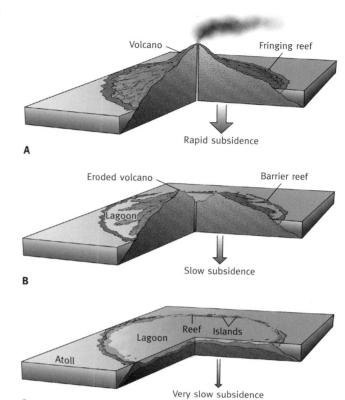

FIGURE 51.17 Relationship between coral atoll reefs and marine volcanoes. The coral reef originally develops around the rim of a subsiding volcanic cone (A). As the cone erodes, the corals continue to build upward, leaving a lagoon surrounded by a ring-like reef (B). When the cone has disappeared below the water, the circular atoll is the only feature remaining at the ocean surface (C).

KEY TERMS

atoll *page 671*

backshore *page 660*

barrier island *page 665*

baymouth bar *page 664*

beach *page 660*

beach mass balance *page 661*

berm *page 660*

coral reef *page 670*

emergent coast *page 670*

foreshore *page 660*

longshore bar *page 660*

nearshore *page 660*

offshore bar *page 664*

sandspit *page 664*

sea arch *page 668*

sea cave *page 666*

sea cliff *page 666*

stack *page 668*

submergent coast *page 670*

tombolo *page 664*

uplifted marine terrace *page 670*

wave-cut platform *page 668*

REVIEW QUESTIONS

1. Describe a typical beach profile. Why would different beach profiles develop in summer and winter?

2. How do sandspits and baymouth bars form?

3. How do barrier islands form?

4. Describe the processes by which irregular, embayed coastlines become straightened.

5. What has been the fundamental cause of the many submergent coastlines encountered throughout the world?

REFERENCES AND FURTHER READINGS

BIRD, E. C. F.   *Coasts: An Introduction to Coastal Geomorphology* (New York: Blackwell, 3rd ed., 1984).

BIRD, E. C. F.   *Submerging Coasts: The Effects of a Rising Sea Level on Coastal Environments* (New York: Wiley, 1993).

CARTER, R. W. G., Ed.   *Coastal Environments: An Introduction to the Physical, Ecological and Cultural Systems of Coastlines* (Orlando, Fla.: Academic Press, 1989).

CHARLIER, R. H., and DE MEYER, C.   *Coastal Erosion: Response and Management* (New York: Springer-Verlag, 1997).

COAKLEY, J. P. "Nearshore sediment studies in western Lake Erie," Proceedings of the 15th Conference on Great Lakes Research, International Association of Great Lakes Research (1972), 330–343

DAVIS, R. A., Jr., and FITZGERALD, D.   *Beaches and Coasts* (Malden, Mass.: Blackwell, 2002).

DEAN, C.   *Against the Tide: The Battle for America's Beaches* (New York: Columbia Univ. Press, 1999).

DOLAN, R., and LINS, H.   "Beaches and Barrier Islands," *Scientific American* (July 1987), 68–77.

FRENCH, P. W.   *Coastal and Estuarine Management* (London/New York: Routledge, 1997).

FRENCH, P. W.   *Coastal Defences: Processes, Problems and Solutions* (London/New York: Routledge, 2001).

HANSOM, J. D.   *Coasts* (London/New York: Cambridge Univ. Press, 1988).

HARDISTY, J.   *Beaches: Form and Process* (Winchester, Mass.: Unwin Hyman Academic, 1990).

HASLETT, S.   *Coastal Systems* (London/New York: Routledge, 2001).

LEATHERMAN, S. P.   *America's Best Beaches* (Miami, Fla.: www.topbeaches.com, annual).

LENCEK, L., and BOSKER, G.   *The Beach: The History of Paradise on Earth* (New York: Penguin Putnam, 1999).

PETHICK, J. S.   *An Introduction to Coastal Geomorphology* (London: Edward Arnold, 1984).

SHAW, J. R. "Beach and Offshore Changes at Point Pelee National Park, Lake Erie 1974–1981," *Canadian Technical Report of Hydrography and Ocean Sciences, Fisheries and Ocean*s, no. 76 (Ottawa: Supply and Services, 1986).

SNEAD, R. A.   *Coastal Landforms and Surface Features: A Photographic Atlas and Glossary* (Stroudsburg, Pa.: Dowden, Hutchinson & Ross, 1982).

STEERS, J. A.   *Applied Coastal Geomorphology* (Cambridge, Mass.: MIT Press, 1971).

THOMSON, R.   *Oceanography of the British Columbia Coast* (Ottawa: Fisheries and Aquatic Sciences Special Publication 56, 1981).

TRENHAILE, A. S.   *The Geomorphology of Rock Coasts* (London/New York: Oxford Univ. Press, 1987).

TRENHAILE, A. S.   *Coastal Dynamics and Landforms* (New York: Oxford Univ. Press, 1997).

VILES, H., and SPENCER, T.   *Coastal Problems: Geomorphology, Ecology and Society at the Coast* (New York: Oxford Univ. Press, 1995).

"Where's the Beach? America's Vanishing Coastline," *Time* (August 10, 1987), 38–47.

WEB RESOURCES

http://cciw.ca/ccsea/intro.html   This is the website of the Canadian Coastal Science and Engineering Association.

http://daac.gsfc.nasa.gov/DAAC_DOCS/geomorphology/GEO_6/GEO_CHAPTER_6.HTML   NASA's geomorphology site provides descriptions of major coastal landforms, with graphics depicting worldwide distribution of tectonic coastlines and shelf types.

http://gc.ca.nrgc.ca/index/cphp   This site includes information about coastal processes and research in Canada.

http://gsea.nr.can.gc.ca/coastweb/coastmap_e.php   This is the website of the Geological Survey of Canada's Atlantic sections. It includes information about the coastal information system, coastal map examples, dynamic segmentation, and references.

http://www.cciw.ca/nwri/nwri.htm   The Canadian Centre for Inland Water website includes information about water and related topics, Great Lakes coastal processes, sediments, and landforms.

http://www.nwri.ca   The website of the National Water Research Institute, Environment Canada, includes information, research, and links to sites dealing with coastal and other water-related themes. The major NWRI facility is at the Canadian Centre for Inland Water in Burlington, Ontario.

http://www.pgc.nrcan.gc.ca/marine/indexe_html   This website has information about coastal processes and research in Canada.

http://www.dal.ca/~mbutler/aszisc.htm   The website of the Atlantic Coastal Zone Information Steering Committee includes a guide to coastal information in Atlantic Canada and links to other coast-related sites.

Defining Physiographic Realms and Regions: The Spatial Variation of Landscapes

Barrier Lake, Kananaskis Country, Alberta, in summer.

OBJECTIVES

- To introduce physio-graphic realms and regions
- To discuss briefly the physiographic realms of North America
- To discuss in greater detail the regions that constitute the physiographic realms of North America, espe-cially in Canada

When you fly across North America, you pass over a panorama of changing landscapes. Even from a height of 12 km, the great canyons of the Colorado Plateau, the jagged relief of the Rocky Mountains, the undulating expanses of the Prairies, and the en echelon folds of the Appalachians leave clear impressions, and you would not mistake one for another.

The landscapes of the continents are not jumbled and disorganized. On the contrary, each area has distinct and characteristic properties.

In our everyday language we use words to identify those properties: the Rocky *Mountains,* the *Prairies,* the St. Lawrence *Valley,* the Canadian *Shield.* In other parts of the world the mountains of the Alps, the Amazon Basin, and the lowlands of western Siberia are recognized in the same way. Physical geographers, like other geographers, use the **regional concept** to classify and categorize spatial information. And the Rocky Mountains and the Prairies are just that—regions in the North American landscape.

Throughout this book we have paid attention to the spatial arrangement of the natural phenomena under investigation. For example, the major systems and processes that operate in the atmosphere were detailed, and a map of climate regions at the global scale was used to show the spatial expression of these systems and processes. Discussion of aspects of the biosphere, world and regional maps of soils, flora, and fauna summarized the evidence.

Now it is time to discuss the regionalization of natural landscapes at several levels of generalization. It is one thing to look down from a plane and recognize the Rocky Mountains or the Appalachians, but it is quite another to draw lines on maps that spatially define those regions. Here the approach of geographers differs from that of geologists, because the physical-geographical approach is more comprehensive. Geologists identify *geomorphological* regions, in which geological factors form the key criteria. Physical geographers use geological criteria as well, but add other environmental elements such as soils, vegetation, and climate when *physiographic* regions are established. An extensive mountain range on homogeneous rock, for instance, would constitute a geomorphological region. But that surface may lie under two spatially discrete climatic regimes, so that the north of it lies under steppe and the south under savanna. Physical geographers would recognize two physiographic regions on this basis.

Defining Physiographic Realms and Regions

Regionalization is essentially a form of spatial classification, and for such a system to be useful, it must be hierarchical; that is, its components must have different ranks. Biologists have established a *taxonomy* that categorizes the many millions of plants and animals into a hierar-

chical system with seven ranks. In descending order, the animal *kingdom* (to which humans belong) is followed by the *phylum* (division) named chordata, the *class* of mammals, the *order* of primates, the *family* of hominids, the *genus* designated *Homo,* and the *species* known as *Homo sapiens* (the subspecies is *Homo sapiens sapiens*). Note that each rank is more specific than the previous one. Historians define eras, ages, and periods, being ever more specific, to conceptualize the sequence of events they study. Human geographers divide the inhabited world into approximately a dozen geographic *realms,* such as Europe, South Asia, and Subsaharan Africa. These realms, in turn, are subdivided into *regions.* Europe, for example, consists of five regions: the British Isles, Western Europe, Northern Europe, Southern (Mediterranean) Europe, and Eastern Europe. Each of these regions contains its own subdivisions, so that Northern Europe has a Scandinavian *subregion.* In this hierarchical geographic classification, then, the *first-order* unit is the realm (Europe), the *second-order* unit is the region (Northern Europe), and the *third-order* unit is the subregion (Scandinavia).

In physical geography a similar hierarchical system can be used. The most general and broadest unit is the **physiographic realm**, incorporating a wide range of environmental conditions in which relief plays a dominant role. Each physiographic realm is divided into two or more **physiographic regions** based, as noted previously, on criteria ranging from climate and vegetation to soils and fauna. And physiographic regions can be divided into subregions and even smaller spatial units.

This notion can be applied to North America. The landscape of the continents is incredibly complex, but it is possible to delineate large-scale physiographic areas. All the continents are composed of four structural elements, and these can be used as a basis to define the largest physiographic units. These physiographic realms can be identified as follows (Fig. 52.1):

1. The Ancient Shield or Craton (the Canadian Shield)
2. The Platform Borderlands or Interior Basin (e.g., the Prairies and Great Plains) that flank the Shield area are also part of the Craton
3. The Marginal Linear Fold Mountain Belts or Orogens (Orogenic Belts) close to the continental margins (e.g., the Western Cordillera and the Appalachian-Caledonide Mountains)
4. The Gulf-Atlantic Coastal Plain and other smaller coastal plain areas (including the Arctic Coastal Plain), significant parts of which are now covered by the sea

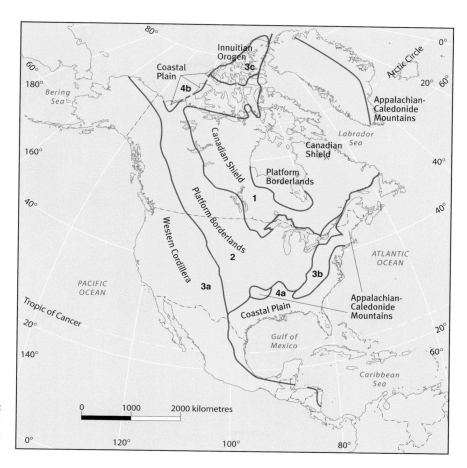

FIGURE 52.1 First-order physiographic realms of continental North America. Each realm contains second-order physiographic regions (see Fig. 52.5).

The Canadian Shield

The Canadian (or Laurentian) Shield is exposed in central and eastern Canada and the northern parts of the Prairie provinces, and it forms the landscape of much of Nunavut and the Northwest Territories and Greenland (Fig. 52.2). It is composed of highly deformed and metamorphosed Precambrian rocks dated to over 570 million years old. Some of the rocks are much older, going back 3.5 to 4 billion years. The Shield is now tectonically stable and has been subdivided on the basis of geological structures and lithology rather than in terms of physiography. The landscape is characterized by undulating topography with rock outcrops separated by basins filled with lakes, wetlands, or areas of thin podzolic and gleysolic soils supporting boreal forest. The present terrain was created by the glacial stripping of the overlying regolith and soils and exposure of the weathering front during the Late Cenozoic glaciations. Farther south the forest becomes mixed with deciduous species. To the north the forest peters out, and the trees become smaller as the temperatures become colder. The Clay Belt is the name given to the area around Senneterre, Kapuskasing, and Hearst; this area differs from the rest

of the Shield in that the ancient rocks are overlain by deep deposits of *varved* clays. These were deposited in an extensive proglacial lake, or proglacial lakes (Lake Barlow and Lake Ojibway) about 10,500 years ago.

The exposed part of the Canadian Shield, though huge, represents only a small part of Shield's actual size. The Shield underlies most of North America and forms the continent's geological core. It was thought to be the product of ancient orogenies but recent studies suggest that it developed as a consequence of (1) extraterrestrial impacts, (2) crustal differentiation, or (3) plate tectonics and extraterrestrial impacts.

Extraterrestrial Impacts It is suggested that the Shield areas of the world originated from a bombardment of the newly formed Earth by enormous meteorites or comets between 3.5 and 4 billion years ago. This bombardment caused the primary basalt crust and the upper mantle rocks to melt (impact melts) and resolidify as new rock types. The impacts also caused the eruption of vast amounts of magma/lava (some of which mixed with the impact-melt material) and the emplacement of granite intrusions. Such impacts may

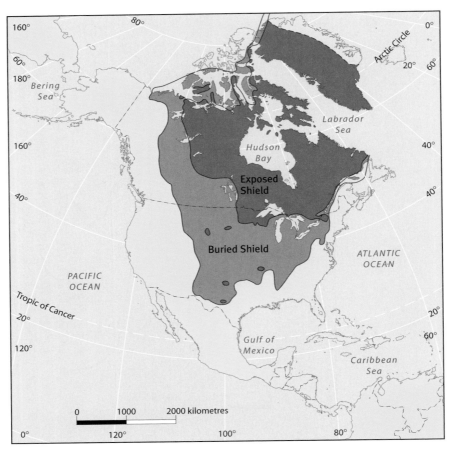

FIGURE 52.2 Map showing the extent of the exposed Canadian Shield and the buried part of the shield underlying much of North America.

have cracked the basaltic crust and initiated plate tectonic movement.

The most ancient rocks of the Shield areas date from the time of the bombardment (a relatively small geological time window of 0.5 billion years). Some workers believe that as many as 25 large impacts may have occurred in this period. The style of the rocks that have been dated to this period has not been found in rocks dated either to before or after this period, suggesting that these rocks had an extraordinary genesis. A huge crater-like feature called an *astron* has been found extending under the Shield rocks of northern Ontario from Hudson Bay to the south shore of Lake Superior. This underground crater is similar in form to the *ring craters* formed by meteoric impacts on the Moon and Mars. The meteorite that formed this feature is estimated to have been between 100 and 140 km in diameter.

Crustal Differentiation   Another suggestion is that the oldest Shield rocks formed by crustal differentiation as the Earth cooled down as it formed. The denser

basaltic crust was separated in this way from the less-dense, overlying granitic crust.

Plate Tectonics, and Extraterrestrial Impacts and Plate Tectonics   Still another idea relates the development of the Shield areas to tectonic collisions and the accretion of exotic terranes. As is known from more-recent collision and accretion episodes, such as those involving the Rocky Mountains and Coast Mountains, these are associated with the creation of fold mountains. In terms of the Shield areas, it is possible that long-continued weathering and erosion over many eons, plus the glaciations during the Late Cenozoic, have removed most of the evidence of these features. It is possible that impacts caused the fracturing of the Earth's primary basaltic crust and initiated plate tectonic activity.

Platform Borderlands (Interior Basin)

Platform Borderlands occur where the Shield is covered by a relatively thin veneer (less than 2 km) of mostly undeformed and unmetamorphosed Phanerozoic (having visible fossils, less than 570 Ma) sedimentary rocks derived from the weathering and erosion of the Shield—these rocks are mainly limestones, dolostones, and shales which were laid down in a shallow subtropical sea that invaded the interior of North America during Palaeozoic times. The rocks are flat-lying and in places gently dipping because of isostatic uplift of the Shield after the glaciations and because of intraplate subsidence (e.g., of the Michigan Basin). In consequence, these rocks in Southern Ontario dip to the southwest at approximately 3 degrees. The horizontal and near-horizontal disposition of these rocks is indicative of relative tectonic stability. Examples of regions within this area are the Prairies, the Great Plains, the Hudson Bay Lowlands, Southern Ontario, and the St. Lawrence Valley.

The Marginal Linear Fold Mountain Belts or Orogens

These are formed from highly deformed and metamorphosed Phanerozoic sedimentary rocks associated with the diapiric emplacement of intrusive rocks (batholiths), the eruption of volcanic lavas, and the accretion of exotic terranes associated with tectonic plate collision and subduction. These belts have been, or in the case of the western Orogen, still are, seismically and volcanically active.

There are three linear fold mountain belts in North America:

1. The Western Cordillera (the Rocky, Coast, and Cascade Mountains, the Central American Mountains, e.g., the Sierra Madre Occidental of Mexico and various plateaux)
2. The Appalachian-Caledonide Mountains, which extend up the eastern side of North America from Alabama, through the Atlantic provinces, along the eastern side of Greenland, and into Scotland and Scandinavia (Skanderna Mountains)
3. The Innuitian Orogen in the far north of the Canadian Arctic archipelago

The Gulf-Atlantic Coastal Plain and Other Smaller Coastal Plains

Coastal plains are characterized by low relief. The two best-developed coastal plains in North America are the Gulf-Atlantic Coastal Plain and the Arctic Coastal Plain. The Gulf-Atlantic Coastal Plain runs down the eastern seaboard of the United States and around the Gulf of Mexico as far as Central America. The Arctic Coastal Plain, is found on the extreme north-western parts of the Canadian Arctic archipelago and in areas of the mainland of the Northwest Territories (e.g., the Mackenzie Delta).

These are the first-order physiographic realms of the continent. Each contains second-order physiographic regions, many of which have very familiar names. As noted above, the Western Cordillera, for instance, includes the Rocky Mountains (extending south from coastal northern Alaska through Canada and the United States into Mexico and Central America) and the ranges paralleling the Pacific coast (Coast Mountains, Cascades, Sierra Nevada, etc.). This realm also contains the Interior Plateau of British Columbia, the Colorado Plateau, and other non-mountainous areas. Thus the level of generalization in first-order realms is high.

Physiographic realms of the first order present a useful generalization for certain purposes—for example, in a comparison with equally general climatic distributions. But for more detailed analysis, second-order regions are more practical. Accordingly, the Western Cordillera is subdivided into such regions as the Coast, Cascade, and Sierra Nevada Mountains, the Interior Plateau of British Columbia, the Columbia and Colorado Plateaux, the Rocky Mountains into northern (including the Canadian Rockies), middle, and southern regions, and so on. Each of these regions, in turn, is subject to further subdivision at progressively lower orders. Thus the level of **regionalization**, like the level of classification, should always be linked to specific objectives. In the case of physiographic realms, what is wanted is an overview of the continent's grand panorama of landscapes.

Criteria and Boundaries

Physiography involves more than the physical landscape and its constituent landforms. It involves all the natural features on the earth's surface—landforms, climate, soils, vegetation, hydrography, and other factors that relate to spatial changes in the overall natural landscape. The concept came into use in physical geography many years ago and has been the basis of many seminal works, including N. M. Fenneman's *Physiography of the Western United States* (1931) and *Physiography of the Eastern United States* (1938). Later W. W. Atwood refined the logic behind the idea, and in his benchmark volume *The Physiographic Provinces of North America* (1940), he used a new designation for the second-order regions. In 1987 W. L. Graf, in *Geomorphic Systems of North America*, employed the term *geomorphic province* in place of *realm*. The physiographic regions of Canada were demarcated by H. S. Bostock in 1971 (in his contribution to *The Geology and Economic Minerals of Canada*), although classifications had been put forward much earlier in provincial reports (e.g., L. J. Chapman and D. F. Putnam's *The Physiography of Southern Ontario* [1951] and Holland's *Landforms of British Columbia* [1964]) and have been reiterated in papers by Stearns, Bird, and Bally et al.

Many physical geographers have abandoned physiography for process studies, but others continue to demonstrate its validity and utility, most recently in *The Physical Geography of North America*, edited by A. R. Orme (2002). These developments are noted because, in the process, the distinction between physiography and geomorphology has become blurred.

How are the boundaries of physiographic realms and their constituent regions established? In some instances nature leaves no doubt and the visual evidence is overwhelming. Along much of the western edge of the Prairies/Great Plains, the Rocky Mountains rise sharply (Fig. 52.3A), terminating the rather level surface of the Interior Plains and marking the beginning of a quite different region (and realm) in terms of relief, slopes, rock types, landforms, vegetation, and other aspects as well.

But as Fig. 52.3B indicates, the transition is far less clear and much less sharp in (most) other instances. The eastern boundary of the Great Plains is a good case in point. Somewhere in the tier of provinces/states from British Columbia, Alberta, North and South Dakota, through Nebraska, Kansas, and Oklahoma, the Great Plains terminate and the Interior Lowlands begin. Exactly where this happens depends on the criteria used to

define the two adjacent regions and the method used to draw the dividing line. Sometimes a persistent linear landform, such as an escarpment, may serve effectively, overshadowing by its prominence the other transitions in the landscape (Fig. 52.3B). Where such a natural dividing line does not present itself, another solution must be found.

Nature rarely draws sharp dividing lines. Vegetation biomes, climate regions, and soil belts merge into one another in *transition zones,* and the lines drawn on maps to delineate them are the products of human calculations, not those of nature. In such a situation we can establish dividing lines for each individual criterion (vegetative change, change of climate, soil change, and so on), superimpose the maps, and draw an "average line" to delineate the physiographic realm, region, or subregion as a whole, as shown in Fig. 52.4. Still another solution is to place a grid of squares over the area in which the boundary is expected to lie, and then assign numerical values to each of the criteria mapped in each square; the physiographic boundary can then be mapped by computer. But as always, everything ulti-

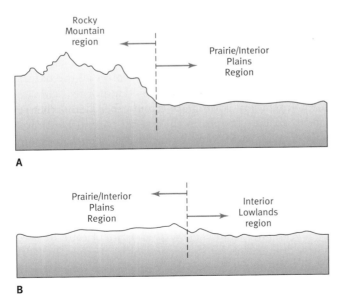

FIGURE 52.3 Topographic features that mark the western (**A**) and eastern (**B**) physiographic boundaries of the Prairie/Interior Plains region.

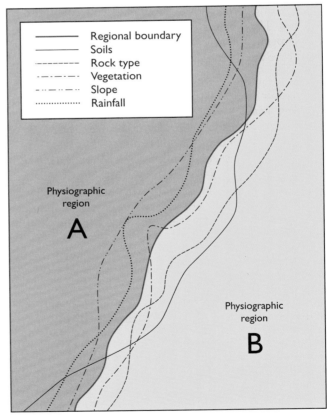

FIGURE 52.4 Derivation of a composite regional boundary (or "average line") from boundaries of several individual criteria.

mately depends on our choice of criteria and our ability to map them or attach quantitative values.

Physiographic Realms and Regions of North America

Figure 52.1 shows the physiographic realms of North America; some regional detail is added to distinguish the level of generalization involved. As has been noted above, the Western Cordillera, for example, consists not

only of mountains but also of intermontane basins and plateaux. The Platform Borderlands (Interior Plains) incorporate not only the Prairies and the Great Plains but even some highlands. We can now focus on each of these physiographic realms and their regional components, assisted further by the even more detailed mapping of their distribution within North America shown in Fig. 52.5.

1. The Canadian Shield

The **Canadian Shield realm** is a vast area of mostly exposed Precambrian igneous and metamorphic rocks, the

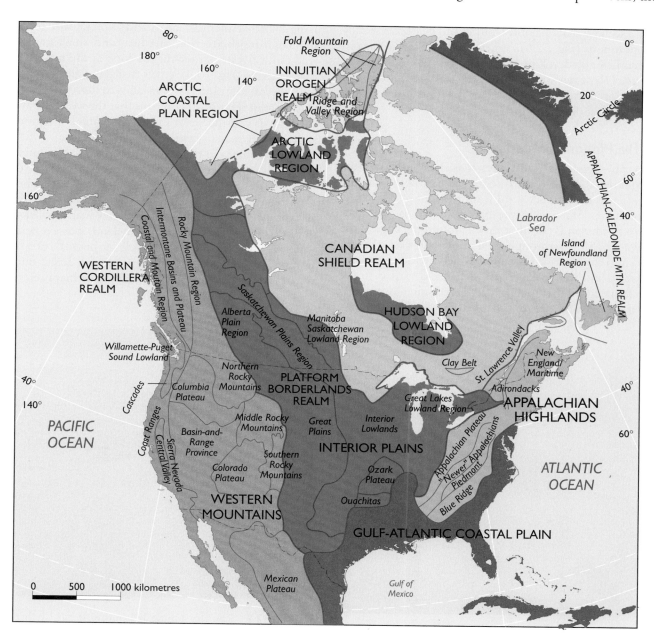

FIGURE 52.5 Physiographic realms and regions of North America.

original core of the North American landmass. The Shield makes up about 50 percent of Canada's area. It is a realm marked by a low undulating topography of rock knobs and basins. The basins are either filled with lakes, wetlands, or areas with thin unproductive soils (except in the Clay Belt). It is noted for its mineral deposits, especially iron, copper, nickel, and zinc. These metal deposits are associated with past tectonic and volcanic activity or meteoric impacts (e.g., Sudbury). This realm was the source of the great Laurentian ice sheets of the Late Cenozoic Ice Age that scoured the rocks and hollowed out the basins now filled with many lakes and wetlands. Low hills and a few isolated mountains diversify a scenery that is slightly rolling and characteristically monotonous (Fig. 52.6). Where the meagre glacial soils are sufficiently developed to sustain vegetation, stands of spruce (*Picea spp.*), pine (*Pinus spp.*), and fir (*Abies spp.*) trees clothe the landscape. Here is found much of the boreal forest described in Unit 27.

2. The Platform Borderlands

The physiographic realm known as the **Platform Borderlands** (also called the Interior Plains and the Central Lowlands) extends eastward from the foot of the Rocky Mountains. Starting in the Arctic Lowlands, the Platform Borderlands continue down around the edge of the Canadian Shield, through the Prairies and Great Plains, and into the Interior Lowlands, which include Southern Ontario and the St. Lawrence Valley and extend to the western edge of the Appalachian-Caledonide Mountains in the east. This realm also includes the Hudson Bay Lowlands (Fig. 52.1). The Platform Borderlands constitute a broad area of generally low relief that is mainly underlain by Phanerozoic sedimentary rocks. The Prairies and Great Plains are in large part sustained by glacial till accumulated during periods of deglaciation in the Late Cenozoic Ice Age. If you fly over the Prairies between Winnipeg and Edmonton, you can see moraines and other glacial and fluvioglacial features, such as drumlins, eskers, and kames, stretching across the surface, bearing witness to the importance and impact of past glacial processes.

The Canadian Prairies and the Great Plains region (which occupies the south-western sector of this low-lying North American heartland) are known for the monoculture production of wheat and small grains as well as for livestock ranching. A look at the map of climate regions (Fig. 16.3) shows that these areas are drier than the adjacent Interior Lowlands to the east. The vegetation map (Fig. 27.2) confirms that the western part of the Prairies and the Great Plains is essentially a region of short, rather sparse grasses (short-grass prairie), whereas the moister areas to the east (Manitoba and the Interior Lowlands) are covered with denser, taller grasses (tall-grass prairie) and trees. The soil map (Fig. 25.15) shows the western areas to be a region of semi-arid chernozems (mollisols) with some areas of solonetzs (natric soils) and vertisols, whereas the Interior Lowlands possess better-watered luvisols (alfisols) as well as pockets of chernozems. Of course, these differences occur across transitional zones, and the relatively small-scale maps referred

FIGURE 52.6 Crystalline, glaciated, vegetated Canadian Shield east of Yellowknife, Northwest Territories.

FIGURE 52.7 The dry prairie of southwestern Alberta, an area characterized by rainshadow conditions, short grass prairie, and chernozems, solonetzs, and vertisolic soils.

to are summaries based on artificial indices. But the typical scenery of the Prairies–Great Plains reflects a dryness that implies a number of significant differences between that region and the Interior Lowlands, which is the reason for separating them (Fig. 52.7).

To the south of the Interior Lowlands lies a comparatively small upland area called the Interior Highlands. This region can be separated into the Ozark Plateau in the north and the Ouachita Mountains in the south. The Ozark Plateau consists of slightly domed sedimentary rocks that have been eroded but still stand over 450 m above the average elevation of the Interior Lowlands to the north (i.e., the Mississippi River Valley). The Ouachita Mountains are a continuation of the Appalachian-Caledonide Mountains.

In Canada the Platform Borderlands can be divided into a number of physiographic regions based on geology, landscape, climate, and vegetation:

1. The Great Lakes Lowland
2. The St. Lawrence Lowlands
3. The Prairies
4. The Arctic Lowlands
5. The Hudson Bay Lowlands

The Great Lakes Lowland This area is separated from the St. Lawrence Valley by a finger of the Canadian Shield that juts southward toward Lake Ontario in the area around Kingston (the Frontenac Axis). It is underlain by a thin veneer of Palaeozoic rocks on top of the Canadian Shield. The rocks dip gently to the south-west toward the Michigan Basin. Erosion has etched out a series of plains or valleys in the less-resistant shales and has left a number of escarpments formed out of limestone and dolostone (the Black River, the Niagara, and the Onondaga Escarpments). The most prominent of the escarpments is the Niagara Escarpment, which runs from Manitoulin Island, through the Bruce Peninsula, and down through Hamilton to Niagara Falls and into New York State.

The other escarpments have been partially buried by glacial deposits. Rivers such as the Trent, Rouge, Don, Humber, and Credit eroded the landscape before the Late Cenozoic glaciations by a process called *uniclinal shifting*, cutting wide, low relief plains as they moved down-dip along the less-resistant strata. The Late Cenozoic glaciations excavated the Great Lakes basins and deposited a series of glacial tills and lake deposits that now blanket the terrain. Since the end of the glaciations, the rivers have been re-established and have begun re-excavating their drainage basins.

Much of the lowland area between the cuestas was flooded as the Great Lakes formed. Erosion of the glacial

materials by coastal processes has caused slope failures along the cliffs and a variety of coastal aggradational landforms, such as spits of various kinds, baymouth bars, and tombolos.

The luvisolic soils that developed in the glacial deposits are extremely productive, supplying a wide range of agricultural products to the many large cities in the Golden Triangle, from Oshawa to Niagara Falls. Before European settlement, much of the area was covered by a deciduous forest of the type known as a *Carolinian forest*, having many of the plant and animal species found in areas as far south as the Carolinas. This forest extended as far as the Rouge River. North of this was a mixed-forest area developed on luvisols and podzols.

The St. Lawrence Lowlands This extends for approximately 400 km, stretching along the St. Lawrence River from close to the Frontenac Axis near Kingston to the vicinity of Quebec City and reappearing on the Île d'Anticosti in the Gulf of St. Lawrence. The landscape is carved on Early Palaeozoic sandstones and shales with some limestone beds. Limestone is common toward the western end of the St. Lawrence Valley, where it forms bare, poorly-drained lowlands and low-relief plateaux. Shales are dominant east of Montreal but are covered by a considerable thickness of glacial deposits. At the end of the Wisconsinan glaciation of the Late Cenozoic, this area was inundated by the sea (the Champlain Sea) before the land could isostatically adjust. This inundation deposited Leda clays, which are sensitive and susceptible to flow failures. Tectonism in the Cretaceous period caused rifting of the Bonnechere graben and the intrusion of a series of stocks and batholiths (the Monteregian Hills), which have now been exposed by erosion (e.g., Mount Royal, Mount St. Bruno, St. Hilaire, Rougemont, and Mount Johnson). The glacial deposits have developed into the fertile soils that are the basis for a successful agricultural sector, which supplies vegetables, fruit, and milk products to the cities of the area and to other parts of Canada.

The Prairies This area is a continuation of the same kind of rocks and physiography seen in the Great Lakes Lowland and the Great Plains of the United States. It is developed on the same lithologies and the same kind of geological structures, but these have been covered in many places by an extremely thick sequence of glacial deposits (in some cases more than 200 m thick). The bedrock is exposed in some river valleys and in escarpments. The drainage networks have developed on the thick glacial materials and bear little relation to the underlying bedrock so far below. Much of the scenery is the outcome of many glaciations and the meltwater produced by deglaciation, which was ponded-up in extensive proglacial lakes (e.g., Lake Agassiz) and discharged through rivers flowing from the ice margins. Differences in geology, glacial deposits, climate, and vegetation lead to the distinctions drawn between the aspen parkland, the tall-grass and the short-grass prairie areas. The aspen parkland occurs in the northern and north-eastern transition of the Prairie region and melds into the boreal forest. The climate here is cooler and moister than in the other areas, and the soils are predominantly luvisols and podzols. Tall-grass prairie occurs in a zone paralleling the parkland, in slightly warmer and less moist conditions. The soils here are dominated by chernozems. The short-grass prairie is found in an area often called the Palliser Triangle. This is an area characterized by aridity and warmer summer temperatures. It occurs in south-western Saskatchewan and south-eastern Alberta. Within this area there are dry valleys (badlands, coulees) and many steep slopes that have been cut into by gullies and rills. Dust storms are common and there are significant areas of sand dunes (see Unit 49).

These areas roughly correspond to differences in elevation and position in the region. The region can be divided into three physiographic sub-regions that form a series of topographic steps from the Canadian Shield in the north, northeast, and east to the Alberta Foothills in the west:

1. **The Manitoba Lowland, the Saskatchewan Lowland**, and their extension to the north, **the Slave Lowland**, lie between the Shield and the Manitoba Escarpment. The Manitoba Escarpment has been formed into a series of plateaux (e.g., Turtle Mountain, south of the Assiniboine River, to the Wapawekka Hills, north of the Saskatchewan River in north-central Saskatchewan; these plateau areas have elevations ranging from 300 to 500 m above sea level). The lowlands are cut into by large river valleys such as the Saskatchewan River Valley. In Manitoba this area is dominated by Lake Winnipeg, Lake Manitoba, and the Red River Valley.

2. The **Saskatchewan Plains** and Peace Hills and Plains are developed on Cretaceous shales and are approximately 400 km wide. This sub-region continues into northern Alberta and the extreme northern area of British Columbia. It occurs between the Manitoba Escarpment in the east and the Missouri Coteau on the western edge. This subregion is crossed by large, entrenched, flat-bottomed valleys, such as the Assiniboine, Qu'Ap-

pelle, and Saskatchewan River valleys, which functioned as glacial spillways during deglaciation.

3. The Alberta Plains include undulating parkland reminiscent of the Saskatchewan Plains (e.g., between Edmonton and Red Deer), extremely arid areas (e.g., the Great Sand Hills to the east of the parkland), and, in the south near the Rockies, the Border Plateau and a series of residual Cenozoic outlier hills (e.g., Wintering Hills and Hand Hills). An **outlier** is an upland area formed by part of a rock formation separated from the main body of the rockbed by erosion. The general elevation of the **Alberta Plain** rises toward the Foothills. Large river systems, with their sources in the Rocky Mountains, flow across this area and have cut significant valleys, for example, the Bow, the Oldman, and the Belly Rivers. Glacial meltwater drained through these valleys and through a network of now-dry flat-bottomed channels, such as Chin and Seven Persons Coulees, which occur south of, and that roughly parallel, the course of the Saskatchewan River between Lethbridge and Medicine Hat.

The Arctic Lowlands   These lowlands are formed on horizontal or nearly horizontal Late Proterozoic and Palaeozoic sedimentary strata between the Innuitian Orogen and the Canadian Shield. The subregion includes an array of different topographic units, including basins (e.g., the Foxe Plain on Baffin Island, and the Boothia Plain and the Victoria Lowland on the mainland) and upland areas (e.g., the Lancaster Plateau on southern Ellesmere and Somerset Islands, and the Shaler Mountains on Victoria Island, which rise to 830 m). These areas are characterized by glacial and cryospheric processes. The lower areas of this subregion are now inundated by the ocean to form marine channels that separate the various islands and the islands from the mainland (e.g., M'Clintock Channel, Lancaster Sound, and the Gulf of Boothia).

The Hudson Bay Lowlands   This subregion has been developed on a thin veneer of Palaeozoic limestones and dolostones deposited over the irregular surface of the Canadian Shield. These rocks are a continuation of the same kind of strata seen in the Prairies, the Great Lakes Lowland, and other parts of the Platform Borderlands. There is evidence of the carbonate rocks continuing under the beds of Hudson Bay and James Bay. In places the Shield rocks break through the limestones and dolostones to form low ridges and hills, a good example being the quartzite ridges on both sides of the Churchill River estuary. In many places the Shield rocks form inliers, such as the Sutton Ridge area in Northern Ontario south of Winisk, which is associated with an approximately 230-km-long Precambrian inlier. An **inlier** is an area of underlying rock exposed by the erosion of the rock beds on top of it. Like many of these features, this inlier has a northwest to southeast trend. The whole area has been covered by glacial, lacustrine, and marine deposits of various kinds that are responsible for the poor drainage conditions of the generally flat lowland area. The Precambrian basement rocks also contribute to the poor drainage.

The Hudson Bay area was the source area for a series of Laurentide ice sheets that formed in the Late Cenozoic. The weight of the mass of ice (about 2–3 km deep) caused the crust to sag down, and on deglaciation, with the removal of this immense load, the crust has undergone isostatic readjustment. This has created a staircase of raised beaches around parts of the Hudson Bay Lowlands. The bay is extremely shallow at its margin, and in some places low tides expose over 5 km of mudflats.

Around Hudson and James Bays, the area is treeless and the landscape quite flat and covered by peat marshes and gravel-beach ridges associated with raised shorelines. The southern parts of the area are warmer and somewhat drier than the more northerly parts. Boreal forest occurs here, with areas of muskeg and bog. Nearly all the rest of the Hudson Bay Lowlands can be described as a huge bowl of muskeg and string bogs that are underlain by permafrost and ground ice; these conditions lead to the creation of *palsas* and *earth hummocks* (about 1–3 m high).

3. The Marginal Linear Fold Mountain Belts

The composite area made up of the low-lying topographic realms of the North American interior just discussed is flanked on all sides by highlands and mountains, together forming the Marginal Linear Fold Mountain Belts. These include the Western Cordillera, the Appalachian-Caledonide Mountains, and the Innuitian Orogen.

The Western Cordillera

Along its entire length the Platform Borderlands of North America are flanked on the west by the high mountains of the **Western Cordilleran realm**; these mountains are much more rugged than those of the Appalachian-Caledonide realm. In fact, when people travel west from Calgary into the Rockies, they are actually leaving the structural continent of North America and going on to rocks that have been accreted onto the western edge of the continent over eons of collision and subduction. The Western Cordillera undoubtedly consti-

tutes North America's most varied physiographic realm, its topography ranging from high alpine mountains to high plateaus and areas of basin-and-range terrain. The Western Cordilleran realm can be divided into three major belts of rock types, structures, and landscapes:

1. The Rocky Mountains
2. The Intermontane Basin and Plateaux region
3. The Coast and Insular Mountains and Valleys

The Rocky Mountains Region   The Rocky Mountains extend down the western side of North America from northernmost Alaska, through the Yukon Territory and the provinces of British Columbia and Alberta (forming the boundary between them), through the United States to New Mexico, and then to Mexico, where they are known as the Sierra Madre Oriental (Eastern Sierra Madre Mountains). The Rockies, formed much later than the Appalachian-Caledonide Mountains, rise as much as 2700 m above their surroundings to elevations that in places exceed 4200 m above sea level (Fig. 52.8). None of the Appalachians' regularity exists in the Rockies, which consist of mountain ranges extending in different directions for varying distances, valleys of very different sizes, and even large sediment-filled basins between the mountains, such as the Rocky Mountain Trench in British Columbia and the Tintina and Shakwak Trenches in the Yukon. The Rocky Mountain Trench is about 1600 km long, and its width varies from 4 to over 15 km. The altitude of the floor varies from 60 to 1000 m above sea level. The

FIGURE 52.8 Rocky Mountain vista in Banff, Alberta.

trench is drained by six major river sytems, including the Kootenay, Columbia, Fraser, and the Findley-Parsnip Rivers (the last two form part of the Peace River network). The lower parts of the Findley and Parsnip Rivers have been drowned because of the construction of the W. A. C. Bennett Dam on the Peace River at Hudson's Hope, B.C. The dam has created an enormous reservoir called Williston Lake, approximately 200 km long and with a surface area of 1733 km². It is the largest reservoir in British Columbia and the ninth largest lake in the world.

The underlying rocks include igneous batholiths (especially in the northern section), volcanics, metamorphosed rocks, and sedimentary strata. There is intense thrusting and folding as well as large-scale block faulting, all reflected in the high-relief topography (see Fig. 45.1B). The Rockies exhibit all the evidence of Late Cenozoic mountain glaciation, with glacial troughs, cirques, arêtes, horns, and a wide range of classic alpine glacial and fluvioglacial aggradational landforms. As a result, this is one of the great tourist and ski-resort areas of the world. There is still some permanent ice and snow on the mountains in parts of the U.S. Rockies, in Alaska, and in Canada. The largest icefield in North America outside of the Arctic is located in the Canadian Rockies—the Columbia Icefields in Jasper National Park. Glaciers still inhabit many of the valleys in the northern parts of the mountain chain and in other places occur at higher elevations (see Fig. 47.2). As Fig. 52.1 shows, the Rocky Mountains physiographic region is rather narrow but extremely long.

Several major valleys and plateaux and plains dissect the Western Cordillera into a number of different sections:

PERSPECTIVES ON THE HUMAN ENVIRONMENT

Passes in the Rocky Mountains

The promise of a transcontinental railway to link central and eastern Canada with the Pacific was one of the main reasons that British Columbia entered Confederation on July 20, 1871. Such a railway could link the Atlantic with the Pacific; it could cut out the long voyage around Cape Horn to Seattle, Victoria, or New Westminster; goods could be shipped to and fro across the country; and the West would be opened up to settlement and to agricultural and other developments. However, unless a suitable pass or passes could be found for a railway line, the western mountains seemed to be a barrier to all these advances.

The exploration for a route through the Rocky Mountains was very protracted and arduous. Between 1857 and 1859 a British expedition led by Captain John Palliser (1817–1877) traversed the Prairies and scouted out some of the major passes through the Rocky, Columbia, and Selkirk Mountains. The expedition's final report was given to the British government in 1863 but was not acted upon. Nevertheless, it did cause great interest in Canada, especially later when a transcontinental

railway was proposed. The Canadian Pacific Railway had surveying teams looking at all the possible routes through the mountains. They concentrated on three passes to begin with (Kicking

FIGURE 52.9   Rogers Pass

Horse, Yellowhead, and Crowsnest), but exploration revealed another possibility (Rogers Pass).

The Kicking Horse or Kootenay Pass (1627 m above sea level) is located between Lake Louise, Alberta, and Field, B.C. This is the route now taken by the Trans-Canada Highway and the main line of the Canadian Pacific Railway. The pass was named after a horse ridden by Dr. James Hector, the geologist and surgeon with the Palliser Expedition (1858). Before the pass was discovered, the party had broken into two groups, one led by Hector and the other by Lt. Thomas Blakiston, Royal Artillery, the magnetic observer and ornithologist of the expedition (Palliser had temporarily returned to Britain). The Hector party was struggling up the pass from the west side, and near Wapta Falls one of the packhorses fell into the river. Hector helped to rescue the animal, but in the commotion his own horse galloped away. When Hector eventually found his horse, it shied and kicked him in the chest.

The Yellowhead Pass (1146 m) and the long-abandoned settlement of Tete Jaune Cache were both named after a Hudson's Bay Company trader and trapper of the early 1800s. Pierre Hastination (also known as Bostonais), a fair-haired Iroquois Métis. He was given the nickname "Tete Jaune" (Yellowhead) by the French voyageurs who met him. In 1825 he was sent to survey the Yellowhead area by the HBC and discovered the pass that now bears his nickname. He was murdered in 1828.

By 1830 the pass was being used by hunters and trappers. It became known as the Leather Pass because of the large quantities of moose hide transported through it. Red River carts started to use the pass in 1841. Some people went through the pass in an attempt to get to the Cariboo goldfields during the rush of 1856, and in the 1860s settlers used it on their way to Kamloops and Prince George.

The Crowsnest Pass (1395 m) was one of the better routes for the CPR rail line. Coal was discovered in the pass in the 1840s, and lumbering began in the 1880s. A mill was established by the McLaren Timber Company at Blairmore, and by 1887 it was supplying railway ties to the CPR. Railway surveyors surveyed the pass in 1892, and the construction of the line was completed six years later. Coal mining began at Frank in 1901, and the town became an important coal depot for CPR locomotives. Frank became widely known because of the massive rock avalanche that decimated the town in 1903. Despite the catastrophe, the rail link to the Pacific was reopened after only a few weeks.

The Crowsnest Pass got its name from the Asini Wachi Wininiwak (Hill or Mountain Cree) and Siksika (Blackfoot) names for the mountain that dominates the valley. The peak was known as Kah-ko-ioo-wut-tshis-tun and Ma-sto-eeas, names that both mean "the nest of crows" (or ravens). This name was recorded in a preliminary report by Lt. Thomas Blakiston, R.A.

Rogers Pass (1330 m) (Fig. 52.9) was named after an American who worked as an explorer and surveyor for the CPR—Major Albert Bowman Rogers, U.S. Cavalry, retired (1829–1889). In 1881 the Canadian Pacific Railway asked Rogers to find a suitable pass through the Selkirk Mountains for the rail line. The company promised to pay him $5000, to give him a gold watch, and also promised to name the pass after him. After he encountered many difficulties, including almost losing his nephew (an expedition member) and nearly starving to death, his party discovered the pass in July 1882. In fact, Rogers concluded that both the Crowsnest and Rogers Passes were the best routes for the railway line. Soon after finding the pass, Major Rogers returned to the United States, where he worked for the Great Northern Railway.

1. The **Canadian** (or **Northern**) **Rocky Mountains** extend from Alaska and the Yukon down to the Snake and Columbia Plains.
2. The **Middle Rocky Mountains** are found south of the Snake and Columbia Plains down to the Wyoming or Great Divide Basin. Yellowstone in the northwest corner of Wyoming is found in the northern part of this subregion. Yellowstone is a caldera (a supervolcano) that sits over a hot spot in the mantle. It was once an enormous volcanic centre that erupted in two phases, between 2.1 million and 1.3 million years ago and 1.3 million and 640,000 years ago. There are many rhyolite lava flows and considerable geothermal activity (hot springs, bubbling mud pools, and geysers). The United States Geological Survey closely monitors this area and considers it to be well overdue for another eruption. Farther south and west are the Grand Teton Mountains, which are formed on an uplifted fault block.

3. The **Southern Rockies** are found in Colorado. The mountains that make up the eastern boundary rise sharply out of the adjacent Great Plains along a range called the Front Range in Colorado. This range and other similar ranges in this subregion consist mainly of crystalline rocks with upturned sedimentary layers along their sides. The crystalline rocks near the Cripple Creek area of the Front Range yielded half a billion U.S. dollars worth of gold ore between 1890 and 1962. Some large rivers rise in this area, such as the Rio Grande and the Colorado.

The Intermontane Basins and Plateaux Region   This region lies west of the Rocky Mountain region and parallels the Rockies from Alaska to Mexico. It is a complex region that can be subdivided, as described on pages 683–685. The western boundary of the Rocky Mountain region is not as sharp as the eastern boundary (Fig. 52.3A) , because the Intermontane Basins and Plateaux lie at considerable elevations and do not usually provide the dramatic wall-like effect that offsets the Rockies from the Prairies and Great Plains.

The overall physiography of the Intermontane region is quite different, however. Here, there are expanses of low relief underlain by slightly disturbed sedimentary strata or by volcanic beds; isolated fault-block mountains; areas of internal drainage; spectacular canyons and escarpments; and, in much of the region, arid environments. Because it includes such diverse areas as the Interior Plateaux of the Yukon and British Columbia, the Columbia and Colorado Plateaux, as well as the Mexican Highlands and the Basin-and-Range subregion, the Intermontane region could be considered to be a number of different regions. Certainly, the strongest bond among these areas is their *intermontane* location—that is, their position between the two major north–south mountain corridors, with the Rockies on one side and the high ranges near the Pacific coast on the other. But internally there is a strong basis for dividing this region into a number of discrete areas (see Fig. 52.5).

The **Nechako-Fraser Plateau subregion** forms an undulating upland covered with glacial sediments in the central interior of British Columbia (Fig. 52.10). The plateau is formed by a mixed assemblage of rocks dominated by Cenozoic intrusive and basaltic rocks erupted from fissures as flood basalts (e.g., the Chasm; see Fig. 52.11). Roughly triangular in shape, the plateau is wider (approximately 300 km) in the Prince George area in the north and narrows to the south. Its elevation increases to the south between the Cascades and the Monashees (part of the Rocky Mountains). The surface is cut into

FIGURE 52.10   The Nechako-Fraser Plateau.

FIGURE 52.11   The Chasm, carved out of the Fraser Plateau, is located in Chasm Provincial Park, British Columbia.

by deep river valleys, especially in the south (e.g., those of the Thompson, Fraser, and Okanagan Rivers). There are large lakes in the Thompson and Okanagan Valleys. This area lies in the rain shadow of the Coast and Insular Mountain Belt, and in the south it has a semi-arid climate. The uplands are covered in mountain woodland, grassland, and arid sagebrush. The Okanagan Valley and other interior valleys are famous for their vineyards and soft fruit orchards (peaches, cherries, and so forth). Cities like Kelowna and Penticton are rapidly developing as resort and cottage areas, offering skiing during the winter and sun in the summer. These communities have also attracted many retirees from Greater Vancouver and the Prairies. Farther north around Kamloops, Clinton, and Williams Lake on the plateau and in the Thompson and Fraser Valleys, cattle ranching dominates.

In the Prince George area the landscape is more subdued, with low hills separated by small plainlands. Here the streams flow in shallower valleys and the countryside is covered with coniferous forest. Saline and epsomite lakes, indicative of semi-arid conditions, dot the plateau surface, even toward its northern end.

The **Columbia Plateau subregion** lies wedged between the Northern Rockies to the east and the Cascades to the west. It forms one of the largest lava surfaces in the world (see Fig. 34.3). It has a maximum elevation of approximately 1800 m above sea level, and the relief is rather low and undulating in the main. Volcanic and other mountains rise dramatically above the flood basalt surface in some areas. The southern boundary of the area is determined by the extent of the lava flows, but in many places this is not clear in terms of the topography. Part of this region is significant because of the unusual scenery of the Channelled Scablands of the Palouse country southeast of Spokane, Washington (huge dry valleys, massive dry waterfalls or coulees, giant ripple-marked areas, and enormous bars of extremely large sediments, with boulders as large as Volkswagen Beetles). This scenery was created by a series of incredibly large floods (up to 40 or 60 events) that occurred because of the catastrophic draining of Glacial Lake Missoula, which was caused by a series of collapses of an ice dam (see Unit 45).

The **Colorado Plateau subregion**, by contrast, this area is underlain by mainly horizontal or nearly horizontal sedimentary rocks that, in the semi-arid environment, have been weathered into vivid colours (*colorado* is a Spanish word for red) and carved by erosion into uniquely spectacular landscapes. The eastern boundary of the plateau meets the Rocky Mountains. On the western side a long fault-scarp separates the plateau from the Basin-and-Range subregion (which also borders on the plateau on the south side). The southern boundary is not marked by a change of altitude or by topographic contrasts, but by the drainage divide between the plateaux' two major stream systems, the Colorado and the Rio Grande.

The Colorado Plateau is traversed by several sets of steep-sided canyons with multicoloured layers of sedimentary rocks. The Grand Canyon of northern Arizona, shown in Fig. 31.8, is of course world famous. The dry-

ness of this region keeps weathering processes to a minimum, preserving the valley walls (which rise about 1600 to 2000 m above the Colorado river and its tributaries) and enhancing the coloration of the exposed strata. Such streams as the Colorado, San Juan, and Little Colorado have cut vigorously into the plateau as it was uplifted by tectonism. The plateau surface lies approximately 3500 m above sea level. The relatively flat upper surface is broken by fault scarps, and erosion has created numerous mesas, buttes, columns, badlands, and even natural arches. No brief description could adequately summarize the distinct character of the Colorado Plateau. It is unlike any other region of North America.

The **Basin-and-Range subregion** lies south of the Columbia Plateau and south and west of the Colorado Plateau (Fig. 52.5). This is actually an entire region of basins separated by highland areas. Many of the basins are internally drained and are not connected to other surface depressions by permanent streams. A large number of linear mountain ranges rise above these basins, and are generally 80 to 130 km long and from 8 to 24 km wide. They rise 600 to 1525 m above the basin floors (reaching 2100 to 3000 m above sea level). Mainly oriented north–south, these mountains have a steep side and a more gently sloping side, which suggests some kind of structural control).

Aridity is also a hallmark of the Basin-and-Range subregion. The basins are mostly dry, the streams are ephemeral, vegetation is sparse, and wind action plays a major role in sculpting the landscape. Many old shoreline features can be found along the margins of some of the basins. These are relics of the **pluvial** lakes that filled the basins during wetter periods of the Pleistocene and Holocene epochs. The subregion's most famous existing body of water is the Great Salt Lake in northern Utah. The lake's volume varied enormously in the Pleistocene, the Holocene, and the historical period. Its high salt content suggests that it is a remnant of a much larger lake that evaporated and shrank to the present size (see Fig. 46.10)—a story of contraction and withering shared by all of the regions bodies of water. Late in the nineteenth century the Great Salt Lake's area was approximately 5000 km², but early last century, during an extended period of drought, the lake almost disappeared. In recent years it has once again expanded (to about 6000 km²), flooding a lakeside resort and portions of a shoreline interstate highway, but another lengthy drought could swiftly reverse the trend.

The Coast and Insular Mountains and Valleys Region Geologically known as the Coast Plutonic Complex, the **Coast and Insular Mountains and Valleys region** forms the westernmost physiographic area of

North America. It too extends north–south, parallel to the other regions in this realm, from Alaska to Central America. This region incorporates three zones that lie approximately parallel to the Pacific coastline. In the interior, farthest from the coast, lie a series of high continuous mountain ranges that include the Cascade Mountains of British Columbia, Washington, and Oregon and the Sierra Nevada of California. Bordering these ranges on the west are several large valleys, including Hecate Strait, between Haida Gwaii and the northern B.C. mainland (now inundated by the sea), the Strait of Georgia–Puget Sound–Willamette Lowland in the Pacific northwest, and the Central Valley of California. Figure 52.12 shows an intensely cultivated and drained section of the Lower Fraser Valley (part of the Georgia–Puget Sound–Willamette Lowland). Separating these valleys from the Pacific Ocean are the Coast Ranges, which include the Coast and Insular Mountains of British Columbia, the Olympic Mountains of Washington, and the Klamath Mountains of northern California.

Except for the intermittent plains and low hills in the major valleys, the topography in this subregion is rugged, the relief high, and the rocks and geological structures extremely varied. Subduction and orogeny (mountain building) are in progress, earthquakes are frequent, and movement can be observed along active transform faults (e.g., along the Queen Charlotte–Denali Fault off British Columbia or the famous San Andreas Fault system). The shoreline is marked by steep slopes and deep water, pounding waves, cliffs, and the associated landforms of high-relief coasts. Elevations in the interior mountains rival those of the Rockies in places, with some mountains exceeding 5400 m. This is the leading edge of the North American lithospheric plate (see Unit 32), and the landscapes of this coastal area decidedly reflect the tectonic forces at work here. Stratovolcanoes of the Cascade volcanic arc rise above the general level of the mountains (e.g., Mount St. Helens, Mount Rainier, Mount Adams, Lassen Peak, Mount Shasta, and Meager Mountain).

The **Mexico–Central American Cordilleran subregion** forms the southernmost subregion of the Western Cordillera. This area is characterized by many high volcanic mountains. It is the physiographic expression of the margin between the Cocos plate on the Pacific side and the Caribbean plate on the eastern side of Central America (see Fig. 32.3). The mountains continue into South America (where they become the Andes). This is a landscape marked by much evidence of crustal instability and dominated by volcanic landforms, such as the composite cones and wide craters of Popocatépetl, La Malinche, and Poco de Orizaba in central Mexico; El

Chicon in southern Mexico; Santa Maria, Fuego, and Pacaya in Guatemala; San Cristobal, Conception, and La Madena in Nicaragua; and Arenal and Poas in Costa Rica (Fig. 52.13). There have also been recent lava flows, and evidence of major slope failures and lahars prevail. Destructive earthquakes also occur frequently in this geologically hazardous region. The Michoacan earthquake (magnitude 8) of September 1985, for example, caused extensive damage in Mexico City and killed 15,000 people. In the prevailing warm and humid climate, however, the volcanic rocks weather to yield fertile soils, and people often live clustered around the lower slopes of active volcanoes. Deforestation is widespread, but where natural vegetation survives, it is dense and extremely varied. The variation is related to the zonation of plant communities at different elevations on the slopes of the volcanic and fold mountains. The environments range from hot coastal lowlands to cool mountainous uplands (see Unit 19).

The Appalachian-Caledonide Mountains

The **Appalachian-Caledonide Mountain realm** is found to the east of the Platform Borderlands and extends northeastwards from Alabama and Georgia, through New England and Atlantic Canada. It can be further traced to the eastern side of Greenland, through Scotland, and into Scandinavia. Some of the contrasts within this realm are the result of the northern section of this mountain chain being glaciated during Late Cenozoic times, while the southern part was not. Appalachian rocks vary considerably, from very tightly folded sedimentary layers to eroded horizontal strata and exposed igneous intrusions. Parallel tree-clad ridges separated by populated valleys prevail in the central zone of the realm (e.g., Pennsylvania; see Fig. 36.15). Toward the west a plateau area dominates, but in many areas to the east a more rugged terrain has developed on crystalline rocks. The Appalachian-Caledonide Mountain realm actually consists of a complex mix of physiographic regions, the most famous, perhaps, being the ridge-and-valley topography of the "Newer" Appalachians, a discrete region shown in Fig. 52.5. But this type of topography, as the map shows, only exists in the central corridor of the Appalachian-Caledonide realm. In the east-central and more northeastern sections there are other distinct areas. All are grouped together because they share a common geological history related to the opening and closing of a series of proto-Atlantic (Iapetus) oceans in what is now called a Supercontinent or Wilson Cycle. This cycle led to subduction, thrusting, folding, and the accretion of exotic terranes and subsequent spreading during four phases from the Late Cambrian and to the initiation in the Late Cretaceous of a new spreading margin in what

FIGURE 52.12 A cultivated section of the Lower Fraser Valley.

FIGURE 52.13 Popocatépetl is an active volcano located less than 65 km southeast of Mexico City, towering over the Valley of Mexico to a height of 5465 m. Ominously, the huge volcano—with more than 25 million people living within 100 km of its crater—ended a long quiescent period in 1994 and has erupted several times since, including the eruption shown here in December 2000, when thousands of people were evacuated. Popocatépetl is only one of dozens of active volcanoes that mark the mountain backbone of Mexico and Central America.

is now the Mid Atlantic Ridge, which caused the fragmentation of the Appalachian-Caledonide Mountains and the development of the North Atlantic Ocean.

The Appalachian-Caledonide Mountains in Atlantic Canada
The Appalachian-Caledonide Mountains in Atlantic Canada can be divided into three regions:

1. The Appalachian-Caledonide region of the island of Newfoundland
2. The Appalachian-Acadian region of the Maritime provinces
3. The Appalachian-Acadian region of the Gaspé Peninsula and Northern Plateau of New Brunswick

The Appalachian-Caledonide Region of the Island of Newfoundland The island of Newfoundland is the northernmost region of this realm in Canada. Plate tectonics and orogeny have imparted a predominantly southwest to northeast trend on many of the major topographic features (e.g., the hill ridges of the Central Upland and the peninsulas and bays around the Avalon Peninsula). The oldest rocks in Newfoundland are found along the Northern Peninsula and west coast of the island and include some very rare rock types, including ophiolites and other seafloor crustal rocks that have been obducted over continental crust during thrusting. The youngest rocks are found in the Avalon Peninsula and date from the Late Proterozoic era.

The island can be divided into four subregions on the basis of topography, rock types, and structures.

1. The *Western Upland Plateaux and Plains* area (e.g., the Long Range and the Humber Hills) includes the magnificent alpine glacial scenery in and around Gros Morne National Park. The northern part of the Northern Peninsula near Hare Bay is a plain underlain by limestone that exhibits many smaller karst features, such as swallow holes. The eastern boundary of this subregion is a fault scarp in the south (Southern Long Ranges), but this is not as apparent farther north.
2. The *Western Lowlands and Hills* area is located to the east of the Western Upland. This area includes the Deer Lake–White Bay Basin as well as two lowland areas that are separated by a plateau.
3. The *Central Uplands* subregion is tilted to the north. The highest parts are on its southern and western edges. This area is dominated by the drainage basins of the Gander and Exploits Rivers.
4. The *Avalon Peninsula* in the east has a topography determined to a great extent by geological structures; massive headland areas generally correspond with anticlines, while large bays are asso-

ciated with synclines. At some point the surface of this area was levelled and it remains quite a flat rocky upland with many lakes and is bounded by steep sea cliffs.

The rock types and the structures seen in Newfoundland can be traced across the Atlantic Ocean to Scotland, where the same kind of structural and physiographic division exists: the rugged Northern Highlands, the Grampian Hills, the Central fault–guided Lowlands (the Midland Valley), and the Southern Uplands.

The Appalachian-Acadian Region of the Maritime Provinces This region exhibits the same kind of structural grain as many other parts of the Appalachian-Caledonide Mountains. In eastern New Brunswick, Prince Edward Island, northern Nova Scotia, and under the seabed of the Gulf of St. Lawrence, the rocks are Late Palaeozoic sandstones and shales associated with coal seams. These rock types are not very resistant to erosion, and they were deeply eroded during the Cenozoic to form extensive lowland plains in the areas just cited. Near the Northumberland Strait the topography is quite hilly. The Northumberland Strait and the large branching estuaries that invade the plains in many places are river- and glacier-cut valleys that were subsequently drowned as the sea level rose at the end of the Wisconsinan glaciation. To the south and east of the lowland area are a series of Hercynian mountain blocks or horsts (e.g., the Caledonian Hills on the western shore of Chignecto Bay; the Cobequid Hills that cross the isthmus of Nova Scotia, north of the Minas Basin in Cumberland and Colchester counties; the Pictou-Antigonish Hills near St. George's Bay; and the Cape Breton Highlands). The surface of the Cape Breton Highlands is undulating and is characterized by barrens, muskeg, and many small lakes. High, fault-scarp cliffs occur along the highland coastline on the northern and western sides. This area has one of the most visually stunning landscapes/seacapes of North America. South and east of the Hercynian mountain blocks are a series of lowlands formed in easily erodable Triassic clastic rocks; these include the Bay of Fundy and the Minas Basin, both now inundated by the sea, and the agriculturally important Annapolis Valley. The Truro Plateau and the Cape Breton Plateau are formed from the same rocks, overlain by lavas or intruded by granites. The Atlantic or "Southern" Uplands, which occur along the Atlantic Coast of Nova Scotia and Cape Breton, are composed of granites and metamorphic rocks and are dissected by river valleys. Many of these have been modified by glaciation, and their lower parts have been drowned by the sea to form large bays and inlets, such as Halifax Harbour.

The Appalachian-Acadian Region of the Gaspé Peninsula and the Northern Plateau of New Brunswick This region forms a continuation of the hills and valleys of the New England region. Its western boundary is the Appalachian Fault. The fault thrusts Early Palaeozoic rocks over continental-shelf sediments. The fault is buried by tills in most places but can be seen occasionally as a low rock bluff. The land east of the fault rises gently up to the hills of the Cantons de l'Est/Eastern Townships (Estrie Region). The rocks in this area once formed high mountains, but long periods of erosion led to the rocks' removal to form a lowland area with residual hills.

This area was uplifted at the same time streams cut down into it, resulting in a series of levels in the landscape. These are best seen in the middle reaches of the Chaudière Valley. Here a river and its tributaries flow through narrow gorges that have been excavated some 130 m into the upland (Beauce Plateau). East of the Sutton Mountains a series of isolated hills have developed on igneous rocks (e.g., Mount Orford, Owls Head, and Mount Megantic). In the middle of the area lie hills developed on lavas and quartzites. These have a southwest to northeast orientation. The Border Range is a third line of hills along Canada's border with New Hampshire and Maine; these hills are merely a continuation of the White Mountains of New England. Flat upland surfaces that have been deeply dissected by stream erosion occur between the ranges. Parts of some of the valleys are occupied by lakes, such as Lake Memphremagog, Lake Magog, and Lake Megantic. Glacial sediments have partially filled some valleys.

The eastern part of this area includes the Gaspé Peninsula and the Northern Plateau of New Brunswick. This area forms a broad plateau. Parallel curved folds in the strata cause curved ridges on the plateau surface in some areas. In the Gaspé Peninsula, Palaeozoic sedimentary and igneous rocks have been downfolded to form a syncline with less-resistant Devonian strata along the centre axis and arced parallel ridges and valleys running parallel to the Gaspé coast.

In the interior of the Gaspé a relatively flat upland rises to between 400 and 500 m. Southeast flowing streams have cut across the structures and down the strike of the rock beds. In places fault scarps rise to 600 m. This upland forms the southern edge of the Shickshock Mountains. These mountains are the highest in Appalachian Canada and include Mount Jacques Cartier, which is 1270 m high.

Appalachian Mountains Region in the United States
New England Appalachians Figure 52.5 shows the northernmost region of the Appalachian Mountains

realm in the United States—the **New England Appalachians**. This region is quite different from other areas of the Appalachians in the U.S. because of the effect of glaciation. It is dotted with lakes, penetrated by arms of the Atlantic Ocean, and bounded by a higher-relief coastline. It is in reality an extension of the type of rocks, structures, and landscape seen in Atlantic Canada. Major topographic features include the Green Mountains of Vermont and the White Mountains of New Hampshire, both underlain by ancient crystalline rocks. Elevations exceed 1800 m in the mountains, but overall the topography has none of the regularity and parallelism that mark the ridge-and-valley terrain of the "Newer" Appalachians to the south. In fact, the New England Appalachians are extremely varied and quite rugged in places. Glacial till covered by an extensive forests helps to give this region its special identity.

The Appalachian Plateau   The **Appalachian Plateau region** is noteworthy for its deposits of bituminous, or soft, coal. It has an irregular topography eroded out of horizontal and slightly dipping strata. Parts of this area could be described as low mountains because the major streams have cut valleys over 450 m deep and because the summit elevations reach 1200 m in such areas as central West Virginia. In fact, during colonial times these mountains were an obstacle to early settlement west of the Appalachians.

The "Newer" Appalachians   The ridge-and-valley topography of the **"Newer" Appalachians** is enough to make this region distinct (Fig. 52.14), especially when compared to the irregular terrain of the Appalachian Plateau. Parallel vegetation-clad ridges have remarkably even summits between 900 and 1200 m above sea level. The eastern edge of this physiographic region is marked by a wider lowland corridor called the Great Valley of the Appalachians (Fig. 52.15). This valley contains fertile limestone- and shale-derived soils and has been tilled by the famous Pennsylvania "Dutch" (actually German—the term is derived from *Deutsch*) farmers since before the American Revolution. It has also served as an important route. At the height of the American Civil War, the Confederate Army of North Virginia, under the command of General R. E. Lee, attempted to encircle Washington, D.C., by advancing up the Great Valley, but it was repulsed in July 1863 by the Union Army of the Potomac (led by General George C. Meade) at the climactic Battle of Gettysburg as it fought to round the northern end of the Blue Ridge Mountains.

Blue Ridge Section   East of the Great Valley, extending from Georgia to Gettysburg, Pennsylvania, lie the Blue Ridge Mountains. This region is underlain by ancient, mostly highly metamorphosed crystalline rocks rather than by the sedimentary rocks that underlie the Appalachian Plateau and the "Newer" Appalachians. The **Blue Ridge section** forms the "Older' Appalachians by virtue of the age of the rocks and the successive periods of orogeny.

The Piedmont   Toward the east, the mountainous topography of the Blue Ridge section yields to the much lower relief of the **Piedmont** (Fig. 52.15). *Piedmont* is the French term for foothills. This region is still considered part of the upland, compared to the neighbouring Gulf-Atlantic Plain beyond the Fall Line (discussed below), but it is not nearly so rugged as the interior Appalachian ranges. In the Blue Ridge section the Appalachians can rise to over 2000 m, but in the Piedmont the maximum elevation is about 900 m along the region's inner boundary, declining from there toward the Fall Line contact with the Coastal Plain. The underlying strata of the Piedmont, however, are the same as those of the Blue Ridge—ancient metamorphosed crystalline rocks. Thus the difference is principally a matter of topography and relief.

The Ouachita Mountains   Another region of the Appalachian-Caledonide Mountains is formed by the Ouachita Mountains. These are a somewhat lower range, but they exhibit the same kind of ridge-and-valley topography and, much like other parts of the realm, are suited to forestry, cattle raising, and resort and vacation-home development. Elevations reach to about 780 m in the central section and less than 300 m along the region's periphery. These mountains are separated from the rest of the Appalachians by an intervening lowland that did not undergo the same crustal readjustments that occurred in the main Appalachians and the Ouchitas.

The Innuitian Orogen

The **Innuitian Orogen region** is located in the extreme northwest of the islands of the Canadian Arctic Archipelago. It is characterized by a very varied topography. The area can be divided into two belts. The northernmost belt is formed by the Grandtland and Axel Heiberg Mountains (of central and western Axel Heiberg Island) and the British Empire and United States Ranges of Ellesmere Island. These are mountain ranges of folded Mesozoic and Palaeozoic sedimentary rocks with minor intrusions – *the Fold Mountain Region*. The highest summits reach approximately 2730 m. On Axel Heiberg Island the mountains are almost buried by an icefield, with only the tallest peaks sticking out above the ice surface (nunataks). At the south end of Axel Heiberg Island is the Eureka Upland, an area of ridged terrain crossed by numerous steep-walled glacial troughs. The same kind of terrain occurs on Ellesmere Island, but many glaciers inhabit the troughs and the lower ends of many of these valleys have been inundated by the sea to form fjords in the latter area.

The inner belt of somewhat less-rugged ridge-and-valley terrain—the *Ridge-and-Valley region*—extends the length of the Innuitian region from the northeastern part of Ellesmere Island to the west of the Parry Islands. It is developed on subparallel folds of Palaeozoic carbonate rocks, shales, and sandstones.

4. The Gulf-Atlantic Coastal Plain and Other Smaller Coastal Plain Areas

Another major physiographic realm extends along much of the eastern seaboard of North America from the vicinity of New York City (including Long Island) southwestwards to the Caribbean coast of Costa Rica in Central America. This is the **Gulf-Atlantic Coastal Plain**. It is bounded on the inland side by the Piedmont (the eastern foothills of the Appalachians), the various components of the Platform Borderlands, the Mexican Plateau, and the Central American Cordillera. It incorporates all of Florida and attains its greatest width in the lower basin of the Mississippi Valley; the Mississippi Delta is included in the realm (Fig. 52.16). In Texas the boundary between the Coastal Plain and the Great Plains is in places rather indistinct, although a fault scarp does separate the two realms in southern Texas.

In the eastern United States the boundary between the Gulf-Atlantic Coastal Plain and the Appalachian-Caledonide Mountains is marked by the *Fall Line,* which can be seen as a series of falls and rapids in rivers leaving the highlands and entering the plain. This physical boundary has developed along a line of contact between the less-resistant sedimentary rocks of the Coastal Plain and the older, more-resistant rocks of the Piedmont. In early American history the places where streams crossed the Fall Line marked not only the head of ocean navigation but also the source of local water power. Not surprisingly these functions attracted people and economic activities, and major cities such as Philadelphia, Baltimore, and Richmond developed.

The seaward boundary of the Coastal Plain is, of course, the continental coastline. This shoreline, however, has changed position in recent geological times as sea level has fluctuated; for example, during the Wisconsinan glaciation of the Late Cenozoic Ice Age, sea level was approximately 100 m lower than it is today. This lower sea level exposed the continental shelf and increased the width of this realm. With deglaciation and the attendant rise in sea level about 10,000 years before the present, part of the Coastal Plain was again covered by the ocean. A case can be made, therefore, that the Gulf-Atlantic Coastal Plain actually continues to the

FIGURE 52.14 A striking evenness of the summit levels marks this section of the ridge-and-valley terrain in central Pennsylvania. (See Fig. 36.15 for a satellite view.)

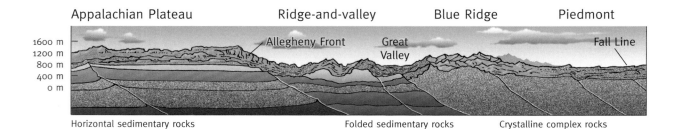

FIGURE 52.15   Caption to come

edge of the continental shelf. The realm's coastline, as pointed out in Unit 51, has characteristics of a low-relief coast, exhibiting offshore barrier islands, lagoons, and beaches. The deepest indentations and irregularities occur north of the Carolinas, where Chesapeake Bay is the largest embayment; otherwise the shoreline is quite straight. Coral reefs appear off the coast in the warmer waters and are especially well developed off southernmost Florida and Mexico's Yucatan Peninsula. The coastline is constantly changing, especially in the area where the Mississippi Delta is building outward into the Caribbean.

The whole of the Gulf-Atlantic Coastal Plain lies below about 300 m in elevation and comprises a realm of low relief and little topographic variety. Sedimentary rocks sloping gently seaward underlie the entire Coastal Plain. In the northernmost region there is a cover of glacial materials. Areas of low hills occur in the Carolinas and northern Florida, and to the west of the Mississippi River a series of low ridges lie more or less parallel to the Gulf coastline. The lower Mississippi Valley and

Delta form another distinct region, as does the karst terrain in central Florida (see Fig. 44.7), where numerous sinkholes and small lakes pockmark the landscape. The Coastal Plain also lies substantially in near-tropical latitudes, and the soil map (see Fig. 25.15) indicates the presence of characteristically tropical soil types (red-yellow podzolics and lateritic soils). There are deciduous forests in the eastern and southeastern United States, grasslands in Texas and northern Mexico, and some savanna country in Yucatan and nearby Central America.

The other significant coastal plain is the **Arctic Coastal Plain**, which includes all of the coastal landscapes along the coast of the Arctic Ocean. It extends from Meighen Island to Alaska. The plain occurs seaward of the Innuitian Orogen, the Platform Borderlands, and the Western Cordillera. It can be divided on the basis of differences in topography into a number of subregions, such as the Mackenzie Delta and the Yukon Coastal Plain on the mainland and the Island Coastal Plain on the islands from Meighen Island to Banks Island.

FIGURE 52.16 New Orleans, Louisiana, is only one of many major port cities that developed on the Gulf-Atlantic Coastal Plain. The Mississippi River is in the foreground. Much of the urban area lies below sea level and faces devastating flooding in the event of a major hurricane striking here. Parts of the Mississippi Delta and the Gulf of Mexico can be seen in the background.

CANADIAN GEOGRAPHERS IN THE FIELD

"This photo shows unusual patterns in the drying bed of Last Chance Lake, near Clinton, B.C. I have been working with an old undergraduate friend, Professor Robin Renault, a geochemist in the Geological Sciences Department at the University of Saskatchewan, on the patterned lakes and travertine mounds of Interior B.C. We want to find out why certain saline and epsomite lakes dry out to form these patterns while others do not (geochemistry? freezing?)."

Peter Long is a Pleistocene geomorphologist. He was trained at the University of London in the UK and has been at York University for 18 years.

The Physiographic Imprint

These, then, are the prominent physiographic realms and regions of North America in general and of Canada in particular. What is seen in the landscape today is the result of all the building forces and erosional systems discussed in this book. Geological forces produced the structures in the upper layer of the crust that exert so much control over the formation of landscape. Crustal deformation from plate movement continues to modify what exists—slowly in most places but quite rapidly in certain active zones. Solar radiation powers atmospheric circulation, and the hydrological cycle rides on the movement of air, delivering water to the interiors of the continents and feeding drainage networks of all sizes.

Water on the surface of the continents comes under the force of gravity and is subject to various laws of physics as it carries on its erosion and deposition of material. Glacial and other cryospheric processes leave their mark on high-altitude and high-latitude terrain. Weathering and slope processes contribute to the sculpting of the landscape, while deposition covers lower-lying areas. Soils develop over long periods of time, and vegetation anchors them.

The totality is summarized in one view of the landscape, which reflects and reveals the work of forces from below and above. The physiographic map records the total imprint made by all these environmental processes and helps in the understanding of the spacial variation of landforms and landscapes.

KEY TERMS

Alberta Plain region *page 682*

Appalachian-Caledonide Mountain Realm *page 688*

Appalachian Plateau region *page 691*

Arctic Coastal Plain region *page 693*

Arctic Lowlands region *page 682*

Basin-and-Range subregion *page 687*

Blue Ridge section *page 691*

Canadian or Northern Rocky Mountains subregion *page 685*

Canadian Shield realm *page 679*

Coast and Insular Mountains and Valleys *page 687*

Colorado Plateau subregion *page 687*

Columbia Plateau subregion *page 687*

Gaspé Peninsula–Northern Plateau of New Brunswick region *page 690*

Great Lakes Lowland region *page 681*

Gulf-Atlantic Coastal Plains region *page 692*

Hudson Bay Lowland subregion *page 682*

inlier *page 683*

Innuitian Orogen region *page 691*

Intermontane Basins and Plateaux region *page 686*

Island of Newfoundland region *page 689*

Manitoba and Saskatchewan Lowland (and Slave Lowland) region *page 682*

Mexico–Central American Cordilleran subregion *page 688*

Middle Rocky Mountains subregion *page 685*

Nechako-Fraser Plateau subregion *page 686*

New England Appalachians region *page 690*

"Newer" Appalachians region *page 691*

outlier *page 682*

physiographic realm *page 674*

physiographic region *page 674*

physiography *page 677*

Piedmont region *page 691*

Platform Borderlands *page 680*

pluvial *page 687*

regional concept *page 674*

regionalization *page 677*

Rocky Mountain region *page 683*

St. Lawrence Lowlands region *page 681*

Saskatchewan Plains region *page 682*

Southern Rocky Mountains subregion *page 686*

Western Cordilleran realm *page 683*

REVIEW QUESTIONS

1. List the physiographic realms of North America. Draw their approximate boundaries on a sketch map.

2. Describe the general topography of each of the physiographic realms of Canada?

3. What and where is the Fall Line?

4. How do the Northern Rocky Mountains differ from the Southern Rocky Mountains?

5. How does the Canadian Shield differ from the Interior Plains?

6. What processes are evident in the Coast and Insular Mountains and Valleys of British Columbia?

REFERENCES AND FURTHER READINGS

ADAMS, J., and CLAGUE, J. J. "Neotectonics and Large-Scale Geomorphology of Canada Progress," *Physical Geography* v. 17 (1992), 248–264.

ATWOOD, W. W. *The Physiographic Provinces of North America* (New York: Ginn/Blaisdell, 1940).

BALLY, A. W., and PALMER, A. R., Eds. *The Geology of North America: An Overview,* Vol.A . *Decade of North American Geology* (Boulder: Geological Society of America, 1989).

BIRD, J. B. *The National Landscapes of Canada: A Study in Regional Earth Science* (Toronto, John Wiley, 2nd ed, 1980).

BIRD, J. B. *The Physiography of Arctic Canada* (Baltimore: Johns Hopkins Press, 1967).

BOSTOCK, H. S. "Provisional Physiographic Map of Canada" (Geological Survey of Canada Paper 64-35, 1964; GSC Map 1245A, 1970).

BOSTOCK, H. S. "Physiographic Subdivisions of Canada," in Douglas, R. J. W., Ed., *Geology and Economic Minerals of Canada* (Ottawa: Queen's Printer, Economic Geology Report 1, 1971), 10–30.

BRIDGES, E. M. *World Geomorphology* (London/New York: Cambridge Univ. Press, 1990).

CHAPMAN, L. J. and PUTNAM, D. F. *The Physiography of Southern Ontario* (Toronto: Government of Ontario, Ontario Geological Survey Special Vol. 2, 3rd ed., 1984).

CONEY, P., and BECK, M. "The Growth of Western North America," *Scientific American* (November 1982), 70–84.

CURRAN, H. A., et al. *Atlas of Landforms* (New York: Wiley, 3rd ed., 1984).

FENNEMAN, N. M. *Physiography of the Western United States* (New York: McGraw-Hill, 1931).

FENNEMAN, N. M. *Physiography of the Eastern United States* (New York: McGraw-Hill, 1938).

GRAF, W. L., et al., Eds. *Geomorphic Systems of North America*, Vol. 2. *Decade of North American Geology* (Boulder: Geological Society of America, 1987).

HOFFMAN P. F. "United Plates of America, The Birth of a Craton, Early Proterozoic Assembly and Growth of Laurentia," *Annual Review of Earth and Planetary Sciences* 16 (1988), 543–603.

HOLLAND, S. S. *Landforms of British Columbia: A Physiographic Outline* (Victoria: B.C. Department of Mines and Petroleum Resources Bulletin 48 1964).

HUNT, C. B. *Natural Regions of the United States and Canada* (San Francisco: Freeman, 2nd ed., 1974).

LOOMIS, F. B. *Physiography of the United States* (New York: Doubleday, 1938).

MOLLARD, J. D., and Janes, J. R. *Airphoto Interpretation and the Canadian Landscape,* Surveys and Mapping Branch, Energy, Mines and Resources Canada (Ottawa: Supply and Services Canada, 1984).

ORME, A. R., Ed. *The Physical Geography of North America* (New York: Oxford Univ. Press, 2002).

PIRKLE, E. C., and YOHO, W. H. *Natural Landscape of the United States* (Dubuque, Iowa: Kendall-Hunt, 3rd ed., 1982).

SHORT, N. M., and BLAIR, J. R. W. *Geomorphology from Space: A Global Overview of Regional Landforms,* NASA Scientific and Technical Information Branch (Washington: NASA, 1986).

SLAYMAKER, H. O. "Physiography of Canada and Its Effects on Geomorphic Processes," in R. J. Fulton, Ed., *Quaternary Geology of Canada and Greenland* (Ottawa, Ont.: Geological Survey of Canada, Geology of Canada, No. 1, 1989), 581–583.

STEARN, C. W. "Canada," in Fairbridge, R. W., Ed., *Encyclopedia of World Regional Geology* (Stroudsburg, Pa: Dowden, Hutchinson and Ross, 1975), 139–144.

THORNBURY, W. D. *Regional Geomorphology of the United States* (New York: Wiley, 1965).

TRENHAILE, A. S. *Geomorphology: A Canadian Perspective* (Toronto: Oxford University Press, 2004).

WINTERS, H. A., et al. *Battling the Elements: Weather and Terrain in the Conduct of War* (Baltimore, Md.: Johns Hopkins Univ. Press, 1998).

WEB RESOURCES

http://tapestry.usgs.gov The USGS merges topographic and geologic information on colored interactive maps. State and physiographic maps of North America are available with description of all features. A puzzle quiz for self-testing purposes can be accessed. A QuickTime panoramic multimedia map presentation highlights this site.

http://wrgis.wr.usgs.gov/docs/usgsnps/province/appalach.html The USGS provides a brief geologic history of the Appalachian Highlands, using imagery from NASA satellites. Links to relief maps and an image gallery are available.

Appendix A   SI and Customary Units and Their Conversions

Appendix A provides a table of units and their conversion from older units to Standard International (SI) units.

Length

Metric Measure

1 kilometre (km)	= 1000 metres (m)
1 metre (m)	= 100 centimetres (cm)
1 centimetre (cm)	= 10 millimetres (mm)

Nonmetric Measure

1 mile (mi)	= 5280 feet (ft)
	= 1760 yards (yd)
1 yard (yd)	= 3 feet (ft)
1 foot (ft)	= 12 inches (in)
1 fathom (fath)	= 6 feet (ft)

Conversions

1 kilometre (km)	= 0.6214 mile (mi)
1 metre (m)	= 3.281 feet (ft)
	= 1.094 yards (yd)
1 centimetre (cm)	= 0.3937 inch (in)
1 millimetre (mm)	= 0.0394 inch (in)
1 mile (mi)	= 1.609 kilometres (km)
1 foot (ft)	= 0.3048 metre (m)
1 inch (in)	= 2.54 centimetres (cm)
	= 25.4 millimetres (mm)

Area

Metric Measure

1 square kilometre (km²)	= 1,000,000 square metres (m²)
	= 100 hectares (ha)
1 square metre (m²)	= 10,000 square centimetres (cm²)
1 hectare (ha)	= 10,000 square metres (m²)

Nonmetric Measure

1 square mile (mi²)	= 640 acres (ac)
1 acre (ac)	= 4840 square yards (yd²)
1 square foot (ft²)	= 144 square inches (in²)

Conversions

1 square kilometre (km²)	= 0.386 square mile (mi²)
1 hectare (ha)	= 2.471 acres (ac)
1 square metre (m²)	= 10.764 square feet (ft²)
	= 1.196 square yards (yd²)
1 square centimetre (cm²)	= 0.155 square inch (in²)
1 square mile (mi²)	= 2.59 square kilometres (km²)
1 acre (ac)	= 0.4047 hectare (ha)
1 square foot (ft²)	= 0.0929 square metre (m²)
1 square inch (in²)	= 6.4516 square centimetres (cm²)

Volume

Metric Measure

1 cubic metre (m³)	= 1,000,000 cubic centimetres (cm³)
1 litre (l)	= 1000 millilitres (ml)
	= 0.001 cubic metre (m³)
1 millilitre (ml)	= 1 cubic centimetre (cm³)

Nonmetric Measure

1 cubic foot (ft³)	= 1728 cubic inches (in³)
1 cubic yard (yd³)	= 27 cubic feet (ft³)

Conversions

1 cubic metre (m³)	= 264.2 gallons (U.S.) (gal)
	= 35.314 cubic feet (ft³)
1 litre (l)	= 1.057 quarts (U.S.) (qt)
	= 33.815 fluid ounces (U.S.) (fl oz)
1 cubic centimetre (cm³)	= 0.0610 cubic inch (in³)
1 cubic mile (mi³)	= 4.168 cubic kilometres (km³)
1 cubic foot (ft³)	= 0.0283 cubic metre (m³)
1 cubic inch (in³)	= 16.39 cubic centimetres (cm³)
1 gallon (gal)	= 3.784 litres (l)

Mass

Metric Measure

1000 kilograms (kg)	= 1 metric tonne (t)
1 kilogram (kg)	= 1000 grams (g)

Nonmetric Measure

1 short ton (ton)	= 2000 pounds (lb)
1 long ton	= 2240 pounds (lb)
1 pound (lb)	= 16 ounces (oz)

Conversions

1 metric tonne (t)	= 2205 pounds (lb)
1 kilogram (kg)	= 2.205 pounds (lb)
1 gram (g)	= 0.03527 ounce (oz)
1 pound (lb)	= 0.4536 kilogram (kg)
1 ounce (oz)	= 28.35 grams (g)

Pressure

standard sea-level air pressure	= 101.325 kilopascals (KPa)
	= 1013.25 millibars (mb)
	= 14.7 lb/in²

Temperature

To change from Fahrenheit (F) to Celsius (C)

$$°C = \frac{°F - 32}{1.8}$$

To change from Celsius (C) to Fahrenheit (F)

$$°F = °C \times 1.8 + 32$$

Energy and Power

1 calorie (cal)	= the amount of heat that will raise the temperature of 1 g of water 1°C (1.8°F)
1 joule (J)	= 0.239 calorie (cal)
1 watt (W)	= 1 joule per second (J/s)
	= 14.34 calories per minute (cal/min)

Appendix B World Political Map, 2004

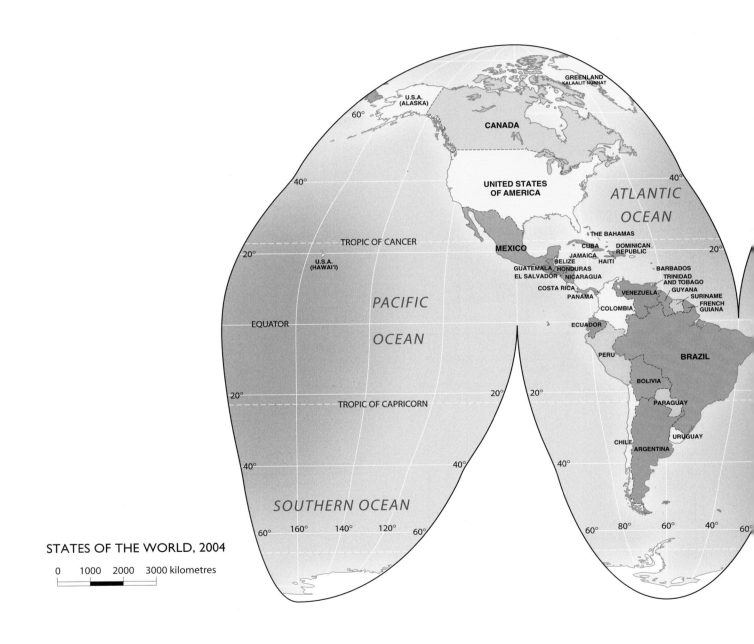

STATES OF THE WORLD, 2004

0   1000   2000   3000 kilometres

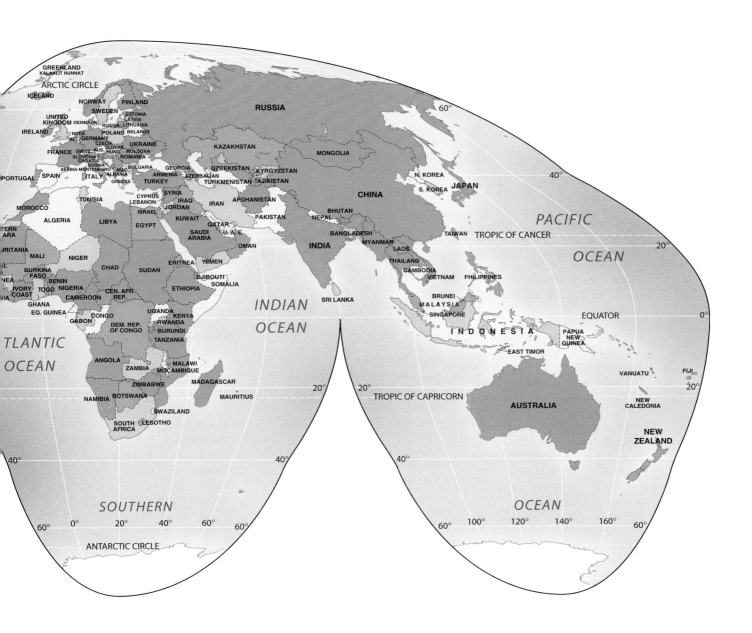

Pronunciation Guide

Aa (AH-AH)
Abilene (abba-LEEN)
Ablation (uh-BLAY-shunn)
Abyssal (uh-BISSLE)
Acacia (uh-KAY-shuh)
Aconcagua (ah-konn-KAH-gwah)
Adiabatic (addie-uh-BATTICK)
Adriatic (ay-dree-ATTIK)
Aeolian (A-OH-lee-un)
Agassiz (AG-uh-see)
Akrotiri (ah-krah-TIRRI)
Albedo (al-BEE-doh)
Albuquerque (ALBA-ker-kee)
Aleutian (uh-LOOH-shun)
Algae (AL-jee)
Algeria (al-JEERY-uh)
Also Sprach Zarathustra (ull-ZOH shprahch zahra-TOOS-trah)
Amalfi (ah-MAHL-fee)
Ameliorate (uh-MEEL-yer-ate)
Amensalism (uh-MEN-sull-ism)
Amino (uh-MEE-noh)
Anacostia (anna-KOSS-tee-uh)
Anatexis (ANA-teksis)
Andesite (an-DES-ite)
Anemometer (anna-MOM-muh-der)
Anion (AN-eye-on)
Antarctica (ant-ARK-tick-uh)
Antimony (ANN-tuh-moh-nee)
Antipodally (an-TIPPUD-lee)
Anyang (ahn-YAHNG)
Aphelion (ap-HEELY-un)
Appalachia (appa-LAY-chee-uh)
Aqaba (AH-kuh-buh)
Aquiclude (AK-kwuh-cloode)
Aquifer (AK-kwuh-fer)
Archipelago (ark-uh-PELL-uh-goh)
Arequipa (ah-ruh-KEE-puh)
Arête (uh-RETT)
Aridisol (uh-RID-ih-sol)
Armero (ahr-MAIR-roh)
Arroyo (uh-ROY-yoh)
Artois (ahr-TWAH)
Aruba (ah-ROO-bah)
Asthenosphere (ass-THENNO-sfeer)
Aswan (as-SWAHN)
Atacama (ah-tah-KAH-mah)
Atoll (AT-tole)

Aurora borealis (aw-ROAR-ruh baw-ree-ALLIS)
Autotroph (AW-doh-troaf)
Azores (AY-zoars)
Azoric (ay-ZOAR-rick)
Azurite (AZH-uh-rite)

Bahamas (buh-HAH-muzz)
Bahía (buh-HEE-uh)
Baja (BAH-hah)
Bajada (buh-HAH-dah)
Bali (BAH-lee)
Bangladesh (bang-gluh-DESH)
Baobab (BAY-oh-bab)
Baotou (bau-TOH)
Barchan (BAR-kan)
Barents (BARRENS)
Barnaul (bar-nuh-OOL)
Basal (BASE-ull)
Basalt (buh-SALT)
Bayeux (bye-YER ["r" silent])
Baykal (bye-KAHL)
Beijing (bay-ZHING)
Bellary (buh-LAHR-ree)
Bengal (BENG-gahl)
Benguela (ben-GWAY-luh)
Bergeron (BEAR-guh-roan)
Bering (BEH-ring)
Berkshire (BERK-sheer)
Bhuj (BOODGE)
Bingham (BING-um)
Biota (bye-OH-tuh)
Bioturbate (BIO-turbait)
Biome (BYE-ohm)
Bitung (bih-TOONG)
Bogor (BOH-goar)
Boise (BOY-zee)
Bonneville (BON-uh-vill)
Borneo (BOAR-nee-oh)
Brahmaputra (brahm-uh-POOH-truh)
Breccia (BRETCH-ee-uh)
Brunisol (BREWN-i-sol)
Buoy (BOY)
Butte (BYOOT)
Bylot (BYE-lot)

Cairo (KYE-roh)
Caldera (kal-DERRA)
Calve (KALV)

Calving (KAL-ving)
Camille (kuh-MEEL)
Canandaigua (kannan-DAY-gwah)
Capri (kuh-PREE)
Caribbean (kuh-RIB-ee-un/ karra-BEE-un)
Caribou (KARRA-boo)
Castel Sant'Angelo (kuh-STELL sunt-UN-jeh-loh)
Catena (kuh-TEENA)
Cation (CAT-eye-on)
Caucasus (KAW-kuh-zuss)
Cayuga (kah-YOO-gah)
Celsius (SELL-see-us)
Cenozoic (senno-ZOH-ik)
Chang Jiang (chung-jee-AHNG)
Changnon (CHANG-nun)
Chaparral (SHAP-uh-RAL)
Chemotrophic (KEMO-trofik)
Chengdu (chung-DOO)
Chernozem (CHURN-o-zem)
Cherrapunji (cherra-POON-jee)
Chesapeake (CHESSA-peek)
Chicxulub (CHEEK-soo-loob)
Chile (CHILLI/CHEE-lay)
Chimborazo (chim-buh-RAH-zoh)
Chinook (shin-NOOK)
Chernobyl (CHAIR-nuh-beel)
Chugach (CHEW-gash)
Chukotskiy (chuh-KAHT-skee)
Chyulu (chee-OO-loo)
Cineole (SIN-ee-ole)
Cirque (SERK)
Cirrus (SIRRUS)
Clayey (CLAY-ee)
Coachella (koh-CHELLA)
Cocos (KOH-kuss)
Conduit (KONN-doo-it)
Coniferous (kuh-NIFF-uh-russ)
Contentious (kon-TEN-shuss)
Coriolis, Gustave-Gaspard (kaw-ree-OH-liss, goo-STAHV gus-SPAH)
Corrasion (kaw-RAY-zhunn)
Costa Rica (koss-tuh REE-kuh)
Cretacious (kreh-TAY-shuss)
Crete (KREET)
Crevasse (kruh-VASS)
Croatia (kroh-AY-shuh)
Cryosol (KRY-o-sol)

Cryoturbate (KRYO-turbait)
Crystalline (KRISS-tuh-ine)
Cuesta (KWESTA)
Cumbre Vieja (KUM-brai VI-eha)
Cumulonimbus (kyoo-myoo-loh-NIMBUS)
Cumulus (KYOO-myoo-luss)
Cvijic, Jovan (SVEE-itch, yoh-VAHN)

Dacite (DASITE)
Dakar (duh-KAHR)
Davisian (duh-VISSY-un)
de Candolle, Alphonse (duh kawn-DOLE, ahl-FAWSS)
Debris (deh-BREE)
Deciduous (deh-SID-yoo-uss)
Deltaic (del-TAY-ik)
Denali (deh-NAH-lee)
Deoxyribonucleic (day-oxie-RYBO-noo-CLAY-ik)
Desertification (deh-ZERT-iff-uh-KAY-shun)
Diapir (DY-a-peer)
Diapirism (DY-a-peer-izm)
Diastrophism (dye-ASTRO-fizzum)
Diurnal (dye-ERR-nul)
Dokuchayev, Vasily (dock-koo-CHYE-eff, VAH-zilly)
Doline (DO-lina)
Drakensberg (DRAHK-unz-berg)
du Toit (doo-TWAH)

Echidna (eh-KID-nuh)
Ecliptic (ee-KLIP-tick)
Ecuador (ECK-wah-dor)
Ecumene (ECK-yoo-mean)
Edaphic (ee-DAFFIK)
Edifice (ED-ifiss)
Eemian (EE-mee-un)
El Faiyum (el-fye-YOOM)
El Niño (el-NEEN-yoh)
Ellesmere (ELZ-meer)
Ely (EELY)
Emu (EE-myoo)
Endemism (en-DEM-izzum)
Epeirogeny (eh-pye-RODGE-enny)
Ephemeral (ee-FEMMA-rull)
Epiphyte (EPPY-fite)
Epoch (EH-pok)
Equinox (EE-kwuh-nox)
Eratosthenes (eh-ruh-TOS-thuh-neeze)
Estuary (ESS-tyoo-erry)
Eucalyptus (yoo-kuh-LIP-tuss)
Euphorbia (yoo-FOR-bee-uh)

Fahrenheit (FARREN-hite)
Falkland (FAWK-lund)
Felsenmeer (FEL-zen-mair)
Fenneman (FEN-uh-mun)

Fiji (FEE-jee)
Filchner-Ronne (FILK-ner ROH-nuh)
Findeisen (FIN-dyzen)
Firn (FERN)
Fissure (FISHER)
Fjord (FYORD)
Foehn (FERN ["r" silent])
Franz Josef (frahnss YOH-zeff)
Fuji (FOO-jee)
Fungi (FUN-jye)

Galapagos (guh-LAH-pah-guss)
Galena (guh-LEENA)
Ganges (GAN-jeeze)
Gaseous (GASH-uss)
Geiger (GHYE-guh)
Gelisol (JELLY-sol)
Geodesy (jee-ODD-uh-see)
Geostrophic (jee-oh-STROFFIK)
Geosynchronous (jee-oh-SIN-krunn-uss)
Geyser (GUY-zer)
Gibraltar (jih-BRAWL-tuh)
Gila (HEE-luh)
Giza (GHEE-zah)
Gleysol (GLAY-sol)
Gneiss (NICE)
Gnomonic (no-MONIC)
Gondwana (gond-WAHNA)
Goudie (GOWDY)
Graben (GRAH-ben)
Granule (GRAN-yule)
Grebe (GREEB)
Greenwich (GREN-itch)
Gros Piton (groh-peet-TAW)
Guangzi-Zhuang (GWAHNG-zee JWAHNG)
Guatemala (gwut-uh-MAH-lah)
Guilin (gway-LIN)
Guinea (GHINNY)
Gujarat (GOO-jah-raht)
Gulkana (gull-KAN-uh)
Gunz (GOONZ)
Guyana (guy-ANNA)
Guyot (GHEE-oh)
Gypsum (JIP-sum)
Gyre (JYER)

Haiphong (hye-FONG)
Halemaumau (HALI-maw-u-maw-u)
Halide (HAY-lyde)
Halong (hah-LONG)
Hatteras (HATTA-russ)
Heimaey (HAY-may)
Hematite (HEE-muh-tite)
Herbaceous (her-BAY-shuss)
Herodotus (heh-RODDA-tuss)
Hierarchical (hyer-ARK-ik-kull)
Hilo (HEE-loh)

Himalayas (him-AHL-yuzz/himma-LAY-uzz)
Hindu Kush (HIN-doo KOOSH)
Hjulstrom (HUIL-strom)
Holocene (HOLLO-seen)
Homo sapiens (HO-mo SAY-pi-ans)
Huang He (HWAHNG-HUH)
Huascarán (wahss-kuh-RAHN)
Hulwan (hil-WAHN)
Humus (HYOO-muss)
Hygroscopic (hye-gruh-SKOPPIK)

Iapetus (IA-pet-us)
Icarus (ICK-uh-russ)
Igneous (IGG-nee-us)
Indigenous (in-DIDGE-uh-nuss)
Indonesia (indo-NEE-zhuh)
In situ (in-SYE-too)
Inuit (IN-yoo-it)
Ion (EYE-on)
Iquitos (ih-KEE-tohss)
Irrawaddy (ih-ruh-WODDY)
Isarithmic (eye-suh-RITH-mik)
Ischia (ISS-kee-uh)
Isohyet (EYE-so-hyatt)
Isostasy (eye-SOSS-tuh-see)
Iteshi (ih-TESHI)
Izu (EE-zoo)

Jawa (JAH-vuh)
Juan de Fuca (WAHN duh FYOO-kuh)

Kafue (kuh-FOO-ee)
Kakogawa (kah-koh-GAH-wah)
Kalaallit nunaat (KALAI-lit NUN-aat)
Kalimantan (kalla-MAN-tan)
Kamchatka (komm-CHUT-kuh)
Kariba (kuh-REEBA)
Kaskawulsh (KASS-kuh-WULSH)
Katabatic (kat-uh-BATTIK)
Kauai (KOW-eye)
Kazakhstan (KUZZ-uck-stahn)
Kenya (KEN-yuh)
Keuka (KYOO-kuh)
Khamsin (KAM-sin)
Khasi (KAH-see)
Kibo (KEE-boh)
Kilauea (kill-uh-WAY-uh)
Kilimanjaro (kil-uh-mun-JAH-roh)
Klamath (KLAM-uth)
Koala (koh-AH-luh)
Kodiak (KOH-dee-ak)
Komatiites (KO-maty-ites)
Köppen, Wladimir (KER-pin ["r" silent], VLAH-duh-meer)
Kosciusko (kuh-SHOO-skoh)
Kotzebue (kot-seh-BYOO)
Krakatau (krak-uh-TAU)

Küchler (KOO-kler)
Kunming (koon-MING)
Kurashio (koora-SHEE-oh)
Kurile (CURE-ile)
Kuznetsk (kooz-NETSK)
Kyushu (kee-YOO-shoo)

La Niña (lah-NEEN-yah)
Laccolith (LACK-oh-lith)
Lahar (luh-HAHR)
Lancashire (LANKA-sher)
Langarone (lahn-gah-ROH-neh)
Lanier (luh-NEAR)
Laredo (luh-RAY-doh)
Larvae (LAR-vee)
Lascaux (lass-SKOH)
Laurasia (law-RAY-zhuh)
Laurentian (law-REN-shun)
Lead [ice-surface channel] (LEED)
Lemur (LEE-mer)
Levee (LEH-vee)
Li (LEE)
Liana (lee-AHNA)
Lichen (LYE-ken)
Linnaean (LINNY-un)
Littoral (LITT-uh-rull)
Loess (LERSS)
Loihi (loh-EE-hee)
Loma Prieta (loh-muh-pree-AY-tuh)
Lumbricus terrestris (LUM-bri-kus
   Ter-es-tris)
Luvisol (LOOV-i-sol)

Maasai (muh-SYE)
Machu Picchu (mah-CHOO
   PEEK-choo)
Madagascar (madda-GAS-kuh)
Mafic (MAFFIK)
Magellan (muh-JELLUN)
Malachite (MALLA-kite)
Malawi (muh-LAH-wee)
Mali (MAH-lee)
Manaus (muh-NAUSS)
Manyara (mun-YAH-rah)
Maquis (mah-KEE)
Marsupial (mar-SOOPY-ull)
Martinique (mahr-tih-NEEK)
Massif (mass-SEEF)
Maui (MAU-ee)
Mauna Kea (MAU-nuh KAY-uh)
Mauna Loa (MAU-nuh LOH-uh)
Mauritania (maw-ruh-TAY-nee-uh)
Mawensi (mah-WENN-see)
Mawsim (MAW-zim)
Maya (MYE-uh)
Meander (mee-AN-der)
Medieval (meddy-EE-vull)
Melbourne (MEL-bun)
Mercalli (mair-KAHL-lee)

Mercator, Gerhardus (mer-CATER,
   ghair-HAR-duss)
Meru (MAY-roo)
Mesa (MAY-suh)
Mescal (MESS-kull)
Mesozoic (meh-zoh-ZOH-ik)
Mica (MYE-kuh)
Michoacán (mitcho-ah-KAHN)
Mindel (MINDLE)
Minot (MYE-not)
Mirnyy (MEAR-nyee)
Mistral (miss-STRAHL)
Miyazaki (mee-YAH-zah-kee)
Moho (MOH-hoh)
Mohorovičić, Andrija (moh-hoh-
   ROH-vih-chik, ahn-DREEA)
Mohs, Friedrich (MOZE,
   FREED-rick)
Mojave (moh-HAH-vee)
Moldau (MOAL-dau)
Monadnock (muh-NAD-nok)
Mont Blanc (mawn-BLAHNK)
Montreal (mun-tree-AWL)
Moraine (more-RAIN)
Moray Firth (MAW-ray FERTH)
Morisawa (mawry-SAH-wah)
Muehrcke (MERR-kee)
Myanmar (mee-ahn-MAH)

Nairobi (nye-ROH-bee)
Namib (nah-MIB)
Namibia (nuh-MIBBY-uh)
Naples (NAYPLES)
Nazca (NAHSS-kuh)
Neap (NEEP)
Nefudh (neh-FOOD)
Negev (NEGGEV)
Nepal (nuh-PAHL)
Nevado del Ruiz (neh-VAH-doh
   del roo-EESE)
New Guinea (noo-GHINNY)
New Madrid (noo-MAD-rid)
Ngorongoro (eng-gore-ong-GORE-oh)
Niche (NITCH)
Niger [River] (NYE-jer)
Niger [Country] (nee-ZHAIR)
Nigeria (nye-JEERY-uh)
Nkhata (eng-KAH-tah)
Nouakchott (noo-AHK-shaht)
Novaya Zemlya (NOH-vuh-yuh
   zem-lee-AH)
Nuée ardente (noo-AY ahr-DAHNT)
Nunatak (NOON-uh-tak)

Oahu (ah-WAH-hoo)
Oblate spheroid (OH-blate
   SFEER-roid)
Obsidian (ob-SIDDY-un)
Oja (OH-jah)
Okhotsk (oh-KAHTSK)

Ophiolites (O-fio-lites)
Orinoco (aw-rih-NOH-koh)
Orogenic (aw-ruh-JENNIK)
Orogeny (aw-RODGE-uh-nee)
Orographic (aw-roh-GRAFFIK)
Oscillation (oss-uh-LAY-shunn)
Osterbygd (AR-star-bade)
Ouachita (wah-CHEE-tuh)
Owasco (oh-WAH-skoh)
Oxisol (OCK-see-sol)
Oyashio (oy-yuh-SHEE-oh)

Pahoehoe (pah-HOI-hoi)
Paleontology (pay-lee-un-
   TOLLO-jee)
Paleozoic (pay-lee-oh-ZOH-ik)
Pamlico (PAM-lih-koh)
Pampas (PAHM-pahss)
Pangaea (pan-GAY-uh)
Papua (PAP-oo-uh)
Paricutín (pah-ree-koo-TEEN)
Patagonia (patta-GOH-nEE-ah)
Pedon (PED-on)
Pele (PAY-lay)
Pelée (peh-LAY)
Pelourinho (peh-loo-REE-noh)
Penck, Walther (PENK, VULL-tuh)
Peneplain (PEN-uh-plane)
Periglacial (perry-GLAY-shull)
Petit Piton (peh-tee-peet-TAW)
Phanerozoic (FANero-zo-ic)
Philippines (FILL-uh-peenz)
Phreatic (free-ATTIK)
Physiography (fizzy-OGG-ruh-fee)
Phytogeography (FYE-toh-jee-
   OGGRA-fee)
Piedmont (PEAD-mont)
Pierre (South Dakota) (PEER)
Pinatubo (pin-uh-TOO-boh)
Planar (PLANE-ahr)
Planetesimal (planna-TEZ-ih-mull)
Platypus (PLATT-uh-puss)
Pleistocene (PLY-stoh-seen)
Pliny (PLY-nee)
Pliocene (PLY-oh-seen)
Podocarp (POD-oh-carp)
Podsol (POD-zol)
Pompeii (pom-PAY)
Pontchartrain (PON-shar-train)
Popocatépetl (poh-puh-CAT-uh-petal)
Prague (PRAHG)
Primeval (pry-MEE-vull)
Psychrometer (sye-KROM-muh-der)
Puget (PYOO-jet)
Pyrenees (PEER-unease)

Quaoar (KWAH-wahr)
Quartic (KWOAR-tik)
Quasar (KWAY-zahr)

Quaternary (kwah-TER-nuh-ree)

Qinghai-Xizang (ching-HYE sheedz-AHNG)

Quartzite (KWARTS-ite)

Quito (KEE-toh)

Rainier (ruh-NEER)

Raisz (ROYCE)

Rawinsonde (RAW-in-sond)

Rayleigh (RAW-ley)

Reykjavik (RAKE-yah-veek)

Rhine (RYNE)

Rhône (ROAN)

Rhumb (RUM)

Rhyolite (RYE-oh-lyte)

Richter (RICK-tuh)

Rio de Janeiro (REE-oh day zhah-NAIR-roh)

Rio de la Plata (REE-oh day lah PLAH-tah)

Roche Moutonnée (ROSH moot-tonn-NAY)

Rondônia (roh-DOAN-yuh)

Rotorua (roh-tuh-ROO-uh)

Ruhr (ROOR)

Ruwenzori (roo-wen-ZOARY)

Sahel (suh-HELL)

St. Lucia (saint LOO-shuh)

St. Pierre (sah PYAIR)

Saltation (sawl-TAY-shunn)

Salvador (SULL-vuh-dor)

Sami (SAA-mi)

San Andreas (san an-DRAY-us)

San Gorgonio (san gore-GOH-nee-oh)

San Joaquin (san wah-KEEN)

San Juan (sahn HWAHN)

Sangamon (SANG-guh-mun)

Santorini (santo-REE-nee)

São Gabriel de Cachoeira (sau GAH-bree-ell day kah-choh-AY-rah)

Saragosa (sarra-GOH-suh)

Schist (SHIST)

Scotia (SKOH-shuh)

Seine (SENN)

Seismic (SIZE-mik)

Seismograph (SIZE-moh-graff)

Seneca (SEH-neh-kuh)

Serengeti (serren-GETTY)

Sesquioxide (SESS-kwee-OXIDE)

Seychelles (say-SHELLZ)

Sial (SYE-al)

Siberia (sye-BEERY-uh)

Sicily (SIH-suh-lee)

Sierra Madre Oriental (see-ERRA mah-dray orry-en-TAHL)

Sierra Nevada (see-ERRA neh-VAH-dah)

Silicic (sih-LISS-ik)

Silurian (sih-LOORY-un)

Sima (SYE-muh)

Skaneateles (skan-nee-AT-luss)

Slovenia (sloh-VEE-nee-uh)

Soledad (SOLE-uh-dad)

Solifluction (sol-ih-FLUK-shun)

Solonetz (SOLON-etz)

Solstice (SOL-stiss)

Solum (SOH-lum)

Somali (suh-MAH-lee)

Soufrière (soo-free-AIR)

Spatial (SPAY-shull)

Spheroidal (sfeer-ROY-dull)

Spodosol (SPODDA-sol)

Sri Lanka (sree-LAHN-kah)

Stalactite (stuh-LAK-tite)

Stalagmite (stuh-LAG-mite)

Steppe (STEP)

Stratigraphy (struh-TIG-gruh-fee)

Strauss, Richard (SHTRAUSS, RIK-art)

Striation (strye-AY-shunn)

Suffosion (suh-FOH-zhunn)

Sulawesi (soo-luh-WAY-see)

Sulphur (SULL-fer)

Sumatera (suh-MAH-truh)

Sumbay (SOOM-bye)

Surficial (ser-FISH-ull)

Surtsey (SERT-see)

Susquehanna (suss-kwuh-HANNA)

Svalbard (SVAHL-bard)

Swakopmund (SFAHK-awp-munt)

Swaziland (SWAH-zee-land)

Synoptic (sih-NOP-tik)

Syria (SEARY-uh)

Tagus (TAY-guss)

Taiga (TYE-guh)

Taklimakan (tahk-luh-muh-KAHN)

Talus (TAY-luss)

Tana (TAHN-nuh)

Tanganyika (tan-gan-YEE-kuh)

Tangshan (tung-SHAHN)

Tanzania (tan-zuh-NEE-uh)

Tapir (TAY-per)

Tephra (TEFF-ruh)

Terrane (teh-RAIN)

Tertiary (TER-shuh-ree)

Teton (TEE-tonn)

Thalweg (THAWL-weg)

Thames (TEMZ)

Thera (THEERA)

Theroux (thuh-ROO)

Tianjin (tyahn-JEEN)

Tiber (TYE-ber)

Tibetan (tuh-BETTEN)

Tierra del Fuego (tee-ERRA dale FWAY-goh)

Titanium (tye-TANEY-um)

Tombolo (TOM-boh-loh)

Toroweap (TOAR-ruh-weep)

Torricelli (toar-ruh-CHELLY)

Travertine (TRAVVER-teen)

Trivandrum (truh-VAN-drum)

Tsavo (TSAH-voh)

Tselinograd (seh-LINN-uh-grahd)

Tsunami (tsoo-NAH-mee)

Tucson (TOO-sonn)

Tunguska (toon-GOOSE-kuh)

Turkana (ter-KANNA)

Turukhansk (too-roo-KAHNSK)

Tuscarora (tuska-ROAR-ruh)

Tuya (TUH-ya)

Uinta (yoo-IN-tuh)

Ukraine (yoo-CRANE)

Uranus (yoo-RAY-nuss)

Ustalf (YOO-stalf)

Uvala (oo-VAH-luh)

Vaiont (vye-YAW)

Valdez (val-DEEZE)

Venezuela (veh-neh-SWAY-luh)

Verkhoyansk (vair-koy-YUNSK)

Vesuvius (veh-ZOO-vee-us)

Vicariance (vye-CARRY-unss)

Vietnam (vee-et-NAHM)

Viña del Mar (VEEN-yah-del-MAHR)

Viscous (VISS-kuss)

Viti Levu (vee-tee-LEH-voo)

Vltava (VAHL-tuh-vuh)

Waialeale (wye-ahl-ay-AHL-ay)

Wasatch (WAH-satch)

Wawona (wah-WOH-nuh)

Weddell (weh-DELL)

Wegener, Alfred (VAY-ghenner, AHL-fret)

Whataroa (wotta-ROH-uh)

Willamette (wuh-LAMMET)

Wrangell (RANG-gull)

Wrangellia (rang-GHELLIA)

Wüste (VISS-tuh)

Xerophyte (ZERO-fite)

Xian (shee-AHN)

Yakutat (YAK-uh-tat)

Yosemite (yoh-SEM-uh-tee)

Yucatán (yoo-kuh-TAHN)

Yugoslavia (yoo-goh-SLAH-vee-uh)

Yungay (YOONG-GYE)

Yunnan (yoon-NAHN)

Zagros (ZAH-gross)

Zambezi (zam-BEEZY)

Zimbabwe (zim-BAHB-way)

Zoogeography (ZOH-OH-jee-oggra-fee)

Glossary of Terms

A horizon   Upper soil layer, which is often darkened by organic matter.

Aa   Angular, jagged, blocky shaped lava formed from the hardening of not especially fluid lavas.

Ablation zone   Glacier's lower zone of loss. *Ablation* refers to all forms of loss at the lower end, including melting and evaporation.

Ablation till   Glacial material carried along on the top of a glacier or ice sheet. The material is mainly supplied by slope and aeolian processes.

Abrasion (glacial)   Glacial erosion process of scraping, produced by the impact of rock debris carried in the ice upon the bedrock surface below.

Abrasion (stream)   Erosive action of boulders, pebbles, and smaller grains of sediment as they are carried along a stream channel. These fragments dislodge other particles along the stream bed and banks, thereby enhancing the deepening and widening process.

Absolute base level   Elevational level lying a few metres below sea level.

Absolute zero   Lowest possible temperature, where all molecules cease their motion; occurs at $-273°C$ or $0°K$.

Abyssal plain   Large zone of relatively low-relief seafloor, constituting one of the deepest areas of an ocean basin.

Accretion   Process where bodies of rock, derived from other lithospheric plates, are attached to the margins of a shield-anchored, continental landmass. These geologically consistent fragments can be regional in extent and are known as terranes.

Acid precipitation   Abnormally acidic rain, snow, or fog resulting from high levels of the oxides of sulphur and nitrogen that exist as industrial pollutants in the air.

Active dune   Unstable sand dune in a desert that is continually being shaped and moved by the wind; cannot support vegetation.

Active factor of soil formation   Energy-giving factors, e.g., climate and organisms. Soil cannot form without these factors.

Active layer (talik)   Soil above the permafrost table, which is subject to annual thawing and freezing.

Active volcano   Volcano that has erupted in recorded human history.

Actual evapotranspiration (AE)   Amount of water that can be lost to the atmosphere from a land surface with any particular soil moisture conditions.

Addition   Soil-layer formation process involving the gains made by the soil through the adding of organic matter from plant growth, or sometimes when loose surface material moves downslope and comes to rest on the soil; expressed as a dark-colored upper layer, whose appearance is attributable to that added organic matter.

Adiabatic   With air being a poor conductor of heat, a parcel of air at one temperature that is surrounded by air at another temperature will neither gain nor lose heat energy over a short period of time. When such non-transfer of heat occurs, the process is called *adiabatic.*

Adiabatic lapse rate   When a given mass of air is forced to expand, its temperature decreases. If a parcel of air rises to a higher altitude, it expands and cools adiabatically. Its lapse rate is therefore referred to as an *adiabatic lapse rate.*

Advection   Horizontal movement of material in the atmosphere.

Aeolian   Related to wind.

Aerosols   Tiny solid or liquid particles suspended in the atmosphere.

Aggradation   Combination of processes that builds up the surface through the deposition of material that was removed from elsewhere by degradation; contributes to the lowering of relief by reducing the height differences between the high and low places in an area.

Air mass   Very large parcel of air (more than 1600 km across) in the boundary layer of the troposphere, which possesses relatively uniform qualities of density, temperature, and humidity in the horizontal dimension. It is also bound together as an organized whole, a vital cohesion because air masses routinely migrate for hundreds of kilometres as distinct entities.

Albic horizon   White or ash-coloured leached (eluviated) Ae horizon characteristic of Podzolic soils.

Albedo   Proportion of incoming solar radiation that is reflected by a surface; the whiter the colour of the surface (albedo derives from the Latin word *albus,* meaning white), the higher its albedo.

Aleutian low   Local name for the northernmost Pacific Ocean's Upper Midlatitude Low, which is centred approximately at 60°N near the archipelago constituted by Alaska's Aleutian Islands.

Alfisol One of the 12 Soil Orders of the U.S. Soil Taxonomy, found in moister, less continental climate zones; characterized by high mineral content, moistness, and sizeable clay accumulation in the **B** horizon. Equivalent to the Luvisolic order of the CSSC.

Allogenic succession Plant succession in which vegetation change is brought about by some external environmental factor, such as disease.

Alluvial apron (*see* **bajada**)

Alluvial fan Fan-shaped deposit consisting of alluvial material located where a mountain stream emerges onto a plain or valley.

Alluvial soil (*see* **alluvium**)

Alluvium Material deposited by a stream composing its floodplain. It is a fining-upwards sequence with channel lag (coarser) material deposited on the bed of a meandering stream at the bottom of a sequence. This is deposited as the channel migrates across and down the floodplain, and the former thalweg is abandoned. On top of this are sand and gravel deposits of the point bar on the inside bank of the meander. Capping the sequence is a layer of fine material (clays and silts) that are deposited from slack water on the floodplain surface during Overbank flows.

Alp A higher area in a glaciated upland that escaped ice erosion (occurs above the trimline). The landscape here is stream cut and rounded. This feature gave its name to the European Alps.

Alpine (mountain) glacier Rivers of ice that form in mountainous regions; confined in valleys that usually have steep slopes (valley or inlet glaciers).

Alpine permafrost On the world map of permafrost, patches of high-altitude permafrost at lower latitudes associated with major highland zones, such as the Canadian Rockies and the Tibetan Plateau.

Alpine sequence A four-glacial chronological sequence devised by Albrecht Penck and Edouard Bruckner in the early twentieth century. They used the difference in height of outwash deposits in the valleys draining off the German Alps as evidence for four glaciations. This sequence was later proved to be far to simplistic.

Amensalism Biological interaction in which one species is inhibited by another.

Anatexis The melting of subducted plate material in the lower crust and/or upper mantle. This process incorporates material from the surrounding crust and mantle, sediments dragged down on top of the subducting slab, and seawater penetrating down associated faults.

Andisol One of the 12 soil orders of the U.S. Soil Taxonomy; established to include certain weakly developed, parent-material-controlled soils, notably those developed on volcanic ash, which are locally distributed throughout the Pacific Ring of Fire, Hawaii, and the world's other volcanic zones.

Angle of incidence (*see* **solar elevation**)

Angle of Repose Maximum angle a granular material can maintain without becoming unstable and failing. (*see* **threshold angle**)

Anion Negatively charged ion, such as those of carbonates, nitrates, and phosphates.

Annual temperature cycle Pattern of temperature change during the course of a year.

Annular drainage Concentric stream pattern that drains the interior of an excavated geological dome (*see* Fig. 42.10B).

Antarctic circle Latitude (66½°S) marking the northern boundary of the Southern Hemisphere portion of the Earth's surface that receives a 24-hour period of sunlight at least once each year.

Antarctic Ice Cap Continental glacier that covers almost all of Antarctica, enabling the study of what conditions were like elsewhere in the world during much of the Late Cenozoic Ice Age.

Antecedent stream Stream exhibiting transverse drainage across a structural feature that would normally impede its flow because the stream predates the structure and kept cutting downward as the structure was uplifted around it.

Anticline Archlike upfold with the limbs dipping away from its axis.

Anticyclone Atmospheric high-pressure cell involving the divergence of air, which subsides at and flows spirally out of the centre. The isobars around an anticyclone are generally circular in shape, with their values increasing toward the centre. In the Northern Hemisphere, winds flow clockwise around an anticyclone; in the Southern Hemisphere, winds flow counterclockwise around an anticyclone.

Antipode Location on the exact opposite point of the near spherical Earth. The North Pole is the antipode of the South Pole.

Apex (delta) Upstream end of a delta, where the stream begins to fan outward into several distributary channels.

Aphelion Point in the Earth's orbit that occurs every July 4th, where the distance to the Sun is maximized (ca. 152.5 million km).

"Apparent" flows Slides of rock or regolith that appear to be flows because of a veneer of flowed material that obscures the underlying side block.

Aquiclude Impermeable rock layer that resists the infiltration of groundwater; consists of tightly packed or interlocking particles, such as in shale.

Aquifer Porous and permeable rock layer that can at least be partially saturated with groundwater.

Aquifer, confined One that lies between two aquicludes; often obtains its groundwater from a distant area, where it eventually reaches the surface.

Aquifer, unconfined One that obtains its groundwater from local infiltration.

Archipelago Group of islands, often elongated into a chain.

Arctic circle Latitude (66½°N) marking the southern boundary of the Northern Hemisphere portion of the Earth's surface that receives a 24-hour period of sunlight at least once each year.

Area symbols Representation of two-dimensional spaces on a map, with colours or black-and-white areal patterns representing specific quantitative ranges (which are identified in the map legend).

Arête Knifelike, jagged ridge that separates two adjacent glaciers, glacial valleys, or cirques.

Arid (B) climates Dry climates where potential evapotranspiration always exceeds the moisture supplied by precipitation; found in areas dominated by the subtropical high-pressure cells, in the interiors of continents far from oceanic moisture sources, and in conjunction with rainshadow zones downwind from certain mountain ranges.

Aridisol One of the 12 soil orders of the U.S. Soil Taxonomy, and the most widespread on the world's landmasses; dry soil (unless irrigated) associated with arid climates, light in colour, and often containing horizons rich in calcium, clay, or salt minerals. Equivalent to the Chernozemic and Soloetzic soil orders of the CSSC.

Arroyo Small, steep-sided, flat-floored gully, which has been cut into the surface of an alluvial fan and may continue onto the valley floor beyond. Found only in semiarid and arid environments, these channels are usually dry but can contain ephemeral streamflow when intermittent local precipitation occurs.

Artesian well One that flows under its own natural pressure to the surface; usually associated with a confined aquifer that is recharged from a remote location where that aquifer reaches the surface.

Artificial beach nourishment The dumping of slightly coarser material on an eroding beach to maintain its size. Can be done by truck or pipeline.

Ash (volcanic) Solid, cinder-like fragments of lava and pyroclastic origin, smaller than volcanic bombs, that are exploded into the air during an eruption. Most fall to the ground close to the erupting volcano.

Aspect Directional orientation of a steep mountain slope. In the Northern Hemisphere, southerly aspects receive far more solar radiation than do northward-facing slopes, with all the environmental consequences such a differential implies.

Asteroid A small planetary body in orbit around the Sun. It is larger than a meteorite but smaller than a planet (its size is usually measured in hundreds of km). Most are found in the Asteroid belt between the orbits of Mars and Jupiter, but the orbits of some asteroids take them close to the Sun and across the paths of the planets such as the Earth. These asteroids are called "Near Earth Objects." Some of these may have collided with the Earth.

Asthenosphere Plastic layer of the upper mantle that underlies the lithosphere, which is able to move over it.

Astron A very large, circular impact crater formed by an asteroid, e.g., like the feature that extends from Hudson Bay to the south shore of Lake Superior under rocks of the Canadian Shield in northwestern Ontario.

Atmosphere Blanket of air that adheres to the Earth's surface, which contains the mixture of gases essential to the survival of all terrestrial life forms.

Atolls Ringlike coral reefs surrounding empty lagoons; grew on the rims of eroded volcanic cones.

Atterberg limits Geotechnical engineering limits defining when an Earth material acts as a solid, plastic or liquid. Mainly influenced by the amount and type of clays and the amount of moisture.

Attrition Wave erosion process where larger rock fragments are reduced to smaller fragments as loose material is continuously moved about in churning water.

Aurora australis Name given to the *aurora* phenomenon that occurs in the Southern Hemisphere's upper middle and high latitudes.

Aurora borealis Vivid sheetlike displays of light in the nighttime sky of the upper middle and high latitudes in the Northern Hemisphere; caused by the intermittent penetration of the thermosphere by ionized particles.

Autotroph Organism that manufactures its own organic materials from inorganic chemicals. A good example is phytoplankton, food-producing plants that manufacture carbohydrates.

Avalanches A mass movement involving the turbulent failure of material down a slope. The material travels as a turbulent density current down the slope on a layer of compressed air and is preceded by an airblast that can flatten trees, cause defoliation, etc. A landslide which can occur in pure snow, rock, or debris or mixtures of material.

Axis (Earth's) Imaginary line that extends from the North Pole to the South Pole through the centre of the Earth. The planet's rotation occurs with respect to this axis.

Azonal flow *Meridional* (north–south) flow of upper atmospheric winds (poleward of 15 degrees of latitude), particularly the subtropical and Polar Front jet streams. Periodic departures from the zonal (west-to-east) flow of these air currents are important because they help to correct the heat imbalance between polar and equatorial regions.

Azores High Eastern segment of the North Atlantic Ocean's semipermanent subtropical high-pressure cell (often called the Bermuda High) that is usually centered above the Azores Islands; an important component of the North Atlantic Oscillation (NAO).

B horizon Middle soil layer, which often receives dissolved and suspended particles from above.

Backshore Beach zone that lies landward of the foreshore; extends from the high-water line to the dune line.

Backslope (dune) Windward slope of a sand dune.

Backwash Return flow to the sea of the thinning sheet of water that slid up the beach as swash undertow.

Bajada Coalesced assemblage of alluvial fans that lines a highland front (also known as *alluvial apron*); primarily a desert feature.

Ballistic, Ballistically An object that is set in motion and then moves under the force of gravity. An object moving in such a manner.

Barchan Crescent-shaped sand dune with its points lying downwind. Convex side of this dune is the windward side.

Barometer Instrument that measures atmospheric pressure.

Barrens An uninhabited wilderness with a harsh climate. Characterized by rock outcrop and shallow sandy and stony soils with a sparse grass cover, wetland areas, and widely dispersed short or stunted trees.

Barrier island Permanent offshore elongated ridge of sand, positioned parallel to the shoreline and separated from it by a lagoon; may have formed originally as an offshore bar during the last glaciation, migrated coastward, and grew as it shifted.

Basal ice Bottom ice layer of a glacier or ice sheet.

Basal (or Peripheral) sliding Lubrication and movement at the base or periphery (sides and base) of a glacier or ice sheet caused by the pressure melting of base (or periphery) caused by pressure melting. Only occurs in Wet-based or Temperate ice.

Basal (or Lodgement) till Till material that is carried englacially and subglacially and is deposited under the ice.

Base level Elevational level below which a stream cannot erode its bed. Ultimate base level is sea level.

Baseflow stream regime Baseflow, or groundwater, is the source of most of a stream's discharge.

Batholith Massive, discordant body of intrusive igneous rock (pluton), which has destroyed and melted most of the existing geological structures it has invaded.

Bauxite Aluminum hydroxide soil horizon.

Bay Broad indentation into a coastline.

Baymouth bar Sandspit that has grown all the way across the mouth of a bay.

Beach Coastal zone of sediment that is shaped by the action of waves; constructed of sand and other materials, derived from both local and distant sources.

Beach drift Larger process associated with longshore drift, which operates to move huge amounts of beach sand or shingle downshore in the direction of the longshore current.

Bedding plane Distinct junction between two sedimentary rock strata.

Below bankfull discharge A stream discharge that is below the height of the banks. Occurs most of the time.

Benioff zone An inclined zone of earthquake foci associated with subduction. The magnitude of the earthquakes increase with depth.

Berm Beach ridge that lies in the backshore beach zone; deposited during storms and beyond the reach of normal daily wave action.

Bermuda High Local name for the North Atlantic Ocean's Subtropical High pressure cell, which is generally centered over latitude 30°N; also known as the Azores High.

Biodiversity *Biological diversity;* variety of the Earth's life forms and the ecological roles they play.

Biofilm A thin coating of algae or bacteria covering a cave wall or other rock face, boulder, or tree.

Biogenic Refers to processes or activities of living organisms.

Biogeography Geography of plants (*phytogeography*) and animals (*zoogeography*).

Biological weathering Decay and disintegration of rock minerals via biological means. Earthworms and plant roots are important in the development of soil, lichens contribute to the breakdown of rocks, and humans, of course, play various roles in the disintegration of rocks and the operation of soil-formation processes.

Biomass Total living organic matter, encompassing all plants and animals, produced in a particular geographical area.

Biome Broadest subdivision of the plant and animal world, an assemblage and association of plants and animals, which forms a regional ecological unit of subcontinental dimensions.

Biosphere Zone of terrestrial life, the habitat of all living things; includes the Earth's vegetation, animals, human beings, and the soil layer.

Biota Total complement of living species found in a given area.

Bioturbation Mixing of the soil by animals or plants.

Birdfoot Delta A stream delta shaped like a bird's foot.

Black-and-white smokers Geothermal hot springs related to midocean ridge spreading sites. The seawater infiltrates the crust close to a magma body. Gets superhot and melts some of the minerals in the crustal rock on the way back to the seabed. On release, the minerals are precipitated to form a chimney around the spring. The colour depends on the minerals involved.

Blocky (angular) soil structure Involves irregularly shaped peds with straight sides that fit against the flat surfaces of adjacent peds, thereby giving a soil considerable strength (*see* Fig. 24.5).

Block streams (*see* rock glaciers)

Bluffs Low cliffs that border the outer edges of an alluvium-filled floodplain or a lake.

Body wave Seismic waves that travel through the interior of the Earth (**P** waves and **S** waves).

Boiling point (water) Key setting in the calibration of the temperature scales. On the Celsius scale water boils at 100°C.

Bomb (storm) Mild winter weather disturbance that drifts northward along the Eastern seaboard of North America, and then suddenly "explodes" into a furious snowstorm, paralyzing the nation's most heavily populated region.

Bombs (volcanic) Just-solidified masses of lava that rain down on a volcano during an explosive eruption. They originate as gas-rich magma whose gases explode when they reach the surface, hurling projectiles of solid lava into the air (which soon fall back to the ground).

Bottomset beds Finest deltaic deposits, usually laid down ahead of the delta, where the coastal water is quiet.

Boulder field (*see* rock sea)

Braided stream Carries a high sediment load when in flood. The flow subdivides into many intertwined channels, reuniting some distance downstream. The flow decreases as sediment is deposited in banks, giving the "braided" appearance.

Breaker Forward collapse of the wave crest since an incoming wave can no longer push water upward as it encounters the ever shallower ocean bottom.

Breccia Clastic sedimentary rocks where the pebble-sized fragments are angular and jagged.

Brunisol A Canadian soil order characterized by the weak development of a reddish brown B horizon lacking in clays and other compounds. The soils in this order are more developed than Regosols. Equivalent to the Inceptisol soil order of the U.S. Soil Taxonomy.

Butte Small, steep-sided, caprock-protected hill, usually found in dry environments; an erosional remnant of a plateau.

C horizon Bottom soil layer in which the weathering of parent material proceeds.

Calcification Pedogenetic regime associated with arid conditions in which calcium carbonate or other salts are brought up into the soil by the capillary rise of groundwater.

Calcite Calcium carbonate ($CaCO_3$), the common mineral that is the main constituent of limestone.

Caldera Steep-walled, circular volcanic basin usually formed by the collapse of a volcano whose magma chamber emptied; can also result from a particularly powerful eruption that blows off the peak and crater of a volcano.

Caliche A hardened calcium-rich layer in soils in arid areas. Protects underlying less-resistant rocks to form pillars, buttes, and mesas.

Calorie One calorie is the amount of heat energy required to raise the temperature of 1 g of water by 1°C; not the same unit as the calories used to measure the energy value of food (which are 1000 times larger).

Calving When an ice sheet or glacier enters the sea, the repeated breaking away of the leading edge of that glacier into icebergs.

Canadian High Local name for northern North America's Polar High, centred over far northwestern Canada.

Canadian System of Soil Classification The Canadian soil taxonomy.

Canopy A canopy is formed by the inter-fingering of tree crowns, e.g., in a tropical rainforest.

Canyon Steep-sided gorge.

Capillary action Rise of groundwater upward through soil pores owing to the tension between water molecules.

Carbon dioxide (CO_2) cycle Dominated by exchanges occurring between air and sea. CO_2 is directly absorbed by the ocean from the atmosphere and is released during the photosynthesis of billions of small organisms known as plankton.

Carbonation Reaction of weak carbonic acid (formed from water and carbon dioxide) with minerals. Carbonic acid, in turn, reacts with carbonate rocks such as limestone in a form of chemical weathering that can be quite vigorous in certain humid areas, where solution and decay lead to the formation of karst landscapes.

Carbonic acid Weak acid (H_2CO_3), formed from water and carbon dioxide, that is instrumental in the important chemical weathering process known as carbonation.

Caribbean karst Rarest karst topography, associated with nearly flat-lying limestones; underground erosion dominated by the collapse of roofs of subsurface conduits, producing a characteristic sinkhole terrain.

Carnivore Animal that eats herbivores and other animals.

Carolinian forest A vegetation zone of deciduous forest with minor areas of long grass prairie and savanna found in south-western Ontario, south of a line drawn due west from Kingston. Much of it has been cleared for agricultural or urban development. The plants and animals have affinities with more southerly areas (e.g., the Carolinas), e.g., black walnut, tulip tree, sassafras, paw paw, southern flying squirrel.

Catastrophic flooding Massive flooding that is much greater than usual overbank flows. Has a periodicity of 50, 100, 150, or 200 years, etc.

Cartography Science, art, and technology of map-making and map use.

Catena Derived from a Latin word meaning chain or series, refers to a sequence of soils appearing in regular succession on landform features of uniform rock type; most frequently associated with hillsides where the same parent material has produced an arrangement of different soil types because of differences in drainage.

Cation Positively charged ion, such as those of calcium.

Cave Any substantial opening in bedrock, large enough for an adult to enter, which leads to an interior open space.

Cave shaft Vertical cave entrance.

Celsius scale Metric temperature scale most commonly used throughout the world (except in the U. S.). The boiling point of water is set at 100°C and its freezing point at 0°C.

Cementation During the lithification process of compaction as the grains of sediments are tightly squeezed together, water in the intervening pore spaces, which contains dissolved minerals, is deposited on the grain surfaces and acts as a glue to bond the grains together.

Cenozoic Era on the geological time scale, extending from 65 million years ago to the present; subdivided into the Tertiary and Quaternary Periods.

Champlain sea An invasion of the sea into the St. Lawrence valley at the end of the Wisconsinan and early Holocene (8000–11000 years ago) caused by the Laurentide ice sheet weighing down the crust in that area.

Channel flows Flows that affect a small channelized area of a slope.

Chaparral Name given to the dominant Mediterranean scrub vegetation in southern California.

Chemical weathering Decomposition of rock minerals via chemical means. In any rock made up of a combination of minerals, the chemical breakdown of one set of mineral grains leads to the disintegration of the whole mass.

Chernozemic soil order A Canadian soil order characteristic of the moister areas of the Prairies. Charaterized by having a thick (mull) humus rich **A** horizon over a calcium rich **B** horizon.

Chinook Name given to the *foehn* winds that affect the leeward areas of mountain zones in the western plateaux of North America, e.g., Alberta.

Chlorophyll Green pigment found in plant surfaces that ensures that the correct wavelength of light is absorbed for the process of photosynthesis, and that enables this process to take place.

Cinder cone Volcanic landform consisting mainly of pyroclastics. Often formed during brief periods of explosive activity, they normally remain quite small.

Cinders (volcanic) (*see* **ash** [volcanic])

Circle of illumination At any given moment on our constantly rotating planet, the boundary between the halves of the Earth that are in sunlight and darkness.

Circum-Pacific earthquake belt Aspect of the Pacific Ring of Fire, the lengthy belt of subduction zones that girdles the Pacific Basin. Here the heaviest concentration of earthquake epicentres as well as active volcanoes occurs.

Cirque Amphitheatre-like basin, high up on a mountain, that is the source area of an alpine glacier.

Cirrus Cloud category that encompasses thin, wispy, streaklike clouds consisting of ice particles rather than water droplets; occur only at altitudes higher than 6000 m.

Clastic sedimentary rocks Sedimentary rocks composed of broken and fragmentary particles eroded from previously existing rocks.

Clay Smallest category of soil particles. Clay particles are smaller than 0.002 mm, with the smallest in the colloidal range possessing diameters of less than one micrometre (1μm).

Cleavage Tendency of minerals to break in certain directions along bright plane surfaces, revealing zones of weakness in the crystalline structure, e.g., slate, shale.

Climate Long-term conditions (over at least 30 years) of aggregate weather over a region, summarized by averages and measures of variability; a synthesis of the succession of weather events we have learned to expect at any given location.

Climatic controls Features of the Earth's surface—such as the distribution of land and water bodies, ocean currents, and highlands—that shape the climate of an area by influencing its temperature and moisture regimes.

Climatic normal Average value for one of many weather parameters during a 30-year period for worldwide locations, published (in table form) by the World Meteorological Organization.

Climatic optimum Period of maximum warmth during the Holocene interglacial epoch; was experienced between 7000 and 5000 years ago.

Climatic state Average, together with the variability and other statistics, of the complete set of atmospherical, hydrospherical, and cryospherical variables over a specified period of time in a specified domain of the Earth–atmosphere system.

Climatology Geographical study of climates. This includes not only climate classification and the analysis of their regional distribution, but broader environmental questions that concern climate change, interrelationships with soil and vegetation, and human–climate interaction.

Climax community Achieved at the end of a plant succession. The vegetation and its ecosystem are in complete harmony (dynamic equilibrium) with the soil, the climate, and other parts of the environment.

Climograph Graph that simultaneously displays, for a given location, its key climatic variables of average temperature and precipitation, showing how they change monthly throughout the year.

Closed system Self-contained system exhibiting no exchange of energy or matter across its boundaries (interfaces).

Cloud Visible mass of suspended, minute water droplets or ice crystals.

Coalescence process Raindrop-producing process that dominates in the tropical latitudes.

Coast General reference to the strip of land and sea where the various coastal processes combine to create characteristic landscapes. The term *shore* has a more specific meaning.

Cockpit karst In tropical karst areas, the sharply contrasted landscape of prominent karst towers and the irregular, steep-sided depressions lying between them. *Cockpit* refers to the depressions.

Cohesional resistance Resistance against movement caused by cohesion or sticking together of slope materials, e.g., clays.

Cold-air drainage Category of local-scale wind systems governed by the downward oozing of heavy, dense, cold air along steep slopes under the influence of gravity; produces katabatic winds (such as southeastern France's *mistral*) that are fed by massive pools of icy air that accumulate over such major mountain regions as the Alps and the Rocky Mountains.

Cold front Produced when an advancing cold air mass hugs the surface and displaces all other air as it wedges itself beneath the preexisting warmer air mass. Cold fronts have much steeper slopes than warm fronts and thus produce more abrupt cooling and condensation (and more intense precipitation).

Cold (or Polar) ice Ice that does not reach pressure melting point because it is in very cold areas or because it does not have sufficient mass. The ice is frozen to the ground. Movement is restricted to ice layers above the ice/ground interface.

Cold lahar A mudflow caused by rainfall mobilizing a pre-existing blanket of volcanic ash.

Cold (or Periglacial) loess Loess derived from Sandar.

Collapse sink Collapsed sinkhole in which the rock ceiling of the sinkhole collapses into the underground solution cavity.

Collapse sinkhole In karst terrain, a surface hollow created by the collapse or failure of the roof or overlying material of a cave, cavern, or underground channel.

Colloids Tiny soil particles formed from the disintegration of soil minerals and humus. They can be observed in suspension in the soil solution, making it look turbid.

Colluvium Soil particles that have washed downslope and have come to rest on the slope; give rise to colluvial soils.

Color (mineral) One of the most easily observable properties of a mineral; used in its identification.

Column (cave) Coalescence of a stalactite and a stalagmite that forms a continuous column from the floor to the roof of a cave.

Compaction Lithification process where deposited sediments are compressed by the weight of newer, overlying sediments. This pressure will compact and consolidate lower strata, squeezing their sediments tightly together. Usually occurs in conjunction with cementation.

Composite volcano Volcano formed, usually above a subduction zone, by the eruption of a succession of lavas, pyroclastics, and ash that accumulate as a series of alternating layers; the larger and more durable composite volcanoes are called *stratovolcanoes*.

Comprehensive Soil Classification System (CSCS) U.S. soil classification system based on the characteristics of the soils. Now called the U.S. Soil Taxonomy.

Compressional stress Stress associated with the convergence of lithospheric plates. The lithosphere is forced to occupy less space and the rocks respond by breaking, bending, folding, sliding, squeezing upward and downward, and crushing tightly together.

Concave Refers to a surface that is rounded inward, like the inside surface of a sphere.

Concoidal Shell-like.

Concordant intrusion Intrusive magma that did not disrupt or destroy surrounding, existing geological structures but conformed to them.

Condensation Process by which a substance is transformed from the gaseous to the liquid state.

Condensation nuclei Small airborne particles around which liquid droplets can form when water vapor condenses; almost always present in the atmosphere in the form of dust or salt particles.

Conduction   Transport of heat energy from one molecule to the next.

Cone of depression   Drop (drawdown) in a local water table that immediately surrounds a well when water is withdrawn faster than it can be replaced by water flowing through that tapped aquifer.

Confined aquifer   (*see* **aquifer, confined**)

Conformal map projection   Map projection that preserves the true shape of the area being mapped.

Conic map projection   One in which the transfer of the Earth grid is from a globe onto a cone, which is then cut and laid flat.

Coniferous   Cone-bearing.

Conservation   Careful management and use of natural resources, the achievement of significant social benefits from them, and the preservation of the natural environment.

Constant gases   Atmospheric gases always found in the same proportions. Two of them constitute 99 percent of the air, nitrogen (78 percent) and oxygen (21 percent).

Contact metamorphism   Metamorphic change in rocks induced by their local contact with molten magma or lava.

Constant of Channel maintenance   The unit area of drainage basin needed to sustain a unit length of stream channel (km^2/km). The reciprocal of drainage density.

Continent (geological)   Geologists define a continent as having granitic crust (SIAL) over basaltic crust (SIMA).

Continental drift   Notion hypothesized by Alfred Wegener concerning the fragmentation of Pangaea and the slow movement of continents away from this core supercontinent. Not the same as plate tectonics.

Continental effect   Lack of the moderating influence of an ocean on air temperature, which is characteristic of inland locations; this produces hotter summers and colder winters relative to coastal locations at similar latitudes.

Continental ice sheets (or glaciers)   Huge masses of ice that bury large areas beneath them.

Continental rise   Transitional zone of gently sloping seafloor that begins at the foot of the continental slope and leads downward to the lowest (abyssal) zone of an ocean basin.

Continental shelf   Gently sloping, relatively shallow, submerged plain just off the coast of a continent, extending to a depth of ca. 180 m.

Continental shield   Large, stable, relatively flat expanse of very old rocks that may constitute one of the earliest "slabs" of solidification of the primeval Earth's molten crust into hard rocks or formed by meteoric impact; forms the geological core of a continental landmass.

Continental slope   Steeply plunging slope that begins at the outer edge of the continental shelf (ca. 180 m [600 ft] below the sea surface) and ends in the depths of the ocean floor at the head of the continental rise.

Continentality   Variation of the continental effect on air temperatures in the interior portions of the world's landmasses; the greater the distance from the moderating influence of an ocean (known as the maritime effect), the greater the extreme in summer and winter temperatures (northeastern Eurasia is the classic example of such extreme annual temperature cycles).

Contouring   Representation of surface relief using isolines of elevation above sea level; an important basis of topographical mapping.

Conurbation   Coalescence of two or more metropolitan areas. The Golden Horseshoe around the measurement of Lake Ontario is the only one in Canada. The U.S. northeastern seaboard's Megalopolis consists of a continuous corridor of connected metropolises that stretches from south of Washington, D.C., to north of Boston.

Convection cell   Rising column of air.

Convectional precipitation   Convection is the spontaneous vertical movement of air in the atmosphere. Convectional precipitation occurs after condensation of this rising air, e.g., related to a thunderstorm.

Convergent evolution   Theory that holds that organisms in widely separated biogeographic realms, although descended from diverse ancestors, develop similar adaptations to measurably similar habitats.

Convergent-lifting precipitation   Precipitation produced by the forced lifting of warm, moist air where low-level windflows converge; most pronounced in the equatorial latitudes, where the Northeast and Southeast Trades come together in the Inter-Tropical Convergence Zone (ITCZ), especially over the oceans.

Convex   Refers to a surface that is rounded outward, like the outside surface of a sphere.

Coral reef   Aggradational reef formed from the skeletal remains of marine organisms.

Core (drilling)   Tubelike sample of seafloor sediment or other rock that is captured and brought to the surface in a hollow drill pipe. The drill pipe is thrust perpendicularly into the ocean floor, and the sample it brings up shows the sequence of sedimentary accumulation.

Core (Earth's)   (*see* **inner core; outer core**)

Coriolis force   Force that, owing to the rotation of the Earth, tends to deflect all objects moving over the surface of the Earth away from their original paths. In the absence of any other forces, the deflection is to the right in the Northern Hemisphere and to the left in the Southern Hemisphere; the higher the latitude, the stronger the deflection.

Corrasion Mechanical coastal-erosion process whereby waves break off pieces of rock from the surface under attack. The sediment-loaded water, now a much more powerful erosive agent, continues to be hurled against that surface.

Counterradiation Longwave radiation emitted by the Earth's surface that is absorbed by the atmosphere and reradiated (also as longwave radiation) back down to the surface.

Coversands Aeolian sands deposited during deglaciation.

Craton A stable area of a continent that has not undergone deformation for a very long time. In North America the Craton is composed of the Canadian Shield and the Platform Borderlands.

Creep Slowest form of mass movement; involves the slow, imperceptible motion of a soil layer downslope, as revealed in the slight downhill tilt of trees and other stationary objects.

Crevasse One of the huge vertical cracks that frequently cut the rigid, brittle upper layer of a glacier or ice sheet.

Critical threshold The point where stability and instability are finely balanced.

Cross-bedding Consists of successive rock strata deposited not horizontally but at varying inclines. Like ripple marks on sand, this usually forms on beaches and in dunes.

Crustal spreading Geographical term for seafloor spreading. Not all crustal spreading occurs on the ocean floor. (*see* **rift valley**)

Crustal warping (*see* **diastrophism**)

Cryosol Canadian soil order distinguished by the presence of ice or permafrost in the profile.

Cryosphere Name for the ice system of the Earth, which constitutes one of the five subsystems of the total Earth System.

Cryoturbation Frost churning of mineral or organic soil materials in cryosolic soils (gelisols).

Crystalline rocks Rocks composed of minerals that exhibit a regularly repeating molecular structure; can also be used generally to refer to igneous and metamorphic rocks as opposed to sedimentary rocks.

Cuesta Long ridge with a steep escarpment on one side and a gently dipping slope and rockbeds on the other.

Cumulonimbus Very tall cumulus clouds, extending from about 500 m at the base to over 10 km at the top, often associated with violent weather involving thunder, lightning, and heavy winds and rains.

Cumulus Cloud category that encompasses thick, puffy, billowing masses that often develop to great heights; subclassified according to height (*see* p. 151).

Cuspate Foreland a "fang"-shaped beach or spit-form caused by the convergence of two longshore currents or drift systems

Cut and fill (beach) Cut and fill refers to the cycle of beach erosion and deposition. Erosion usually occurs because of more storms and greater wave action during the winter months, while deposition normally takes place during the summer when there are fewer storms and less wave energy.

Cuirasse A protective Duricrust cover such as a laterite or a caliche.

Cut bank Another name for a meander cliff. The outer bend of a meander bend which is undercut by stream flow.

Cycle of erosion Model of landscape development suggested by W.M. Davis in the later part of the nineteenth century which postulated a short period of uplift followed by an extremely long (eons in length) period of erosion during which the landscape was worn down to a nearly flat surface (a peneplain).

Cyclic autogenic succession Plant succession in which one type of vegetation is replaced by another, which in turn is replaced by the first, with other series possibly intermixed.

Cyclogenesis Formation, evolution, and movement of midlatitude cyclones.

Cyclone Atmospheric low-pressure cell involving the convergence of air, which flows into and spirally rises at the center. The isobars around a cyclone are generally circular in shape, with their values decreasing toward the center. In the Northern Hemisphere, winds flow counterclockwise around a cyclone; in the Southern Hemisphere, winds flow clockwise around a cyclone.

Cyclonic precipitation Precipitation associated with the passage of the warm and cold fronts that are basic components of the cyclones that shape the weather patterns of the midlatitudes; often used as a synonym for *frontal precipitation*.

Cylindrical map projection One in which the transfer of the Earth grid is from a globe onto a cylinder, which is then cut and laid flat.

DALR (*see* **dry adiabatic lapse rate**)

Daylight-saving time By law, all clocks in a time zone are set one hour forward from standard time for at least part of the year. In Canada, all provinces observe Daylight Saving Time, with the exception of Saskatchewan.

Debris or Rock avalanche (*see* **avalanches**)

Debris or Rock fall or Topple The fall or tumbling of rock or debris down a slope. Topple involves the falling over of slabs of rock or debris and the fall of material down slope.

Debris flow A Hillslope process involving the viscous flow of debris. Essentially an excessively loaded flow of water.

Debris torrents A Hillslope process involving an excessively-loaded channel flow containing rock, debris and tree material, caused by the build up of material in an mountain drainage basin and mobilization by intense rainfall and/or snow melt.

Deciduous Of trees and other plants that drop their leaves seasonally.

Deflation Process whereby wind sweeps along a surface and carries away the finest particles.

Deflation hollow A basin excavated by Aeolian activity.

Deforestation (*see* **tropical deforestation**)

Deformation Any change in the form and/or structure of a body of crustal rock caused by an Earth movement.

Deglaciation Melting and receding of glaciers that accompanies the climatic warm-up after the peak of a glacial period has been reached.

Degassing 1) Gasses erupted during a volcanic eruption, or 2) The release of carbon dioxide in to the cave atmosphere when dripstone (secondary calcite) is deposited.

Degradation Takes place through a combination of processes that erode the landscape.

Delta Often major sedimentary deposit surrounding and extending beyond the mouth of a river where it empties into the sea or a lake; frequently assumes a triangular configuration, hence its naming after the Greek letter of that shape.

Deltaic plain Flat, stable landward portion of a delta that is growing seaward.

Dendritic drainage Tree-limb-like stream pattern that is the most commonly observed; indicates surface of relatively uniform hardness or one of flat-lying sedimentary rocks.

Dendrochronology Study of the width of annual growth rings in trees.

Density Amount of mass per volume in an object or a portion of the atmosphere.

Denudation Erosion of the landscape.

Depletion Soil-layer formation process involving the loss of soil components as they are carried downward by water, plus the loss of other material in suspension as the water percolates through the soil from upper to lower layers. While the upper layers are depleted accordingly, the dissolved and suspended materials are redeposited lower down in the soil.

Deranged drainage Drainage that is confused, i.e., many short sections of stream separated by intervening wetlands and lakes.

Desert biome Characterized by sparse, xerophytic vegetation or even the complete absence of plant life.

Desert climate (BW) Most arid of climates, usually experiencing no more than 250 mm of annual precipitation.

Desert (or Hot) loess Aeolian silt and fine sand derived from deserts.

Desert pavement A desert lag deposit of coarser material (gravel, stones) left behind as wind winnows the finer material and carries it away. Also called Reg (Arabia) Gibber Plain (Australia) or Gobi (central Asia). Often covered by desert varnish.

Desertification Process of desert expansion into neighboring steppe lands as a result of human degradation of fragile semiarid environments.

Dew Fine water droplets that condense on surfaces at and near the ground when saturated air is cooled. The source of this condensate is the excess water vapor beyond the saturation level of that air parcel, whose capacity to contain water decreases as its temperature drops.

Dew point Temperature at which air becomes saturated and below which condensation occurs.

Diapir, Diapirism A rising mass of magma in the crust or an igneous intrusion. The process of magma rising in the crust and intruding pre-existing rocks.

Diastrophism Vertical and horizontal movements of the earth's crust.

Diffuse radiation Proportion of incoming solar energy (22 percent) that reaches the Earth's surface after first being scattered in the atmosphere by clouds, dust particles, and other airborne materials.

Dyke (dike) Discordant intrusive igneous form in which magma has cut vertically across preexisting strata, forming a kind of "barrier" wall.

Dip Angle at which a rock layer tilts from the horizontal.

Direct radiation Proportion of incoming solar energy that travels directly to the Earth's surface; globally, this averages 31 percent.

Discharge (stream) (Q) Volume of water passing a given cross-section of a river channel per unit of time; measured as average water velocity multiplied by the cross-sectional area (m^3/s).

Discordant intrusion Intrusive magma that did not conform to but cut across or otherwise disrupted surrounding, existing geological structures.

Dispersal Evolution of a modern species from an ancestral species that arrived in a given area by movement over land, swimming, rafting, or flying.

Disruption (of a surface) The erosion or change of a surface caused by raindrop impact. There is microcratering, material is re-oriented or disoriented, some particles are thrown down slope, finer material is eroded leaving micro-pillars of finer material under gravel particles or stones etc.

Dissolution   Chemical weathering process in which soluble rocks such as limestone are dissolved.

Dissolved solids   Another term used for material in solution in groundwater or stream water.

Distributaries   Several channels into which a river subdivides when it reaches its delta; caused by the clogging of the river mouth by deposition of fine-grained sediment as the stream reaches base level and water velocity declines markedly. Also used for channels of a braided stream.

Diurnal temperature cycle   Pattern of temperature change during the course of a day.

Drainage divide   Topographical barrier, usually a mountain ridge or higher ground, that separates two drainage basins.

Doldrums   Equatorial zone of periodic calm seas and unpredictable breezes where the Northeast and Southeast Trades converge. The crews of sailing ships dreaded these waters because their vessels risked becoming stranded in this becalmed area.

Doline   A depression in Karstic terrain caused by the collapse of a cave roof.

Dolostone (dolomite)   Soluble magnesium carbonate rock ($CaMg[CO_3]_2$), in addition to calcite-rich limestone, that can form karst topography.

Dormant volcano   Volcano that has not been seen to erupt but shows evidence of recent activity.

Doubling time   Number of years required for a given human population to double itself in size. For the world as a whole, in 2003 that figure stood at 48 years.

Downthrown block   Block that moves downward with respect to adjacent blocks when vertical movement occurs during faulting.

Drag structures   Structures formed as a thawed soil moves down slope, "pulling out" the underlying materials.

Drainage basin   Area occupied by a complete stream system formed by the trunk river and all its tributaries.

Drainage density   Total length of the stream channels that exist in a unit area of a drainage basin (km/km^2).

Drainage divide (or Watershed)   The boundary separating one Drainage basin from another. Usually formed by higher ground.

Drainage network   A trunk stream and its tributaries. A stream system.

Drawdown   Amount of drop in a local water table that occurs when water is withdrawn through a well faster than it can be replaced by new groundwater in the aquifer; commonly forms a cone of depression around the well.

Drift (glacial)   (*see* **glacial drift**)

Drift (ocean surface)   Term often used as a synonym for ocean current when the rate of movement lags well behind the average speeds of surface winds blowing in the same direction. Currents are characterized by a slow and steady movement that very rarely exceeds 8 km/h.

Driftless area   Area in southwestern Wisconsin that was never covered by the continental ice sheets that repeatedly buried adjacent areas of the middle of North America.

Dripstone   Secondary calcium carbonate deposited in a cave or around a spring

Drought   Below-average availability of water in a given area over a period lasting at least several months or years.

Drumlin   An asymmetrical whaleback or hogback hill, oval in plan. Cut by subglacial mega-floods.

Dry adiabatic lapse rate (DALR)   Lapse rate of an air parcel not saturated with water vapor: $-1°C/100$ m.

Dry-bulb temperature   On a psychrometer, temperature reading of the thermometer whose bulb is not swaddled in a wet cloth. Air temperature.

Dune   Accumulation of sand that is shaped by wind action.

Dune crest   Top of a sand dune where the backslope and slip face meet.

Duricrust   An indurated cuirasse or crust, e.g., laterite or caliche.

Dust Bowl   Environmental disaster that plagued the Prairies and Great Plains for most of the 1930s. The continued heavy ploughing of much of this region during a prolonged drought (in a futile attempt to keep raising wheat on a large scale) resulted in the loosened topsoil falling prey to the ever-present wind. Huge dust clouds soon formed, which carried the soil away and deposited it as dunes, forcing thousands of farm families to abandon their fields and migrate out of the area.

Dust dome   Characteristic shape taken by the large quantities of dust and gaseous pollutants in a city's atmosphere.

Dust (volcanic)   Fine solid lava fragments, smaller than particles of volcanic ash, that are exploded into the air during an eruption. These lighter materials fall to the ground farthest from a volcano, but also can be carried for substantial distances by prevailing windflows if they are exploded high enough into the troposphere.

Dynamic equilibrium   An equilibrium state where the fundamental controls vary over time, e.g., rainfall, temperature, etc.

Debris or Earth flow   Form of slope process in which a section of soil or weathered bedrock, lying on a rather steep slope, becomes saturated by heavy rains until it is lubricated enough to flow.

Earth System Shells or layers that make up the total Earth System range from those of the planet's deepest interior to those bordering outer space. This book focuses on the five key Earth layers: atmosphere, lithosphere, hydrosphere, cryosphere, and biosphere.

Earthquake Shaking and trembling of the Earth's surface; caused by sudden releases of stresses that have been building slowly within the crust.

Earthworm An hermaphroditic annelid found in soil. The most important soil fauna in temperate soils.

Easterly wave Wavelike perturbation in the constant easterly flow of the Northeast and Southeast Trades, which produces this type of distinctive weather system. Westward-moving air is forced to rise on the upwind side (producing often heavy rainfall) and descend on the fair-weather downwind side of the low-pressure wave trough.

Echelon faults A series of nearly parallel faults produced by compressional forces when the crust is horizontally shortened. Sometimes the crustal block between two reverse faults is pushed upward to form a horst.

Ecological niche The way a group of organisms makes its living in nature, or the environmental space within which an organism operates most efficiently.

Ecosystem Linkage of plants or animals to their environment in an open system as far as energy is concerned. An ecological system.

Ecumene Portion of the world's land surface that is permanently settled by human beings.

Edaphic factors Factors concerned with the soil.

Eddies Localized loops of water circulation detached from the mainstream of a nearby current, which move along with the general flow of that current. Occur in the ocean and streams.

Ediacaran (Ediacaran fauna) An era of Late Proterozoic. A very early fossil fauna.

El Niño Periodic, large-scale, abnormal warming of the sea surface in the low latitudes of the eastern Pacific Ocean that produces a (temporary) reversal of surface ocean currents and airflows throughout the equatorial Pacific. These regional events have global implications, disturbing normal weather patterns in many parts of the world.

Electromagnetic spectrum Continuum of electric and magnetic energy, as measured by wavelength, from the high-energy shortwave radiation of cosmic rays to the low-energy longwave radiation of radio and electric power.

ELR (*see* **environmental lapse rate**)

Eluviation Means "washed out" and refers to the soil process that involves removal from the **Ae** horizon and downward transportation of soluble minerals and microscopic, colloid-sized particles of organic matter, clay, and aluminum and iron oxides.

Emergent coast Coastal zone whose landforms have recently emerged from the sea, through either tectonic uplift or a drop in sea level, or both.

Empirical Real world, as opposed to an abstract theoretical model. Based on measurement and scientific study.

Endemism Biotic complex of an isolated (or once isolated) area, many of whose species of plants, animals, and other life forms exist nowhere else on Earth. The species in such places are particularly vulnerable to extinction through the environmental changes introduced by humans, e.g., New Zealand and Australia.

Englacial Material carried within a glacier or ice sheet. When melted out becomes a part of Basal Tills.

ENSO Acronym for El Niño–Southern Oscillation, the reversal of the flow of ocean currents and prevailing winds in the equatorial Pacific Ocean that disturbs global weather patterns.

Entisol One of the 12 soil orders of the U.S. Soil Taxonomy, which contains all the soils of recent origin. Equivalent to the Regisolic soil order.

Entrenched meanders Meanders of a stream incised into hard bedrock from overlying floodplain topography; caused by the uplifting of the land or fall base level.

Entropy The complete dissipation (usage and/or wastage) of energy.

Entropy surface The lowest point to which the landscape can erode beyond which there is no energy available.

Environmental lapse rate (ELR) Nonadiabatic lapse rate at any particular time or place. The troposphere's (nonadiabatic) normal lapse rate averages $-0.64°C/100$ m.

Epeirogeny Vertical movement of the Earth's crust over very large areas that produces little or no bending or breaking of the uplifted (or downward thrusted) rocks.

Ephemeral plant One that completes its life cycle within a single growing season.

Ephemeral stream Intermittently flowing stream. Precipitation (and subsequent streamflow) is periodic, and when the rains end, the stream soons runs dry again.

Epicentre Point on the Earth's surface directly above the *focus* (place of origin) of an earthquake.

Epiphyte Tropical rainforest plant that uses trees for support, but is not parasitic.

Equal-area map projection One in which all the areas mapped are represented in correct proportion to one another.

Equator   Parallel of latitude running around the exact middle of the globe, defined as 0° latitude.

Equatorial low   Inter-Tropical Convergence Zone (ITCZ) or thermal low-pressure belt of rising air that straddles the equatorial latitudinal zone; fed by the wind-flows of the converging Northeast and Southeast Trades.

Equilibrium   A system state where input equals output (Steady state).

Equilibrium Line   A line that separates the accumulation zone from the ablation zone on a glacier or ice sheet.

Equinox   One of the two days (around March 21 and September 23) in the year when the Sun's noontime rays strike the Earth vertically at the Equator. In Northern Hemisphere terminology, the March 21 event is called the spring (vernal) equinox and the September 23 event is called the fall (autumnal) equinox.

Erg   Sand sea; large expanse of sandy desert landscape.

Erosion   Carrying away of weathered rock material and associated processes, where the Earth's surface is reshaped.

Escarpment   (*see* **cuesta**)

Esker   Glacial outwash landform. A long ribbonlike ridge of sand and gravel in the landscape because it was formed by the clogging of a river course within or with a glacier, the debris from which remain after the ice melts.

Estuary   Drowned (submerged) mouth of a river valley that has become a branch of the sea or large lake.

Etchplanation   The process of (deep) weathering and removal by erosional processes exposing a landscape.

Evaporation   Also known as vaporization, process by which water changes from the liquid to the gaseous (water vapor) state. It takes 597 cal of heat energy to change the state of 1 g of water at 0°C from a liquid to a gas.

Evaporites   Rock deposits resulting from the evaporation of the water in which these materials were once dissolved; include halite (salt) epsomite and gypsum.

Evapotranspiration   Combined processes by which water (1) evaporates from the land surface and (2) passes into the atmosphere through the leaf pores of plants (transpiration).

Evergreen   Of trees and other plants that keep their leaves year-round.

Exfoliation (spalling)   Special kind of jointing that produces a joint pattern resembling a series of concentric shells, much like the layers of an onion. Following the release of confining pressure, the outer layers progressively peel away and expose the lower layers.

Extinct volcano   Volcano that shows no sign of life and exhibits evidence of long-term weathering and erosion.

Extrusive igneous rocks   Rocks formed from magma that cooled and solidified, as lava, ash, and pyroclastics on the Earth's surface.

Eye (hurricane)   Open vertical tube that marks the center of a hurricane, often reaching an altitude of 16 km.

Eye wall (hurricane)   Rim of the eye or open vertical tube that marks the center of a well-developed hurricane. The tropical cyclone's strongest winds and heaviest rainfall occur here.

Factor of Safety (f)   An engineering way of determining the threshold angle of a slope and slope stability. The critical threshold is *f = 1*. *f>1* means stability, while *f<1* indicates instability.

Factors of Soil Formation   The factors of soil formation are Climate, Organisms (both active factors), Topography, Parent Materials, and Time (all passive factors). Time is the only independent factor. Soil is also considered a factor because once a soil forms it becomes as factor too influencing further soil forming processes.

Fall (autumn)   In Northern Hemisphere terminology, season that begins at the fall (autumnal) equinox around September 23 and ends at the winter solstice on December 22.

Fall (autumnal) equinox   In Northern Hemisphere terminology, equinox that occurs when the Sun's noontime rays strike the Equator vertically around September 23.

Fall Line   In North America, follows the boundary between the Appalachians and the Coastal Plain and connects the waterfalls that mark the inland limit of ocean navigation on the rivers that cross it. Because these falls were also local sources of water power, they attracted people and activities and gave rise to such major cities as Richmond, Washington, etc.

Fault   Fracture in crustal rock involving the displacement of rock on one side of the fracture with respect to rock on the other side.

Fault-block mountains   Horstlike highlands thrust upward along parallel axes by compressional forces; especially common in Atlantic Canada.

Fault breccia   Crushed, jagged rock fragments that often lie along a fault trace.

Fault-line scarp   Scarp that originated as a fault scarp but was modified, perhaps even displaced, by erosion.

Fault plane   Surface of contact along which blocks on either side of a fault move.

Fault scarp   Exposed clifflike face of a fault plane created by geological action without significant erosional change.

Fault trace   Lower edge of a fault scarp; line on the surface where a fault scarp intersects the surface.

Felsenmeer   (*see* **rock sea**)

Felsic   Light-coloured minerals or igneous or metamorphic rocks, e.g., quartz and felspars.

Feng Lin   Name given to Karst towers in southern China.

Fertigation Contraction of "fertilize" and "irrigation," an Israeli-perfected technique for the large-scale raising of crops under dry environmental conditions. Via subterranean pipes, the roots of genetically engineered plants are directly fed a mixture of brackish underground water and chemical fertilizers that supply just the right blend of moisture and nutrients for the crop to thrive.

Fetch Uninterrupted distance traveled by a wind or an ocean wave.

Field capacity Maximum amount of water that a soil can hold by capillary tension against the downward pull of gravity.

Finger lake Elongated lake that fills much of an even longer, fairly narrow glacial trough.

Fining-upwards sequence A sequence of floodplain deposits starting with coarser material at the base and getting finer upwards. (*see* **alluvium**)

Firn Granular, compacted snow.

Firn line (*see* **snow line**)

Fissure eruption Volcanic eruption that comes not from a pipe-shaped vent but from a lengthy crack in the lithosphere. The lava that erupts does not form a mountain but extends in horizontal sheets across the countryside, sometimes forming a plateau (e.g., flood basalts).

Fixed dune Stable sand dune that supports vegetation, which slows or even halts the dune's wind-generated movement.

Fjord A drowned glacial trough or the drowned lower end of a glacial trough.

Flashy stream regime A stream regime that is dominated by sporadic surface runoff that occurs during and just after a storm or snowmelt, e.g., an ephemeral stream. Flashy as in flash flood.

Flood Episode of abnormally high stream discharge. Water overflows from the stream channel and temporarily covers its floodplain (which continues to build from the alluvium that is deposited by the floodwaters).

Floodplain Flat, low-lying ground adjacent to a stream that is flooded.

Flow regime Discrete region of outward ice flow in a continental ice sheet; possesses its own rates of snow accumulation, ice formation, and velocity.

Fluvial Denotes running water; derived from Latin word for river, *fluvius*.

Fluvioglacial Stratified material (usually sand and gravel) carried from glacier or ice sheet by melt-water streams.

Focus (earthquake) Place of origin of an earthquake, which can be near the surface or deep inside the crust or upper mantle.

Foehn Rapid movement of warm dry air (caused by a plunge in altitude), frequently experienced on the leeward or rain-shadow side of a mountain barrier, whose

moisture has mostly been removed via the orographic precipitation process. The name is also used specifically to designate such local winds in the vicinity of central Europe's Alps; in the western plateaux of North America, these airflows are called *chinook* winds.

Fog Cloud layer in direct contact with the Earth's surface.

Fold Individual bend or warp in layered rock.

Foliation Unmistakable banded appearance of certain metamorphic rocks, such as gneiss and schist; bands formed by minerals realigned into parallel strips during metamorphism.

Food chain Stages through which energy in the form of food goes within an ecosystem.

Foreset beds Sedimentary deposits that are built from the leading edge of the topset beds as a delta grows seaward. Later these will be covered by the extension of the topset beds.

Foreshore Beach zone that is alternatively water-covered during high tide and exposed during low tide; zone of beach drift and related processes.

Fossil fuels Coal, oil, and natural gas.

Fossorial Burrowing or living below the ground surface.

Fracture (mineral) When minerals do not break in a clean cleavage, they still break or fracture in a characteristic way. Obsidian, for example, fractures in an unusual shell-like (concoidal) manner that is a useful identifying quality.

Freezing Process by which a substance is transformed from the liquid to the solid state.

Freezing nuclei Perform the same function for ice particles that condensation nuclei perform for water droplets; small airborne particles (of dust or salt) around which ice crystals can form when liquid water freezes or water vapor sublimates.

Freezing point (water) Key setting in the calibration of temperature scales. On the Celsius scale water freezes at 0°C.

Friction (Roughness) The resistance encountered when water, gas or material etc. moves over another a surface or another material, e.g., water moving over the bed and along the banks of a stream encounters friction because of sand, gravel, or pebbles jutting out from the channel perimeter.

Frictional force Drag that slows the movement of air molecules in contact with, or close to, the Earth's surface; varies with the "roughness" of the surface. There is less friction with movement across a smooth water surface than across the ragged skyline of a city centre.

Front (weather) Surface that bounds an air mass, along which contact occurs with a neighboring air mass possessing different qualities. This narrow boundary zone usually marks an abrupt transition in air density, temperature, and humidity. A moving front is the leading edge of the air mass built up behind it.

Frontal precipitation Precipitation that results from the movement of fronts whereby warm air is lifted, cooled, and condensed; also frequently called *cyclonic precipitation.*

Frost action Form of physical weathering in which water penetrates the joints and cracks of rocks, expands and contracts through alternate freezing and thawing, and eventually shatters the rocks.

Frost creep Movement of particles within the active layer (talik) above the permafrost under the influence of gravity. On the surface, soil will move downslope during the thawing phase.

Frost heaving Upward displacement of rocks and rock fragments within the active layer (talik) above the permafrost after they have been loosened by frost wedging; triggered by freezing of the ground that expands the total mass of rock materials.

Frost shattering (*see* **frost wedging**)

Frost thrusting Horizontal movement of rocks and rock fragments within the active layer (talik) above the permafrost.

Frost wedging Forcing apart of a rock when the expansion stress created by the freezing of its internal water into ice exceeds the cohesive strength of that rock body.

Galaxy Organized, disklike assemblage of billions of stars. Our solar system belongs to the Milky Way galaxy, which measures about 120,000 light-years in diameter.

Gelisol One of the 12 soil orders of the U.S. Soil Taxonomy, found in cold, dry environments whose surfaces are underlain by permafrost. Such soils show evidence of cryoturbation (frost churning) and/or ice segregation in the seasonally thawing active layer (talik) that lies above the permafrost table. Equivalent to the cryosolic soil order.

General circulation Global atmospheric circulation system of wind belts and semipermanent pressure cells. In each hemisphere, the former include the Trades, Westerlies, and Polar Easterlies. The latter include the Equatorial Low (ITCZ) and, in each hemisphere, the Subtropical High, Upper Midlatitude Low, and Polar High.

Geodesy Precise study and measurement of the size and shape of the Earth.

Geographic information system (GIS) Assemblage of computer hardware and software that permits spatial data to be collected, recorded, stored, retrieved, manipulated, analyzed, and displayed to the user.

Geography Literally means *Earth description.* As a modern academic discipline, it is concerned with the explanation of the physical and human characteristics of the Earth's surface.

Geological structure Landscape features originally formed by geological processes, which are sculpted by streams and other erosional agents into characteristic landforms.

Geological time scale Standard timetable or chronicle of Earth history used by scientists; sequential organization of geological time units, whose dates continue to be refined by ongoing research.

Geomorphology Literally means *Earth shape* or *form;* geography of landscape and its evolution, a major subfield of physical geography.

Geostrophic wind Wind that results when the Coriolis and pressure-gradient forces balance themselves out. It follows a relatively straight path that minimizes deflection and lies parallel to the isobars.

Geosynchronous orbit Orbit in which a satellite's revolution of the Earth is identical to the planet's rotational speed. Therefore the satellite is "fixed" in a stationary position above the same point on the Earth's surface.

Geothermal energy Energy whose source is underground heat. Where magma chambers lie close to the surface, groundwater is heated and emerges onto the surface as steam or hot water from a geyser or a hot spring.

Geyser Hot spring that periodically expels jets of heated water and steam.

GIS (*see* **geographic information system**)

Glacial burst flood (*see* **jökulhlaup**)

Glacial creep The internal deformation in a glacier or ice sheet caused by the differential movement of the ice layers caused by weight and gravity. Occurs in cold and wet-based ice.

Glacial drift Unsorted till and stratified drift.

Glacial erratic Boulder that was transported by an ice sheet or glacier far from its source area.

Glacial outwash (sandur) Meltwater-deposited sand and gravel, which are sorted into layers.

Glacial striations Scratches on a rock surface made when boulders or pebbles (embedded in moving ice) were dragged across it.

Glacial surge An increase in the velocity of glacier flow caused by meltwater building up under the ice because of an increase in melting or damming of the glacier's plumbing system. This means that the ice is lubricated or floats on a layer of watering decreasing friction. Ends when most of the subglacial water discharges, often when a sediment or ice dam collapses causing a jökulhlaup.

Glacial trough Valley that has been eroded by a glacier; distinctively **U**-shaped in cross-sectional profile.

Glaciation Period of global cooling during which continental ice sheets form and alpine glaciers expand.

Glacier Body of ice, formed on land, which exhibits motion.

Gleization A Pedogenetic regime dominated by water logging which restricts the microbial breakdown of organic matter. Characterized by a thick Organic layer with a thin layer of bluish-grey (gley) clay (because of the reduction of iron) underneath. Generally occurs in wet sites at the base of slopes, or upslope from Organic soils.

Gley A soil developed by the above process. (*see* **gleization**)

Gleysol A Canadian soil order of soils developed as above. (*see* **gleization**)

Global Positioning System (GPS) Constellation of more than two dozen linked orbiting satellites that broadcast signals to portable receivers anywhere on the Earth's surface. The simultaneous detection of these signals enables the person on the ground (or at sea or on an aircraft) to calculate precisely the latitude, longitude, and elevation of the receiver's location.

Global warming theory Notion, popular among scientists that human fossil-fuel consumption is causing atmospheric warming that will melt glaciers, raise sea levels, and inundate low-lying coastal areas. Since the mid-1990s, however, competing theories of climate change are receiving considerable attention and gaining new proponents.

Gneiss Metamorphic rock derived from granite that usually exhibits pronounced foliation.

Gondwana Southern portion of the primeval supercontinent, Pangaea.

GPS (*see* **Global Positioning System**)

Graben Crustal block that has sunk down between two fairly parallel normal faults in response to tensional forces.

Gradational process Process that works to wear down the geological materials built up on the Earth's landmasses.

Graded stream Stream in which slope and channel characteristics are adjusted over time to provide just the velocity required for the transportation of the load supplied from the drainage basin, given the available discharge.

Gradient (river) Slope of a river channel as measured by the difference in elevation between two points along the stream course.

Gravity Force of attraction that acts among all physical objects as a result of their *mass* (quantity of material of which they are composed).

Great circle Circle formed along the edge of the cut when a sphere is cut in half. On the surface of the sphere, that circle is the shortest distance between any two points located on it.

Greenhouse effect Widely used analogy describing the blanket-like effect of the atmosphere in the heating of the Earth's surface. Shortwave insolation passes through the "glass" of the atmospheric "greenhouse," heats the surface, is converted to longwave radiation, which can-

not penetrate the "glass," and thereby results in trapping heat that raises the temperature inside the "greenhouse."

Greenpeace An international environmental and anti-nuclear organization formed by a group of Canadian activists originally to stop U.S. atmospheric nuclear testing in Alaska.

Ground heat flow Heat that is conducted into and out of the Earth's surface; also known as *soil heat flow.*

Ground moraine Blanket of unsorted glacial till that was laid down at the base of a melting glacier or ice sheet.

Groundwater Water contained within the lithosphere. This water, hidden below the ground, accounts for about 25 percent of the world's freshwater.

Groyne, Groyne field A groyne is a wooden or concrete structure built perpendicular to the shore, which is designed to retain beach material by stopping some beach and longshore sediment transport.

Gully, Gullying Large erosional features cut in to a slope by running water. Larger than a rill. Cannot be obliterated by ploughing or bulldozing. They are usually only subject to discharge during and just after rainstorms or snowmelt. They form the very ends of the stream network. A Hillslope process involving the erosion of gullies.

Gyre Cell-like circulation of surface currents that often encompasses an entire ocean basin. For example, the subtropical gyre of the North Atlantic Ocean consists of the huge loop formed by four individual, continuous legs—the North Equatorial, Gulf Stream, North Atlantic Drift, and Canaries currents.

Habitat Environment a species normally occupies within its geographical range.

Hail Precipitation consisting of ice pellets, which form in a cloud that has more ice crystals than water droplets.

Hanging valley Valley formed by the intersection of a tributary glacier with a trunk glacier. When the ice melts away, the tributary valley floor usually is at a higher elevation and thus "hangs" above the main valley's floor.

Hardpan Colloquial term for an indurated horizon in the soil, e.g., podzol.

Hawaiian High Local name for the North Pacific Ocean's Subtropical High pressure cell, which is generally centered over latitude 30°N; also known as the Pacific High.

Headward erosion Upslope extension, over time, of the "head" or source of a river valley, which lengthens the entire stream network.

Heat-island intensity Maximum difference in temperature between neighboring urban and rural environments.

Hercynian A Carboniferous orogeny responsible for the creation of block mountains in the Appalachian-

Caledonide mountains and other areas, including Swabian, Schwarzwald (Black Forest) and Carpathian horsts.

Hemisphere   Half-sphere; used precisely, as in Northern Hemisphere (everything north of 0° latitude), or sometimes more generally, as in land hemisphere (the significant concentration of landmasses on roughly one side of the Earth).

Herbivore   Animal that lives on plants, or more generally the first consumer stage of a food chain.

Heterosphere   Upper of the atmosphere's two vertical regions, which possesses a variable chemical composition and extends upward from an elevation of 80 to 100 km to the edge of outer space.

High mountains   Terrain of less than 50 percent gentle slope whose local relief exhibits variations in excess of 900 m.

Highland (H) climates   Climates of high-elevation areas that exhibit characteristics of climates located poleward of those found at the base of those highlands. The higher one climbs, the colder the climate becomes—even in the low latitudes. Thus **H** climate areas are marked by the vertical zonation of climates, as in South America's Andes.

Hills   Terrain of less than 50 percent gentle slope whose local relief exhibits variations of 0 to 300 m.

Hillslope process   A slope process in which the debris is moved by flowing water or another agent.

Histosol   One of the 12 soil orders of the U.S. Soil Taxonomy; organic soil associated with poorly drained, flat-lying areas. Equivalent to the Organic soil order.

Hogback   Prominent steep-sided ridge whose rockbeds dip sharply.

Holocene   Current interglacial epoch, extending from 10,000 years ago to the present on the geological time scale.

Homosphere   The lower of the atmosphere's two vertical regions, which possesses a relatively uniform chemical composition and extends from the surface to an elevation of 80 to 100 km.

Horizonation   Differentiation of soils into layers called horizons.

Horn   Sharp-pointed, Matterhorn-like mountain peak that remains when several cirques attain their maximum growth by headward erosion into an upland area.

Horst   Crustal block that has been raised between two reverse faults by compressional forces.

Hortonian Overland Flow   Runoff generated when rainfall intensity is greater than infiltration capacity.

Hot lahar   A mudflow caused by a volcanic eruption.

Hot spot   Place of very high temperatures in the upper mantle that reaches the surface as a "plume" of extraordinarily high heat. A linear series of shield volcanoes can form on lithospheric plates moving over this plume, as happened in the case of the Hawaiian island chain.

Hot spring   Spring whose water temperature averages above 10°C; often emanates from a crustal zone that contains magma chambers near the surface.

Humid continental climate (Dfa/Dwa, Dfb/Dwb)   Collective term for the milder subtypes of the humid microthermal climate, found on the equatorward side of the **D**-climate zone.

Humid microthermal climate   (*see* **microthermal climates**)

Humid subtropical climate (Cfa)   Warm, perpetually moist mesothermal climate type that is found in the southeastern portion of each of the five major continents.

Humification   The process of turning organic matter into humus.

Humus   Decomposed and partially decomposed organic matter that forms a dark layer at the top of the soil; important to a soil's fertility.

Hurricane   Tropical cyclone capable of inflicting great damage. A tightly organized, moving low-pressure system, normally originating at sea in the warm most air of the tropical atmosphere, exhibiting wind speeds in excess of 33 m per second. As with all cyclonic storms, it has a distinctly circular wind and pressure field.

Hydration   Expansion in volume often occurs in the process, which contributes to the breakdown of rocks.

Hydraulic action   Erosional work of running water in a stream or in the form of waves along a coast. In a stream, rock material is dislodged and dragged away from the valley floor and sides; where waves strike a shoreline, the speed and weight of the water, especially when air is compressed into rock cracks by the power of the waves, can fracture and erode coastal rocks quite rapidly.

Hydrograph   Graph of a river's discharge over time.

Hydrological cycle   Complex system of exchange involving water in its various forms as it continually circulates among the atmosphere, lithosphere, hydrosphere, cryosphere, and biosphere.

Hydrology   Systematic study of the Earth's water in all its states.

Hydrolysis   Form of chemical weathering that involves moistening and the transformation of rock minerals into other mineral compounds associated with hydration.

Hydrosphere   Sphere of the Earth System that contains all the water that exists on and within the solid surface of our planet and in the atmosphere above.

Hygrophyte Plant adapted to the moisture of wet environments.

Hygroscopic water Thin films of water that cling tenaciously to most soil particles but are unavailable to plant roots.

Hypocentre Another name for an epicentre.

Hypothetical continent model Earth's landmasses generalized into a single, idealized, shield-shaped continent of uniform low elevation.

Iapetus Name given to early or proto-oceans, such as the proto-Atlantic. The name is from one of the Greek Titans, father of Atlas.

Ice age Stretch of geological time during which the Earth's average atmospheric temperature is lowered; causes the expansion of ice sheets in the high latitudes and the growth of alpine glaciers in lower latitudes.

Ice cap Regional mass of ice smaller than a continent-sized ice sheet (less than 50,000 km² in size). While the Scandinavian Ice Sheet covered northern Europe, an ice cap covered the Alps in central Europe. Name given to ice cover of Greenland and Antarctica.

Icecap climate (EF) World's coldest climate, the harsher of the two subtypes of the **E**-climate zone.

Ice crystal process Most common process where precipitation forms and falls to Earth; rainfall in the tropical latitudes, however, is produced by the coalescence process.

Icelandic Low Local term for the northernmost North Atlantic Ocean's Upper Midlatitude Low, centered approximately at 60°N near Iceland.

Ice sheet (*see* **continental glaciers**)

Ice shelf Smaller ice sheet that is a floating, seaward extension of a continental glacier, such as Antarctica's Ross Ice Shelf.

Ice tongues Relatively small outlet glaciers that extend into the sea at the margin of a continental ice sheet or ice cap.

Ice wedges A ground ice feature formed by water freezing in a crack in the soil surface.

Ice-wedge casts The "fossil" of the above exhibiting infilling by finer soil material.

Ice-wedge polygons Polygonal features formed by the freezing and thawing of sediments that fill surface cracks caused by very cold winter temperatures in periglacial zones.

Igneous rocks (Primary) rocks that formed directly from the cooling of molten magma; igneous is Latin for "formed from fire."

Illuviation Soil process in which downward-percolating water carries soluble minerals and colloid-sized particles of organic matter and minerals from the **A** into the **B** horizon, where these materials are deposited in pore spaces and against the surfaces of soil grains.

Impact melt A rock that has been melted by the heat and pressure caused by a meteorite or cometary impact.

Impermeable Surface that does not permit water to pass through it.

Impurities (atmospheric) Solid particles floating in the atmosphere whose quantities vary in time and space. Among other things, they play an active role in the formation of raindrops.

Inceptisol One of the 12 soil orders of the Soil Taxonomy; forms quickly, is relatively young (though older than an entisol), has the beginnings of a **B** horizon, and contains significant organic matter.

Incised stream (*see* **entrenched meanders**)

Independent controls (of geomorphological systems) Climate, Geology, and Base Level.

Indurated Irreversibly hardened, e.g., an ironpan or laterite.

Inert gas Chemically inactive gas that does not combine with other compounds. Argon, an inert atmospheric gas, makes up almost 1 percent of dry air.

Infiltration Flow of water into the Earth's surface through the pores and larger openings in the soil mass.

Infiltration capacity Rate at which a soil is able to absorb water percolating downward from the surface.

Infrared radiation Low-energy longwave radiation of the type emitted by the Earth and the atmosphere.

Inlier A "window" or area of underlying rock exposed by the erosion of the overlying rock beds.

Inner core Solid, most inner portion of the Earth, consisting mainly of nickel and iron.

Inselbergs Rounded or sugar-loaf shaped residual hills left behind by the erosion of deeply weathered areas by slope and stream erosion. Residuals on an etchplain.

In situ In place, not moved.

Insolation Incoming solar radiation.

Intensity (earthquake) Size and damage of an earthquake as measured—on the Modified Mercalli Scale—by the impact on structures and human activities on the cultural landscape.

Interactive mapping In geographic information systems (GIS) methodology, the constant dialogue via computer demands and feedback to queries between the map user and the map.

Interception Blocking of rainwater through vegetation from reaching the ground. Raindrops land on leaves and other plant parts and evaporate before they can penetrate the soil below.

Interface   Surface-like boundary of a system or one of its component subsystems. The transfer or exchange of matter and energy takes place here.

Interfluve   Ridge that separates two adjacent stream valleys.

Interglacial   Period of warmer global temperatures between deglaciation and the onset of the next glaciation.

International date line   For the most part is antipodal to the prime meridian and follows the 180th meridian. Crossing the line toward the west involves skipping a day, whereas crossing the line toward the east means repeating a day.

Inter-Tropical Convergence Zone (ITCZ)   Thermal low-pressure belt of rising air that straddles the equatorial latitudinal zone, which is fed by the windflows of the converging Northeast and Southeast Trades.

Intrusive igneous rocks   Rocks formed from magma that cooled and solidified below the Earth's surface.

Inversion   (*see* **temperature inversion**)

Involutions   Patterns or structures in a soil or deposit caused by cryoturbation (freezing and thawing).

Ion   Atom or cluster of electrically charged atoms formed by the breakdown of molecules.

Isarithmic mapping   Commonly used cartographic device to represent three-dimensional volumetric data on a two-dimensional map; involves the use of isolines to show the surfaces that are mapped.

Island (volcanic) arc   Volcanic island chain produced in a zone where two oceanic plates are converging. One plate will subduct the other, forming deep trenches as well as spawning volcanoes that may protrude above sea level in an island-arc formation (Alaska's Aleutian archipelago is a classic example). Volcanic arc is used for a group of volcanoes associated with fold mountain belts (orogens).

Isobar   Line connecting all points having identical atmospheric pressure.

Isohyet   Line connecting all points receiving an identical amount of precipitation.

Isoline   Line connecting all places possessing the same value of a given phenomenon, such as "height" above the flat base of the surface being mapped.

Isostasy   Derived from an ancient Greek term (*iso* = the same; *stasy* = to stand), the condition of vertical equilibrium between the floating landmasses and the asthenosphere beneath them. This situation of sustained adjustment is maintained despite the forces that constantly operate to change the landmasses.

Isotherm   Line connecting all points experiencing identical temperature.

Isotope   Related form of a chemical element; has the same number of protons and electrons but different numbers of neutrons.

ITCZ   (*see* **Inter-Tropical Convergence Zone**)

Jet stream   Two concentrated, high-altitude, west-to-east flowing "rivers" of air that are major features of the upper atmospheric circulation system poleward of latitude 15° in both the Northern and Southern Hemispheres. Because of their general occurrence above the subtropical and subpolar latitudes, they are respectively known as the *subtropical jet stream* and the *Polar Front jet stream*. A third such corridor of high-altitude, concentrated windflow is the *tropical easterly jet stream*, a major feature of the upper air circulation equatorward of latitude 15°N. This third jet stream, however, flows in the opposite, east-to-west direction and occurs only above the tropics of the Northern Hemisphere.

Joint   Fracture in a rock in which no displacement movement has taken place.

Joint plane   Planes of weakness and separation in a rock; produced in an intrusive igneous rock by the contraction of cooling magma (sedimentary and metamorphic rocks also display forms of jointing).

Jointing   Tendency of rocks to develop parallel sets of fractures without any obvious movement such as faulting.

Jökulhlaup (Icelandic)   A glacial burst flood.

Jungle   Thick rainforest vegetation caused by secondary growth along a riverbank or because of clearance.

Kame   Mound of glacial debris or stratified drift at the edge of a glacier or ice sheet; often found as deltaic deposits where meltwater streams flowed into temporary lakes near the receding ice. Associated with kettles.

Kame and Kettle topography   A landscape made up of Kames and Kettles (also called Thermokarst).

Karst   Distinctive landscape associated with the underground chemical erosion of particularly soluble limestone bedrock.

Katabatic winds   Winds that result from cold-air drainage; especially prominent under clear conditions where the edges of highlands plunge sharply toward lower-lying terrain.

Karren   Solution widened joints exposed in a limestone pavement. Also applied to solution eroded rills down a limestone slope.

Kelp transport   The movement of sand and shingle held in the holdfasts by kelp (a large form of seaweed).

Kelvin scale   *Absolute* temperature scale used by scientists, based on the temperature of absolute zero (−273°C). A kelvin is identical to a Celsius degree (°C), so that water boils at 373 K (100°C) and freezes at 273 K (0°C).

Kettle, Kettle Lake   A depression caUSed by the melting of subsurface ice, usually proglacially (close to the terminus a glacier or ice sheet). A lake formed in a kettle.

Kinetic energy Energy of movement.

L-F-H horizon The litter layers at the top of a soil profile. **L** stands for Litter (plant debris etc.), **F** for fermentation or a state of partial decomposition, and **H** for Humus, the end-product of organic decomposition in soils.

L (long) wave Surface seismic wave that travels along the Earth's crust.

La Niña Lull or cool ebb in low-latitude Pacific Ocean surface temperatures that occurs between El Niño peaks of anomalous sea-surface warming.

Laccolith Concordant intrusive igneous form in which a magma pipe led to a subterranean chamber that grew, domelike, pushing up the overlying strata into a gentle bulge without destroying them.

Lacustrine Related to lakes.

Lag deposit Coarse material left behind when finer material is winnowed and eroded by wind or water.

Lagoon Normally shallow body of water that lies between an offshore barrier island and the original shoreline.

Lahar (*see* **Cold** or **Hot lahar**)

Land breeze Offshore airflow affecting a coastal zone, resulting from a nighttime pressure gradient that steers local winds from the cooler (higher pressure) land surface to the warmer (lower pressure) sea surface.

Landform Single and typical unit that forms parts of the overall shape of the Earth's surface; also refers to a discrete product of a set of geomorphological processes.

Land Hemisphere The roughly one-half of the Earth that contains most of the landmasses (Northern Hemisphere); the opposite of the water (oceanic) hemisphere.

Landscape Aggregation of landforms, often of the same type; also refers to the spatial expression of the processes that shaped those landforms.

Avalanche (Landslide) Form of mass movement that travels downslope very rapidly. In effect, it is a collapse of a slope and does not need water as a lubricant (can be triggered by an earthquake, undercutting, glacial oversteeping as well as by human activities).

Lapse rate Rate of decline in temperature as altitude increases. The average lapse rate of temperature with height in the troposphere is −0.64°C/100 m.

Late Cenozoic Ice Age Last great ice age that ended 10,000 years ago; spanned the entire Pleistocene epoch (1,800,000 to 10,000 years ago) plus the latter portion of the preceding Pliocene epoch, possibly beginning as far back as 3,500,000 years ago.

Latent heat "Hidden" heat involved in the processes of melting, freezing, evaporation, and condensation (*see* latent heat of fusion; latent heat of vaporization).

Latent heat of fusion Heat energy involved in melting, the transformation of a solid into a liquid. A similar amount of heat is given off when a liquid freezes into a solid.

Latent heat of vaporization Heat energy involved in the transformation of a liquid into a gas or vice versa.

Lateral moraine Moraine situated along the edge of a mountain glacier, consisting of debris that fell from the adjacent valley wall.

Laterite (oxisol, lateritic) Name sometimes given to a very hard iron oxide or aluminum hydroxide soil horizon that is reddish in color (*later* is Latin for brick); found in wet tropical areas.

Laterite or ore (oxic) horizon In moist equatorial and tropical areas, where humus is minimal, downward-percolating rainwater leaches the soil and leaves behind compounds rich in iron and aluminum. Sometimes these aluminum and iron oxides are so concentrated that they develop into a hard layer, red or orange in colour, known as laterite or oxic horizon. (Farmers call it *hardpan*.)

Laterization The Pedogenetic regime by which Laterites and Bauxites form.

Latitude Angular distance, measured in degrees north or south, of a point along a parallel from the Equator.

Laurasia Northern portion of the supercontinent, Pangaea.

Laurentide Ice Sheet Huge Late Cenozoic continental ice sheet that covered all of Canada east of the Rocky Mountains and expanded repeatedly to bury areas as far south as the Ohio and Missouri Valleys.

Lava Magma that reaches and cooks the Earth's surface.

Leaching (leached) Soil process in which downward-percolating water dissolves and washes away many of the soil's mineral substances and other ingredients.

Lead (ice surface) Channel of water that opens across a surface of sea ice during the warmer period of the year.

Leap year Occurs every fourth year, when a full day (February 29) is added to the calendar to allow for the quarter-day beyond the 365 days it takes the Earth to complete one revolution of the Sun.

Leeward Protected side of a topographical barrier with respect to the winds that flow across it; often refers to the area downwind from the barrier as well, which is said to be in the "shadow" of that highland zone.

Legend (map) Portion of a map where its point, line, area, and volume symbols are identified.

Lessivation (lessivated) The process of washing clay particles down a soil profile from the **A** to the **B** horizon. Lessivated is a term used for soils that have been affected by this process, e.g., Luvisols.

Levee, artificial   Artificially constructed levee built to reinforce a natural levee, most often along the lowest course of a river.

Levee, natural   River-lining ridge of alluvium deposited along some streams when they overflow their banks during a periodic flood. When the river contracts after the flood, it stays within these self-generated "dikes" or levees. Controversy exists about this feature. (*see* **Levee, artifcial**)

Liana   Tropical rainforest vine, rooted in the ground, with leaves and flowers in the tree canopy above.

Light-year   Distance traveled by a pulse of light in one year. Light travels at a speed of 300,000 km (186,000 mi) per second; a light-year thus involves a distance of 9.46 trillion km.

Limestone   Sedimentary rock formed from the respiration and photosynthesis of marine organisms in which calcium carbonate is distilled from seawater or from calcium with sediments or brine concentration. Finely textured and therefore resistant to weathering when exposed on the surface, it is susceptible to solution that can produce karst landscapes both above and below the ground.

Line symbols   Represent linkages and/or flows that exist between places on a map.

Linear autogenic succession   Plant succession that occurs when the plants themselves initiate changes in the environment that consequently cause vegetation changes.

Liquid limit   An Atterberg limit separating a plastic state from the liquid state. Dependent on moisture and clay content.

Liquifaction   The complete collapse of structure/competence in an unconsolidated material caused by saturation and earthquake shaking.

Lithification   Rock formation; the process of compression, compaction, and cementation whereby a sediment is transformed into a sedimentary rock.

Lithology   Rock type of a local area, which greatly influences its landform and landscape development.

Lithomarge   A deep pallid sandy layer found under laterites.

Lithoprobe   A Canadian program to gather knowledge about the structural and tectonic make-up of North America.

Lithosphere   Outermost shell of the solid Earth, lying immediately below the land surface and ocean floor (*lithos* means rock); composed of the Earth's thin crust together with the solid uppermost portion of the upper mantle that lies just below.

Lithospheric plate   One of the fragmented, rigid segments of the lithosphere (also called a *tectonic plate,* which denotes its active mobile character). These segments or plates move in response to the plastic flow in the hot asthenosphere that lies just below the lithosphere.

Little Ice Age (Neoglacial)   Period of decidedly cooler global temperatures that prevailed from 1430 to 1850 (averaging about 1.5°C lower than in the 1940s). During these four centuries, glaciers in most parts of the world expanded considerably.

Littoral zone   Coastal zone.

Loam   An agricultural term for soil containing grains of all three texture size categories—sand, silt, and clay—within certain proportions. The term, however, refers not to a size category but to a certain combination of variously sized particles.

Local base level   Base level for a stream that flows into a lake at whatever altitude it may lie.

Loess   Deposit of very fine silt or dust laid down after having been blown some distance (perhaps hundreds of kilometres) by the wind; characterized by its fertility and ability to stand in steep vertical walls. Related to deserts (hot loess) or periglacial areas.

Lone waves (L waves)   Seismic waves that travel across the Earth's surface causing the ground to move from side to side.

Long grass prairie   Type of vegetation characteristic of less arid areas of the Prairies. Exhibits greater plant size and a greater plant density.

Longitude   Angular distance, measured in degrees east or west, of a point along a meridian from the prime meridian.

Longitudinal dune   Long ridgelike sand dune that lies parallel to the prevailing wind.

Longshore bar   Ridge of sand parallel to the shoreline that develops in the nearshore beach zone.

Longshore current   Water current that runs along the shoreline similar to the longshore drift of sand, which is generated by the refracted, oblique-angled arrival of waves onshore; can also develop from tidal action and from coastal storms.

Littoral (Longshore) drift   Movement of sand and shingle along the shoreline in the flow of water (*longshore current*) generated by the refracted, oblique-angled arrival of waves onshore.

Longwave radiation   Radiation emitted by the Earth, which has much longer wavelengths—and involves much lower energy—than the solar (shortwave, higher energy) radiation emitted by the Sun.

Low mountains   Terrain of less than 50 percent gentle slope whose local relief exhibits variations of 300 to 900 m.

Lower mantle   Solid interior shell of the Earth, which encloses the liquid outer core.

Lustre (mineral)   Surface sheen of a mineral that, along with color, can be a useful identifying quality.

Luvisolic soil order A Canadian soil order. Lessivated (washed) soils or soils that exhibit the translocation of particulate clays from the **A** to the **B** horizon.

Mafic Dark coloured (minerals), e.g., olivine or biotite.

Magma Liquid molten mass from which igneous rocks are formed.

Magnetosphere Upper portion of the thermosphere, which constitutes the outermost of the atmosphere's layers. Here the Earth's magnetic field is often more influential than its gravitational field in the movement of particles.

Magnitude (earthquake) Amount of shaking of the ground during an earthquake as measured by a seismograph.

Mangrove Type of vegetation, exhibiting stiltlike roots and a leafy crown, that grows in seawater on low-lying, muddy coasts in tropical and subtropical environments. In certain places, such as tidal flats and river mouths, these trees congregate thickly. In North America they are most evident along the southwesternmost shore of Florida where the Everglades meet the sea.

Map projection Orderly arrangement of meridians and parallels, produced by any systematic method, that can be used for drawing a map of the spherical Earth on a flat surface.

Marble Metamorphosed limestone. The hardness and density of this rock is preferred by sculptors for statues that can withstand exposure to the agents of weathering and erosion for millennia.

Marine west coast climate (Cfb, Cfc) Perpetually moist mesothermal climate type associated with midlatitude coasts (and adjacent inland areas not blocked by mountain barriers) bathed by the prevailing Westerlies year-round, whose maritime influences produce temperature regimes devoid of extremes.

Maritime effect Moderating influence of the ocean on air temperature, which produces cooler summers and milder winters relative to inland locations at similar latitudes, e.g., Vancouver, British Columbia.

Mass balance The inputs and outputs of mass in a system, such as a stream, glacier, or beach.

Mass movement A slope process where the debris rolls or tumbles down slope because of gravity.

Master horizons Soil horizons marked by capital letters: **A, B, C, R,** and **W.**

Meander A bend or curve in a stream.

Meander belts Stream meander development zones that themselves form giant meanders.

Meander cliff (*see* **cut bank**)

Meanders Smooth, rounded curves or bends of streams that can become quite pronounced as floodplain

development proceeds; also characteristic of many ocean currents, which, after the passage of storms, can produce such extreme loops that many detach and form localized eddies.

Medial moraine Moraine—situated well away from a glacier's edges—formed by the intersection of two lateral moraines when a substantial tributary glacier meets and joins a trunk glacier.

Mediterranean climate (Csa, Csb) West coast mesothermal climate whose signature dry summers result from the temporary poleward shift of the subtropical high-pressure zone.

Mediterranean scrub biome (scleraphilous forest) Consists of widely spaced evergreen or deciduous trees and often dense, hard-leaf evergreen scrub; sometimes referred to as chaparral or maquis. Thick waxy leaves are well adapted to the long dry summers and burning.

Mega-Floods (*see* **catastrophic flooding**)

Megatherm Plant adapted to withstand considerable heat.

Mega-Yardang Found in some areas of the Gobi desert and on Mars. (*see* **yardang**)

Melting Change from the solid state to the liquid state. At 0°C it takes about 80 cal of heat energy to change 1 g of water from a solid into a liquid.

Mercalli scale (Modified) Scale that measures earthquake intensity, the impact of a quake on the human landscape; ranges upward from intensity I to intensity XII.

Mercator map projection Most famous of the cylindrical projections, the only one on which any straight line is a line of true and constant compass bearing.

Meridian On the Earth grid, a north–south line of longitude. These range from 0° (prime meridian) to 180°E and W (180°E and W, of course, are the same line—the international date line [written simply as 180°]).

Meridional circulation North–south (*azonal*) movement of air.

Mesa Flat-topped, steep-sided upland capped by a resistant rock layer; normally found in dry environments.

Mesopause Upper boundary of the mesosphere, lying approximately 80 km above the surface.

Mesophyte Plant adapted to environments that are neither extremely moist nor extremely dry.

Mesosphere Third layer of the atmosphere, lying above the stratosphere. Here temperatures again decline with increasing elevation as they do in the troposphere.

Mesotherm Plant adapted to withstand intermediate temperatures that are not excessively high or low.

Mesothermal Climates exhibiting a moderate amount of heat; the **C** climates.

Mesothermal (C) climates Moderately heated climates that are found on the equatorward side of the middle latitudes, where they are generally aligned as interrupted east–west belts; transitional between the climates of the tropics and those of the upper midlatitudes where polar influences begin to produce harsh winters.

Mesozoic Era on the geological time scale, extending from 248 million to 65 million years ago.

Metabolic heat Heat produced by human bodies (from the conversion of the chemical energy in the food we eat).

Metabolic Processes Processes that maintain living things, e.g., breathing, digestion.

Metamorphic rocks (Secondary) rocks that were created from the transformation, by heat and/or pressure, of existing rocks.

Meteoric Impact The impact of a meteorite forming a crater.

Meteorology Systematic, interdisciplinary study of the short-term atmospheric phenomena that constitute weather.

Metropolis Metropolitan area consisting of a central city and its surrounding suburban ring, e.g., Vancouver or Toronto, may become an outer city in its own right, capturing an increasingly large share of the metropolis' population and economic activity, e.g., Burnaby and Mississauga.

Microclimate Climate region on a localized scale.

Micro- and Meso-fauna An assemblage of very small or small animals.

Micrometre (μm) One millionth of a metre.

Microtherm Plant adapted to withstand low temperatures.

Microthermal Northern Hemisphere climates exhibiting a comparatively small amount of heat; the **D** climates.

Microthermal (D) climates Weakly heated continental climates of the Northern Hemisphere's upper midlatitudes, where the seasonal rhythms swing from short, decidedly warm summers to long, often harsh winters; mostly confined to the vast interior expanses of North America and Eurasia poleward of 45°N.

Mid-Atlantic Ridge Submarine volcanic mountain range that forms the midoceanic ridge that extends through the entire North and South Atlantic Oceans, from Iceland in the north to near-Antarctic latitudes in the south.

Midoceanic ridge High submarine volcanic mountain ranges like the Mid-Atlantic ridge, part of a global system of such ranges most often found in the central areas of the ocean basins. Here new crust is formed by upwelling magma, which continuously moves away toward the margins of the ocean basins.

Midstream bar Midchannel sandbar that is deposited where sediment-clogged water of a stream significantly slows in velocity.

Milankovitch Forcing The cyclical variability in Earths axial tilt and orbit around the Sun that could cause climatic changes.

Millennium Period of 1000 years.

Mineral Naturally occurring inorganic element or compound having a definite chemical composition, physical properties, and, usually, a crystalline structure.

Mineral spring Hot spring containing large quantities of minerals dissolved from surrounding rocks. Its mineral water is sometimes used for medicinal purposes.

Mistral **winds** Katabatic windflow, affecting France's Rhône Valley each winter, which involves the cold-air drainage of the massive pool of icy air that accumulates over the nearby high-lying French and Swiss Alps.

Mixing ratio Ratio of the mass of water vapour to the total mass of the dry air containing that water vapour.

Model Creation of an idealized (somewhat simplified) representation of reality in order to demonstrate its most important properties.

Moder humus Type of humus found under deciduous forest which is mixed in with the mineral soil by soil microorganisms, e.g., earthworms.

Moho Abbreviation for the Mohorovičić discontinuity.

Mohorovičić discontinuity Contact plane between the Earth's crust and the mantle.

Mohs Hardness Scale Standard mineral-hardness measurement scale used in the Earth sciences; ranges from 10 (the hardest substance, diamond) down to 1 (talc, the softest naturally occurring mineral).

Mollisol One of the 12 soil orders of the Soil Taxonomy, found in the world's semiarid climate zones; characterized by a thick, dark surface layer and high alkaline content. Equivalent to the Chernozemic soil order.

Moment Magnitude Scale Most widely used measure of the severity of an earthquake's ground motion, which evolved from the Richter Scale developed in the 1930s; based on the size of the fault along which a quake occurs and the distance the rocks around it slip.

Monadnock Prominent (not yet eroded) remnant of an upland on a peneplain in the cycle of erosion model.

Monotremes An ancient family of egg-laying mammals of which only two species survive, e.g., platypuses and echidnas.

Monsoon Derived from the Arabic word for "season," a regional windflow that streams onto and off certain landmasses on a seasonal basis. The moist onshore winds of summer bring the *wet monsoon* whereas the offshore winds of winter are associated with the *dry monsoon*.

Monsoon rainforest climate (Am) Tropical monsoon climate, characterized by sharply distinct wet and dry seasons.

Moon Satellite that orbits a planet, probably originating from the clustering of planetesimals. All solar system planets except Mercury and Venus have such bodies. Our Moon orbits the Earth once every 27.3 days at an average distance of 385,000 km.

Mor humus A raw humus formed from coniferous debris. It forms a discrete mat of needles, cones and twigs on top of the mineral soil.

Moraine Ridge, mound, or sheet of glacial debris deposited during the melting phase of a glacier.

Morphology Shape or form.

Mudflow Flow form of slope process involving a stream of fluid, lubricated mud; most common where heavy rains strike an area that has long been dry and where weathering has loosened ample quantities of fine-grained material.

Mull humus A type of humus intimately mixed with mineral soil material, characteristic of grassland areas. Much of the humic material is supplied by the rotting of the extensive root systems of grasses.

Multispectral systems Paraphernalia of remote-sensing platforms, which today increasingly employ sets of scanners simultaneously attuned to several different spectral bands, greatly enhancing observation quality and interpretive capabilities.

Munsell Soil Color Chart A colour classification system using values for colours, hues, and chroma.

Muskeg In the northern coniferous forest biome, the particular assemblage of low-growing leathery bushes and stunted trees that concentrate in the waterlogged soil bogs and lake-filled depressions.

Mutation Variation in reproduction in which the message of heredity (DNA) contained in the genes is imperfectly passed on and from which new species may originate.

Mutualism Biological interaction in which there is a coexistence of two or more species because one or more is essential to the survival of the other(s); also called *symbiosis*.

Neap tide Least extreme tidal range that occurs when the Moon's pull works at right angles against the Sun's attraction and the Earth's rotational bulge.

Nearshore Beach zone that is located seaward of the foreshore, submerged even during an average low tide.

Longshore bars and troughs develop here in this zone of complex, ever-changing topography.

Negative feedback mechanism Feedback mechanism that operates against change to keep a system in its original condition.

Net radiation Amount of radiation left over when all the incoming and outgoing radiation flows have been tallied; totals about one-fourth of the shortwave radiation originally arriving at the top of the atmosphere.

Neve Another name for the Accumulation zone of a glacier.

Niche (*see* **ecological niche**)

Nonclastic sedimentary rocks Derived not from particles of other rocks, but from chemical solution by deposition and evaporation or from organic deposition.

Nonrenewable resource One that when used at a certain rate will ultimately be exhausted. (Metallic ores and petroleum are good examples.)

Nonsilicates Minerals consisting of compounds that do not contain the silicon and oxygen of the silicates; include the carbonates, sulfates, sulfides, and halides.

Non-utilization Primary production, etc. that is not eaten and is decomposed.

Normal fault Tensional fault exhibiting a moderately inclined fault plane that separates a block that has remained fairly stationary from one that has been significantly downthrown.

North Atlantic Oscillation (NAO) Alternating pressure gradient between the North Atlantic Ocean's semipermanent upper midlatitude low-pressure cell (the Icelandic Low) and its semipermanent subtropical high-pressure cell (the Bermuda High, especially its eastern segment—the Azores High) centered above the Azores Islands. Its fluctuations affect the warmth and moisture of windflows in Europe, and the NAO's complicated workings also involve the North Atlantic Drift ocean current, the sinking of warm water near Greenland and Iceland, the upwelling of cold water off northwest Africa, and many lesser components.

North Pole "Top" of the Earth, at latitude 90°N; one of two places (the other being the South Pole) where the planet's axis intersects the surface.

Northeast Trades Surface wind belt that generally lies between the Equator and 30°N; the Coriolis force deflects equatorward-flowing winds to the right, thus recurving north winds into northeast winds.

Northern coniferous forest biome Upper midlatitude boreal forest (known in Russia as the snowforest or *taiga*); dominated by dense stands of slender, cone-bearing, needleleaf trees, such as spruce, pine, and fir.

Northern Hemisphere The half of the Earth located north of the Equator (0° latitude); the northernmost point is the North Pole (90°N).

Nuée ardente Cloud of hot and noxious volcanic gas that races downslope following a spectacular explosion associated with unusually high pressures inside the erupting volcano; incinerates everything in its path.

Numerical weather prediction Computer weather forecasting method used by the Atmospheric Environment Service, based on projections by small increments of time up to 48 hours into the future.

Nunatak Mountain peak of a buried landscape that protrudes through the overlying glacier or ice sheet.

O horizon In certain soils, such as organic and gleysolic soils, the uppermost layer—lying above the **A** horizon—consisting entirely of organic material in various stages of decomposition.

Obduction (Obducted) The reverse of subduction. A type of collision along a lithospheric plate margin where oceanic crust is over part of a continent carrying plate, exposing ophiolites and in some cases the Moho, e.g., the Gros Morne area of Newfoundland.

Oblate spheroid (Minor) departure in the shape of Planet Earth from that of a perfect sphere. The Earth, as an oblate spheroid, bulges slightly at the Equator and is slightly flattened at the poles.

Occluded front Surface boundary between cold and cool air in a mature midlatitude cyclone; caused by the cold front undercutting and lifting the warm air entirely off the ground.

Oceanic trench Prominent seafloor feature, often adjacent to an island arc, in a zone where two oceanic plates converge and one subducts the other. The greatest depths of the world ocean lie in such trenches in the Pacific east of the Philippines (Challenger Deep in the Mariana Trench, ~10,900 m).

Offshore bar Sandbar that lies some distance from the beach and is not connected to land. A longshore bar is an example.

Ogive A dirt-band or sediment-rich layer in a glacier or ice sheet.

Open system System whose boundaries (interfaces) freely permit the transfer of energy and/or matter across them.

Open wave Early maturity stage in the development of a midlatitude cyclone. Surface cyclonic air motion transforms the original kink on the stationary front into an open wave, around which cold and warm air interact in distinct ways.

Ophiolites A suite of rocks characteristic of the oceanic crust, e.g., pillowed basalt lavas, sheeted dykes, gabbro.

Optimum (biogeographic) range For each plant and animal species, the geographic area where it can maintain a large, healthy population.

Orders of magnitude Sizes of geographical entities. Figure 1.7 shows the entire range of magnitudes, including those that geographers usually operate within.

Organic matter One of the four soil components; material that forms from living matter.

Organic soil order A Canadian soil order including all soils formed from rotting and rotted organic debris and associated with poorly drained sites.

Organisms Living things.

Orogenic belt Chain of linear mountain ranges.

Orographic precipitation Rainfall (and sometimes snowfall) produced by moist air parcels that are forced to rise over a mountain range or other highland zone. Such air parcels move in this manner because they are propelled by both steering winds and the push of other air parcels piling up behind them.

Outcrop curvature The pulling out of rock beds by the creep process. Can be seen in some road- or rail-cuts.

Outlier Upland area formed by part of a bed formation separated from the main body of the rock bed by erosion, e.g., an outlier of limestone separated by erosion from an escarpment.

Outer core Liquid shell that encloses the Earth's inner core, whose composition involves similar materials.

Overbank deposits Fine grained muds which fall out of suspension from slack water on a floodplain.

Overbank flow (Flood) Water spreads out from the channel and covers part or all of the floodplain. Fine grained muds fall out of suspension in standing pools of water and form Overbank Deposits capping the *fining-upwards sequence* characteristic of floodplain deposits.

Overthrust fault Compressional fault in which the angle of the fault plane is very low.

Overturned fold Extremely compressed fold, which doubles back on itself with an axial plane that is oriented beyond the horizontal.

Oxbow lake Lake formed when two adjacent meanders link up and one of the bends in the channel, shaped like a bow, is cut off.

Oxidation/Reduction The reaction of oxygen with a mineral (e.g., ferric iron). The removal of oxygen from a mineral (e.g., ferrous iron).

Oxisol One of the 12 soil orders of the U.S. Soil Taxonomy, found in tropical areas with high rainfall; heavily leached and usually characterized by pronounced laterite horizon, red or orange in colour. (*see* **laterite**)

Oxygen cycle Oxygen is put back into the atmosphere as a by-product of photosynthesis, and is lost when it is inhaled by animals or chemically combined with other materials during oxidation.

Ozone hole Seasonal depletion of ozone above the Antarctic region, which very likely is caused by the discharge of artificial chemical compounds called chlorofluorocarbons (CFCs). Evidence is mounting that a global thinning of the ozone layer is also taking place.

Ozone layer Also known as the ozonosphere, the ozone-rich layer of the stratosphere that extends between 15 and 50 km above the surface. The highest concentrations of ozone are usually found at the level between 20 and 25 km.

Ozonosphere Synonym for ozone layer.

P wave Seismic body wave that travels through the Earth, which is also a "push" or compressional wave; moves material in its path parallel to the direction of wave movement, and can even travel through material in a liquid state.

Pacific Ring of Fire Circum-Pacific belt of high volcanic and seismic activity, stretching around the entire Pacific Basin counterclockwise through western South America, western North America, Kamcharka, and Asia's island archipelagoes (from Japan to Indonesia) as far as New Zealand.

Pack ice Floating sea ice that forms from the freezing of ocean water.

Pahoehoe Ropy-patterned lava; forms where very fluid lavas develop a smooth "skin" upon hardening, which wrinkles as movement continues.

Palaeozoic Era of ancient life on the geological time scale extending from 570 million to 248 million years ago.

Palsa A mound in organic terrain caused by the growth of ground ice.

Pangaea Primeval supercontinent, hypothesized by Alfred Wegener, that broke apart and formed the continents and oceans as we know them today; consisted of two parts—a northern Laurasia and a southern Gondwana.

Panthalassa Primeval world ocean. (*see* **Pangea**)

Parabolic dune Crescent-shaped sand dune with its points lying upwind. The concave side of this dune is the windward side.

Parallel On the Earth grid, an east–west line of latitude. These parallels range from 0° (Equator) to 90°N and S (the North and South Poles, respectively, where the east–west line shrinks to a point).

Parallel retreat (Slopes) Slopes retain the same angle but erode backwards.

Parallelism Constant tilt of the Earth's axis (at 66½° to the plane of the ecliptic), which remains parallel to itself at every position in its annual revolution of the Sun.

Parent material Earth, materials that form soils.

Passive factor of soil formation Energy-receiving factors, e.g., Topography, Parent Material, and Time. These cannot form soil without the active factors (Climate and Organisms).

Patterned ground Periglacial rock and soil debris shaped or sorted by frost action in such a manner that it forms designs on the surface resembling rings, polygons, lines, and the like (*see* Fig. 48.7).

Ped Naturally occurring aggregate or "clump" of soil and its properties.

Pedalfers Soils that base-poor because of leaching, but which retain iron and aluminum oxides in their profiles. Characteristic of the more humid areas of eastern North America.

Pediment Smooth, gently sloping bedrock surface that underlies the alluvial apron of a mountain front and extends outward from the foot of the highlands; primarily a desert feature.

Pediplain Surface formed by the coalescence of numerous pediments after a long period of erosion has led to parallel slope retreat.

Pedocals Soils that retain calcium and other bases in their profiles. Characteristic of the more arid areas of western North America.

Pedogenetic Regimes Soil-forming regimes related to differences in the dominance of one or more soil forming factors which influence the additions, losses, transformations and translocations that occur in the soils.

Pedology Soil science; study of soils.

Pedon Column of soil drawn from a specific location, extending from the soil surface all the way down to the level where the bedrock shows signs of being transformed into **C**-horizon material.

Peneplain (Peneplanation) A nearly-flat plain developed over an extremely long period of erosion and down-wearing of the landscape. The end-result of the cycle of erosion model. Peneplanation is the process of developing a peneplain.

Perched aquifer Pockets of groundwater situated above the level of the local water table. This type of confined aquifer is often associated with karst areas.

Perched water table Separate local water table that forms at a higher elevation than the nearby main water table; caused by the effects of a local aquiclude.

Percolation Downward movement of water through the pores and other spaces in the soil under the influence of gravity.

Perennial plant One that persists for a long time.

Periglacial High-latitude or high-altitude environment on the perimeter of a glaciated area, or with low temperatures.

Periglacial (or Cold) loess Aeolian silt and fine sand deposit derived from a sandur.

Perihelion Point in the Earth's orbit, which occurs every January 3, where the distance to the Sun is minimized (about 147.5 million km).

Permafrost Perennially frozen layer of subsoil (frozen for >2 years) that is characteristic of the colder portions of the **D**-climate zone as well as the entire **E**-climate zone; can exceed 300 m in depth.

Permafrost table Upper surface of the permafrost (analogous to the water table). The soil above is subject to annual thawing and freezing (talik).

Permeability The ability of a surface or Earth materials (soil, sediments, rock) to allow water or air to infiltrate and pass through it. Permeability is related to the connectedness and size of pores, root holes and other voids in the material. Sands, gravels and rocks such as limestones are permeable. Clays are porous but have low permeability.

pH scale Used to measure acidity and alkalinity of substances on a scale ranging from 0 to 14, with 7 being neutral. Below 7 increasing acidity is observed as 0 is approached, whereas above 7 increasing alkalinity is observed as 14 is approached.

Phanerozoic A unit of the geological time scale starting about 570 million years ago and characterized by rock units having visible fossils.

Photochemical pollution Form of secondary pollution in which the effects of sunlight play a role, e.g., smog.

Photosynthesis Process in which plants convert carbon dioxide and water into carbohydrates and oxygen through the addition of solar energy. Carbohydrates are a significant component of the food and tissue of both plants and animals.

Phreatic eruption Extraordinarily explosive volcanic eruption involving the penetration of water into a superheated magma chamber. Such explosions of composite volcanoes standing in water can reach far beyond a volcano's immediate area.

Phreatic zone (*see* **zone of saturation**)

Physical geography Geography of the physical world. Figure 1.4 diagrams the subfields of physical geography.

Physical (Mechanical) weathering Disintegration of rocks by physical means through the imposition of certain stresses, such as freezing and thawing or the expansion of salt crystals (salt burst hydration).

Physiographic realm First-order subdivision of the North American continent at the broadest scale; characterized by an appropriate uniformity of landscapes, landforms, and other physiographic elements.

Physiographic region Second-order subdivision of the North American continent at a more detailed scale than the physiographic realm; characterized by an appropriate uniformity of landscapes, landforms, and other physiographic elements.

Physiography Literally, *landscape description*. It involves all the natural features on the Earth's surface, including not only the landscapes and landforms but also the climate, soils, vegetation, hydrography, and other factors that may relate to spatial changes in the overall natural landscape.

Phytogeography Geography of flora or plant life; where botany and physical geography overlap.

Phytomass Total living organic plant matter produced in a given geographic area; often used synonymously with biomass, because biomass is measured by weight (plants overwhelmingly dominate over animals in total weight per unit area).

Phytoplankton Microscopic green autotrophic plants at the lowest rung of the food chain.

Pingo Moundlike, elliptical hill in a periglacial zone whose core consists of ice rather than rock or soil.

Pipkrake effect The movement of larger material (gravel, etc.) down slope caused by undermining.

Plain On a land surface of more than 50 percent gentle slope, a low-lying area that exhibits less than 90 m of local relief.

Planar map projection One in which the transfer of the Earth grid is from a globe onto a plane, involving a single point of tangency.

Plane of the ecliptic Plane formed by the Sun and the Earth's orbital path.

Planet Dark solid body, much smaller in size than a star, whose movements in space are controlled by the gravitational effects of a nearby star.

Planetesimal Asteroid-sized body that, during the formation of the solar system, combined with swarms of similar bodies to eventually become compressed into forming one of the nine planets.

Plankton (*see* **phytoplankton; zooplankton**)

Plant nutrients In a soil, the plant-food substances that circulate through the humus-vegetation system (such as nitrogen compounds and phosphates).

Plant succession Process in which one type of vegetation is replaced by another.

Plastic Limit An Atterberg limit separating a solid state and plastic state. Determined by moisture and clay content.

Plasticity Index The relationship between the Plastic and Liquid Atterberg Limits. The closeness of the limits indicates possible instability (the closer, the more unstable).

Plate tectonics Study of those aspects of tectonics that treat the processes by which the lithospheric plates move over the asthenosphere.

Platform Borderlands The areas developed on a thin veneer of gently dipping sedimentary rocks of Phanerozoic age that cover un-exposed parts the Shield areas of continents.

Plateau On a land surface of more than 50 percent gentle slope, a tableland that exhibits more than 90 m of local relief. Moreover, most of the gently sloping area occurs in the lower half of the plateau's elevational range, and plateaus are also bounded on at least one side by a sharp drop or rise in altitude.

Platy soil structure Involves layered peds that look like flakes stacked horizontally.

Pleistocene Epoch that extended from 1.8 million to 10,000 years ago on the geological time scale; includes the latter half of the last great (Late Cenozoic) Ice Age, which began about 3.5 million years ago, as well as the emergence of humans.

Plucking (quarrying) Glacial erosion process in which fragments of bedrock beneath the glacier or ice sheet are extracted from the surface as the ice advances.

Plunging fold Anticline or syncline whose axis dips from the horizontal.

Pluton Body of intrusive igneous rock.

Pluvial lake Lake that developed in a presently dry area during times of heavier precipitation associated with glaciations. Glacial Lake Bonneville, the (much larger) forerunner of Utah's Great Salt Lake, is a classic example.

Podzolic soil order A soil order of the Canadian System of Soil Classification characterized by the leaching of bases and the retention of iron and aluminum oxides in the profile.

Podzolic horizon An illuvial **B** horizon characteristic of Podzolic Soils. (*see* **spodic horizon**)

Podzolization A Pedogenetic regime characterized by the leaching of bases and the retention of iron and aluminum oxides in the soil profile.

Point bar An accumulation of sediment (sand and/or gravel) on the inner bank (slip-off slope) of a meander bend.

Point symbols Exhibit the location of each occurrence of the phenomenon being mapped, and frequently its quantity.

Polar (E) climates Climates in which the mean temperature of the warmest month is less than 10°C (50°F). The tundra (**ET**) subtype exhibits warmest month temperatures between 0°C (32°F) and 10°C (50°F), whereas in the (coldest) ice-cap (**EF**) subtype the average temperature of the warmest month does not reach 0°C (32°F).

Polar Easterlies High-latitude wind belt in each hemisphere, lying between 60 and 90 degrees of latitude. The Coriolis force is strongest in these polar latitudes, and the equatorward-moving air that emanates from the Polar High is sharply deflected in each hemisphere to form the Polar Easterlies.

Polar Front Latitudinal zone, lying at approximately 60°N and S, where the equatorward-flowing Polar Easterlies meet the poleward-flowing Westerlies. The warmer Westerlies are forced to rise above the colder Easterlies, producing a semipermanent surface low-pressure belt known as the *Upper Midlatitude Low.*

Polar Front jet stream Upper atmosphere jet stream located above the subpolar latitudes, specifically the Polar Front; at its strongest during the half-year centered on winter.

Polar High Large semipermanent high-pressure cell centered approximately over the pole in the uppermost latitudes of each hemisphere.

Pollutant Any substance that impacts an organism negatively.

Pollution (air) Air is said to be polluted when its composition departs significantly from its natural composition of such gases as nitrogen and oxygen.

Pollution plume When prevailing winds exceed 13 km/h, dust domes begin to detach themselves from the cities over which they are centered. The polluted air streams out as a plume above the downwind countryside.

Polynyas Polynyas are ice free areas in polar seas. They are associated with a concentration of marine life.

Polythermal A glacier or ice sheet having both cold and wet-based ice.

Pool A deeper part of a stream channel usually associated with meander bends.

Pores/voids The interstices of a rock, sediment, or soil.

Porosity (rock) Water-holding capacity of a rock. Volume of pores per unit volume of rock.

Porosphere A material with a lot of interconnected pores, such as a soil where pores are created by plant roots and earthworm burrowing.

Positive feedback mechanism Feedback mechanism that induces progressively greater change from the original condition of a system.

Potential energy Energy an object has by virtue of its position relative to another object.

Potential evapotranspiration (PE) Maximum amount of water that can be lost to the atmosphere from a land surface with abundant available water.

Precambrian Era that precedes the Palaeozoic Era on the geological time scale, named after the oldest period of the Palaeozoic, the Cambrian; extends backward from 570 million years ago to the origin of the Earth, now estimated to be about 4.6 billion years ago.

Precipitation Any liquid water or ice that falls to the Earth's surface through the atmosphere (rain, snow, sleet, and hail).

Predation   Biological interaction in which one species eats members of another species.

Pressure (atmospheric)   Weight of a column of air at a given location, determined by the force of gravity and the composition and properties of the atmosphere at that location. *Standard sea-level air pressure* produces a reading of 760 mm on the mercury barometer. In terms of weight, it is also given as 1013.25 millibars (mb).

Pressure melting point   The point or temperature where basal melting is caused by the pressure exerted by an overlying mass of ice.

Pressure gradient force   The difference in surface pressure over a given distance between two locations is called the *pressure gradient*. When that pressure gradient exists, it acts as a force that causes air to move (as wind) from the place of higher pressure to that of lower pressure.

Prevailing Westerlies   (*see* **westerlies**)

Primary circulation   (*see* **general circulation**)

Primary landform   Structure created by tectonic activity.

Primary pollutant   Gaseous or solid pollutant that comes from an industrial or domestic source or the internal combustion engine of a motor vehicle.

Primary producers (Production)   The first trophic level in an Ecosystem composed of autotrophs (plants on land, algae in water).

Primary rocks   Igneous rocks, the only rock type created directly from the solidification of the Earth's primeval molten crust.

Primary seral succession   (*see* **linear autogenic succession**)

Prime meridian   North–south line on the Earth grid, passing through the Royal Observatory at Greenwich, London, defined as having a longitude of 0°.

Prismatic soil structure   Involves peds arranged in columns, giving a soil vertical strength.

Proglacial lake   A lake impounded between the snout of a glacier or a margin of an ice sheet and higher ground such as a terminal moraine or an escarpment, e.g., Glacial Lake Agassiz.

Proterozoic   The last Pre-Cambrian Geological Era between the Archaean and The Palaeozoic Eras (1.6 Ga to 570 Ma). Includes the Varangian and Ediacarian Periods.

Proxy climatic data   Indirect evidence of past climatic change; found all over the natural world, such as in seafloor sediment deposits and the concentric annual growth rings of trees.

Psychrometer   Instrument consisting of two thermometers. The bulb of one is swaddled in a wet cloth or sock, the other is not. It is used to measure relative humidity, specific humidity, and the mixing ratio.

Puddling and sealing   The decrease in the permeability of a surface caused by the re-orientation of soil materials (e.g., clay flakes) causing the closing of pores, etc. resulting from raindrop impact.

Pyroclastics   Collective name for the pre-existing rock lava fragments that are erupted explosively from a volcano.

Quartzite   Very hard metamorphic rock that resists weathering; formed by the metamorphosis of sandstone (made of quartz grains and a silica cement).

Quaternary   Second of the two periods of the Cenozoic Era on the geological time scale, extending from 1.8 million years ago to the present.

R horizon   Layer at the base of the soil where the bedrock is breaking up and weathering into the particles from which soil is being formed; **R** stands for regolith.

Radial drainage   Stream pattern that emanates outward in many directions from a central mountain or dome area.

Radiant heat   Heat flows in the form of shortwave or longwave electromagnetic radiation. The composite flows of radiant heat tallied on the surface and in the atmosphere make up net radiation.

Radiation   Transmission of energy in the form of electromagnetic waves. A wide range of energy occurs within the electromagnetic spectrum.

Radiosonde   Radio-equipped weather instrument packages that are carried aloft by balloon.

Rain   Precipitation consisting of large liquid water droplets.

Rain shadow effect   Dry conditions—often at a regional scale as in western North America—which occur on the leeward side of a mountain barrier that experiences orographic precipitation. The passage of moist air across that barrier wrests most of the moisture from the air, whose adiabatic warming as it plunges downslope sharply lowers the dew point and precipitation possibilities e.g., Interior Plateau of British Columbia and Alberta.

Rainsplash erosion   The preferential erosion of fine material caused by the impact of raindrops on a bare soil surface on a slope.

Range (animal)   Area of natural occurrence of a given animal species; often changes over time, and in some cases even seasonally. (*see also* **optimum range**)

Rawinsonde   High-altitude radar tracking of radiosonde balloons, which provides information about wind speed and directions at various vertical levels in the atmosphere.

Rayleigh waves (R Waves)   Seismic waves that travel across the Earth's surface and cause the surface to move up and down, much like ocean waves do in the sea.

Recessional moraine   Morainal ridge marking a place where glacial retreat was temporarily halted.

Rectangular drainage   Stream pattern dominated by right-angle contacts between streams and tributaries, but not as pronounced as in trellis drainage.

Recumbent fold   Highly compressed fold, which doubles back on itself with an axial plane that is near horizontal.

Recurved spit   A sand beach built out from the coast which has a curved seaward or lakeward end.

Red-yellow podzolic   A well-developed luvisolic soil found to the south of the margins of the Pleistocene ice sheets in North America. They are characterized by a strongly developed clay-rich **B** horizon. (Equivalent to the U.S. Soil Taxonomy Ultisol order).

Regime   (*see* **soil regime**)

Regional concept   Used to classify and categorize spatial information. Regions are artificial constructs developed by geographers to delineate portions of the Earth's surface that are marked by an overriding sameness or homogeneity (in our case, physiography [*see* Unit 52]).

Regional subsystem   Particular interconnection, at any given place within the total Earth System, of the five spheres or subsystems (atmosphere, hydrosphere, cryosphere, lithosphere, biosphere).

Regolith   Weathered, broken, loose material overlying bedrock, usually derived from the rock below (then called saprolite), but sometimes transported to the area. First stage in the conversion of bedrock to soil; located at the base of the soil in the **R** horizon (**R** for regolith).

Regosolic soil order   A Canadian soil order composed of recently or poorly developed soils in areas that are geomorphologically active or recently deposited. Equivalent to the Entisol order of the U.S. Soil Taxonomy.

Reinvigorated stream   One that has newly increased its erosive power and cuts downward into its own floodplain and other alluvial deposits; caused by either a relative fall in the stream's base level or tectonic uplift.

Relative humidity   Proportion of water vapor present in a parcel of air relative to the maximum amount of water vapor that air could hold at the same temperature.

Relaxation   The undergoing of change or adaptiion to current environmental conditions, e.g., slope failures.

Relief   Vertical distance between the highest and lowest elevations in a given area.

Remote sensing   Technique for imaging objects without the sensor being in immediate contact with the local scene.

Renewable resource   One that can regenerate as it is exploited.

Rescue effect   When a successful species disperses into a less suitable environment, it often manages to survive because the species' numbers are constantly replenished by a continuing stream of migrants.

Residual soil   Simplest kind of soil formation in which a soil forms directly from underlying rock. When this occurs, the dominant soil minerals bear a direct relationship to that original rock.

Respiration   Biological term for the chemical combination of oxygen and other materials to create new products (chemists call this process *oxidation*). Heat increases the plants' rates of respiration; respiration runs counter to photosynthesis because it breaks down available carbohydrates and combines them with oxygen.

Reverse fault   Result of one crustal block overriding another along a steep fault plane between them; caused by compression of the crust into a smaller horizontal space.

Revetments   Blocks of concrete of gabions put along a stream bank or a coast to stop or slow down erosion.

Revised Universal Soil Loss Equation (RUSLE I and II)   A set of revisions to the Universal Soil Loss Equation (USLE).

Revolution   One complete circling of the Sun by a planet. It takes the Earth precisely one year to complete such an orbit.

Rhizosphere   The root zone of a soil.

Rhumb line   Any straight line drawn on a cylindrical Mercator map projection, which is automatically a line of true and constant compass bearing.

Rhyolites   A fine-grained extrusive form of granite.

Richter Scale   Open-ended numerical scale, first developed in the 1930s, which measures earthquake magnitude; ranges upward from 0 to 8+, and has evolved into the *Moment Magnitude Scale*.

Riffle   A shallower part of a stream channel found between pools and associated with straightaways.

Rift   Opening of the crust, normally into a trough or trench, that occurs in zone of plate divergence or spreading. (*see* **rift valley**)

Rift valley   Develops in a continental zone of plate divergence where tensional forces pull the crustally thinning surface apart. The rift valley is the trough that forms when the land sinks between parallel faults in strips.

Rill, Rilling   A micro-channel cut into a slope which can be eliminated by ploughing or bulldozing. A hillslope process where rills are eroding a slope.

Rip current   Very strong, narrow, short-distance, stream-like current that moves seaward from the shoreline cutting directly across the oncoming surf.

Rip-Rap (*see* **revetments**)

River Cliff (*see* **cut bank**)

Roche moutonnée Landform created by glacial smoothing and plucking; asymmetrical mound that results from abrasion to one side (the side from which it advanced) and plucking on the leeward side.

Rock Any naturally formed, firm, and consolidated aggregate mass of mineral matter, of organic or inorganic origin, that constitutes part of the planetary crust. (*see* **igneous, sedimentary,** and **metamorphic rocks**)

Rock cycle Cycle of transformation that affects all rocks and involves all parts of the Earth's crust. Plutons form deep in the crust, uplift pushes them to the surface, weathering and erosion wears them down, and the sediments they produce become new mountains.

Rock fall (movement) Fastest form of mass movement that involves the free fall or downslope rolling of rock pieces loosened by weathering. These boulders form a talus cone or scree slope at the base of the cliff from which they broke away.

Rock flour Very finely ground-up debris carried downslope by a mountain glacier; when deposited, it is often blown away by the wind. Stays aloft in water causing the characteristic greenish colour of the Rocky Mountains, for example.

Rock glacier In high-relief periglacial areas, a tongue of boulder-like rock debris that has slowly moved downslope as a unit; may have been consolidated by a since eroded matrix of finer sediments, or cemented together by long melted ice.

Rock sea Area of blocky rock fragments formed when weathered rocks—particularly from frost wedging—remain near their original location (also called *blockfield* or *felsenmeer,* and *boulder field* when the rock fragments are dominated by large boulders).

Rock steps Step-like valley profile (in the postglacial landscape) often created as alpine glaciers move down valley.

Rock terrace Terrace of hard bedrock that results from the resumed downward cutting of a reinvigorated stream that removes the entire sequence of floodplain deposits.

Rockslide Landslide type of mass movement consisting mainly of rock materials.

Rotation Spinning of a planet on its axis, the imaginary line passing through its center and both poles. It takes the Earth one calendar day to complete one full rotation.

Rotational slump A mass movement where the plane of failure takes the shape of an arc. Common in deep regoliths and sediments.

Runoff Removal—as overland flow via the network of streams—at the land surface of the surplus precipitation that does not infiltrate the soil or accumulate on the ground through surface detention.

S wave Seismic body wave that is also a shear or "shake" wave; moves objects at right angles to its direction of movement, but (unlike **P** waves) cannot travel through material in a liquid state.

Sahel Derived from the Arabic word for shore, the name given to the east–west semiarid (**BSh**) belt that constitutes the "southern shore" of North Africa's Sahara; straddles latitude 15°N and stretches across the entire African continent. Suffered grievous famine in the 1970s that killed hundreds of thousands, and since then has periodically been devastated by severe droughts.

Salinization Pedogenetic Regime characteristic of extremely arid environments where salts are deposited in the soil or on the soil surface by the evaporation of groundwater.

SALR (*see* **saturated [wet] adiabatic lapse rate**)

Salt burst hydration Form of physical weathering in arid regions. Salt crystals behave much like ice in the process of frost action, entering rock joints dissolved in water, staying behind after evaporation, growing and prying apart the surrounding rock, and weakening the internal structure of the host landform.

Saltation Transportation process that entails the bouncing of sand- and gravel-sized fragments along the bed of a moving stream or in the nearshore zone, or moved by wind.

Sami The culturally acceptable name for the "Lapps" of northern Scandinavia.

Sand Coarsest grains in a soil. Sand particles range in size from 2 to 0.05 mm.

Sandspit Elongated extension of a beach into open water where the shoreline reaches a bay or bend; built and maintained by littoral or longshore drift.

Sandstone Common sedimentary rock possessing sand-sized grains.

Sandur (Icelandic, plural: Sandar) An outwash plain.

Santa Ana wind Hot, dry, *foehn*-type wind that occasionally affects Southern California. Its unpleasantness is heightened by the downward funneling of this airflow from the high inland desert through narrow passes in the mountains that line the Pacific coast.

Saturated air Air that is holding all the water vapor molecules it can possibly contain at a given temperature.

Saturated (wet) adiabatic lapse rate (SALR) Lapse rate of an air parcel saturated with water vapor in which condensation is occurring; unlike the *dry adiabatic lapse rate* (DALR) the value of the SALR is variable, depending on the amount of water condensed and the latent heat released. A typical value for the SALR at 20°C is −0.44°C/100 m.

Saturation overland flow Runoff generated by the complete filling of all soil pores by water.

Savanna biome Transitional vegetation of the environment between the tropical rainforest and the subtropical desert; consists of tropical grasslands subject to sporadic burning with widely spaced trees.

Savanna climate (Aw) Tropical wet-and-dry climate located in the transition, still tropical latitudes between the subtropical high-pressure and equatorial low-pressure belts.

Scale Ratio of the size of an object on a map to the actual size of the object it represents.

Scarp Steep Face of a cuesta or escarpment.

Schist Common metamorphic rock so altered that its previous form is impossible to determine; fine-grained, exhibits wavy bands, and breaks along parallel planes (but unevenly, unlike slate).

Sclerophyllous forest Scrub forest, Chaparral, Mediterranean type vegetation characterized by succulent species and subject to periodic burning.

Scree slope Steep accumulation of weathered rock fragments and loose boulders that rolled downslope in free fall. Also called talus.

Sea arch Small island penetrated by the sea at its base. Island originated as an especially resistant portion of a headland that was eroded away by waves.

Sea breeze Onshore airflow affecting a coastal zone, resulting from a daytime pressure gradient that steers local winds from the cooler (higher pressure) sea surface onto the warmer (lower pressure) land surface.

Sea cave Cave carved by undercutting waves that are eroding the base of a sea cliff.

Sea cliff Especially steep coastal slope that develops when headlands are eroded by waves.

Seafloor spreading Process wherein new crust is formed by upwelling magma at the midoceanic ridges, and then continuously moves away from its source toward the margins of the ocean basin; *see* **crustal spreading.**

Seamount Undersea abyssal-zone volcanic mountain reaching over 1000 m above the ocean floor.

Secondary circulation Regional air circulation system. The monsoon phenomenon is a classic example.

Secondary landform Landform that is the product of weathering and erosion.

Secondary pollutant Produced in the air by the interaction of two or more primary pollutants or from reactions with normal atmospheric constituents.

Secondary rocks Rock types derived from preexisting rocks—sedimentary and metamorphic rocks.

Sediment yield Measurement of the total volume of sediment leaving a drainage basin (t/yr).

Sedimentary rocks (Secondary) rocks that formed from the deposition and compression of rock and mineral fragments or precipitation of material in solution.

Seismic Pertaining to earthquakes.

Seismic reflection When a seismic wave traveling through a less dense material reaches a place where the density becomes much greater, it can be bounced back or reflected.

Seismic refraction When a seismic wave traveling through a less dense material reaches a place where the density becomes greater, it can be bent or refracted.

Seismic waves Pulses of energy generated by earthquakes that can pass through the Earth.

Seismograph Device that measures and records the seismic waves produced by earthquakes.

Sensible heat flow Environmental heat we feel or sense on our skins.

Sensitive (or Quick) clays Spherical clay-sized material (not clay minerals) that are prone to liquefy when wetted and shaken.

Serac a block of glacial ice between crevasses.

Sere, Seral An assemblage of plants, relating to an assemblage of plants.

Sesquioxide Oxide containing the ratio of 1½ oxygen atoms to every metallic atom.

Shaft (solution feature) In karst terrain, a pipelike vertical conduit that leads from the bottom of a solution hollow. Surface water is funneled down the shaft to join a subsurface channel or the groundwater below the water table.

Shale Soft, finest grained of the sedimentary rocks; formed from compacted mud, mud rock.

Shear strength Forces that act against down slope movement, e.g., cementation, cohesion, friction, weight, normal stress.

Shear stress The Force acting to move material down slope, influenced by weight and gravity.

Shear zone Occurs at the base of ice where mobile wet-based ice tries to get over immobile cold ice. Responsible for bringing basal material in to a glacier or ice sheet.

Sheet erosion Erosion produced by sheet flow as it removes fine-grained surface materials.

Sheet flow Surface runoff of rainwater not absorbed by the soil (also called *sheet wash*); forms a thin layer of water that moves downslope without being confined to local stream channels.

Shield volcano   Formed from fluid basaltic lavas that flow in sheets which are built up gradually by successive eruptions. In profile their long horizontal dimensions peak in a gently rounded manner that resembles a shield (the main island of Hawai'i has some of the world's most active shield volcanoes).

Shingle   Gravel and/or pebbles forming a beach.

Shingle beach   Beach consisting of gravel and/or pebbles; associated with high-energy shorelines.

Shoaling   Near-shore impact of ever shallower water on an advancing, incoming wave.

Shore   Has a more specific meaning than *coast;* denotes the narrower belt of land bordering a body of water, the most seaward portion of a coast (the *shoreline* is the actual contact border).

Shoreline   Within a *shore zone,* the actual contact border between land and water.

Short grass prairie   A vegetation of sparse short grasses separated by areas of bare surface characteristic of the more arid areas of the prairies and Great Plains.

Shortwave radiation   Radiation coming from the Sun, which has much shorter wavelengths—and involves much higher energy—than the terrestrial (longwave, lower energy) radiation emitted by the Earth.

SIAL   Derived from the chemical symbols for the minerals **si**licon and **al**uminum; refers to the generally lighter coloured, less dense rocks of the continents, which are dominated by granite or granite rocks.

Siberian High   Local name for northern Asia's Polar High, which is centered over the vast north-central/northeastern region of Russia known as Siberia.

Silicates   Minerals consisting of compounds containing silicon and oxygen and, mostly, other elements as well.

Sill   Concordant intrusive igneous form in which magma has inserted itself as a thin layer between strata of preexisting rocks without disturbing those layers to any great extent.

Silt   Next smaller category of soil particles after sand, the coarsest variety. Silt particles range in size from 0.5 to 0.002 mm.

SIMA   Derived from the chemical symbols for the minerals **si**licon and **ma**gnesium; refers to the generally darker coloured rocks of the ocean floors, which are dominated by basalt.

Slash and Burn   Swidden or shifting cultivation. Parts of a forest are cut down and burned (to supply nutrients) for agriculture. The soil nutrients are used up very quickly and the plots are left while another area is cut and burned for new fields.

Slate   Metamorphosed shale; a popular building material, it retains shale's quality of breaking along parallel planes.

Sleet   Precipitation consisting of pellets of ice produced by the freezing of rain before it reaches the surface; if it freezes after hitting the surface, it is called *freezing rain.*

Slickensides   Smooth, mirrorlike surfaces on a scarp or face produced by the movement of rocks along the fault plane or soil either side of a crack.

Slip face   Leeward slope of a sand dune.

Slope (river)   (*see* **gradient** [**river**])

Slope creating process   A process responsible for slope formation, e.g., tectonism, stream incision, wave erosion.

Slope decline   A model of slope evolution. Slopes wear down over time. See Peneplanation.

Slope flows   Flows affecting a large area of a slope.

Slope modifying process   A hillslope process which cannot form slopes but can modify slopes, e.g., wash, rilling.

Slopefoot process   Undercutting of the base of the slope by a stream or wave action.

Slope processes   All erosional processes affecting slopes, e.g., mass movements and hillslope processes.

Slope replacement   A model of slope evolution. Slopes retreat backwards and leave or are replaced by a less steep slope.

Slope retreat   A model of slope evolution. Slopes retain their angle and erode backwards. (*see* **pediplanation**)

Slough (Meander scar)   Dried up, curved linear depression on a floodplain, which is evidence of an old stream channel that was once a meander or an oxbow lake.

Slumping   Type of mass movement in which a major section of regolith, soil, or weakened bedrock comes down a steep slope as a backward-rotating slump block.

Smog   Poor-quality surface-level air lying beneath a temperature inversion layer in the lower atmosphere. The word is derived from the contraction of "smoke" and "fog."

Snow   Precipitation consisting of large ice crystals called snowflakes; formed by the ice-crystal process whose crystals do not have time to melt before they reach the ground.

Snow line   High-altitude boundary above which snow remains on the ground throughout the year.

Snowball Earth   A glacial period which affected most, if not all of the Earth, during part of the Late Proterozoic Era (1.6 Ga. to 600 Ma.).

Soil   Mixture of fragmented and organic matter and weathered grains of minerals and rocks with variable proportions of air and water. The mixture has a fairly distinct layering, and its development is influenced by climate and living organisms.

Soil air Fills the pores or spaces among the mineral particles, water, and organic matter in the soil; contains more carbon dioxide and less oxygen and nitrogen than atmospheric air does.

Soil body Geographical area within which soil properties remain relatively constant.

Soil colour The coloration of a soil horizon. Can be scientifically described using a Munsell Soil Color Chart.

Soil components These are four in number: minerals, organic matter, water, and air.

Soil consistence Subjective measure of a moist or wet soil's stickiness, plasticity, cementation, and hardness. This test is done in the field by rolling some damp soil in the hand and observing its behaviour.

Soil creep Soil creep is a mass movement process in which the topsoil moves downslope over bedrock or regolith because of its weight.

Soil formation factors These are five in number: parent material, climate, organisms, topography, and time.

Soil geography Systematic study of the spatial patterns of soils, their distribution, and the interrelationships with climate, vegetation, and humankind.

Soil heat flow Heat conducted into and out of the Earth's surface; also known as *ground heat flow*.

Soil horizon Soil layer. The differentiation of soils into layers is called *horizonation*.

Soil moisture Water that has infiltrated into the soil; any further movement of this water is by processes other than infiltration.

Soil order In Soil taxonomy, the broadest possible classification of the Earth's soils into one of 12 major categories; a very general grouping of soils with broadly similar composition, the presence or absence of certain diagnostic horizons, and similar degrees of horizon development, weathering, and leaching.

Soil profile Entire array of soil horizons (layers) from the surface top to bottom.

Soil regime Variations in behaviour of changeable elements in the soil-formation environment. The term implies some regularity in the (spatial) pattern, but recognizes change within it. Thus even if their parent material remained constant all over the world, soils would differ because they would form under varying temperature, moisture, biogeographic, and other conditions.

Soil storage capacity For agricultural purposes, the product of the average depth in centimetres to which roots grow and the water storage per centimetre for that soil type.

Soil taxonomy Soil classification scheme used by contemporary pedologists and soil geographers.

Soil texture Size of the particles in a soil; more specifically, the proportion of sand, silt, and clay in each soil horizon.

Sol Russian word for soil (Russians were pioneers in the modern science of pedology); used as a suffix for some soil types in the Canadian System of Soil Classification and all soil types in the U.S. Soil Taxonomy.

Solar constant Average solar energy received every minute at the top of the Earth's atmosphere: 1.95 cal/cm^2.

Solar elevation Number of degrees above the horizon of the noontime Sun, the position at which the solar rays strike the surface at their highest daily angle; also called *angle of incidence*.

Solar system Sun and its nine orbiting planets (plus *their* orbiting satellites). In order of increasing distance from the Sun, these planets are Mercury, Venus, Earth, Mars, Jupiter, Saturn, Uranus, Neptune, and Pluto.

Solifluction/Gelifluction An intensified form of creep usually found in a permafrost area. Solifluction is the flow of super-saturated soil which has reached its liquid limit. It can occur in any environment. Gelifluction is the term used for this solifluction associated with frozen ground or permafrost.

Solonetzic Soil Order A CSSC Soil Order including saline and alkaline soils. No equivalent at the order level in the U.S. Soil Taxonomy.

Solstice (*see* **summer solstice; winter solstice**)

Solum Consists of the **A** and **B** horizons of a soil, that part of the soil in which plant roots are active and play a role in the soil's development.

Solution (stream) Transportation process where rock material is dissolved and carried within a solids stream. Also called dissolved.

Solution load Stream load carried dissolved in water. Supplied by Baseflow. (*see* **dissolved solids**)

Solution sinkhole In karst terrain, a funnel-shaped surface hollow (with the shaft draining the center) created by solution; ranges in size from a bathtub to a stadium.

Solution weathering The weathering and removal of the weathered minerals in a dissolved state or in solution.

Source region Extensive geographical area, possessing relatively uniform characteristics of temperature and moisture, where large air masses can form.

South Pole "Bottom" of the Earth, at latitude 90°S; one of two places (the other being the North Pole) where the planet's axis intersects the surface.

Southeast Trades Surface wind belt that generally lies between the Equator and 30°S. The Coriolis force deflects equatorward flowing winds to the left, thus recurving south winds into southeast winds.

Southern Hemisphere   The half of the Earth located south of the Equator (0° latitude); the southernmost point is the South Pole (90°S).

Southern Oscillation   Periodic, anomalous reversal of the pressure zones in the atmosphere overlying the equatorial Pacific; associated with the occurrence of the El Niño phenomenon. As the sea surface temperatures change and water currents reverse, corresponding shifts occur in the windflows above.

Spatial   Pertaining to space on the Earth's surface; synonym for geographic(al).

Species   Population of physically and chemically similar organisms within which free gene flow takes place.

Species dominance   Relationship between the most abundant and important species residing in a given geographical area, and the lesser species that live in the same environment.

Species-richness gradient   Phenomenon involving the general decline over distance in the number of species per unit area, as one proceeds from the equatorial to the higher latitudes.

Specific humidity   Ratio of the weight (mass) of water vapor in the air to the combined weight (mass) of the water vapour plus the air itself.

Spheroidal (granular) soil structure   Involves peds that are usually very small and often nearly round in shape, so that the soil looks like "a layer of bread crumbs."

Spheroidal weathering (spalling)   Product of the chemical weathering process of hydrolysis. In certain igneous rocks such as granite, hydrolysis combines with other processes to cause the outer shells of the rock to flake off in what looks like a small-scale version of *exfoliation*.

Spodosol   One of the 12 soil orders of the U.S. Soil Taxonomy, which develops where organic soil acids associated with pine needle decay cause the depletion of most **A** horizon minerals. That **Ae** horizon is characterized by an ash-gray colour, the signature of silica that is resistant to dissolving by organic acids. Equivalent to the Podzolic soil order.

Spodic horizon   An illuvial **B** horizon characteristic of Podzolic Soils. (*see* **podzolic horizon**)

Sporadic burning   Burning (Fire) that occurs from time to time, because of the build up of plant debris and lightning strikes.

Sporadic permafrost   Permafrost that occurs sporadically in areas south of the Discontinuous permafrost zone, such as near the tops of high mountains.

Spring (season)   Northern Hemisphere season that begins at the spring (vernal) equinox around March 21

and ends at the summer solstice on June 22. The Southern Hemisphere spring begins at the equinox that occurs around September 23 and ends at the solstice on December 22.

Spring tide   Highest tidal range that occurs when the Earth, Moon, and Sun are aligned.

Spring (vernal) equinox   In Northern Hemisphere terminology, the equinox that occurs when the Sun's noontime rays strike the Equator vertically on or around March 21.

Spring (water)   Surface stream of flowing water that emerges from the ground.

Spur   Ridge that thrusts prominently from the crest or side of a mountain.

Stability (of air)   Parcel of air whose vertical movement is such that it returns to its original position after receiving some upward force. However, if an air parcel continues moving upward after receiving such a force, it is said to be unstable.

Stack   Column-like island that is a remnant of a headland eroded away by waves.

Stade, Stadial   A glacial advance.

Stalactite   Rock formation composed of dripstone hanging from the roof of a cave.

Stalagmite   Upward tapering, pillar-like rock formation composed of dripstone standing on the floor of a cave.

Standard parallel   Parallel of tangency between a globe and the surface onto which it is projected.

Standard (sea-level) air pressure   Average weight of the atmospheric column pressing down on the Earth's surface. It produces a reading of 760 mm on the mercury barometer. In terms of weight, it is also given as 1013.25 millibars (mb).

Stationary front   Boundary between two stationary air masses.

Steady-state system   System in which inputs and outputs are constant and equal.

Steppe climate (BS)   Semiarid climate, transitional between fully developed desert conditions (**BS**) and the subhumid margins of the bordering **A, C,** and **D** climate regions.

Stepped Long Profile (Glacial)   A stepped floor of a glacial trough, thought to be a result of the polythermal nature of ice associated with extension and compressive flow which causes crevasses and basal shearing.

Stepped Long Profile (Stream)   A long profile characteristic of both formerly glaciated and tropical areas.

Stock   Discordant pluton that is smaller than a batholith.

Stone Lines   Lines of stones that are dragged out into the soil and on to the soil surface by the creep process.

Stone net   Hexagon-like arrangement of stones that is common in the periglacial soils of the Arctic and near-Arctic regions; created when ice forms on the underside of rocks in the soil, a process that wedges rocks upwards and eventually results in their meeting to form lines and patterns.

Storm   Organized, moving atmospheric disturbance.

Storm surge   Wind-driven wall of water hurled ashore by the approaching centre of a hurricane, which can surpass normal high tide levels by more than 5 m; often associated with a hurricane's greatest destruction.

Straightaways   The parts of stream channels between meander bends. Associated with riffles.

Strand   A long wide sandy beach.

Strata   Layers.

Stratification   Layering.

Stratified drift   One of two types of glacial drift; material transported by glaciers and later sorted and deposited by the action of running water, either within the glacier or as it melts. Fluvioglacial deposit.

Stratigraphy   Order and arrangement of rock strata.

Stratopause   Upper boundary of the stratosphere, lying approximately 52 km above the surface.

Stratosphere   Atmospheric layer lying above the troposphere. Here temperatures are either constant or start increasing with altitude.

Stratovolcano   Large composite volcano.

Stratus   Cloud-type category encompassing layered and fairly thin clouds that cover an extensive geographic area; subclassified according to height.

Streak (mineral)   Colour of a mineral in powdered form when rubbed against a porcelain plate; used in mineral identification.

Stream capacity   Maximum load of sediment that a stream can carry at a given discharge (volume of water).

Stream competence   Erosional effectiveness of a stream as measured by the velocity of water movement: the faster the flow, the greater the ability to move more and larger material.

Stream perimeter   The bed and banks of a stream.

Stream piracy   Capture of a segment of a stream by another stream.

Stream profile   Longitudinal, downward curve of a stream from its head in an upland area to its mouth.

Stream turbulence   Irregularity in the water movement in a stream related to the interaction of sediment size and riverbed roughness.

Strike   Compass direction of the line of intersection between a rock layer and a horizontal plane.

Strike-slip fault   (*see* **transcurrent fault**)

Subduction   Process that takes place when an oceanic plate converges head-on with a plate carrying a continental landmass at its leading edge. The lighter continental plate overrides the denser oceanic plate and pushes it downwards.

Subduction zone   Area in which the process of subduction is taking place.

Subglacial   material carried under a glacier or ice sheet. Sub-glacial melt-water streams flow in tunnels under a glacier of ice sheet.

Subglacial cavity   A cave under a glacier.

Sublimation   Process where a solid can change directly into a gas. The reverse process is also called sublimation (or deposition). The heat required to produce these transformations is the sum of the latent heats of fusion and vaporization.

Submarine canyon   Submerged river valley on the continental shelf. Before the rise in sea level (of about 120 m) over the past 10,000 years, the shelf was mostly dry land across which the river flowed to its former outlet.

Submergent coast   Drowned coastal zone, more common than uplifted, emergent coasts; submergence caused in large part by the rise in sea level (about 120 m) of the past 10,000 years.

Subpolar gyre   Oceanic circulation loop found only in the Northern Hemisphere. Its southern limb is a warm current steered by prevailing westerly winds, but the complex, cold returning flows to the north are complicated by sea-ice blockages and the configuration of landmasses vis-à-vis outlets for the introduction of frigid Arctic waters.

Subsidence   Vertical downflow of air toward the surface from higher in the troposphere.

Subsurface processes   Hillslope processes that occur within a slope (e.g., eluviation, solution, and lessivation).

Subsystem   Component of a larger system. It can act independently, but operates within, and is linked to, the larger system.

Subtropical gyre   Circulates around the Subtropical High that is located above the center of the ocean basin; dominates the oceanic circulation of both hemispheres, flowing clockwise in the Northern Hemisphere and counterclockwise in the Southern Hemisphere.

Subtropical High   Semipermanent belt of high pressure that is found at approximately 30 degrees of latitude in both the Northern and Southern Hemispheres. The subsiding air at its center flows outward toward both the lower and higher latitudes.

Subtropical jet stream Jet stream of the upper atmosphere that is most commonly located above the subtropical latitudes; evident throughout the year.

Suffosion sinkhole Collapse sinkhole created when an overlying layer of unconsolidated material is left unsupported.

Sulphidic bacteria Bacteria that can form sulphuric acid.

Sulphidic cave A cave formed by Sulphidic bacterial action.

Summer In Northern Hemisphere terminology, the season that begins on the day of the summer solstice (June 22) and ends on the day of the fall (autumnal) equinox (around September 23).

Summer solstice Each year, day of the poleward extreme in the latitude where the Sun's noontime rays strike the Earth's surface vertically. In the Northern Hemisphere that latitude is 23½°N (the Tropic of Cancer) and the date is June 22; in the Southern Hemisphere that latitude is 23½°S (the Tropic of Capricorn) and the date is December 22.

Supercontinent cycle The growth and break up of supercontinents such as Pangaea. Also called a Wilson Cycle.

Superimposed stream River exhibiting transverse drainage across a structural feature that would normally impede its flow because the feature was at some point buried beneath the surface on which the stream developed. As the feature became exposed the stream kept cutting through it.

Supraglacial Means on the top of a glacier or ice sheet. (*see* **ablation till**)

Surf Water zone just offshore dominated by the development and forward collapse of breaking waves.

Surface creep Rolling or dragging movement of fairly large rock fragments by the wind that pushes them along the ground, especially during windstorms.

Surface detention Water that collects on the surface in pools and hollows, bordered by millions of tiny natural dams, during a rainstorm that deposits more precipitation than the soil can absorb.

Exotic (suspect terrane) Rocks possessing properties that sharply distinguish it from surrounding regional rocks; terrane consisting of a "foreign" rock mass that is mismatched to its large-scale geological setting that has been accreted.

Suspension (stream) Transportation process whereby very fine clay- and silt-sized sediment is carried within a moving stream.

Suspension (wind) Transportation process whereby very fine clay- and silt-sized particles are kept aloft and carried high in the air by the wind.

Sustainable development Inexact term used widely by social scientists and policymakers; generally understood to mean development that meets the needs of the present without compromising the ability of future generations to meet their own needs.

Swallow hole In karst terrain, the place where a surface stream "disappears" to flow into an underground channel.

Swash Thinning sheet of water that slides up the beach after a wave reaches shore and has broken.

Swells Long rolling waves that can travel thousands of kilometres across the ocean surface until they break against a shore.

Symbiosis (*see* **mutualism**)

Syncline Troughlike downfold with its limbs dipping toward its axial plane.

Synoptic weather chart Map of weather conditions covering a wide geographical area at a given moment in time.

System Any set of related objects or events and their interactions. Usually connected by a flow of energy, water, or material.

Taiga Russian word for "snowforest." Boreal (coniferous) forest.

Taiga climate (Dfc/Dwc, Dfd/Dwd) Collective term for the harsher subtypes of the humid microthermal climate, found on the poleward side of the **D**-climate zone.

Talik A term used for the active layer in permafrost areas.

Talus cone Steep accumulation of weathered rock fragments and loose boulders that have rolled downslope in free fall.

Talus creep Creep of stones or boulders down a talus cone.

Tarn Small circular lake on the floor of a cirque basin.

Taxonomy Classification.

Tectonic plate (*see* **lithospheric plate**)

Tectonics Study of the movements and deformation of the Earth's crust.

Teleconnections Relationships involving long-distance linkages between weather patterns that occur in widely separated parts of the world; El Niño is a classic example.

Temperate deciduous forest biome Dominated by broadleaf trees. Herbaceous plants are also abundant, especially in spring before the trees grow new leaves.

Temperate evergreen forest biome Dominated by needleleaf trees; especially common along western mid-latitude coasts where precipitation is abundant.

Temperate grassland biome   Occurs over large midlatitude areas of continental interiors. Perennial and sod-forming grasses are dominant.

Temperate karst   Marked by disappearing streams, jagged rock masses, solution depressions, and extensive cave networks; forms more slowly than tropical karst.

Temperature   Index used to measure the kinetic energy possessed by molecules; the more kinetic energy they have, the faster they move. Temperature, therefore, is an abstract term that describes the energy (speed of movement) of molecules.

Temperature gradient   Horizontal rate of temperature change over distance.

Temperature inversion   Condition in which temperature increases with altitude rather than decreases—a positive lapse rate. It inverts what we, on the surface, believe to be the "normal" behavior of temperature change with increasing height.

Tensional stress   Stress associated with the divergence of lithospheric plates. As the lithosphere spreads, rocks are being pulled apart and they thin, break, and fault; sometimes blocks of crust sink down to form rift valleys.

Tephra   Loose assemblage of pyroclastics.

Terminal Groyne Scour   Erosion at the down-shore end of a groyne field. Sediment is held back by the groynes and the water erodes the shoreline to produce sediment to transport.

Terminal moraine   Rock debris, carried in and just ahead of the leading front of a glacier, and deposited as an irregular ridge when the ice's forward progress stops. These ridges are important to Earth scientists because they mark the farthest extent of an ice lobe.

Termite   Colonial isopod that collects vegetation debris and concentrates it in its nests termitaria.

Termitaria   Above ground nests of termites. Composed of fine soil material, termite saliva and faeces. Eroded termitaria supply the fine topsoil found on the top of Laterites in many savanna areas.

Terraces, paired   Higher lying remnants of an old floodplain that stand above the bluffs lining the newer floodplain of a rejuvenated river. When they lie at the same elevation, these terraces are said to be paired.

Terrane   Geological region of "consistent" rocks in terms of age, type, and structure. Mismatched subregions can occur and are known as suspect terranes.

Tertiary   First of the two periods of the Cenozoic Era of recent life on the geologic time scale, extending from 65 million to 1.8 million years ago.

Thalweg   The wandering low flow channel in a stream bed.

Thermohaline circulation   Describes the deep-sea system of oceanic circulation, which is controlled by differences in the temperature and salinity of subsurface water masses.

Thermometer   Instrument for measuring temperature. Most commonly these measurements are made by observing the expansion and contraction of mercury inside a glass tube.

Thermosphere   Fourth layer of the atmosphere, lying respectively above the troposphere, stratosphere, and mesosphere. In this layer, temperatures increase as altitude increases.

Threshold angle   The angle at which mass movements stop on a slope. The angle of repose or stability.

Threshold angle model   A model of slope evolution. Slopes are created by Stream Incision, brought down to their Threshold Angle by Mass Movements and then sustained (or slightly modified) by Hillslope Processes.

Thrust fault   Compressional fault in which the angle of the fault plane is very low; sometimes called *overthrust fault*.

Thunderstorm   Local storm dominated by thunder, lightning, heavy rain, and sometimes hail; exhibits a definite life cycle involving developing, mature, and dissipation stages.

Tidal bore (or Eagre)   A wall of water that moves up a coastal reach of a stream caused by an incoming tide. The incoming water moves up-stream over the down-stream flowing stream water. The wall of water can be a few cm to many metres high.

Tidal current   Tidal movement of seawater into and out of bays and lagoons.

Tidal range   Average vertical difference between sea levels at high tide and low tide.

Tide   Cyclical rise and fall of sea level controlled by the Earth's rotation and the gravitational pull of the Moon and Sun. Daily two high tides and two low tides occur within a period slightly longer than 24 hours.

Till   One of the two types of glacial drift; solid material (ranging in size from boulders to clay particles) carried at the base of a glacier that is deposited as an unsorted mass when the ice melts back.

Time   An independent and passive factor of soil formation.

Time-independent   A process not dependent on time.

Tilth   Aerated, mixed, humus-rich top soil formed by earthworms and other soil organisms. Ploughing fields produces a tilth.

Time zone   Approximately 15-degree-wide longitudinal zone, extending from pole to pole, which shares the same local time. In Canada, from east to west, the time zones are known as Newfoundland, Atlantic, Eastern, Central, Mountain, and Pacific.

Tombolo   Sandspit that forms a link between the mainland and an offshore island.

Toponymy   Place names.

Topset beds   Horizontal layers of sedimentary deposits that underlie a deltaic plain.

Tornado   Small vortex of air, averaging 100 to 500 m (330 to 1650 ft) in diameter, that descends to the ground from rotating clouds at the base of a severe thunderstorm, accompanied by winds whose speeds range from 50 to 130 m/s. As tornadoes move across the land surface, they evince nature's most violent weather and can produce truly awesome destruction in the natural and cultural landscapes.

Tornado Alley   North–south corridor in the eastern Great Plains of the central United States, which experiences tornadoes with great frequency; extends from central Texas northward through Oklahoma and Kansas to eastern Nebraska.

Tower (karst)   In tropical karst landscapes, a cone-shaped, steep-sided hill that rises above a surface that may or may not be pocked with solution depressions.

Traction   Transportation process that involves the sliding or rolling of particles along a riverbed.

Trans-Eurasian earthquake belt   Second in the world only to the Circum-Pacific belt, a belt of high earthquake incidence that extends east-southeastward from the Mediterranean Sea across southwestern and southern Asia to join the Circum-Pacific belt off Southeast Asia.

Transcurrent fault   Transverse fault in which crustal blocks move horizontally in the direction of the fault; also known as a *strike-slip fault* because movement at a transcurrent fault occurs along the strike of the fault.

Transform fault   Special case of transcurrent faulting in which the transverse fault marks the boundary between two lithospheric plates that are sliding past each other. California's San Andreas Fault is a classic example.

Transformation   Soil-layer formation process involving the weathering of rocks and minerals and the continuing decomposition of organic material in the soil. Weathering is most advanced in the upper soil layers.

Translocation   Movements of material in solution or in particulate form down a soil profile (e.g., the leaching of bases), up a soil profile (e.g., salts brought up into the soil by groundwater under capillary action), or moved horizontally within the soil (e.g., water moving clay-sized material down slope through the soil mass).

Transpiration   Passage of water into the atmosphere through the leaf pores of plants.

Transport-limited slopes   A slope form that is influenced to a great extent by erosional processes rather than weathering. Weathered material builds up to cover the slope.

Transported soil   When a soil is totally independent of the underlying solid rock because the parent material has been transported and deposited by one or more agents, often far from its source area.

Transverse dune   Ridgelike sand dune that is positioned at a right angle to the prevailing wind; usually straight or slightly curved.

Transverse fault   (*see* **transcurrent fault**)

Transverse stress   Lateral stress produced when two lithospheric plates slide horizontally past each other.

Treeline   The latitudinal or altitudinal limit of tree growth (mainly because of cold temperatures and/or the lack of soil).

Trellis drainage   Stream pattern that resembles a garden trellis; flows only in two orientations, more or less at right angles to each other; often develops on parallel-folded sedimentary rocks.

Tributaries   In a stream system, the smaller branch streams that connect with and feed the main artery (trunk stream); terminology also applies to glacier systems.

Tributary glacier   Smaller glacier that feeds a trunk (main) glacier.

Trimline   The upper limit of glacial erosion in a mountainous area. The trimline separates the glacially over-steepened and straightened walls of a glacial trough from the alp above.

Trophic (feeding) levels   Position in an Ecosystem based on energy or food flow, the trophic levels are Primary Producer, Herbivore, Carnivore and Decomposer.

Tropic of Cancer   Most northerly latitude (23½°N) where the Sun's noontime rays strike the Earth's surface vertically (on June 22, the day of the Northern Hemisphere summer solstice).

Tropic of Capricorn   Most southerly latitude (23½°S) where the Sun's noontime rays strike the Earth's surface vertically (on December 22, the day of the Northern Hemisphere winter solstice).

Tropical (A) climates   Dominated by warmth (due to low-latitude location) and moisture (from the rains of the Inter-Tropical Convergence Zone); contained within a continuous east–west belt astride the Equator, varying latitudinally from 30 to 50 degrees wide.

Tropical cyclone   (*see* **hurricane**)

Tropical deforestation   Clearing and destruction of tropical rainforests to make way for expanding settlement frontiers and the exploitation of new economic opportunities.

Tropical depression   Easterly wave of increased intensity, but exhibiting wind speeds of less than 21 m/s. Its low-pressure trough has deepened and begun to assume a rotating, cyclonic organization. Further intensification of the depression would next transform it into a tropical storm.

Tropical gyre Narrow, low-latitude oceanic circulation loop, in both the Northern and Southern Hemispheres, comprised of the equatorial currents and returning countercurrents; reinforced by the converging winds of the Northeast and Southeast Trades.

Tropical karst Dominated by steep-sided, vegetation-covered hill terrain; solution features are larger than in slower forming temperate karst landscapes.

Tropical rainforest biome Vegetation dominated by tall, closely spaced evergreen trees; a teeming arena of life that is home to a greater number and diversity of plant and animal species than any other biome.

Tropical rainforest climate (Af) Due to equatorial proximity, exhibits the greatest effects of heat and moisture of any climate type.

Tropical savanna climate (*see* **savanna climate**)

Tropical storm Intensified tropical depression, exhibiting a deep central low-pressure cell, rotating cyclonic organization, and wind speeds between 21 and 33 m/s. Further intensification would transform the system into a tropical cyclone (hurricane).

Tropopause Upper boundary of the troposphere along which temperatures stop decreasing with height.

Troposphere Bottom layer of the atmosphere in which temperature usually decreases with altitude.

True flow A Hillslope process in which the sediment is carried in a viscous state.

Truncated spurs Straightened and oversteepened hillsides that have been cut by a glacier, straightening the glacially eroded valley.

Trunk glacier Main glacier, which is fed by tributary glaciers.

Trunk stream Main stream in a drainage network, which is fed by all the tributary streams.

Tsunami (Harbour wave) Seismic sea wave, set off by a crustal disturbance, which can reach gigantic proportions.

Tundra biome Microtherm plant assemblage of the coldest environments; dominated by perennial mosses, lichens, and sedges.

Tundra climate (ET) Milder subtype of the **E**-climate zone, named after its distinct vegetation assemblage of mosses, lichens, and stunted trees.

Turf or Stone garlands These are concentrations of turf or stones found around the ends of tongues of solifluction lobes. Seen from above they look like garlands.

Ultisol One of the 12 soil orders of the U.S. Soil Taxonomy; usually quite old, not particularly fertile, and located in warm subtropical environments with pronounced wet seasons. Equivalent to Red-yellow podzolic/Lateritic soils.

Ultraviolet radiation High-energy, shortwave radiation associated with incoming solar energy.

Unconfined aquifer (*see* **aquifer, unconfined**)

Unconformity Gap in the geological history of an area as found in the rock record, owing to a hiatus in deposition, followed by erosion of the surface, with further deposition continuing later; more specifically, can also refer to the contact between the eroded strata and the strata of resumed deposition.

Underfit stream Small stream lying in a large river valley that seems incapable of having sculpted that valley. Stream piracy is one cause.

Understory Plants growing below the tree canopy, undergrowth.

Undertow (*see* **backwash**)

Universal Soil Loss Equation (USLE) An equation that is used to estimate soil erosion by runoff.

Uplifted marine terrace In an emergent coastal zone, a wave-cut platform that has been exposed and elevated by tectonic uplift or a lowering of sea level (or both).

Upper mantle Viscous interior shell of the Earth, which encloses the solid lower mantle. The uppermost part of the upper mantle, however, is solid, and this zone, together with the crust that lies directly above it, is called the lithosphere.

Upper Midlatitude Low Semipermanent surface low-pressure belt, lying at approximately 60°N and S, where the equatorward flowing Polar Easterlies meet the poleward flowing Westerlies. At this sharp atmospheric boundary, known as the Polar Front, the warmer Westerlies are forced to rise above the colder Easterlies.

Upthrown block Block that moves upward with respect to adjacent blocks when vertical movement occurs during faulting.

Upwelling Rising of cold water from the ocean depths to the surface; affects the local climatic environment because cold water lowers air temperatures and the rate of evaporation.

Urban heat island Form taken by an isotherm representation of the heat distribution within an urban region. The central city has higher temperatures than the surrounding areas.

U.S. Soil Taxonomy The comprehensive soil classification system developed and used in the U.S.

Uvala In karst terrain, a large surface depression created by the coalescence of two or more neighbouring sinkholes.

Vadose zone (*see* **zone of aeration**)

Valley train (*see* **sandur**)

Vapour pressure Pressure exerted by the molecules of water vapour in air.

Vapour-pressure gradient Difference in vapour pressure between two locations. A common situation involves air near a water surface, which contains a large number of water vapour molecules and thus exhibits a relatively high vapour pressure, and air at some distance from that surface, which contains fewer vapour molecules and therefore a lower vapour pressure.

Vaporization Synonym for evaporation.

Variable gases Atmospheric gases present in differing quantities at different times and places; three are essential to life: carbon dioxide, water vapor, and ozone.

Varves Paired layers of alternating Finer and coarser sediments caused by seasonal variations in deposition on a lakebed.

Velocity (stream) Rate of speed (m/s) at which water moves in a stream channel. This rate varies within the stream.

Vent Opening through the Earth's crust from which lava erupts. Most eruptions occur through pipe-shaped vents that build volcanic mountains, but fissure eruptions also occur through lengthy cracks that exude sheets of lava (flood basalts).

Venturi effect Restriction of a pipe or stream cross-section causes an increase in the velocity of water (or air) flow. Occurs because of riffles in a stream.

Vertical zonation Characteristic of **H** climates, the distinct arrangement of climate zones according to altitudinal position. The higher one climbs, the colder and harsher the climate becomes.

Vertisolic soil order An soil order the Canadian System or Soil Classification characterized by surface cracking and swelling because of dessication and moisture or freezing and thawing. Fine material is blown into the cracks when open, exposing a lower layer at the surface. The soil material is inverted in this way, hence the name. Equivalent to the Vertisol order of the U.S. Soil Taxonomy.

Vicariance Modern species evolved from an ancestral species that arrived in a given part of the world after being carried along as landmasses parted over tens of millions of years.

Viscosity Property of a fluid that resists flowing.

Viscous Syrup-like; capable of flowing slowly.

Voids (*see* **pores**)

Volcanic (Island) Arc An arc-shaped group of volcanoes or volcanic islands.

Volcanic ash (*see* **ash [volcanic]**)

Volcanic bombs (*see* **bombs [volcanic]**)

Volcanic dome Small volcanic mound built by oozing lava without pyroclastic activity; often forms inside the crater following an explosive eruption, e.g., Mt. St. Helen's.

Volcanic Explosivity Index A classification of volcanic eruptions based on criteria such as energy release, the volume of ash erupted, etc.

Volcanic hazard A process related to volcanism which is a hazard to life, e.g., lava flows, gas emissions, ashfall, lahars, etc.

Volcanic risk The possibility of volcanic eruptions or processes related to volcanic eruptions happening in a specific area.

Volcanism Eruption of molten rock at the Earth's surface, often accompanied by rock fragments and explosive gases.

Volcano Vent in the Earth's surface through which magma, solid rock, debris, and gases are erupted. This ejected material usually assumes the shape of a shield or a conical hill or mountain.

Volume symbols Describe surfaces on a map, which can be generalizations of real surfaces or representations of conceptual surfaces.

W horizon A water-logged layer in Organic, Gleysolic and thawed Cryosolic soils. Occurs because either, part the soil is underwater (Organic and Gleysolic soils) or because of a soil layer stopping drainage (e.g., permafrost under the talik, indurated ironpan in some Podzolic soils).

Wadi An Arabic term for a canyon or gorge.

Wallace's Line A.R. Wallace's controversial boundary line that purportedly separates the unique faunal assemblage of Australia from the very different animal assemblage of neighbouring Southeast Asia. Wallace's line, suggested over a century ago, is still the subject of debate today.

Warm front Produced when an advancing warm air mass infringes on a preexisting cooler one. When they meet, the lighter warmer air overrides the cooler air mass, forming the gently upward sloping warm front (producing far more moderate precipitation than that associated with steeply sloped cold fronts).

Warm sector In an open-wave, midlatitude cyclone, the wedge of warm air enclosed by the cold and warm fronts.

Wash (sheetwash, slopewash) A Hillslope process in which a sheet of water pulses over a slope.

Wash load The very finest material carried in suspension by the turbulence of stream flow which is usually flushed out of a stream into a lake or the sea.

Water balance The measurement of the inflow (precipitation), outflow (evapotranspiration and smog), and net annual surplus or deficit of water at a given location.

Water gap Pass in a ridge or mountain range through which a stream flows.

Water (Oceanic) Hemisphere The roughly one-half of the Earth that contains most of the surface water (Southern Hemisphere); the opposite of the *land hemisphere*.

Water-logged Filled with water. Saturated.

Water resources Subfield of physical geography involving its intersection with hydrology; systematic study of the surface and subsurface water supplies potentially available for human use.

Water table Top of the (phreatic) zone of saturation; does not lie horizontally, but follows the general profile of the land surface above.

Water vapour Invisible gaseous form of water; the most widely distributed variable gas of the atmosphere.

Watershed (*see* **drainage basin**)

Waterspout Tornado that forms and moves over a water surface.

Wave crest Top of a wave. The wave's height is the vertical distance between the wave crest and the wave trough.

Wave-cut platform Abrasion platform that develops at the foot of a sea cliff, marking its recession. Its nearly flat bedrock surface slopes seaward.

Wave height Vertical distance between wave crest (top) and wave trough (bottom).

Wave length Horizontal distance between one wave crest (or wave trough) and the next.

Wave of translation Swell nearing shore that has "felt" the rising ocean bottom and whose internal water motion (as a wave of oscillation) begins to be affected by it; the wave's erosional work has begun.

Wave period Time interval between the passage of two successive wave crests past a fixed point.

Wave refraction Near-shore bending of waves coming in at an oblique angle to the shoreline. Shoaling slows part of the wave, which progressively bends as the faster end "catches up."

Wave trough Bottom of a wave. The wave's height is the vertical distance between wave crest and wave trough.

Waves of oscillation Waves that move water particles in a circular up-and-down path. Their depth is one-half their length.

Weather Immediate and short-term conditions of the atmosphere that impinge on daily human activities.

Weathering Chemical alteration and physical disintegration of Earth materials by the action of air, water, and organisms; more specifically, the breakdown of rocks in situ, their disintegration and decomposition without distant removal of the products.

Weathering-limited slopes A slope form that is greatly influenced by weathering rather than erosional process-es. The slope form is not covered by regolith and is closely related to the characteristics of a particular rock type.

Westerlies Two broad midlatitude belts of prevailing westerly winds, lying between approximately 30° and 60° in both hemispheres; fed by the Coriolis-force-deflected, poleward windflow emanating from the Subtropical High on the equatorward margin of the Westerlies wind belt.

Wet-based (Temperate) ice Ice that can reach pressure melting point because it occurs in warmer climates than cold ice or it has more mass to cause basal melting. It is mobile and therefore can erode the ground below.

Wet-bulb temperature On a psychrometer, temperature reading of the thermometer whose bulb is swaddled in a wet cloth or sock (this produces a lower temperature than that of the surrounding air due to cooling caused by the evaporation process). Used to calculate humidity.

Wilson Cycle (*see* **supercontinent cycle**)

Wilting point Practical lower limit to moisture contained within a soil. Below this point, a crop dries out, suffering permanent injury.

Wind Movement of air relative to the Earth's surface. Winds are always named according to the direction from which they blow.

Wind abrasion (sandblasting) Erosion of rock surfaces by windborne sand particles.

Wind-chill index Index that tells us subjectively how cold we would feel under given combinations of wind speed and air temperature.

Windward Exposed, upwind side of a topographic barrier that faces the winds that flow across it.

Winter In Northern Hemisphere terminology, the season that begins on the day of the winter solstice (December 22) and ends on the day of the spring (vernal) equinox (around March 21).

Winter solstice Day each year of the poleward extreme in latitude *in the opposite hemisphere* where the Sun's noontime rays strike the Earth's surface vertically. In the Northern Hemisphere, that date is December 22 when the Sun is directly above latitude $23\frac{1}{2}°$S (the Tropic of Capricorn); in the Southern Hemisphere, that date is June 22 when the Sun is directly above latitude $23\frac{1}{2}°$N (the Tropic of Cancer).

Wisconsinan glaciation Most recent glaciation of the Late Cenozoic Ice Age, consisting of early and late stages.

Wrangellia Assemblage of exotic terranes in northwestern North America, named after the Alaskan mountain range where the phenomenon was first identified.

Xerophyte Plant adapted to withstand the aridity of dry environments.

Yardang Desert landform shaped by wind abrasion in the form of a low ridge lying parallel to the prevailing wind direction; most common in dry sandy areas underlain by soft bedrock.

Younger Dryas A return of glacial conditions during deglaciation in Europe between about 12,900 and 11,500 years ago and thought to have been caused by the discharge of glacial meltwater from Lake Agassiz and the Great Lakes in to the North Atlantic. It had a very rapid onset. Named after an alpine-tundra wildflower (*Dryas sp.*).

Zenith Point in the sky directly overhead, 90° above the horizon.

Zonal flow Westerly flow of winds that dominates the upper atmospheric circulation system poleward of 15 degrees latitude in each hemisphere.

Zone of accumulation (Néné) Glacier's upper zone of growth, where new snow is added and turned into ice over a long period.

Zone of aeration Upper of the two subterranean zones that contain groundwater; lies above the water table and is normally unsaturated, except during heavy rainfall (also known as *vadose zone*).

Zone of intolerance Geographic area beyond a plant or animal species' zone of physiological stress. Conditions here are extreme for that species and it cannot survive, except possibly for short, intermittent periods.

Zone of physiological stress Marginal geographical area for a plant or animal species that surrounds its optimum range. Here the species survives in smaller numbers, but increasingly encounters environmental stress as the outer spatial limit to its existence is neared.

Zone of saturation Lower of the two subterranean zones that contain groundwater; lies below the water table and is also known as the *phreatic zone*.

Zoogeographical realm Largest and most generalized regional unit for representing the Earth's fauna; reflects evolutionary centers for animal life as well as the influence of barriers over time.

Zoogeography Geography of animal life or fauna; where zoology and physical geography overlap.

Zooplankton Microscopic animal life forms that float in the ocean and freshwater bodies; eaten by small fish, which in turn are eaten by larger fish.

Credits

Unit 21 Figs. 21.2, 21.3, From L. P. Herrington, "Biophysical Adaptations of Man Under Climatic Stress," *Meteorological Monographs*, Vol. 2, No. 8, pp. 30–34, © 1954 by the American Meteorological Society. Fig. 21.6: From *Urbanization and Environment* by Thomas R. Detwyler and Melvin G. Marcus, © 1972 by Wadsworth Publishing Company, Inc. Fig. 21.7: From Stanley A. Changon, Jr., "Recent Studies of Urban Effects on Precipitation in the United States," in *Urban Climates*, Paper No. 254, pp. 325–341, © 1971 by World Meteorological Organization.

Unit 22 Fig. 22.6: Adapted from Paul Harrisson and Fred Pearce, eds., *AAAS Atlas of Population and Environment*, University of California Press, 2000, pp.76–77. Fig. 22.10: Adapted from "Water," *National Geographic* Special Edition, November 1993, p. 61, © 1993 National Geographic Society.

Unit 24 Fig. 24.1: From *Fundamentals of Soil Science*, eighth revised edition, by Henry D. Foth, copyright © John Wiley & Sons, Inc. Fig. 24.2: After USDA, Soil Conservation Service, n.d. Fig. 24.7: From S. R. Eyre, *Vegetation and Soils: A World Picture*, Aldine, 1963, p. 259, © S. R. Eyre. Fig. 24.8: From Daniel H. Yaalon, *Transactions of the International Congress of Soil Science*, Vol. 4, V. 16, p. 120 © 1960 by the International Society of Soil Science.

Unit 25 Fig. 25.2: After USDA, n.d. Table 25.3: After Peter W. Birkeland, *Soils and Geomorphology*, Oxford University Press, 3 rev. ed., 1999, pp. 40–41.

Unit 26 Fig. 26.1: From Léo F. Laporte, Encounter with the Earth, Canfield Press, p. 120, © 1975 by Léo F. Laporte. Fig. 26.3: After H. Lieth and E. Box, *Publications in Climatology*, C. W. Thornthwaite Laboratory of Climatology, Vol. 25, No. 3, 1972, p. 42. Figs. 26.5, 26.6: From *Geography: A Modern Synthesis*, 3/ed., by Peter Haggett, copyright © 1983 by Peter Haggett, published by Harper-Collins Publishers. Fig. 26.7: Adapted from *Fundamentals of Ecology*, Third Edition by Eugene P. Odum, copyright © 1971 by Saunders College Publishing. Fig. 26.8: © *Biol. Bull.*, Vol. XXI, No. 3, pp. 127–151, and Vol. XXII, No. 1, pp. 1–38. Fig. 26.9: After C. B. Cox et al., Biogeography, 1973, p. 61, © Blackwell Scientific Publications Ltd. Fig. 26.14: From Carl Zimmer, *Evolution: Triumph of an Idea*, HarperCollins, 2001, p. 185.

Unit 27 Fig. 27.2: Adapted from *Planets and People*, Resource Publication of the Association of American Geographers, Thomas R. Vale, 1982. Figs. 27.3, 27.4: Figures adapted from *Environmental Science*, Third Edition by Jonathan Turk, Amos Turk, and Karen Arms, copyright © 1984 by Saunders College Publishing.

Unit 28 Fig. 28.6: After *Guide to the Mammals of Pennsylvania*, by Joseph F. Merritt, published by the University of Pittsburgh Press, © 1987 by the University of Pittsburgh Press.

Unit 31 Fig. 31.4: Adapted from Brian J. Skinner and Stephen C. Porter, *The Dynamic Earth: An Introduction to Physical Geology*, John Wiley & Sons, 3 rev. ed., 1995, p. 427.

Unit 32 Fig. 32.4: Data from the U.S. Coast and Geodetic Survey and NOAA. Fig. 32.11: Same source as Fig. 3.12, p. 490.

Unit 33 Figs. 33.1, 33.4 Courtesy of LITHOPROBE, Canada's natural resource project, headquartered at The University of British Columbia, Vancouver, Canada, http://www.lithoprobe.ca. Fig. 33.2: Same source as Fig. 9.10, p. 143.

Unit 34 Fig. 34.5: From Stephen L. Harris, *Fire Mountains of the West: The Cascade and Mono Lake Volcanoes*, © 1991 Mountain Press Publishing Company. Fig. 34.8 Reproduced with permission from Environment Canada, 2004.

Unit 35 Fig. 35.6: Data from U.S. Coast and Geodetic Survey. Fig. 35.8: After NOAA, n.d. Tables 35.1, 35.2: From *The Way the Earth Works*, by P. J. Wyllie, published by John Wiley & Sons, copyright © John Wiley & Sons, Inc.

Unit 36 Figs. 36.2, 36.5, 36.10, 36.12, and 36.13: Same source as Fig. 3.12, pp. 416, 417, 424, and 426.

Unit 37 Fig. 37.4: Same source as Fig. 3.12, p. 293.

Unit 39 Fig. 39.4: After Arthur Bloom, *The Surface of the Earth*, © 1969, p. 90, published by Prentice-Hall, Inc., Englewood Cliffs, N.J. Fig. 39.5: From Léo F. Laporte, *Encounter With the Earth*, Canfield Press, p. 97, © 1975 by Léo F. Laporte. Fig. 39.6, 39.7, 39.9, 39.12, and 39.17: Same source as Fig. 3.12, p. 323. Fig. 39.11: After U.S. Geological Survey, Professional Paper 950, n.d. Fig. 39.13: Courtesy of Roger Wheate, University of Northern British Columbia.

Unit 40 Fig. 40.2: After *Physical Geography: Earth Systems*, Scott Foresman & Co., Glenview, Illinois, 1974, © John J. Hidore. Fig. 40.6: After J. P. Bruce and R. H. Clark, *Introduction to Hydrometeorology*, Pergamon Press, Elmsford, New York, 1966, © J. P. Bruce and R. H. Clark. Fig. 40.7: Adapted from Brian J. Skinner and Stephen C. Porter, *The Dynamic Earth: An Introduction to Physical Geology*, John Wiley & Sons, 1989, p. 199. Fig. 40.8: From Léo F. Laporte, *Encounter With the Earth*, Canfield Press, p. 249, © Léo F. Laporte. Fig. 40.10: Adapted from *Introduction to Physical Geography*, Second edition by H. M. Kendall, R. M. Glendinning, C. H. McFadden, and R. F. Logan, copyright © 1974 by Harcourt Brace Jovanovich, Inc. Fig. 40.12: Same source as Fig. 9.10, p. 245.

Unit 41 Fig. 41.2: Adapted from Environment Canada, 2004. Fig. 41.9: Same source as 40.7, p. 221. Fig. 41.11: Same source as Fig. 3.12, p. 279. Fig. 49.13: From Marie Morisawa, *Streams: Their Dynamics and Morphology*, © 1968 McGraw-Hill, Inc.

Unit 42 Fig. 42.10 Adapted from Environment Canada, 2004.

Unit 43 Figs. 43.2a, 43.10, and 43.14: Same source as Fig. 3.12, pp. 274, 287, and 290. Fig. 43.12b Adapted from Environment Canada, 2004.

Unit 44 Fig. 44.4: Same source as Fig. 3.12, p. 256. Fig. 44.5: From a portion of Glasgow North (Kentucky) Quadrangle, 7.5 minute series, U.S. Geological Survey, n.d.

Unit 45 Figs. 45.2a, 45.2b: Same source as Fig. 3.12, p. 345. Fig. 45.3: After NASA, n.d. Fig. 45.6: Same source as Fig. 40.7, p. 270.

Unit 46 Fig. 46.4: From J. F. Lovering and J. R. V. Prescott, Laast of Lands . . . Antarctica, Melbourne University Press, 1979, data from Gordon and Goldberg, "Circumpolar Characteristics of Antarctic Waters," American Geographical Society, Antarctic Map Folio Series 1970, and Kort, "The Antarctic Ocean," *Scientific American*, Vol. 207, 1962. Figs. 46.6, 46.10, and 46.13: Adapted from Richard Foster Flint, *Glacial and Pleistocene Geology*, John Wiley & Sons, 1957, pp. 227 ff., copyright © Harrison L. Flint. Fig. 46.8: Same source as Fig. 3.12, p. 365. Fig 46.11: Adapted from William D. Thornbury, *Principles of Geomorphology*, John Wiley & Sons, 2 rev. ed., 1969, p. 399.

Unit 47 Fig. 47.8: After Armin K. Lobeck, *Geomorphology*, McGraw-Hill Book Company, 1932. Fig. 47.11: Same source as Fig. 40.7, p. 268.

Unit 48 Fig. 48.3: Same source as Fig. 3.12, p. 361.

Unit 49 Figs. 49.4, 49.6, and 49.7: Same source as Fig. 3.12, pp. 316, 322, and 324. Fig. 49.10: After U.S. Bureau of Reclamation, 1960.

Unit 50 Figs. 50.1, 50.4, and 50.6: After Keith Stowe, *Essentials of Ocean Science*, 1987, pp. 84, 87, and 124, published by John Wiley & Sons, copyright © 1987 by John Wiley & Sons, Inc. Figs. 50.2, 50.3a, and 50.5: Same source as Fig. 3.12, pp. 385, 386, and 387.

Unit 51 Figs 51.1, 51.7: Same source as Fig. 3.12, pp. 392, 393. Fig. 51.6: Same source as Fig. 40.7, p. 297. Fig. 51.17: Same source as Fig. 9.10, p. 302.

Unit 52 Fig. 52.2 Adapted from J.B. Bird, *The Natural Landscapes of Canada* (Toronto, ON: John Wiley & Sons, 1980). Fig. 52.15: Adapted from Antony R. Orme, ed., *The Physical Geography of North America*, Oxford University Press, 2002, p. 293.

Credits for Photographs

Unit 1 *Opener*: Goddard Space Flight Center/NASA. Figure 1.2: © National Geographic Image Collection. Fig. 1.3: © James Gurney/National Geographic Image Collection. Fig. 1.5: © AbleStock Photos. Fig. 1.6: H. J. de Blij. Fig. 1.8: © AbleStock Photos.

Unit 2 *Opener*: H. J. de Blij. Fig. 2.6: Tibor G. Toth/National Geographic Image Collection.

Unit 3 *Opener*: H. J. de Blij. Fig. 31.A: © The British Museum. Fig. 3.16: © Canadian Space Agency, image received by the Canada Centre for Remote Sensing, processed by RADARSAT International, Inc.

Unit 4 *Opener*: Photo by NASA (computer enhancement © David Smart/DRK Photo). Fig. 4.1: © S. Nielsen/DRK Photo. Fig. 4.4: © by Fred Espenak, www.MrEclipse.com. Fig. 4.5: Jet Survey/Science Photo Library. Fig. 4.7: NASA/JPL/Cornell. Fig. 4.8: JSC/NASA. Fig. 4.9: Corbis; Original image courtesy of NASA/Corbis.

Unit 5 *Opener*: JSC/NASA. Fig. 5.3: Mike Grandmaison@firstlight.ca.

Unit 6 Fig. 6.2: Bill Lowry/Ivy Images. Fig. 6.8: 000 – Ivy Images.

Unit 7 *Opener*: © Fred Bruemmer/DRK Photo. Fig. 7.4: © Kim Heacox/DRK Photo.

Unit 8 *Opener*: NASA/Science Photo Library. Fig. 8.1: The Mansell Collection/Timepix. Fig. 8.4: © NASA/Photo Researchers, Inc. Fig. 8.7: Dick Hemingway.

Unit 9 *Opener*: H. J. de Blij.

Unit 10 *Opener*: H. J. de Blij. Fig. 10.6: © Geospace/Science Photo Library.

Unit 11 *Opener*: H. J. de Blij. Fig. 11.1: O. Brown, R. Evans, and M. Carle, University of Miami, Rosentiel School of Marine and Atmospheric Science, Miami, Florida.

Unit 12 Fig. 12.6: H. J. de Blij. Fig. 12.8a: O. Bierwagon/Ivy Images. Fig. 12.8b: Daniel Gulin/CORBIS/MAGMA. Fig. 12.8c: CP/Jonathan Hayward. Fig. 12.8d: CP/London Free Press/Sue Reeve.

Unit 13 *Opener*: H. J. de Blij . Fig. 13.2: JSC/NASA. Fig. 13.4: H. J. de Blij. Fig. 13.6: © Jim Zuckerman/Corbis. Fig. 13.7: CP/Jeff McIntosh.

Unit 14 *Opener*: © University of Dundee/Photo Researchers, Inc. Fig. 14.2: © Warren Faidley/DRK Photo.

Unit 15 *Opener*: Dick Hemingway. Fig. 15.1: Courtesy of The Weather Network. Fig. 15.3: Meteorological Service of Canada, Environment Canada, reproduced with the permission of Environment Canada, 2004. Fig. 15.10: © Peter Menzel Photos.

Unit 16 *Opener*: © Steve McCurry/Magnum Photos.

Unit 17 *Opener*: H. J. de Blij. Figs. 17.1, 17.2: H. J. de Blij. Fig. 17.6: © Wolfgang Kachler/Corbis. Fig. 17.7: © John Moss/Photo Researchers, Inc. Fig. 17.10: © T. A. Wiewandt/DRK Photo. Fig. 17.12: © Steve McCurry/Magnum Photos.

Unit 18 *Opener*: H. J. de Blij. Fig. 18.4a: © Richard A. Cooke/Corbis. Fig. 18.4b: © IFA/Peter Arnold, Inc. Fig. 18.5: H. J. de Blij. Fig. 18.11: © Robert Glusic/Getty Images.

Unit 19 *Opener*: H. J. de Blij. Fig. 19.2: © Doug Wilson/Corbis. Fig. 19.3: Winston Fraser/Ivy Images. Fig. 19.6: © Robert Glusic/Getty Images. Fig. 19.11: H. J. de Blij.

Unit 20 *Opener*: H. J. de Blij. Fig. 20.1: © Tom Bean/Corbis. Fig. 20.2: © Kenneth Garrett/Woodfin Camp and Associates. Fig. 20.6a: © NASA. Fig. 20.6b: © Science Photo Library/Photo Researchers Inc. Fig. 20.8: Photo by Van Trestick/Corbis Sygma.

Unit 21 *Opener*: H. J. de Blij. Fig. 21.4: Francis Lépine/Valan Photos. Fig. 21.9: NASA/PHOTO RESEARCHERS, INC. Fig. 21.8: © Bettmann/Corbis. Fig. 21.10: © AFP/Corbis. Fig. 21.11: NASA/SCIENCE PHOTO LIBRARY.

Unit 22 *Opener*: www.slidefarm.com. Figs. 22.1, 22.2: Randall Schaetzl. Fig. 22.3: H. J. de Blij. Fig. 22.4: O. Bierwagon/Ivy Images. Fig. 22.7: Barrett and McKay Photo. Fig. 22.8: H. J. de Blij. Fig. 22.9: Saskatchewan Archives Board R-A4665.

Unit 23 *Opener*: H. J. de Blij. Figs. 23.1, 23.2, 23.4: H. J. de Blij. Fig. 23.7: Randall Schaetzl. Fig. 23.8: © Dan Suzio/Photo Researchers, Inc.

Unit 24 *Opener*: H. J. de Blij. Figs. 24.3b, 24.4b, 24.5b, 24.6b: Randall Schaetzl.

Unit 25 *Opener*: H. J. de Blij. Figs. 25.3, 25.4, 25.6, 25.7, 25.8, 25,9, 25.10, 25.11, 25.14: Randall Schaetzl. Fig. 25.5: Photo from Soil and Land Resources Division, University of Idaho. Fig. 25.13: H. J. de Blij.

Unit 26 *Opener*: H. J. de Blij. Fig. 26.2: © Pete Oxford/DRK Photo. Figs. 26.4, 26.13: H. J. de Blij. Fig. 26.10: John Fowler/Valan Photos. Fig. 26.14: Peter Bird, Animal and Plant Control Commission, South Australia.

Unit 27 *Opener*: H. J. de Blij. Figs. 27.5, 27.6: H. J. de Blij. Fig. 27.7: David Tanaka. Fig. 27.8: Bill Ivy/Ivy Images. Fig. 27.9: Raymond Gehman/CORBIS/MAGMA. Fig. 27.10: H. J. de Blij. Fig. 27.11: © John Cancalosi/DRK Photo.

Unit 28 *Opener*: H. J. de Blij. Figs. 28.1, 28.2, 28.5, 28.7: H. J. de Blij.

Unit 29 *Opener*: H. J. de Blij. Fig. 29.1: Mark E. Gibson/DRK Photo. Fig. 29.7a, 29.7b, 29.10, 29.11: H. J. de Blij. Fig. 29.9: University of British Columbia. Fig. 29.13: © Tom Bean/DRK Photo. Fig. 29.14: © Richard Bergmann/Photo Researchers Inc.

Unit 30 *Opener*: H. J. de Blij. Fig. 30.2: © Mickey Gibson/Earth Scences. Fig 30.3a: © Phillip Hayson/Photo Researchers, Inc. Fig. 30.3b: © E. R. Degginger/Earth Scenes. Figs. 30.5, 30.6: H. J. de Blij. Fig. 30.7: © Kevin Schaefer/Peter Arnold, Inc.

Unit 31 Figs. 31.1, 31.3, 31.6, 31.10, 31.11: H. J. de Blij. Fig. 31.7: © Dominique Braud/Earth Scenes. Fig. 31.8: Tom Bean/Corbis.

Unit 32 *Opener*: H. J. de Blij. Figs. 32.2, 32.3: Tibor G. Toth/National Geographic Image Collection. Fig. 32.10: © John S. Shelton. Fig. 32.13: www.slidefarm.com.

Unit 33 *Opener*: H. J. de Blij. Fig.33.5: H. J. de Blij. Fig. 33.6: © Montheath, C./Earth Scenes. Fig. 33.9: © Earth Satellite Corporation/Science Photo Library/Photo Researchers. Fig. 33.10: © Carson Baldwin, JR./Earth Scenes.

Index